W9-DIE-621

MODERN
DICTIONARY
of
ELECTRONICS

Rudolf F. Graf

HOWARD W. SAMS & CO., INC.
THE BOBBS-MERRILL CO., INC.
INDIANAPOLIS · KANSAS CITY · NEW YORK

THIRD EDITION

THIRD PRINTING — 1970

Copyright © 1962, 1963 and 1968 by Howard W. Sams & Co., Inc., Indianapolis, Indiana 46206. Printed in the United States of America.

All rights reserved. Reproduction or use, without express permission, of editorial or pictorial content, in any manner, is prohibited. No patent liability is assumed with respect to the use of the information contained herein.

Library of Congress Catalog Card Number 68-13873

PREFACE

No truly authoritative dictionary can be the work of one person. Rather, it is the culmination of the unceasing efforts of many people. The field of electronics is constantly expanding and so its language and vocabulary must be augmented with newly originated words and phrases if effective communication of thoughts and ideas are to be established. The originators give the words their initial meanings, but the exact definitions change with technological advances and actual usage by others.

The content of this dictionary is thus an analysis of words and their meanings as determined by common usage, and as researched and written by its author and editors. Because the field of electronics is constantly expanding, its language and vocabulary must grow along with it. More than 4000 new terms and additions to existing terms have been added in this third edition. Many of the new terms are related to fields, phenomena, or processes that were little-known or even nonexistent when the first edition was published in 1962.

Every entry in the second edition was reviewed and many were revised for this new book in order to keep pace with current usage. Where more than one definition exists for a term, the different meanings are arranged numerically. This method, however, does not necessarily imply a preferred order of meanings.

The emphasis of this dictionary is on the broad subject of electronics. Within this field it contains over 16,000 definitions of current terms from radio, television, communications, radar, electronic instrumentation, industrial and medical electronics, microelectronics, computers, data processing, lasers, logic, semiconductors, and fiberoptics.

I gratefully acknowledge the permission granted once again by Mr. E. K. Gannett of the IEEE to use definitions and illustrations which originally were prepared by them. My thanks also go to the other organizations and trade sources who have so kindly supplied their material and granted permission to use it.

I should like to take this opportunity to dedicate this book to my children, Jeffrey and Debbie, while at the same time extending gratitude to my lovely wife Bettina, whose untiring efforts and truly invaluable assistance have made it possible for me to prepare this edition of the dictionary.

Samuel Johnson once said, "Dictionaries are like watches. The worst is better than none, and the best cannot expect to be quite true." With that thought in mind, the users of this volume are cordially invited to submit to the publisher comments and suggestions for additions or changes of definitions given here, so that future editions will better reflect the current usage of the language of electronics.

RUDOLF F. GRAF

HOW TO USE THIS DICTIONARY

This MODERN DICTIONARY OF ELECTRONICS follows the standards accepted by prominent lexicographers. All terms of more than one word are treated as one word. For example, "bridged-T network" appears between "bridged tap" and "bridge duplex system." Abbreviations are also treated alphabetically; the initials "ARRL" follow the term "arrester" rather than appearing at the beginning of the A's.

For ease in quickly locating a specific term, catchwords for the first and last entries which appear on each page are shown at the top.

Illustrations have been positioned with the terms they depict and are clearly captioned so they can be immediately associated with the proper definition.

Moderate cross-referencing has been used as an aid in locating terms which you might look for in more than one place. For example, when looking up "Esaki diode" you'll be referred to "tunnel diode." However, occasionally you may look for a term and not find it. In such instances, always think of the term in its most logical form; i.e., you will find "acoustic resonator" in the A's and not in the R's. In other words, when looking up the definition for a specific device, such as a "dipole antenna," refer to the modifier "dipole" rather than to "antenna."

A unique feature is the *Pronunciation Guide* beginning after the definitions. This Guide shows syllabic division and pronunciations, based on accepted industry usage, for over 1100 commonly mispronounced words. Because the language is in constant flux, pronunciations and spellings acceptable five years ago may be obsolete today. Witness the evolution of the word "ampere." Originally it was pronounced "AHMpair," the French pronunciation. In this country, accepted usage simplified the term to "AMpeer" (just as "Schmidt" became "Smith"). Today the accepted pronunciation is "AMper."

Since it follows the most authoritative standards of the industry, this dictionary will serve as an excellent guide on spelling, hyphenation, abbreviation, capitalization, etc.

It is hoped you will find MODERN DICTIONARY OF ELECTRONICS helpful, informative, and satisfactory in every way. Should you care to pass along any comments or suggestions which come to mind as a result of its use, we will be most happy to hear from you.

Howard W. Sams

A

A—1. Abbreviation for angstrom unit, used in expressing wavelength of light. Its length is 10^{-8} centimeter. 2. Chemical symbol for argon, an inert gas used in some electron tubes. 3. Symbol for area of a plane surface.

a—1. Abbreviation for atto (10^{-18}). 2. Abbreviation for ampere.

A— (A-minus or A-negative)—Sometimes called F—. Negative terminal of an A-battery or negative polarity of other sources of filament voltage. Denotes the terminal to which the negative side of the filament-voltage source should be connected.

A+ (A-plus or A-positive)—Sometimes called F+. Positive terminal of an A-battery or positive polarity of other sources of filament voltage. The terminal to which the positive side of the filament voltage source should be connected.

ab—The prefix attached to names of practical electric units to indicate the corresponding unit in the cgs (centimeter grams second) electromagnetic systems—e.g., abampere, abvolt, abcoulomb.

abac—See Alignment Chart.

abampere—Centimeter-gram-second electromagnetic unit of current. The current which, when flowing through a wire one centimeter long bent into an arc with a radius of one centimeter, produces a magnetic field intensity of one oersted. One abampere is equal to 10 amperes.

A-battery—Source of energy which heats the filaments of vacuum tubes in battery-operated equipment.

abc—Abbreviation for automatic bass compensation, a circuit used in some equipment to increase the amplitude of the bass notes to make them appear more natural at low volume settings.

abcoulomb—Centimeter-gram-second electromagnetic unit of electrical quantity. The quantity of electricity passing any point in an electrical circuit in one second when the current is one abampere. One abcoulomb is equal to 10 coulombs.

aberration—In lenses a defect that produces inexact focusing. Aberration may also occur in electron optical systems, causing a halo around the light spot.

abfarad—Centimeter-gram-second electromagnetic unit of capacitance. The capacitance of a capacitor when a charge of one abcoulomb produces a difference of potential of one abvolt between its plates. One abfarad is equal to 10^9 farads.

abhenry—Centimeter-gram-second electromagnetic unit of inductance. The inductance in a circuit in which an electromotive force of one abvolt is induced by a current changing at the rate of one abampere per second. One abhenry is equal to 10^9 henrys.

abmho—Centimeter-gram-second electromagnetic unit of conductance. A conductor or circuit has a conductance of one abmho when a difference of potential of one abvolt between its terminals will cause a current of one abampere to flow through the conductor. One abmho is equal to 10^9 mho.

abnormal glow—In a glow tube, a current discharge of such magnitude that the cathode area is entirely surrounded by a glow. A further increase in current results in a rise in its density and a drop in voltage.

abnormal propagation—The phenomenon of unstable or changing atmospheric and/or inospheric conditions acting upon transmitted radio waves. Such waves are prevented from following their normal path through space, causing difficulties and disruptions of communications.

abnormal reflections—See Sporadic Reflections.

abohm—Centimeter-gram-second electromagnetic unit of resistance. The resistance of a conductor when, with an unvarying current of one abampere flowing through it, the potential difference between the ends of the conductor is one abvolt. One abohm is equal to 10^{-9} ohm.

abort—To cut short or break off (an action, operation, or procedure) with an aircraft, guided missile, or the like—especially because of equipment failure. An abort may occur at any point from start to countdown or takeoff to the destination. An abort can be caused by human technical or meteorological errors, miscalculation, or malfunctions.

AB power pack—Assembly in a single unit of the A- and B-batteries of a battery-operated circuit. Also, a unit that supplies the necessary A and B voltages from an a-c source of power.

abrasion machine—A laboratory device for determining the abrasive resistance of wire or cable. The two standard types of machines are the squirrel cage with square steel bars and the abrasive grit types.

abrasion resistance—A measure of the ability of a wire or wire covering to resist damage due to mechanical causes. Usually expressed as inches of abrasive tape travel.

abscissa—Horizontal, or X-, axis on a chart or graph.

absolute address—An address used to specify the location in storage of a word in a computer program, not its position in the program.

absolute altimeter—Electronic instrument which furnishes altitude data with regard to the surface of the earth or any other surface immediately below the instrument—as distinguished from an aneroid altimeter, the readings of which depend on air pressure.

absolute altitude—Altitude with respect to the earth's surface, as differentiated from the altitude with respect to sea level.

absolute code—A code using absolute addresses and absolute operation codes—i.e., a code that indicates the exact location where the reference operand is to be found or stored.

absolute coding—Computer coding using absolute addresses.

absolute delay—The time interval between the transmission of two synchronized radio, loran, or radar signals from the same or different stations.

absolute efficiency—Ratio of the actual output of a transducer to that of a corresponding ideal transducer under similar conditions.

absolute error—1. The amount of error expressed in the same units as the quantity containing the error. 2. Loosely, the absolute value of the error—i.e., the magnitude of the error without regard to its algebraic sign.

absolute gain of an antenna—The gain in a given direction when the reference antenna is an isotropic antenna isolated in space.

absolute humidity—Amount of water vapor present in a unit volume of atmosphere.

absolute maximum rating—Limiting values of operating and environmental conditions, applicable to any electron device of a specified type as defined by its published data, and not to be exceeded under the worst probable conditions. Those ratings beyond which the life and reliability of a device can be expected to decline.

absolute minimum resistance—The resistance between the wiper and the termination of a potentiometer, when the wiper is adjusted to minimize that resistance.

absolute Peltier coefficient—The product of the absolute temperature and the absolute Seebeck coefficient of a material.

absolute pressure—Pressure of a liquid or gas measured relative to a vacuum (zero pressure).

absolute pressure transducer — A pressure transducer that accepts simultaneously two independent pressure sources, and the output of which is proportional to the pressure difference between the sources.

absolute scale—*See* Kelvin Scale.

absolute Seebeck coefficient—The integral from absolute zero to the given temperature of the quotient of the Thomson coefficient of a material divided by its absolute temperature.

absolute system of units—Also called coherent system of units. A system of units in which a small number of units is chosen as fundamental—e.g., units of mass, length, time, and charge. Such units are termed absolute units. All other units are derived from them by taking a definite proportional factor in each of those laws which is chosen as the basic laws for expressing the relationships between the physical quantities. The proportional factor is generally taken as unity.

absolute temperature—Temperature measured from absolute zero, a theoretical level defined as −273.2°C or −459.7°F or 0°K.

absolute units—A system of units based on physical principles, in which a small number of units are chosen as fundamental and all other units derived from them—i.e. abohm, abcoulomb, abhenry, etc.

absolute value—The numerical value of a number or symbol without reference to its algebraic sign. Thus, |3| is the absolute value of +3 or −3. An absolute value is signified by placing vertical lines on both sides of the number or symbol.

absolute value device—A computing element that produces an output equal to the magnitude of the input signal, but always of one polarity.

absolute zero—Lowest possible point on the scale of absolute temperature; the point at which all molecular activity ceases. Absolute zero is defined as −273.2°C, −459.7°F, or 0°K.

absorber—1. In a nuclear reactor, a substance that absorbs neutrons without reproducing them. Such a substance may be useful in control of a reactor or, if unavoidably present, may impair the neutron economy. 2. Any material or device which absorbs and dissipates radiated energy.

absorption—1. Dissipation of the energy of a radio or sound wave into other forms as a result of its interaction with matter. 2. The process by which the number of particles or photons entering a body of matter is reduced by interaction of the particle or radiation with the matter. Similarly, the reduction of the energy of a particle while traversing a body of matter. This term is sometimes erroneously used for capture. 3. Penetration of a substance into the body of another.

Absorption circuit.

absorption circuit—A tuned circuit that dissipates energy taken from another circuit.

absorption coefficient—1. Measure of sound-absorbing characteristics of a unit area of a given material, compared with the sound-absorbing characteristics of an open space (total absorption) having the same area. 2. Ratio or loss of intensity caused by absorption, to the total original intensity of radiation.

absorption control—Control of a nuclear reactor by use of a neutron absorber. Adjustment is made by varying the effective amount of absorber in or near the core. The most common arrangement is to incorporate the absorber in rods which can be moved in or out to produce the desired effect.

absorption current — The current flowing into a capacitor following its initial charge, due to a gradual penetration of the electric stress into the dielectric. Also, the current which flows out of a capacitor following its initial discharge.

absorption dynamometer — An instrument for measuring power, in which the energy of a revolving wheel or shaft is absorbed by the friction of a brake.

absorption fading — A slow type of fading, primarily caused by variations in the absorption rate along the radio path.

absorption frequency meter — *See* Absorption Wavemeter.

absorption loss — That part of transmission loss due to dissipation or conversion of electrical energy into other forms (e.g., heat), either within the medium or attendant upon a reflection.

absorption marker — A sharp dip on a frequency-response curve due to the absorption of energy by a circuit sharply tuned to the frequency at which the dip occurs.

absorption modulation — Also called loss modulation. A system for amplitude-modulating the output of a radio transmitter by means of a variable-impedance device (such as a microphone or vacuum-tube circuit) inserted into or coupled to the output circuit.

absorption trap — A parallel-tuned circuit coupled either magnetically or capacitively to absorb and attenuate interfering signals.

absorption wavemeter — Also called absorption frequency meter. An instrument for measuring frequency. Its operation depends on the use of a tuned electrical circuit or cavity loosely coupled to the source. Maximum energy will be absorbed at the resonant frequency, as indicated by a meter or other device. Frequency can then be determined by reference to a calibrated dial or chart.

absorptivity — A measure of the portion of incident radiation or sound energy absorbed by a material.

A-B test — Direct comparison of two sounds by playing first one and then the other. May be done with two tape recorders playing identical tapes (or the same tape), two speakers playing alternately from the same tape recorder, or two amplifiers playing alternately through one speaker, etc.

abvolt — Centimeter-gram-second electromagnetic unit of potential difference. The potential difference between two points when one erg of work is required to transfer one abcoulomb of positive electricity from a lower to a higher potential. An abvolt is equal to 10^{-8} volt.

ac — Abbreviation for alternating current.

a-c bias — The alternating current, usually of a frequency several times higher than the highest signal frequency, that is fed to a record head in addition to the signal cur-

rent. The a-c bias serves to linearize the recording process.

accelerating conductor or relay — One which causes the operation of a succeeding device to begin in the starting sequence after the proper conditions have been established.

accelerating electrode — An electrode in a cathode-ray or other electronic tube to which a positive potential is applied to increase the velocity of electrons or ions toward the anode. A klystron tube does not have an anode but does have accelerating electrodes.

acceleration — The rate of change in velocity. Often expressed as a multiple of the acceleration of gravity ($g = 32.2$ ft/sec²).

acceleration at stall — The value of servomotor angular acceleration calculated from the stall torque of the motor and the moment of inertia of the rotor. Also called torque-to-inertia ratio.

acceleration switch — A type of limit switch which senses acceleration forces above a preset value and in a particular direction. Commonly used in aerospace equipment, it triggers sensors or arming networks when a specific gravitational force has been reached.

acceleration time — In a computer, the elapsed time between the interpretation of instructions to read or write on tape and the possibility of information transfer from the tape to the internal storage, or vice versa.

acceleration voltage — Potential between a cathode and anode or other accelerating element in a vacuum tube. Its value determines the average velocity of the electrons.

accelerator — A device for imparting a very high velocity to charged particles such as electrons or protons. Fast-moving particles of this type are used in research or in studying the structure of the atom itself.

accelerator dynamic test — A test performed on an accelerometer by means of which information is gathered pertaining to the overall behavior frequency response and/or natural frequency of the device.

Accelerometer.

accelerometer — An instrument or device, often mounted in an aircraft, guided missile, or the like; used to sense accelerative forces and convert them into corresponding electrical quantities usually for measuring, indicating or recording purposes. It does not measure velocity or distance, only changes in velocity.

9

accentuation—Also called pre-emphasis. The emphasizing of any certain band of frequencies, to the exclusion of all others, in an amplifier or electronic device. Applied particularly to the higher audio frequencies in frequency-modulated (f-m) transmitters.

accentuator—Network or circuit used for pre-emphasis or increase in amplitude of a given band of frequencies, usually audio.

acceptable-environmental-range test — A test to determine the range of environmental conditions for which an equipment maintains at least the minimum required reliability.

acceptable quality level—The maximum percentage of defective components considered to be acceptable as an average for a process or the lowest quality a supplier is permitted to present continually for acceptance. (Abbreviated AQL.)

acceptance sampling plan—A plan for the inspection of a sample as a basis for acceptance or rejection of a lot or taking another sample.

acceptance test—A test to demonstrate the degree of compliance of a purchaser's equipment with his requirements and specifications.

acceptor—Also called acceptor impurity. An impurity lacking sufficient valence electrons to complete the bonding arrangement in the crystal structure. When added to a semiconductor crystal, it accepts an electron from a neighboring atom and thus creates a hole in the lattice structure of the crystal.

acceptor circuit—A circuit which offers minimum opposition to a given signal.

acceptor impurity—*See* Acceptor.

access arm—In a computer storage unit, a mechanical device which positions the reading and writing mechanism.

access time—Also called waiting time. The time interval between the instant a memory or storage device requests information and the instant this information begins to be available in useful form.

a-c circuit breaker—A device which is used to close and interrupt an a-c power circuit under normal conditions, or to interrupt this circuit under faulty or emergency conditions.

accompaniment manual — In an organ, the keyboard used for playing the accompaniment to the melody. Also called the lower manual, or great manual.

accompanying audio (sound) channel—Also known as co-channel sound frequency. The r-f carrier frequency which supplies the sound to accompany a television picture.

accordion—A type of contact used in some printed-circuit connectors. The contact spring is given a z shape to permit high deflection without excessive stress.

a-c coupling—Coupling of one circuit to another circuit through a capacitor or other device which passes the varying portion but not the static (d-c) characteristics of an electrical signal.

accumulator—In an electronic computer, a device which stores a number and which, on receipt of another number, adds the two and stores the sum. An accumulator may have properties such as shifting, sensing signals, clearing, complementing, and so forth.

accuracy—1. The maximum error in the measurement of a physical quantity in terms of the output of an instrument when referred to the individual instrument calibration. Usually given as a percentage of full scale. 2. The quality of freedom from mistake or error in an electronic computer—that is, of conformity to truth or to a rule.

accuracy rating of an instrument — The limit, usually expressed as a percentage of full-scale value, not exceeded by errors when the instrument is used under reference conditions.

ac/dc—Electronic equipment capable of operation from either an a-c or d-c primary power source.

a-c/d-c receiver—A radio receiver designed to operate directly from either an a-c or a d-c source.

a-c directional overcurrent relay—A device which functions on a desired value of a-c overcurrent flowing in a predetermined direction.

a-c dump—The intentional, accidental, or conditional removal of all alternating-current power from a system or component. An a-c dump usually results in the removal of all power, since direct current is usually supplied through a rectifier or converter.

a-c erasing head—In magnetic recording, a device using alternating current to produce the magnetic field necessary for removal of previously recorded information.

acetate—A basic chemical compound in the mixture used to coat recording discs.

acetate base—The transparent plastic film which forms the tough backing for acetate magnetic recording tape.

acetate disc—A mechanical recording disc, either solid or laminated, made mostly from cellulose nitrate lacquer plus a lubricant.

acetate tape—A sound-recording tape with a smooth, transparent acetate backing. One side is coated with an oxide capable of being magnetized.

a-c generator—1. A rotating electrical machine that converts mechanical power into alternating current. Also known as an alternator. 2. A device, usually an oscillator, designed for the purpose of producing alternating current.

A-channel—One of two stereo channels (usually the left) to the microphones, speakers, or other equipment associated with this channel.

achieved reliability—Reliability determined on the basis of actual performance of nominally identical items under equivalent environmental conditions. Also called operational reliability.

achromatic—1. In color television, a term meaning a shade of gray from black to white, or the absence of color (without color). 2. Black-and-white television, as distinguished from color television. 3. A term applied to lenses, signifying their more or less complete correction for chromatic aberation.

achromatic lens—A lens which has been corrected for chromatic aberration. Such a lens is capable of bringing all colors of light rays to approximately the same point of focus. This it does by combining a concave lens of flint glass with a convex lens of crown glass.

achromatic locus—Also called achromatic region. On a chromaticity diagram an area that contains all points representing acceptable reference white standards.

achromatic region—*See* Achromatic Locus.

acid—A chemical compound which dissociates and forms hydrogen ions when in aqueous solution.

acid depolarizer—An acid, such as nitric acid, sometimes introduced into a primary cell to prevent polarization.

aclinic line—Also called isoclinic line. On a magnetic map, an imaginary line which connects points of equal magnetic inclination or dip.

a-c magnetic biasing—In magnetic recording, the method used to remove random noise and/or previously recorded material from the wire or tape. This is done by introducing an alternating magnetic field at a substantially higher frequency than the highest frequency to be recorded.

a-c noise—Noise which displays a rate of change which is fast relative to the response capability of the device.

a-c noise immunity—A measure of a logic circuit's ability to maintain the prescribed logic state in the presence of such noise. It is defined in terms of the amplitude and pulse width of an input noise signal to which the element will not respond.

Acorn tube.

acorn tube—A button- or acorn-shaped vacuum tube with no base, for uhf applications. Electrodes are brought out through the glass envelope on the side, top, and bottom.

acoustic—Also acoustical. Pertaining to sound or the science of sound.

acoustic absorption loss—The energy lost by conversion into heat or other forms when sound passes through or is reflected by a medium.

acoustic absorptivity—The ratio of sound energy absorbed by a surface to the sound energy arriving at the surface. Equal to 1 minus the reflectivity of the surface.

acoustical attenuation constant—The real part of the acoustical propagation constant. The commonly used unit is the neper per section or per unit distance.

acoustical-electrical transducer—A device designed to transform sound energy into electrical energy and vice versa.

acoustical mode—A mode of crystal-lattice vibration that does not produce an oscillating dipole.

acoustical ohm—A measure of acoustic resistance, reactance, or impedance. One acoustical ohm is equal to a volume velocity of 1 cubic centimeter per second when produced by a sound pressure of 1 microbar.

acoustical phase constant—The imaginary part of the acoustical propagation constant. The commonly used unit is the radian per section or per unit distance.

acoustical reflectivity—*See* Sound-Reflection Coefficient.

acoustical transmittivity—*See* Sound-Transmission Coefficient.

acoustic burglar alarm—Also called acoustic intrusion detector. A burglar alarm that is responsive to sounds produced by an intruder. Concealed microphones connected to an audio amplifier trip an alarm when sounds exceed a predetermined normal level.

acoustic capacitance—In a sound medium, a measure of volume displacement per dyne per square centimeter. The unit is centimeter to the fifth power per dyne.

acoustic clarifier—A system of cones loosely attached to the baffle of a speaker and designed to vibrate and absorb energy during sudden loud sounds, thereby suppressing them.

acoustic compliance—1. The measure of volume displacement of a sound medium when subjected to sound waves. 2. That type of acoustic reactance which corresponds to capacitive reactance in an electrical circuit.

acoustic delay line—A device which retards one or more signal vibrations by causing them to pass through a solid or liquid.

acoustic depth finder—*See* Fathometer.

acoustic dispersion—The change of the speed of sound with frequency.

acoustic elasticity—1. The compressibility of the air in a speaker enclosure as the cone moves backward. 2. The compressibility of any material through which sound is passed.

acoustic feedback—Also called acoustic regeneration. The mechanical coupling of a portion of the sound waves from the output of an audio-amplifying system to a preceding part or input circuit (such as the microphone) of the system. When excessive, acoustic feedback will produce a howling sound in the speaker.

acoustic filter—A sound-absorbing device that selectively suppresses certain audio frequencies while allowing others to pass.

acoustic frequency response—The voltage-attenuation frequency measured into a resistive load, producing a bandwidth approaching sufficiently close to the maximum.

acoustic generator—A transducer such as a speaker, headphones, or a bell, which converts electrical, mechanical, or other forms of energy into sound.

acoustic homing system—A missile guidance system which responds to noise radiated by the target.

acoustic horn—Also called horn. A tube of varying cross section having different terminal areas which change the acoustic impedance to control the directivity of the sound pattern.

acoustic impedance—Total opposition of a medium to sound waves. Equal to the force per unit area on the surface of the medium, divided by the flux (volume velocity or linear velocity multiplied by area) through that surface. Expressed in ohms and equal to the mechanical impedance divided by the square of the surface area. One unit of acoustic impedance is equal to a volume velocity of one cubic centimeter per second produced by a pressure of 1 microbar. Acoustic impedance contains both acoustic resistance and acoustic reactance.

acoustic inertance—A type of acoustic reactance which corresponds to inductive reactance in an electrical circuit. (The resistance to movement or reactance offered by the sound medium because of the inertia of the effective mass of the medium.) Measured in acoustic ohms.

acoustic intensity—The limit approached by the quotient of acoustical power being transmitted at a given time through a given area divided by the area as the area approaches zero.

acoustic interferometer—An instrument for measuring the velocity or frequency of sound waves in a liquid or gas. This is done by observing the variations of sound pressure in a standing wave, established in the medium between a sound source and a reflector, as the reflector is moved or the frequency is varied.

acoustic intrusion detector—*See* Acoustic Burglar Alarm.

acoustic labyrinth—Special speaker enclosure having partitions and passages to prevent cavity resonance and to reinforce bass response.

acoustic lens—An array of obstacles that refract sound waves in the same way that an optical lens refracts light waves. The dimensions of these obstacles are small compared to the wavelengths of the sounds being focused.

acoustic line—Mechanical equivalent of an electrical transmission line. Baffles, labyrinths, or resonators are placed at the rear of a speaker to help reproduce the very low audio frequencies.

acoustic memory—A computer memory using an acoustic delay line. The line employs a train of pulses in a medium such as mercury or quartz.

acoustic mine—Also called sonic mine. An underwater mine that is detonated by sound waves, such as those from a ship's propeller or engines.

acoustic mirage—The distortion of a sound wavefront by a large temperature gradient in air or water. This creates the illusion of two sound sources.

acoustic ohm—The unit of acoustic resistance, reactance, or impedance. One acoustic ohm is present when a sound pressure of 1 dyne per square centimeter produces a volume velocity of 1 cubic centimeter per second.

acoustic phase constant—The imaginary part of the acoustic propagation constant. The commonly used unit is the radian per section or per unit distance.

acoustic pickup—In nonelectrical phonographs, the method of reproducing the material on a record by linking the needle directly to a flexible diaphragm.

acoustic radiator—In an electroacoustic transducer, the part that initiates the radiation of sound vibration. A speaker cone or headphone diaphragm is an example.

acoustic radiometer—An instrument for measuring sound intensity by determining the unidirectional steady-state pressure caused by the reflection or absorption of a sound wave at a boundary.

acoustic reactance—That part of acoustic impedance due to the effective mass of the medium—that is, to the inertia and elasticity of the medium through which the sound travels. The imaginary component of acoustic impedance and expressed in acoustic ohms.

acoustic reflectivity—The ratio of the rate of flow of sound energy reflected from the surface on the side of incidence, to the incident rate of flow.

acoustic refraction—A bending of sound waves when passing obliquely from one medium to another in which the velocity of sound is different.

acoustic regeneration—*See* Acoustic Feedback.

acoustic resistance—That component of acoustic impedance responsible for the dissipation of energy due to friction between molecules of the air or other medium through which sound travels. Measured in acoustic ohms and analogous to electrical resistance.

acoustic resonance—An increase in sound intensity as reflected waves and direct waves which are in phase combine. May also be due to the natural vibration of air columns or solid bodies at a particular sound frequency.

acoustic resonator—An enclosure which intensifies those audio frequencies at which the enclosed air is set into natural vibration.

acoustics—1. Science of production, transmission, reception, and effects of sound. 2. In a room or other location, those characteristics which control reflections of sound waves and thus the sound reception in it.

acoustic scattering — The irregular reflection, refraction, or diffraction of a sound wave in many directions.

acoustic shock — Physical pain, dizziness, and sometimes nausea brought on by hearing a loud, sudden sound.

acoustic system — Arrangement of components in devices designed to reproduce audio frequencies in a specified manner.

acoustic transmission system — An assembly of elements adapted for the transmission of sound.

acoustic treatment — Use of certain sound-absorbing materials to control the amount of reverberation in a room, hall, or other enclosure.

acoustic wave — A traveling vibration by which sound energy is transmitted in air, in water, or in the earth. The characteristics of these waves may be described in terms of change of pressure, of particle displacement, or of density.

acoustic wave filter — A device designed to separate sound waves of different frequencies. (Through electroacoustic transducers, such a filter may be associated with electric circuits.)

acoustoelectric effect — Generation of an electric current in a crystal by a traveling longitudinal sound wave.

a-c plate resistance — Also called dynamic plate resistance. Internal resistance of a vacuum tube to the flow of alternating current. Expressed in ohms, the ratio of a small change in plate voltage to the resultant change in plate current, other voltages being held constant.

a-c power supply — A power supply that provides one or more a-c output voltages — e.g., a-c generator, dynamotor, inverter, or transformer.

acquisition — 1. The process of locating the orbit of a satellite or trajectory of a space probe so that tracking or telemetry data can be gathered. 2. The process of pointing an antenna or telescope so that it is properly oriented to allow gathering of tracking or telemetry data from a satellite or space probe.

acquisition and tracking radar — A radar set which locks on to a strong signal and tracks the object emitting or reflecting the signal. May be airborne or on the ground. Tracking radars use a dish-type antenna reflector to produce a searchlight-type beam.

acquisition radar — A radar set that detects an approaching target and feeds approximate position data to a fire-control or missile-guidance radar, which then takes over the function of tracking the target.

a-c receiver — A radio receiver designed to operate from an a-c source only.

a-c reclosing relay — A device which controls the automatic reclosing and locking out of an a-c circuit interrupter.

a-c relay — A relay designed to operate from an alternating-current source.

a-c resistance — Total resistance of a device in an a-c circuit. (*Also see* High-Frequency Resistance.)

a-c time overcurrent relay — A device which has either a definite or an inverse time characteristic and functions when the current in an a-c circuit exceeds a predetermined value.

actinic — In radiation, the property of producing a chemical change, such as the photographic action of light.

actinium — A radioactive element discovered in pitchblende by the French chemist Debierne in 1889. Its atomic number is 89; its atomic weight, 227.

actino electric effect — The property of some special materials whereby when an electric current is impressed on them, their resistance changes with light.

actino electricity — Electricity produced by the action of radiant energy on crystals.

actinometer — An instrument that measures the intensity of radiation by determining the amount of fluorescence produced by that radiation.

action area — In the rectifying junction of a metallic rectifier, that portion which carries the forward current.

action current — A brief and very small electric current which flows in a nerve during a nervous impulse.

action potential — The instantaneous value of the voltage between excited and resting portions of an excitable living structure.

activation — 1. Making a substance artificially radioactive by placing it in an accelerator such as a cyclotron, or by bombarding it with neutrons. 2. To treat the cathode or target of an electron tube in order to create or increase its emission. 3. The process of adding electrolyte to a cell to make it ready for operation.

activation time — The time interval from the moment activation is initiated to the moment the desired operating voltage is obtained in a cell or battery.

activator — An additive that improves the action of an accelerator.

active area — The portion of the rectifying junction of a metallic rectifier that carries forward current.

active communications satellite — *See* Active Comsat.

active component — 1. An electrical or electronic element capable of controlling voltages or currents to produce gain or switching action in a circuit (e.g., transistor, vacuum tube, or saturable reactor). Also called active device, or active element. 2. A device, the output of which is dependent on a source of power other than the main input signal.

active comsat — Also called active communication satellite. A communication satellite in which on-board receivers and transmitters receive signals beamed at them from a ground terminal, amplify them greatly, and

13

retransmit them to another ground terminal. Less sensitive receivers and less powerful transmitters can be used on the ground than are needed for passive comsats.

active current—In an alternating current, a component in phase with the voltage. The working component as distinguished from the idle or wattless component.

active decoder—A device that is associated with a ground station and automatically indicates the radar beacon reply code that is received in terms of its number or letter designation.

active device—*See* Active Component.

active electric network—An electric network containing one or more sources of energy.

active element—*See* Active Component.

active filter—A device employing passive network elements and amplifiers. It is used for transmitting or rejecting signals in certain frequency ranges, or for controlling the relative output of signals as a function of frequency.

active guidance—*See* Active Homing.

active homing—Also called active guidance. A missile system using a radar system in the missile itself to provide target information and to guide itself to the target.

active infrared detection—An infrared detection system in which a beam of infrared rays is transmitted toward one or more possible targets, and the rays reflected from the target are detected.

active jamming—Intentional radiation or reradiation of electromagnetic waves to impair the use of a specific portion of the electromagnetic-wave spectrum.

active leg—Within a transducer, an electrical element which changes its electrical characteristics as a function of the applied stimulus.

active line—A horizontal line which produces the tv picture, as opposed to the lines occurring during blanking (horizontal and vertical retrace).

active maintenance downtime—The time during which work is actually being done on an item from the recognition of an occurrence of failure to the time of restoration to normal operation. This includes both preventive and corrective maintenance.

active material—1. In the plates of a storage battery, lead oxide or some other active substance which reacts chemically to produce electrical energy. 2. The fluorescent material, such as calcium tungstate, used on the screen of a cathode-ray tube.

active mixer and modulator—A device requiring a source of electrical power and using nonlinear network elements to heterodyne or combine two or more electrical signals.

active network—A network containing passive and active (gain) elements.

active pressure—In an a-c circuit, the pressure which produces a current, as distinguished from the voltage impressed upon the circuit.

active RC network—A network formed by resistors, capacitors, and active elements.

active repair time—That portion of corrective maintenance downtime during which repair work is being done on the item, including preparation, fault-location, part-replacement, adjustment and recalibration, and final test time. It may also include part procurement time under shipboard or field conditions.

active satellite—A satellite which receives, regenerates, and retransmits signals between stations. *See also* Communications Satellite.

active sonar—*See* Sonar.

active substrate—A substrate in which active elements are formed to provide discrete or integrated devices. Examples of active substrates are single crystals of semiconductor materials within which are transistors, resistors, and diodes, or combinations of these elements. Another example is ferrite substrates within which electromagnetic fields are used to perform logical, gating, or memory functions.

active systems—In radio and radar, systems which require transmitting equipment, such as a beacon or transponder, to be carried in the vehicle.

active tracking system—Usually, a system which requires the addition of a transponder or responder on board the vehicle to repeat or retransmit information to the tracking equipment—e.g., dovap, secor, azusa.

active transducer—A type of transducer in which its output waves depend on one or more sources of power, apart from the actuating waves.

active wire—The wire of an armature winding that produces useful voltage. That portion of the winding in which induction takes place.

activity—1. In a piezoelectric crystal, the magnitude of oscillation relative to the exciting voltage. 2. The intensity of a radioactive source. 3. Operations that result in the use or modification of the information in a computer file.

activity curve—A graph showing how the activity of a radioactive source varies with time

activity ratio—The ratio of the number of records in a computer file which have activity to the total number of records in the file.

a-c transducer—A transducer which, for proper operation, must be excited with alternating currents only. Also a device, the output of which appears in the form of an alternating current.

actual power—The average of values of instantaneous power taken over 1 cycle.

actuating system—1. In a device or vehicle, a system that supplies and transmits energy for the operation of a mechanism or other device. 2. A manually or automatically operated mechanical or electrical device which operates electrical contacts to effect signal transmission.

actuating time—The time at which a specified contact functions.

actuator—1. In a servo system, the device which moves the load. 2. The part of a relay that converts electrical energy into mechanical motion.

a-c voltage—*See* Alternating Voltage.

acyclic machine—A direct-current machine in which the voltage generated in the active conductors maintains the same direction with respect to those conductors at all times.

adapter—A fitting designed to change the terminal arrangement of a jack, plug, socket, or other receptacle, so that other than the original electrical connections are possible.

Adapter.

adaptive control system—A device the parameters of which are automatically adjusted to compensate for changes in the dynamics of the process to be controlled. An afc circuit utilizing temperature-compensating capacitors to correct for temperature changes is an example.

adaptive telemetry—Telemetry having the ability to select certain vital information or any change in a given signal.

Adcock antenna—A pair of vertical antennas separated by one-half wavelength or less and connected in phase opposition to produce a figure-8 directional pattern.

Adcock direction finder—A radio direction finder using one or more pairs of Adcock antennas for directional reception of vertically polarized radio waves.

Adcock radio range—A type of radio range utilizing four vertical antennas (Adcock antennas) placed at the corners of a square, with a fifth antenna in the center.

a-d converter—Abbreviation for analog-to-digital converter.

add-and-subtract relay—A stepping relay capable of being operated so as to rotate the movable contact arm in either direction.

addend—A quantity which, when added to another quantity (called the augend), produces a result called the sum.

adder—1. A device which forms the sum of two or more numbers, or quantities, impressed on it. 2. In a color tv receiver, a circuit which amplifies the receiver primary signal coming from the matrix. Usually there is one adder circuit for each receiver primary channel.

addition record—A new record created during the processing of a file in a computer.

additive—Sometimes referred to as the key. A number, series of numbers, or alphabetical intervals added to a code to put it in a cipher.

additive color—A system which combines two colored lights to form a third.

additive primaries—Primary colors which can be mixed to form other colors, but which cannot themselves be produced by mixing other primaries. Red, green, and blue are the primaries in television because, when added in various proportions, they produce a wide range of other colors. For this reason, red, green, and blue are called additive primaries.

additron—An electrostatically focused, beam-switching tube used as a binary adder in high-speed digital computers.

address—1. An expression, usually numerical, which designates a specific location in a storage or memory device or other source or destination of information in a computer. 2. An identification, as represented by a name, label, or number, for a register, location in storage, or any other data source or destination such as the location of a station in a communications network. 3. Loosely, any part of an instruction that specifies the location of an operand for the instruction. 4. *Also see* Instruction Code.

address computation—The process by which the address part of an instruction in a digital computer is produced or modified.

addressed memory—In a computer, memory sections containing each individual register.

address modification—In a computer, a change in the address portion of an instruction or command such that, if the routine which contains that instruction or command is repeated, the computer will go to a new address or location for data or instructions.

address part—In an electronic-computer instruction, a portion of an expression designating location. (*Also see* Instruction Code.)

add-subtract time—The time required by a digital computer to perform addition or subtraction. It does not include the time required to obtain the quantities from storage and put the result back into storage.

add time—The time required in a digital computer to perform addition. It does not include the time required to obtain the quantities from storage and put the result back into storage.

ADF—*See* Automatic Direction Finder.

adiabatic damping—A reduction in the size of an accelerator beam as the energy of the beam is increased.

adiabatic demagnetization—A technique used to obtain temperatures within thousandths of a degree of absolute zero. It consists of applying a magnetic field to a substance at a low temperature and in good thermal contact with its surroundings, insulating the substance thermally, and then removing the magnetic field.

A-display—Also called A-scan. A radar scope presentation in which time (distance or range) is one co-ordinate (usually horizontal) and the target appears displaced perpendicular to the time base.

adjacent- and alternate-channel selectivity —A measure of the ability of a receiver to differentiate between a desired signal and between signals which differ in frequency from the desired signal by the width of one channel or two channels, respectively.

adjacent audio (sound) channel—The r-f carrier frequency which contains the sound modulation associated with the next lower-frequency television channel.

adjacent channel—That frequency band immediately above or below the one being considered.

adjacent-channel attenuation — *See* Selectance.

adjacent-channel interference — Undesired signals received on one communication channel from a transmitter operating on a channel immediately above or below.

adjacent-channel selectivity—The ability of a receiver to reject signals on channels adjacent to the channel of the desired station.

adjacent video carrier—The r-f carrier that carries the picture modulation for the television channel immediately above the channel to which the receiver is tuned.

adjustable resistor—A resistor which has the resistance wire partly exposed to enable the amount of resistance in use to be adjusted occasionally by the user. Adjustment requires the loosening of a screw, the subsequent moving of the lug, and retightening of the screw.

adjustable voltage divider—A wirewound resistor with one or more movable terminals that can be slid along the length of the exposed resistance wire until the desired voltage values are obtained.

adjusted circuit—Also called bolted-fault level. In a circuit the current measured under short-circuit conditions with the leads that are normally connected to the circuit breaker bolted together.

adjusted decibels—The noise level in a transmission system at any point in the system above a reference noise, when the noise meter used has been adjusted to represent the interfering effect under specified conditions. Abbreviated dba.

admittance—The ease with which an alternating current flows in a circuit. The reciprocal of impedance and usually expressed in mhos. Symbol is Y or y.

ADP—Abbreviation for automatic data processing.

adsorption—The deposition of a thin layer of gas or vapor particles or gas onto the surface of a solid. The process is known as chemisorption if the deposited material is bound to the surface by a simple chemical bond.

advance ball—In mechanical recording, a rounded support (often sapphire) which is attached to a cutter and rides on the surface of the recording medium. Its purpose is to maintain a uniform mean depth of cut and to correct for small irregularities on the surface of the disc.

advance wire—An alloy of copper and nickel, used in the manufacture of electric heating units and some wirewound resistors.

aeolight—A glow lamp which employs a cold cathode and a mixture of inert gases and in which the intensity of illumination varies with the applied signal voltage. This lamp is used to produce a modulated light for motion-picture sound recordings.

aerial—*See* Antenna.

aerial cable—A cable installed on a pole line or similar overhead structure.

aerodiscone antenna—An aircraft antenna that is aerodynamically shaped and is physically small compared to other antennas having similar electrical characteristics. Its radiation pattern is omnidirectional and linearly polarized.

aerodrome control radio station—A radio station providing communications between an aerodrome control tower and aircraft or mobile aeronautical radio station.

aerodynamics—The science of the motion of air and other gases. Also, the forces acting on bodies when they move through such gases, or when such gases move against or around the bodies.

aeromagnetic—Pertaining to the magnetic field of the earth as surveyed from the air.

aeronautical advisory station — A station used for civil defense and advisory communications with private aircraft stations.

aeronautical broadcasting service—The broadcasting service intended for the transmission of information related to air navigation.

aeronautical broadcast station—A radio station which broadcasts meteorological information and notices to airmen.

aeronautical fixed service—A fixed service intended for the transmission of information relating to air navigation and preparation for and safety of flight.

aeronautical fixed station—A station operating in the aeronautical fixed service.

aeronautical ground station—A radio station operated for the purpose of providing air-to-ground communications in connection with the operation of aircraft.

aeronautical marker-beacon station — A land station operating in the aeronautical radionavigation service and providing a signal to designate a small area above the station.

aeronautical mobile service—A radio service between aircraft and land stations or between aircraft stations.

aeronautical radio beacon station—A radionavigation land station in the aeronautical radionavigation service, the emission of which enables an aircraft or other mobile service to determine its bearing or its position in relation to the aeronautical radio beacon station.

aeronautical radionavigation service — A

radionavigation service intended for use in the operation of aircraft.

aeronautical radio service—1. Service carried on between aircraft stations and/or land stations. 2. Special radio for air navigation.

aeronautical station—A land station (or in certain instances a shipboard station) in the aeronautical mobile service that carries on communications with aircraft stations.

aeronautical telecommunication agency—An agency to which is assigned the responsibility for operating a station or stations in the aeronautical telecommunication service.

aeronautical telecommunication log—A record of the activities of an aeronautical telecommunication station.

aeronautical telecommunications—Any telegraph or telephone communications of sign signals, writing, images, and sounds of any nature, by wire, radio or other system or process of signaling, used in the aeronautical service.

aeronautical telecommunication service—Telecommunication service provided for aeronautical purposes.

aeronautical telecommunication station—A station in the aeronautical telecommunication service.

aeronautical utility land station—A land station located at an airport control tower and used for communications connected with the control of ground vehicles and aircraft on the ground.

aeronautical utility mobile station—A mobile station used at an airport for communications with aeronautical utility land stations, ground vehicles, and aircraft on the ground.

aerophare—*See* Radio Beacon.

AES—Abbreviation for Audio Engineering Society.

af—*See* Audio Frequency.

afc—*See* Automatic Frequency Control.

afterglow—Also called phosphorescence. The light that remains in a gas-discharge tube after the voltage has been removed, or on the phosphorescent screen of a cathode-ray tube after the exciting electron beam has been removed.

afterheat—The heat produced by the continuing decay of radioactive atoms in a reactor after fission has stopped. Most of the afterheat is due to the radioactive decay of fission products.

afterpulse—In a photomultiplier, a spurious pulse induced by a preceding pulse.

agc—*See* Automatic Gain Control.

aging—1. Storing a permanent magnet, capacitor, rectifier, meter, or other device, sometimes with voltage applied, until its desired characteristics become essentially constant. 2. The change of a component or a material with time under defined environmental conditions, leading to improvement or deterioration of properties.

agonic line—An imaginary line on the earth's surface, all points of which have zero magnetic declination.

AGREE—Advisory Group on Reliability of Electronics Equipment.

aided tracking—A system of tracking a target signal in bearing, elevation, or range (or any combination of these variables) in which manual correction of the tracking error automatically corrects the rate at which the tracking mechanism moves.

AIEE—Abbreviation for American Institute of Electrical Engineers. Now merged with IRE to form IEEE.

airborne intercept radar—Short-range airborne radar employed by fighter and interceptor planes to track down their targets.

airborne noise—Undesired sound in the form of fluctuations of air pressure about the atmospheric pressure as a mean.

air capacitor—A capacitor in which air is the only dielectric material between its plates.

aircarrier aircraft station—A radio station aboard an aircraft that is engaged in or essential to the transportation of passengers or cargo for hire.

air cell—A cell in which depolarization at the positive electrode is accomplished chemically by reduction of the oxygen in the air.

air column—The air space within a horn or acoustic chamber.

air condenser—*See* Air Capacitor.

air-cooled tube—An electron tube in which the generated heat is dissipated to the surrounding air directly, through metal heat-radiating fins, or with the aid of channels or chimneys that increase the air flow.

Air-core coil.

air-core coil—A number of turns of spiral wire in which no metal is used in the center.

air-core transformer—A transformer (usually rf) having two or more coils wound around a nonmetallic core. Transformers wound around a solid insulating substance or on an insulating coil form are included in this category.

aircraft bonding—Electrically connecting together all of the metal structure of the aircraft, including the engine and metal covering of the wiring.

aircraft flutter—Flickering in a tv picture as the signal is reflected from flying aircraft. The reflected signal arrives in or out of phase with the normal signal and thus strengthens or weakens the latter.

aircraft station—A radio station installed on aircraft and continuously subject to human control.

airdrome control station—A station used for communication between an airport control tower and aircraft.

air gap—1. A nonmagnetic discontinuity in a ferromagnetic circuit. For example, the space between the poles of a magnet—although filled with brass, wood or any other nonmagnetic material—is nevertheless called an air gap. This gap reduces the tendency toward saturation. 2. The air space between two magnetically or electrically related objects.

air lock—A small chamber, located at the entrance to an area, the doors of which are so interlocked that only one can be opened at a time. This acts as an air seal to maintain the condition of the air within the area.

airport runway beacon—A radio-range beacon which defines one or more approaches to an airport.

airport surveillance radar — Radar equipment or a radar system used in air-traffic control. Used in conjunction with precision approach radar to scan the airspace for a distance of approximately thirty to sixty miles around an airport. It shows, on an indicator in the airport control tower, the location of all airborne aircraft below a certain altitude, as well as obstructions to flight within its range.

air-position indicator—Airborne computing system which presents a continuous indication of aircraft position on the basis of aircraft heading, air speed, and elapsed time.

air-spaced coax—A coaxial cable in which air is basically the dielectric material. The conductor may be centered by means of a spirally wound synthetic filament, by beads, or by braided filaments. This construction is also referred to as an air dielectric.

air-to-ground communication — Transmission of radio signals from an aircraft to stations or other locations on the earth's surface, as differentiated from ground-to-air, air-to-air, or ground-to-ground.

air-to-ground radio frequency—The frequency or band of frequencies agreed upon for transmission from an aircraft to an aeronautical ground station.

air-to-surface missile—A missile designed to be dropped from an aircraft. An internal homing device or the aircraft's radio guides it to a surface target.

airwaves—Slang expression for radio waves used in radio and television broadcasting.

alacritized switch—A mercury switch treated to yield a low adhesional force between the rolling surface and mercury pool, resulting in a decreased differential angle.

alarm relay—A relay, other than an annunciator, used to operate, or to operate in connection with, a visual or audible alarm.

albedo—The reflecting ability of an object. It is the ratio of the amount of light reflected compared to the amount received.

Alexanderson alternator—An early mechanical generator used as a source of low-frequency power for transmission or induction heating. It is capable of generating frequencies as high as 200,000 hertz.

algebraic adder—A computer circuit which can form an algebraic sum.

algol—An international problem language designed for the concise, efficient expression of arithmetic and logical processes and the control (iterative, etc.) of these processes. From ALGOrithmic Language.

algorithm—A fixed step-by-step procedure for finding a solution to a problem.

align—To adjust the tuned circuits of a receiver or transmitter for maximum signal response.

aligned-grid tube—A multigrid vacuum tube in which at least two of the grids are aligned one behind the other to give such effects as beam formation and noise suppression.

alignment—The process of adjusting components of a system for proper interrelationship. The term is applied especially to (1) the adjustment of tuned circuits in a receiver to obtain the desired frequency response, and (2) the synchronization of components in a system.

alignment chart—Also called nomograph or abac. Chart or diagram consisting of two or more lines on which equations can be solved graphically. This is done by laying a straightedge on the two known values and reading the answer at the point where the straightedge intersects the scale for the value sought.

Alignment chart.

alignment pin—1. A pin in the center of the base of a tube. A projecting rib on the pin assures that the tube is correctly inserted into its socket. 2. Any pin or device that will insure the correct mating of two components designed to be connected.

alignment tool—A special screwdriver or socket wrench used for adjusting trimmer or padder capacitors or cores in tuning inductances. It is usually constructed partly or entirely of nonmagnetic material. (*Also see* Neutralizing Tool.)

alive—Electrically connected to a source of potential difference, or electrically charged to have a potential different from that of the earth.

alive circuit—One which is energized.

alkali—A compound which forms hydroxyl ions when in aqueous solution. Also called a base.

Alkaline cell.

alkaline cell—Also called alkaline-manganese. A primary cell similar to the zinc-carbon cell except that a potassium hydroxide (KOH) electrolyte is used. This cell has about 50 to 100 percent more capacity than the zinc-carbon cell. Nominal cell voltage is 1.5 volts.

all-diffused monolithic integrated circuit—Also called compatible monolithic integrated circuit. A microcircuit consisting of a silicon substrate into which all of the circuit parts (both active and passive elements) are fabricated by diffusion and related processes.

allen screw—A screw having a hexagonal hole or socket in its head. Often used as a setscrew.

allen wrench—A straight or bent hexagonal rod used to turn an Allen screw.

Alligator clip.

alligator clip—A spring-loaded metal clip with long, narrow meshing jaws, used for making temporary electrical connections.

allocate—In a computer, to assign storage locations to main routines and subroutines, thus fixing the absolute values of symbolic addresses.

allocated channels—A channel assigned to a specific user.

allocated frequency band—A segment of the radio-frequency spectrum established by competent authority designating the use which may be made of the frequencies contained therein.

allocated-use circuit—1. A circuit in which one or more channels have been allocated for the exclusive use of one or more services by a proprietary service; may be a uni-

lateral or joint circuit. 2. Communication link specifically assigned to user(s) warranting such facilities.

alloy—A composition of two or more elements, of which at least one is a metal. It may be either a solid solution, a heterogeneous mixture, or a combination of both.

alloy deposition—The process of depositing an alloy on a substrate.

alloy-diffused transistor—A transistor with a diffused base and alloyed emitter.

alloyed contact—An ohmic contact formed by an alloy process.

alloy junction—Also called fused junction. A junction produced by alloying one or more impurity metals to a semiconductor. A small button of impurity metal is placed at each desired location on the semiconductor wafer, heated to its melting point, and cooled rapidly. The impurity metal alloys with the semiconductor material to form a P or N region, depending on the impurity used.

alloy-junction photocell—A photodiode in which an alloy junction is produced by alloying (mixing) an indium disc with a thin wafer of N-type germanium.

alloy-junction transistor—Also called fused-junction transistor. A semiconductor wafer of P- or N-type material with two dots containing P- or N-type impurities fused, or alloyed, into opposite sides of the wafer to provide emitter and base junctions. The base region comprises the original semiconductor wafer.

alloy process—A fabrication technique in which a small part of the semiconductor material is melted together with the desired metal and allowed to recrystallize. The alloy developed is usually intended to form a p-n junction or an ohmic contact.

alloy transistor—A transistor in which the emitter and collector junctions are both alloy junctions.

all-pass network—A network designed to introduce phase shift or delay but not appreciable attenuation at any frequency.

all-wave antenna—A receiving antenna suitable for use over a wide range of frequencies.

all-wave receiver—A receiver capable of receiving stations on all the commonly used wavelengths in short-wave bands as well as in the broadcast band.

alnico—An alloy consisting mainly of ALuminum, NIckel, and CObalt plus iron. Capable of very high flux density and magnetic retentivity. Used in permanent magnets for speakers, magnetrons, etc.

alpha—Emitter-to-collector current gain of a transistor connected as a common-base amplifier. For a junction transistor, alpha is less than unity, or 1.

alphabetic coding—A system of abbreviation used in preparing information for input into a computer. Information may then be reported in the form of letters and words as well as in numbers.

alphabetic-numeric—Having to do with the alphabetic letters, numerical digits, and special characters used in electronic data processing work.

alpha cutoff frequency—The frequency at which the current gain of a common-base transistor stage has decreased to 0.707 of its low-frequency value. Gives a rough indication of the useful frequency range of the device.

alphameric (alphanumeric)—Generic term for alphabetic letters, numerical digits, and special characters which are machine-processable.

alphanumeric—Pertaining to a character set that contains both letters and numerals and usually other characters.

alphanumeric code—A code used to express numerically the letters of the alphabet.

alpha particle—A small, electrically charged particle thrown off at a very high velocity by many radioactive materials including uranium and radium. Identical to the nucleus of a helium atom, it is made up of two neutrons and two protons. Its electrical charge is positive and is equal in magnitude to twice that of an electron.

alpha ray—A stream of fast-moving alpha particles which produce intense ionization in gases through which they pass, are easily absorbed by matter, and produce a glow on a fluorescent screen. The lowest-frequency radioactive emissions.

alternate channel—A channel located two channels above or below the reference channel.

alternate-channel interference — Interference caused in one communication channel by a transmitter operating in the channel after an adjacent channel. (*Also see* Second-Channel Interference.)

alternate frequency—The frequency assigned for use at a certain time, or for a certain purpose, to replace or supplement the frequency normally used.

alternate mode—A means of displaying on an oscilloscope the output signals of two or more channels by switching the channels, in sequence, after each sweep.

alternate routine—A secondary or backup communications path to be used if the normal (primary) routing is not possible.

alternating-charge characteristic — The function relating, under steady-state conditions, the instantaneous values of the alternating component of transferred charge to the corresponding instantaneous values of a specified periodic voltage applied to a nonlinear capacitor.

alternating current—Abbreviated ac. A flow of electricity which reaches maximum in one direction, decreases to zero, then reverses itself and reaches maximum in the opposite direction. The cycle is repeated continuously. The number of such cycles per second is the frequency. The average value of voltage during any cycle is zero.

alternating current/direct current — A term applied to electronic equipment indicating it is capable of operation from either an alternating-current or direct-current primary power source.

alternating-current erasing head—An erasing head, used in magnetic recording in which alternating current produces the magnetic field necessary for erasing. Alternating-current erasing is achieved by subjecting the medium to a number of cycles of a magnetic field of a decreasing magnitude. The medium is, therefore, essentially magnetically neutralized.

alternating-current pulse — An alternating-current wave of brief duration.

alternating-current transmission—In television, that form of transmission in which a fixed setting of the controls makes any instantaneous value of signal correspond to the same value of brightness only for a short time.

alternating quantity—A periodic quantity which has alternately positive and negative values, the average value of which is zero over a complete cycle.

alternating voltage—Also called a-c voltage. Voltage that is continually varying in value and reversing its direction at regular intervals, such as that generated by an alternator or developed across a resistance or impedance through which alternating current is flowing.

alternation—One-half of a cycle—either when an alternating current goes positive and returns to zero, or when it goes negative and returns to zero. Two alternations make one cycle.

alternator—A device for converting mechanical energy into electrical energy in the form of an alternating current.

alternator transmitter—A radio transmitter that generates power by means of a radio-frequency alternator.

altimeter—An instrument that indicates the altitude of an aircraft above a specific reference level, usually sea level or the ground below the aircraft. It may be similar to an aneroid barometer that utilizes the change of atmospheric pressure with altitude, or it may be electronic.

altimeter station—An airborne transmitter, the emissions from which are used to determine the altitude of an aircraft above the surface of the earth.

altitude—The vertical distance of an aircraft or other object above a given reference plane such as the ground or sea level.

altitude delay—The synchronization delay introduced between the line of transmission of the radar pulse and the start of the trace on the indicator. This is done to eliminate the altitude circle on the plan-position indicator-type display.

alto-troposphere—A portion of the atmosphere about 40 to 60 miles above the surface of the earth.

alumina—A ceramic used for insulators in electron tubes for substrates in thin-film circuits. It can withstand continuously high temperatures and has a low dielectric loss over a wide frequency range.

aluminized-screen picture tube—A cathode-ray picture tube which has a thin layer of aluminum deposited on the back of its fluorescent surface to improve the brilliance of the image and also prevent ion-spot formation.

aluminum-electrolytic capacitor—A capacitor with two aluminum electrodes (the anode has the oxide film) separated by layers of absorbent paper saturated with the operating electrolyte. The aluminum-oxide film or dielectric is repairable in the presence of an operating electrolyte.

am—*See* Amplitude Modulation.

amateur—Also called a ham. A person licensed to operate radio transmitters as a hobby. Any amateur radio operator.

amateur bands—Certain radio frequencies assigned exclusively to radio amateurs. In the United States of America, the Federal Communications Commission (FCC) makes these assignments.

amateur station—A radio transmitting station operated by one or more licensed amateur operators.

amateur-station call letters—A group of numbers and letters assigned exclusively to a licensed amateur operator to identify his station.

ambient—Surrounding. (*Also see* Ambient Noise; Ambient Temperature.)

ambient level—The level of interference emanating from sources other than the test sample, such as inherent noise of the measuring device and extraneous radiated fields.

ambient light—Normal room light.

ambient-light filter—A filter used in front of a television picture-tube screen to reduce the amount of ambient light reaching the screen, and to minimize reflections of light from the glass face of the tube.

ambient noise—Acoustic noise in a room or other location. Usually measured with a sound-level meter. The term "room noise" commonly designates ambient noise at a telephone station.

ambient pressure—The general surrounding atmospheric pressure.

ambient temperature—Temperature of air or liquid surrounding any electrical part or device. Usually refers to the effect of such temperature in aiding or retarding removal of heat by radiation and convection from the part or device in question.

ambient temperature range—The range of environmental temperatures in the vicinity of the unit, over which the unit may be operated safely and within specifications. For forced-air cooled units, the ambient temperature is measured at the air intake.

ambiguity—1. An undesirable tendency of a synchro or servo system to seek a false null position, in addition to the proper null position. 2. Inherent error resulting from multiple-bit changes in a polystrophic code. (Proper logic design prevents such errors.)

ambiguous count—A count on an electronic scaler that is obviously impossible.

American Institute of Electrical Engineers (AIEE) — Now merged with IRE to form IEEE.

American Morse code—A system of dot-and-dash signals originated by Samuel F. B. Morse and still used to a limited extent for wire telegraphy in North America. It differs from the International Morse code used in radiotelegraph transmission.

American Radio Relay League (ARRL)—An organization of amateur radio operators.

American Standards Association (ASA)—A national federation of 123 trade associations, technical and professional societies, and consumer groups whose purpose is to develop uniform and voluntary standards of performance, dimension, and terminology.

American wire gage (AWG)—The system of notation generally adopted in the United States for measuring the size of solid wires.

a-m/f-m receiver—A device capable of converting either amplitude- or frequency-modulated signals into audio frequencies.

a-m/f-m tuner—A device capable of converting either amplitude- or frequency- modulated signals into low-level audio frequencies.

ammeter — An instrument for measuring either direct or alternating electric current (depending on its construction). Its scale is usually graduated in amperes, milliamperes, microamperes, or kiloamperes.

ammeter shunt—A low-resistance conductor placed in parallel with the meter movement so most of the current flows through this conductor and only a small part passes through the movement itself. This extends the usable range of the meter.

amp—Abbreviation for ampere.

ampacity—Current-carrying capacity expressed in amperes.

amperage—The number of amperes flowing in an electrical conductor or circuit.

ampere—1. A unit of electrical current or rate of flow of electrons. One volt across 1 ohm of resistance causes a current flow of 1 ampere. A flow of 1 coulomb per second equals 1 ampere. An unvarying current is passed through a solution of silver nitrate of standard concentration at a fixed temperature. A current that deposits silver at the rate of .001118 gram per second is equal to 1 ampere, or 6.25×10^{18} electrons per second passing a given point in a circuit. 2. The constant current which, if maintained in two straight parallel conductors of infinite length, of negligible circular sections, and placed 1 meter apart in a vacuum will produce between these conductors a force equal to 2×10^{-7} newton per meter of length.

ampere-hour—A current of one ampere flowing for one hour. Multiplying the current in amperes by the time of flow in hours gives the total number of ampere-hours. Used mostly to indicate the amount of energy a storage battery can deliver before it needs recharging, or the energy a primary battery can deliver before it needs replacing. One ampere-hour equals 3,600 coulombs.

ampere-hour capacity—The amount of current a battery can deliver in a specified length of time under specified conditions.

ampere-hour meter — An electrical meter which measures the amount of current (amperes) per unit of time (hours) which has been consumed in a circuit.

Ampere's rule—Current in a certain direction is equivalent to the motion of positive charges in that direction. The magnetic flux generated by a current in a wire encircles the current in the counter clockwise direction when the current is approaching the observer.

ampere-turn—The magnetomotive force produced by a coil, derived by multiplying the number of turns of wire in the coil by the current (in amperes) flowing through it.

amp-hr — Abbreviation for ampere-hour or ampere-hours.

Amplidyne.

amplidyne—A special direct-current generator used extensively in servo systems as a power amplifier. The response of its output voltage to changes in field excitation is very rapid, and its amplification factor is high.

amplification—Increase in size of a medium in its transmission from one point to another. May be expressed as a ratio or, by extension of the term, in decibels.

amplification factor (μ)—1. In a vacuum tube, the ratio of a small change in plate voltage to a small change in grid voltage required to produce the same change in plate current (all other electrode voltages and currents being held constant). 2. In any device, the ratio of output magnitude to input magnitude.

amplified agc — An automatic gain-control circuit in which the control voltage is amplified before being applied to the tube or transistor, the gain of which is to be controlled in accordance with the strength of the incoming signal.

amplified back bias—Degenerative voltage developed across a fast time-constant circuit within a stage of an amplifier and fed back into a preceding stage.

amplifier—A device which draws power from a source other than the input signal and which produces as an output an enlarged reproduction of the essential features of its input. The amplifying element may be an electron tube, transistor, magnetic circuit, or any of various devices.

amplifier noise—All spurious or unwanted signals, random or otherwise, that can be observed in a completely isolated amplifier in the absence of a genuine input signal.

amplifier nonlinearity—The inability of an amplifier to produce an output at all times proportionate to its input.

amplify — To increase in magnitude or strength, usually said of a current or voltage.

amplistat—A self-saturating type of magnetic amplifier.

Amplitron—A broad-band crossed-field amplifier with a re-entrant electron stream. The electron stream interacts with the backward wave of a nonre-entrant r-f structure. (Raytheon.)

amplitude—The magnitude of variation in a changing quantity from its zero value. The word must be modified with an adjective such as peak, rms, maximum, etc., which designates the specific amplitude in question.

amplitude-controlled rectifier—A rectifier circuit in which a thyratron is the rectifying element.

amplitude distortion—In an amplifier or other device, that which occurs when the output amplitude is not a linear function of the input amplitude. (Note: Amplitude distortion is measured with the system operating under steady-state conditions and with a sinusoidal input signal. When other frequencies are present, the term "amplitude" applies to the fundamental only.)

amplitude fading—Fading in which the amplitudes of all frequency components of a modulated carrier wave are uniformly attenuated.

amplitude-frequency response—The variation of gain, loss, amplification, or attenuation of a device or system as a function of frequency. Usually measured in the region where the transfer characteristic is essentially linear.

amplitude gate—*See* Slicer.

amplitude-level selection — The choice of the voltage level at which an oscilloscope sweep is triggered.

amplitude limiter—A circuit or stage which automatically reduces the amplification to prevent signal peaks from exceeding a predetermined level.

amplitude-modulated transmitter—A transmitter in which the amplitude of its radio-frequency wave is varied at a low frequency rate—usually in the audio or video range. This low frequency is the intelligence (information) to be conveyed.

amplitude-modulated wave — A constant-frequency waveform in which the amplitude varies in step with the frequency of an impressed signal.

amplitude modulation—1. Modulation in which the amplitude of a wave is the characteristic subject to variation. 2. Those systems of modulation in which each component frequency (f) of the transmitted intelligence produces a pair of sideband frequencies at carrier frequency plus (f) and carrier frequency minus (f). 3. In special cases, the carrier may be suppressed; either the lower or upper sets of sideband frequencies may be suppressed; the lower set of sideband frequencies may be produced by one or more channels of information. The carrier may be transmitted without intelligence-carrying sideband frequencies. The resulting emission bandwidth is proportional to the highest frequency component of the intelligence transmitted.

Amplitude modulation.

amplitude-modulation noise level — Undesired amplitude variations of a constant radio-frequency signal, especially in the absence of any intended modulation.

amplitude noise—The effect on radar accuracy of the fluctuations in amplitude of the signal returned by the target. These fluctuations are caused by any change in aspect if the target is not a point source.

amplitude of noise — When impulse-type noise is of random occurrence and so closely spaced that the individual wave shapes are not separated by the receiving equipment, then the noise has the waveshape and characteristics of random noise. Random-noise amplitude is proportional to the square root of the bandwidth. If the impulses are separated, the noise no longer has the wave shape of random noise and its amplitude is directly proportional to the bandwidth of the transmission system.

amplitude permeability — The relative permeability at a stated value of field strength and under stated conditions, the field strength varying periodically with time and no direct magnetic-field component being present.

amplitude range—The ratio, usually expressed in decibels, between the upper and lower limits of program amplitudes which contain all significant energy contributions.

amplitude resonance—The condition that exists when any change in the period or frequency of the periodic agency (but not its amplitude) decreases the amplitude of the oscillation or vibration of the system.

amplitude selection—The process of selecting that portion of a waveform which lies above or below a given value, or between two given values.

amplitude separator—A television-receiver circuit that separates the control impulses from the video signal.

amplitude-suppression ratio—In frequency modulation, the ratio of the magnitude of the undesired output to the magnitude of the desired output of an f-m receiver when the applied signal is simultaneously amplitude- and frequency-modulated. Generally measured with an applied signal that is amplitude-modulated 30% at a 400-hertz rate and is frequency-modulated 30% of the maximum system deviation at a 1,000-hertz rate.

amplitude versus frequency distortion—Distortion caused by the nonuniform attenuation or gain of the system, with respect to frequency under specified terminal conditions.

a-m tuner—A device capable of converting amplitude-modulated signals into low-level audio frequencies.

amu—Abbreviation for atomic mass unit.

anacoustic zone — Zone of silence in space where distances between air molecules are so great that sound waves are not propagated.

analog—In electronic computers a physical system in which the performance of measurements yields information concerning a class of mathematical problems.

analog channel — A computer channel in which the transmitted information can have any value between the defined limits of the channel.

analog communications—A system of telecommunications employing a nominally continuous electrical signal that varies in frequency, amplitude, etc., in some direct correlation to nonelectrical information (sound, light, etc.) impressed on a transducer.

analog computer—A computer operating on the principle of creating a physical (often electrical) analogy of the mathematical problem to be solved. Variables such as temperature or flow are represented by the magnitude of a physical phenomenon such as voltage or current. The computer manipulates these variables in accordance with the mathematical formulas "analogued" on it.

analog data—A physical representation of information such that the representation bears an exact relationship to the original information. The electrical signals on a telephone channel are an analog data representation of the original voice. 2. Data represented in a continuous form, as contrasted with digital data represented in a discrete (discontinued) form. Analog data are usually represented by physical variables, such as voltage, resistance, rotation, etc.

analog network—A circuit or circuits that represent physical variables in such a manner as to permit the expression and solution of mathematical relationships between the variables, or to permit the solution directly by electric or electronic means.

analog output—As distinguished from digital output. Here the amplitude is continuously proportionate to the stimulus, the proportionality being limited by the resolution of the device.

analog recording—A method of recording in which some characteristic of the record current, such as amplitude or frequency, is continuously varied in a manner analogous to the time variations of the original signal.

analog representation — A representation that does not have discrete values, but is continuously variable.

analog switch—A device that either transmits an analog signal without distortion, or completely blocks it.

analog-to-digital converter—A device which produces a digital output from an input in the form of physical motion or electrical voltages.

Analytical Engine—An early form of general-purpose digital computer invented in 1833 by Charges Babbage.

analyzer—1. An instrument or other device designed to examine the functions of components, circuits, or systems, and their relations to each other, as contrasted with an instrument designed to measure some specific parameter of such a system or circuit. 2. Of computers, a routine the purpose of which is to analyze a program written for the same or a different computer. This analysis may consist of summarizing instruction references to storage and tracing sequences of jumps.

anastigmat—A lens system designed so as to be free from the aberration called astigmatism.

anchor—An object, such as a metal rod, set into the ground to hold the end of a guy wire.

ancillary equipment — Equipment not directly employed in the operation of a system, but necessary for logistic support, preparation of flight or assessment of target damage —e.g. test equipment, vehicle transport.

AND circuit—Synonym for AND gate.

Anderson bridge—A bridge normally used for the comparison of self-inductance with capacitance. It is a 6-branch network in which an outer loop of four arms is formed by four nonreactive resistors and the unknown inductor. An inner loop of three arms is formed by a capacitor and a fifth resistor in series with each other and in parallel with the arm opposite the unknown

inductor. The detector is connected between the junction of the capacitor and the fifth resistor and at that end of the unknown inductor separated from a terminal of the capacitor by only one resistor. The source is connected to the other end of the unknown inductor and to the junction of the capacitor with two resistors of the outer loop. The balance is independent of frequency.

Anderson bridge.

AND gate—In an electronic computer, a gate circuit with more than one control (input) terminal. No output signal will be produced unless a pulse is applied to all inputs simultaneously.

anechoic enclosure—A term originally applied to audio-frequency low-reflection enclosures. Now applied generally to low-reflection enclosures.

anechoic room—An enclosure in which reflected sound energy is negligible. Used for measurement of microphone and speaker characteristics.

anemometer—An instrument used for measuring the force or speed of wind.

angels — Short-duration radar reflections in the lower atmosphere. Most often caused by birds, insects, organic particles, tropospheric layers, or water vapor.

angle—1. A fundamental mathematical concept formed when two straight lines meet at a point. The lines are the sides of the angle, and the point of intersection is the vertex. 2. A measure of the distance along a wave or part of a cycle, measured in degrees. 3. The distance through which a rotating vector has progressed.

angle modulation—Modulation in which the angle of a sine-wave carrier is the characteristic varied from its normal value. Phase and frequency modulation are particular forms of angle modulation.

angle noise—Tracking error introduced into radar by variations in the apparent angle of arrival of the echo from a target due to finite target size. (This effect is caused by variations in the phase front of the radiation from a multiple-point target as the target changes its aspect with respect to the observer.)

angle of advance—*See* Braid Angle.

angle of arrival—Angle made between the line of propagation of a radio wave and the earth's surface at the receiving antenna.

angle of azimuth—The angle measured clockwise in a horizontal plane, usually from the north. The north used may be true north, Y-north, or magnetic north.

angle of beam—The angle which encloses most of the transmitted energy from a di- rectional-antenna system.

angle of convergence—Angle formed by the lines of sight of both eyes when focusing on an object.

angle of deflection—The angle formed be- tween the new position of the electron beam in a cathode-ray tube and the normal posi- tion before deflection.

angle of departure—The angle of the line of propagation of a radio wave with respect to a horizontal plane at the transmitting antenna.

angle of divergence—In cathode-ray tubes, a measure of its spread as the electron beam travels from the cathode to the screen. The angle formed by an imaginary center line and the border line of the electron beam. In good tubes, this angle is less than 2°.

angle of elevation—The angle between the horizontal plane and the line ascending to the object.

angle of incidence—The angle between a wave or beam striking a surface and a line perpendicular to that surface.

Angle of lag.

angle of lag—The angular phase difference between one sinusoidal function and a sec- ond having the same frequency. Expressed in degrees, the amount the second function must be retarded to coincide with the first.

Angle of lead.

angle of lead—1. The time or angle by which one alternating electrical quantity leads an- other of the same cyclic period. 2. The angle through which the commutator brushes of a generator or motor must be moved from the normal position to prevent sparking.

angle of radiation—The angle between the surface of the earth and the center of the

beam of energy radiated upward into the sky from a transmitting antenna.

angle of reflection—The angle between a wave or beam leaving a surface and a line perpendicular to that surface.

angle of refraction—The angle between a wave or beam as it passes through a medium and a line perpendicular to the surface of that medium.

angle tracking noise—Any deviation of the tracking axis from the center of reflectivity of a target. The resultant of servonoise, re- ceiver noise, angle noise, and amplitude noise.

angstrom unit—A unit of measurement of a wavelength of light and other radiation. Equal to one ten-thousandth of a micron or one hundred-millionth of a centimeter (10^{-8} cm). The visible spectrum extends from about 4,000 to 8,000 angstrom units. Blue light has a wavelength in the region of 4,700 angstroms; yellow, 5,800; and red, 6,500.

angular acceleration—The time rate of change in angular velocity.

angular accelerometer—A device capable of measuring the magnitude of, and/or varia- tions in, angular acceleration.

angular aperture—The largest angular ex- tent of wave surface which an objective can transmit.

angular deviation loss—The ratio of the re- sponse of a microphone or speaker on its principal axis to the response at a specified angle from the principal axis (expressed in decibels).

angular distance—The angle subtended by two bodies at the point of observation. It is equal to the distance in wavelengths mul- tiplied by 2π radians or by 360°.

angular frequency—Frequency expressed in radians per second. It is equal to the num- ber of hertz (cycles per second) multiplied by 2π.

angular length—Length expressed in radians or equivalent angular measure equal to 2π radians, or 360°, multiplied by the length in wavelengths.

angular phase difference—Phase difference between two sinusoidal functions expressed as an angle.

angular rate—The rate of change of bearing.

angular velocity—The rate at which an angle changes. Expressed in radians per second, the angular velocity of a periodic quantity is the frequency multiplied by 2π. If the periodic quantity results from uniform rota- tion of a vector, the angular velocity is the number of radians per second passed over by the rotating vector. Generally designated by the Greek letter omega (ω).

anhysteresis—The process whereby a ma- terial is magnetized by applying a unidirec- tional field upon which is superimposed an alternating field of gradually decreasing am- plitude.

anion—A negatively charged ion which, during electrolysis, is attracted toward the anode. A corresponding positive ion is called the cation.

anisotropic—A material that has better magnetic characteristics along one axis than any other.

anisotropic body—A body in which the value of any given property depends on the direction of measurement, as opposed to a body that is isotropic.

anisotropic magnet—A magnetic material having a better magnetic characteristic along the preferred axis than along any other.

anisotropy—Directional dependence of magnetic properties, leading to the existence of easy or preferred directions of magnetization. Anisotropy of a particle may be related to its shape, to its crystalline structure, or to the existence of strains within it.

annealed wire—A wire which has been softened by heating (soft-drawn wire).

annealing—The process of heating any solid material such as glass or metal, followed by slow cooling. This generally lowers the tensile strength and thereby improves the ductility.

annular—Ringed; ring-shaped.

annular transistor—A mesa transistor in which the semiconductor regions are arranged in concentric circles about the emitter.

annulling network—An arrangement of impedance elements connected in parallel with filters to annul or cancel capacitive or inductive impedance at the extremes of the passband of a filter.

annunciation relay—1. An electromagnetically operated signaling apparatus which indicates whether a current is flowing or has flowed in one or more circuits. 2. A non-automatic reset device which gives a number of separate visual indications upon the functioning of protective devices, and which may also be arranged to perform a lockout function.

annunciator—A visual device consisting of a number of pilot lights or drops. Each light or drop indicates the condition which exists or has existed in an associated circuit and is labeled accordingly.

anode—1. The positive electrode such as the plate of a vacuum tube; the element to which the principal stream of electrons flows. 2. In a cathode-ray tube, the electrodes connected to a source of positive potential. These anodes are used to concentrate and accelerate the electron beam for focusing. 3. The less noble and/or higher-potential electrode of an electrolytic cell at which corrosion occurs. This may be an area on the surface of a metal or alloy, the more active metal in a cell composed of two dissimilar metals, or the positive electrode of an impressed-current system.

anode-balancing coil—A set of mutually coupled windings used to maintain approximately equal currents in anodes operating in parallel from the same transformer terminal.

anode breakdown voltage—The potential required to cause conduction across the main gap of a gas tube when the starter gap is not conducting and all other tube elements are held at cathode potential.

anode-bypass capacitor—Also called plate-bypass capacitor. A capacitor connected between the anode and ground in an electron tube circuit. Its purpose is to bypass high-frequency currents and keep them out of the load.

anode characteristic—A graph that shows how the anode current of an electron tube is affected by changes in the anode voltage.

anode circuit breaker—A device used in the anode circuits of a power rectifier for the primary purpose of interrupting the rectifier circuit if an arc-back should occur.

anode current—The electron flow in the element designated as the anode. Usually signifies plate current.

anode dark space—In a gas tube, a narrow, dark zone next to the surface of the anode.

anode dissipation—The power dissipated as heat in the anode of an electron tube because of the bombardment by electrons and ions.

anode efficiency—*See* Plate Efficiency.

anode-load impedance—*See* Plate-Load Impedance.

anode modulation—*See* Plate Modulation.

anode neutralization—Also called plate neutralization. A method of neutralization in which a portion of the anode-cathode a-c voltage is shifted 180° and applied to the grid-cathode circuit through a neutralizing capacitor.

anode power input—*See* Plate Power Input.

anode power supply—The means for supplying power to the plate of an electron tube at a more positive voltage than that of the cathode. (*Also see* Plate Power Supply.)

anode pulse modulation—*See* Plate Pulse Modulation.

anode rays—Positive ions coming from the anode of an electron tube; these ions are generally due to impurities in the metal of the anode.

anode saturation—*See* Plate Saturation.

anode sheath—A layer of electrons surrounding the anode in mercury-pool arc tubes.

anode strap—A metallic connector between selected anode segments of a multicavity magnetron, used principally for mode separation.

anode supply—Also called plate supply. The direct-voltage sources used in an electron-tube circuit to place the anode at a high positive potential with respect to the cathode.

anode terminal—The semiconductor-diode terminal that is positive with respect to the other terminal when the diode is biased in the forward direction.

anode voltage—The potential difference existing between the anode and cathode.

anode voltage drop (of a glow-discharge, cold-cathode tube)—Difference in potential between cathode and anode during conduction, caused by the electron flow through the tube resistance (IR drop).

anodizing—An electrochemical oxidation process used to improve the corrosion resistance or to enhance the appearance of a metal surface. Aluminum and magnesium parts are frequently anodized.

anomalous propagation—1. Propagation that is unusual or abnormal. 2. The conduction of uhf signals through atmospheric ducts or layers in a manner similar to that of a waveguide. These atmospheric ducts carry the signals with less than normal attenuation over distances far beyond the optical path taken by uhf signals. Also called superrefraction. 3. In sonar, pronounced and rapid variations in the strength of the echo due to large, rapid focal fluctuations in propagation conditions.

A — N radio range—A navigational aid which provides four equisignal zones for aircraft guidance. Deviation from the assigned course is indicated aurally by the Morse code letters A (•—) or N (—•). Oncourse position is indicated by an audible merging of the A and N code signals into a continuous tone.

A — N signal—A radio-range, quadrant-designation signal which indicates to the pilot whether he is on course or to the right or left.

answerback—The response of a terminal to remote-control signals. *Also see* Handshaking.

antenna—Also called aerial. That portion, usually wires or rods, of a radio transmitter or receiver station used for radiating waves into or receiving them from space.

antenna array—A system of two or more antennas coupled together to obtain desirable directional effects.

antenna bandwidth—The range of frequencies over which the impedance characteristics of the antenna are sufficiently uniform that the quality of the radiated signal is not significantly impaired.

antenna beam width—The angle, in degrees, between two opposite half-power points of an antenna beam.

antenna coil—In a radio receiver or transmitter, the inductance through which antenna current flows.

antenna coincidence—That instance when two rotating, highly directional antennas are pointed toward each other.

antenna-conducted interference—Any signal that is generated within a transmitter or receiver, and appears as an undesired signal at the antenna terminals of the device—e.g., harmonics of a transmitter signal, or the local-oscillator signal of the receiver.

antenna cores—Ferrite cores of various cross-sections for use in radio antennas.

antenna coupler—1. A radio-frequency transformer used to connect an antenna to a transmission line or to connect a transmission line to a radio receiver. 2. A radio-frequency transformer, link circuit, or tuned line used to transfer radio-frequency energy from the final plate-tank circuit of a transmitter to the transmission line feeding the antenna.

antenna cross talk—A measure of undesired power transfer through space from one antenna to another. Usually expressed in decibels, the ratio of power received by one antenna to the power transmitted by the other.

antenna current—The radio-frequency current that flows in an antenna.

antenna detector—A device consisting of an antenna and electronic equipment to warn aircraft crew members of their being observed by radar sets. (Usually located in the nose or tail of the aircraft and illuminates a light on one or more panels when radar signals are detected.)

antenna-directivity diagram—A curve representing, in polar or Cartesian coordinates, a quantity proportional to the gain of an antenna in the various directions in a particular plane or cone.

antenna disconnect switch—A safety switch or interlock plug used to remove driving power from the antenna to prevent rotation while work is being performed.

antenna duplexer—A circuit that permits two transmitters to transmit simultaneously from the same antenna without interaction between them.

antenna effect—1. Cause of error in a loop antenna due to the capacitance to ground. 2. In a navigational system, any undesirable output signal that results when a directional antenna acts as a nondirectional antenna.

antenna effective area—In any specified direction, the square of the wavelength multiplied by the power gain (or directive gain) in that direction, and divided by 4π. (When power gain is used, the effective area is that for power reception; when directive gain is used, the effective area is that for directivity.)

antenna factor—The value in db that must be added to a two-terminal voltmeter reading to obtain the actual induced antenna open-circuit voltage or the electric-field strength.

POWDERED-IRON CORE   WINDING

Antenna core.

antenna field—1. The region defined by a group of antennas. 2. A group of antennas placed in a geometric configuration which is specific for a particular trajectory measuring system. 3. The effective free-space energy distribution produced by an antenna or group of antennas.

antennafier—An integrated low-profile antenna and amplifier for use with compact, portable communications systems.

antenna gain—The effectiveness of a directional antenna in a particular direction, compared against a standard (usually an isotropic antenna). The ratio of standard antenna power to the directional antenna power that will produce the same field strength in the desired direction.

antenna ground system—That portion of an antenna closely associated with the earth and including an extensive conducting surface which may be the earth itself.

antenna height—The average antenna height above the terrain from two to ten miles from the antenna. In general, the antenna height will be different in each direction from the antenna. The average of these various heights is considered the antenna height above average terrain.

antenna-induced microvolts—The voltage that exists across the open-circuited antenna terminals, as calculated from a measurement.

antenna lens—An arrangement of metal vanes or dielectric material used to focus a microwave beam in a manner similar to an optical lens.

antenna lobe—*See* Lobe.

antenna matching—Selection of components to make the impedance of an antenna equal to the characteristic impedance of its transmission line.

antennamitter—An integrated low-profile antenna and oscillator for use with compact, portable communications systems.

antenna pair—Two antennas located on a base line of accurately surveyed length. The signals received by these antennas are used to determine quantities related to a target position.

antenna pattern—Also called antenna polar diagram. A plot of angle *versus* free-space field intensity at a fixed distance in the hori-

zontal plane passing through the center of the antenna.

antenna-pattern measuring equipment—Devices used to measure the relative field strength or intensity existing at any point or points in the space immediately surrounding an antenna.

antenna pedestal—A structure which supports an antenna assembly (motors, gears, synchros, rotating joints, etc.).

antenna polar diagram—*See* Antenna Pattern.

antenna power—The square of the antenna current of a transmitter, multiplied by the antenna resistance at the point where the current is measured.

antenna power gain—The power gain of an antenna in a given direction is four times the ratio of the radiation intensity in that direction to the total power delivered to the antenna. (The term is also applied to receiving antennas.)

antenna reflector—In a directional-antenna array, an element which modifies the field pattern in order to reduce the field intensity behind the array and increase it in front. In a receiving antenna, the reflector reduces interference from stations behind the antenna.

antenna relay—A relay used in radio stations to automatically switch the antenna to the receiver or transmitter and thus protect the receiver circuits from the r-f power of the transmitter.

antenna resistance—The total resistance of a transmitting antenna system at the operating frequency. The power supplied to the entire antenna circuit, divided by the square of the effective antenna current referred to the feed point. Antenna resistance is made up of such components as radiation resistance, ground resistance, radio-frequency resistance of conductors in the antenna circuit, and equivalent resistance due to corona, eddy currents, insulator leakage, and dielectric power loss.

antenna resonant frequency—The frequency (or frequencies) at which an antenna appears to be a pure resistance.

antenna stabilization—A system for holding a radar beam steady despite the roll and pitch of a ship or airplane.

antenna switch—Switch used for connecting an antenna to or disconnecting it from a circuit.

antenna system—An assembly consisting of the antenna and the necessary electrical and mechanical devices for insulating, supporting, and/or rotating it.

antenna terminals—On an antenna, the points to which the lead-in (transmission line) is attached.

antenna tilt error—The angular difference between the antenna tilt angle shown on the mechanical indicator, and the electrical center of the radar beam.

antenna wire—A wire, usually of high ten-

Antenna pattern.

sile strength such as copperweld, bronze, etc., with or without insulation, used as an antenna for radio and electronic equipment.

antiaircraft missile — A guided missile launched from the surface against an airborne target.

anticapacitance switch — A switch with widely separated legs, designed to keep capacitance at a minimum in the circuits being switched.

anticathode—Also called target. The target of an X-ray tube on which the stream of electrons from the cathode is focused and from which the X rays are radiated.

anticlutter circuit—In a radar receiver, an auxiliary circuit which reduces undesired reflection, to permit the detection of targets which otherwise would be obscured by such reflections.

anticlutter gain control—A device which automatically and gradually increases the gain of a radar receiver from low to maximum within a specified period after each transmitter pulse. In this way, short-range echoes producing clutter are amplified less than long-range echoes.

anticoincidence — A nonsimultaneous occurrence of two or more events (usually, ionizing events).

anticoincidence circuit — A counter circuit that produces an output pulse when either of two input circuits receives a pulse, but not when the two inputs receive pulses simultaneously.

anticollision radar—A radar system used in an aircraft or ship to warn of possible collision.

antiferroelectricity—The property of a class of crystals which also undergo phase transitions from a higher to a lower symmetry. They differ from the ferroelectrics in having no electric dipole moment.

antiferroelectric materials—Those materials in which spontaneous electric polarization occurs in lines of ions; adjacent lines are polarized in an antiparallel arrangement.

antiferromagnetic materials—Those materials in which spontaneous magnetic polarization occurs in equivalent sublattices; the polarization in one sublattice is aligned antiparallel to the other.

antiferromagnetic resonance—The absorption of energy from an oscillating electromagnetic field by a system of processing spins located on two sublattices, with the spins on one sublattice going in one direction and the spins on the other sublattice in the opposite direction.

antihunt—A stabilizing signal or equalizing circuit used in a closed-loop feedback system of a servomechanism to prevent the system from hunting, or oscillating. Special types of antihunt circuits are the anticipator, derivative, velocity feedback, and damper.

antihunt circuit—A circuit used to prevent excessive correction in a control system.

antihunt device—A device used in positioning systems to prevent hunting or oscillation of the load around an ordered position. The device may be mechanical or electrical. It usually involves some form of feedback.

antijamming — 1. Art of minimizing the effect of enemy electronic countermeasures to permit echoes from targets detected by radar to be visible on the indicator. 2. Controls or circuit features incorporated to minimize jamming.

antijamming radar data processing—Use of data from one or more radar sources to determine target range in the presence of jamming.

antilogarithm—The number from which a given logarithm is derived. For example, the logarithm of 4261 is 3.6295. Therefore the antilogarithm of 3.6295 is 4261.

antimagnetic—Made of alloys that will not remain in a magnetized state.

antimicrophonic — Specifically designed to prevent microphonics. Possessing the characteristic of not introducing undesirable noise or howling into a system.

antimissile missile — A missile which is launched to intercept and destroy another missile in flight.

antinodes—Also called loops. The points of maximum displacement in a series of standing waves. Two similar and equal wave trains traveling at the same velocity in opposite directions along a straight line result in alternate antinodes and nodes along the line. Antinodes are separated from their adjacent nodes by half the wavelength of the wave motion.

antinoise carrier-operated device—A device commonly used to mute the audio output of a receiver during standby or no carrier periods. Usually the automatic volume control voltage is used to control a squelch tube which, in turn, controls the bias applied to the first audio tube so that it is permitted to operate only when a carrier is present at the receiver input. Thus, the receiver output is heard when a signal is received, and is muted when no signal is present.

antinoise microphone—A microphone which discriminates against acoustic noise. A lip or throat microphone is an example.

antiproton—An elementary atomic particle which has the same mass as a proton but is negatively charged.

antiresonant circuit—A parallel-resonant circuit offering maximum impedance to the series passage of the resonant frequency.

antiresonant frequency—1. The frequency at which the impedance of a system is very high. 2. Of a crystal unit, the frequency for a particular mode of vibration at which, neglecting dissipation, the effective impedance of the crystal unit is infinite.

antiresonant frequency of a crystal unit—For a particular mode of vibration, the frequency at which (neglecting dissipation) the effective impedance of the crystal unit is infinite.

antisidetone—In a telephone circuit, special circuits and equipment which are so arranged that only a negligible amount of the power generated in the transmitter reaches the associated receiver.

antisidetone circuit—A telephone circuit which prevents sound, introduced in the local transmitter, from being reproduced in the local receiver. (Reduces sidetones.)

antisidetone induction coil — An induction coil designed for use in an antisidetone telephone set.

antisidetone telephone set—A telephone set with an antisidetone circuit.

antistickoff voltage—A small voltage, usually applied to the rotor winding of the coarse synchro control transformer in a two-speed system. The antistickoff voltage acts to eliminate the possibility of ambiguous behavior in the system.

antitransmit-receive switch — Abbreviated ATR switch. An automatic device employed in a radar system to prevent received energy from being absorbed in the transmitter.

aperiodic — Having no fixed resonant frequency or repetitive characteristics or no tendency to vibrate. A circuit that will not resonate within its tuning range is often called aperiodic.

aperiodic antenna—An antenna designed to have a constant impedance over a wide frequency range (for example, a terminated rhombic antenna).

aperiodic damping—Also called overdamping. The condition of a system when the amount of damping is so large that, when the system is subjected to a single disturbance, either constant or instantaneous, the system comes to a position of rest without passing through that position. While an aperiodically damped system is not strictly an oscillating system, it has such properties that it should become an oscillating system if the damping is sufficiently reduced.

aperiodic function—A function having no repetitive characteristics.

aperture—1. In a unidirectional antenna, that portion of the plane surface which is perpendicular to the direction of maximum radiation and through which the major part of the radiation passes. 2. In an opaque disc, the hole or window placed on either side of a lens to control the amount of light passing through. 3. Also called aperture time. The amount of uncertainty about the exact time when the encoder input was at the value represented by a given output code. In general, the aperture is equal to the conversion time; it may be reduced by the use of sample-and-hold circuits.

aperture compensation—Reduction of aperture distortion by boosting the high-frequency response of a television-camera video amplifier.

aperture distortion—In a television signal, the distortion due to the finite dimension of the camera-tube scanning beam. The beam covers several mosaic globules simultaneously, resulting in a loss of picture detail.

aperture illumination — The field distribution in amplitude and phase through the aperture.

aperture mask—Also called shadow mask. A thin sheet of perforated material placed directly behind the viewing screen in a three-gun color picture tube to prevent the excitation of any one color phosphor by either of the two electron beams not associated with that color.

aperture plate—A ferrite memory plate containing a large number of uniformly spaced holes arranged in parallel rows and interconnected by plated conductors to provide a magnetic memory plane.

A power supply—A power supply used as a source of heating current for the cathode or filament of a vacuum tube.

apparent bearing—The direction from which the signal arrives with respect to some reference direction.

apparent power—The product of voltage and current of a single-phase circuit in which the two reach their peaks at different times.

apparent source—*See* Effective Acoustic Center.

Applegate diagram—A graphical representation of electron bunching in a velocity-modulated tube, showing their positions along the drift space. This bunching is plotted on the vertical coordinate, against time along the horizontal axis.

Appleton layer—In the ionosphere, a region of highly ionized air capable of reflecting or refracting radio waves back to earth. It is made up of the F_1 and F_2 layers.

appliance—Any electrical equipment used in the home and capable of being operated by a nontechnical person. Included are units that perform some task that could be accomplished by other, more difficult means, but usually not those used for entertainment (radios, tv's, hi-fi sets, etc.).

application factor—A modifier of the failure rate. It is based on deviations from rated operating stress (usually temperature and one electrical parameter).

applicator (applicator electrodes)—Appropriately shaped conducting surfaces between which an alternating electric field is established for the purpose of producing dielectric heating.

applied voltage—The potential between a terminal and a reference point in any circuit or device.

applique circuit—A special circuit provided to modify existing equipment in order to allow for some special usage.

approach-control radar—Any radar set or system used in a ground-controlled approach system—e.g., an airport-surveillance radar, precision approach radar, etc.

approach path—In radio aircraft navigation,

that portion of the flight path in the immediate vicinity of a landing area where such flight path terminates at the touchdown point.

AQL — Abbreviation for acceptable quality level.

OUTER AQUADAG COATING

INNER AQUADAG COATING

Aquadag.

aquadag—A conductive graphite coating on the inner side walls of some cathode-ray tubes. It serves as an electrostatic shield or as a postdeflection and an accelerating anode. Also applied to outer walls and grounded; here it serves, with the inner coating, as a capacitor to filter the applied high voltage.

arbitrary function fitter—A circuit having an output voltage or current that is a presettable, adjustable, usually nonlinear function of the input voltage(s) or current(s) fed to it.

arc—1. A luminous discharge of electricity through a gas. Characterized by a change in space potential in the immediate vicinity of the cathode; this change is approximately equal to the ionization potential of the gas. 2. A prolonged electrical discharge, or series of prolonged discharges, between two electrodes. (Both produce a bright-colored flame, as contrasted to a dim corona-glow discharge).

arcback—Also called backfire. Failure of the rectifying action in a tube, resulting from the flow of a principal electron stream in the reverse direction due to the formation of a cathode spot on the anode. This action limits the peak inverse voltage which may be applied to a particular rectifier tube.

arc converter—A form of oscillator utilizing an electric arc to generate an alternating or pulsating current.

arc discharge—A discharge between electrodes in gas or vapor. Characterized by a relatively low voltage drop and a high current density.

arc drop—The voltage drop between the anode and cathode of a gas rectifier tube during conduction.

arc-drop loss—In a gas tube, the product of the instantaneous values of arc-drop voltage and current averaged over a complete cycle of operation.

arc-drop voltage—The voltage drop between the anode and cathode of a gas rectifier tube during conduction.

arc failure—1. A flashover in the air near an insulation surface. 2. An electrical failure in the surface heated by a flashover arc. 3. An electrical failure in the surface damaged by the flashover arc.

arc furnace—An electric furnace heated by arcs between two or more electrodes.

arcing—The production of an arc—for example, at the brushes of a motor or at the contact of a switch.

arcing contacts—Special contacts on which the arc is drawn after the main contacts of a switch or circuit breaker have opened.

arcing time—1. The interval between the parting, in a switch or circuit breaker, of the arcing contacts and the extension of the arc. 2. The time elapsing, in a fuse, from the severance of the fuse link to the final interruption of the circuit under the specified condition.

arc lamp—Application of an electric arc to produce a brilliant light. Used extensively in spotlights and motion-picture projectors.

arc oscillator—A negative-resistance oscillator comprised of a sustained d-c arc and a resonant circuit.

arcover voltage—Under specified conditions, the minimum voltage required to create an arc between electrodes separated by a gas or liquid insulation.

arc percussive welding—A type of welding in which the materials to be welded are separated by a gap, across which an arc is struck; the arc melts the surfaces of the materials, and the materials are simultaneously brought together. *See also* Pulse Arc Welding.

arc resistance—The length of time that a material can resist the formation of a conductive path by an arc adjacent to the surface of the material. Also called tracking resistance.

arc suppressor—*See* Spark Suppressor.

arc-through—A loss of control in multi-electrode gas tubes. As a result, the principal electron stream flows during a scheduled nonconducting period.

area redistribution—A method of measuring the duration of irregularly shaped pulses. A rectangle is drawn having the same peak amplitude and the same area as the original pulse under consideration. Because the same time units are used in measuring the original and the new pulse, the width of the rectangle is considered the duration of the pulse.

argon—An inert gas used in discharge tubes and some electric lamps. It gives off a purple glow when ionized.

argon glow lamp—A glow lamp containing argon gas which produces a pale blue violet light.

argument — The independent variable of a function.

arithmetic check—A check of a computation making use of the arithmetical properties of the computation.

arithmetic element—Synonym for arithmetic unit.

arithmetic mean—Usually, the same as average. It is obtained by first adding quantities together and then dividing by the number of quantities involved. It also means a figure midway between two extremes and is found by adding the minimum and maximum together and dividing by two.

arithmetic operation—In an electronic computer, the operations in which numerical quantities form the elements of the calculation, including the fundamental operations of arithmetic (addition, subtraction, multiplication, comparison, and division).

arithmetic organ—*See* Arithmetic Unit.

arithmetic shift—In a digital computer, the multiplication or division of a quantity by a power of the base used in the notation.

arithmetic unit—Also called arithmetic element or arithmetic organ. In an automatic digital computer, that portion in which arithmetical and logical operations are performed on elements of information.

armature—The moving element in an electromechanical device such as the rotating part of a generator or motor, the movable part of a relay, or the spring-mounted, iron portion of a bell or buzzer.

armature contacts—1. Contacts mounted directly on the armature. 2. Sometimes used for movable contacts.

armature core—An assembly of laminations forming the magnetic circuit of an armature.

armature gap—The space between the armature and pole face.

armature hesitation—A delay or momentary reversal of the motion of the armature.

armature-hesitation contact chatter—Chatter caused by delay or momentary reversal in direction of the armature motion of a relay during either the operate or the release stroke.

armature-impact contact chatter—Chatter caused by impact of the armature of a relay on the pole piece in operation, or on the backstop in release.

armature overtravel—That portion of the available stroke occurring after the contacts of a relay have touched.

armature reaction—In an armature, the reaction of the magnetic field produced by the current on the magnetic lines of force produced by the field coil of an electric motor or generator.

armature rebound—Return motion of the armature of a relay after it strikes the backstop.

armature-rebound contact chatter—Chatter caused by the partial return of the armature of a relay to its operated position as a result of rebound from the backstop in release.

armature relay—A relay operated by an electromagnet which, when energized, causes an armature to be attracted to a fixed pole or poles.

armature slot—In the core of an armature, a slot or groove into which the coils or windings are placed.

armature stud—In a relay, an insulating member that transmits the motion of the armature to an adjacent contact member.

armature travel—The distance traveled during operation by a specified point on the armature of a relay.

armature voltage control—A means of controlling the speed of a motor by changing the voltage applied to its armature windings.

armature wire—Stranded annealed copper wire, straight lay, soft loose white cotton braid. It is used for low-voltage, high-current rotor winding motors and generators. Straight lay permits forming in armature slots, and compressibility.

armchair copy—Amateur term for clear, static-free signals.

armed sweep—*See* Single Sweep.

arming the oscilloscope sweep—Closing a switch which enables the oscilloscope to trigger on the next pulse.

armor—A metallic cover placed over the insulation of wire or cable to protect it from abrasion or crushing.

armored cable—Two or more insulated wires collectively provided with a metallic covering, primarily to protect the insulated wires from damage.

armor clamp—A fitting for gripping the armor of a cable at the point where the armor terminates or where the cable enters a junction box.

Armstrong frequency-modulation system—A phase-shift modulation system originally proposed by E. H. Armstrong.

Armstrong oscillator.

Armstrong oscillator—An inductive feedback oscillator that consists of a tuned grid circuit and an untuned tickler coil in the plate circuit. Feedback is controlled by varying the coupling between the tickler and the grid circuit.

array—In an antenna, a group of elements arranged to provide the desired directional characteristics. These elements may be antennas, reflectors, directors, etc.

array antenna—An antenna comprising a number of radiating elements, generally similar, arranged and excited to obtain directional effects.

array device—A group of many similar, basic, complex, or integrated devices without separate enclosures. Each has at least one of its electrodes connected to a common conductor, or all are connected in series.

arrester—1. Also called a lightning arrester. A protective device used to provide a bypass path directly to ground for lightning discharges that strike an antenna or other conductor. 2. A power-line device capable of reducing the voltage of a surge applied to its terminals, interrupting current if present, and restoring itself to original operating conditions.

ARRL — Abbreviation for American Radio Relay League.

arrowhead—A linearly polarized, frequency-independent, log-periodic antenna.

ARSR—Abbreviation for Air Route Surveillance Radar.

articulation— (Sometimes called intelligibility.) In a communications system, the percentage of speech units understood by a listener. The word "articulation" is customarily used when the contextual relationships among the units of speech material are thought to play an unimportant role; the word "intelligibility," when the context is thought to play an important role in determining the listener's perception.

articulation equivalent—The articulation of speech reproduced over a complete telephone connection, expressed numerically in terms of the trunk loss of a working reference system which is adjusted to give equal articulation.

artificial antenna—Also called dummy antenna. A device which simulates a real antenna in its essential impedance characteristics and has the necessary power-handling capabilities, but which does not radiate or receive radio waves. Used mainly for testing and adjusting transmitters.

artificial ear—A microphone-equipped device for measuring the sound pressures developed by an earphone. To the earphone it presents an acoustic impedance equivalent to the impedance presented by the human ear.

artificial echo—1. Received reflections of a transmitted pulse from an artificial target, such as an echo box, corner reflector, or other metallic reflecting surface. 2. A delayed signal from a pulsed radio-frequency signal generator.

artificial horizon—A gyroscopically operated instrument that shows, within limited degrees, the pitching and banking of an aircraft with respect to the horizon. Lines or marks on the face of the instrument represent the aircraft and the horizon. The relative positions of the two are then easily discernible.

artificial ionization—Introduction of an artificial reflecting or scattering layer into the atmosphere to permit beyond-the-horizon communications.

artificial line—A lumped-constant network designed to simulate some or all the characteristics of a transmission line over a desired frequency range.

artificial line duct—A balancing network simulating the impedance of the real line and distant terminal apparatus. It is employed in a duplex circuit to make the receiving device unresponsive to outgoing signal currents.

artificial load—Also called dummy load. A dissipative but essentially nonradiating device having the impedance characteristics of an antenna, transmission line, or other practical utilization circuit.

artificial radioactivity — Radioactivity induced in stable elements under controlled conditions by bombarding them with neutrons or high-energy, charged particles. Artificially radioactive elements emit beta and/or gamma rays.

artificial voice—A small speaker mounted in a specially shaped baffle that is proportioned to simulate the acoustical constants of the human head. It is used for calibrating and testing close-talking microphones.

artos stripper—A machine which, when properly adjusted, will automatically measure to a predetermined length, cut, strip, count, and tie wire in bundles.

artwork—An accurately scaled configuration used to produce a master pattern.

ASA—Abbreviation for American Standards Association.

ASA code—A code recommended by the American Standards Association for industry-wide use in the transmission of information.

asbestos—A nonflammable material generally used for heat insulation, such as in a line-cord resistor.

A-scan.

A-scan—Also called A-display. On a cathode-ray indicator, a presentation in which time (range or distance) is one co-ordinate (horizontal) and signals appear as perpendicular deflections to the time scale (vertical).

A-scope—An oscilloscope that uses an A-scan to present the range of a target as the distance along a horizontal line from the transmitted pulse pip to the target, or echo pip. Signals appear as vertical excursions of the horizontal line, or trace.

aspect ratio—Ratio of frame width to frame height. In the United States the television standard is 4/3.

asperities—Local microscopic points on an electrode surface at which there is considerable field enhancement. They lead to a dependence of electric strength on electrode area (area effect).

aspheric—Not spherical; an optical element having one or more surfaces that are not spherical.

ASR—1. Abbreviation for airport surveillance radar. 2. Abbreviation for automatic send-receive set. A combination teletypewriter, transmitter, and receiver with transmission capability from either a keyboard or paper tape. Most often used in a half-duplex circuit.

ASRA—Abbreviation for automatic stereophonic recording amplifier. An instrument developed by Columbia Broadcasting System for stereo recording. Compression of the vertical component of the stereo recording signal is automatically decreased or increased as required by the recording conditions.

assemble—In digital computer programming, to put together subprograms into a complete program.

assembly—1. A complete operating unit, such as a radio receiver, made up of subassemblies such as an amplifier and various components. 2. Process in which instructions written in symbolic form by the programmer are changed to machine language by the computer.

assembly program—A computer program flexible enough to incorporate subroutines into the main program.

assignable cause—A definitely identified factor contributing to a quality variation.

assigned frequency—The center of the frequency band assigned to a station.

assigned frequency band—The frequency band, the center of which coincides with the frequency assigned to the station, and the width of which equals the necessary bandwidth plus twice the absolute value of the frequency tolerance.

astable circuit—A circuit which continuously alternates between its two unstable states at a frequency determined by the circuit constants. It can be readily synchronized by applying a repetitive input signal of slightly higher frequency. A blocking oscillator is an example of an astable circuit.

astable multivibrator (free-running)—A circuit having two momentarily stable states, between which it continuously alternates, remaining in each for a period controlled by the circuit parameters and switching rapidly from one to the other.

Astable multivibrator.

astatic—1. Having no particular orientation or directional characteristics; such as a vertical antenna. 2. Being in neutral equi-librium; having no tendency toward any change of position.

astatic galvanometer—A sensitive galvanometer used for detecting small currents. Consists of two small magnetized needles of equal size and strength arranged in parallel and with their north and south poles adjacent, suspended inside the galvanometer coil. Since the resultant magnetic moment is zero, the earth's magnetic field does not affect the system.

astigmatism—A type of spherical aberration in which the rays from a single point of an object do not converge on the image, thereby causing a blurred image. Astigmatism in an electron-beam tube is a focus defect in which electrons in different axial planes come to focus at different points.

astrionics—Electronics as involved with astronautics.

astrocompass—An instrument for determining direction relative to the stars. It is unaffected by the errors to which magnetic or gyrocompasses are subject.

astrodome—A rigid hemispherical structure used to cover large tracking instruments to protect them from the elements. It is usually constructed so that the dome rotates with the instrument.

astronautics—The science and art of operating space vehicles.

astrotracker—A device for tracking stars.

A-supply—The A-battery, transformer filament winding, or other voltage source that supplies power for heating the filaments of vacuum tubes.

asymmetrical cell—A cell, such as a photoelectric cell, in which the impedance to the flow of current is greater in one direction than in the other direction.

asymmetrical distortion—Distortion affecting a two-condition or binary modulation or restitution, in which all the significant intervals corresponding to one of the two significant conditions have longer or shorter durations than the corresponding theoretical durations of the excitation. If this particular requirement is not met, distortion is present.

asymmetric sideband transmission — *See* Vestigial Sideband Transmission.

asymmetry control—In pH meters, an adjustment sometimes provided to compensate for differences in the electrodes.

asymptote—A line which comes nearer and nearer a given curve but never touches it.

asymptotic breakdown voltage—A voltage that will break down insulation if applied over a long period of time.

asynchronous—Not having a constant period.

asynchronous computer—An automatic digital computer in which an operation is started by a signal denoting that the previous operation has been completed.

asynchronous device—A device in which the speed of operation is not related to any frequency in the system to which it is connected.

asynchronous machine — Any machine in which its speed of operation is not proportionate to the frequency of the system to which the machine is connected.

AT-cut crystal—A quartz-crystal slab cut at a 35° angle with respect to the optical, or Z-axis, of the crystal. It has practically a zero temperature coefficient and is used at frequencies of about 0.5 to 10 megahertz.

atmosphere—1. The body of air surrounding the earth. 2. A unit of pressure defined as the pressure of 760 mm of mercury at 0° C. Approximately 14.7 pounds per square inch.

atmospheric absorption—The energy lost in the transmission of radio waves due to dissipation in the atmosphere.

atmospheric absorption noise—The dominant noise factor, at frequencies above 1000 MHz, caused by the absorption of energy from radio waves by oxygen and water vapor in the atmosphere.

atmospheric duct—Within the troposphere, a condition in which the variation of refractive index is such that the propagation of an abnormally large proportion of any radiation of sufficiently high frequency is confined within the limits of a stratum. This effect is most noticeable above 3,000 MHz.

atmospheric electricity — Static electricity between clouds, or between clouds and the earth.

atmospheric noise—Also called atmospherics. The noise heard during radio reception because of atmospheric interference.

atmospheric pressure—The barometric pressure of air at a particular location on the earth's surface. The nominal, or standard, value of atmospheric pressure is 760 mm of mercury (14.7 pounds per square inch) at sea level. Atmospheric pressure decreases at higher altitudes.

atmospheric radio wave—A radio wave that is propagated by reflections in the atmosphere. May include the ionospheric wave, the tropospheric wave, or both.

atmospheric radio window—That portion of the frequency spectrum that will allow radio-frequency waves to pass through the earth's atmosphere (approximately 10 to 10,000 MHz).

atmospheric refraction — The bending of the path of electromagnetic radiation from a distant point as the radiation passes obliquely through varying air densities.

atmospherics—Also referred to as static, atmospheric noise, and strays. In a radio tuner or receiver, noise due to natural weather phenomena and electrical charges existing in the atmosphere.

Atom.

atom—The smallest portion of an element which exhibits all properties of the element. It is pictured as composed of a positively charged nucleus containing almost all the mass of the atom, surrounded by one or more electrons. In the neutral atom, the number of electrons is such that their total charge (negative) exactly equals the positive charge in the nucleus.

atomic battery—*See* Nuclear Battery.

atomic charge—The electronic charge of an ion, equal to the number of ionization multiplied by the charge on one electron.

atomic energy—*See* Nuclear Energy.

atomic fission—*See* Fission.

atomic frequency — The natural vibration frequency of an atom.

atomic fuel—A fissionable material—i.e., one in which the atomic nucleus may be split to release energy.

atomic fusion—*See* Fusion.

atomic mass unit—Abbreviated amu. Used to express the relative masses of isotopes. It is so proportioned that the mass of a neutral atom of the naturally most abundant isotope of oxygen (O16) is 16.00000 atomic mass units.

atomic migration—The progressive transfer of a valance electron from one atom to another within the same molecule.

atomic number—The number of protons (positively charged particles) in the nucleus of an atom. All elements have different atomic numbers, which determine their positions in the periodic table. For example, the atomic number of hydrogen is 1; that of oxygen is 8; iron, 26; lead, 82; uranium, 92.

atomic power—*See* Nuclear Energy.

atomic ratio—The ratio of quantities of different substances to the number of atoms of each.

atomic reactor—*See* Nuclear Reactor.

atomic theory—A generally accepted theory concerning the structure and composition of substances and compounds. It states that everything is composed of various combinations of ultimate particles called atoms.

atomic weight—The approximate weight of the number of protons and neutrons in the nucleus of an atom. The atomic weight of oxygen, for example, is approximately 16 (actually it is 16.0044)—it contains 8 neutrons and 8 protons. Aluminum is 27 and contains 14 neutrons and 13 protons. If expressed in grams, these weights are called gram atomic weights.

ATR tube — Abbreviation for antitransmit-receive tube. A gas-filled, radio-frequency switching tube used to isolate the transmitter while a pulse is being received.

attachment cord—*See* Patch Cord.

attack—The length of time it takes for a tone in an organ to reach full intensity after a key is depressed. On most organs this effect is adjustable by either a switch or potentiometer.

attack time—The interval required for an

ATR (switch) tube.

Attenuators.

propagation ratio which indicates the relative decrease in energy.

input signal, after suddenly increasing in amplitude, to attain a specified percentage (usually 63%) of the ultimate change in amplification or attenuation due to this increase.

attenuating — Decreasing electrical current, voltage, or power in a communicating channel. Refers to audio, radio, or carrier frequencies.

attenuation—The decrease in amplitude of a signal during its transmission from one point to another. It may be expressed as a ratio or, by extension of the term, in decibels.

attenuation constant—1. The real component of the propagation constant. 2. For a traveling plane wave at a given frequency, the rate at which the amplitude of a field component (or the voltage or current) decreases exponentially in the direction of propagation, in nepers or decibels per unit length.

attenuation distortion—1. In a circuit or system, its departure from uniform amplification or attenuation over the frequency range required for transmission. 2. Distortion that causes a decrease in the amplitude of a field component (voltage or current) in the direction of propagation.

attenuation equalizer—A corrective network designed to make the absolute value of the transfer impedance of two chosen pairs of terminals substantially constant for all frequencies within a desired range.

attenuation-frequency distortion — A form of wave distortion in which the relative magnitudes of the different frequency components of the wave are changed.

attenuation network—1. A network providing relatively slight phase shift and substantially constant attenuation over a range of frequencies. 2. The arrangement of circuit elements, usually impedance elements, inserted in circuitry to introduce a known loss or to reduce the impedance level without reflections.

attenuation ratio — The magnitude of the

attenuator—1. An adjustable resistive network for reducing the amplitude of an electrical signal without introducing appreciable phase or frequency distortion. 2. A distributed network that absorbs part of a signal and transmits the remainder with a minimum of distortion or delay.

attenuator tube—A gas-filled, radio-frequency switching tube in which a gas discharge, initiated and regulated independently from the radio-frequency power, is used to control this r-f power by reflection or absorption.

atto—Prefix meaning 10^{-18}. Abbreviated a.

audibility—1. The ability to be heard, usually construed as being heard by the human ear. 2. The ratio of the strength of a specific sound to the strength of a sound that can barely be heard. Usually expressed in decibels.

audible—Capable of being heard, in most contexts by the average human ear.

audible tones—Sounds composed of frequencies which the average human can detect.

audio—Pertaining to frequencies corresponding to a normally audible sound wave. These frequencies range roughly from 15 to 20,000 hertz.

audio amplifier — *See* Audio-Frequency Amplifier.

audio band—The range of audio frequencies passed by an amplifier, receiver, transmitter, etc. (*Also see* Audio Frequency.)

audio-channel wire—A small-diameter wire, shielded and jacketed, used primarily in radio and television for wiring consoles, panels, etc.

audio component—That portion of any wave or signal which contains frequencies in the audible range (between 15 and 20,000 hertz).

audio frequency—Abbreviated af. Any frequency corresponding to a normally audible sound wave. Audio frequencies range roughly from 15 to 20,000 hertz.

audio-frequency amplification—An increase in voltage, current, or power of a signal at the audio frequency.

audio-frequency amplifier—Also called audio amplifier. A device which contains one or more electron tubes or transistors (or both) and which is designed to amplify signals within a frequency range of about 20 to 20,000 hertz.

audio-frequency choke—An inductance used to impede the flow of audio-frequency currents.

audio-frequency noise — In the audio-frequency range, any electrical disturbance introduced from a source extraneous to the signal.

audio-frequency oscillator—An oscillator circuit using an electron tube, transistor, or other nonrotating device capable of producing audio signals.

audio-frequency peak limiter — A circuit generally used in the audio system of a radio transmitter to prevent overmodulation. It keeps the signal amplitude from exceeding a predetermined value.

audio-frequency shift modulator—A system of facsimile transmission over radio, in which the frequency shift required is applied through an 800-hertz shift of an audio signal, rather than shifting the transmitter frequency. The radio signal is modulated by the shifting audio signal, usually at 1500 to 2300 hertz.

audio-frequency transformer — Also called audio transformer. An iron-core transformer for use with audio-frequency currents to transfer signals from one circuit to another. Used for impedance matching or to permit maximum transfer of power.

audiogram—Also called threshold audiogram. A graph showing hearing loss, percent of hearing loss, or percent of hearing as a function of frequency.

audio-level meter—An instrument that measures audio-frequency power with reference to a predetermined level. Usually calibrated in decibels.

audiometer — An instrument for measuring hearing acuity. Measurements may be made with speech signals (usually recorded) or with tone signals.

audion—A three-electrode vacuum tube introduced by Dr. Lee de Forest.

audio oscillator—*See* Audio-Frequency Oscillator.

audio patch bay—Specific patch panels provided for termination of all audio circuits and equipment used in the channel and technical-control facility. This equipment can also be found in transmitting and receiving stations.

audio peak limiter — *See* Audio-Frequency Peak Limiter.

audiophile—A person who is interested in good musical reproduction for his own personal listening and who uses the latest audio equipment and techniques.

audio signal—An electrical signal the frequency of which is within the audio range.

audio spectrum—The continuous range of audio frequencies extending from the lowest to the highest (from about 15 to 20,000 hertz.

audio taper — Semilogarithmic change of resistance. Used on tone controls in audio amplifiers to compensate for the lower sensitivity of the human ear when listening to low-volume sounds.

audio transformer — *See* Audio-Frequency Transformer.

audiovisual—Involving both sight and sound. (As audiovisual education uses films, slides, phonograph records, and the like, to supplement instruction.)

audiovisual system—A system of communications which simultaneously transmits pictorial and audio signals.

augend—In an arithmetic addition, the number increased by having another number (called the addend) added to it.

augmented operation code—In a computer, an operation code that is further defined by information contained in another portion of an instruction.

aural—Pertaining to the ear or to the sense of hearing. (*Also see* Audio.)

aural radio range—A radio range the courses of which are normally followed by interpretation of an aural signal.

aural signal—The signal corresponding to the sound portion of a television program. In general, the audible component of a signal.

aural transmitter—The equipment used to transmit the aural (sound) signals from a television broadcast station.

aurora—Sheets, streamers, or streaks of pale light often seen in the skies of the northern and southern hemispheres. The aurora borealis and aurora australis.

auroral absorption — Absorption of radio waves due to auroral activity. (*Also see* Aurora.)

authorized carrier frequency — A specific carrier frequency authorized for use, from which the actual carrier frequency is permitted to deviate, solely because of frequency instability, by an amount not to exceed the frequency tolerance.

autoalarm—Also called automatic alarm receiver. A device which is tuned to the international distress frequency of 500 kHz and which automatically actuates an alarm if any signal is received.

auto call—An alerting device which sounds a preset code of signals in a building, to page those persons whose code is being sounded.

autodyne circuit—A vacuum-tube circuit which serves simultaneously as an oscillator and as a heterodyne detector.

autodyne reception—A type of radio reception employed in regenerative receivers for the reception of c-w code signals. In this system the incoming signal beats with the signal from an oscillating detector to produce an audible beat frequency.

auto-man—A locking switch which controls the method of operation—i.e., automatic or manual.

automata—A plural form of automaton.

automatic—Self-regulating or self-acting; capable of producing a desired response to certain predetermined conditions.

automatic-alarm receiver — Complete receiving, selecting, and warning device capable of being actuated automatically by intercepted radio-frequency signals forming the international automatic-alarm signal.

automatic back bias—A radar-receiver technique which consists of one or more automatic gain-control loops to prevent large signals from overloading a receiver, whether by jamming or by actual echoes.

automatic bass compensation—A circuit used in a receiver or audio amplifier to make the bass notes sound more natural at low volume settings. The circuit, which usually consists of resistors and capacitors connected to taps on the volume control, automatically compensates for the poor response of the human ear to weak sounds.

automatic bias—*See* Self-Bias.

automatic brightness control—A circuit used in television receivers to keep the average brightness of the reproduced image essentially constant. Its action is similar to that of an automatic volume-control circuit.

automatic check—An operation performed by equipment built into an electronic computer to automatically verify proper operation.

automatic chrominance control—A color-television circuit which automatically controls the gain of the chrominance bandpass amplifier by varying the bias.

automatic circuit breaker—A device that automatically opens a circuit, usually by electromagnetic means, when the current exceeds a safe value. Unlike a fuse, which must be replaced once it blows, the circuit breaker can be reset manually when the current is again within safe limits.

automatic coding—A technique by which a digital computer is programmed to perform a significant portion of the coding of a problem.

automatic color purifier—*See* Automatic Degausser.

automatic computer—A computer which automatically handles long sequences of reasonable operations without further intervention from a human being.

automatic contrast control—A television circuit which automatically changes the gain of the video i-f and r-f stages to maintain proper contrast in the television picture.

automatic crossover—A type of current-limiting circuit on a power supply provided with an adjustment for setting the short-circuit current to an adjustable maximum value.

automatic current limiting—An overload-protection mechanism designed to limit the maximum output current of a power supply to a preset value. Usually it automatically restores the output when the overload is removed.

automatic cutout—A device operated by electromagnetism or centrifugal force, to automatically disconnect some parts of an equipment after a predetermined operating limit has been reached.

automatic data processing—The processing of digital information by automatic computers and other machines. Abbreviated ADP. Also called integrated data processing.

automatic degausser—Also called automatic color purifier and degausser. An arrangement of degaussing coils mounted around a color-television picture tube. These coils are energized only for a short while after the set is turned on. They serve to demagnetize any parts of the picture tube that may have been affected by the earth's magnetic field or the magnetic field of any nearby home appliance.

automatic direction finder—Abbreviated ADF. Also called an automatic radio compass. An electronic device, usually for marine or aviation application, which provides a radio bearing to any transmitter whose frequency is known but whose direction and location are not.

automatic error correction—A technique, usually requiring the use of special codes and/or automatic retransmission, which detects and corrects errors occurring in transmission. The degree of correction depends upon coding and equipment configuration.

automatic exchange—A telephone exchange in which connections are made between subscribers by means of devices set in operation by the originating subscriber's instrument and without the intervention of an operator.

automatic focusing—A method of electrostatically focusing a television picture tube; the focusing anode is internally connected through a resistor to the cathode and thus requires no external focusing voltage.

automatic frequency control—Abbreviated afc. A circuit that automatically maintains the frequency of an oscillator within specified limits.

automatic gain control—1. Abbreviated agc. A type of circuit used to maintain the output volume of a receiver constant, regardless of variations in the signal strength applied to the receiver. 2. A self-acting compensation device which maintains the output of a transmission system constant within narrow limits in the face of wide variations in the attenuation of the system. 3. A radar circuit which prevents saturation of the radar receiver by long blocks of received signals, or by a carrier modulated at low frequency.

automatic gain stabilization—A circuit, used in certain identification friend-or-foe equipment and radar beacon systems, which serves to maintain optimum sensitivity in a superregenerative stage by keeping the noise-pulse load constant. The system prevents random noises from triggering the automatic transmitter associated with the receiver.

automatic grid bias—Grid-bias voltage provided by the difference in potential across a resistance (or resistances) in the grid or cathode circuit due to grid or cathode current or both.

automatic level compensation—A system which automatically compensates for variations in the circuit. *See also* Automatic Volume Control.

automatic light control—The process by

which the illumination incident upon the face of a television pickup device is automatically adjusted as a function of scene brightness.

automatic modulation control—A transmitter circuit that reduces the gain for excessively strong audio input signals without affecting the strength of normal signals, thus permitting higher average modulation without overmodulation; this is equivalent to an increase in the carrier-frequency power output.

automatic noise limiter — A vacuum-tube circuit that automatically clips off all noise peaks above the highest peak of the desired signal being received. This circuit prevents strong atmospheric or man-made interference from being troublesome.

automatic pedestal control—The process by which the pedestal height of a television signal is automatically adjusted as a function of the input or other specified parameter.

automatic phase control—A circuit used in color television receivers to synchronize the burst signal with the 3.58-MHz color oscillator.

automatic pilot—*See* Autopilot.

automatic programming—Any technique designed to simplify the writing and execution of programs in a computer. Examples are assembly programs which translate from the programmer's symbolic language to the machine language, those which assign absolute addresses to instruction and data words, and those which integrate subroutines into the main routine.

automatic radio compass—A radio direction finder which automatically rotates the loop antenna to the correct position. A bearing can then be secured from the indicator dials without mechanical adjustments or calculation. (*Also see* Automatic Direction Finder.)

automatic record changer — An electrically operated mechanism which automatically feeds, plays, and rejects a number of records in a preset sequence. It consists of a motor, turntable, pickup arm, and changer. Modern changers are designed to play automatically $16\frac{2}{3}$-, $33\frac{1}{3}$-, 45-, and 78-rpm records.

automatic relay — A means of selective switching which causes automatic equipment to record and retransmit communications.

automatic reset—1. A stepping relay that returns to its home position either when it reaches a predetermined contact position or when a pulsing circuit fails to energize its driving coil within a given time. 2. An overload relay that restores the circuit as soon as the cause of the overload is corrected.

automatic reset relay—1. A stepping relay that returns to its home position either when it reaches a predetermined contact position or when a pulsing circuit fails to energize the driving coil within a given time. It may either pulse forward or be spring-reset to the home position. 2. An overload relay that re-

stores the circuit as soon as an overcurrent situation is corrected.

automatic scanning—A variable-speed sweep of the entire frequency range of an RFI meter. It may also include the scanning of a portion of this frequency range over a predetermined sector.

automatic scanning receiver — A receiver which can automatically and continuously sweep across a preselected frequency, either to stop when a signal is found or to plot signal occupancy within the frequency spectrum being swept.

automatic selective control (or transfer) relay—A device which operates to select automatically between certain sources or conditions in an equipment, or performs a transfer operation automatically.

automatic sensitivity control — A circuit used for automatically maintaining the receiver sensitivity at a predetermined level. It is similar to an automatic gain control, but it affects the receiver constantly rather than during the brief interval selected by the range gate. 2. The self-acting mechanism which varies the system sensitivity as a function of the specified control parameters. This may include automatic target control, automatic light control, or any combination thereof.

automatic sequencing — The ability of a computer to perform successive operations without additional instructions from a human being.

automatic short-circuit protection—An automatic current-limiting system which enables a power supply to continue operating at a limited current, and without damage, into any output overload, including a short circuit. The output voltage is restored to normal when the overload is removed, as distinguished from a fuse or circuit-breaker system which opens with overload and must be reclosed manually to restore power.

automatic shutoff — In a tape recorder, a switching arrangement which automatically shuts the recorder off when the tape breaks or runs out. Also, a switching arrangement which stops the record changer after the last record.

automatic starter—A device which, after being given the initial impulse by means of a push button or similar device, starts a system or motor automatically in the proper sequence.

automatic target control — The self-acting mechanism which controls the vidicon target potential as a function of the scene brightness.

automatic telegraph transmission—A form of telegraphy in which signals are transmitted mechanically from a perforated tape.

automatic telegraphy—A form of telegraphy in which signals are transmitted and/or received automatically.

automatic threshold variation—A constant false-alarm rate scheme which is an open-loop type of automatic gain control in which the decision threshold is varied continuously in proportion to the incoming intermediate frequency and video noise level.

automatic time switch—A combination of a switch with an electric or spring-wound clock arranged to turn an apparatus on and off at predetermined times.

automatic tracking—In radar, the process whereby a mechanism, actuated by the echo, automatically keeps the radar beam locked on the target, and may also determine the range simultaneously.

automatic transfer equipment—Equipment which automatically transfers a load so that a source of power may be selected from one of several incoming lines.

automatic tuning—An electrical, mechanical, or electrical/mechanical system that automatically tunes a circuit to a predetermined frequency when a button or other control is operated.

automatic video-noise leveling—A constant false-alarm rate scheme in which the video-noise level at the output of the receiver is sampled at the end of each range sweep and the receiver gain is readjusted accordingly to maintain a constant video-noise level at the output.

automatic voltage regulator—A device or circuit which maintains a constant voltage, regardless of any variation in input voltage or load.

automatic volume compression—*See* Volume Compression.

automatic volume control (avc)—1. A self-acting compensation device which maintains the output of a transmission system constant within narrow limits in the face of wide variations in attenuation in that system. 2. A self-acting device which maintains the output of a radio receiver or amplifier substantially constant within relatively narrow limits while the input voltage varies over a wide range. 3. *See also* Automatic Level Compensation.

automatic volume expansion—Also called volume expansion. An audio-frequency circuit that automatically increases the volume range by making loud portions louder and weak ones weaker. This is done to make radio reception sound more like the actual program, because the volume range of programs is generally compressed at the point of broadcast.

automatic zero and full-scale calibration correction—A system of zero and sensitivity stabilization in which electronic servos are used that compare demodulated "zero" and "full-scale" signals with reference voltages.

automation—1. The method or act of making a manufacturing or processing system partially or fully automatic. 2. The entire field of investigation, design, development, application, and methods of rendering or making processes or machines self-acting or self-moving; rendering automatic.

automaton—1. A device that automatically follows predetermined operations or responds to encoded instructions. 2. Any communication-linked set of elements. 3. A machine which exhibits living properties.

automonitor—1. To instruct an automatic digital computer to produce a record of its information-handling operations. 2. A program or routine for this purpose.

autopilot—Also called automatic pilot, gyropilot, or robot pilot. A device containing amplifiers, gyroscopes, and servomotors which automatically control and guide the flight of an aircraft or guided missile. The autopilot detects any deviation from the planned flight and automatically applies the necessary corrections to keep the aircraft or missile on course.

auto radio—A radio receiver designed to be installed in an automobile and powered by the storage battery of the automobile.

autoradiography—Self-portraits of radioactive sources made by placing the radioactive material next to photographic film. The radiations fog the film and thus leave an image of the source.

autoregulation induction heater—An induction heater in which a desired control is effected by the change in characteristics of a magnetic charge as it is heated at or near its Curie point.

autostarter—*See* Autotransformer Starter.

Autosyn—A trade name of the Bendix Corp. for a remote-indicating instrument or system based on the synchronous-motor principle in which the angular position of the rotor of a motor at the measuring source is duplicated by the rotor of the indicator motor.

auto tracking—Also called automatic tracking operation. A master/slave connection of two or more power supplies, each of which has one of its output terminals in common with one of the output terminals of all of the other supplies, such connections being characterized by one-knob control and proportional output voltage from all supplies. Useful where simultaneous turn-up, turndown, or proportional control of all power supplies in a system is required.

autotransformer—1. A transformer with a single winding (electrically) in which the whole winding acts as the primary winding, and only part of the winding acts as the secondary (step-down); or part of the winding acts as the primary and the whole winding acts as the secondary (step-up). 2. A voltage, current, or impedance transforming device in which parts of one winding are common to both the primary and secondary circuits.

Autotransformer.

autotransformer starter — Also called a compensator or autostarter. A motor starter having an autotransformer to furnish a reduced voltage for starting. Includes the necessary switching mechanism.

auxiliary actuator — A mechanism which may be attached to a switch to modify its characteristics.

auxiliary circuit—Any circuit other than the main circuit.

auxiliary contacts — In a switching device, contacts, in addition to the main circuit contacts, which function with the movement of the latter.

auxiliary memory—See Auxiliary Storage.

auxiliary relay—1. A relay which responds to the opening or closing of its operating circuit, to assist another relay or device in the performance of a function. 2. A relay actuated by another relay and used to control secondary circuit functions such as signals, lights, or other devices. Also called slave relay.

auxiliary-station line filter — A line filter for use at repeated points to separate frequencies of different carrier systems, using the same line pair. For example, such a filter might be used at a high-frequency carrier-system repeater to bypass the low-frequency carrier system and voice frequencies around the repeater.

auxiliary storage — Also called auxiliary memory. Storage capacity in a digital computer, in addition to the main memory.

auxiliary switch—A switch actuated by some device such as a circuit breaker, for signaling, interlocking, or other purpose.

auxiliary transmitter—A transmitter held in readiness in case the main transmitter of a broadcasting station fails.

availability—1. The ratio, expressed as a percent, of the time during a given period that an equipment is correctly operating to the total time in that period. Also called operating ratio. 2. The probability that a system is operating satisfactorily at any point in time when used under stated conditions, where the total time considered includes operating time, active repair time, administrative time, and logistic time.

available conversion gain—Ratio of available output-frequency power from the output terminals of a transducer to the available input-frequency power from the driving generator, with terminating conditions specified for all frequencies which may affect the result. Applies to outputs of such magnitude that the conversion transducer is operating in a substantially linear condition.

available gain—The ratio of the available power at the output terminals of the network to the available power at the input terminals of the network.

available line—In a facsimile system, that portion of a scanning line which can be used for picture signals. Expressed as a percentage of the length of the scanning line.

available machine time—Time after the application of power during which a computer is operating correctly.

available power—1. The mean square of the open-circuit terminal voltage of a linear source, divided by four times the resistive component of the source impedance. 2. Of a network, the power that would be delivered to a conjugately matched load. It is the maximum power that a network can deliver. Available power, though defined in terms of an output load impedance, is independent of that impedance.

available power gain—Sometimes called completely matched power gain. Ratio of the available power from the output terminals of a linear transducer, under specified input-termination conditions, to the available power from the driving generator. The available power gain of an electrical transducer is maximum when the input-termination admittance is the conjugate of the driving-point admittance at the input terminals of the transducer.

available signal-to-noise ratio—Ratio of the available signal power at a point in a circuit, to the available random-noise power.

avalanche—Rapid generation of a current flow with reverse-bias conditions as electrons sweep across a junction with enough energy to ionize other bonds and create electron-hole pairs, making the action regenerative.

avalanche breakdown—In a semiconductor diode, a nondestructive breakdown caused by the cumulative multiplication of carriers through field-induced impact ionization.

avalanche conduction—A form of conduction in a semiconductor in which charged-particle collisions create additional hole-electron pairs.

avalanche diode—Also called breakdown diode. A silicon diode that has a high ratio of reverse-to-forward resistance until avalanche breakdown occurs. After breakdown the voltage drop across the diode is essentially constant and is independent of the current. Used for voltage regulating and voltage limiting. Originally called zener diode, before it was found that the Zener effect had no significant role in the operation of diodes of this type.

avalanche impedance — See Breakdown Impedance.

avalanche noise—A phenomenon in a semiconductor junction in which carriers in a high-voltage gradient develop sufficient energy to dislodge additional carriers through physical impact.

avc—See Automatic Volume Control.

average—See Arithmetic Mean.

average absolute pulse amplitude — The average of the absolute value of instantaneous amplitude taken over the pulse duration. Absolute value means the arithmetic value regardless of algebraic sign.

average brightness—The average illumination in a television picture.

average calculating operation—A typical computer calculating operation longer than an addition and shorter than a multiplication, often taken as the mean of nine additions and one multiplication.

average electrode current—The value obtained by integrating the instantaneous electrode current over an averaging time and dividing by the average time.

average life—See Mean Life.

average noise factor—See Average Noise Figure.

average noise figure—Also called average noise factor. In a transducer, the ratio of total output noise power to the portion attributable to thermal noise in the input termination, the total noise being summed over frequencies from zero to infinity and the noise temperature of the input termination being standard (290° K).

average power output of an amplitude-modulated transmitter—The radio-frequency power delivered to the transmitter output terminals, averaged over a modulation cycle.

average pulse amplitude—The average of the instantaneous amplitudes taken over the pulse duration.

average rate of transmission—Effective speed of transmission.

average value—The value obtained by dividing the sum of a number of quantities by the number of quantities. The average value of a sine wave is 0.637 times the peak value.

average voltage—The sum of the instantaneous voltages in a half-cycle waveshape, divided by the number of instantaneous voltages. In a sine wave, the average voltage is equal to 0.637 times the peak voltage.

aviation channels—A band of frequencies, below and above the standard broadcast band, assigned exclusively for aircraft and aviation applications.

aviation services—The aeronautical mobile and radionavigation services.

avionics—An acronym designating the field of AVIation electrONICS.

Avogadro's number—The number (N) of molecules in a gram-molecule or the number of atoms in a gram-atom of a substance. The number $N = 6.02 \times 10^{23}$ molecules.

AWG—American Wire Gage. A means of specifying wire diameter. The higher the number, the smaller the diameter.

Axial leads.

axial leads—Leads coming out the ends and along the axes of a resistor, capacitor, or other axial part, rather than out the side.

axial ratio—Ratio of the major axis to the minor axis of the polarization ellipse of a wave guide. This term is preferred over ellipticity, because mathematically ellipticity is 1 minus the reciprocal of the axial ratio.

axis—The straight line, either real or imaginary, passing through a body around which the body revolves or around which parts of a body are symmetrically arranged.

Ayrton-Perry winding—Two conductors connected in parallel so that the current flows in opposite directions in each conductor and thus neutralizes the inductance between the two.

Ayrton shunt—Also called universal shunt. A high-resistance parallel connection used to increase the range of a galvanometer without changing the damping.

azel display—A modified type of plan-position indicator presentation showing two separate radar displays on one cathode-ray screen. One display presents bearing information, and the other shows elevation.

azimuth—The angular measurement in a horizontal plane and in a clockwise direction.

azimuth alignment—Alignment of the recording and reproducing gaps so that their center lines lie parallel with one another. Misalignment of the gaps causes a loss in output at short wavelengths.

azimuth gain reduction—A technique which allows control of the radar receiver system throughout any two azimuth sectors.

azimuth rate—The rate of change of true bearing.

azimuth resolution—The angle or distance by which two targets must be separated in azimuth to be distinguished by a radar set, when the targets are at the same range.

azimuth stabilization—The presentation of indications on a radar display so that north, or any specific reference line of direction, is always at the top of the screen.

azimuth-stabilized, plan-position indicator—A ppi scope on which the reference bearing (usually true or magnetic north) remains fixed with respect to the indicator, regardless of the vehicle orientation.

azimuth versus amplitude—An electronic counter-countermeasures receiver with plan-position indicator-type display attached to the main antenna, used to display strobes due to jamming aircraft. It is useful in making passive fixes when two or more radar sites can operate together.

azusa—A short base-line continuous-wave phase-comparison electronic tracking system operating on the C-band, wherein a single station provides two direction cosines and slant range.

B

B—1. Symbol for the base of a transistor. 2. Symbol for magnetic flux. 3. Abbreviation for photometric brightness. 4. B or b. Abbreviation for susceptance.

B— (B-minus or B-negative) — Negative terminal of a B battery or the negative polarity of other sources of anode voltage. Denotes the terminal to which the negative side of the anode-voltage source should be connected.

B+ (B-plus or B-positive)—Positive terminal of a B battery or the positive polarity of other sources of anode voltage. The terminal to which the positive side of the anode voltage source should be connected.

babble—1. The aggregate cross talk from a large number of disturbing channels. 2. In a carrier, or other multiple-channel system, the unwanted disturbing sounds which result from the aggregate cross talk or mutual interference from other channels.

babble signal—A type of electronic deception signal used to confuse enemy receivers. Generally it has characteristics of enemy transmission signals. It can be composed by superimposing incoming signals on previously recorded intercepted signals. This composite signal can then be radiated as a jamming signal.

BABS (Blind Approach Beacon System)— A pulse-type ground-based navigation beacon used for runway approach. The BABS ground beacon is installed beyond the far end of the runway on the extended center line. When interrogated by an aircraft, it retransmits two diverging beams, one of short and the other of long duration pulses. The beams are transmitted alternately, but because of the fast switching, the aircraft receives what appears to be a continuous transmission of both beams. The cathode-ray tube in the aircraft displays both long and short pulses superimposed on each other. When the aircraft is properly aligned with the runway, the pulses will be of equal amplitude.

back bias—1. A degenerative or regenerative voltage which is fed back to circuits before its originating point. Usually applied to a control anode of a tube. 2. A voltage applied to a grid of a tube (or tubes) to restore a condition which has been upset by some external cause. 3. *Also see* Reverse Bias.

backbone — A high-voltage, high-capacity transmission line or group of lines having a limited number of large-capacity connections between loads and points of generation.

back contact—Relay, key, jack, or other contact designed to close a circuit and permit current to flow when, in the case of a relay, the armature has released or fallen back, or in other cases, when the equipment is inoperative.

back current—Also called reverse current. The current which flows when reverse bias is applied to a semiconductor junction.

back diode—A tunnel diode that is usually chosen for its reverse-conduction characteristics.

back echo—An echo due to the back lobe of an antenna.

back emission—Also called reverse emission. Emission from an electrode occurring only when the electrode has the opposite polarity from that required for normal conduction. A form of primary emission common to rectifiers during the inverse portion of their cycles.

backfire—*See* Arcback.

Back focal length.

back focal length—Distance from the center of a lens to its principal focus on the side of the lens away from the object.

background—1. The picture white of the copy being scanned when the picture is black and white only. Also undesired printing in the recorded copy of the picture being transmitted, resulting in shading of the background area. 2. Noise heard during a radio program; this noise is caused by atmospheric interference or operation of the receiver at such high gain that inherent tube and circuit noises become noticeable.

background control—In color television, a potentiometer used as a means of controlling the d-c level of a color signal at one input of a tricolor picture tube. The setting of this control determines the average (or background) illumination produced by the associated color phosphor.

background count—Count caused by radiation from sources other than the one being measured.

background noise—1. The total system noise, independent from the presence or absence of a signal. The signal is not included as part of the noise. 2. In a receiver, the noise in the absence of signal modulation in the carrier. 3. Any unwanted sound that intrudes upon program material, such as sounds produced as a result of surface imperfections of a disc record.

background radiation—Radiation due to the presence of radioactive material in the vicinity of the measuring instrument.

background response — In radiation detectors, response caused by ionizing radiation from sources other than that to be measured.

backlash—1. In a potentiometer, the maximum difference that occurs in shaft position

43

when the shaft is moved to the same actual output-ratio point from opposite directions. Resolution and contact-width effects must be excluded from this measure. 2. The shortest distance between nondriving tooth surfaces of adjacent teeth in mating gears or the amount of clearance between the teeth or mating gears. Usually measured at the common pitch circle.

Backlash.

backloaded horn—A speaker enclosure arranged so the sound from the front of the cone feeds directly into the room, while the sound from the rear feeds into the room via a folded horn.

back loading—A form of horn loading particularly applicable to low-frequency speakers; the rear radiating surface of the speaker feeds the horn and the front part of the speaker is directly exposed to the room.

back lobe—In the radiation pattern of a directional antenna, that part which extends backward from the main lobe.

back pitch—The winding pitch of the back end of the armature—that is, the end opposite the commutator.

backplate—In a camera tube, the electrode to which the stored-charge image is capacitively coupled.

back porch—In a composite picture signal, that portion which lies between the trailing edge of a horizontal-sync pulse and the trailing edge of the corresponding blanking pulse. A color burst, if present, is not considered part of the back porch.

back-porch effect—The continuation of collector current in a transistor for a short time after the input signal has dropped to zero. The effect is due to storage of minority carriers in the base region. It also occurs in junction diodes.

back-porch tilt—The slope of the back porch from its normal horizontal position. Positive and negative refer respectively to upward and downward tilt to the right.

back scatter—Return, due to scatter, of a portion of electromagnetic radiation toward its source.

backscatter—Propagation of extraneous signals by F- or E- region reflection in addition to the desired ionospheric scatter mode. The undesired signal enters the antenna through the back lobes.

back scattering—1. Radiation of unwanted energy to the rear of an antenna. 2. The

reflected radiation of energy from a target toward the illuminating radar.

back-shunt keying—A method of keying a transmitter, in which the radio-frequency energy is fed to the antenna when the telegraph key is closed and to an artificial load when the key is open.

backstop—That part of the relay which limits the movement of the armature away from the pole face or core. In some relays, a normally closed contact may serve as a backstop.

backswing—The amplitude of the first maximum excursion in the negative direction after the trailing edge of a pulse expressed as a percentage of the 100% amplitude.

back-to-back circuit—Two tubes or semiconductor devices connected in parallel but in opposite directions so that they can be used to control current without introducing rectification. Also called inverse-parallel connection.

backup—1. An item kept available to replace an item which fails to perform satisfactorily. 2. An item under development intended to perform the same general function performed by another item also under development.

backup facility—A communications-electronics facility which is established for the purpose of replacing or supplementing another facility or facilities, under real or simulated emergency conditions.

backup item—An additional item to perform the general functions of another item. It may be secondary to an identified primary item or a parallel development to improve the probability of success in performing the general function.

backwall—The plate in a pot core which connects the center post to the sleeve.

backwall photovoltaic cell—A cell in which light must pass through the front electrode and a semiconductor layer before reaching the barrier layer.

backward-acting regulator—A transmission regulator in which the adjustment made by the regulator affects the quantity which caused the adjustment.

backward diode—A highly doped, alloyed germanium junction that operates on the principle of quantum-mechanical tunneling. The diode is "backward" because its easy-current direction is in the negative-voltage rather than the positive-voltage region of the i-v curve. The backward diode has a negative-resistance region, but the resultant "valley" of its i-v curve is much less pronounced than in tunnel diodes.

backward wave—In a traveling-wave tube, a wave having a group velocity opposite the direction of electron-stream motion.

backward-wave oscillator—An oscillator employing a special vacuum tube in which oscillatory currents are produced by using an oscillatory electromagnetic field to bunch the electrons as they flow from cathode to anode.

backward-wave tube—A traveling-wave tube in which the electrons travel in a direction opposite to that in which the wave is propagated.

back wave—*See* Spacing Wave.

baffle—1. In acoustics, a shielding structure or partition used to increase the effective length of the external transmission path between two points (for example, between the front and back of an electroacoustic transducer). A baffle is often used in a speaker to increase the acoustic loading of the diaphragm. 2. In a gas tube, an auxiliary member placed in the arc path and having no separate external connection. 3. A device for deflecting oil or gas in a circuit breaker.

baffle plate—A metal plate inserted into a waveguide to reduce the cross-sectional area for wave-conversion purposes.

bail—A loop of wire used to prevent permanent separation of two or more parts assembled together—e.g., the bail holding dust-caps on round connectors.

Bakelite—A trademark of the Bakelite Corp. for its line of plastic and resins. Formerly, the term applied only to its phenolic compound used as an insulating material in the construction of radio parts.

balance—1. The effect of blending the volume of various sounds coming over different microphones in order to present them in correct proportion. 2. The maintenance of equal average volume from both speaker systems of a stereo installation.

balance control—On a stereo amplifier, a differential gain control used to vary the volume of one speaker system relative to the other without affecting the over-all volume level. As the volume of one speaker increases and the other decreases, the sound appears to shift from left to center to right, or vice versa.

balanced—1. Electrically alike and symmetrical with respect to ground. 2. Arranged to provide balance between certain sets of terminals.

balanced amplifier—An amplifier circuit with two identical signal branches, connected to operate in phase opposition and with their input and output connections each balanced to ground; for example, a push-pull amplifier.

balanced armature—An armature which is approximately in equilibrium with respect to both static and dynamic forces.

balanced-armature unit—The driving unit used in magnetic speakers, consisting of an iron armature pivoted between the poles of a permanent magnet and surrounded by coils carrying the audio-frequency current. Variations in the audio-frequency current cause corresponding changes in the armature magnetism and corresponding movements of the armature with respect to the poles of the permanent magnet.

balanced circuit—1. A circuit with two sides electrically alike and symmetrical to a common reference point, usually ground. 2. A circuit terminated by a network that has infinite impedance losses.

balanced converter—*See* Balun.

balanced currents—Also called push-pull currents. In the two conductors of a balanced line, currents which are equal in value and opposite in direction at every point along the line.

balanced detector—A demodulator for frequency-modulation systems. In one form, the output consists of the rectified difference of the two voltages produced across two resonant circuits, one circuit being tuned slightly above the carrier frequency and the other slightly below.

balanced line—A line or circuit utilizing two identical conductors. Each conductor is operated so that the voltages on them at any transverse plane are equal in magnitude and opposite in polarity with respect to ground. Thus, the currents on the line are equal in magnitude and opposite in direction. A balanced line is preferred where minimum noise and cross talk are desired.

balanced-line system—A system consisting of a generator, balanced line, and load adjusted so that the voltages of the two conductors at all transverse planes are equal in magnitude and opposite in polarity with respect to ground.

balanced low-pass filter—A low-pass filter designed to be used with a balanced line.

balanced method—A method of measurement in which the reading is taken at zero. It may be a visual or audible reading, and in the latter case the null is the no-sound setting.

balanced modulator—An amplitude modulator in which the control grids of two tubes are connected for parallel operation, and the screen grids and plates for push-pull operation. After modulation, the output contains the two sidebands without the carrier.

balanced network—A hybrid network in which the impedances of the opposite branches are equal.

balanced oscillator—Any oscillator in which (1) the impedance centers of the tank circuits are at ground potential and (2) the voltages between either end and the centers are equal in magnitude and opposite in phase.

balanced termination—For a system or network having two output terminals, a load presenting the same impedance to ground for each output terminal.

balanced transmission line—A transmission line having equal conductor resistances per unit length and equal impedances from each conductor to earth and to other electrical circuits.

balanced voltages—Also called push-pull voltages. On the two conductors of a balanced line, voltages (relative to ground) which are equal in magnitude and opposite in polarity at every point along the line.

balanced-wire circuit—A circuit with two sides electrically alike and symmetrical to ground and other conductors. Commonly refers to a circuit the two sides of which differ only by chance.

balancer—In a direction finder, that portion used for improving the sharpness of the direction indication. It balances out the capacitance effect between the loop and ground.

balance-to-unbalance transformer — A device for matching a pair of lines, balanced with respect to earth, to a pair of lines not balanced with respect to earth.

balancing network — An electrical network designed for use in a circuit in such a way that two branches of the circuit are made substantially conjugate (i.e., such that an electromotive force inserted into one branch produces no current in the other).

balancing unit—1. An antenna-matching device used to permit efficient coupling of a transmitter or receiver having an unbalanced output circuit to an antenna having a balanced transmission line. 2. A device for converting balanced to unbalanced transmission lines, and vice versa, by placing suitable discontinuities at the junction between the lines instead of using lumped components.

ball—In face bonding, a method of providing chips with contact.

ballast lamp—A lamp which maintains a nearly constant current by increasing its resistance as the current increases.

ballast resistor—A special type of resistor used to compensate for fluctuations in alternating-current power-line voltage. It is usually connected in series with the power supply to a receiver or amplifier. The resistance of a ballast resistor increases rapidly with increases in current through it, thereby tending to maintain an essentially constant current despite variations in the line voltage.

ballast tube—A current-controlling resistance device designed to maintain a substantially constant current over a specified range of variations in the applied voltage to a series circuit.

ball bonding—A type of thermocompression bonding which uses a flame to cut a wire as it leaves a capillary feed tube. The molten end of the wire solidifies into a ball, which is pressed against the bonding pad on an integrated circuit.

ballistic galvanometer—An instrument that indicates the effect of a sudden rush of electrical energy, such as the discharge current of a capacitor.

ballistic-missile early-warning system—An electronic system for providing detection and early warning of attack by enemy intercontinental ballistic missiles.

ballistic trajectory—In the trajectory of a missile, the curve traced after the propulsive force is cut off and the body of the missile is acted upon only by gravity, aerodynamic drag, and wind.

ballistrocardiogram—A waveform of the impulse imparted to or incurred by the body as a result of the displacement of blood upon each heartbeat. The period of the cycle of this waveform is the time interval between heart beats. Typically taken in one of two ways—by measuring the seismic disturbance imparted to the table upon which the patient is lying supine, or by measuring the deflection of a heavy metal bar placed across the patient's ankles while he is lying supine.

balop—Contraction of balopticon, an apparatus for the projection of opaque images in conjunction with a television camera.

balopticon—*See* Balop.

balun—Also called balanced converter or "bazooka." An acronym from BALanced to UNbalanced. A device used for matching an unbalanced coaxial transmission line to a balanced two-wire system.

banana jack—A jack that accepts a banana plug. Generally designed for panel mounting.

banana plug—A plug with a banana-shaped spring-metal tip and with elongated springs to provide a low-resistance compression fit.

band—1. Any range of frequencies which lies between two defined limits. 2. A group of radio channels assigned by the FCC to a particular type of radio service:

Very low freq.	(vlf)	10-30 kHz.
Low freq.	(lf)	30-300 kHz.
Medium freq.	(mf)	300-3,000 kHz.
High freq.	(hf)	3-30 MHz.
Very high freq.	(vhf)	30-300 MHz.
Ultrahigh freq.	(uhf)	300-3,000 MHz.
Superhigh freq.	(shf)	3,000-30,000 MHz.
Extremely high freq.	(ehf)	30-300 GHz.

3. A group of tracks or channels on a magnetic drum in an electronic computer. (*Also see* Track.)

band center—The geometric mean between the limits of a band of frequencies.

banded cable — Two or more cables banded together by stainless-steel strapping.

Band-elimination filter characteristic.

band-elimination filter—Also called band-stop filter. A wave filter with a single attenuation band, neither of the cutoff frequencies being zero or infinite. The filter passes frequencies on either side of this band.

bandpass—The number of hertz expressing the difference between the limiting frequencies at which the desired fraction (usually half-power) of the maximum output is obtained.

bandpass-amplifier circuit—A stage designed to uniformly amplify signals of certain frequencies only.

bandpass filter—A wave filter with a single transmission band, neither of the cutoff frequencies being zero or infinite. The filter attenuates frequencies on either side of this band.

bandpass flatness—The variations in gain in the bandpass of a filter or tuned circuit.

bandpass response—Also called flat-top response. The response characteristic in which a definite band of frequencies is transmitted uniformly.

band-rejection filter—A filter having a single attenuation band, with neither of the cutoff frequencies being zero or infinite.

band selector—Also called bandswitch. A switch used to select any one of the bands in which a receiver, signal generator, or transmitter is designed to operate.

B and S gage—Brown and Sharpe wire gage, where the conductor sizes rise in geometrical progression. Adopted as the American Wire Gage standard.

bandspreading—1. The spreading of tuning indications over a wide range to facilitate tuning in a crowded band of frequencies. 2. The method of double-sideband transmission in which the frequency band of the modulating wave is shifted upward so that the sidebands produced by modulation are separated from the carrier by a frequency at least equal to the bandwidth of the original modulating wave. In this way, second-order distortion products may be filtered out of the demodulator output.

bandspread tuning control—A separate tuning control provided on some short-wave receivers to spread the stations in a single band of frequencies over an entire tuning dial.

band-stop filter — See Band-Elimination Filter.

bandswitch—A switch used to select any one of the frequency bands in which an electronic apparatus may operate.

bandwidth—1. The range within the limits of a band. The width of a bandpass filter is generally taken as the limits between which its attenuation is not more than 3.0 decibels greater than its average attenuation throughout its passband. Also used in connection with receiver selectivity, transmitted frequency spectrum occupancy, etc. 2. In a given facsimile system, the difference in hertz between the highest and lowest frequency components required for the adequate transmission of the facsimile signals. 3. The least frequency interval of a wave, outside of which the power spectrum of a

time-varying quantity is everywhere less than some specified fraction of its value at a reference frequency. 4. The range of frequencies of a device, within which its performance, with respect to some characteristic, conforms to a specified standard.

Bandwidth.

bang-bang controller — A discontinuity-type nonlinear system that contains time delay, dead space, and hysteresis.

bank—An aggregation of similar devices (e.g. transformers, lamps, etc.) connected and used together. In automatic switching, a bank is an assemblage of fixed contacts over which one or more wipers or brushes move to establish electric connections.

bank-and-wiper switch—A switch in which the electromagnetic ratchets or other mechanisms are used, first, to move the wipers to a desired group of terminals, and second, to move the wipers over the terminals of this group to the desired bank contacts.

bank winding—Also called banked winding. A compact multilayer form of coil winding used for reducing distributed capacitance. Single turns are wound successively in two or more layers, the entire winding proceeding from one end of the coil to the other without being returned.

bantam tube — A compact tube having a standard octal base but a considerably smaller glass envelope than the standard glass octal tube has.

bar—1. See Microbar. 2. A subdivision of a crystal slab. 3. A vertical or horizontal line on a television screen, used for testing.

bare conductor — A conductor not covered with any insulating material.

bar generator—A generator of pulses or repeating waves which are equally separated in time. These pulses are synchronized by the synchronizing pulses of a television system so that they produce a stationary bar pattern on a television screen.

bar-graph monitoring oscilloscope—An oscilloscope for observation of commutated signals appearing as a series of bars with lengths proportional to channel modulation. The same oscilloscope is commonly used for setup and troubleshooting observations.

barium—An element the oxide of which is used in the cathode coating of vacuum tubes.

barium titanate—A ceramic that has electric properties and is capable of withstanding much higher temperatures than Rochelle salt crystals. Used in crystal pickups and sonar transducers.

Barkhausen effect—A succession of abrupt changes which occur when the magnetizing force acting on a piece of iron or other magnetic material is varied.

Barkhausen interference — Interference caused by Barkhausen oscillations.

Barkhausen-Kurz oscillator — Circuit for generating ultrahigh frequencies. Its operation depends on the variation in the electrical field around the positive grid and less positive plate of a triode; the variation is caused by oscillatory electrons in the interelectrode spaces.

Barkhausen oscillation—A form of parasitic oscillation in the horizontal-output tube of a television receiver; it results in one or more narrow, dark, ragged vertical lines near the left side of the picture or raster.

Barkhausen oscillator—See Barkhausen-Kurz Oscillator.

Barkhausen tube—See Positive-Grid Oscillator Tube.

bar magnet—A bar of metal that has been so strongly magnetized that it holds its magnetism and thereby serves as a permanent magnet.

barn—A unit of measure of nuclear cross sections. Equal to 10^{-24} square centimeters.

Barnett effect—The magnetization resulting from the rotation of a magnetic specimen. The rotation of a ferromagnet produces the same effect as placing the ferromagnet in a magnetic field directed along the axis of rotation. On the macroscopic model, the domains of a ferromagnet can be considered a group of electron systems, each acting as an independent gyroscope or gyrostat.

barometer—An instrument for measuring atmospheric pressure. There are two types of barometers commonly used in meteorology—the mercury barometer and the aneroid barometer.

barometric pressure—The weight of the atmosphere per unit of surface. The standard barometer reading at sea level and 59° F is 29.92 inches of mercury absolute.

bar pattern—A pattern of repeating lines or bars on a television screen. When such a pattern is produced by pulses which are equally separated in time, the spacing between the bars on the television screen can be used to measure the linearity of the horizontal or vertical scanning systems.

bar quad—See B-quad.

barrage jamming—Simultaneous jamming of a number of adjacent channels or frequencies.

bar relay—A relay in which a bar actuates several contacts simultaneously.

barrel distortion—In camera or image tubes, the distortion which results in a monotonic decrease in radial magnification in the reproduced image away from the axis of symmetry of the electron optical system. In tv receivers, barrel distortion makes all four sides of the raster curve out like a barrel.

barretter—A voltage-regulator tube consisting of an iron-wire filament in a hydrogen-filled envelope. The filament is connected in series with the circuit to be regulated and maintains a constant current over a given voltage variation.

barretter mount — A wave-guide mount in which a barretter can be inserted to measure electromagnetic power.

barricade shield—A type of movable shield for protection from radiation.

barrier—A partition for the insulation or isolation of electric circuits or electric arcs.

barrier capacitance — See Depletion-Layer Capacitance.

barrier-film rectifier — A rectifier in which a film having unilateral (single-direction) conductivity is in contact with metal or other normally conducting plates.

barrier grid—A grid close to, or in contact with, a storage surface of a charge storage tube. It establishes an equilibrium voltage for secondary-emission charging and serves to minimize redistribution.

barrier layer—See Depletion Layer.

barrier-layer cell — A type of photovoltaic cell in which light acting on the surface of the contact between layers of copper and cuprous oxide causes an electromotive force to be produced.

barrier-layer rectification—See Depletion-Layer Rectification.

barrier region—See Depletion Region.

barrier shield—A wall or enclosure shielding the operator from an area where radioactive material is being used or processed by remote-control equipment.

barrier voltage — The voltage necessary to cause electrical conduction in a junction of two dissimilar materials, such as a P-N junction diode.

base—1. The region between the emitter and collector of a transistor which receives minority carriers injected from the emitter. It is the element which corresponds to the control grid of an electron tube. 2. In a vacuum tube, the insulated portion through which the electrodes are connected to the pins. 3. On a printed-circuit board, the portion that supports the printed pattern. 4. Also see Positional Notation and Radix. 5. See Alkali.

baseband—The frequency band occupied by the aggregate of the transmitted signals used to modulate a carrier. The term is com-

Barrel distortion.

monly applied where the ratio of the upper to the lower limit of the frequency band is larger than unity.

base electrode—An ohmic or majority-carrier contact to the base region of a transistor.

base film—The plastic substrate that supports the coating of magnetic recording tape. The base film of most instrumentation and computer tapes is made of polyester. For less critical uses, cellulose acetate and polyvinyl chloride are employed.

basegroup—Designating a number of carrier channels in a particular frequency range that forms a basic unit (channel bank) for further modulation to a final frequency band.

base insulator—Heavy-duty insulator used to support the weight of an antenna mast and to insulate the mast from the ground of some other surface.

base line—1. In radar displays, the visual line representing the track of the radar scanning beam. 2. In graphical presentations, the horizontal scale, often representing time, bias, or some other variable.

base-line break—In radar, a technique which uses the characteristic break in the base line on an A-scope display due to a pulse signal of significant strength in noise jamming.

base load—In a d-c converter, the current which must be taken from the base to maintain a saturated state.

base-loaded antenna—A vertical antenna the electrical height of which is increased by adding inductance in series at the base.

base material—An insulating material (usually a copper-clad laminate) used to support a conductive pattern.

base number—The radix of a number system (10 is the base number, or radix, for the decimal system; 2 for the binary system).

base pin—*See* Pin.

base point—*See* Radix Point.

base region—In a transistor, the interelectrode region into which minority carriers are injected.

base resistance—Resistance in series with the base lead in the common-T equivalent circuit of a transistor.

base ring—Ohmic contact to the base region of power transistors; so called because it is ring-shaped.

base spreading resistance—In a transistor, the resistance of the base region caused by the resistance of the bulk material of the base region.

base station—A land station, in the land mobile service, carrying on a service with land mobile stations. (A base station may secondarily communicate with other base stations incident to communications with land mobile stations.) Sometimes defined as a station in a land mobile system which remains in a fixed location and communicates with mobile stations.

base voltage—The voltage between the base

terminals of a transistor and the reference point.

basic frequency—In any wave, the frequency which is considered the most important. In a driven system, it would in general be the driving frequency, while in most periodic waves it would correspond to the fundamental frequency.

basic linkage—In a computer, a linkage that is used repeatedly in one routine, program, or system and that follows the same set of rules each time it is used.

basic-Q—*See* Nonloaded Q.

basic rectifier—A metallic rectifier in which each rectifying element consists of a single metallic rectifier cell.

basic switch—A precision snap-acting switch of either the open type, skeleton type, or the type encased within an envelope. A basic switch is normally used within a protective enclosure or as a component.

basket winding—A coil winding in which adjacent turns are separated except at the points of crossing.

bass—Sounds in the low audio-frequency range. On the standard piano keyboard, all notes below middle C (256 hertz).

bass boost—A deliberate adjustment of the amplitude-frequency response of a system or component to accentuate the lower audio frequencies.

bass-boosting circuit—A circuit that attenuates the higher audio frequencies in order that low or bass frequencies will be emphasized by comparison.

bass compensation—Emphasizing the low-frequency response of an audio amplifier at low volume levels to compensate for the lowered sensitivity of the human ear to weak low frequencies.

bass control—A manual tone control that has the effect of changing the level of bass frequencies reproduced by an audio amplifier.

bass reflex—A method of extending the low-frequency range of a speaker and its response. Accomplished by an opening in the cabinet enclosing the speaker.

Bass-reflex enclosure.

bass-reflex enclosure—*See* Vented Baffle.

bass response—1. The extent to which a

speaker or audio-frequency amplifier handles low audio frequencies. 2. The ability of any device to pick up or reproduce low audio frequencies.

batch process — A method of fabricating monolithic resistors, capacitors, and diodes with the same process at the same time.

batch processing—In a computer, a method of processing in which a number of similar input items are grouped for processing during the same machine run.

bat handle—Standard form of a toggle-switch lever having a shape similar to that of a baseball bat.

bathtub capacitor—A type of capacitor enclosed in a metal housing having broadly rounded corners like those on a bathtub.

bathyconductorgraph—A device used from a moving ship to measure the electrical conductivity of sea water at various depths.

bathythermograph—A device that automatically plots a graph showing temperature as a function of depth when lowered into the sea.

Batten system—A method developed by W. E. Batten for coordinating single words in a computer to identify a document. Sometimes called peek-a-boo system.

battery—A d-c voltage source consisting of two or more cells which converts chemical, nuclear, solar, or thermal energy into electrical energy.

battery acid—A solution that serves as the electrolyte in a storage battery. In the common lead-acid storage battery, the electrolyte is diluted sulphuric acid.

battery capacity—The amount of energy obtainable from a storage battery, usually expressed in ampere-hours.

battery charger—Device used to convert alternating current into a pulsating direct current which can be used for charging a storage battery.

battery clip—A metal clip with a terminal to which a connecting wire can be attached, and with spring jaws that can be quickly snapped onto a battery terminal or other point to which a temporary connection is desired.

battery receiver—A radio receiver that obtains its operating power from one or more batteries.

battle short—A switch for short-circuiting safety interlocks and lighting a red warning light.

bat wing—An element on an f-m or tv transmitting or receiving antenna; so called because of its shape.

baud—A unit of signaling speed derived from the duration of the shortest code element. Speed in bauds is the number of code elements per second.

bay—1. A portion of an antenna array. 2. A vertical compartment in which a radio transmitter or other equipment is housed.

bayonet base—A base having two projecting pins on opposite sides of a smooth cylindrical base; the pins engage corresponding slots in a bayonet socket and hold the base firmly in the socket.

bayonet coupling — A quick-coupling device. Connection is accomplished by rotating two parts under pressure. Pins on the side of the male connector engage slots on the side of the female connector.

bayonet socket—A socket for bayonet-base tubes or lamps; it has slots on opposite sides and one or more contact buttons at the bottom.

bazooka—*See* Balun.

B battery—The battery that furnishes the required d-c voltages to the plate and screen-grid electrodes of the vacuum tubes in a battery-operated circuit.

BCD—Abbreviation for Binary-Coded Decimal.

B channel—One of two stereo channels, usually the right, together with the microphone, speakers, or other equipment associated with this channel.

BCI — Abbreviation for BroadCast Interference, a term denoting interference by transmitters with reception of broadcast signals on standard broadcast receivers.

B-display.

B-display—On a radarscope, a type of presentation in which the target appears as a bright spot. Its bearing is indicated by the horizontal coordinate and its range by the vertical coordinate.

beacon—A device which emits a signal for use as a guidance or warning aid. Radar beacons aid the radar set in locating and identifying special targets which may otherwise be difficult or impossible to sense.

beacon delay—The amount of inherent delay within the beacon—i.e., the time between the arrival of a signal and the response of the beacon. In a pulse beacon, delay ordinarily is measured between the leading db points of the triggering pulse and the reply pulse.

beacon receiver—A radio receiver for converting into perceptible signals the waves emanating from a radio beacon.

beacon skipping—A term used to describe a condition where beacon return pulses are missing at the interrogating radar. Beacon skipping can be caused by interference, over-interrogation of the beacon, antenna nulls, or pattern minima.

beacon stealing—The loss of beacon tracking by a (desired) radar due to (interfering) interrogation signals from another radar.

beacon time sharing—A technique by which two or more radars may interrogate and track a long-recovery type of beacon without exceeding the duty cycle of the beacon. This technique is accomplished by the proper sequencing of the various radar interrogations. It is necessary to insure that the total of all interrogations does not exceed the beacon duty cycle and that enough time is allowed for the modulator section of the beacon to recover before it receives the next interrogation.

beaded coax—A coaxial cable in which the dielectric consists of beads made of various materials.

beaded support—Ceramic and plastic beads used to support the inner conductor in coaxial transmission lines.

beaded transmission line — A line using beads to support the inner conductor in coaxial transmission lines.

bead thermistor—A thermistor consisting of a small bead of semiconducting material such as germanium placed between two wire leads. Used for microwave power measurement, temperature measurement, and as a protective device. The resistance decreases as the temperature increases.

beam—1. A flow of electromagnetic radiation concentrated in a parallel, converging, or diverging pattern. 2. The unidirectional or approximately unidirectional flow of radiated energy or particles.

beam alignment — The adjustment of the electron beam in a camera tube (on tubes employing low-velocity scanning) to cause the beam to be perpendicular to the target at the target surface.

beam angle—The angle between the directions, on either side of the axis, at which the intensity of the radio-frequency field drops to one-half the value it has on the axis.

beam antenna—An antenna that concentrates its radiation into a narrow beam in a definite direction.

beam bender—*See* Ion-Trap.

beam bending—Deflection of the scanning beam of a camera tube by the electrostatic field of the charges stored on the target.

beam blanking—Interruption of the electron beam in a cathode-ray tube by the application of a pulse to the control grid or cathode.

beam candlepower—The candlepower of a bare source which, if located at the same distance as the beam, would produce the same illumination as the beam.

beam convergence—The converging of the three electron beams of a three-gun color picture tube at a shadow mask opening.

beam crossover—The point of overlap of a beam from an antenna that is mutated or rotated about the center line of the antenna radiation direction. The crossover point is normally at the 0.7 power point. The received energy, when commutated into four quadrants, provides the necessary information for the servoamplifier error signal used to align the antenna to a target.

beam-coupling coefficient—In a microwave tube, the ratio of the amplitude, expressed in volts, of the velocity modulation produced by a gap to the radio-frequency gap voltage.

beam current—The current carried by the electron stream that forms the beam in a cathode-ray tube.

beam cutoff—In a television picture tube or cathode-ray tube, the condition in which the control-grid potential is so negative with respect to the cathode that electrons cannot flow and thereby form the beam.

beam-deflection tube — An electron-beam tube in which current to an output electrode is controlled by the transverse movement of an electron beam.

beam-forming electrode—Electron-beam focusing elements in power tetrodes and cathode-ray tubes.

beam hole—An opening through a reactor shield and, generally, through the reactor reflector which permits a beam of radioactive particles or radiation to be used for experiments outside the reactor.

beam-index color tube—A color picture tube in which the signal generated by an electron beam after deflection is fed back to a control device or element in such a way that an image in color is provided.

beam-lead bonding — A free-bonding technique in which thick, gold extensions of the thin-film terminals of the semiconductor devices and circuits are electroformed so they extend beyond the edges of the chips.

beam modulation—*See* Z-Axis Modulation.

beam parametric amplifier — A parametric amplifier in which a modulated electron beam provides a variable reactance.

beam-positioning magnet — A magnet used with a tricolor picture tube to influence the direction of one of the electron beams so that it will have the proper spatial relationship with the other two beams.

beam-power tube—An electron-beam tube in which directed electron beams are used to contribute substantially to its power-handling capability, and in which the control and screen grids essentially are aligned.—*See* illustration on page 52.

beam relaxor—A type of sawtooth scanning-oscillator circuit which generates but does not amplify the current wave required for magnetic deflection in a single beam-power pentode.

beam-rider control system — A system whereby the control station sends a beam to

Beam-power tube.

Beam-switching tube.

the target, and the missile follows this beam until it collides with the target.

beam-rider guidance — A form of missile guidance wherein a missile, through a self-contained mechanism, automatically guides itself along a radar beam.

beam splitting—A process for increasing the accuracy in locating targets by radar. By noting the azimuths at which one radar scan first discloses a target and at which radar data from it ceases, beam splitting calculates the mean azimuth for the target.

beam spreader—An optical element the purpose of which is to impart a small angular divergence to a colliminated incident beam.

beam switching — A method of obtaining more accurately the bearing and/or elevation of an object by comparing the signals received when the beam is in a direction differing slightly in bearing and/or elevation. When these signals are equal, the object lies midway between the beam axes.

beam-switching tube—A multiposition, high-vacuum, constant-current distributor. The beam-switching tube consists of many identical "arrays" around a central cathode. Each array comprises (1) a spade which automatically forms and locks the electron beam, (2) a target-output electrode which

gives the beam current its constant characteristics, and (3) a high-impedance switching grid which switches the beam from target to target. A small cylindrical magnet, permanently attached to the glass envelope, provides a magnetic field. This field, in conjunction with an applied electric field, comprises the crossed fields necessary for operation of this tube. It is used in electronic switching and in distributing such as counting, timing, sampling, frequency dividing, coding, matrixing, telemetering, and controlling.

beam width—1. The angular width of a radio, radar, or other beam measured between two reference lines. 2. The width of a radar beam measured between lines of half-power intensity.

bearing—1. The horizontal direction of an object or point, usually measured clockwise from a reference line or direction through 360°. 2. Support for a rotating shaft. 3. The horizontal angle at a given point, measured from a specific reference datum, to a second point relative to another as measured from a specific reference datum.

bearing cursor—A mechanical bearing line of a plan-position indicator type of display for reading the target bearing.

bearing loss—The loss of power through friction in the bearings of an electric motor (brushes removed and no current in the windings).

bearing resolution—The minimum angular

Beam-rider guidance.

separation in a horizontal plane between two targets at the same range that will allow an operator to obtain data on either individual target.

beat—Periodic variations that result from the superimposition of waves having different frequencies. The term is applied both to the linear addition of two waves, resulting in a periodic variation of amplitude, and to the nonlinear addition of two waves, resulting in new frequencies, of which the most important usually are the sum and difference of the original frequencies.

beat frequency—One of the two additional frequencies produced when two different frequencies are combined. One beat frequency is the sum of the two original frequencies; the other is the difference between them.

beat-frequency oscillator — Abbreviated bfo. An oscillator that produces a signal which mixes with another signal to provide frequencies equal to the sum and difference of the combined frequencies.

beating—The combining of two or more frequencies to produce sum and difference frequencies called beats.

beating-in—Interconnecting two transmitter oscillators and adjusting one until no beat frequency is heard in a connected receiver. The oscillators are then at the same frequency.

beating oscillator—*See* Local Oscillator.

beat note—The wave of difference frequency created when two waves of different frequencies are combined. The beat note is equal to the difference in frequency between the two.

beat reception—*See* Heterodyne Reception.

beats—Beat notes which are generally at a sufficiently low audio frequency that they can be counted.

beat tone—Musical tone due to beats, produced by the heterodyning of two high-frequency wave trains.

beaver tail—A fan-shaped radar beam, wide in the horizontal plane and narrow in the vertical plane. The beaver tail is swept up and down for height finding.

bedspring—A broadside antenna array with a flat reflector.

before start—The interval before the starting circuit to a timer has been operated. The timer is fully reset and all contacts are in the precycle position.

bel—The fundamental unit in a logarithmic scale for expressing the ratio of two amounts of power. The number of bels is equal to the $\log_{10} P_1/P_2$, where P_1 is the power level being considered and P_2 is an arbitrary reference level. The decibel, equal to 1/10 bel, is a more commonly used unit.

B eliminator—A power pack that changes the a-c power-line voltage to the d-c source required by the vacuum tubes. In this way, batteries can be eliminated.

bell—An electrical device consisting of a hammer vibrated by an electromagnet. The hammer strikes the sides of the bell and emits a ringing noise. The electromagnet attracts an armature or piece of soft iron forming part of the hammer lever. A contact breaker then opens the circuit and cuts off the attraction. A spring draws the hammer back to its original position, closing the circuit and repeating the action.

Bellini-Tosi direction finder—An early radio direction-finder system consisting of two loop antennas at right angles to each other and connected to a goniometer.

bellows—A pressure-sensing element consisting of a ridged metal cylinder closed at one end. A pressure difference between its outside and inside will cause the cylinder to expand or contract along its axis.

bellows contact—A contact in which a multileaf spring is folded. This type provides a more uniform spring rate over the full tolerance range of the mating unit.

bell transformer—A small iron-core transformer; its primary coil is connected to an a-c primary line, and its secondary coil delivers 10 to 20 volts for operation of a doorbell, buzzer, or chimes.

bell wire—Cotton-covered copper wire, usually No. 18, used for doorbell and thermostat connections in homes and for similar low-voltage work.

bend—A change in the direction of the longitudinal axis of a waveguide.

bend waveguide—A section of waveguide in which the direction of the longitudinal axis is changed.

Benito—A c-w navigational system in which the distance to an aircraft is determined on the ground by measuring the phase difference of an audio signal transmitted from the ground and retransmitted by the aircraft. Bearing information is obtained by ground direction finding of the aircraft signals.

TRANSMITTING ANTENNA

WIRE MESH REFLECTING SCREEN

RECEIVING ANTENNA

Bedspring antenna.

beta—Symbolized by the Greek letter *beta* (β). Also called current-transfer ratio. 1. The current transfer ratio (gain) of a transistor in the common-emitter circuit arrangement. This is the ratio of a-c collector current to a-c base current. 2. A symbol used to denote B quartz.

beta circuit—In a feedback amplifier, the circuit which transmits a portion of the amplifier output back to the input.

beta cutoff frequency — The frequency at which the beta of a transistor is 3 decibels below the low-frequency value.

beta particle—A small electrically charged particle thrown off by many radioactive materials. It is identical to the electron and possesses the smallest negative electrical charge found in nature. Beta particles emerge from radioactive material at high speeds, sometimes close to the speed of light.

beta ray—A stream of beta particles.

betatron—A large doughnut-shaped accelerator which produces artificial beta radiation. Electrons (beta particles) are whirled through a changing magnetic field. They gain speed with each trip and emerge with high energies (on the order of 100 million electron volts in some instances).

bev—A Billion Electron Volts. An electron possessing this much energy travels at a speed close to that of light—186,000 miles a second.

bevatron—A very large circular accelerator in which protons are whirled between the poles of a huge magnet to produce energies in excess of 1 billion electron volts.

Beverage antenna—*See* Wave Antenna.

beyond-the-horizon propagation—*See* Scatter Propagation.

beyond-the-horizon transmission—*See* Scatter Propagation.

Bezel.

bezel—1. A holder designed to receive and position the edges of a lens, meter, window, or dial glass. 2. The flange or cover used for holding an external graticule or crt cover in front of the crt in an oscilloscope. May also be used for mounting a trace-recording camera or other accessory item.

bfo—Abbreviation for beat-frequency oscillator.

B-H curve—Curve plotted on a graph to show successive states during magnetization of a ferromagnetic material. A normal magnetization curve is a portion of a symmetrical hysteresis loop. A virgin magnetization curve shows what happens the first time the material is magnetized.

B-H meter—A device for measuring the intrinsic hysteresis loop of a sample of magnetic material.

bias—1. The electrical, mechanical, or magnetic force applied to a relay, vacuum tube, or other device for the purpose of establishing an electrical or mechanical reference level for the operation of the device. 2. Direct-current potential applied to the control grid of a vacuum tube. 3. Bias derived from a direct current, used on signaling or telegraph relays or electromagnets to secure the desired time spacing of transitions from marking to spacing. 4. A method of restraining a relay armature, by means of spring tension, to secure a desired time spacing of transitions from marking to spacing. 5. The average direct-current voltage between the control grid and cathode of a vacuum tube. 6. The effect on teletypewriter signals produced by the electrical characteristics of the line and the equipment. 7. Energy applied to a relay to hold it in a given position.

bias cell—A dry cell used in the grid circuit of a vacuum tube to provide the necessary C-bias voltage.

bias current—The current through the base-emitter junction of a transistor. It is adjusted to set the operating point of the transistor.

bias distortion—1. Distortion resulting from operation on a nonlinear portion of the characteristic curve of a vacuum tube or other device, due to improper biasing. 2. In teletype circuits, the uniform shifting of mark pulses from their proper position in relationship to the start pulses.

biased induction—Symbolized by B_b. The biased induction at a point in a magnetic material which is subjected simultaneously to a periodically varying magnetizing force and a biasing magnetizing force and is the algebraic mean of the maximum and minimum values of the magnetic induction at the point.

bias-induced noise—The difference between bulk-erased and zero-modulation noise.

biasing magnetizing force—Symbolized by H_b. A biasing magnetizing force at a point in a magnetic material which is subjected simultaneously to a periodically varying magnetizing force and a constant magnetizing force and is the algebraic mean of the maximum and minimum values of the combined magnetizing forces.

bias meter—Used in teletypewriter work for measuring signal bias directly in percent. A positive reading on the meter indicates a marking-signal bias; a negative reading indicates a spacing-signal bias.

bias oscillator—An oscillator used in magnetic recorders to generate an a-c signal in the range of 40 to 80 kHz for the purpose of magnetic biasing to obtain a linear recording characteristic. Usually the bias oscillator also serves as the erase oscillator.

bias resistor—A resistance connected into a self-biasing vacuum-tube circuit to produce the voltage drop necessary to provide a desired biasing voltage.

bias-set frequency—In direct magnetic tape

recording, a specified recording frequency employed during the adjustment of bias level for optimum record performance (not the frequency of the bias).

bias telegraph distortion — Distortion in which all mark pulses are lengthened (positive bias) or shortened (negative bias). It can be measured with a steady stream of "unbiased reversals" (square waves having equal-length mark and space pulses). The average lengthening or shortening does not give true bias distortion unless other types of distortion are negligible.

bias windings—Control windings of a saturable reactor, by means of which the operating condition is translated by an arbitrary amount.

Biconical antenna.

biconical antenna—An antenna which is formed by two conical conductors, having a common axis and vertex, and excited at the vertex. When the vertex angle of one of the cones is 180°, the antenna is called a discone.

bidirectional—Responsive in opposite directions. An ordinary loop antenna is bidirectional because it has maximum response from the opposite directions in the plane of the loop.

bidirectional antenna—An antenna having two directions of maximum response.

bidirectional current—A current which is both positive and negative.

bidirectional microphone—A microphone in which the response predominates for sound incidences of 0° and 180°.

bidirectional pulses—Pulses, some of which rise in one direction and the remainder in the other direction.

bidirectional pulse train—A pulse train, some pulses of which rise in one direction and the remainder in the other direction.

bidirectional transducer — *See* Bilateral Transducer.

bidirectional transistor—A transistor which is specified with parameter limits in both the normal and inverted configuration and has substantially the same electrical characteristics when the terminals normally designed as emitter and collector are interchanged.

bifilar resistor — A resistor wound with a wire doubled back on itself to reduce the inductance.

bifilar transformer—A transformer in which the turns of the primary and secondary windings are wound together side-by-side and in the same direction. This type of winding results in near unity coupling, so that there is a very efficient transfer of energy from primary to secondary.

bifilar winding—A method of winding non-inductive resistors in which the wire is folded back on itself and then wound double, with the winding starting from the point at which the wire is folded.

bifurcated contact — A movable contact which is forked (divided) to provide two contact-mating surfaces in parallel for a more reliable contact.

bilateral amplifier—An amplifier capable of receiving as well as transmitting signals; it is used primarily in transceivers.

bilateral antenna—An antenna, such as a loop, having maximum response in exactly opposite directions (180° apart).

bilateral bearing—A bearing which indicates two possible directions of wave arrival. One of these is the true bearing, and the other is a bearing displaced 180° from the true bearing.

bilateral circuit — A circuit wherein equipment at opposite ends is managed, operated, and maintained by different services.

bilateral element—A two-terminal element, the voltage-current characteristic of which has odd symmetry around the origin.

bilateral network—A network in which a given current flow in either direction results in the same voltage drop.

bilateral transducer — Also called bidirectional transducer. A transducer capable of transmission simultaneously in both directions between at least two terminations.

billboard antenna—Broadside array consisting of stacked dipoles with flat reflectors.

bimag—*See* Tape-wound Core.

bimetallic strip—A strip formed of two dissimilar metals welded together. Because the metals have different temperature coefficients of expansion, the strip bends or curls when the temperature changes.

bimetallic thermometer—A device containing a bimetallic strip which expands or contracts as the temperature changes. A calibrated scale indicates the amount of change in temperature.

bimorph cell—Two crystal elements (usually Rochelle salt) in rigid combination, arranged to act as a mechanical transformer in headphones, microphones, pickups, and speakers.

binary—1. A numbering system using a base number, or radix, of 2. In the binary system, there are only two digits—1 and 0. 2. Pertaining to a characteristic or property involving a selection, choice, or condition in which there are two possibilities. 3. Another range for bistable multivibrator.

binary cell—In an electronic computer, an elementary unit of storage which can be placed in either of two stable states.

binary chain — A series of binary circuits, each of which can exist in either one of two states, arranged so each circuit can affect or modify the condition of the next circuit.

binary channel—A transmission facility limited to the use of two symbols.

binary code—A code in which each code element is one of two distinct kinds or values—for example, the presence and absence of a pulse.

binary-coded—Expressed by a series of binary digits (0's and 1's).

binary-coded character—A decimal digit, alphabetic letter, punctuation mark, etc., represented by a fixed number of consecutive binary digits.

binary-coded decimal—Abbreviated BCD. A system of number representation in which each decimal digit of a number is expressed by binary numbers.

binary-coded digit—One element of a notation system for representing a decimal digit by a fixed number of binary positions.

binary-coded octal system—An octal numbering system in which each octal digit is represented by a three-place binary number.

binary counter—*See* Binary Scaler.

binary digit—*See* Bit.

binary magnetic core—A ring-shaped magnetic material which can be made to take either of two stable states of magnetic polarization.

binary notation—*See* Binary Number System.

binary number system—A number system using two symbols (usually denoted 0 and 1) and having 2 as its base, just as the decimal system uses 10 symbols (0, 1, . . . , 9) and has a base of 10. Also called binary notation.

binary numeral—The binary representation of a number—e.g., "101" is the binary numeral and "V" is the Roman numeral of the number of fingers on one hand.

binary point—The point which marks the place between integral powers of two and fractional powers of two in a binary number.

binary pulse-code modulation—A form of pulse-code modulation in which the code for each element of information consists of one of two distinct kinds, e.g., pulses and spaces.

binary scaler—Also called binary counter. 1. A counter which produces one output pulse for every two input pulses. 2. A counting circuit, each stage of which has two distinguishable states.

binary search—Also called dichotomizing search. A search in which a set of items is divided into two parts; one part is rejected, and the process is repeated on the accepted part until those items with the desired property are found.

binary signaling—A communications mode in which information is passed by the presence and absence, or plus and minus variations, of one parameter of the signaling medium.

binary system—A system of mathematical computation based on powers of 2.

binary-to-decimal conversion—The process of converting a number written in binary notation to the equivalent number written in the ordinary decimal notation.

binaural—Two-eared; applied to a kind of recording that is played into separate headphones to create a sense of depth.

binaural disc—A stereo record with two separate signals, one on each wall of its recorded grooves. Stereophonic sound is obtained by feeding each signal into its own speaker.

binaural effect—The effect which makes it possible for a person to distinguish the difference in arrival time or intensity of sound at his ears and thereby determine the direction from which a sound is arriving.

binaural recorder—A tape recorder which employs two separate recording channels, or systems, each with its own microphone, amplifier, recording and playback heads, and earphones. Recordings using both channels are made simultaneously on a single magnetic tape having two parallel tracks. During playback, the original sound is reproduced with a depth and realism unequalled by any other recording method. For a true binaural effect, headphones are necessary.

Binaural sound reproducing system.

binaural sound—Sound recorded or transmitted by pairs of equipment so as to give the listener the effect of having heard the original sound.

binder—A substance, like cement, used to hold particles together and thus provide mechanical strength in carbon resistors and phonograph records.

binding energy—The minimum energy required to dissociate a nucleus into its component neutrons and protons. Neutron or proton binding energies are those energies required to remove a neutron or a proton, respectively, from a nucleus. Electron binding energy is that energy required to remove an electron from an atom or a molecule.

Binding post.

binding post—A bolt-and-nut terminal for making temporary electrical connections.

binistor—A four-terminal controlled rectifier semiconductor which provides bistable, negative-resistance characteristics.

binomial array—A directional antenna array used for reducing minor lobes and providing maximum response in opposite directions.

biochemical fuel cell — An electrochemical generator of electrical power in which bi-organic matter is used as the fuel source. In the usual electrochemical reaction, air serves as the oxidant at the cathode and microorganisms are used to catalyze the oxidation of the bi-organic matter at the anode.

bioelectrogenesis—The practical application of electricity drawn directly from the bodies of animals, including humans, to power electronic devices and appliances.

bioelectronics—The application of electronic theories and techniques to the problems of biology.

biological shield—A mass of absorbing material placed around a reactor or radioactive source to reduce the radiation to a level that is safe for human beings.

biometrics — The science of statistics as applied to biological observations.

bionics—1. The science of applying biological techniques to the design of electronic devices and systems. 2. The science of systems which function in a manner resembling living systems.

biotelemetry—The technique of measuring or monitoring vital processes and transmitting data without wires to a point (or points) remote from the subject.

biotelescanner—A device that can analyze and radio data on life forms during space exploration.

bipolar—Having two poles.

bipolar electrode—An electrode without metallic connection with the current supply, one face of which acts as an anode surface and the opposite face as a cathode surface when an electric current is passed through a cell.

bipolar magnetic driving unit—A headphone or speaker unit having two magnetic poles acting directly on a flexible iron diaphragm.

bipolar transistor—A transistor that uses both negative and positive charge carriers.

biquinary notation—A numerical system of notation based on a double scale of five.

biscuit—*See* Preform.

bistable—1. A circuit element with two stable operating states—e.g., a flip-flop in which one transistor is saturated while the other is turned off. It changes state for each input pulse or trigger. 2. A device capable of assuming either one of two stable states.

bistable multivibrator (flip-flop) — A circuit having two stable states; it will stay in either one indefinitely until appropriately triggered after which it immediately switches to the other state.

bistable relay — A relay that requires two pulses to complete one cycle composed of two conditions of operation. Also called locked, interlocked, and latching relay.

biswitch—A two-terminal integrated device which basically performs the function of two PNPN switches interconnected so as to provide bilateral switching.

bit—Abbreviation for binary digit. A unit of information equal to one binary decision, or the designation of one of two possible and equally likely values or states (such as 1 or 0) of anything used to store or convey information. It may also mean "yes" or "no."

bit density—The number of bits of information contained in a given area, such as the number of bits written along an inch of magnetic tape.

bit rate—The speed of transmission of bits.

black—A signal produced at any point in a facsimile system by the scanning of a selected area of subject copy having maximum density.

black and white—*See* Monochrome.

black and white transmission—*See* Monochrome Transmission.

black area—An area with encrypted signal only present.

black-body — 1. An idealized emitter for which total radiated energy and the spectral distribution of the energy are accurately known functions of temperature. These relationships are given by Planck's law. 2. A solid that radiates or absorbs energy with no internal reflection of the energy at any wavelength. Physically it may be a hollow sphere coated on the inside with lampblack and with an opening through which energy may enter or leave.

black box—1. A term used loosely to refer to any subcomponent that is equipped with connects and disconnects so that it can be readily inserted into or removed from a specified place in a larger system (e.g., the complete missile or some major subdivision) without benefit of knowledge of its detailed

Bistable multivibrator.

internal structure. 2. A term pertaining to either the functional transformation that acts upon a specified input to give a particular output or to the apparatus for accomplishing this transformation (without regard to the detailed circuitry used). 3. A useful mathematical approach to an electronic circuit which concerns itself only with the input and output, and ignores the interior elements, discrete or integrated.

black compression—Also called black saturation. The reduction in the gain of a television picture signal at those levels corresponding to dark areas in the picture with respect to the gain at that level corresponding to the midrange light value in the picture. The over-all effect of black compression is to reduce contrast in the low lights of the picture.

blacker-than-black—The amplitude region of the composite video signal below the reference black level in the direction of the synchronizing pulses.

blacker-than-black level—A voltage value used in an electronic television system for control impulses. It is greater than the value representing the black portions of the image.

black level—That level of the picture signal corresponding to the maximum limit of black peaks.

black light—Invisible light radiation. May be either ultraviolet or infrared radiation, both of which are invisible.

black-light emitter—A source of electromagnetic radiation in the ultraviolet or infrared region, just outside the visible spectrum.

black peak—A peak excursion of the picture signal in the black direction.

black saturation—*See* Black Compression.

black signal — Also called picture black. A signal produced at any point in a facsimile system by the scanning of a maximum-density area of the subject copy.

blackout—1. Interruption of radiocommunication due to excess absorption caused by solar flares. During severe blackouts, all frequencies above approximately 1500 kHz are absorbed excessively in the daylight zone. 2. Passive defense that consists of interrupting all forms of communication or identification.

black transmission — 1. In an amplitude-modulation facsimile system a form of transmission in which the maximum transmitted power corresponds to the maximum density of the copy. 2. In a frequency-modulation system, a form of transmission, in which the lowest transmitted frequency corresponds to the maximum density of the copy.

blank—1. The result of the final operation on a crystal. 2. To cut off the electron beam of a cathode-ray tube. 3. A code character to denote the presence of no information rather than the absence of information. In the Baudot code, it is composed of all spacing pulses. In paper tape, it is represented by a feedhole without intelligence holes.

blanked picture signal—The signal resulting from adding blanking to a picture signal. Adding the sync signal to the blanked picture signal forms the composite picture signal.

blanketing—The overriding of a signal by a more powerful one or by interference, so that a receiver is unable to receive the desired signal.

blank groove—*See* Unmodulated Groove.

blanking—The process of making a channel or device noneffective for the desired interval. In television, blanking is the substitution for the picture signal, during prescribed intervals, of a signal the instantaneous amplitude of which is such as to make the return trace invisible. *See also* Gating.

blanking level—Also called pedestal level. In a composite picture signal, the level that separates the range of the composite picture signal containing picture information from the range containing synchronizing information.

blanking pulse—A square wave (positive or negative) used to switch off electronically a part of a television or radar set for a predetermined length of time.

blanking signal—A wave made up of recurrent pulses related in time to the scanning process and used to effect blanking. In television, this signal is composed of pulses at line and field frequencies, which usually originate in a central sync generator and are combined with the picture signal at the pickup equipment in order to form the blanked picture signal. The addition of a sync signal completes the composite picture signal.

blanking time—The length of time the electron beam of a cathode-ray tube is cut off.

blanking zone—*See* Blanking Pulse.

blank tape—*See* Raw Tape.

blasting—Overloading of an amplifier or speaker, resulting in severe distortion of loud sounds.

bleeder current—The current drawn continuously from a power supply by a resistor. Used to improve the voltage regulation of the power supply.

bleeder resistor—1. A resistor used to draw a fixed current. Also used, as a safety measure, to discharge a filter capacitor after the circuit is de-energized. 2. A resistor placed in the power supply of a radio receiver or other electronic device to stabilize the voltage supply.

bleeding whites—An overloading condition in which white areas in a television picture appear to flow into the black areas.

blemish—On the storage surface of a charge-storage tube, an imperfection which produces a spurious output.

blind approach—An aircraft landing approach when visibility is poor, usually made with the aid of instruments and radiocommunication.

blind zone—An area from which echoes cannot be received; generally, an area shielded from the transmitter by some natural obstruction and therefore from which there can be no return.

blip—Sometimes referred to as pip. On a cathode-ray display, a spot of light or a base-line irregularity representing the radar reflection from an object.

blip-scan ratio—The ratio between a single recognizable blip on a radar scope and the number of scans necessary to produce it. The blip-scan ratio of any given radar set varies with the range, antenna tilt, level of operator and set performance, target aspect, wind, etc.

blivet—*See* Land.

Bloch wall—The transition layer separating adjacent ferromagnetic domains.

block—A set of things, such as words, characters, or digits, handled as a unit by a computer.

block diagram—A diagram in which the essential units of any system are drawn in the form of blocks, and their relationship to each other is indicated by appropriately connected lines. The path of the signal or energy may be indicated by lines and/or arrows.

blocked impedance — The input impedance of a transducer when its output is connected to a load of infinite impedance.

blockette—In digital computer programming, a subgroup, or subdivision, of a group of consecutive machine words transferred as a unit.

block-grid keying — A method of keying a continuous-wave transmitter by operating the amplifier stage as an electronic switch. During the spacing interval when the key is open, the bias on the control grid becomes highly negative and prevents the flow of plate current so that the tube has no output. During the marking interval when the key is closed, this bias is removed and full plate current flows.

blocking—Application of an extremely high bias voltage to a transistor, vacuum tube, or metallic rectifier to prevent current from flowing in the forward direction.

blocking capacitor—A capacitor which introduces a comparatively high series impedance for limiting the flow of low-frequency alternating or direct current without materially affecting the flow of high-frequency alternating current.

blocking layer—*See* Depletion Layer.

blocking oscillator — Also called squegging oscillator. An electron-tube oscillator that operates intermittently as its grid bias increases during oscillation to a point where the oscillations stop, and then decreases until oscillation resumes.

blocking-oscillator driver—A circuit which develops a square pulse used to drive the modulator tubes, and which usually contains a line-controlled blocking oscillator that shapes the pulse into the square wave.

blocking relay — A device which initiates a pilot signal to block tripping on external faults in a transmission line or in other apparatus under predetermined conditions, or which co-operates with other devices to block tripping or to block reclosing on an out-of-step condition or on power swings.

block protector—A rectangular piece of carbon, *Bakelite* with a metal insert, or porcelain with a carbon insert which, in combination with each other, make one element of a protector. They form a gap which will break down and provide a path to ground for excessive voltages.

block sort—A computer sorting technique in which the file is first divided according to the most significant character of the key, and the separate portions are then sorted one at a time. It is used particularly for large files.

blooming—An increase in the size of the scanning spot on a cathode-ray tube, caused by defocusing when the brightness control is set too high. The result is expansion and consequent distortion of the image. May also be caused by insufficient high voltage.

blow—The opening of a circuit because of excessive current, particularly when the current is heavy and a melting or breakdown point is reached.

blower—An electric fan used to supply moving air for cooling purposes.

blown jacket—The common term given to an outer covering of insulation of a cable that was applied by the controlled inflation of the cured jacket tube and the pulling of the cable through it.

blowout coil—An electromagnetic device used to establish a magnetic field in the space where an electrical circuit is broken and thus displace and extinguish the arc.

blowout magnet—A strong permanent magnet or electromagnet used for reducing or deflecting the arc between electrodes or contacts.

blue-beam magnet—A small permanent magnet used to adjust the static convergence of the electron beam for blue phosphor dots in a three-gun color picture tube.

blue glow — The glow normally seen in vacuum tubes containing mercury vapor; it is due to ionization of the molecules of mercury vapor.

blue gun—In a three-gun, color picture tube, the electron gun whose beam strikes the phosphor dots emitting the blue primary color.

blue restorer—The d-c restorer in the blue channel of a three-gun color-television picture-tube circuit.

blue video voltage—The signal voltage that controls the grid of the blue gun in a three-gun picture tube. This signal is a reproduction of the blue output signal of the color-tv camera.

bobbin—A small insulated spool which serves as a support for a coil or wirewound resistor.

bobbin core—*See* Tape-wound Core.

body capacitance — Capacitance introduced into an electrical circuit by the proximity of the human body.

body electrodes—Electrodes placed on or in the body to couple electrical impulses from the body to an external measuring or recording device.

boffle — A speaker enclosure, developed by H. A. Hartley, containing a group of stretched, resilient sound-absorbing screens.

bogey—The average, or published, value for a tube characteristic. A bogey tube would be one having all characteristics of a bogey value.

bogey electron device—An electron device the characteristics of which have the published nominal values for the type.

boiling point—The temperature at which a liquid vaporizes when heated. The exact point depends on the absolute pressure at the liquid-vapor surface.

Superconducting bolometer.

bolometer—A radiation detector that converts incident radiation into heat which, in turn, causes a temperature change in the material used in the detector. This change is then measured to give an indication of the amount of incident radiant energy.

bolted fault level—*See* Adjusted Circuit.

bombardment — 1. The directing of high-speed electrons at an electrode, causing secondary emission of electrons, fluorescence, disintegration, or the production of X rays. 2. The process of directing high-speed particles at atoms to cause ionization or transmutation.

bond—1. Electrical interconnection made with a low-resistance material between a chassis, metal shield cans, or cable shielding braid, in order to eliminate undesirable interaction and interference resulting from high-impedance paths between them. 2. *See* Valence Bond.

bonded assembly—An assembly, the supporting frame and metallic noncircuit elements of which are connected so as to be electrically shorted together.

bonded-barrier transistor — A transistor made by alloying the base with the alloying material on the end of a wire.

bonded NR diode—An N junction semiconductor device in which the negative resistance arises from a combination of avalanche breakdown and conductivity modulation due to the current through the junction.

bonded pickup—*See* Bonded Transducer.

bonded strain gage—A pressure transducer that uses a pressure-sensing system consisting of strain-gage elements firmly bonded to a pressure-responsive member. Thermal stability and insensitivity to shock and vibration are improved by means of this bonded construction.

bonded transducer—Also called bonded pickup. A transducer which employs the bonded strain-gage principle of transduction.

bonding—1. Soldering or welding together various elements, shields, or housings of a device to prevent potential differences and possible interference. 2. A method used to produce good electrical contact between metallic parts of any device. Used extensively in automobile and aircraft to prevent static buildup. Also refers to the connectors and straps used to bond equipment. 3. The means employed to obtain an electromagnetically homogenous mass having an equipotential surface.

bonding conductor—A conductor which serves to connect exposed metal surfaces together.

bond strength—A measure of the amount of stress required to separate a layer of material from the base to which it is bonded. Peel strength, measured in pounds per inch of width, is obtained by peeling the layer; pull strength, measured in pounds per square inch is obtained by a perpendicular pull applied to a surface of the layer.

bone conduction — The process by which sound is conducted to the inner ear through the cranial bones.

book capacitor—A two-plate trimmer capacitor that has its plates hinged together like the pages of a book. The capacitance is varied by changing the angle between the plates.

Boolean algebra—A system of mathematical logic dealing with classes, propositions, on-off circuit elements, etc. Associated by operators as AND, OR, NOT, EXCEPT, IF...THEN, etc., thereby permitting computations and demonstration as in any mathematical system. Named after George Boole, famous English mathematician and logician, who introduced it in 1847.

Boolean calculus—Boolean algebra modified to include time.

Boolean function—A mathematical function in Boolean algebra.

boom—A mechanical support for a microphone, used in a television studio to suspend the microphone within range of the actors' voices, but out of camera range.

boost capacitor—A capacitor used in the damper circuit of a television receiver to supply a boosted B voltage.

boost charge—The partial charge of a storage battery, usually at a high current rate for a short period.

boosted B voltage—In television receivers the voltage resulting from the combination of the B-plus voltage from the power supply and the average value of voltage pulses coming through the damper tube from the horizontal deflection-coil circuit. The pulses are partially or wholly smoothed by filtering. This boosted voltage may be several hundred volts higher than the B-plus voltage.

booster—1. A carrier-frequency amplifier, usually a self-contained unit, connected between the antenna or transmission line and a television or radio receiver. 2. An intermediate radio or tv station which retransmits signals from one fixed station to another. 3. A small, self-contained transformer designed to be connected to a cathode-ray tube socket to increase the filament voltage and thereby extend the life of the tube.

booster amplifier—A circuit used to increase the output current or the voltage capabilities of an operational amplifier circuit without loss of accuracy (ideally) or inversion of polarity. Usually applied inside the loop for accuracy.

booster voltage—The additional voltage supplied by the damper tube of a television receiver to the horizontal-output, horizontal-oscillator, and vertical-output tubes, resulting in a greater sawtooth sweep output.

boot—1. A form placed around the wire termination of a multiple-contact connector for the purpose of containing the liquid potting compound until it hardens. 2. A protective housing, usually made from a resilient material, used to protect connector or other terminals from moisture.

bootstrap circuit—A single-stage amplifier in which the output load is connected between the negative end of the plate supply and the cathode, the signal voltage being applied between the grid and cathode. The name "bootstrap" arises from the fact that the change in grid voltage also changes the potential of the input source (with respect to ground) by an amount equal to the output signal.

boresight error—The angular deviation of the electrical boresight of an antenna from its reference boresight.

boss—*See* Land.

bottom metalization—The metalization which may be provided over the back portion of an uncased IC chip facilitating its face-up attachment.

bounce—An unnatural, sudden variation in the brightness of a television picture.

boundary—An interface between P and N

material at which donor and acceptor concentrations are equal.

boundary defect—In a crystal, the boundary area between two adjacent perfect crystal regions that are tilted slightly with respect to each other.

bound charge—On a conductor, the charge which, owing to the inductive action of a neighboring charge, will not escape to ground; residual charge.

bound circuit—A circuit designed to limit the excursion of a signal. The limit value it establishes may be nominal when used for protection, or highly precise when used operationally.

bound electron—An electron bound to the nucleus of an atom by electrostatic attraction.

Bow-tie antenna.

bow-tie antenna—An antenna generally used for uhf reception. It consists of two triangles in the same plane, with a reflector behind them. The transmission line is connected to the points which form a gap.

boxcar circuit—A circuit used in radar to sample voltage waveforms and store the latest value sampled.

boxcar lengthener—A circuit that lengthens a series of pulses without changing their heights.

boxcars—Long pulses that are separated by very short spaces.

B power supply—A power supply which provides the plate and screen voltages applied to a vacuum tube.

B-quad—A quad arrangement similar to the S-quad except for a short between the junctions of the two sets of series elements. Also called bridge quad or bar quad.

Bragg's law—An expression of the conditions under which a system of parallel atomic layers in a crystal will reflect an X-ray beam with maximum intensity.

braid—1. A weave of organic or inorganic fiber used as a covering for a conductor or group of conductors. 2. A woven metal tube used as shielding around a conductor or group of conductors. When flattened, it is used as a grounding strap.

braided wire—A flexible wire made up of small strands woven together.

brain waves—The patterns of lines produced on the moving chart of an electroencephalograph as the result of electrical potentials produced by the brain, picked up by electrodes, and amplified in the machine.

braking magnet—*See* Retarding Magnet.

branch—1. In an electronic network, a section between two adjacent branch points. 2. A portion of a network consisting of one or more two-terminal elements in series.

branch circuit—In a wiring system, that portion extending beyond the final over-current device protecting the circuit.

branch current—The current in the branch of a network.

branch impedance—In a passive branch, the impedance obtained by assuming a driving force across and a corresponding response in the branch, no other branch being electrically connected to the one under consideration.

branching—In a computer, a method of selecting, on the basis of the computer results, the next operation to execute while the program is in progress.

branch order—An instruction used to link subroutines into the main program of a computer.

branch point—1. In an electric network, the junction of more than two conductors. *(Also see* Node.) 2. In a computer, a point in the routine where one of two or more choices is selected under control of a routine.

branch voltage—The voltage across a branch of a network.

brass pounder—Amateur term for a Morse code operator, especially one who spends long hours handling "traffic."

breadboard construction—An arrangement in which electronic components are fastened temporarily to a board for experimental work.

breadboard model — An assembly in rough form to prove the feasibility of a circuit, device, system, or principle.

break—1. An open circuit. 2. An interruption in radio transmission to permit transmission from the other end.

break-before-make contacts — Contacts which interrupt one circuit before establishing another.

break contact — In a switching device, the contact which opens a circuit upon operation of the device (normally closed contact).

breakdown—1. An electric discharge through an insulator, insulation on wire, or other circuit separator, or between electrodes in a vacuum or gas-filled tube. 2. The phenomenon occurring in a reverse-biased semiconductor diode. The start of the phenomenon is observed as a transition from a region of high dynamic resistance to one of substantially lower dynamic resistance. This is done to boost the reverse current.

breakdown diode—*See* Avalanche Diode.

breakdown impedance—Also called avalanche impedance. The small-signal impedance at a specified direct current in the breakdown region of a semiconductor diode.

breakdown region—The entire region of the volt-ampere characteristic beyond the initiation of breakdown due to reverse current in a semiconductor-diode characteristic curve.

breakdown strength—*See* Dielectric Strength.

breakdown torque—The maximum torque a motor will develop, without an abrupt drop in speed, as the rated voltage is applied at the rated frequency.

breakdown voltage — 1. That voltage at which an insulator or dielectric ruptures, or at which ionization and conduction take place in a gas or a vapor. 2. The voltage measured at a specified current in the breakdown region of a semiconductor diode. Also called zener voltage. 3. The voltage required to jump an air gap.

Breaker points.

breaker points — The low-voltage contacts that interrupt the current in the primary circuit of the ignition system of a gasoline engine.

break frequency—In a plot of log gain (attenuation) versus log frequency, the frequency at which the asymptotes of two adjacent linear slope segments meet.

break-in keying—In the operation of a radio-telegraph communication system, a method by which the receiver is capable of receiving signals during transmission spacing intervals.

break-in operation—A method of radiocommunication involving break-in keying which allows the receiving operator to interrupt the transmission.

break-in relay — A relay used for break-in operation.

break-make contact — Also called transfer contact. A contact form in which one contact opens its connection to another contact and then closes its connection to a third contact.

breakout—The exit point of a conductor or number of conductors along various points of a main cable of which the conductors are a part. This point is usually harnessed or sealed with some synthetic-rubber compound.

breakover voltage — The value of positive anode voltage at which an scr with the gate circuit open switches into the conductive state.

breakpoint—A place in a routine specified by an instruction, instruction digit, or other condition, where the routine may be interrupted by external intervention or by a monitor routine.

breakpoint instruction — In the programming of a digital computer an instruction which, together with a manual control, causes the computer to stop.

breakpoint switch — A manually operated switch which controls conditional operation at breakpoints; it is used primarily in debugging.

breakup—*See* Color Breakup.

breathing—Amplitude variations similar to "bounce," but at a slow, regular rate.

breezeway—In the NTSC color system, that portion of the back porch between the trailing edge of the sync pulse and the start of the color burst.

B-register—A computer register that stores a word which will change an instruction before the computer carries out that instruction.

bremsstrahlung — Electromagnetic radiation emitted by a fast-moving charged particle (usually an electron) when it is slowed down (or accelerated) and deflected by the electric field surrounding a positively charged atomic nucleus. X rays produced in ordinary X-ray machines are bremsstrahlung. (In German, the term means "braking radiation.")

brevity code—A code which has as its sole purpose the shortening of messages rather than the concealment of their content.

Brewster angle—The angle of incidence at which the reflection of parallel-polarized electromagnetic radiation at the interface between two dielectric media equals zero.

bridge—1. In a measuring system, an instrument in which part or all of a bridge circuit is used to measure one or more electrical quantities. 2. In a fully electronic stringed instrument, the part that converts the mechanical vibrations produced by the strings into electrical signals.

bridge circuit—A network arranged so that, when an electromotive force is present in one branch, the response of a suitable detecting device in another branch may be zeroed by suitable adjustment of the electrical constants of still other branches.

bridged tap—The portion of a cable pair connected to a circuit which is not a part of the useful path.

Bridged-T network.

bridged-T network—A T-network in which the two series impedances of the T are bridged by a fourth impedance.

bridge duplex system — A duplex system based on the Wheatstone-bridge principle in which a substantial neutrality of the receiving apparatus to the transmitted currents is obtained by an impedance balance. Received currents pass through the receiving relay, which is bridged between the points that are equipotential for the transmitted currents.

Bridge rectifier.

bridge hybrid—*See* Hybrid Junction

bridge quad—*See* B-quad.

bridge rectifier—A full-wave rectifier with four elements connected in the form of a bridge circuit so that d-c voltage is obtained from one pair of opposite junctions when an alternating voltage is applied to the other pair of junctions.

bridge transformer—*See* Bridging Transformer.

bridging—The shunting of one electrical circuit by another.

bridging amplifier—An amplifier with an input impedance sufficiently high that its input may be bridged across a circuit without substantially affecting the signal level of the circuit.

bridging connection—A parallel connection by means of which some of the signal energy in a circuit may be withdrawn with imperceptible effect on the normal operation of the circuit.

bridging contacts—A set of contacts in which the moving contact touches two stationary contacts simultaneously during transfer.

bridging gain—Ratio between the power a transducer delivers to a specified load impedance under specified operating conditions, and the power dissipated in the reference impedance across which the transducer input is bridged. Usually expressed in decibels.

bridging loss—Ratio between the power dissipated in the reference impedance across which the input of a transducer is bridged, and the power the transducer delivers to a specified load impedance under specified operating conditions. Usually expressed in decibels.

bridging transformer—Also called bridge transformer and hybrid coil. A transformer designed to couple two circuits having at least nominal ohmic isolation and operating at different impedance levels, without introducing significant frequency or phase distortion, or significant phase shift.

brightness—The attribute of visual perception in accordance with which an area appears to emit more or less light. Used with cathode-ray tubes.

brightness control—In a television receiver, the control which varies the average brightness of the reproduced image.

brightness signal—*See* Luminance Signal.

brilliance—1. The degree of brightness and clarity in a reproduced cathode-ray tube. 2. The degree to which the higher audio frequencies sound like the original when reproduced by a receiver or public-address amplifier.

brilliance control—A potentiometer used in a three-way speaker system to adjust the output level of the tweeter for proper relative volume between the treble and the lower audio frequencies produced by the complete speaker system.

broad band—As applied to data transmission, the term denotes transmission facilities capable of handling frequencies greater than those required for high-grade voice communications (higher than 3 to 4 kilohertz).

broad-band amplifier—An amplifier which has an essentially flat response over a wide frequency range.

broad-band antenna—An antenna which is capable of receiving a wide range of frequencies.

broad-band electrical noise—Also called random noise. A signal that contains a wide range of frequencies and has a randomly varying instantaneous amplitude.

broad-band interference—Interference occupying a frequency range that is much greater than the bandwidth of the equipment being used to measure it.

broad-band random vibration—Single-frequency component vibrations that are random in both phase and amplitude at minute increments of frequency throughout a specified bandwidth. Typically it occurs when intense, high-power-level noise impinges on structures.

broad-band tube (TR and pre-TR tubes)—A gas-filled, fixed-tuned tube incorporating a bandpass filter suitable for radio-frequency switching.

broadcast—Radio or television transmission intended for public reception, for which receiving stations make no receipt.

broadcast band—The band of frequencies extending from 535 to 1605 kHz.

broadcasting—The transmitting of speech, music, or visual programs for commercial or public-service motives to a relatively large audience (as opposed to two-way radio, for example, which is utilitarian and is directed toward a limited audience).

broadcasting service—A radiocommunication service in which the transmissions are intended for direct reception by the general public. This service may include sound transmissions, television transmissions, or other types of transmissions.

broadcasting station—A station in the broadcasting service.

broadside—A direction perpendicular to an axis or plane.

broadside array—An antenna array whose direction of maximum radiation is perpendicular to the line or plane of the array (depending on whether the elements lie on a line or a plane). A uniform broadside array is a linear array whose elements contribute fields of equal amplitude and phase.

broad tuning—A tuned circuit or circuits which respond to frequencies within one band or channel, as well as to a considerable range of frequencies on each side.

brush—A piece of conductive material, usually carbon or graphite, which rides on the commutator of a motor and forms the electrical connection between it and the power source.

brush discharge—An intermittent discharge of electricity which starts from a conductor when its potential exceeds a certain value but is too low for the formation of an actual spark. It is generally accompanied by a whistling or crackling noise.

brush-discharge resistance—*See* Corona Resistance.

brush rocker—A movable rocker, or "yoke," on which the brush holders of a dynamo or motor are fixed so that the position of the brushes on the commutator can be adjusted.

brush station—In a computer, a position where the holes of a punched card are sensed, particularly when this is done by a row of brushes sweeping electrical contacts.

brute-force filter—A type of power-pack filter which depends on large values of capacitance and inductance to smooth out pulsations, rather than on the resonant effects of a tuned filter.

brute supply—One that is completely unregulated. It employs no circuitry to maintain the output voltage constant with a changing input line or load variations. The output voltage varies in the same percentage and in the same direction as the input line voltage. If the load current changes, the output voltage changes inversely—an increase in load current drops the output voltage.

B & S—Abbreviation for Brown and Sharpe gage. A wire-diameter standard that is the same as AWG.

B scope—A type of radarscope that presents the range of an object by a vertical deflection of the signal on the screen, and the bearing by a horizontal deflection.

"B" service—FAA service pertaining to transmission and reception by teletype or radio of messages containing requests for and approval to conduct an aircraft flight, flight plans, in-flight progress reports, and aircraft arrival reports.

B supply or B+ supply—A source for supplying a positive voltage to the anodes and other positive electrodes of electron tubes.

Bucky diaphragm.

buck—To oppose, as one voltage bucking another, or the magnetic fields of two coils bucking each other.

bucket—A general term for a specific reference in storage in a computer, such as a section of storage, the location of a word, a storage cell, etc.

bucking coil—A coil connected and positioned in such a way that its magnetic field opposes the magnetic field of another coil. The hum-bucking coil of an electrodynamic speaker is an example.

bucking voltage—A voltage which is opposite in polarity to another voltage in the circuit and hence bucks, or opposes, the latter voltage.

buckling—The warping of the plates of a battery due to an excessively high rate of charge or discharge.

Bucky diaphragm—A grid composed of narrow strips of lead arranged with X-ray–transparent spaces between adjacent strips and placed between the specimen and the X-ray film. Used to reduce scattered radiation.

buffer—1. A circuit or component which isolates one electrical circuit from another. Usually refers to electron-tube amplifiers used for this purpose. 2. A vacuum-tube stage used chiefly to prevent undesirable interaction between two other stages. In a transmitter, it generally follows the master-oscillator stage. 3. An isolating circuit used in an electronic computer to avoid reaction of a driven circuit on the corresponding driver circuit. 4. A storage device used to compensate for a difference in the rate of flow of information or the time or occurrence of

events when transmitting information from one device to another. 5. A computer circuit having an output and a multiplicity of inputs and designed so that the output is energized whenever one or more inputs are energized. Thus, a buffer performs the circuit function equivalent to the logical OR.

buffer amplifier—An amplifier designed to isolate a preceding circuit from the effects of a following circuit.

buffer capacitor — A capacitor connected across the secondary of a vibrator transformer, or between the anode and cathode of a cold-cathode rectifier tube, to suppress voltage surges that might otherwise damage other parts in the circuit.

buffer element—A low-impedance inverting driver circuit. Because of its very low source impedance the element can supply substantially more output current than the basic circuit. As a consequence, the buffer element is valuable in driving heavily loaded circuits or minimizing rise-time deterioration due to capacitive loading.

buffer storage—In a computer, a synchronized element of storage between two other forms of storage. Computation may continue while data are being transferred between the buffer and the other storage.

bug—1. A semiautomatic telegraph sending key consisting of a lever which is moved to one side to produce a series of correctly spaced dots, and to the other side to produce a dash. 2. A circuit fault due to improper design or construction. 3. An electronic listening device, generally small and

65

concealed, used for commercial or military espionage.

build—The increase of diameter due to insulation.

building-out—Addition to an electric structure of an element or elements electrically similar to an element or elements of the structure, to bring a certain property or characteristic to a desired value.

building-out circuit—A short section of transmission line, or a network which is shunted across a transmission line, for the purpose of impedance matching.

building-out network—A network designed to be connected to a basic network so that the combination will simulate the sending-end impedance, neglecting dissipation, of a line having a termination other than that for which the basic network was designed.

building-out section—A short section of transmission line, either open or short-circuited at the far end, shunted across another transmission line for use on an impedance-matching transformer.

bulb—The glass envelope which encloses an incandescent lamp or an electronic tube.

bulb-temperature pickup—A temperature transducer in which the sensing element is enclosed in a metal tube or sheath to protect it against corrosive liquids or other contaminants.

bulge—The difference between the actual characteristic and a linear characteristic of the attenuation-frequency characteristic of a transmission line.

bulk degausser—*See* Bulk Eraser.

bulk-erased noise—The noise arising when a bulk-erased tape is reproduced with the erase and record heads completely de-energized. Ideally, this noise is governed by the number of magnetic particles that pass by the head in unit time.

bulk eraser—Also called bulk degausser or degausser. Equipment for erasing a roll of tape. The roll is usually rotated while a 60-hertz a-c erasing field is decreased, either by withdrawing the roll from an electromagnet or by reducing the a-c supply to an electromagnet.

bulk noise—*See* Excess Noise.

bulk resistor—A resistor made by providing ohmic contacts between two points of a homogeneous, uniformly doped crystal of silicon material.

bump contracts—A small mound of material formed on the chip substrate, to register with terminal pads, as then the chip is employed in "flip-chip circuits."

bunched pair—A group of pairs tied together or otherwise associated for identification.

buncher—1. The input resonant cavity in a conventional klystron oscillator. 2. In a velocity-modulated tube, the electrode which concentrates the electrons in the constant-current electron beam into bunches.

buncher gap—*See* Input Gap.

buncher resonator—The input cavity reso-

nator in a velocity-modulated tube. It serves to modify the velocity of the electrons in the beam.

bunching—1. Grouping pairs together for identification and testing. 2. In a velocity-modulated electron stream the action that produces an alternating convection-current component as a direct result of the differences of electron transit time produced by the velocity modulation.

bunching parameter—One-half of the product of the bunching angle in the absence of velocity modulation and the depth of velocity modulation.

bunching time—The time in the armature motion of a relay during which all three contacts of a bridging-contact combination are electrically connected.

bunching voltage—The radio-frequency voltage between the grids of the buncher resonator in a velocity-modulated tube such as a klystron. Generally, the term implies the peak value of this oscillating voltage.

Bunch stranding.

bunch stranding—A method in which a number of wires are twisted together in a common direction and with a uniform pitch to form a finished, stranded wire.

bundled cable—Individual insulated wires laced together to form a bundle to facilitate handling.

buried cable—A cable installed underground and not removable except by disturbing the soil.

buried layer—A low-resistivity material introduced into a silicon substrate.

burned-in image—An image which remains in a fixed position in the output signal of a camera tube after the camera has been turned to a different scene.

burn-in—Operation of a device to stabilize its failure rate.

burn-in period—*See* Early Failure Period.

burst—1. A sudden increase in the strength of a signal. 2. The cosmic-ray effect upon matter, causing a sudden intense ionization that gives rise to great numbers of ion pairs at once. (*Also see* Color Burst.)

burst pedestal—A rectangular pulselike television signal which may be part of the color burst. The amplitude of the color-burst pedestal is measured from the alternating-current axis of the sine-wave portion of the horizontal pedestal.

burst pressure—The maximum pressure to which a device can be subjected without rupturing.

bus—1. In a computer, one or more conductors used as a path over which information is transmitted from any of several sources to any of several destinations. 2. The term used to specify an uninsulated conductor (a bar or wire); may be solid, hollow, square, or round. 3. Sometimes used to specify a bus bar. 4. The communications path between two switching points.

bus bar—A heavy copper strap or bar used to carry heavy currents or to make a common connection between several circuits.

bus reactor—A current-limiting reactor connected between two different buses or two sections of the same bus for the purpose of limiting and localizing the disturbance due to a fault on either bus.

bussback—The connection, by a common carrier, of the output portion of a circuit back to the input portion of a circuit. (*Also see* Loopback Test.)

busy test—In telephony, a test to find out whether certain facilities which may be desired, such as a subscriber line or a trunk, are available for use.

Butler oscillator—A two-tube (or transistor) crystal-controlled oscillator in which the crystal forms the positive feedback path when excited in its series-resonant mode.

butterfly resonator—Also called butterfly capacitor. A tuning device that combines both inductance and capacitance in such a manner that it exhibits resonant properties at very high and ultrahigh frequencies (characterized by a high tuning ratio and Q). So called because the shape of the rotor resembles the opened wings of a butterfly.

Butterworth filter—A filter network that exhibits the flattest possible response in the passband. The response is monotonic, rolling off smoothly into the stop band, where it approaches a constant slope of 6 db/octave.

butt joint—1. A splice or other connection formed by placing the ends of two conductors together and joining them by welding, brazing, or soldering. 2. A connection between two waveguides which maintains electrical continuity by providing physical contact between the ends.

button—1. The metal container in which the carbon granules of a carbon microphone are held. 2. Also called dot. A piece of metal used for alloying onto the base wafer in making alloy transistors.

button silver-mica capacitor—A stack of silvered mica sheets encased in a silver-plated brass housing. The high-potential

terminal is connected through the center of the stack. The other capacitor terminal is formed by the metal shell, which connects at all points around the outer edge of the electrodes. This design permits the current to fan out in a 360° pattern from the center terminal, providing the shortest possible electrical path between the center terminal and chassis. The internal series inductance is thus kept small.

button stem—In a tube, the glass base onto which the mount structure is assembled. The pins may be sealed into the glass; if so, no base is needed. In some large tubes, the stiff wires are passed directly into the base pins to give added strength. (*Also see* Pressed Stem.)

button up—To close or completely seal any operating device.

buzzer—A signaling device in which an armature vibrates to produce a raucous, nonresonant sound.

BV_{EBO}—The reverse-breakdown voltage of the emitter-to-base junction of a transistor with the collector open-circuited.

BX cable.

BX cable—Insulated wires in flexible metal tubing, used for wiring buildings and electrical and electronic equipment.

bypass—A shunt (parallel) path around one or more elements of a circuit.

bypass capacitor—A capacitor used for providing a comparatively low-impedance a-c path around a circuit element.

bypass filter—A filter providing a low-attenuation path around some other circuit or equipment.

B—Y signal—One of the three color-difference signals in color television. The B—Y signal forms a blue primary signal for the picture tube when combined—either inside or outside the picture tube—with a luminance or Y signal.

byte—A single group of bits processed together (in parallel). It can consist of a variable number of bits.

C

C—Symbol for capacitor, capacitance, carbon, coulomb, centigrade or Celsius, transistor collector, candle, velocity of light.

C— (C minus)—The negative terminal of a C battery, or the negative polarity of other sources of grid-bias voltage. Used to denote the terminal to which the negative side of the grid-bias voltage source should be connected.

C+ (C plus)—Positive terminal of a C battery, or the positive polarity of other sources of grid-bias voltage. The terminal to which the positive side of the grid-bias voltage source should be connected.

cabinet—A protective housing for electrical or electronic equipment.

cable—1. An assembly of one or more conductors, usually within a protective sheath, and so arranged that the conductors can be used separately or in groups. 2. A stranded conductor (single-conductor cable) or a combination of conductors insulated from one another (multiple-conductor cable).

cable assembly—A cable with plugs or connectors on each end for a specific purpose. It may be formed in various configurations.

cable clamp—A device used to give mechanical support to the wire bundle or cable at the rear of a plug or receptacle.

cable core—That portion of an insulated cable lying under the protective covering or jacket.

cable coupler—A device used to join lengths of similar or dissimilar cable having the same electrical characteristics.

cable fill—The ratio of the number in use to the total number of pairs in a cable.

cable filler—Material used in multiple-conductor cables to occupy the spaces between the insulated conductors.

cable Morse code—A three-element code used mainly in submarine-cable telegraphy. Dots and dashes are represented by positive and negative current impulses of equal length, and a space by the absence of current.

cable run—The path occupied by a cable on cable racks or other support from one termination to another.

cable sheath—A protective covering of rubber, neoprene, resin, or lead over a wire or cable core.

cable splice—A connection between two or more separate lengths of cable. The conductors in one length are individually connected to conductors in the other length, and the protecting sheaths are so connected that protection is extended over the joint.

cable terminal—A means of electrically connecting a predetermined number of cable conductors in such a way that they can be individually selected and extended by conductors outside the cable.

cable vault—A vault in which the outside plant cables are spliced to the tipping cables.

cabling—The method by which a group of insulated conductors is mechanically assembled (or twisted together).

cactus needle—A phonograph needle made from the thorn of a cactus plant.

cadmium—A metallic element widely used for plating steel hardware or chassis to improve its appearance and solderability and to prevent corrosion. It is also used in the manufacture of photocells.

cadmium selenide photoconductive cell—A photoconductive cell that uses cadmium selenide as the semiconductor material. It has a fast response time and high sensitivity to longer light wavelengths, such as those emitted by incandescent lamps and some infrared light sources.

cadmium sulfide photoconductive cell—A photoconductive cell in which a small wafer of cadmium sulfide is used to provide an

extremely high dark-light resistance ratio. Some of the cells can be used directly as a light-controlled switch operated directly from the 120-volt a-c power line.

Cage antenna.

cage antenna—An antenna comprising a number of wires connected in parallel and arranged in the form of a cage. This is done to reduce the copper losses and increase the effective capacity.

calculating—Computing a result by multiplication, division, addition, or subtraction, or by a combination of these operations. A data-processing function.

calculating punch—A punched-card machine that reads data from a group of cards and punches new data in the same or other cards.

calculator—1. A device capable of performing arithmetic. 2. A calculator as in 1 which requires frequent manual intervention. 3. Generally and historically, a device for carrying out logical and arithmetical digital operations of any kind.

calendar age—Age of an item or object measured in terms of time elapsed since it was manufactured.

calendar life—That period of time expressed in days, months, or years during which an item may remain installed and in operation, but at the end of which the item should be removed and returned for repair, overhaul, or other maintenance.

calibrate—To ascertain, by measurement or by comparison with a standard, any variations in the readings of another instrument, or to correct the readings.

calibrated interference measurements—Measurements in which the meter is calibrated against a known sine wave or impulse-generator output and interference readings are taken directly from the output indicating meter on the receiver.

calibrated triggered sweep—In a cathode-ray oscilloscope, a sweep that occurs only when initiated by a pulse and moves horizontally at a known rate.

calibration—1. The process of comparing an instrument or device with a standard to determine its accuracy or to devise a corrected scale. 2. Taking measurements of various parts of electronic equipment to determine the performance level of the equipment and whether it conforms to technical order specifications.

calibration accuracy—Finite degree to which a device can be calibrated (influenced by sensitivity, resolution, and reproducibility of the device itself and the calibrating equipment). Expressed as a per cent of full scale.

calibration curve—A smooth curve connecting a series of calibration points.

calibration marker—On the screen of a radar indicator, the markings that divide the range scale into accurate intervals for range determination or checking against mechanical indicating dials, scales, or counters.

call—1. A transmission made for the purpose of identifying the transmitting station and the station for which the transmission is intended. 2. To transfer control to a specified closed subroutine. 3. In communication the action performed by the calling party, or the operations necessary in making a call, or the effective use made of a connection between two stations.

call circuit— A communication circuit between switching points used by traffic forces for transmitting switching instructions.

call in—To transfer control of a digital computer temporarily from a main routine to a subroutine, which is inserted in the sequence of calculating operations to fulfill a subsidiary purpose.

call letters—A series of government-assigned letters, or letters and numbers, which identify a transmitting station.

call sign—Any combination of characters or pronounceable words which identifies a communication facility, a command, an authority, an activity, or a unit; used primarily for establishing and maintaining communications.

call word— A call number which is exactly the size of one machine word.

calomel electrode — An electrode consisting of mercury in contact with a solution of potassium chloride saturated with mercurouse chloride (calomel). (*Also see* Glass Electrode.)

calorimeter—An apparatus for measuring quantities of heat. Used to measure microwave power in terms of heat generated.

calorimeter system—A precision r-f wattmeter as well as an efficient dummy load able to absorb energy at any frequency band. It can absorb and measure any level of microwave energy, and functions by circulating a known amount of liquid through a suitably designed low vswr load. The load is located in a wave-guide or coaxial section that mates to the termination of the r-f energy source being measured or absorbed.

camera—*See* Television Camera.

camera cable—A cable or group of wires that carry the picture signal from the television camera to the control room.

camera chain—A television camera, associated control units, power supplies, monitor, and connecting cables necessary to deliver a picture for broadcasting.

camera signal—The video-output signal of a television camera.

camera tube—An electron-beam tube in which an electron current or charge-density image is formed from an optical image and scanned in a predetermined sequence to provide an electric signal.

can—A metal shield placed around a tube, coil, or transformer to prevent electromagnetic or electrostatic interaction.

canal ray—Also called positive ray. Streams of positive ions that flow from the anode to the cathode in an evacuated tube.

candle—The unit of luminous intensity. One candle is defined as the luminous intensity of 1/60th square centimeter of a black-body radiator operating at the solidification temperature of platinum.

candlepower—Luminous intensity expressed in terms of standard candles.

candoluminescence — A phenomenon that produces white light without need for very high temperatures.

cannibalization — A method of maintenance or modification in which the required parts are removed from one system or assembly for installation on a similar system or assembly.

capacitance—1. Abbreviated C. Also called capacity. In a capacitor or a system of conductors and dielectrics, that property which permits the storage of electrically separated charges when potential differences exist between the conductors. The capacitance of a capacitor is defined as the ratio between the electric charge that has been transferred from one electrode to the other and the resultant difference in potential between the electrodes. The value of this ratio is dependent on the magnitude of the transferred charge.

$$C \text{ (farad)} = \frac{Q \text{ (coulomb)}}{V \text{ (volt)}}$$

2. In the case of fluid devices, it accumulates fluid by virtue of its volume and the pressure head available.

capacitance between two conductors — The ratio between the charge transferred from one conductor to the other and the resultant difference in the potentials of the two conductors when insulated from each other and from all other conductors.

capacitance divider—A circuit made up of capacitors and used for measuring the value of a high-voltage pulse by making available only a small, known fraction of the total pulse voltage for measurement.

capacitance meter—An instrument for measuring capacitance. If the scale is graduated in microfarads, the instrument is usually designated a microfaradmeter.

Capacitance divider.

Capacitors.

capacitance-operated intrusion detector— A boundary alarm system in which the approach of an intruder to an antenna wire encircling the protected area (a few feet above ground) changes the antenna-ground capacitance and thereby sets off the alarm.

capacitance ratio— The ratio of maximum to minimum capacitance, as determined from a capacitance characteristic, over a specified voltage range.

capacitance relay— An electronic circuit incorporating a relay which responds to a small change in capacitance, such as that created by bringing the hand or body near a pickup wire or plate.

capacitive coupling— Also called electrostatic coupling. The association of two or more circuits with one another by means of mutual capacitance between them. Between stages of an amplifier, that type of interconnection which employs a capacitor in the circuit, between the plate of one tube and the grid of the succeeding tube.

capacitive divider— Two or more capacitors placed in series across a source, making available a portion of the source voltage across each capacitor. The voltage across each capacitor will be inversely proportional to its capacitance.

capacitive feedback— The process of returning part of the energy in the plate or output circuit of a vacuum tube to the grid, or input, circuit by means of a capacitance common to both circuits.

capacitive load— A predominantly capacitive load—i.e., one in which the current leads the voltage.

capacitive reactance— Symbolized by X_c. The impedance a capacitor offers to ac or pulsating dc. Measured in ohms and equal to $\frac{1}{2\pi f C}$, where f is in hertz and C is in farads.

capacitive speaker — *See* Electrostatic Speaker.

capacitive storage welding — A particular type of resistance welding whereby the energy is stored in banks of capacitors, which are then discharged through the primary of the welding transformer. The secondary current generates enough heat to produce the weld.

capacitive transduction— Conversion of the measurand into a change in capacitance.

capacitive tuning— Tuning by means of a variable capacitor.

capacitivity— *See* Dielectric Constant.

capacitor— A device consisting essentially of two conducting surfaces separated by an insulating material or dielectric such as air, paper, mica, glass, plastic film, or oil. A capacitor stores electrical energy, blocks the flow of direct current, and permits the flow of alternating current to a degree dependent upon the capacitance and the frequency.

capacitor antenna— Also called condenser antenna. An antenna which consists of two conductors or systems of conductors and the essential characteristic of which is its capacitance.

capacitor bank— A number of capacitors connected together in series, parallel, or in series-parallel.

capacitor color code— Color dots or bands placed on capacitors to indicate one or more of the following: capacitance, capacitance tolerance, voltage rating, temperature coefficient, and the outside foil (on paper capacitors).

capacitor-input filter— A power-supply filter in which a capacitor is connected directly across, or in parallel with, the rectifier output.

capacitor microphone— *See* Electrostatic Microphone.

capacitor motor— A single-phase induction motor with the main winding arranged for direct connection to the power source, together with an auxiliary winding connected in series with a capacitor.

capacitor pickup — A phonograph pickup which depends for its operation on the variation of its electrical capacitance.

capacitor series resistance— An equivalent resistance in series with a pure capacitance which gives the same resultant losses as the actual capacitor. This equivalent circuit does not represent the variation in capacitor losses with frequency.

capacitor speaker— *See* Electrostatic Speaker.

capacitor-start motor— An a-c split-phase induction motor in which a capacitor is connected in series with an auxiliary winding to provide a means of starting. The auxiliary circuit opens when the motor reaches a predetermined speed.

capacitor voltage — The voltage across the terminals of a capacitor.

capacity—1. The current-output capability of a cell or battery over a period of time. Usually expressed in ampere-hours (amp-hr). 2. Capacitance. 3. The limits, both upper and lower, of the items or numbers which may be processed in a computer register, in the accumulator. When quantities exceed the capacity, a computer interrupt develops and requires special handling. 4. The total quantity of data that a part of a computer can hold or handle, usually expressed as words per unit of time. 5. The capability of a specific system to store data, accept transactions, process data, and generate reports.

capstan—The driven spindle or shaft in a tape recorder—sometimes the motor shaft itself—which rotates against the tape, pulling it through the machine at a constant speed during recording and playback modes of operation. The rotational speed and diameter of the capstan thus determine the tape speed.

capstan idler—*See* Pressure Roller.

captive screw—Screw-type fastener that is retained when unscrewed and cannot easily be separated from the part it secured.

capture effect — 1. The selection of the stronger of two frequency-modulated signals of the same frequency, with the complete rejection of the weaker signal. If both signals are of equal strength, both may be accepted and no intelligible signal will result. 2. An effect occurring in a transducer (usually a demodulator) whereby the input wave having the largest magnitude controls the output.

capture ratio—The ability of a tuner to reject unwanted f-m stations and interference on the same frequency as a desired one, measured in db. The lower the figure, the better the performance of the tuner.

carbon—One of the elements, consisting of a nonmetallic conductive material occurring as graphite, lampblack, diamond, etc. Its resistance is fifty to several hundred times that of copper and decreases as the temperature increases.

carbon brush — A current-carrying brush made of carbon, carbon and graphite, or carbon and copper.

carbon-contact pickup—A phonograph pickup which depends for its operation on the variation in resistance of carbon contacts.

carbon-film resistor—A resistor formed by vacuum-depositing a thin carbon film on a ceramic form.

carbonize—To coat with carbon.

carbonized filament — A thoriated-tungsten filament treated with carbon. A layer of tungsten carbide formed on the surface slows down the evaporation of the active emitting thorium and thus permits higher operating temperatures and much greater electron emission.

carbonized plate—An electron-tube anode that has been blackened with carbon to increase its heat dissipation.

Carbon microphone.

carbon microphone—A microphone which depends for its operation on the variation in resistance of carbon contacts.

carbon-pile regulator—An arrangement of carbon discs the series resistance of which decreases as more pressure or compression is applied.

carbon resistor—Also called composition resistor. A resistor consisting of carbon particles which are mixed with a binder molded into a cylindrical shape, and then baked. Terminal leads are attached to opposite ends. The resistance of a carbon resistor decreases as the temperature increases.

carbon transfer recording—A type of facsimile recording in which carbon particles are deposited on the record sheet in response to the received signal.

carborundum—A compound of carbon and silicon used in crystals to rectify or detect radio waves.

carcinotron—A voltage-tuned, backward-wave oscillator tube used to generate frequencies ranging from uhf up to 100GHz or more.

card—*See* Punched Card and Printed Circuit Board.

card bed — A mechanical device for holding punch cards to be transported past the punching and reading stations.

Card bed.

card code—An arbitrary code in which holes punched in a card are assigned numeric or alphabetic values.

card column—One of 20 to 90 single-digit columns in a tabulating card. When punched, a column contains only one digit, one letter, or one special code.

Cardew voltmeter—The earliest type of hot-wire instrument. It consisted of a small-diameter platinum-silver wire sufficiently long to give a resistance high enough to be connected directly across the circuit being measured. The wire was looped over pulleys and it expanded as current flowed, causing the pointer to rotate.

Cardew voltmeter.

card face — The printed side of a punched card if only one side is printed.

card feed — A mechanism that moves punch cards, one at a time, into a machine.

card field—On a punch card, the fixed columns in which the same type of information is routinely entered.

card hopper—*See* Card Stacker.

cardiac monitor — An instrument that usually has an oscilloscope display of the heart wave, and combines the features of several cardiac instruments such as an electrocardiograph, cardiotachometer, etc. May also allow upper and lower limits to be set and trigger audible and/or visual alarms when these limits are exceeded.

card image—1. A representation in storage of the holes punched in a card, in such a manner that the holes are represented by one binary digit and the unpunched spaces are represented by the other binary digit. 2. In machine language, a duplication of the data contained in a punch card.

Cardioid diagram.

cardiograph—An instrument (or recording of instruments) for measuring the form or force of heart motion.

cardioid diagram—Heart-shaped polar diagram showing the response or radiation characteristic of certain directional antennas, or the response characteristic of certain types of microphones.

cardioid microphone — A microphone that has a heart-shaped response pattern that gives nearly uniform response for a range of about 180° in one direction and a minimum response in the opposite direction.

cardiostimulator—A device used to stimulate the heart and/or regulate its beat. *Also see* Pacemaker and Defibrillator.

card jam—A pile-up of cards in a machine.

card machine — A machine used to transfer information from or to punched cards.

card programmed—1. The capability of being programmed by punched cards. 2. The capability of performing sequences of calculating operations according to instructions contained in a stack of punched cards.

card punch—A device to record information in cards by punching holes in the cards to represent letters, digits, and special characters.

card reader—A device designed to read punched cards and convert each hole into an electrical impulse for use in a computer system.

card row — On a punched card, one of the horizontal lines of punching positions.

card sensing—The process of sensing or reading the information in punched cards and converting this information, usually into electrical pulses.

card stacker—A mechanism that stacks cards in a pocket or bin after they have passed through a computer. Also called card hopper.

carillon—A bell tower designed to play from a keyboard. In an organ, this may be achieved by tube synthesis of bell-like tones struck with felt hammers, or completely electronically.

Carnot theorem — A thermodynamic principle which states that a cycle continuously operating between a low temperature and a high temperature can be no more efficient than a reversible cycle operating between the same temperatures.

carriage tape—*See* Control Tape.

carrier—1. A wave of constant amplitude, frequency, and phase which can be modulated by changing amplitude, frequency, or phase. 2. An entity capable of carrying an electric charge through a solid (e.g., holes and conduction electrons in semiconductors).

carrier-amplitude regulation—The change in amplitude of the carrier wave in an amplitude-modulated transmitter when symmetrical modulation is applied.

carrier beat — In facsimile transmission, an undesirable heterodyne of signals, each synchronous with a different stable oscillator, causing a pattern in received copy. Where one or more of the oscillators is fork-controlled, this is called fork beat.

carrier chrominance signal—In color television, sidebands of a modulated chrominance subcarrier, plus any unsuppressed subcarrier, added to the monochrome signal to convey color information.

carrier color signal — In color television, sidebands of a modulated chrominance subcarrier, plus the chrominance subcarrier, if not suppressed, which are added to the monochrome signal to convey color information.

carrier concentration—The number of carriers in a cubic centimeter of semiconductor material.

carrier control—A control by the presence or absence of an r-f carrier.

carrier current—The current associated with a carrier wave.

carrier-current communication—The superimposing of a high-frequency alternating current on ordinary telephone, telegraph, and power-line frequencies for telephone communication and control.

carrier-current control—Remote control in which the receiver and transmitter are coupled together through power lines.

carrier frequency—1. The frequency (hertz) of the wave modulated by the intelligence wave; usually a radio frequency (rf). 2. The reciprocal of the period of a periodic carrier.

carrier-frequency interconnection — In the formation of carrier networks, the transfer of groups of channels between terminals of wire-line cable or radio carrier systems at carrier frequencies.

carrier-frequency peak-pulse power — The power, averaged over that carrier-frequency cycle, which occurs at the maximum pulse of power (usually half the maximum instantaneous power).

carrier-frequency pulse—A carrier that is amplitude-modulated by a pulse. The amplitude of the modulated carrier is zero before and after the pulse.

carrier-frequency range — The continuous range of frequencies within which a transmitter may normally operate. A transmitter may have more than one carrier-frequency range.

carrier-frequency stereo disc—A stereo disc with two laterally-cut channels. One channel is cut in the usual manner. The second channel is employed to frequency-modulate a supersonic carrier frequency. The playback cartridge delivers the signal for one channel plus the carrier frequency containing the other channel. The latter must then be demodulated to obtain the second channel.

carrier-isolating choke coil — An inductor inserted in series with a line on which carrier energy is applied to impede the flow of carrier energy beyond that point.

carrier leak — The carrier-frequency signal remaining after suppression in a suppressed carrier system.

carrier level — The strength, expressed in decibels, of an unmodulated carrier signal at a particular point in a system.

carrier lifetime—The time required for excess carriers doped into a semiconductor to recombine with other carriers of the opposite sign.

carrier line—A transmission line used for multiple-channel carrier communications.

carrier loading—The insertion of additional lump inductance in a cable section of a transmission line utilized for carrier transmission up to about 35 kHz. Loading serves to minimize impedance mismatch between cable and open wire, and to reduce the cable attenuation.

carrier mobility—The average drift velocity of carriers per unit electric field in a homogeneous semiconductor. The mobility of electrons is usually different from that of holes.

carrier noise level—Also called residual modulation. The noise level produced by undesired variations of a radio-frequency signal in the absence of any intended modulation.

carrier power output rating — The power available at the output terminals of a transmitter when the output terminals are connected to the normal-load circuit or to a circuit equivalent thereto.

carrier repeater—An assembly, including an amplifier (or amplifiers), filters, equalizers, level controls, etc., used to raise the carrier signal level to a value suitable for traversing a succeeding line section while maintaining an adequate signal-to-noise ratio.

carrier shift—1. The transmission of radio teletypewriter messages by shifting the carrier frequency in one direction for a marking signal and in the opposite direction for a spacing signal. 2. The condition resulting from imperfect modulation, whereby the positive and negative excursions of the envelope pattern are unequal, thus effecting a change in the power associated with the carrier.

carrier signaling — In a telephone system, the method by which ringing, busy signals, or dial-signaling relays are operated by the transmission of a carrier-frequency tone.

carrier suppression—The method of operation in which the carrier wave is not transmitted.

carrier swing—The total deviation of a frequency- or phase-modulated wave from the lowest to the highest instantaneous frequency.

carrier system — A means of obtaining a number of channels over a single path by modulating each channel upon a different carrier frequency and demodulating at the receiving point to restore the signals to their original form.

carrier tap choke coil—A carrier-isolating choke coil inserted in series with a line tap.

carrier tap transmission choke coil—An inductor inserted in series with a line tap to control the amount of carrier energy flowing into the tap.

carrier telegraphy—That form of telegraphy

in which the transmitted signal is formed by modulating the alternating current, under control of the transmitting apparatus, before supplying it to the line.

carrier telephony—Ordinarily applied only to wire telephony. That form of telephony in which carrier transmission is used, the modulating wave being at an audio frequency.

carrier terminal—Apparatus at one end of a carrier transmission system, whereby the processes of modulation, demodulation, filtering, amplification, and associated functions are effected.

carrier-to-noise ratio—Ratio of the magnitude of the carrier to the magnitude of the noise after selection and before any nonlinear process such as amplitude limiting and detection. This ratio is expressed in many different ways—for example, in terms of peak values in the case of impulse noise, and in terms of root-mean-square values in the case of random noise.

carrier-transfer filter—A group of filters arranged to form a carrier-frequency crossover or bridge between two transmission circuits.

carrier transmission—That form of electrical transmission in which a single-frequency wave is modulated by another wave containing the information.

carrier type d-c amplifier—An amplifier system which converts a d-c input to modulated a-c amplifiers, and synchronously detects to provide amplified d-c output.

carrier wave—The single-frequency wave which is transmitted and which is modulated by another wave containing the information.

carry—1. A signal or expression produced in an electronic computer by an arithmetic operation on a one-digit place of two or more numbers expressed in positional notation and transferred to the next higher place for processing there. 2. A signal or expression—as defined in (1)—which arises when the sum of two digits in the same digit place equals or exceeds the base of the number system in use. If a carry into a digit place will result in a carry out of the same digit place and the normal adding circuit is bypassed when this new carry is generated, the result is called a high-speed or "stand-on-nines" carry. If the normal adding circuit is used, the result is called a cascade carry. If a carry resulting from the addition of carries is not allowed to propagate, the process is called a partial carry; if it is, a complete carry. A carry generated in the most significant digit place and sent directly to the least significant place is called an end-around carry. 3. In direct subtraction, a signal or expression—as defined in (1) above—which arises when the difference between the digits is less than zero. Such a carry is frequently called a borrow. 4. The action of forwarding a carry. 5. The command directing a carry to be forwarded.

carry time—The time required for a computer to transfer a carry digit to the next higher column and add it there.

Cartridge.

cartridge—A removable phonograph pickup.

cartridge fuse—A tubular fuse the end caps of which are enclosed in a glass or composition insulating tube to confine the arc or vapor when the fuse blows.

cascade—*See* Tandem.

cascade amplifier—A multiple-stage amplifier in which the output of each stage is connected to the input of the next stage.

cascade connection—Two or more similar component devices arranged in tandem, with the output of one connected to the input of the next.

cascade control—Also called piggy-back control. An automatic control system in which the control units, linked in chain fashion, feed into one another in succession. Each unit thus regulates the operation of the next in line.

cascaded carry—In a computer, a system of executing the carry process in which carry information cannot be passed on to place (N + 1) unless the Nth place has received carry information or produced a carry.

cascaded feedback canceler—Also called velocity-shaped canceler. A sophisticated moving-target indicator canceler which provides clutter and chaff rejection.

cascaded thermoelectric device—A thermoelectric device having two or more stages that are arranged thermally in series.

cascode amplifier—An amplifier using a neutralized grounded-cathode input stage followed by a grounded-grid output stage. The circuit has high gain, high input impedance, and low noise.

case pressure—The total differential pressure in the internal cavity of a transducer and the ambient pressure. The term is commonly used to summarize the limiting combined differential and/or line-pressure capabilities of differential transducers.

case temperature—The temperature on the surface of the case at a designated point.

Cassegrain antenna—An antenna the feed of which is positioned near the vertex of the reflector, with a small subreflector placed near the focal point. The feed illuminates

Cascode amplifier.

the subreflector, and the subreflector redirects the waves toward the main reflector, which then forms the radiated beam (called the secondary beam or pattern). The shapes of the subreflector and main reflector are so chosen that the secondary rays will emerge parallel to the main-reflector axis.

casting-out-nines check—A partial verification of an arithmetical operation on two or more numbers. It involves casting out nines from the numbers and from the results.

catalyst—Also called hardener and promoter. A substance which markedly speeds up the cure of a casting or molding compound when added in a minor quantity as compared to the amounts of primary reactants.

catatastrophic failure—A sudden failure without warning, as opposed to degradation failure. Or, a failure the occurrence of which can prevent the satisfactory performance of an entire assembly or system.

catcher—In a velocity-modulated vacuum tube, an electrode on which the spaced electron groups induce a signal. The output of the tube is taken from this element.

catena—A chain or connected series.

catenate—*See* Concatenate.

catenation—*See* Concatenation.

cathamplifier—A push-pull amplifier in which the push-pull transformer is in the cathode circuit.

cathode—1. In an electron tube the electrode through which a primary source of electrons enters the interelectrode space. 2. General name for any negative electrode. 3. The lower-potential electrode of a corrosion cell where the action of the corrosion current may reduce or eliminate corrosion, or the negatively charged metallic parts of an impressed-current system. 4. When a semiconductor diode is biased in the forward direction, that terminal of the diode which is negative with respect to the other terminal.

cathode activity—Measure of the efficiency of an emitter. The mathematical relationship between two values of emission current measured under two conditions of cathode temperature.

cathode bias—A method of biasing a vacuum tube by placing the biasing resistor in the common cathode-return circuit, thereby making the cathode more positive—rather than the grid more negative—with respect to ground.

cathode-coupled amplifier—A cascade amplifier in which the coupling between two stages is accomplished by a common-cathode resistor.

cathode coupling—The use of an input or output element in the cathode circuit for coupling energy to another stage.

cathode current—*See* Electrode Current.

cathode-current density—The current per square centimeter of cathode area, expressed as amperes or milliamperes per centimeter squared.

cathode dark space—Also called Crookes' dark space. The relatively nonluminous region between the cathode and negative glow in a glow-discharge—cold-cathode tube.

cathode emission—The process whereby electrons are emitted from the cathode structure.

Cathode follower.

cathode follower—Also called grounded-plate amplifier. A vacuum-tube circuit in which the input signal is applied to the control grid, and the output is taken from the cathode. Electrically, such a circuit possesses a high input impedance and a low output impedance characteristic and a gain of less than unity. The equivalent circuit using a transistor is called an emitter follower.

cathode glow—The luminous glow which covers the surface of the cathode in a glow-discharge—cold-cathode tube, between the cathode and the cathode dark space.

cathode guide—The element of a glow tube used in switching the neon glow from one indicated number to the next.

cathode heating time—The time required for the cathode to attain a specified condition—for example, a specified value of emission or a specified rate of change in emission.

cathode interface—A resistive and capacitive layer formed between the nickel sleeve and oxide coating of an indirectly-heated cathode. Raising the cathode temperature will largely nullify the layer.

75

cathode keying—A method of keying a radiotelegraph transmitter by opening the plate return lead to the cathode or filament center tap.

cathode luminous sensitivity (of a multiplier phototube)—The photocathode current divided by the incident luminous flux.

cathode modulation—A form of amplitude modulation in which the modulating voltage is applied to the cathode circuit.

cathode pulse modulation—Modulation produced in an amplifier or oscillator by applying externally generated pulses to the cathode circuit.

cathode radiant sensitivity — The current leaving the photocathode divided by the incident radiant power of a given wavelength.

cathode ray—A stream of electrons emitted, under the influence of an electric field, from the cathode of an evacuated tube or from the ionized region nearby.

cathode-ray charge-storage tube — A charge-storage tube in which the desired information is written by means of a cathode-ray beam.

cathode-ray instrument—*See* Electron-Beam Instrument.

cathode-ray oscillograph — An apparatus capable of producing, from a cathode-ray tube, a permanent record of the value of an electrical quantity as a function of time.

cathode-ray oscilloscope—A test instrument which, when properly adjusted, makes possible the visual inspection of alternating-current signals. It consists of an amplifier, time-base generating circuits, and a cathode-ray tube for transformation of electrical energy into light energy.

SECOND ANODE OR ACCELERATING ANODE

AQUADAG COATING

SUPPORT & FEED WIRES

CONTROL GRID

CATHODE & HEATER ENCLOSED IN GRID CYLINDER

HORIZONTAL DEFLECTION PLATES

FIRST ANODE OR FOCUS ANODE

VERTICAL DEFLECTION PLATES

AQUADAG COATING

Cathode-ray tube.

cathode-ray tube—Abbreviated crt. A tube in which its electron beam can be focused to a small cross section on a luminescent screen and can be varied in position and intensity to produce a visible pattern.

cathode-ray tuning indicator — Commonly called magic eye. A small-diameter cathode-ray tube that visually indicates whether an apparatus such as a radio receiver is tuned precisely to a station.

cathode resistor—A resistance connected in the cathode circuit of a tube so that the voltage drop across it will supply the proper cathode-biasing voltage.

cathode spot—On the cathode of an arc, the area from which electrons are emitted at a current density of thousands of amperes per square centimeter and where the temperature of the electrode is too low to account for such currents by thermionic emission.

cathode sputtering—*See* Sputtering.

cathodic protection—The control of the electrolytic corrosion of an underground or underwater metallic structure by the application of an electric current through a sacrificial anode in such a way that the structure is made to act as a cathode of an electrolytic cell.

cathodolumninescence — Luminescence produced by the bombardment with high-velocity electrons of a metal in a vacuum. Small amounts of the metal are vaporized in an excited state by the bombardment and emit radiation characteristic of the metal.

cation—A positive ion that moves toward the cathode in a discharge tube, electrolytic cell, or similar equipment. The corresponding negative ion is called an "anion."

catv — Abbreviation for community antenna television.

catwhisker—A small, pointed wire used to make contact with a sensitive area on the surface of a crystal or semiconductor.

cavitation—In ultrasonic cleaning, the local formation of cavities in a liquid as the total pressure in that region is reduced.

cavitation noise — The noise produced in a liquid by the collapse of the bubbles created by cavitation.

cavity — A metallic enclosure inside which resonant fields may be excited at a microwave frequency.

cavity filter—A selective tuned device having the proper coupling means for insertion into a transmission line to produce attenuation of unwanted off-frequency signals.

cavity impedance—The impedance that appears across the gap of the cavity of a microwave tube.

cavity magnetron—A magnetron having a number of resonant cavities forming the anode; used as a microwave-transmitting oscillator.

cavity radiation — The radiation (heat) emerging from a small hole leading to a constant-temperature enclosure. Such radiation is identical with black-body radiation at the same temperature, no matter what the nature of the inner surface of the enclosure.

cavity resonator—A space which is normally bounded by an electrically conducting surface and in which oscillating electromagnetic energy is stored; the resonant frequency is determined by the geometry of the enclosure.

X-band reflex-klystron
resonant cavity.

TR cavity.

Re-entrant wavemeter cavity.

Cavities.

cavity-resonator frequency meter—A cavity resonator used for determining the frequency of an electromagnetic wave.

cavity-tuned, absorption-type frequency meter—A device used for measuring frequency. Its operation depends on the use of an enclosure with a conductive inner wall; the resonant frequency of the wall is determined by its internal dimensions.

cavity-tuned, heterodyne-type frequency meter—A device for measuring frequency. Its operation depends on the use of an enclosure, the resonant frequency of which is determined by its internal dimensions.

cavity-tuned, transmission-type frequency meter—A device for measuring frequency. Its operation depends on the use of an enclosure with a conductive inner wall; the resonant frequency of the wall is determined by its internal dimensions.

C-band—A radio-frequency band of 3.9 to 6.2 GHz, with wavelengths of 7.69 to 4.84 cm. It includes the top two sidebands of S-band, and the bottom three sidebands of the X-band.

C—battery—Also called grid battery. The energy source which supplies the voltage for biasing the grid of a vacuum tube.

C-bias—*See* Grid Bias.

CCIF—Abbreviation for International Telephone Consultative Committee.

CCIR—Abbreviation for International Radio Consultative Committee.

CCIT—Abbreviation for International Telegraph Consultative Committee.

CCS—Abbreviation for continuous commercial service. Refers to the power rating of transformers, tubes, resistors, etc. Used for rating components in broadcasting stations and some industrial applications.

ccw—Abbreviation for counterclockwise.

C-display—A type of radar display in which the signal is a bright spot, with the bearing as the horizontal and the elevation angle as the vertical co-ordinate.

celestial guidance—A system of guidance in which star sightings that are automatically taken during the flight of a missile provide position information used by the guidance equipment.

cell—1. A single unit that produces a direct voltage by converting chemical energy into electrical energy. 2. A single unit that produces a direct voltage by converting radiant energy into electrical energy—for example, a solar or photovoltaic cell. 3. A single unit that produces a varying voltage drop because its resistance varies with illumination. 4. Elementary unit of storage. 5. In corrosion processes, a source of electric potential that is responsible for corrosion. It consists of an anode and a cathode immersed in an electrolyte and electrically bonded together. The anode and cathode may be separate metals or dissimilar areas on the same metal. The different metals will develop a difference in potential that is accompanied by corrosion of the anode. When this cell involves an electrolyte as it does in corrosion processes, it is referred to as an electrolytic cell.

cell counter—An electronic instrument used to count white or red blood cells or other very small particles.

cell-type enclosure—A prefabricated basic shielded enclosure of double-walled copper-mesh construction. The original screen-room design.

cell-type tube (TR, ATR, and PRE-TR tubes)—A gas-filled, radio-frequency switching tube which operates in an external resonant circuit. A tuning mechanism may be incorporated into the external resonant circuit or the tube.

cellulose-nitrate discs—*See* Lacquer Disc.

Celsius temperature scale—Also called centigrade temperature scale. A temperature scale based on the freezing point of water defined as 0°C. and the boiling point defined as 100°C. both under conditions of normal atmospheric pressure (760 mm of mercury).

77

center frequency—1. Also called resting frequency. The average frequency of the emitted wave when modulated by a symmetrical signal. 2. The frequency at the center of a spectrum display (for linear frequency scanning). It is usually tunable.

centering control—One of two controls used to shift the position of the entire image on the screen of a cathode-ray tube. The horizontal-centering control moves the image to the right or left, and the vertical-centering control moves it up or down.

centering diode—A clamping circuit used in some types of plan-position indicators.

center of gravity—A point inside or outside a body and around which all parts of the body balance each other.

center of mass—On a line between two bodies, the point around which the two bodies would revolve freely as a system.

center poise—Scale of viscosity for insulating varnishes.

center ring—The part that supports the stator in an induction-motor housing. The motor end shields are attached to the ends of the center ring.

center tap—A connection at the electrical center of a winding, or midway between the electrical ends of a resistor or other portion of a circuit.

Center tap.

center-tapped winding—An internal tap at the center of a winding (three external leads).

center wire—A fine loop of wire used in proportional counters as an anode. A high voltage is applied to it to set the conditions for radiation measurement.

centigrade temperature scale — The older name for a Celsius temperature scale in the English-speaking countries. Officially abandoned by international agreement in 1948, but still in common usage.

centimeter waves — Microwave frequencies between 3 and 30 GHz, corresponding to wavelengths of 1 to 10 centimeters.

central processing unit—Also called central processor. Part of a computer system which contains the main storage, arithmetic unit, and special register groups. Performs arithmetic operations, controls instruction processing, and provides timing signals and other housekeeping operations.

Central Radio Propagation Laboratory—An organization, reporting to the Department of Commerce through the National Bureau of Standards, which is responsible for the collection, correlation, and analysis of data on which radio-propagation predictions are based, and issuance of radio-propagation predictions, and research on radio propagation and measurement methods and standards.

centrifugal force—The force which acts on a rotating body and which tends to throw the body farther from the axis of its rotation.

centripetal force—The force which compels a rotating body to move inward toward the center of rotation.

Ceracircuits — A trademark of the Sprague Electric Company for hybrid thick-thin film integrated circuits that consist of discrete passive and semiconductor active elements attached to precision resistor substrates to form functional electronic modules.

ceramic—A clay-like material, consisting primarily of magnesium and aluminum oxides, which after molding and firing is used as an insulating material. It withstands high temperatures and is less fragile than glass. When glazed, it is called porcelain.

ceramic-based microcircuit—A microminiature circuit printed on a ceramic substrate. Usually consists of combinations of resistive, capacitive, or conductive elements fired on a waferlike piece of ceramic.

ceramic capacitor—A capacitor the dielectric of which is a ceramic material such as steatite or barium titanate, the composition of which can be varied to give a wide range of temperature coefficients. The electrodes are usually silver coatings, fired on opposite sides of the ceramic disc or slab, or fired on the inside and outside of a ceramic tube. After connecting leads are soldered to the electrodes, the unit is usually given a protective insulating coating.

ceramic microphone—A microphone with a ceramic cartridge.

ceramic permanent magnet—A permanent, nonmetallic magnet made from pressed and sintered mixtures of metallic-oxide powders, usually oxides of barium and iron.

ceramic pickup—A phonograph pickup with a ceramic cartridge.

ceramic transducer—*See* Piezoelectric Transducer.

Cerenkov radiation — Light emitted when charged particles pass through a transparent material at a velocity greater than that of light in that material. It can be seen, for example, as a blue glow in the water around the fuel elements of pool reactors. P.A. Cerenkov was the Russian scientist who first explained the origin of this light.

Cerenkov rebatron radiator — A device in which a tightly bunched velocity-modulated electron beam is passed through a hole in a dielectric. The reaction between the higher velocity of the electrons passing through the hole and the slower velocity of the electromagnetic energy passing through the dielectric results in radiation at some frequency higher than the frequency of modulation of the electron beam.

cermet—A metal-dielectric mixture used in making thin-film resistive elements. The first half of the term is derived from *cer*amic and the second half from *met*al.

cesium—A chemical element having a low work function. Used as a getter in vacuum tubes and in cesium-oxygen-silver photocell cathodes.

cesium-vapor lamp—A low-voltage arc lamp for producing infrared radiation.

C_{gk}—Symbol for grid-cathode capacitance in a vacuum tube.

C_{gp}—Symbol for grid-plate capacitance in a vacuum tube.

cgs electromagnetic system of units—A coherent system of units for expressing the magnitude of electrical and magnetic quantities. The most common fundamental units of these quantities are the centimeter, gram, and second. Their unit of current (ab-ampere) is of such a magnitude that if maintained constant in two straight parallel conductors having an infinite length and negligible circular sections and placed one centimeter apart in a vacuum, a force equal to 2 dynes per centimeter of length will be produced.

cgs electrostatic system of units—A coherent system of units for expressing the magnitude of electrical and magnetic quantities. The most common fundamental units of these quantities are the centimeter, gram, and second. Their unit of electrical charge (statcoulomb) is of such a magnitude that two equal unit point charges one centimeter apart in a vacuum will repel each other with a force of one dyne.

chad—The piece of material removed when a hole or notch is formed in a storage medium such as punched tape or punched cards.

chadless tape—A type of punched paper tape in which each chad is left fastened by about a quarter of the circumference of the hole. Chadless punched paper tape must be sensed by mechanical fingers, because chad interferes with reliable electrical or photoelectrical reading.

chafe—Undesirable rubbing with friction.

chaff—A general name applied to radar-confusion reflectors which consist of thin, narrow, metallic strips of various length and frequency responses used to reflect radar echoes.

chaining—In a computer, a system of storing records such that each record belongs to a list or group of records and has a linking field for tracing the chain.

chain printer—In a computer, a high-speed printer having type slugs carried on the links of a revolving chain.

chain radar system—A radar system comprising a number of radars or radar stations located at various sites along a missile-flight path. These radar stations are linked together by data and communication lines for target acquisition, target positioning, and/or data-recording purposes. The target-acquisition link makes it possible for any radar to position any other radar on target.

chain reaction—A reaction that stimulates its own repetition. In a fission chain reaction a fissionable nucleus absorbs a neutron and fissions, releasing additional neutrons. These in turn can be absorbed by other fissionable nuclei, releasing still more neutrons. A fission chain reaction is self-sustaining when the number of neutrons released in a given time equals or exceeds the number of neutrons lost by absorption in nonfissioning material or by escape from the system.

challenger—*See* Interrogator.

chance failure—*See* Random Failure.

channel—1. A portion of the spectrum assigned for the operation of a specific carrier and the minimum number of sidebands necessary to convey intelligence. 2. A single path for transmitting electric signals. (Note: The word "path" includes separation by frequency division or time division. Channel may signify either a one-way or two-way path, providing communication in either one direction only or in two directions.) *Also see* Alternate Channel. 3. In electric computers, that portion of a storage medium which is accessible to a given reading station. 4. The path along which information, particularly a series of digits or characters, may flow. 5. In computer circulating storage, one recirculating path containing a fixed number of words stored serially by word. 6. The main current path between the source and the drain in a field-effect transistor or other semiconductor.

channel balance—Equal response on both left and right channels.

channel capacity—The maximum possible information rate through a channel, subject to the constraints of that channel. May be either per second or per symbol.

channel frequency—The band of frequencies which must be handled by a carrier system to transmit a specific quantity of information.

channeling—The utilization of a modulation-frequency band for the simultaneous transmission from two or more communication channels in which the channel separation is accomplished by the use of carriers or subcarriers, each in a different discrete frequency band forming a subdivision of the main band. This covers a special case of multiplex transmission.

channel interval—The time allocated to a channel, including on and off time.

channelizing—The process of subdividing wideband transmission facilities for the purpose of putting many different circuits requiring comparatively narrow bandwidths on a single wideband facility.

channel pulse—Intelligence on a channel, by virtue of the modulation characteristic.

channel pulse synchronization—Synchronization of a local-channel rate oscillator by comparison and phase lock with separate channel synchronizing pulses.

channel reliability—The percentage of time

that the channel meets the arbitrary standards established by the user.

channel reversal—Shifting the outputs of a stereo system so the channel formerly heard from the left speaker now comes from the right and vice versa.

channel-reversing switch—A switch that reverses the connections of two speakers in a stereo system with respect to the channels, so that the channel heard previously from the right speaker is heard from the left and vice versa.

channel sampling rate — The number of times per second that individual channels are sampled. This is different from commutation rate, since it is possible for more than one channel to be applied to a given commutator input (with subcommutation).

channel selector—A switch or dial used for selecting a desired channel.

channel separation—In stereo the electrical or acoustical difference between the left and right channels. Inadequate separation can lessen the stereo effect; excessive separation can exaggerate it beyond natural proportions.

channel strip—An amplifier, or other device having a sufficiently wide bandpass to amplify one television channel.

channel subcarrier—The channel required to convey telemetric data involving a subcarrier band.

channel synchronizing pulse separator—A device for separating channel synchronizing pulses from commutated signals.

channel-to-channel connection — A device for rapid data transfer between two computers. A channel adapter is available that permits the connection between any two channels on any two systems. Data are transferred at the rate of the slower channel.

channel-utilization index—In a computer, the ratio between the information rate (per second) through a channel and the channel capacity (per second).

channel wave—Any elastic wave propagated in a sound channel because of a low-velocity layer in the solid earth, the sea, or the atmosphere.

character—1. In electronic computers, one of a set of elementary symbols which may be collectively arranged in order to express information. These symbols may include the decimal digits 0 through 9, the letters A through Z, punctuation and typewriter symbols, and any other single symbol which a computer may read, store, or write. 2. One of a set of symbols used to present information on a display tube.

character crowding—The effect of reducing the time interval between subsequent characters read from tape. It is caused by a combination of mechanical skew, gap scatter, jitter, amplitude variation, etc. Also called packing.

character emitter—In a computer, an electromechanical device that puts out coded pulses.

characteristic—An inherent and measurable property of a device. Such a property may be electrical, mechanical, thermal, hydraulic, electromagnetic, or nuclear; and it can be expressed as a value for stated or recognized conditions. A characteristic may also be a set of related values (usually in graphical form).

Characteristic curve.

characteristic curve—A graph plotted to show the relationship between changing values. An example would be a curve showing plate-current changes as the grid voltage varies.

characteristic distortion — Displacement of signal transitions due to the persistence of transients caused by preceding transitions.

characteristic frequency — The frequency which can be easily identified and measured in a given emission.

characteristic impedance—Also called surge impedance. 1. The driving-point impedance of a line if it were of infinite length. 2. In a delay line, the value of terminating resistance which provides minimum reflection to the network input and output. 3. The ratio of voltage to current at every point along a transmission line on which there are no standing waves. 4. The square root of the product of the open- and short-circuit impedance of the line.

characteristic impedance of free space—The relationship between the electric and magnetic intensities of space due to the expansion of the impedance concept to electromagnetic fields.

characteristic spread—The range between the minimum and maximum values for a given characteristic that is considered normal in any large group of tubes or other devices.

characteristic telegraph distortion—Distortion which does not affect all signal pulses alike. Rather, the effect on each transition depends on the signal previously sent, because remnants of previous transitions or transients persist for one or more pulse lengths.

characteristic wave impedance—The ratio of the transverse electric vector to the transverse magnetic vector at the point it is crossed by an electromagnetic wave.

character reader — A computer input device which can directly recognize printed or writ-

MU-METAL SHIELD
COIL ADJUSTERS
YOKE AJUSTER
HELICAL ACCELERATOR
VIEWING SCREEN
ELECTRON GUN
SELECTION PLATES
MATRIX
CONVERGENCE COIL
DEFLECTION YOKE
REFERENCE PLATES
DISPLAYED CHARACTER
(DOTTED LINE INDICATES PATH OF ELECTRON BEAM)

Charactron.

ten characters; they need not first be converted into punched holes in cards or paper or polarized magnetic spots.

character recognition — In a computer, the act of reading, identifying, and encoding a printed character.

character sensing — To detect the presence of characters optically, magnetically, electrostatically, etc.

Charactron—Trade name of General Dynamics/Electronics for a specially constructed cathode-ray tube used to display alphanumeric characters and other special symbols directly on its screen.

charge—1. The electrical energy stored in a capacitor or battery or held on an insulated object. 2. The quantity of electrical energy in (1) above.

charge carrier—A mobile hole or conduction electron in a semiconductor.

charge density—The charge per unit area on a surface, or charge per unit volume in space.

charged particle — An ion, an elementary particle that carries a positive or negative electric charge.

charger—A device used to convert alternating current into a pulsating direct current which can be used for charging a storage battery.

charge retention—The ability of a battery to hold its energy once it has been charged.

charge-storage tube—A storage tube which retains information on its surface in the form of electric charges.

charge transfer—The process in which an ion takes an electron from a neutral atom of the same type with a resultant transfer of electronic charge.

charging—The process of converting electrical energy to stored chemical energy.

charging current—The current that flows into a capacitor when a voltage is first applied.

charging rate—The rate of current flow used in charging a battery.

chassis—1. A sheet-metal box, frame, or simple plate on which electronic components and their associated circuitry can be mounted. 2. The entire equipment (less cabinet) when so assembled. (*Also see* Printed-Circuit Board.)

chassis ground—A connection to the metal structure that supports the electrical components which make up the unit or system.

chatter—1. Prolonged undesirable opening and closing of electrical contacts. 2. The vibration of a cutting stylus in a direction other than the direction in which it is driven.

chatter time—The interval of time from initial actuation of a contact to the end of chatter.

check—The partial or complete verification of the correctness of equipment operations, the existence of certain prescribed conditions, and/or the correctness of results.

check digit—A digit carried along with a machine word and used to report information about the other digits in the word so that if a single error occurs, the check fails and an error alarm signal is initiated.

checkerboard—*See* Worst-Case Noise Pattern.

check point—In a computer routine, a point at which it is possible to store sufficient information to permit restarting the computation from that point.

check-point routine—A computer routine in which information for a check point is stored.

check problem—A problem which, when incorrectly solved, indicates an error in the programming or operation of a computer.

check register—A special register provided in some computers to temporarily store transferred information for comparison with a second transfer of the same information in order to verify that the information transferred each time agrees precisely.

check routine — A program the purpose of which is to determine whether a computer or a program is operating correctly.

81

checksum — In a computer, a summation of digits or bits summed according to an arbitrary set of rules and primarily used for checking purposes.

cheese antenna—An antenna with a cylindrical parabolic reflector enclosed by two plates perpendicular to the cylinder and so spaced that more than one mode can be propagated in the desired direction of polarization. It is fed on the focal line.

chelate—A molecule in which a central inorganic ion is covalently bonded to one or more organic molecules, with at least two bonds to each molecule; used as a laser dopant.

chemical deposition—The process of depositing a substance on a surface by means of the chemical reduction of a solution.

chemically deposited printed circuit — A printed circuit formed on a base by the reaction of chemicals alone. Dielectric, magnetic, and conductive circuits can be applied.

chemically reduced printed circuit — A printed circuit formed by chemically reducing a metallic compound.

chemisorption—*See* Adsorption.

Child's law—Also known as the three-halves power equation. It states that the current in a thermionic diode varies directly with the three-halves power of the anode voltage and inversely with the square of the distance between electrodes.

chip—1. Also called thread. In mechanical recording, the material removed from the recording medium by the recording stylus as it cuts the groove. 2. In punched cards, a piece of cardboard removed in the punching process. 3. A single substrate on which all the active and passive elements of an electronic circuit have been fabricated utilizing the semiconductor technologies of diffusion, passivation, masking, photoresist, and epitaxial growth. A chip is not ready for use until it is packaged and provided with terminals for connection to the outside world.

chirp—1. An all-encompassing term for the various techniques of pulse expansion-pulse compression applied to pulse radar. A technique to expand narrow pulses to wide pulses for transmission, and to compress wide received pulses to the original narrow pulse width and waveshape. This improves the signal-to-noise ratio without degradation to the range resolution and range discrimination. 2. A colloquial expression for a coded pulse. In coding the pulse, the carrier frequency is increased in a linear manner for the duration of the pulse, and when the pulse is translated to an audio frequency, it sounds like a chirp. 3. A change in the pitch of code signals, generally due to poor regulation of the transmitter power supply.

choke—An inductance used to impede the flow of pulsating direct current or alternating current by means of its self-inductance.

choke coil—Also called impedance coil. An inductor (reactor) used to limit or suppress the flow of alternating current without appreciable effect on the flow of direct current.

choke flange—A waveguide flange with a grooved surface; the groove is so dimensioned that the flange forms part of a choke joint.

choke-input filter—A power-supply filter in which a choke is the first element in series with the input.

choke joint—1. A connector between two sections of transmission line in which the gap between sections to be connected is built out to form a series-branching transmission line carrying a standing wave, in which actual contact falls at or near a current minimum. 2. A joint for connecting two sections of waveguide together. Permits efficient energy transfer without the necessity of an electrical contact at the inside surface of the guide.

chopped mode — A time-sharing method of displaying output signals of two or more channels with a single crt gun, in sequence, at a rate not referenced to the sweep.

chopper—1. A device for interrupting a current or a light beam at regular intervals. Choppers are frequently used to facilitate amplification. 2. An electromechanical switch for the production of modified square waves. The waves are of the same frequency as a driving sine wave and bear a definite relationship to it. 3. An electromechanical or electronic device used to interrupt a d-c or low-frequency a-c signal at regular intervals to permit amplification of the signal by an a-c amplifier. It may also be used as a demodulator to convert an a-c signal to dc. 4. A rotating shutter for interrupting an otherwise continuous stream of particles. Choppers can release short bursts of neutrons with known energies. Used to measure nuclear cross sections.

chopper amplifier—A circuit that amplifies a low-level signal after it has gone through a chopper.

chopper stabilization—1. The addition of a chopper amplifier to the regulator input circuitry of a regulated power supply in order to reduce output drift. 2. A method of improving the d-c drift of an amplifier by utilization of chopper circuits.

chopper-stabilized amplifier — An amplifier configuration utilizing a carrier-type d-c amplifier to reduce the effect of input offset and drift of a direct-coupled amplifier.

chopping—Removal by electronic means of one or both extremities of a wave at a predetermined level.

chord — A harmonious combination of tones

Chokes.

sounded together through the use of one or more fingers on either or both hands. On chord organs a full chord is selected by depressing a single chord button.

chord organ — An organ with provision for playing a variety of chords, each produced by means of a single button or key.

chorus — A natural electromagnetic phenomenon in the vlf range. Probably originates in the exosphere. Also called "dawn chorus" because it sounds like birds at dawn. It generally consists of a multitude of rising tones, each tone rising from 1-2 kHz to 3-4 kHz and usually lasting 0.1 to 0.5 second.

Christmas-tree pattern — 1. *See* Optical Pattern. 2. A pattern resembling a Christmas tree, sometimes produced on the screen of a television receiver when the horizontal oscillator falls out of sync.

chroma — That quality which characterizes a color without reference to its brightness; that quality which embraces hue and saturation. White, black, and gray have no chroma.

chroma-clear raster — Also called white raster. Looks like a clear raster, but each of the three guns in the crt is operating under the influence of a color level determined by a white video signal. In this case, all tv set chroma circuits are working as though the tv set were receiving a color transmission of a completely white scene.

chroma control — A variable resistor which controls saturation by varying the level of chrominance signal fed to the demodulators of a color television receiver.

chromatic aberration — An effect which causes refracted white light to produce an image with colored fringes due to the various colors being bent at different angles.

chromaticity — 1. The combination of the hue and saturation attributes of color. 2. A term quantitatively descriptive of a color, and dependent upon both hue and saturation, but without reference to brilliance.

chromaticity coordinate — The ratio of any one of the tristimulus values of a sample color to the sum of the three tristimulus values.

chromaticity diagram — A plane diagram formed when any one of the three chromaticity co-ordinates is plotted against another.

chromaticity flicker — The flicker which results from fluctuation of the chromaticity only.

chrominance — Colorimetric difference between any color and a reference color of equal luminance, the reference color having a specified chromaticity. In standard color-television transmission, the specified chromaticity is that of the zero subcarrier.

chrominance amplifier — The amplifier that separates the chrominance signal from the total video signal.

chrominance cancellation — A cancellation of the brightness variations produced by the chrominance signal on the screen of a monochrome picture tube.

chrominance-carrier reference — A continu-

Chromaticity diagram.

ous signal having the same frequency as the chrominance subcarrier, and a fixed phase with the color burst. The phase reference of carrier-chrominance signals for modulation or demodulation.

chrominance channel — In color television, a combination of circuits designed to pass only those signals having to do with the reproduction of color.

chrominance component — Either of the I and Q signals which add to produce the complete chrominance signal in NTSC systems.

chrominance demodulator — A demodulator used in color-television reception for deriving video-frequency chrominance components from the chrominance signal and a sine wave of the chrominance subcarrier frequency.

chrominance gain control — In red, green, and blue matrix channels, variable resistors which individually adjust the primary-signal levels. Used in color television.

chrominance modulator — A modulator used in color-television transmission for generating the chrominance signal from the video-frequency chrominance components and the chrominance subcarrier.

chrominance primary — One of two transmission primaries, the amounts of which deter-

Chrominance primaries.

mine the chrominance of a color. Chrominance primaries have zero luminance and are not physical.

chrominance signal—That portion of the composite color signal used to represent electrically the hues and saturation levels of the colors in a televised scene.

chrominance subcarrier — Also called color carrier. An r-f signal which has a specific frequency of 3.579545 MHz and which is used as a carrier for the I and Q signals.

chrominance-subcarrier oscillator — In a color-tv receiver, a crystal-controlled oscillator which generates the subcarrier signal for use in the chrominance demodulators.

chrominance video signals—Output voltages from the red, green, and blue sections of a color-television camera or receiver matrix.

chronistor—A subminiature elapsed-time indicator that uses electroplating principles to totalize the operating time of equipment up to several thousand hours.

chronograph—An instrument for producing a graphical record of time as shown by a clock or other device.

chronometer — A portable timekeeper with compensated balance, capable of showing time with high precision and accuracy.

chronoscope—An instrument for measuring very small intervals of time.

CIE — Initials of the Commission Internationale de l'Eclairage or International Commission on Illumination.

Circle cutter.

circle cutter—A tool consisting of a center drill with an adjustable extension-arm cutter and used to cut holes in panels and chassis.

circle of confusion—The circular image of a point source due to the inherent aberrations in an optical system.

circlotron amplifier—A one-port, nonlinear cross-field high power microwave amplifier which uses a magnetron as a negative-resistance element, much as a maser uses an active material.

circuit—1. An electronic path between two or more points capable of providing a number of channels. 2. A number of conductors connected together for the purpose of carrying an electrical current. 3. The interconnection of a number of devices in one or more closed paths to perform a desired electrical or elec-

tronic function. Examples of simple circuits are high- or low-pass filters, multivibrators, oscillators, and amplifiers.

circuit analyzer — Also called multimeter. Several instruments or instrument circuits combined in a single enclosure and used in measuring two or more electrical quantities in a circuit.

circuit breaker—An automatic device which, under abnormal conditions, will open a current-carrying circuit without damaging itself (unlike a fuse, which must be replaced when it blows).

circuit-breaker cascade system—A system wherein the protective devices are arranged in order of ratings such that those in series will coordinate and provide the required protection.

circuit capacity—The number of communication channels which can be handled by a given circuit at the same time.

circuit dropout—A momentary interruption of a transmission because of the complete failure of a circuit.

circuit efficiency (of the output circuit of electron tubes)—Ratio of the power, at the desired frequency, delivered to a load at the output-circuit terminals of an oscillator or amplifier, to the power, at the desired frequency, delivered to the output circuit by the electron stream.

circuit element—Any basic constituent of a circuit except the interconnections.

circuit hole — On a printed-circuit board, a hole that lies partially or completely within the conductive area.

circuit noise—The noise brought to the receiver electrically from a telephone system, but not the noise picked up acoustically by the telephone transmitters.

circuit noise level—At any point in a transmission system, the ratio of the circuit noise at that point to some arbitrary amount of circuit noise chosen as a reference. This ratio is usually expressed in decibels above reference noise, abbreviated dbrn, signifying the reading of a circuit noise meter; or in adjusted decibels, abbreviated dba, signifying the circuit noise meter reading adjusted to represent interfering effect under specified conditions.

circuit-noise meter—Also called noise-measuring set. An instrument for measuring the circuit-noise level. Through the use of a suitable frequency-weighting network and other characteristics, the instrument gives equal readings for noises of approximately equal interference. The readings are expressed in decibels above the reference noise.

circuit parameters—The values of the physical quantities associated with circuit elements—for example, the resistance (parameter) of a resistor (element), the amplification factor and plate resistance (parameters) of a tube (element), the inductance per unit length (parameter) of a transmission line (element).

circuit protection—Automatic protection of a consequence-limiting nature used to minimize the danger of fire or smoke, as well as the disturbance to the rest of the system which may result from electrical faults or prolonged electrical overloads.

circuit re-entrancy—*See* Re-entrancy.

circuit reliability—The percentage of time the circuit meets arbitrary standards set by the user.

circuitry—A complex of circuits describing interconnection within or between systems.

circular antenna—A horizontally polarized antenna derived essentially from a half-wave antenna but having its elements bent into a circle.

circular electric wave—A wave with circular electric lines of force.

circular magnetic wave—A wave with circular magnetic lines of force.

circular mil—The universal term used to define cross-sectional areas. Equal to the area of a circle one mil (.001 inch) in diameter.

circular mil area—The square of the diameter of a round conductor measured in thousandths of an inch. The circular mil area of a braid is the sum of the circular mil area of each of the wires that make up the braid.

circular polarization—Polarization such that the vector representing the wave has a constant magnitude and rotates continuously about a point.

circular polarized wave—Applied usually to transverse waves. An electromagnetic wave for which the electric and/or magnetic field vector at a point describes a circle.

circular scan—A radar scan in which a given point on the direct beam describes a circle in space, with the antenna at the center.

circular scanning—Scanning in which the direction of maximum radiation generates a plane or a right circular cone with a vertex angle close to 180°.

circular trace—A cro time base produced by applying sine waves of the same frequency and amplitude, but 90° out of phase, to the horizontal- and vertical-deflection plates of a cathode-ray tube. This results in a circular trace, and signals then give inward or outward radial deflections from the circle.

circular waveguide—A waveguide having a circular cross-sectional area.

circulating memory — *See* Circulating Register.

circulating register—Also called circulating memory. A register (or memory) consisting of a means for delaying the information and a means for regenerating and reinserting it into the delaying means. This is accomplished as the information moves around a loop and returns to its starting place after a fixed delay.

circulating storage—A device using a delay line to store information in a train or pattern of pulses. The pulses at the output end are sensed, amplified, reshaped, and re-inserted into the input end of the delay line.

circulator — A microwave coupling device having a number of terminals so arranged that energy entering one terminal is transmitted to the next adjacent terminal in a particular direction.

Citizens band channels—

Channel No.	Frequency (MHz)	Channel No.	Frequency (MHz)
1	26.965	13	27.115
2	26.975	14	27.125
3	26.985	15	27.135
4	27.005	16	27.155
5	27.015	17	27.165
6	27.025	18	27.175
7	27.035	19	27.185
8	27.055	20	27.205
9	27.065	21	27.215
10	27.075	22	27.225
11	27.085	23*	27.255
12	27.105		

*This channel is shared with class-C radio control.

Citizens Radio Service—A type of radio service intended for private or personal use for communication, radio control, and similar purposes. A license can be obtained from the FCC; there is no need to take a technical examination. The frequencies assigned are in the 460-470–MHz and 26.965-27.255–MHz bands.

clamp—*See* Clamping Circuit.

clamper—*See* Clamping Circuit.

clamping — The process that establishes a fixed level for the picture signal at the beginning of each scanning line.

clamping circuit — Also called clamper or clamp. A circuit which adds a fixed bias to a wave at each occurrence of some predetermined feature of the wave. This is done to hold the voltage or current of the feature at (clamp it to) a specified fixed or variable level. (*Also see* D-C Restorer.)

clamping diode—A diode used to fix a voltage level at some point in a circuit.

clapotis—A standing wave in which there is no horizontal motion of the crest. This phenomenon results from the interference caused by the reflection of a wave train from a barrier which the wave train approaches with its crest parallel to the barrier.

clapper—A hinged or pivoted armature.

Clapp oscillator — A Colpitts-type oscillator using a series-resonant tank circuit for improved stability.

Clark cell—An early standard cell that used an anode of mercury, a cathode of zinc amalgam, and an electrolyte containing zinc sulphate and mercurous sulphate. Its voltage is 1.433 at 15°C.

class-A amplifier—An amplifier in which the grid bias and alternating grid voltage are such that plate current flows at all times. To denote that no grid current flows during any part of the input cycle, the suffix *1* is sometimes added to the letter or letters of the class identification. The suffix 2 denotes that grid current flows during part of the input cycle.

class-AB amplifier—An amplifier in which the grid bias and alternating grid voltage are such that plate current flows for more than half but less than the entire electrical cycle. To denote that no grid current flows during any part of the input cycle, the suffix 1 is sometimes added to the letter or letters of the class identification. The suffix 2 denotes that grid current flows during part of the cycle.

class-AO emission—The incidental radiation of an unmodulated carrier wave from a station.

class-A1 emission—A carrier wave (unmodulated by an audio frequency) keyed normally for telegraphy to transmit intelligence in the International Morse Code at a speed not exceeding 40 words per minute (the average word is composed of five letters).

class-A2 emission—A carrier wave which is amplitude-modulated at audio frequencies not exceeding 1,250 hertz. The modulated carrier wave is keyed normally for telegraphy to transmit intelligence in the International Morse Code at a speed not exceeding 40 words per minute, the average word being composed of five letters.

class-A3 emission—A carrier wave which is amplitude-modulated at audio frequencies corresponding to those necessary for intelligible speech transmitted at the speed of conversation.

class-A insulating material—A material or combination of materials such as cotton, silk, and paper suitably impregnated, coated, or immersed in a dielectric liquid such as oil. Other materials or combinations of materials may be included if shown to be capable of satisfactory operation at 105°C.

class-A modulator—A class-A amplifier used for supplying the signal power needed to modulate the carrier.

class-A operation—Operation of a vacuum tube with grid bias such that plate current flows throughout 360° of the input cycle.

class-A signal area—A strong tv signal area for vhf, 2,500 microvolts per meter or greater; and for uhf, 5,000 microvolts per meter or greater.

class-A transistor amplifier—An amplifier in which the input electrode and alternating input signal are biased so that output current flows at all times.

class-B amplifier—An amplifier in which the grid bias is approximately equal to the cutoff value so that, when no exciting grid voltage is applied, the plate current will be approximately zero and will flow for approximately half of each cycle when an alternating grid voltage is applied. To denote that no grid current flows during any part of the input cycle, the suffix 1 is sometimes added to the letter or letters of the

class identification. The suffix 2 denotes that grid current flows during part of the cycle.

class-B insulating material — A material or combination of materials such as mica, glass fiber, asbestos, etc., suitaby bonded. Other materials or combinations, not necessarily inorganic may be included if shown to be capable of satisfactory operation at 130°C.

class-B modulator—A class-B amplifier used specifically for supplying the signal power needed to modulate a carrier.

class-B operation—Operation of a vacuum tube with the grid bias set at or very near cutoff, so that plate current flows for approximately the positive half of each cycle of the input signal.

class-B transistor amplifier—An amplifier in which the input electrode is biased so that when no alternating input signal is applied, the output current is approximately zero, and when an alternating input signal is applied, the output current flows for approximately half a cycle.

class-C amplifier—An amplifier in which the grid bias is appreciably beyond the cutoff point, so that plate current is zero when no alternating grid voltage is applied, and plate current flows for appreciably less than half of each cycle when an alternating grid voltage is applied. To denote that no grid current flows during any part of the input cycle, the suffix 1 is sometimes added to the letter or letters of the class identification. The suffix 2 denotes that grid current flows during part of the cycle.

class-C insulating material—Insulation consisting entirely of mica, porcelain, glass, quartz, or similar inorganic materials. Other materials or combinations of materials may be included if shown to be capable of satisfactory operation at temperatures over 220°C.

class-C operation—Operation of a vacuum tube with grid bias considerably greater than cutoff. The plate current is zero with no input signal to the grid and flows for appreciably less than one-half of each cycle of the input signal.

class-F insulating material—A material or combination of materials such as mica, glass fiber, asbestos, etc., suitably bonded. Other materials or combinations of materials, not necessarily inorganic, may be included if shown to be capable of satisfactory operation at 155°C.

class-H insulating material—A material or combination of materials such as silicone elastomer, mica, glass fiber, asbestos, etc., suitably bonded. Other materials or combinations of materials may be included if shown to be capable of satisfactory operation at 180°C.

class-J oscilloscope—See J-Scope.

class-O insulating material—An unimpregnated material or combination of materials such as cotton, silk, or paper. Other materials or combinations of materials may be included if shown to be capable of satisfactory operation at 90°C.

clavier — Any keyboard, either hand or foot operated.

clean room—An area in which high standards of control of humidity, temperature, dust and all forms of contamination are maintained.

clear—Also called reset. To restore a storage or memory device to a prescribed state, usually to zero.

clearance — The shortest distance through space between two live parts, between live parts and supports or other objects, or between any live part and grounded part.

clearing ends — The operation of removing the sheath from the end of a cable, eliminating all moisture, and checking for crosses, shorts, and grounds in preparation for testing.

clear raster—A raster free of snow such as would be obtained in the absence of a video signal on either the cathodes or the grids of the three guns in the color crt (mostly a function of bias conditions).

click filter—A capacitor and resistor connected across the contacts of a switch or relay to prevent a surge being introduced into an adjacent circuit. (*Also see* Key-Click Filter.)

clipped-noise modulation—A clipping action performed to increase the bandwidth of a jamming signal. Results in more energy in the sidebands, correspondingly less energy in the carrier, and an increase in the ratio of average power to peak power.

clipper—A device the output of which is zero or a fixed value for instantaneous input amplitudes up to a certain value, but is a function of the input for amplitudes exceeding the critical value.

clipper amplifier—An amplifier designed to limit the instantaneous value of its output to a predetermined maximum.

clipper-limiter—Also called slicer. A device the output of which is a function of the instantaneous input amplitude for a range of values lying between two predetermined limits, but is approximately constant at another level for input values above the range.

clipping—The loss of initial or final parts of words or syllables due to less-than-ideal operation of voice-operated devices.

clock—The primary source of synchronizing signals in electronic computers.

clocked flip-flops—Directly coupled units operating on the "master-slave" principle. Information enters the "master" while the trigger input voltage is high, and transfers to the "slave" when the trigger input voltage goes low.

clock frequency—In digital computers, the master frequency of periodic pulses that are used to schedule the operation of the computer.

clock rate—The rate at which a word or characters of a word (bits) are transferred from one internal computer element to another. Clock rate is expressed in cycles (in a parallel-operation machine, in words; in a serial-operation machine, in bits) per second.

clockwise-polarized wave — *See* Right-Handed Polarized Wave.

close coupling—Also called tight coupling. Any degree of coupling greater than critical coupling.

closed array—An array which cannot be extended at either end.

closed circuit—1. A complete electric circuit through which current may flow when a voltage is applied. 2. A program source that is not broadcast for general consumption, but is fed to remote monitoring units by wire.

closed-circuit communication systems — Certain communication systems which are entirely self-contained and do not exchange intelligence with other facilities and systems.

closed-circuit signaling—Signaling in which current flows in the idle conditions and a signal is initiated by increasing or decreasing the current.

closed-circuit television—A television system in which the television signals are not broadcast, but are transmitted over a closed circuit and received only by interconnected receivers.

closed entry—A design that places a limit on the size of a mating part.

closed loop—1. A circuit in which the output is continuously fed back to the input for constant comparison. 2. In a computer, a group of indefinitely repeated instructions.

closed-loop bandwidth — The frequency at which the closed-loop gain drops 3 db from its midband or d-c value.

closed-loop gain — The response of a feedback circuit to a voltage inserted in series with the amplifier input.

closed-loop input impedance—The impedance looking into the input port of an amplifier with feedback.

closed-loop output impedance—The impedance looking into the output port of an operational amplifier with feedback.

closed-loop voltage gain—The voltage gain of an amplifier with feedback.

closed magnetic circuit—A circuit in which the magnetic flux is conducted continuously around a closed path through ferromagnetic materials.

closed routine — In a computer, a routine that is entered by basic linkage from the main routine rather than being inserted as a block of instructions within a main routine.

close-talking microphone—Also called noise-cancelling microphone. A microphone designed to be held close to the mouth of the speaker.

closing rating—In a relay, conditions under which the contact must close, with a prescribed duty cycle and contact life.

cloverleaf antenna—An nondirectional vhf

transmitting antenna that consists of a number of horizontal four-element radiators arranged much like a four-leaf clover, stacked a half-wave apart vertically. These horizontal units are energized to give maximum radiation in the horizontal plane.

clutter—Confusing, unwanted echoes which interfere with the observation of desired signals on a radar display.

clutter gating — The technique which provides switching between moving-target indicators and normal videos. This results in normal video being displayed in regions with no clutter, and moving-target indicator video being switched in only for the clutter areas.

CML—Abbreviation for current mode logic.

C-network—A network composed of three impedance branches in series. The free ends are connected to one pair of terminals, and the junction points to another pair.

coarse-chrominance primary — Also called the Q signal. A zero-luminance transmission primary associated with the minimum bandwidth of chrominance transmission and chosen for its relatively small importance in contributing to the subjective sharpness of the color picture.

coast—On a radar, a memory feature which, when activated, causes the range and/or angle systems to continue to move in the same direction and at the same speed as an original target was moving. Used to prevent lock-up to a stronger target if approached by the target being tracked.

coast station—A land-based radio station in the maritime mobile service. It carries on communications with shipboard stations.

coated cathode—In a vacuum tube, a cathode that has been coated with compounds so as to increase its electron emission (e.g., an oxide-coated cathode).

coated filament — A vacuum-tube filament that has been coated with metal oxides to increase its electron emission.

coating—The magnetic layer, consisting of oxide particles held in a binder that is applied to the base film, used for magnetic recordings.

coating thickness—The thickness of the magnetic coating applied to the base film. Modern tape coatings range in thickness from 170 to 650 microinches, with a preponderance of coatings being approximately 400 microinches thick. In general, thin coatings give good resolution, at the expense of reduced output at long wavelengths; thick coatings give a high output at long wavelengths, at the expense of degraded resolution.

coated tape — See Magnetic-Powder—Coated Tape.

coaxial antenna—An antenna comprised of a quarter-wavelength extension to the inner conductor of a coaxial line, and a radiating sleeve which in effect is formed by folding back the outer conductor of the coaxial line for approximately one-quarter wavelength.

coaxial cable—See Coaxial Line.

coaxial cavity — A cylindical reasonating cavity that has a central conductor in contact with its movable pistons or other reflecting devices. The conductor serves to pick up a desired wave in the microwave region.

coaxial diode—A diode that has the same outer diameter and terminations as a coaxial cable into which the diode is designed to be inserted.

coaxial-fed linear array—A beacon antenna having a uniform azimuth pattern.

coaxial filters—A passive, linear, essentially nondissipative network that transmits certain frequencies and rejects others.

Coaxial line.

coaxial line—Also called coaxial cable, coaxial transmission line, and concentric line. A transmission line in which one conductor completely surrounds the other, the two being coaxial and separated by a continuous solid dielectric or by dielectric spacers. Such a line has no external field and is not susceptible to external fields from other sources.

coaxial-line connector — A connection between two coaxial lines, or between a coaxial line and the equipment.

coaxial-line frequency meter — A shorted section of coaxial line which acts as a resonant circuit and is calibrated in terms of frequency or wavelength.

coaxial relay — A type of relay used for switching high-frequency circuits.

coaxial speaker—A single speaker comprising a high and a low-frequency unit plus an electrical crossover network.

coaxial stub—A short length of coaxial cable joined as a branch to another coaxial cable. Frequently a coaxial stub is short-circuited at the outer end, and its length is so chosen that a high or low impedance is presented to the main coaxial cable at a certain frequency range.

coaxial transistor—A diffused-base, alloy-emitter, epitaxial mesa germanium semiconductor device with a bandwidth product up to 3 gigahertz capable of being operated at medium power.

coaxial transmission line—See Coaxial Line.

COBOL — Acronym for COmmon Business Oriented Language. Used to express problems of data manipulation and processing in English narrative form.

co-channel interference — Interference between two signals of the same type from transmitters operating on the same channel.

Cockcroft-Walton accelerator—A device for accelerating charged particles by the action of a high direct-current voltage on a stream of gas ions, in a straight insulated tube. The voltage is generated by a voltage-multiplier system consisting essentially of a number of condenser pairs connected through switching devices (vacuum tubes). The particles (which are nuclei of an ionized gas, such as protons from hydrogen) gain energies of up to several million electron-volts from the single acceleration so produced. Named for the British physicists J. D. Cockcroft and E.T.S. Walton, who developed this machine in the 1930's.

codan—Acronym for Carrier-Operated Device, Anti-Noise. An electronic circuit that keeps a receiver inactive except when a signal is received.

codan lamp—A visual indication that a usable transmitted signal has been received by a particular radio receiver.

code—1. A communications system in which arbitrary groups of symbols represent units of plain text of varying length. Codes may be used for brevity or security. 2. System of signaling by utilizing dot-dash-space, mark-space, or some other method where each letter or figure is represented by prearranged combinations. 3. System of characters and rules for representing information. 4. Loosely, the set of characters resulting from the use of a code.

code character—One of the elements which make up a code and which represent a specified symbol or value to be encoded. Dot-dot-dot-dash is the Morse code character for the letter V.

coded decimal digit—A decimal digit expressed in terms of four or more ones and zeros.

coded passive reflector antenna—An object intended to reflect Hertzian waves and having variable reflecting properties according to a predetermined code for the purpose of producing an indication on a radar receiver.

coded program—A description of a procedure for solving a problem with a digital computer. It may vary in detail from a mere outline of the procedure to an explicit list of instructions coded in the machine's language.

code element—One of the finite set of parts of which the characters in a code may be composed.

code-practice oscillator—An audio oscillator with a key and either headphones or a speaker, used to practice sending and receiving Morse code.

coder—1. A device which sets up a series of signals in code form. 2. A beacon circuit which forms the trigger-pulse output of a discriminator into a series of pulses and then feeds them to a modulator circuit. 3. A person who prepares instruction sequences from detailed flowcharts and other algorithmic procedures prepared by others, as contrasted with a programmer who prepares the procedures and flowcharts.

coding—1. Converting program flowcharts into the language used by the computer. 2. The assignment of identification codes to transactions, such as a customer code number. 3. A method of representing characters within a computer.

codiphase radar—A radar system including a phased-array radar antenna and signal-processing and beam-forming techniques.

codistor—A multijunction semiconductor device which provides noise-rejection and voltage-regulation functions.

coefficient—The ratio of change under specified conditions of temperature, length, volume, etc.

coefficient of coupling — See Coupling Coefficient.

coefficient of performance of a thermoelectric cooling couple—The quotient of the net rate of heat removal from the cold junction divided by the electrical power input to the thermoelectric couple, assuming perfect thermal insulation of the thermoelectric arms.

coefficient of performance of a thermoelectric cooling device — The quotient of the rate at which heat is removed from the cooled body divided by the electrical power input to the device.

coefficient of performance of a thermoelectric heating couple — The quotient of the rate at which heat is added to the hot junction divided by the electrical power input to the thermoelectric couple, assuming perfect thermal insulation of the thermoelectric arms.

coefficient of performance of a thermoelectric heating device — The quotient of the rate at which heat is added to the heated body divided by the electrical power input to the device.

coercive force—Symbolized by H. The magnetizing force that must be applied to a magnetic material in a direction opposite the residual induction in order to reduce the induction to zero.

coercivity—The property of a magnetic material measured by the coercive force corresponding to the saturation induction for the material.

cogging—Nonuniform angular velocity. The armature coil of a motor tends to speed up when it enters the magnetic field produced by the field coils, and to slow down when leaving it. This becomes apparent at low speeds, and the fewer the coils, the more noticeable it is.

coherent carrier—A carrier, derived from a c-w signal, the frequency and phase of which have a fixed relationship to the frequency and phase of the reference signal.

coherent detection—A method of deriving additional information from the phase of the carrier.

coherent electroluminescence device—See Diode Laser.

coherent interrupted waves—Interrupted continuous waves occurring in wave trains in which the phase of the waves is maintained through successive wave trains.

coherent light—A single frequency of light. Light having characteristics similar to a radiated radio wave that has a single frequency.

coherent light detection and ranging—*See* Colidar.

coherent oscillator—An oscillator within some radar sets which furnishes phase references for target returns during intervals between transmitter pulse, and its output compared with the returns so that the echo becomes coherent video. Coherent video is applied to a cancellation circuit which eliminates nonmoving targets, and only moving targets are supplied to the indicator.

coherent-pulse operation — The method of pulse operation in which a fixed phase relationship is maintained from one pulse to the next.

coherent radiation—A form of radiation in which definite phase relationships exist between radiation at different positions in a cross section of the radiant beam.

coherent reference—The reference signal, usually of stable frequency, to which other signals are phase-locked to establish coherency throughout a system.

coherent system of units—Also called absolute system of units. A system of units in which the magnitude and dimensions of each unit are related to those of the other units by definite simple relationships in which the proportionality factors are usually chosen to be unity.

coherent transponder—A transponder, the output signal of which is coherent with the input signal. Fixed relations between frequency and phase of input and output signals are maintained.

coherer—An early form of detector used in wireless telegraphy.

coil—A number of turns of wire wound around an iron core or onto a form made of insulating material, or one which is self-supporting. A coil offers considerable opposition to the passage of alternating current, but very little opposition to direct current.

coil dissipation—The amount of electrical power consumed by a winding. For the most practical purposes, this equals the I^2R loss.

coil form—An insulating support of ceramic, plastic, or cardboard onto which coils are wound.

coil loading—As commonly understood, the insertion of coils into a line at uniformly spaced intervals. However, the coils are sometimes inserted in parallel.

coil neutralization — *See* Inductive Neutralization.

coil rating—*See* Input-Power Rating.

coil resistance—The total terminal-to-terminal resistance of a coil at a specified temperature.

coil serving—A covering, such as thread or tape, that serves to protect a coil winding from mechanical damage.

coil temperature rise — The increase in winding temperature above the ambient temperature when energized under specified conditions for a given period of time, usually that required to reach a stable temperature.

coil tube — A tubular coil form. (*Also see* Spool.)

coincidence amplifier—An amplifier which produces no output unless two input pulses are applied simultaneously to the circuit.

coincidence circuit—A circuit that produces a specified output pulse when and only when a specified number (two or more) or combination of input terminals receives pulses within a specified time interval.

coincidence gate—A circuit with the ability to produce an output which is dependent upon a specified type or the coincident nature of the output.

coincident-current selection—The selection of a magnetic core, for reading or writing, by the simultaneous application of two or more currents.

cold cathode—A cathode the operation of which does not depend on its temperature being above the ambient temperature.

cold-cathode tube—An electron tube containing a cathode which will emit electrons without being heated.

cold emission—*See* Field Emission.

cold flow—Change of dimension or distortion, caused by sustained application of a force.

cold-pressure welding—A method of making an electrical connection in which the members to be joined are compressed to the plastic range of the metals.

cold rolling—Rolling a magnetic core alloy into the form of a rod so that the metallic grains are oriented in the long direction of the rod.

cold weld—A joint between two metals (without an intermediate material) produced by the application of pressure only.

colidar — Abbreviation for COherent LIght Detection And Ranging. An optical radar system that uses the direct output from a ruby laser source without further pulse modulation.

collate—To combine two or more similarly ordered sets of items to produce another ordered set. Both the number and the size of the individual items may differ from those of the original sets or their sums.

collator—A device to collate sets of punched cards or other documents into a sequence.

collating sequence—1. In digital computers, the sequence in which the characters acceptable to a computer are ordered. The British term is marshalling sequence. 2. An ordering assigned to a set of items, such that any two sets in that assigned order can be collated.

collector—1. An electrode that collects electrons or ions which have completed their functions within an electron tube. 2. The collector of a transistor is an electrode through which a primary flow of carriers leaves the interelectrode region.

collector capacitance — Depletion-layer capacitance associated with the collector junction of a transistor.

collector-coupled logic—*See* Current-Sourcing Logic.

collector current—The direct current flowing in the collector of a transistor.

collector cutoff—The operating condition of a transistor when the collector current is reduced to the leakage current of the collector-base junction.

collector cutoff current—The minimum current that will flow in the collector circuit of a transistor with zero current in the emitter circuit.

collector efficiency—The ratio, usually expressed in percentage, of useful power output to final-stage power-supply power input of a transistor.

collector family—Set of transistor characteristic curves in which the collector current and voltage are variables.

collector junction—Of a semiconductor device, a junction normally biased in the high-resistance direction, so that the current through the junction can be controlled by the introduction of minority carriers.

collector resistance — Resistance in series with the collector lead in the common-T equivalent circuit of a transistor.

collector rings (slip rings)—Metal rings suitably mounted on an electric machine serving, through stationary brushes bearing thereon, to conduct current into or out of the rotating member.

collector transition capacitance — The capacitance across the collector-to-base transition region of a transistor.

collector voltage—The d-c collector supply voltage applied between the base and collector of a transistor.

collimation—The process of adjusting an instrument so that its reference axis is aligned in a desired direction within a predetermined tolerance.

collimation equipment—Equipment designed specifically for aligning optical equipment.

collimator—An optical device that creates a beam made up of parallel rays of light, used in testing and adjusting certain optical instruments.

collinear array—An antenna array in which half-wave elements are arranged end to end on the same vertical or horizontal line.

color balance—The adjustment of electron-gun emissions to compensate for the difference in the light emitting efficiencies of the three phosphors on the screen of the color picture tube.

color-bar pattern—A test pattern (usually a series of vertical bars, each having a specific hue), used for checking the performance of a color-television receiver.

color breakup—Any fleeting or partial separation of a color picture into its display primary components because of a rapid change in the condition of viewing. For example, fast movement of the head, abrupt interruption of the line of sight, and blinking of the eyes are illustrations of rapid changes in the conditions of viewing.

color burst—Also called reference burst. Approximately nine cycles of the chrominance subcarrier added to the back porch of the horizontal blanking pedestal of the composite color signal and used in the color receiver as a phase reference for the 3.579545-MHz oscillator.

color carrier—*See* Chrominance Subcarrier.

colorcast—A color television broadcast.

color code—A system of colors for specifying the electrical value of a component part or for identifying terminals and leads. Also used to distinguish between cable conductors.

color coder—Also called color encoder. In a color-tv transmitter, that circuit or section which combines the camera signals and the chrominance subcarrier to form the transmitted color picture signal.

color contamination—An error in color rendition due to incomplete separation of the paths carrying different color components of the picture. Such errors can arise in the optical, electronic, or mechanical portions of a color-television system as well as in the electrical portions.

color-coordinate transformation — Computation of the tristimulus values of colors in terms of one set of primaries from the tristimulus values of the same colors in another set of primaries. Such computation may be performed electrically in a color-television system.

color decoder—A section or circuit of a color-television receiver used for deriving the signals for the color-display device from the color-picture signal and the color burst.

color-difference signal—The signal produced when the amplitude of a color signal is reduced by an amount equal to the amplitude of the luminance signal. Color-difference signals are usually designated R-Y, B-Y, and G-Y. In a sense, I and Q signals are also color-difference signals because they are formed when specific proportions of R-Y and B-Y color-difference signals have been combined.

color edging—Spurious color at the boundaries of differently colored areas in a picture.

color encoder—*See* Color Coder.

color fidelity—The degree to which a color television system is capable of faithfully reproducing the colors in an original scene.

color flicker—The flicker which results from fluctuation of both the chromaticity and the luminance.

color fringing—Spurious chromaticity at the boundaries of objects in a color-tv picture. It can be caused by the change in relative position of the televised object from field to field, or by misregistration. Color fringing may cause small objects to appear separated into different colors.

colorimeter—An optical instrument designed to compare the color of a sample with that of a standard sample or a synthesized stimulus. (In a three-color colorimeter, the synthesized stimulus consists of three colors of constant chromaticity but variable luminance.)

colorimetric—The measurement of color characteristics, particularly wavelength and primary-color content.

colorimetry — The technique of measuring color and interpreting the results.

color killer—A stage designed to prevent signals in a color receiver from passing through the chrominance channel during monochrome telecasts.

color match—The condition in which the two halves of a structureless photometric field look exactly the same.

color mixture—Color produced by the combination of lights of different colors. The combination may be accomplished by successive presentation of the components, provided the rate of alternation is sufficiently high; or the combination may be accomplished by simultaneous presentation, either in the same or in adjacent areas, provided they are small enough and close enough together to eliminate pattern effects.

color oscillator—In a color-television receiver, the oscillator operating at the burst frequency of 3.579545 MHz. Its frequency and phase are synchronized by the master oscillator at the transmitter.

color phase—The difference in phase between a chrominance primary signal (I or Q) and the chrominance carrier reference.

color-phase alternation—Periodic changing of the color phase of one or more components of the color-television subcarrier between two sets of assigned values.

color-phase diagram — A vector diagram which denotes the phase difference between

Color-phase diagram.

the color-burst signal and the chrominance signal for each of the three primary and complementary colors. This diagram also designates vectorially the peak amplitude of the chrominance signal for each of these colors, and the polarities and peak amplitudes of the in-phase and quadrature portions required to form these chrominance signals.

color-picture signal—1. A signal which represents electrically the three color attributes (brightness, hue, and saturation) of a scene. 2. A combination of the luminance and chrominance signals, excluding all blanking and synchronizing signals.

color-picture tube—An electron tube that provides an image in color by scanning a raster and by varying the intensity at which it excites the phosphors on the screen to produce light of the chosen primary colors.

color primaries—In the color receiver, the saturated colors of definite hue and variable luminance produced by the receiver. These color primaries, when mixed in proper proportions, form other colors.

color purity—Freedom of a color from white

Color picture tube.

light or any colored light not used to produce the desired color.

color-purity magnet—A magnet placed in the neck region of a color-picture tube to alter the electron-beam path and thereby improve color purity.

color registration—The accurate superimposing of the red, green, and blue images that are used to form a complete color picture in a color television receiver.

color sampling rate—In a color television system, the number of times per second that each primary color is sampled.

color saturation—The degree to which white light is absent in a particular color. A fully saturated color contains no white light. If 50% of the light intensity is due to the presence of white light, the color is said to have a saturation of 50%.

color sensitivity—The spectral sensitivity of a light-sensitive device such as a phototube or camera tube.

color signal—Any signal at any point in a color-television system, used for wholly or partially controlling the chromaticity values of a color-television picture. This is a general term encompassing many specific connotations, such as are conveyed by the words, "color-picture signal," "chrominance signal," "carrier-color signal," "monochrome signal" (in color television), etc.

color subcarrier—A monochrome signal to which modulation sidebands have been added to convey color information.

color-sync signal—The series of color bursts (pulses of subcarrier-reference signal) applied to the back porch of the horizontal-sync pedestal in the composite video signal.

color-television receiver—A standard monochrome receiver to which special circuits have been added. Phosphors capable of glowing in the three primary colors are used on the special screen. By using these primary colors and mixing them to produce complementary colors, and by varying their intensity, it is possible to reproduce an image in somewhat the original colors.

color-television signal—The complete signal used to transmit a color picture. Included are horizontal-, vertical-, and color-sync components.

color temperature—The temperature to which a perfectly black body must be heated to match the color of the source being measured. Color-temperature measurements begin at absolute zero and are expressed in degrees Kelvin.

color transmission—The transmission of color-television signals which can be reproduced with different values of hue, saturation, and luminance.

color triad—One cell of a three-color, phosphor-dot screen of a phosphor-dot, color-picture tube. Each triad contains one dot of each of the three color-producing phosphors.

color triangle—A triangle drawn on a chromaticity diagram to represent the entire range of chromaticities obtainable when the 3 prescribed primaries are added. These are represented by the corners of the triangle.

Colpitts oscillator.

Colpitts oscillator—An electron-tube oscillator comprising a parallel-tuned tank circuit connected between grid and plate. The tank capacitance contains two voltage-dividing capacitors in series, with their common connection at cathode potential. When these two capacitances are the plate-to-cathode and grid-to-cathode capacitances of the tube, the circuit is known as an Ultra-audion oscillator.

column—Also called place. In positional notation, a position corresponding to a given power of the radix. A digit located in any particular column is a coefficient of a corresponding power of the radix.

coma—1. An aberration of spherical lenses, occuring in the case of oblique incidence, when the bundle of rays forming the image is unsymmetrical. The image of a point is comet shaped, hence the name. 2. A cathode-ray tube image defect that makes the spot on the screen appear comet shaped when away from the center of the screen.

comb filter—A type of filter network that is, in effect, a multiple-bandpass design that passes only frequencies within a number of narrow bands, or provides outputs corresponding to each of its passbands. Comb filters are so named because their response characteristics have the appearance of a comb.

combination cable—A cable in which the conductors are grouped in combinations such as pairs and quads.

combination microphone—A microphone consisting of two or more similar or dissimilar microphones combined into one.

combination tones—Frequencies produced in a nonlinear device, such as in an audio amplifier having appreciable harmonic distortion.

combiner—A circuit for mixing video, trigger, and scan data from the synchronizer for the modulation of a link.

combiner circuit—One that combines the luminance and chroma channels with the sync signals in color-television cameras.

combustible—*See* Flammable.

command—1. In a computer, one or more

sets of signals which occur as the result of an instruction. (*Also see* Instruction.) 2. An independent signal from which the dependent signals in a feedback-control system are controlled according to the prescribed system relationships. 3. A signal which initiates or triggers an action in the device that receives the signal.

command control—A system whereby functions are performed as the result of a transmitted signal.

command destruct signal—A radio signal for destroying a missile in flight.

command guidance system—A missile guidance system in which both the missile and the target are tracked by radar. The missile is guided by signals transmitted to it while it is in flight. (*Also see* Command Link.)

command link—The portion of a command guidance system used to transmit steering commands to the missile. (*Also see* Command Guidance System.)

command module—*See* Module.

command net— A communication network which connects an echelon of command with some or all of its subordinate echelons for the purpose of command and control.

command reference—In a servo or control system, the voltage or current to which the feedback signal is compared. As an independent variable, the command reference exercises complete control over the system output.

comment—An expression which explains or identifies a particular step in a routine, but which has no effect on the operation of the computer in performing the instructions for the routine.

commercial test (measuring) equipment—Devices used as "working instruments" selected from suppliers' catalogs as suitable for the user's measuring needs and procured as standard ("off-the-shelf") items. This includes measuring devices installed, intact and in consoles. Devices procured from suppliers but modified by user-imposed specifications, in such a manner as to affect console performance, do not fall into this category.

Common-base amplifier.

common-base amplifier — Also called a grounded-base amplifier. A transistor amplifier in which the base element is com-

mon to both the input and the output circuit. It is comparable to the grounded-grid configuration of a triode electron-tube amplifier.

common battery—A system of current supply in which all direct-current energy for a unit of a telephone system is supplied by one source in a central office or exchange.

common-battery office — A central office which supplies transmitter and signal current for its associated stations, and for signaling by the central office equipment from a power source located in the central office.

common business oriented language—Specific language by which business data-processing procedures may be precisely described in a standard form. Intended not only as a means for directly presenting any business program to any suitable computer for which a compiler exists, but also as a means of communicating such procedures among individuals.

common-carrier fixed station—A fixed station that is open to public correspondence.

common-collector amplifier—Also known as an emitter-follower and a grounded-collector amplifier. A transistor amplifier in which the collector element is common to both the input and the output circuit. This configuration is comparable to an electron-tube cathode follower.

Common-collector amplifier.

common communications carrier— A company recognized by an appropriate regulatory agency as having a vested interest in furnishing communications services.

common-emitter amplifier — Also called grounded-emitter amplifier. A transistor amplifier in which the emitter element is common to both the input and the output circuit. This configuration is comparable to a conventional electron-tube amplifier.

common language—A form of representing information which a machine can read and which is common to a group of computers and data-processing machines.

common mode—Signals that are identical with respect to both amplitude and time. Also used to identify the respective parts of two signals that are identical with respect to amplitude and time.

common-mode characteristics—The characteristics pertaining to performance of an operational amplifier where the inverting and noninverting inputs have a common signal.

common-mode gain—The ratio of the common-mode output voltage of a differential amplifier divided by the common-mode input voltage.

common-mode impedance input—The internal impedance between either one of the input terminals of a differential operational amplifier and signal ground.

common-mode input—That signal applied in phase (i.e., common mode) equally to both inputs of a differential amplifier.

common-mode input capacitance — The equivalent capacitance of both inverting and noninverting inputs of an operational amplifier with respect to ground.

common-mode input impedance — The open-loop input impedance of both inverting and noninverting inputs of an operational amplifier with respect to ground.

common-mode input voltage — The maximum voltage that can be applied simultaneously between the two inputs of a differential amplifier and ground without causing damage.

common-mode rejection — Also called in-phase rejection. A measure of how well a differential amplifier ignores a signal which appears simultaneously and in phase at both input terminals (called a common-mode signal). Usually and preferably stated as a voltage ratio, but more often stated in the db equivalent of said ratio at a specified frequency—e.g., "120 db at 60 hertz with 1K source impedance."

common-mode rejection ratio—The ratio of the common-mode input voltage to the output voltage expressed in db. The extent to which a differential amplifier does not provide an output voltage when the same signal is applied to both inputs.

common-mode resistance—The resistance between the input- and output-signal lines or circuit ground. In an isolated amplifier, this is its insulation resistance. (Common-mode resistance has no connection with common-mode rejection.)

common-mode signal — The instantaneous algebraic average of two signals applied to a balanced circuit (i.e., two ungrounded inputs of a balanced amplifier), all signals referred to a common reference.

common-mode voltage—1. The amount of voltage common to both input lines of a balanced amplifier. Usually specified as the maximum voltage which can be applied without breaking down the insulation between the input circuit and ground. (Common-mode voltage has no connection with common-mode rejection.) 2. The voltage on both inputs of a differential input amplifier.

common-mode voltage gain—The ratio of the signal voltage applied at the inputs (in parallel) to the signal voltage between the outputs.

common-mode voltage range—The range of voltage that may be applied to both inputs of an operational amplifier without saturating the input stage. This may limit the output capabilities in the voltage-follower connection.

common-user channels — Communication channels which are available to all authorized agencies for transmission of command, administrative, and logistic traffic.

communication—The transmission of information from one point, person, or equipment to another.

communication band—The band of frequencies due to the modulation (including keying) necessary for a given type of transmission.

communication channel—Part of a radio or wire circuit, or a combination of wire and radio which connects two or more terminals.

communication link—The physical means of connecting one location to another for the purpose of transmitting and receiving information.

communications common carriers — Companies that furnish communications services to the public, regulated by the FCC or appropriate state agencies.

communications receiver—A receiver designed for reception of voice or code signals from stations operating in the communications service.

communication switch—A device used to execute repetitive sequential switching.

communication zone indicator—A device that indicates whether or not long-distance high-frequency broadcasts are successfully reaching their destination.

community antenna television—A television system that receives and retransmits commercial television broadcasts. Microwave transmitters and coaxial cables are used to bring the television signals to subscribers in a community. Abbreviated catv.

commutation—1. A mechanical process of converting the alternating current in the armature of direct-current generators into the direct-current generator output. 2. Sampling of various quantities in a repetitive manner, for transmission over a single channel in telemetering. 3. Repetitive sampling of two or more information channels for transmission over a single link.

commutation capacitors — Cross-connected capacitors in a thyratron inverter. They provide a path such that the start of conduction in one thyratron causes an extinguishing pulse to be applied to the alternate thyratron. Also used in inverter circuits employing semiconductor devices.

commutator—The part of the armature to which the coils of a motor are connected. It consists of wedge-shaped copper segments arranged around a steel hub and insulated from it and from one another. The motor brushes ride on the outer edges of the commutator bars and thereby connect the armature coils to the power source.

compactron—An electron tube based on a building-block concept which involves the standardizing of basic tube sections, diodes, triodes, pentodes; clipping them together as required; and sealing them in a single envelope.

compander—A combination comprised of a compressor at one point in a communication path to reduce the volume range of signals, followed by an expander at another point to improve the ratio of the signal to the interference entering the path between the compressor and expander.

companding—A process in which compression is followed by expansion. Companding is often used for noise reduction, in which case the compression is applied before the noise exposure and the expansion afterward.

compandor—*See* Compander.

companion keyboard — A remote keyboard connected by a multiwire cable to an ordinary keyboard and able to operate it.

comparator—A circuit which compares two signals and supplies an indication of agreement or disagreement.

compare—A computer operation in which two quantities are matched for the purpose of discovering their relative magnitudes or algebraic values.

comparison bridge—A type of voltage-comparison circuit resembling a four-arm electrical bridge. The elements are so arranged that if a balance exists in the circuit, a zero error signal is derived.

compatible IC—A hybrid IC in which the active circuit element is within the silicon planar integrated structure. A passive network, which may be separately optimized, is deposited onto its insulating surface to complete the IC device.

compatible monolithic integrated circuit—A device in which passive components are deposited by thin-film techniques on top of a basic silicon-substrate circuit containing the active components and some passive parts. *Also see* All-Diffused Monolithic Integrated Circuit.

compatibility—1. That property of a color-television system which permits typical, unaltered monochrome receivers to receive substantially normal monochrome from the transmitted signal. 2. In stereo, a system usable with a monophonic program source, or a stereo program that can be reproduced monophonically on a monophonic system.

compensated amplifier — A broad-band amplifier the frequency range of which is extended by the proper choice of circuit constants.

compensated-impurity resistor—A diffused-layer resistor into which are introduced additional N- and P-type impurities.

compensated-loop direction finder—A direction finder employing a loop antenna and a

second antenna system to compensate for polarization error.

compensated semiconductor—A semiconductor in which one type of impurity or imperfection (donor) partially cancels the electrical effects of the other (acceptor).

compensated volume control—*See* Loudness Control.

compensating filter—A filter used to alter the spectral emission of an emulsion to a specified response to different wavelengths.

compensation — The controlling elements which compensate for or offset the undesirable characteristics of the process to be controlled in a system.

compensation signal—A signal recorded on the tape, along with the computer data and on the same track as the data; this signal is used during the playback of data to electrically correct for the effects of tape-speed errors.

compensation theorem—An impedance in a network may be replaced by a generator of zero internal impedance, the generated voltage of which at any instant is equal to the instantaneous potenial difference produced across the replaced impedance by the current flowing through it.

compensator—1. In a direction finder, the portion which automatically applies to the direction indication all or part of the correction for the deviation. 2. An electronic circuit for altering the frequency response of an amplifier system to achieve a specified result. This refers to record equalization or loudness correction.

compile — To bring digital-computer programming subroutines together into a main routine or program.

compiler—An automatic coding system in a computer which generates and assembles a program from instructions written by a programmer.

compiling routine — A routine by means of which a computer can itself construct the program used to solve a problem.

complement—1. In an electronic computer, a number the representation of which is derived from the finite positional notation of another by one of the following rules:
> True complement—Subtract each digit from 1 less than the base; then add 1 to the least significant digit and execute all required carries.
> Base minus 1's complement—Subtract each digit from 1 less than the base (e.g., "9's complement" in the base 10, "1's complement" in the base 2, etc.)
2. To form the complement of a number. (In many machines, a negative number is represented as a complement of the corresponding positive number.)

complementary colors—Two colors are complementary if, when added together in proper proportion such as by projection, they produce white light.

complementary rectifier—Half-wave rectifying circuit elements which are not self-saturating rectifiers in the output of a magnetic amplifier.

complementary-symmetry circuit — An arrangement of PNP and NPN transistors that provides push-pull operation from one input signal.

complementary tracking—A system of interconnection of two or more devices in which one (the master) operates to control the others (the slaves).

complementary transistor amplifier — An amplifier that utilizes the complementary symmetry of NPN and PNP transistors.

complementary transistor logic—A digital logic circuit configuration making use of a complementary transistor emitter coupled AND-OR gate. Basically a two-level diode gate using simultaneous NPN and PNP action.

complementary transistors — Two transistors of opposite conductivity (PNP and NPN) that are operated in the same functional unit.

complementary wave—A wave brought into existence at the ends of a coaxial cable or two-conductor transmission lines, or any discontinuity along the line.

complementary wavelength — The wavelength of light of a single frequency. When combined with a sample color in suitable proportions, the wavelength matches the reference-standard light.

complementor—A circuit or device that produces a Boolean complement. A NOT circuit.

complete carry—A system of executing the carry process in a computer. All carries, and any other carries to which they give rise, are allowed to propagate to completion in this system.

complex components—Indivisible and non-repairable components having more than one function.

complex function—An integrated device in which three or more circuits are integral to a single silicon chip. In addition, the circuits are interconnected on the chip itself to form some electronic function at a higher level of organization than a single circuit. The interconnection pattern for the function is predetermined by the fixed mask; no wiring discretion is available for yield purposes. The input and outputs of all the circuits are not normally exposed to the package terminals. An example of a complex function would be a full adder or a multibit serial shift register.

complex parallel permeability — The complex relative permeability measured under stated conditions on a core with the aid of a coil. The parameter characterizing the induction is the impedance of the coil when placed on the core, expressed as a parallel connection of reactance and resistance. The parameter characterizing the field strength is the reactance the coil would have if placed

on a core of the same dimensions but with unity relative permeability, the distribution of the magnetic field being identical in both cases. The coil should have negligible copper losses.

complex permeability—Under stated conditions, the complex quotient of the moduli of the parallel vectors representing induction and field strength in a material. One of the moduli varies sinusoidally with time, and the component chosen from the other modulus varies sinusoidally at the same frequency.

complex series permeability—The complex relative permeability measured under stated conditions on a core with the aid of a coil. The parameter characterizing the induction in the core is the impedance of the coil when placed on the core, expressed as a series connection of reactance and resistance. The parameter characterizing the field strength is the reactance this coil would have if placed on a core of the same dimensions but with unity relative permeability. The coil should have negligible copper losses, etc.

complex steady-state vibration—A periodic vibration of more than one sinusoid. It includes repeating square waves, sawtooth waves, etc., because these waveforms can be expressed in terms of a Fourier series of sinusoidal terms.

complex tone—A sound wave produced by the combination of simple sinusoidal components of different frequencies. A sound sensation characterized by more than one pitch.

complex wave—A periodic wave made up of a combination of several frequencies or several sine waves superimposed on one another.

complex-wave generator — A device which generates a nonsinusoidal signal having a desired repetitive characteristic and waveform.

compliance—1. The reciprocal of stiffness—i.e., the ability to yield or flex. 2. The ease with which a phonograph stylus responds to an outside force. 3. The mechanical and acoustical equivalent of capacitance.

compliance extension—A form of master/slave interconnection of two or more current-regulated supplies to increase their output-voltage range through series connection.

compliance range — The range of voltage needed to sustain a given constant current throughout a range of load resistances.

compliance voltage—The output voltage of a constant-current supply.

compliance voltage range—The output voltage range of a d-c power supply operating in a constant-current mode.

component — 1. An essential functional part of a subsystem or equipment. It may be any self-contained element with a specific function, or it may consist of a combination of parts, assemblies, accessories, and attachments. 2. In vector analysis, one of the parts of a wave, voltage, or current considered separately.

component density—The volume of a circuit assembly divided by the total number of discrete circuit components utilized, usually expressed in components per cubic foot.

component layout—The physical arrangement of the components in a chassis or printed circuit.

component operating hours — A unit of measurement for the period of successful operation of one or more components (of a specified type) which have endured a given set of environmental conditions.

component stress—Those factors of usage or test, such as voltage, power, temperature, frequency, etc., which tend to affect the failure rate of component parts.

composite cable—A cable in which conductors of different gages or types are combined under one sheath.

composite circuit—A circuit which can be used simultaneously for telephony and direct-current telegraphy or signaling, the two being separated by frequency discrimination.

composite color signal—The color-picture signal plus all blanking and synchronizing signals. Includes luminance and chrominance signals, vertical- and horizontal-sync pulses, vertical- and horizontal-blanking pulses, and the color-burst signal.

composite color sync—The signal comprising all the sync signals necessary for proper operation of a color receiver. Includes the deflection sync signals to which the color sync signal is added in the proper time relationship.

composite conductor—Two or more strands of different metals, such as aluminum and steel or copper and steel, assembled and operated in parallel.

composite controlling voltage—The voltage of the anode of an equivalent diode, combining the effects of all individual electrode voltages in establishing the space-charge limited current.

composited circuit—A circuit which can be used simultaneously for telephony and for direct-current telegraphy or signaling, separation between the two being accomplished by frequency discrimination.

composite filter—A filter with two or more sections.

composite guidance system—A guidance system using a combination of more than one individual guidance system.

composite picture signal—The television signal produced by combining a blanked picture signal with the sync signal.

composite video signal—The complete video signal. For monochrome, it consists of the picture signal and the blanking and synchronizing signals. For color, color-synchronizing signals and color-picture information are added.

composite wave filter—A combination filter consisting of two or more low-pass, high-pass, bandpass, or band-elimination filters.

composition resistor—*See* Carbon Resistor.

compound-connected transistor—Two transistors which are combined to increase the current amplification factor at high emitter currents. This combination is generally employed in power-amplifier circuits.

compound-filled transformer — A transformer which is contained within a case and in which the structural insulating material is supplemented by submergence in a

Composite picture signal.

solid or semisolid insulating material introduced into the case in a fluid state.

compound horn—An electromagnetic horn of rectangular cross section. The four sides of the horn diverge in such a way that they coincide with or approach four planes, with the provision that the two opposite planes do not intersect the remaining planes.

compound modulation—*See* Multiple Modulation.

compound-wound motor—A d-c motor having two separate field windings. One, usually the predominant field, is connected in parallel with the armature circuit and the other is connected in series.

compressed-air loudspeaker—A loudspeaker that has an electrically actuated valve to modulate a stream of compressed air.

compression—A process in which the effective amplification of a signal is varied as a function of the signal magnitude, the effective gain being greater for small than for large signals. In television, the reduction in gain at one level of a picture signal with respect to the gain at another level of the same signal.

compressional wave—In an elastic medium, a wave which causes a change in volume of an element of the medium without rotation of the element.

compression driver unit—A speaker driver unit that does not radiate directly from the vibrating surface. Instead, it requires acoustic loading from a horn which connects through a small throat to an air space adjacent to the diaphragm.

compression ratio—The ratio between the magnitude of the gain (or amplification) at a reference signal level and its magnitude at a higher stated signal level.

compressor—A transducer which, for a given amplitude range of input voltages, produces a smaller range of output voltages. In one important type of compressor, the envelope of speech signals is used to reduce their volume range.

compromise network—In a telephone system, a network used in conjunction with a hybrid coil to balance a subscriber's loop. The network which is adjusted for an average loop length, an average subscriber's set, or both, and gives compromise (not precision) isolation between the two directional paths of the hybrid coil.

Compton effect — The elastic scattering of photons by electrons. Because the total energy and momentum are conserved in the collisions, the wavelength of the scattered radiation undergoes a change that depends on the scattering angle.

computer — Any device, usually electronic, capable of accepting information, comparing, adding, subtracting, multiplying, dividing, and integrating this information, and then supplying the results of these processes in acceptable form.

computer code — Also called machine language. The code by which data are represented within a computer system. An example is a binary-coded decimal.

computing—To perform basic and more involved mathematical processes of comparing, adding, subtracting, multiplying, dividing, integrating, etc.

computing machine — An automatic device which carries out well defined mathematical operations.

concatenate—To link together or unite in a series.

concatenation — The joining or linking of sets or series.

concave—Curved inward.

concentrated-arc lamp—A type of low-voltage arc lamp having nonvaporizing electrodes sealed in an atmosphere of inert gas and producing a small, brilliant, incandescent cathode spot.

concentration gradient—A difference in carrier concentration (holes or free electrons) from point to point in a semiconductor.

concentric cable—*See* Coaxial Line.

concentric groove—*See* Locked Groove.

concentric-lay conductor—A conductor composed of a central core surrounded by one or more layers of helically laid wires. In the most common type of concentric-lay conductor, all wires are of the same size, and the central core is a single wire.

concentric line—*See* Coaxial Line.

concentric stranding—A method of stranding wire in which the final wire is built up in layers such that the inner diameter of a succeeding layer always equals the outer diameter of the underlying layer.

concentric-wound coil—A coil with two or more insulated windings which are wound one over the other.

concurrent processing — The ability of a computer to work on more than one program at the same time.

condensed mercury temperature—The temperature of a mercury-vapor tube, measured on the outside of the tube envelope, in the region where the mercury is condensing in a glass tube or at a designated point on a metal tube.

condenser—*See* Capacitor.

condenser antenna—*See* Capacitor Antenna.

condenser microphone — *See* Electrostatic Microphone.

condenser speaker—*See* Electrostatic Speaker.

conditional—1. In a computer, subject to the result of a comparison made during computation. 2. Subject to human intervention.

conditional jump—Also called conditional transfer of control. An instruction to a computer which will cause the proper one of two (or more) addresses to be used in obtaining the next instruction, depending on some property of one or more numerical expressions or other conditions.

conditional transfer of control—*See* Conditional Jump.

Condor—A c-w navigational system, similar to benito, which automatically measures bearing and distance from a single ground station and displays them on a cathode-ray indicator. The distance is determined by phase comparison, and the bearing, by automatic direction finding.

conductance—Symbolized by G or g. 1. In an element, device, branch, network, or system, the physical property that is the factor by which the square of an instantaneous voltage must be multiplied to give the corresponding energy lost by dissipation as heat or other permanent radiation, or by loss of electromagnetic energy from the circuit. 2. The real part of admittance.

conducted heat—Thermal energy transferred by thermal conduction.

conducted interference—Any unwanted electrical signal conducted on the power lines supplying the equipment under test, or on lines supplying other equipment to which the one under test is connected.

conduction—The transmission of heat or electricity through or by means of a conductor.

conduction band—In a semiconductor, a partially filled energy band in which electrons can move freely, allowing the material to carry an electric current.

conduction current—The power flow parallel to the direction of propagation, expressed in mhos/meter.

conduction-current modulation—1. Periodic variations in the conduction current passing a point in a microwave tube. 2. The process of producing such variations.

conduction electrons—The electrons which are free to move under the influence of an electric field in the conduction band of a solid.

conduction error—The error in a temperature transducer due to heat conduction between the sensing element and the mounting to the transducer.

conduction field—Energy which surrounds a conductor when an electric current is passed through the conductor, and which, because of the difference in phase between the electrical field and magnetic field set up in the conductor, cannot be detached from the conductor.

conductive gasket—A special highly resilient gasket used to reduce r-f leakage in shielding which has one or more access openings.

conductive material—A material in which a relatively large conduction current flows when a potential is applied between any two points on or in a body constructed from the material. Metals and strong electrolytes are examples of conductors.

conductive pattern — The arrangement or design of the conductive lines on a printed-circuit board.

conductivity—1. The conductance between opposite faces of a unit cube of material. The volume conductivity of a material is the reciprocal of the volume resistivity. 2. The ability of a material to conduct current. The reciprocal of resistivity.

conductivity modulation — The change in

conductivity of a semiconductor as the charge-carrier density is varied.

conductivity - modulation transistor — A transistor in which the active properties are derived from minority-carrier modulation of the bulk resistivity of the semiconductor.

conductor—1. A bare or insulated wire or combination of wires not insulated from one another, suitable for carrying an electric current. 2. A body of conductive material so constructed that it will serve as a carrier of electric current.

conduit — A tubular raceway for holding wires or cables designed and used expressly for this purpose.

conduit wiring—Wiring carried in conduits and conduit fittings.

cone—The cone-shaped paper or fiber diaphragm of a speaker.

cone of nulls—A conical surface formed by directions of negligible radiation.

cone of silence — An inverted cone-shaped space directly over the aerial towers of some radio beacons. Within the cone, signals cannot be heard or will be greatly reduced in volume.

confetti—Flecks or streaks of color caused by tube noise in the chrominance amplifier. Because of its colors, confetti is much more noticeable than snow in a black-and-white picture. The chrominance amplifier is therefore cut off during a monochrome program.

confidence—1. The likelihood, expressed in per cent, that a statement is true. 2. The degree of assurance that the stated failure rate has not been exceeded.

confidence factor—The percentage figure expressing confidence level.

confidence interval—A range of values believed to include, with a preassigned degree of confidence, the true characteristic of the lot.

confidence level—The probability (expressed as a percentage), that a given assertion is true or that it lies within certain limits calculated from the date. 2. A degree of certainty.

confidence limits—Extremes of a confidence interval within which there is a designated chance that the true value is included.

configuration—1. The relative arrangement of parts (or components) in a circuit. 2. A listing of the names and/or serial numbers of the assemblies which comprise an equipment.

conformance error — The deviation of a calibration curve from a specified curve line.

conical horn—A horn the cross-sectional area of which increases as the square of the axial length.

conical scanning—A form of scanning in which the beam of a radar unit describes a cone, the axis of which coincides with that of the reflector.

conjugate branches—Any two branches of a network in which a driving force impressed on one branch does not produce a response in the other.

conjugate bridge—A bridge in which the detector circuit and the supply circuits are interchanged, compared with a normal bridge.

conjugate impedance — An impedance the value of which is the conjugate of a given impedance. For an impedance associated with an electric network, the conjugate is an impedance with the same resistance component and a negative reactive component of the original.

connected—A network is connected if, between every pair of nodes of the network, there exists at least one path composed of branches of the network.

connection — 1. The attachment of two or more component parts so that conduction can take place between them. 2. The point of such attachment.

connection diagram—A diagram showing the electrical connections between the parts comprising an apparatus.

connector—A coupling device which provides an electrical and/or mechanical junction between two cables, or between a cable and a chassis or enclosure.

connector assembly—The combination of a mated plug and receptacle.

conoscope—An instrument for determining the optical axis of a quartz crystal.

consequent poles—Additional magnetic poles present at other than the ends of a magnetic material.

consol—*See* Sonne.

console—1. A cabinet for a radio or television receiver that stands on the floor rather than on a table. 2. Main operating unit in which indicators and general controls of a radar or electronic group are installed.

console operator — A person who monitors and controls an electronic computer by means of a central control unit or console.

consonance — Electrical or acoustical resonance between bodies or circuits not connected directly together.

constant — An unvarying or fixed value or data item.

constant-amplitude recording—The disc-recording characteristic in which the groove displacement is directly proportionate to the signal amplitude.

constant current — A current that does not undergo a change greater than the required precision of the measurement when the impedance of the generator is halved.

constant-current characteristic—The relationship between the voltages of two electrodes, the current to one of them as well as all other voltages being maintained constant.

constant-current modulation — Also called Heising modulation. A system of amplitude modulation in which the output circuits of the signal amplifier and carrier-wave generator or amplifier are directly and conduc-

tively coupled by a common inductor. The inductor has an ideally infinite impedance to the signal frequencies and therefore maintains the common plate-supply current of the two devices constant. The signal-frequency voltage thus appearing across the common inductor also modulates the plate supply to the carrier generator or amplifier, with corresponding modulation of the carrier output.

constant-current power supply — A regulated power supply which acts to keep its output current constant in spite of changes in load, line, or temperature. Thus, for a change in load resistance, the output current remains constant to a first approximation, while the output voltage changes by whatever amount necessary to accomplish this.

constant-current transformer — A transformer that automatically maintains a constant current in its secondary circuit under varying conditions of load impedance when supplied from a constant-potential source.

constant-delay discriminator — *See* Pulse Demoder.

constant-K filter—An image-parameter filter comprising a tandem connection of a number of identical prototype L-section filters. Each adjacent pair of L-sections together forms either a T- or π-network. The product of the series and shunt impedances is a constant that is independent of frequency.

constant-K network—A ladder network in which the product of its series and shunt impedances is independent of frequency within the range of interest.

constant-luminance transmission—A type of transmission in which the transmission primaries are a luminance primary and two chrominance primaries.

constant-power-dissipation line — A line superimposed on the output static characteristic curves and representing the points of collector voltage and current, the product of which represents the maximum collector power rating of a particular transistor.

constant-resistance network — A network that will reflect a constant resistance to the output circuit of the driving amplifier when terminated in a resistive load. Loudspeakers do not reflect a constant impedance; therefore, an amplifier does not see a constant resistance. This disadvantage may be somewhat compensated for by the use of negative feedback by the amplifier.

constant-velocity recording — The disc-recording characteristic in which the groove displacement is inversely proportionate to the signal frequency.

constant voltage — A voltage that does not undergo a change greater than the required precision of the measurement when the impedance of the generator is doubled.

constant-voltage/constant-current (cv/cc) output characteristic—A regulated power supply which acts as a constant-voltage source for comparatively large load resistances and as a constant-current source for comparatively small load resistances.

constant-voltage power supply — A regulated power supply which acts to keep its output voltage constant in spite of changes in load, line, or temperature. Thus, for a change in load resistance, the output voltage of this type of supply remains constant to a first approximation, while the output current changes by whatever amount necessary to accomplish this.

constant-voltage transformer — A transformer delivering a fixed predetermined voltage over a limited range of input voltage variations (e.g. 95-125 volts).

consumer's reliability risk — The risk to the consumer that a product will be accepted by a reliability test when the reliability of the product is actually below the value specified for rejection.

Flat.

Convex.
Contacts (side view).

contact—1. One of the current-carrying parts of a relay, switch, or connector that are engaged or disengaged to open or close the associated electrical circuits. 2. (v) To join two conductors or conducting objects in order to provide a complete path for current flow. 3. (n) The juncture point to provide the complete path.

contact-actuation time—The time required for any specified contact on the relay to function. When not otherwise specified, it is the initial actuation time. For some purposes, it is preferable to use either the final or effective actuation time.

contact arc — The electrical (current) discharge that occurs between mating contacts when the circuit is being disestablished.

contact area — The common area between two conductors or a conductor and a connector through which the flow of electricity takes place.

contact arrangement—The combination of contact forms that make up the entire relay-switching structure.

contact bounce—The uncontrolled making and breaking of contact when the relay contacts are closed.

contact chatter—The undesired vibration of mating contacts during which there may or may not be actual physical contact opening. If there is no actual opening but only a change in resistance, it is referred to as dynamic resistance, and it appears as "grass" on the screen of an oscilloscope having adequate sensitivity and resolution.

contact combination—1. The total assembly of contacts on a relay. 2. Sometimes used for contact form.

contact emf — A small voltage established whenever two conductors of different materials are brought into contact.

contact follow—The displacement of a stated point on the contact-actuating member following the initial closure of a contact.

contact force—1. The amount of force exerted by one of a pair of closed contacts on the other. 2. The force exerted by the moving mercury on a stationary contact or electrode in a mercury switch.

contact gap—Also called contact separation. The distance between a pair of mating relay contacts when they are open.

contact length—The length of travel of one contact while touching another contact during the assembly or disassembly of a connector.

contact load—The electrical power demands encountered by a contact set in any particular application.

contact microphone—A microphone designed to pick up mechanical vibrations directly from the sound source and convert them into corresponding electrical currents or voltages.

contact modulator — A switch used to produce modified square waves having the same frequency as, and a definite phase relationship to, a driving sine wave. Also called electromechanical chopper.

contact noise—The random fluctuation of voltage across a junction through which current is flowing from one solid to another.

contactor—A heavy-duty relay used to control electrical circuits.

contactor alarm—A signal calling attention to lowered pressure in a cable gas-pressure system.

contact potential—Also called volta effect. The difference of potential that exists when two dissimilar, uncharged metals are placed in contact. One becomes positively charged and the other negatively charged, the amount of potential depending on the nature of the metals.

contact-potential difference—The difference between the work functions of two materials, divided by the electronic charge generated by them.

contact pressure — The amount of pressure holding a set of contacts together.

contact rating — The electrical power-handling capability of relay or switch contacts under specified environmental conditions and for a prescribed number of operations.

contact rectifier—A rectifier consisting of two different solids in contact. Rectification is due to the greater conductivity across the contact in one direction than in the other.

contact resistance—Total electrical resistance of a contact system, such as the resistance of a relay or a switch measured at the terminals. Usually this resistance is only a fraction of an ohm.

contact retention—The minimum axial load a contact in a connector can withstand in either direction while remaining firmly fixed in its normal position in the insert.

contacts — In a relay, the current-carrying parts that engage or disengage to open or close electrical circuits.

contact separation—The maximum distance between the stationary and movable contacts when the circuit is broken.

contact spring—1. A current-carrying spring to which the contacts are fastened. 2. A non-current-carrying spring that positions and tensions a contact-carrying member.

contact wetting—The coating of a contact surface with an adherent film of mercury.

contact wipe—The sliding or tangential motion between two touching contact surfaces.

contaminated—Made radioactive by addition of a radioactive material.

contents—The information stored in any part of the computer memory.

Continental code—*See* International Morse Code.

continuity—1. A continuous path for the flow of current in an electric circuit. 2. In radio broadcasting, the prepared copy from which the spoken material is presented.

continuity test—An electrical test for determining whether a connection is broken.

continuity writer—In radio broadcasting, the person who writes the copy from which the spoken material is presented.

continuous carrier — A carrier over which transmission of information is accomplished by means which do not interrupt the carrier.

continuous commercial service—*See* CCS.

continuous-duty rating—The rating applied to equipment if operated for an indefinite length of time.

continuously loaded cable — A submarine cable in which the conductors are continuously loaded.

continuous power—The power an amplifier is capable of delivering for at least 30 seconds with a sine-wave signal.

continuous rating—The rating that defines the load which can be carried for an indefinite length of time.

continuous recorder—A recorder that makes its record on a continuous sheet or web rather than on individual sheets.

continuous spectrum—The spectrum which exhibits no structure and appears to represent a continuous variation of wavelength from one to the other.

continuous variable—A variable that may assume any value within a defined range.

continuous-wave radar—A system in which a transmitter sends out a continuous flow of radio energy to the target, which re-radiates (scatters) the energy intercepted and returns a small fraction to a receiving antenna.

continuous waves — Electromagnetic waves generated as a continuous train of identical oscillations. They can be interrupted according to a code, or modulated in amplitude, frequency, or phase in order to convey information. Abbreviated cw.

continuous-wave tracking system—A tracking system which operates by keeping a continuous radio beam on a target and determining its behavior from changes in the antenna necessary to keep the beam on the target.

contrahelical—In the wire and cable industry the term is used to mean the direction of a layer with respect to the previous layer. Thus it would mean a layer spiraling in an opposite direction from the preceding layer within a wire or cable.

Contran — A computer-programming language in which instructions are written at a compiler level, thereby eliminating the need for translation by a compiling routine.

contrast—1. The actual difference in density between the highlights and the shadows. Contrast is not concerned with the magnitude of density, but only with the difference in densities. 2. Amplitude ratio between picture white and picture black. 3. Ratio between the maximum and minimum brightness values in a picture. 4. In optical character recognition, the differences between the color or shading of the printed material on a document and the background on which it is printed.

contrast control—A method of adjusting the contrast in a television picture by changing the amplitude of the video signal.

contrast range — The ratio between the whitest and blackest portions of a television image.

contrast ratio—Ratio of the maximum to the minimum luminance values in a television picture or a portion thereof.

control—Also called a control circuit. 1. In a digital computer, those parts which carry out the instructions in proper sequence, interpret each instruction, and apply the proper signals to the arithmetic unit and other parts in accordance with the interpretation. 2. Sometimes called a manual control. In any mechanism, one or more components responsible for interpreting and carrying out manually initiated directions. 3. In some business applications, a mathematical check. 4. In electronics, a potentiometer or variable resistor.

control ampere turns—The magnitude and polarity of the control magnetomotive force required for operation of a magnetic amplifier at a specified output.

control card—In computer programming, a card containing input data or parameters for a specific application of a general routine.

control characteristic—1. A plot of the load current of a magnetic amplifier as a function of the control ampere turns for various loads and at the rated supply voltage and frequency. 2. The relationship, usually shown by a graph, between the critical grid voltage and the anode voltage of a tube.

control circuits—In a digital computer, the circuits which carry out the instruction in proper sequence, interpret each instruction, and apply the proper commands to the arithmetic element and other circuits in accordance with the interpretation.

control-circuit transformer — A voltage transformer utilized to supply a voltage suitable for the operation of control devices.

control-circuit voltage — The voltage provided for the operation of shunt-coil magnetic devices.

control compartment — A space within the base, frame, or column of a machine used for mounting the control panel.

control counter — In a computer, a device which records the storage location of the instruction word to be operated on following the instruction word in current use.

control data — In a computer, one or more items of data used to control the identification, selection, execution, or modification of another routine, record file, operation, data value, etc.

control electrode—An electrode on which a voltage is impressed to vary the current flowing between other electrodes.

control field—In a sequence of similar items of computer information, a constant location where control information is placed.

control grid—The electrode of a vacuum tube, other than a diode, upon which a signal voltage is impressed to regulate the plate current.

control-grid bias—The average direct-current voltage between the control grid and cathode of a vacuum tube.

control-grid plate transconductance—The ratio of the amplification factor of a vacuum tube to its plate resistance, combining the effect of both into one term.

controlled avalanche device — A semiconductor device that has very specific maximum and minimum avalanche-voltage characteristics and is also able to operate and absorb momentary power surges in this avalanche region indefinitely without damage.

controlled-carrier modulation — Also called variable-carrier or floating-carrier modulation. A modulation system in which the carrier is amplitude-modulated by the signal frequencies, and also in accordance with the envelope of the signal, so that the modulation factor remains constant regardless of the amplitude of the signal.

controlled rectifier—1. A rectifier employing grid-controlled devices such as thyratrons or ignitrons to regulate its own output current. 2. Also called an scr (silicon-controlled rectifier). A four-layer PNPN semiconductor which functions like a grid-controlled thyratron.

controller—An element or group of elements that take data proportional to the difference between input and output of a device or system and convert these data into power

used to restore agreement between input and output.

control locus—A curve which shows the critical value of grid bias for a thyratron.

control panel — A panel having a systematic arrangement of terminals used with removable wires to direct the operation of a computer or punched-card equipment.

control-power disconnecting device—A disconnective device such as a knife switch, circuit breaker, or pullout fuse block used for the purpose of connecting and disconnecting, respectively, the source of control power to and from the control bus or equipment.

control ratio—1. The ratio of the change in anode voltage to the corresponding change in critical grid voltage of a gas tube, with all other operating conditions maintained constant. 2. Also called programming coefficient. The required range in control resistance of a regulated power supply to produce a 1-volt change in output voltage. Expressed in ohms per volt.

control register—In a digital computer, the register that stores the current instruction governing the operation of the computer for a cycle. Also called instruction register.

control section—*See* Control Unit.

control sequence—In a computer, the normal order of execution of instructions.

control tape—In a computer, a paper or plastic tape used to control the carriage operation of some printing output devices. Also called carriage tape.

control unit—That section of an automatic digital computer that directs the sequence of operations, interprets coded instructions, and sends the proper signals to the other computer circuits to carry out the instructions. Also called control section.

control-voltage winding—The motor winding which is excited by a varying voltage at a time phase difference from the voltage applied to the fixed voltage windings of a servomotor.

control winding—In a saturable reactor, the winding used for applying a controlling magnetomotive premagnetization force to the saturable-core material.

convection—The motion in a fluid as a result of differences in density and the action of gravity.

convection cooling—A method of heat transfer which depends on the natural upward movement of the air warmed by the heat dissipated from the device being cooled.

convection current—The amount of time required for a charge in an electron stream to be transported through a given surface.

convection-current modulation — 1. The time variation in the magnitude of the convection current passing through a surface. 2. The process of producing such a variation.

convergence—The condition in which the electron beams of a multibeam cathode-ray tube intersect at a specified point.

convergence coil—One of the two coils associated with an electromagnet, used to obtain dynamic beam convergence in a color-television receiver.

convergence control—A variable resistor in the high-voltage section of a color-television receiver. It controls the voltage applied to the three-gun picture tube.

convergence electrode — An electrode the electric field of which causes two or more electron beams to converge.

convergence magnet—A magnet assembly the magnetic field of which causes two or more electron beams to converge.

convergence phase control—A variable resistor or inductance for adjusting the phase of the dynamic convergence voltage in a color-tv receiver employing a three-gun picture tube.

convergence surface—The surface generated by the point at which two or more electron beams intersect during the scanning process in a multibeam cathode-ray tube.

conversion efficiency—1. The ratio of a-c output power to the d-c input power to the electrodes of an electron tube. 2. The ratio of the output voltage of a converter at one frequency to the input voltage at some other frequency. 3. In a rectifier, the ratio of d-c output power to a-c input-power.

conversion gain—1. The ratio of the inter-mediate-frequency output voltage to the input-signal voltage of the first detector of a superheterodyne receiver. 2. The ratio of the available intermediate-frequency power output of a converter or mixer to the available radio-frequency power input.

conversion loss—The ratio of available input power to available output power under specified test conditions.

conversion time — The length of time required by a computer to read out all the digits in a given coded word.

conversion transconductance — The magnitude of the desired output-frequency component of current divided by the magnitude of the input-frequency component of voltage when the impedance of the output external termination is negligible for all frequencies which may affect the result.

conversion transducer—One in which the signal undergoes frequency conversion. The gain or loss is specified in terms of the useful signal.

conversion voltage gain (of a conversion transducer)—With the transducer inserted between the input-frequency generator and the output termination, the ratio of the magnitude of the output-frequency voltage across the output termination to the magnitude of the input-frequency voltage across the input termination of the transducer.

convert — To change information from one form to another without changing the meaning, e.g., from one number base to another.

converter—1. In a superheterodyne radio receiver, the section which converts the desired incoming r-f signal into a lower carier frequency known as the intermediate frequency. 2. A rotating machine consisting of an electric motor driving an electric generator, used for changing alternating current to direct current. 3. A facsimile device that changes the type of modulation delivered by the scanner. 4. Generally called a remodulator. A facsimile device that changes amplitude modulation to audio-frequency–shift modulation. 5. Generally called a discriminator. A device that changes audio-frequency–shift modulation to amplitude modulation. 6. A conversion transducer in which the output frequency is the sum or difference of the input frequency and an integral multiple of the local-oscillator frequency. 7. A device that accepts an input that is a function of maximum voltage and time, and converts it to an output that is a function of maximum voltage only. 8. *See* Shaft Position Encaser. 9. A device capable of converting impulses from one mode to another, such as analog to digital, or parallel to serial, or one code to another.

converter tube — A multielement electron tube that combines the mixer and local-oscillator functions of a heterodyne conversion transducer.

converter unit—The unit of a radar system in which the mixer of a superheterodyne receiver and usually two stages of intermediate-frequency amplification are located. Performs a preamplifying operation.

converting—Changing data from one form to another to facilitate its transmission, storage, or manipulation of information.

convex—Curved outward.

Cook system—An early stereo-disc recording technique in which the two channels were recorded simultaneously with two cutters on different portions (bands) of a record as concentric spirals. The playback equipment consisted of two pickups mounted side by side so that each played at the correct spot on its own band.

Coolidge tube—An X-ray tube in which the electrons are produced by a hot cathode.

coordinated transpositions—Transpositions which are installed in either electric supply or communication circuits, or in both, for the purpose of reducing inductive coupling, and which are located effectively with respect to the discontinuities in both the electric supply and communication circuit.

coordinater indexing—1. In a computer, a system in which individual documents are indexed by descriptors of equal rank so that a library can be searched for a combination of one or more descriptors. 2. A computer indexing technique in which the coupling of individual words is used to show the interrelations of terms.

coordination—A term describing the ability of the lower rating of two breakers in series to trip before the higher-rating one trips.

copper loss—*See* I^2R Loss.

copper-oxide rectifier—A metallic rectifier in which the rectifying barrier is the junction between metallic copper and cuprous oxide. A disc of copper is coated with cuprous oxide on one side, and a soft lead washer is used to make contact with the oxide layer.

Copper-oxide rectifier.

copper-sulfide rectifier—A semiconductor rectifier in which the rectifying barrier is a junction between magnesium and copper sulfide.

copy—*See* Subject Copy.

copying telegraph—An absolute term for a facsimile system for the transmission of black-and-white copy only.

Corbino effect—A special case of the Hall effect that occurs when a disc carrying a radial current is placed perpendicularly into a magnetic field.

cord—One or a group of flexible insulated conductors covered by a flexible insulation and equipped with terminals.

cord sets—Portable cords fitted with any type of wiring device at one or both ends.

cordwood — A sandwich-type construction wherein components lie in a vertical "cordwood" pattern between horizontal layers.

cordwood module — A high-density circuit module in which discrete components are mounted between and perpendicular to two small, parallel printed-circuit boards to which their terminals are attached.

core—1. A magnetic material placed within a coil to intensify the magnetic field. 2. Magnetic material inside a relay or coil winding.

coreless-type induction heater—A device in which an object is heated by induction without being linked by a magnetic-core material.

core loss—Also called iron loss. Loss of energy in a magnetic core as the result of eddy currents, which circulate through the core and dissipate energy in the form of heat.

core memory — A computer memory device containing magnetic cores.

core plane — A horizontal network of magnetic cores that contains a core common to each storage position.

core storage—In a computer, a form of high-speed storage that uses magnetic cores.

core transformer—A transformer in which the windings are placed on the outside of the core.

core-type induction heater — A device in which an object is heated by induction. Unlike the coreless type, a magnetic core links the inducing winding to the object.

core wrap—Insulation placed over a core before the addition of windings.

corner—An abrupt change in direction of the axis of a waveguide.

corner cut — A corner removed, for orientation purposes, from a card to be used with a computer.

corner effect—The rounding off of the attenuation versus frequency characteristic of a filter at the extremes (or corners) of the passband.

corner frequency — 1. The frequency at which the open-loop gain-versus-frequency curve changes slope. For a servo motor, the product of the corner frequency in radians per second and the time constant of the motor is unity. 2. The frequency at which the two asymptotes of the gain-magnitude curves of an operational amplifier intersect.

corner reflector—A reflecting object consisting of two (dihedral) or three (trihedral) mutually intersecting conducting surfaces. Trihedral reflectors are often used as radar targets.

corner-reflector antenna—An antenna consisting of a primary radiating element and a dihedral corner reflector formed by the elements of the reflector.

Corner-reflector antenna.

corona—A luminous discharge of electricity, due to ionization of the air, appearing on the surface of a conductor when the potential gradient exceeds a certain value.

corona effect (of alternating current)—The effect produced when two wires, or other conductors having a great difference of voltage, are placed near each other.

corona failure—Failure due to corona degradation at areas of high voltage stress.

corona loss—A loss or discharge which occurs when two electrodes having a great difference of pressure are placed near each other. The corona loss takes place at the critical voltage and increases very rapidly with increasing pressure.

corona resistance—That length of time that an insulation material withstands the action of a specified level of field-intensified ionization that does not result in the immediate, complete breakdown of the insulation. Also called ionization resistance, brush-discharge resistance, or slot-discharge resistance.

corona shield—A shield placed around a high-potential point to redistribute electrostatic lines of force and prevent corona.

corona voltmeter—A voltmeter in which the peak voltage value is indicated by the beginning of corona at a known and calibrated electrode spacing.

corrective equalization—*See* Frequency-Response Equalization.

corrective maintenance—The maintenance performed on a nonscheduled basis to restore equipment to satisfactory condition.

corrective network—Also called shaping network. An electric network designed to be inserted into a circuit to improve its transmission or impedance properties, or both.

correlated characteristic—A characteristic known to be reciprocally related to some other characteristic.

correlation—1. The relationship, expressed as a number between minus one and plus one, between two sets of data, etc. 2. A relationship between two variables; the strength of the linear relationship is indicated by the coefficient of correlation.

correlation detection—A method of detection in which a signal is compared, point to point, with an internally generated reference. The output of such a detector is a measure of the degree of similarity of the input and reference signal. The reference signal is constructed in such a way that it is at all times a prediction, or best guess, of what the input signal should be at that time.

correlation direction finder—A satellite station separated from a radar to receive a jamming signal. By correlating the signals received from several such stations, the range and azimuth of many jammers may be obtained.

correlation distance—A term used in tropospheric propagation. The minimum spatial separation between antennas which will give rise to independent fading of the received signals.

Correlation Orientation Tracking and Range System—A system generally using a parabolic antenna for the analysis of a narrow band of radar energy for tracking and ranging purposes.

correlation tracking and ranging—A nonambiguous short–base-line, single-station c-w phase comparison system measuring two direction cosines and a slant range from which space position can be computed.

correlation tracking and triangulation—A trajectory-measuring system composed of several antenna base lines separated by large distances and used to measure direction cosines to an object. From these measurements, the space position is computed by triangulation.

correlation tracking system—A system utilizing correlation techniques in which signals derived from the same source are correlated to derive the phase difference between the signals. This phase difference contains the system data.

corrosion—A chemical action which causes gradual destruction of the surface of a metal by oxidation or chemical contamination. Also caused by reduction of the electrical efficiency between the metal and a contiguous substance or to the disintegrating effect of strong electrical currents or ground-return currents in electrical systems. The latter is known as electrolytic corrosion.

cosecant - squared antenna—An antenna which emits a cosecant-squared beam. In the shaped-beam antenna used, the radiation intensity over part of its pattern in some specified plane (usually the vertical) is proportionate to the square of the cosecant of the angle measured from a specified direction in that plane (usually the horizontal).

cosecant-squared beam—A radar-beam pattern designed to give uniform signal intensity in echoes from distant and nearby objects. It is generated by a spun-barrel reflector. The beam intensity varies as the square of the cosecant of the elevation angle.

cosine law—The law which states that the brightness in any direction from a perfectly diffusing surface varies in proportion to the cosine of the angle between that direction and the normal to the surface.

cosmic noise—Radio static, the origin of which is due to sources outside the earth's atmosphere. The source may be similar to sunspots, or spots on other stars.

cosmic rays—Any rays of high penetrating power produced by transmutations of atoms in outer space. These particles continually enter the earth's upper atmosphere from interstellar space.

coulomb—The quantity of electricity which passes any point in an electric circuit in 1 second when the current is maintained constant at 1 ampere. The coulomb is the unit of electric charge in the mksa systems.

Coulomb's law—Also called law of electric charges or law of electrostatic attraction. The force of attraction or repulsion between two charges of electricity concentrated at two points in an isotropic medium is proportionate to the product of their magnitudes and is inversely proportionate to the square of the distance between them. The force between unlike charges is an attraction, and between like charges a repulsion.

coulometer—An electrolytic cell which measures a quantity of electricity by the amount of chemical action produced.

Coulter counter—An electronic-cell counting instrument operating on the ion-conductivity principle. Designed by J. R. Coulter. (*Also see* cell counter.)

count—In radiation counters, a single response of the counting system.

countdown—A decreasing tally that indicates the number of operations remaining in a series.

counter—1. A circuit which counts input pulses. One specific type produces one output pulse each time it receives some predetermined number of input pulses. The same term may also be applied to several such circuits connected in cascade to provide digital counting. 2. In mechanical analog computers, a means for measuring the angular displacement of a shaft. 3. Sometimes called accumulator. A device capable of changing from one to the next of a sequence of distinguishable states upon receipt of each discrete input signal.

counter circuit—A circuit which receives uniform pulses representing units to be counted and produces a voltage in proportion to their frequency.

counterclockwise polarized wave—*See* Left-Handed Polarized Wave.

counterelectromotive cell — Cells of practically no ampere-hour capacity used to oppose the line voltage.

counterelectromotive force — Abbreviated counter emf. A voltage developed in an inductive circuit by an alternating or pulsating current. The polarity of this voltage is at every instant opposite that of the applied voltage.

Counterpoise.

counterpoise—A system of wires or other conductors, elevated above and insulated from ground, forming a lower system of conductors of an antenna.

counter tube—Also called radiation counter tube. An electron tube that converts an incident particle or burst of incident radiation into a discrete electric pulse. This is generally done by utilizing the current flow through a gas that is ionized by the radiation.

counting efficiency—In a scintillation counter, the ratio, under specified conditions, of the average number of photons or particles of ionizing radiation that produce counts to the average number of photons or particles incident on the sensitive area.

counting-rate meter—A device for indicating the time rate of occurrence of input pulses averaged over a time interval.

counting-type frequency meter—An instrument for measuring frequency. Its operation depends on the use of pulse-counting techniques to indicate the number and/or rate of recurring electrical signals applied to its input circuits.

counts per turn—The total number of code positions per 360° of encoder shaft rotation.

couple — Two or more dissimilar metals or alloys in electrical contact with each other that act as the electrodes of an electrolytic cell when they are immersed in an electrolyte.

coupled circuit — Any network containing only resistors, inductors (self and mutual), and capacitors, and having more than one independent mesh.

coupler—An arrangement of coils or capacitors so placed with respect to each other that there is electromagnetic or electrostatic coupling between their circuits.

coupling—The association of two or more circuits or systems in such a way that power may be transferred from one to another.

coupling angle—In connection with synchronous motors, the mechanical-degree relationship between the rotor and the rotating field.

coupling aperture—Also called coupling hole or coupling slot. An aperture, in the wall of a waveguide or cavity resonator, designed to transfer energy to or from an external circuit.

coupling capacitor—Any capacitor used to couple two circuits together. Coupling is accomplished by means of the capacitive reactance common to both circuits.

coupling coefficient — Also called coefficient of coupling. The degree of coupling that exists between two circuits. It is equal to the ratio between the mutual impedance and the square root of the product of the total self-impedances of the coupled circuits, all impedances being of the same kind.

coupling hole—*See* Coupling Aperture.

coupling loop—A conducting loop projecting into a waveguide or cavity resonator and designed to transfer energy to or from an external circuit.

coupling probe—A probe projecting into a waveguide or cavity resonator and designed to transfer energy to or from an external circuit.

coupling slot—*See* Coupling Aperture.

coupling transformer—A transformer that couples two circuits together by means of its mutual inductance.

covalent bond—A type of linkage between atoms. Each atom contributes one electron to a shared pair that constitutes an ordinary chemical bond.

coverage—A percentage of the completeness with which a braid or shield covers the surface of underlying insulated conductors or conductor.

cpm—Abbreviation for cycles per minute.

C-power supply—A device connected in the circuit between the cathode and grid of a vacuum tube to apply grid bias.

cps—Abbreviation for cycles per second. Now replaced by hertz (Hz).

crash-locator beacon — Airborne equipment consisting of various transmitters, collapsible antennas, etc., designed to be ejected from a downed aircraft and to transmit beacon signals to help searching forces to locate the crashed aircraft.

crater lamp – 1. A glow-discharge type of vacuum tube the brightness of which is proportional to the current passing through the tube. The glow discharge takes place in a cup or crater rather than on a plate as in a neon lamp. 2. A gaseous lamp usually containing neon. Provides a point source of light that can be modulated with a signal.

crazing—Checking of an insulation material when it is stressed and in contact with certain solvents or their vapors.

creepage – The conduction of electricity across the surface of a dielectric.

creepage distance—The shortest distance between conductors of opposite polarities, or between a live part and ground measured over the surface of the supporting material.

creepage path—The path across the surface of a dielectric between two conductors. Lengthening the creepage path reduces the possibility of arc damage or tracking.

creepage surface—An insulating surface that provides physical separation between two electrical conductors of different potential.

creep recovery—The change in no-load output occurring with time after removal of a load which had been applied for a specific period of time.

crest factor—The ratio of the peak voltage to the rms voltage of a waveform (with the d-c component removed.)

crest factor of a pulse—The ratio of the peak amplitude to the rms amplitude of a pulse.

crest value—Also called peak value. The maximum absolute value of a function.

crest voltmeter—A peak-reading voltmeter.

crimp – To compress or deform a connector barrel around a cable so as to make an electrical connection.

crimp contact—A contact whose back portion is a hollow cylinder to allow it to accept a wire. After a bared wire is inserted, a swedging tool is applied to crimp the contact metal firmly against the wire. An excellent mechanical and electrical contact results. A crimp contact often is referred to as a solderless contact.

crippled leapfrog test—In a computer, a variation of the "leapfrog" test in which the test is repeated from a single set of storage locations rather than from a changing set of storage locations.

critical angle—The maximum angle at which a radio wave may be emitted from an antenna and still be returned to the earth by refraction in the ionosphere.

critical area—*See* elemental area.

critical characteristic—A characteristic not having the normal tolerance to variables.

critical coupling—Also called optimum coupling. Between two circuits independently resonant to the same frequency, the degree of coupling which transfers the maximum amount of energy at the resonant frequency.

critical current—That current, at a specified temperature and in the absence of external magnetic fields, above which a material is normal and below which it is superconducting.

critical damping—1. The value of damping which provides the most rapid transient response without overshoot. 2. Operation on the borderline between underdamping and overdamping.

critical dimension – The dimension of a waveguide cross section that determines the cutoff frequency.

critical failure—A failure that causes a system to operate outside designated limits.

critical field—Also called cutoff field. Of a magnetron, the smallest theoretical value of a steady magnetic-flux density, at a steady anode voltage, that would prevent an electron emitted from the cathode at zero velocity from reaching the anode.

critical frequency—Also called penetrating frequency. The limiting frequency below which a magneto-ionic wave component is reflected by an ionospheric layer and above which the component penetrates the layer at vertical incidence. (*Also see* Waveguide Cutoff Frequency.)

critical grid current—The instantaneous value of grid current in a gas tube when the anode current starts to flow.

critical grid voltage – The instantaneous value of grid voltage at which the anode current starts to flow in a gas tube.

critical high-power level—The radio-frequency power level at which ionization is produced in the absence of a control-electrode discharge.

critical item—*See* Critical Part.

critical magnetic field – That field intensity below which at a specified temperature and in the absence of current, a material is superconducting and above which it is normal.

critical part—A part whose failure to meet specified requirements results in the failure of the product to serve its intended purpose. Also called critical item.

critical potential—*See* Ionization Potential.

critical temperature—That temperature below which, in the absence of current and external magnetic fields, a material is superconducting and above which it is normal.

critical voltage—Also called cutoff voltage. In a magnetron, the highest theoretical value of steady anode voltage, at a given steady magnetic-flux density, at which electrons emitted from the cathode at zero velocity will fail to reach the anode.

critical wavelength – The free-space wavelength corresponding to the critical frequency.

cro – Abbreviation for cathode-ray oscilloscope.

Crookes dark space – *See* Cathode Dark Space.

Crosby system—A compatible multiplex f-m stereo broadcast technique in which the right and left signals are combined in phase (sum signal) and transmitted on the main carrier, and also combined out-of-phase (difference signal) and transmitted on the subcarrier. The two signals are combined (matrixed) in the receiving apparatus to restore the right and left channels.

crossbanding—The use of combinations of interrogation and reply frequencies such that either one interrogation frequency is used with several reply frequencies or one reply frequency is used with several interrogation frequencies.

crosscheck—To check a computation by two different methods.

cross color—The interference in a color-television receiver chrominance channel caused by cross talk from monochrome signals.

cross coupling—Unwanted coupling between two different communication channels or their components.

crossed-field amplifier—A high-power electron tube in which direct-current power is converted to microwave power by a combination of crossed electric and magnetic fields.

crossed-pointer indicator—A two-pointer indicator used with instrument landing systems to indicate the position of an aircraft with respect to the glide path.

crossfire—Interfering current in one telegraph or signaling channel resulting from telegraph or signaling currents in another channel.

crossfoot—1. In a computer, to add or subtract numbers in different fields of the same punch card and punch the result into another field of the same card. 2. To compare totals of the same numbers obtained by different methods.

cross-hatching—In a printed-circuit board, the breaking up of large conductive areas where shielding is required.

cross magnetostriction—Under specified conditions, the relative change of dimension in a specified direction perpendicular to the magnetization of a body of ferromagnetic material when the magnetization of the body is increased from zero to a specified value (usually saturation).

cross modulation—A type of intermodulation that occurs when the carrier of the desired signal is modulated by an undesired signal.

cross neutralization—A method of neutralization used in push-pull amplifiers. A portion of the plate-to-cathode a-c voltage of each tube is applied to the grid-to-cathode circuit of the other tube through a neutralizing capacitor.

crossover—The point where two conductors that are insulated from each other cross.

crossover distortion—Distortion that occurs in a push-pull amplifier at the points of operation where the input signals cross over (go through) the zero reference points.

crossover frequency—As applied to electrical dividing networks, the frequency at which equal power is delivered to each of the adjacent-frequency channels when all channels are terminated in the specified load. (*Also see* Transition Frequency.)

crossover network—A selective network which divides its audio input into two or more frequency bands for distribution to speakers.

crossover spiral—*See* Leadover Groove.

cross polarization—The component electric field vector normal to the desired polarization component.

cross-sectional area of a conductor—The summation of all cross-sectional areas of the individual strands in the conductor, expressed in square inches or more commonly in circular mils.

cross talk—Interference which appears in a given transmitting or recording channel but has its origin in another channel. (*Also see* Magnetic Printing.)

cross-talk coupling—Also called cross-talk loss. Cross coupling between speech communication channels or their component parts. Note: Cross-talk coupling is measured between specified points of the disturbing and disturbed circuit and is preferably expressed in decibels.

cross-talk level—The volume of cross-talk energy, measured in decibels, referred to a base.

cross-talk loss—*See* Cross-talk Coupling.

crowbar—A term describing the action which effectively creates a high overload on the actuating member of the protective device. This crowbar action may be triggered by a slight increase in current or voltage.

crowbar voltage protector—A separate circuit which monitors the output of a power supply and instantaneously throws a short circuit (or crowbar) across the output terminals of the power supply whenever a preset voltage limit is exceeded. An scr is usually used as the crowbar device.

crt—Abbreviation for cathode-ray tube.

cryogenic device—A device intended to function best at temperatures near absolute zero.

cryogenic motor—A motor that operates at a temperature below −129°C and that uses a cryogenic fluid or gas to cool its windings and bearings.

cryogenics—The study and use of devices utilizing properties of materials near absolute zero in temperature.

cryosar—A semiconductor device primarily intended for high-speed computer switching and memory applications. This device operates by the low-temperature avalanche breakdown produced by impact ionization of impurities.

cryostat—A refrigerating unit such as that for producing or utilizing liquid helium in establishing extremely low temperatures (approaching absolute zero).

cryotron—A superconductive four-terminal device in which a magnetic field, produced by passing a current through two input terminals, controls the superconducting-to-normal transition—and thus the resistance—between the two output terminals.

cryotronics — A contraction of "cryogenic electronics."

crystal—A solid in which the constituent atoms are arranged with some degree of geometric regularity. In communication practice, a piezoelectric crystal, piezoelectric crystal plate, or crystal rectifier.

crystal anisotropy — A force which directs the magnetization of a single-domain particle along a direction of easy magnetization. To rotate the magnetization of the particle, an applied magnetic field must provide enough energy to rotate the magnetization through a difficult crystal direction.

crystal audio receiver—Similar to the crystal video receiver except for the path detection bandwidth, which is audio rather than video.

crystal calibrator—A crystal-controlled oscillator used as a reference to check and set the frequency tuning of a receiver or transmitter.

crystal can relay—A relay mounted in a can of a specific size and shape; called a crystal can because of its common usage as a mounting for quartz crystals used in frequency-control circuits.

crystal control—Control of the frequency of an oscillator by means of a specially designed and cut crystal.

crystal-controlled oscillator — See Crystal Oscillator.

crystal-controlled transmitter — A radio transmitter in which the carrier frequency is controlled directly by a crystal oscillator.

crystal cutter—A disc cutter in which the mechanical displacements of the recording stylus are derived from the deformities of a crystal having piezoelectric properties.

crystal detector—A mineral or crystalline material which allows electrical current to flow more easily in one direction than in the other. In this way, an alternating current can be converted to a pulsating current.

crystal diode—A rectifying element comprising a semiconductor crystal having two terminals. Its operation is analogous to that of electron-tube diodes.

crystal filter—A highly selective circuit capable of discriminating against all signals except those at the center frequency of a crystal, which serves as the selective element.

crystal headphones—Headphones using Rochelle-salt or other crystal elements to convert audio-frequency signals into sound waves.

crystal holder—A case of insulating material for mounting a crystal. External prongs allow the crystal to be plugged into a suitable socket.

crystal imperfection—Any deviation in lattice structure from that of a perfect single crystal.

crystal microphone—Also called piezoelectric microphone. A microphone which depends for its operation on the generation of an electric charge by the deformation of a body

(usually crystalline) having piezoelectric properties.

crystal mixer—1. A mixer circuit with the frequency of the local oscillator being controlled by a crystal. Normally used in superheterodyne radio receivers. 2. A mixer that utilizes the nonlinear characteristic of a crystal diode to mix two frequencies. Frequently used in radar receivers to convert the received radar signal to a lower i-f signal by mixing it with a local-oscillator signal.

crystal operation—Operation using crystal-controlled oscillators.

Crystal oscillator.

crystal oscillator — Also called crystal-controlled oscillator. An oscillator in which the frequency of oscillation is controlled by a piezoelectric crystal.

crystal oven—A container, maintained at a constant temperature, in which a crystal and its holder are enclosed in order to keep their temperature constant and thereby reduce frequency drift.

Crystal pickup.

crystal pickup — Also called piezoelectric pickup. A phonograph pickup which depends for its operation on the generation of an electric charge by the deformation of a body (usually crystalline) having piezoelectric properties.

crystal pulling—A method of growing crystals in which the developing crystal is gradually withdrawn from a melt.

crystal rectifier—An electrically conductive or semiconductive substance, natural or synthetic, which has the property of rectifying small radio-frequency voltages.

crystal set—A simple type of radio receiver having only a crystal-detector stage for de-modulation of the received signal and no amplifier stages.

crystal slab—A relatively thick piece of crystal from which crystal blanks are then cut.

crystal speaker — Also called piezoelectric speaker. A speaker in which the mechanical displacements are produced by piezoelectric action.

crystal-stabilized transmitter—A transmitter employing automatic frequency control, in which the reference frequency is the same as the crystal-oscillator frequency.

crystal transducer—*See* Piezoelectric Transducer.

crystal video receiver—A radar receiver consisting only of a crystal detector and video amplifier.

C-scope — A rectangular radar display in which targets appear as bright spots with azimuth indicated by the horizontal coordinate and elevation angle by the vertical coordinate.

CT-cut crystal—A natural quartz crystal cut to vibrate below 500 kHz.

CTL—Abbreviation for complementary transistor logic.

cubical antenna—An antenna array, the elements of which are positioned to form a cube.

cue circuit—A one-way communication circuit for conveying program control information.

cup—A single mechanical section of a potentiometer which may contain one or more electrical resistance elements.

cup core—A core which forms a magnetic shield around an inductor. Usually a cylinder with one end closed. A center core inside the inductor is normally used and may or may not be part of the cup core.

cup washer—A washer formed with a recess in one side to retain compression springs or, on binding-post terminals, to prevent escape of connecting wire strands.

curie—A unit used for indicating the strength of radioactive sources in terms of the number of disintegrations per second in the source. One curie is equal to 3.7×10^{10} disintegrations per second.

Curie point—Also called magnetic transition temperature. The temperature above which a ferromagnetic material becomes substantially nonmagnetic.

curing temperature—Temperature at which a material undergoes a curing process.

Curpistor—A subminiature constant-current tube containing two electrodes and filled with radioactive nitrogen.

current—The movement of electrons through a conductor. Measured in amperes, and its symbol is I.

current amplification — 1. The ratio of the current produced in the output circuit of an amplifier to the current supplied to the input circuit. 2. In photomultipliers, the

ratio of the signal output current to the photoelectric signal current from the photocathode.

current amplifier—A device designed to deliver a greater output current than its input current.

current antinode—Also called current loop. The point at which current is a maximum along a transmission-line antenna or other circuit element having standing waves.

current attenuation—The ratio of the magnitude of the current in the input circuit of a transducer to the magnitude of the current in a specified load impedance connected to the transducer.

current-balance relay—A relay in which operation occurs when the magnitude of one current exceeds the magnitude of another current by a predetermined ratio.

current-carrying capacity — The maximum current a conductor (or braid) can carry without heating beyond a safe limit.

current-carrying rating — The current that can be carried continuously or for stated periodic intervals without impairment of the contact structure or interrupting capability.

current density—The amount of electric current passing through a given cross-sectional area of a conductor in amperes per square inch—i.e., the ratio of the current in amperes to the cross-sectional area of the conductor.

current echo—The signal which on a transmission line is reflected as the result of some discontinuity.

current feed—A method of feeding to a point where the current is a maximum (e.g., at the center of a half-wave antenna).

current flicker ¬ Current surges resulting from momentary shorts that can occur within a solid-electrolytic capacitor. They may produce a leakage-current increase, a decrease, no change at all, or a catastrophic failure. Under certain conditions, current flicker can avalanche to cause a short, which under low-impedance circuit conditions results in catastrophic destruction of the capacitor.

current generator—A two-terminal circuit element with a terminal current independent of the voltage between its terminals.

current limiting (automatic)—An overload-protection mechanism which limits the maximum output current of a power supply to a preset value and automatically restores the output when the overload is removed. (*Also see* Short-Circuit Protection.)

current-limiting fuse — A protective device which anticipates a dangerous short-circuit current and opens the circuit, precluding the development of the peak available current.

current-limiting reactor—A form of reactor intended for limiting the current that can flow in a circuit under short-circuit conditions.

current-limiting resistor — A resistor inserted into an electric circuit to limit the flow of current to some predetermined value. Usually inserted in series with a fuse or circuit breaker to limit the current flow during a short circuit or other fault, to prevent excessive current from damaging other parts of the circuit.

current loop—*See* Current Antinode.

current margin—The difference between the steady-state currents flowing through a telegraph receiving instrument corresponding, respectively, to the two positions of the telegraph transmitter.

current-mode logic—Abbreviated CML. A nonsaturating logic circuit that employs the characteristics of a differential amplifier circuit in its design. Because it is nonsaturating, it is the fastest switching logic design. The gate input element is the base of a transistor with a separate transistor for each input.

current node—A point at which current is zero along a transmission line, antenna, or any other circuit element that has standing waves.

current noise—Also called excess noise. A low-frequency-noise caused by current flowing in a resistor, particularly a carbon resistor. The amount varies widely with the type and construction of the resistor. This low-frequency noise is generally measurable only in the region below 100 kHz, and the noise power varies inversely with frequency.

current probe—A type of transformer usually having a snap-around configuration, used for measuring the current in a conductor.

current pump—A circuit that drives, through an external load circuit, an adjustable variable or constant value of current, regardless of the reaction of that load to the current, within rated limits of current, voltage, and load impedance.

current regulator—A device that functions to maintain the output current of a generator or other voltage source at a predetermined value, or varies the voltage according to a predetermined plan.

current relay—A relay that operates at a predetermined value of current. It can be an overcurrent relay, an undercurrent relay, or a combination of both.

current saturation—The condition in which the plate current of a vacuum tube cannot be further increased by increasing the plate voltage.

current-sensing resistor—A resistor of low value placed in series with the load to develop a voltage proportional to the output current. A regulated d-c power supply regulates the current in the load by regulating the voltage across this sensing resistor.

current sensitivity—The current required to give standard deflection on a galvanometer.

current-sinking logic—Also called input-coupled logic. A logic form that requires that current flow out of the input of a circuit and back into the output of the preceding stage, which serves as a current sink instead of a source.

current-sourcing logic—Also called collector-coupled logic. A logic form where current flows from the output of a circuit and is forced into the input of a similar circuit to activate the circuit which drives.

current-stability factor—In a transistor, the ratio of a change in emitter current to a change in reverse-bias current between the collector and base.

current-transfer ratio—*See* Beta.

current transformer—A transformer, intended for measuring or control purposes, designed to have its primary winding connected in series with a circuit carrying the current to be measured or controlled.

Current transformer.

current-type telemeter—A telemeter in which the magnitude of a single current is the translating means.

cursor—1. A mechanically or electronically generated line which moves back and forth over another surface to delineate accurate readings. 2. A mechanical bearing line on a plan position indicator-type display for reading target bearing.

customer set—*See* Subscriber Set.

Cutler feed—A resonant cavity, at the end of a waveguide, which feeds radio-frequency energy to the reflector of the antenna assembly of some airborne antennas.

cutoff—1. Minimum value of bias which cuts off, or stops, the flow of plate current in a tube. 2. The frequency above or below which a selective circuit fails to respond. 3. The frequency of transmission at which the loss exceeds by 10 decibels that observed at 1,000 hertz.

cutoff attenuator—A variable length of waveguide used below the cutoff frequency of the waveguide to introduce variable non-dissipative attenuation.

cutoff current—Transistor collector current with no emitter current and normal collector-to-base bias.

cutoff field—*See* Critical Field.

cutoff frequency—The frequency at which the gain of an amplifier falls below .707 times the maximum gain.

cutoff frequency of a line—The upper frequency limit, usually of a loaded transmission circuit, beyond which the attenuation rises very rapidly.

cutoff limiting—Keeping the output of a vacuum tube below a certain point by driving the control grid beyond cutoff.

cutoff voltage—1. The electrode voltage which reduces the dependent variable of an electron-tube characteristic to a specified value. (*Also see* Critical Voltage.) 2. The voltage at which the discharge is considered complete. This need not be a very low voltage.

cutoff wavelength—The ratio of the velocity of electromagnetic waves in free space to the cutoff frequency of a waveguide.

cutout—1. An electrical device that interrupts the flow of current through any particular apparatus or instrument, either automatically or manually. 2. Pairs brought out of a cable and terminated at some place other than at the end of the cable.

cut-signal branch operation—In systems where radio reception continues without cutting off the carrier, the cut-signal branch operation technique disables a signal branch in one direction when it is enabled in the other to preclude unwanted signal reflections.

cutter—Also called mechanical recording head. An electromechanical transducer which transforms an electric input into a mechanical output (for example, the mechanical motions which a cutting stylus inscribes into a recording medium).

cut-through—The resistance of a solid material to penetration by an object under conditions of pressure, temperature, etc.

cut-through flow test—A test to measure the resistance to deformation of insulation subjected to heat and pressure.

cutting rate—The number of lines per inch the lead screw moves the cutting-head carriage across the face of a recording blank. Standard rates are 96, 104, 112, 128, 136, and greater in multiples of eight lines per inch. For microgroove recordings, 200 to 300 lines per inch are used.

cw—Abbreviation for: 1. Continuous wave. 2. Clockwise.

c-w reference signal—In color television, a sinusoidal signal used to control the conduction time of a synchronous demodulator.

cybernetics—The study of systems of control and communications in humans and animals, and in electrically operated devices such as calculating machines.

cycle—1. The change of an alternating wave

Cycle.

from zero to a negative peak to zero to a positive peak and back to zero. The number of cycles per second (hertz) is called the frequency. (*Also see* Alternation.) 2. An off-on application of power.

cycle counter—A mechanism or device used to record the number of times a specified cycle is repeated.

cycle index—1. In digital computer programming, the number of times a cycle has been executed. 2. The difference between the number of times a cycle has been executed and the number of times it is desired that the cycle be repeated.

cycle life—For rechargeable cells, the total number of discharge/charge cycles before the cell becomes inoperative.

cycle reset—To return a cycle index to its initial value.

cycle shift—In a computer, the removal of the digits of a number or characters from a word from one end of the number or word and their insertion, in the same sequence, at the other end.

cycle timer—A controlling mechanism which opens or closes contacts according to a preset cycle.

cyclically magnetized condition—The condition of a magnetic material after being under the influence of a magnetizing force varying between two specific limits until, for each increasing (or decreasing) value of the magnetizing force, the magnetic-flux density has the same value in successive cycles.

cyclic code—Positional notation, not necessarily binary, in which quantities differing by one unit are represented by expressions which are identical except for one place or column, and the digits in that place or column differ by only one unit. Cyclic codes are often used in mechanical devices because no ambiguity exists at the changeover point between adjacent quantities.

cyclic memory—A memory that continuously stores information but provides access to any piece of stored information only at multiples of a fixed time called the cycle time.

cyclic shift—A shift in which the data moved out of one end of the storing register are reentered into the other end, as in a closed loop.

cycling vibration—Sinusoidal vibration applied to an instrument and varied in such a way that the instrument is subjected to a specified range of vibrational frequencies.

cycloconverter—A step-down static frequency converter that produces a constant or a precisely controllable output frequency from a variable-frequency a-c power input. In general, the frequency ratio chosen is three to one, or greater.

cyclogram—An oscilloscope display obtained by monitoring two voltages having a direct cyclic relationship to each other.

cycloidotron—A fast-wave crossed-field microwave tube similar to the cyclotron resonance tube.

cyclometer register—A set of four or five wheels numbered from 0 to 9 inclusive on their edges, and enclosed and connected by gearing so that the register reading appears as a series of adjacent digits.

cyclotron—A device consisting of an evacuated tank in which positively charged particles (for example, protons, deuterons, etc.) are guided in spiral paths by a static magnetic field while being highly accelerated by a fixed-frequency electric field.

cyclotron frequency—The frequency at which an electron traverses an orbit in a steady, uniform magnetic field and zero electric field. Given by the product of the electronic charge and the magnetic-flux density, divided by 2π times the electron mass.

cyclotron-frequency magnetron oscillations—Those oscillations having substantially the same frequency as that of the cyclotron.

cyclotron radiation—The electromagnetic radiation emitted by charged particles orbiting in a magnetic field. It arises from the centripetal acceleration of the particle moving in a circular orbit.

cyclotron resonance—The effect characterized by the tendency of charge carriers to spiral around an axis in the same direction as an applied magnetic field, with an angular frequency determined by the value of the applied field and the ratio of the charge to the effective mass of the charge carrier.

cylindrical reflector—A reflector which is part of a cylinder, usually parabolic.

cylindrical wave—A wave the equiphase surfaces of which form a family of coaxial cylinders.

Czochralski technique—A method of growing large single crystals by pulling them from a molten state. Usually used for growing single crystals of germanium and silicon.

D

D—Symbol for electrostatic flux density, deuterium, or dissipation factor.

dag—Abbreviation for Aquadag.

Damon effect—The change in susceptibility of a ferrite, caused by a high r-f power input.

damped natural frequency—1. The frequency at which a system with a single degree of freedom will oscillate, in the presence of damping, after momentary displacement from the rest position by a transient force. 2. The rate of free oscillation of a sensing element in the presence of damping.

damped oscillation—The oscillation that occurs when the amplitude of the oscillating quantity decreases with time. If the rate of decrease can be expressed mathematically, the name of the function describes the damping. Thus, if the rate of decrease is expressed as a negative exponential, the system is said to be an exponentially damped system.

damped waves—Waves in which successive cycles at the source progressively diminish in amplitude.

dampen—1. To diminish progressively in amplitude; usually said of waves or oscillations. 2. To deaden vibrations.

damper—*See* Stabilizer.

damper tube—The tube which conducts in the horizontal-output circuit of a television receiver when the current in the horizontal-deflecting yoke reaches its negative peak. This causes the sawtooth deflection current to decrease smoothly to zero instead of continuing to oscillate.

damper winding—In electric motors, a permanently short-circuited winding, usually uninsulated, and arranged so that it opposes rotation or pulsation of the magnetic field with respect to the pole shoes.

damping—1. Reduction of energy in a mechanical or electrical system by absorption or radiation. 2. Act of reducing the amplitude of the oscillations of an oscillatory system, hindering or preventing oscillation or vibration, or diminishing the sharpness of resonance of the natural frequency of a system. 3. The dissipation of kinetic energy in a system by a controlled energy-absorbing medium. A system can be described as being either critically damped, overdamped, or underdamped. 4. The manner in which the pointer settles to its steady indication after a change in the value of the measured quantity. Two general classes of damped motion are: a. Periodic, in which the pointer oscillates about the final position before coming to rest; b. Aperiodic, in which the pointer comes to rest without overshooting the rest position. Sometimes referred to as overdamping.

damping coefficient—The ratio of actual damping to critical damping.

damping constant—The Napierian logarithm of the ratio of the first to the second of two values of an exponentially decreasing quantity separated by a unit of time.

damping diode—A vacuum tube which damps the positive or negative half-cycle of an a-c voltage.

damping factor—1. For any underdamped motion during any complete oscillation, the quotient obtained by dividing the logarithmic decrement by the time required by the oscillation. 2. Numerical quantity indicating ability of an amplifier to operate a speaker properly. Values over 4 are usually considered satisfactory. 2. The ratio of rated load impedance to the internal impedance of an amplifier. 3. *See* Decrement.

damping magnet—A permanent magnet and a movable conductor such as a sector or disc arranged in such a way that a torque (or force) is produced which tends to oppose any relative motion.

damping of an instrument—The manner in which the pointer of an instrument settles to a steady indication after a change in the measured quantity has occurred.

damping ratio—1. The ratio of the degree of actual damping to the degree of damping required for critical damping. May be effected by changes in ambient temperature. 2. Of a galvanometer, the ratio, expressed as a positive number, of a given deflection to the next deflection in the opposite direction. The greater this ratio, the greater the degree of damping. The natural logarithm of this ratio is called the logarithmic decrement.

Daniell cell—A cell having a copper electrode in a copper-sulfate solution and a zinc electrode in a diluted sulfuric acid or zinc-sulfate solution, with the two solutions separated by a porous partition. Generates an essentially constant electromotive force of about 1.1 volts.

daraf—The unit of elastance. It equals the reciprocal of capacitance and is actually farad spelled backward.

dark conduction—Residual electrical conduction in a photosensitive substance in total darkness.

dark current—See Electrode Dark Current.

dark discharge—In a gas, an electric discharge that has no luminosity.

dark-field disc—A disc used in the optical-electronic type of cell counter that controls light transmission.

dark resistance—The resistance of a photoelectric device in total darkness.

dark spot—A phenomenon sometimes observed in a reproduced television image. It is caused by the formation of electron clouds in front of the mosaic screen in the transmitter camera tube.

dark spot signal—The signal existing in a television system while the television camera is scanning a dark spot.

dark-trace tube—A cathode-ray tube with a screen coated with a halide of sodium or potassium. The screen normally is nearly white, and whenever the electron beam strikes, it turns a magenta color which is of long persistence. The screen can be illuminated by a strong light source, so that the reflected image may be made intense enough to be projected.

Darlington amplifier—Also called Darlington pair, double-emitter follower, or B mul-

Darlington amplifier.

tiplier. A transistor circuit which, in its original form, consists of two transistors in which the collectors are tied together and the emitter of the first transistor is directly coupled to the base of the second transistor. Therefore, the emitter current of the first transistor equals the base current of the second transistor. This connection of two transistors can be regarded as a compound transistor with three terminals.

Darlington pair—See Darlington Amplifier.

D'Arsonval current—A high-frequency, low-voltage current of comparatively high amperage.

D'Arsonval galvanometer—A d-c galvanometer consisting of a narrow rectangular coil suspended between the poles of a permanent magnet.

D'Arsonval instrument—See Permanent-Magnet Moving-Coil Instrument.

D'Arsonval movement.

D'Arsonval movement—A meter movement consisting essentially of a small, lightweight coil of wire supported on jeweled bearings between the poles of a permanent magnet. When the direct current to be measured is sent through the coil, its magnetic field interacts with that of the permanent magnet and causes the coil and attached pointer to rotate.

dash—Term used in radiotelegraphy. It consists of three units of a sustained transmitted signal followed by one unit during which no signal is transmitted.

dashpot—A device using a gas or liquid to absorb energy from or retard the movement of the moving parts of a circuit breaker or other electrical or mechanical device.

data—A general term used to denote any or all facts, numbers, letters, and symbols, or facts that refer to or describe an object, idea, condition, situation, or other factors. It connotes basic elements of information which can be processed or produced by a computer. Sometimes data are considered to be expressible only in numerical form, but information is not so limited.

data acquisition system—A system in which a computer at a central computing facility gathers data from multiple remote locations.

data collection—In a computer, the transferring of data from one or more points to a central point. Also called data gathering.

data communication—The transmission of information from one point to another.

data conversion—The changing of data from one form of representation to another.

data element—An element which converts data functions into a usable signal. (*Also see* Element.)

data-flow diagram—An illustration having a configuration such that it suggests a certain amount of circuit operation.

data gathering—*See* Data Collection.

data-handling capacity—The number of bits of information which may be stored in a computer system at one time. The rate at which these bits may be fed to the input either by hand or with automatic equipment.

data-handling system—Semiautomatic or automatic equipment used in the collection, transmission, reception, and storage of numerical data.

data link—Electronic equipment which permits automatic transmission of information in digital form.

data processing—The handling of information in a sequence of reasonable operations.

data-processing machines—A general name for a machine which can store and process numerical and alphabetical information.

data processor—An electronic or mechanical machine for handling information in a sequence of reasonable operations.

data reduction—The process of summarizing a large quantity of experimentally obtained data.

dataset—A circuit termination device used to provide interface between a circuit and terminal input/output equipment.

data synchronizer—A device that controls and synchronizes the transmission of data between an input/output (I/O) device and the computer system.

data transmission—The sending of information from one place to another or from one part of a system to another.

data-transmission equipment—The communications equipment used in direct support of data-processing equipment.

data transmission utilization measure—In a data-transmission system, the ratio of the useful data output to the total data input.

daylight visible range—The maximum range at which, under given conditions, a large black object can be seen against a white sky.

db—Abbreviation for decibel.

dba—Abbreviation for decibels adjusted. Used in conjunction with noise measurements. The reference level is −90 dbm, and the adjustment depends on the frequency-band weighting characteristics of the measuring device.

dbj—A unit used to express relative r-f signal levels. The reference level is zero dbj = 1,000 microvolts. (Originated by Jerrold Electronics.)

dbk—Decibels referred to 1 kilowatt.

dbm—Abbreviation for decibels above (or below) one milliwatt. A quantity of power expressed in terms of its ratio to 1 milliwatt.

db meter—A meter having a scale calibrated to read directly in decibel values at a specified reference level (usually one milliwatt equals zero db).

dbRAP—Decibels above reference acoustical power, which is defined as 10^{-16} watts.

dbRN—Decibels above reference noise. This is a unit used to show the relationship between the interfering effect of a noise frequency, or band of noise frequencies, and a fixed amount of noise power commonly called reference noise. A tone of 1000 hertz having a power level of −90 dbm was selected as the reference noise power because it appeared to have negligible interfering effect and would permit the measurement of interfering effect in positive numbers.

dbv—The increase or decrease in voltage independent of impedance levels.

dbw—Decibels referred to 1 watt.

dbx—Decibels above the reference coupling. Reference coupling is defined as the coupling between two circuits that would be required to give a reading of 0 dba on a two-type noise-measuring set connected to the disturbed circuit when a test tone of 90 dba (using the same weighting as that used on the disturbed circuit) is impressed on the disturbing circuit.

dc—Abbreviation for direct current.

D cable—Two-conductor cable, each conductor having the shape of the capital letter D, with insulation between the conductors and between the conductors and the sheath.

d-c amplifier—*See* Direct-Current Amplifier.

d-c balance—An adjustment of circuitry to avoid a change in d-c level when the gain is changed.

d-c beta—The d-c current gain of a transistor; the ratio of the collector current to the base current that caused it, measured at constant collector-to-emitter voltage.

d-c block—A coaxial component employed to prevent the flow of d-c or video along a transmission line while allowing the uninterrupted flow of r-f. The structure is of a short section of coaxial line, having a capacitance in series with the center and/or outer conductor. The r-f flows with negligible reflection or attenuation, while the video frequencies or d-c are blocked.

dcc—Abbreviation for double cotton-covered.

d-c circuit breaker—A device used to close and interrupt a d-c power circuit under normal conditions or to interrupt this circuit under fault or emergency conditions.

d-c component—The average value of a signal. In television it represents the average luminance of the picture being transmitted, and in radar it is the level from which the transmitted and the received pulses rise.

d-c coupled—The connection by a device which passes the steady-state characteristics of a signal and which largely eliminates the transient or oscillating characteristics of the signal.

d-c dump—The withdrawal of direct-current

power from a computer. This may result in loss of the stored information.

d-c generator—A rotating electric device for converting mechanical power into d-c power.

d-c inserter stage—A television transmitter stage that adds a d-c component known as the pedestal level to the video signal.

d-c leakage current—The conduction current that flows through a capacitor when rated d-c voltage is applied.

d-c noise—The noise arising when reproducing a tape which has been nonuniformly magnetized by energizing the record head with direct current, either in the presence or absence of bias. This noise has pronounced long-wavelength components which can be as much as 20 db higher than those obtained from a bulk-erased tape.

d-c noise margin—The difference between the output voltage level of a driving gate and the input threshold voltage of a driven gate for both the "1" and the "0" states.

d-c operating point—The d-c values of collector voltage and current of a transistor with no signal applied.

d-c overcurrent relay—A device which functions when the current in a d-c circuit exceeds a given value.

d-c patch bay—Specific patch panels provided for termination of all direct-current circuits and equipment used in an installation.

d-c picture transmission—Transmission of the d-c component of the television picture signal. This component represents the background or average illumination of the over-all scene and varies only with the over-all illumination.

d-c plate resistance—The value or characteristic used in vacuum-tube computations. It is equal to the direct-current plate voltage divided by the direct-current plate current and is given the symbol r_p.

d-c reclosing relay—A device which controls the automatic closing and reclosing of a d-c circuit interrupter, generally in response to load-circuit conditions.

d-c resistivity—The resistance of a body of ferromagnetic material having a constant cross-sectional area, measured under stated conditions by means of direct voltage, multiplied by the cross-sectional area, and divided by the length of the body.

d-c restoration—The re-establishment, by a sampling process, of the d-c and the low-frequency component which, in a video signal, have been suppressed by a-c transmission.

d-c restorer—Also called clamper or restorer. A clamping circuit which holds either amplitude extreme of a signal waveform to a given reference level of potential.

d-c shift—An error in transient response, with a time constant approaching several seconds.

d-c short—A coaxial component that provides

a d-c circuit between the center and outer conductors, while allowing the r-f signal to flow uninterrupted. The unit has a high-impedance line shunted across the main coax line. This consequently makes this device frequency dependent. However, it can be acquired in octave bandwidths.

d-c signaling—A transmission method which utilizes direct current.

DCTL — Abbreviation for direct-coupled transistor logic.

d-c transducer—A transducer capable of proper operation when excited with direct current. Its output is given in terms of direct current unless otherwise modified by the function of the stimulus.

d-c transmission—Transmission of a television signal in such a way that the d-c component of the picture signal is still present. This is done to maintain the true level of background illumination.

dcwv—Abbreviation for direct current working volts. The maximum continuous voltage which can be applied to a capacitor.

deac—A device employed in frequency-modulation receivers to de-emphasize the higher frequencies in the received signal so as to restore their proper relative amplitude. (*Also see* De-emphasis.)

deaccentuator — A network or circuit employed in frequency-modulated receivers to de-emphasize the higher frequencies in the received signal to store their proper relative amplitude.

dead—Free from any electric connection to a source of potential difference and from electric charge; having the same potential as that of earth. The term refers only to current-carrying parts which are sometimes alive, or charged.

dead band—1. In a control system, the range of values through which the measurand can be varied without initiating an effective response. 2. Also called dead space, dead zone, or switching blank. A specified range of values in which the incoming signal can be altered without also changing the outgoing response.

deadbeat—Coming to rest without vibration or oscillation — i.e., the pointer which a highly damped meter or galvanometer moves to a new position without overshooting and vibrating about its final position.

deadbeat instrument—A voltmeter, ammeter, or similar device in which the movement is highly damped to bring it to rest quickly.

dead break—An unreliable contact made near the trip point of a relay or switch at low contact pressure. As a result, the switch does not actuate, even though the circuit is interrupted.

dead end—1. In a sound studio, the end with the greater sound-absorbing characteristic. 2. In a tapped coil, the portion through which no current is flowing at a particular bandswitch position.

dead-end tower—An antenna or transmission-line tower designed to withstand unbalanced mechanical pull from all the conductors in one direction, together with the wind strain and vertical loads.

dead room—A room for testing the acoustic efficiency or range of electroacoustic devices such as speakers and microphones. The room is designed with an absolute minimum of sound reflection, and no two dimensions of the room are the same. A ratio of 3 to 4 to 5 is usually employed (e.g., 15′ × 20′ × 25′). The walls, floor, and ceiling are lined with a sound-absorbing material.

dead short—A short circuit having minimum resistance.

dead space—1. An area or zone, within the normal range of a radio transmitter, in which no signal is received. 2. *See* Dead Band.

dead spot—1. A geographic location in which signals from one or more radio stations are received poorly or not at all. 2. That portion of the tuning range of a receiver where stations are heard poorly or not at all because of poor sensitivity.

dead time—The minimum interval, following a pulse, during which a transponder or component circuit is incapable of repeating a specified performance.

dead volume—The total volume of the pressure port cavity of a pressure transducer at the rest position (i.e., with no stimulus applied).

dead zone—1. The range of values over which no corrective action will take place in an automatic control system. 2. *See* Dead Band.

deafness—*See* Hearing Loss.

debug—To examine or test a procedure, routine, or equipment for the purpose of detecting and correcting errors.

debugging—1. Isolating and removing all malfunctions ("bugs") from a computer or other device to restore its operation. 2. A process undertaken to carry an equipment or a group of parts through the initial period during which catastrophic-type failures occur at an abnormally high rate.

debugging period—*See* Early Failure Period.

debunching—Space-charge effect that tends to destroy the electron bunching in a velocity-modulation vacuum tube by spreading the beam due to mutual repulsion of the electrons.

Debye length—A theoretical length that describes the maximum separation at which a given electron is influenced by the electric field of a given positive ion. Also called Debye shielding distance or plasma length.

Debye shielding—*See* Debye Length.

decade—1. The interval between any two quantities having a ratio of 10:1. 2. A group or assembly of 10 units (e.g., a counter which counts to 10 in one column, or a resistor box which inserts resistance quantities in multiples of powers of 10).

decade band—A band having frequency limits related by the equation $f_b - f_a = 10$.

decade box—A special assembly of precision resistors, coils, or capacitors. It contains two or more sections, each having 10 times the value of the preceding section. Each section is divided into 10 equal parts. By means of a 10-position selector switch or equivalent arrangement, the box can be set to any desired value in its range.

decade counter—*See* Decade Scaler.

Decade resistance box.

decade resistance box—A resistance box containing two or more sets of 10 precision resistors.

decade scaler—Counter or scale-of-ten counter. A scaler with a factor of 10. It produces one output pulse for every 10 input pulses.

decalesent point—The temperature at which there is a sudden absorption of heat as the temperature of a metal is raised.

decametric waves—High-frequency band; 3 MHz to 30 MHz.

decay—1. Gradual reduction of a quantity. 2. The decrease in the radiation intensity of any radioactive material with respect to time. 3. In a storage tube, a change in magnitude or configuration of stored information by any cause other than erasing or writing.

decay characteristic—*See* Persistence Characteristic (of a luminescent screen).

decay distance—The distance between an area of wave generation and a point of passage of the resulting waves outside the area.

Decca—A British long-range hyperbolic navigational system that operates in the 70- to 130-kilohertz frequency band. It is a continuous-wave system in which the receiver measures and integrates the relative phase difference between the signal received from two or more synchronized ground stations. One master station and three slave stations are usually arranged in stat formation. Operational range is about 250 miles.

decelerated electrons—Electrons which, after traveling at a great rate of speed, strike a target, become quickly decelerated, and cause the target to emit X rays.

decelerating electrode—In an electron-beam tube, an electrode to which a potential is applied to slow down the electrons in the beam.

deceleration—The act or process of moving, or of causing to move, with decreasing speed; the state of so moving.

deceleration time—In a computer, the time interval between the completion of the reading or writing of a record on a magnetic tape and the time when the tape stops moving.

deception—Deliberate production of false or misleading echoes on enemy radar by the radiation of spurious signals synchronized to the radar or by the reradiation of the radar pulses from extraneous reflectors.

deception device—A device that works to make unfriendly signals either unusable or misleading.

deci—Prefix meaning one-tenth (10^{-1}).

decibel—Abbreviated db. The standard unit for expressing transmission gain or loss and relative power levels. The term "dbm" is used, when a power of one milliwatt is the reference level. Db indicates the ratio of power output to power input:

$$db = 10 \log_{10} \frac{P_1}{P_2}$$

One decibel is 1/10 of a bel.

decibel meter—Also called db meter. An instrument for measuring the electric power level, in decibels, above or below an arbitrary reference level.

decibels above or below 1 milliwatt—The unit used to describe the ratio of the power at any point in a transmission system to a reference level of 1 milliwatt. The ratio expresses decibels above or below this reference level of 1 milliwatt.

decibels above or below 1 watt—A measure of power expressed in decibels to a reference level of 1 watt.

decibels above reference noise—An expression used to describe the ratio of the circuit noise level in a transmission system, at any point, to some arbitrarily chosen reference noise. The expression signifies the reading of a noise meter. Where the circuit noise meter has been adjusted to represent effect under specified conditions, the expression is in adjusted decibels.

decilog—A division of the logarithmic scale used for measuring the logarithm of the ratio of two values of any quantity. The number of decilogs is equal to 10 times the logarithm to the base 10 of the ratio. One decilog therefore corresponds to a ratio of $10^{0.1}$ (i.e. 1.25892+).

decimal—1. Pertaining to a characteristic or property involving a selection, choice, or condition in which there are 10 possibilities. 2. Pertaining to the number representation system with a radix of 10.

decimal attenuator—A system of attenuators arranged so that a voltage or current can be reduced decimally.

decimal notation—The writing of quantities in the decimal numbering system.

decimal numbering system—The popular numbering system using the Arabic numerals 0 through 9 and thus having a base, or radix, of 10. For example, the decimal number 2,345 can be derived in this way:

$$2,000 + 300 + 40 + 5 = 2,345 \text{ or:}$$
$$2 (10^3) + 3 (10^2) + 4 (10^1) + 5 (10^0) = 2,345.$$

In the decimal system, all numbers are obtained by raising the radix (total number of marks, or 10 in this system) to various powers.

decimal point—In a decimal number, the point which marks the place between integral and fractional powers of 10.

decimal-to-binary conversion—The mathematical process of converting a number written in the scale of 10 into the same number written in the scale of 2.

decimetric waves—1. Electromagnetic waves having wavelengths between 0.1 and 1 meter. 2. Ultrahigh frequency band; 300 MHz to 3 GHz.

decineper—One-tenth of a neper.

decinormal calomel electrode—A calomel electrode containing a decinormal potassium chloride solution.

decision—In a computer, the process of determining further action on the basis of the relationship of two similar items of data.

decision box—On a flowchart, a rectangle or other symbol used to mark a choice or branching in the sequence of programming of a digital computer.

decision element—In computers or data-handling systems, a circuit which performs a logical operation—such as AND, OR, NOT, or EXCEPT on one or more binary digits of input information which represent "yes" or "no"—and expresses the result in its output.

declination—The angular difference between the position of a compass needle and the true position of geographical north and south.

declinometer—Also called a compass declinometer. A device for measuring the direction of a magnetic field relative to astronomical or survey coordinates.

decode—In a computer, to obtain a specific output when specific character-coded input lines are activated.

decoder—1. A device for decoding a series of coded signals. 2. In automatic telephone switching, a relay-type translator which determines from the office code of each call the information required for properly recording the call through the switching train. Each decoder has means, such as a cross-connecting field, for establishing the controls desired and readily changing them. Sometimes called matrix. In an electronic computer, a network or system in which a combination of inputs is excited at one time to produce a single output.

decoding—1. The process of obtaining intelligence from a code signal. 2. In multiplex, a process of separating the subcarrier from the main carrier.

decommutation—The process of recovering a signal from the composite signal previously created by a commutation process.

decommutator — Equipment for separating, demodulating, or demultiplexing commutated signals.

decoupling—The reduction of coupling.

decoupling circuit—A circuit used to prevent interaction of one circuit with another.

decoupling network—A network of capacitors and chokes or resistors placed into leads which are common to two or more circuits, to prevent unwanted, harmful interstage coupling.

decoy—A reflecting object used in radar deception, having reflective characteristics of a target.

decrement—1. Progressive diminution in the value of a variable quantity; also the amount by which a variable decreases. When applied to damped oscillations, it is usually called damping factor. 2. A specific part of an instruction word in some binary computers, thus a set of digits.

dee — A hollow, D-shaped accelerating electrode in a cyclotron.

dee line—A structural member that supports the dee of a cyclotron and together with the dee forms the resonant circuit.

de-emphasis—Also called post-emphasis or post-equalization. Introduction of a frequency-response characteristic which is complementary to that introduced in pre-emphasis.

de-emphasis network—A network inserted into a system to restore the pre-emphasized frequency spectrum to its original form.

de-energize—To disconnect a device from its power source.

deep discharge—The withdrawal of all available electrical energy before recharging a cell or battery.

defect — A condition considered potentially hazardous or operationally unsatisfactory and therefore requiring attention.

defect conduction—Hole conduction in the valence band in a semiconductor.

defibrillator—A device used to eliminate fibrillation (irregular beating) of the heart muscle by the application of high-voltage impulses.

definite-purpose relay — A relay with some electrical or mechanical feature which distinguishes it from a general-purpose relay.

definition—1. The fidelity with which the detail of an image is reproduced. When the image is sharp (i.e., has definite lines and boundaries), the definition is said to be good. 2. The degree with which a communication system reproduces sound images or messages.

deflecting coil—An inductor used to produce a magnetic field that will bend the electron beam a desired amount in the cathode-ray tube of an oscilloscope, television receiver, or television camera.

deflecting electrode—An electrode to which a potential is applied in order to deflect an electron beam.

deflecting torque—*See* Torque of an Instrument.

deflection—Movement of the electron beam in a cathode-ray tube as electromagnetic or electrostatic fields are varied to cause the light spot to traverse the face of the tube in a predetermined pattern.

deflection coil—One of the coils in the deflecting yoke.

deflection factor—*See* Deflection Sensitivity.

deflection plane—A plane perpendicular to the cathode-ray-tube axis and containing the deflection center.

deflection plates—Two pairs of parallel electrodes, the pairs set one forward of the other and at right angles to each other, parallel to the axis of the electron stream within an electrostatic cathode-ray tube. An applied potential produces an electric field between each pair. By varying the applied potential, this field may be varied to cause a desired angular displacement of the electron stream.

deflection polarity — The relationship between the direction of displacement of an oscilloscope trace and the polarity of the applied signal wave.

deflection polarity of an oscilloscope—The relationship between the direction of a displacement of the cathode beam and the polarity of the applied signal wave.

deflection sensitivity—Also called deflection factor. The displacement of the electron beam at the target or screen of a cathode-ray tube divided by the change in magnitude of the deflecting field. Deflection sensitivity is usually expressed in millimeters (or inches) per volt applied between the deflecting electrodes, or in millimeters (or inches) per ampere in the deflection coil.

deflection voltage—The voltage applied to the electrostatic plates of a cathode-ray tube to control the movement of the electron beam.

Deflection yoke.

deflection yoke—An assembly of one or more electromagnets for deflecting one or more electron beams.

degassing—The process of driving out and

exhausting the gases of an electron tube occluded in its internal parts.

degausser—Also called automatic degausser and bulk eraser. A device to clarify the color picture by means of coils within the set. The coils deactivate the magnetization which builds up around a color tv set when it is moved around, or when other electrical devices are brought too close to the receiver.

degaussing—Girdling a ship's hull with a web of current-carrying cable that sets up a magnetic field equal in value and opposite in polarity to that induced by the earth's magnetic field, thus rendering the ship incapable of actuating the detonator of a magnetic mine.

degeneracy—The condition in which two or more modes have the same resonant frequency in a resonant device.

degenerate modes—A set of modes having the same resonance frequency (or propagation constant). The members of a set of degenerate modes are not unique.

degenerate parametric amplifier—An inverting parametric device for which the two signal frequencies are identical and equal to one-half the frequency of the pump. (This exact but restrictive definition is often relaxed to include cases where the signals occupy frequency bands which overlap.)

degeneration—*See* Negative Feedback.

degradation—A gradual decline of quality or loss of ability to perform within required limits. The synonym "drift" is often used for electronic devices.

degradation failure—Failure resulting from a gradual change in the performance characteristics of a device or part.

degree of current rectification—The ratio between the average unidirectional current output and the root-mean-square value of the alternating-current input from which it was derived.

degree of voltage rectification—The ratio between the average unidirectional voltage and the root-mean-square value of the alternating voltage from which it was derived.

deion circuit breaker—A circuit breaker built so that the arc that forms when the circuit is broken is magnetically blown into a stack of insulated copper plates, giving the effect of a large number of short arcs in series. Each arc becomes almost instantly deionized when the current drops to zero in the alternating-current cycle, and the arc cannot re-form.

deionization—The process by which an ionized gas returns to its neutral state after all sources of ionization have been removed.

deionization potential—The potential at which ionization of the gas within a gas-filled tube ceases and conduction stops.

deionization time—The time required for the grid of a gas tube to regain control after the anode current has been interrupted.

dekahexadecimal—*See* Sexidecimal Notation.

Dekatron—A cold-cathode counting tube.

delay—The time required for a signal to pass through a device or conductor.

delay circuit—A circuit which delays the passage of a pulse or signal from one part of a circuit to another.

delay coincidence circuit—A coincidence circuit actuated by two pulses, one of which is delayed a specific amount with respect to the other.

delay counter—In a computer, a device that can temporarily delay a program a sufficient length of time for the completion of an operation.

delay distortion—1. Phase-delay distortion (i.e., departure from flatness in the phase delay of a circuit or system over the frequency range required for transmission, or the effect of such departure on a transmitted signal). 2. Also called envelope delay distortion or phase delay. Envelope distortion (i.e., departure from flatness in the envelope delay of a circuit or system over the frequency range required for transmission, or the effect of such departure on a transmitted signal). 3. The amount of variation in delay for various frequency components of the facsimile signal, usually expressed in microseconds from an average delay time.

delayed automatic volume control—Abbreviated delayed avc. An automatic volume-control circuit that acts only on signals above a certain strength. It thus permits reception of weak signals even though they may be fading, whereas normal automatic volume control would make the weak signals even weaker.

delayed avc—*See* Delayed Automatic Volume Control.

delayed contacts—Contacts which are actuated a predetermined time after the start of a (timing) cycle.

delayed ppi—A ppi (plan-position indicator) in which the initiation of the time base is delayed.

delayed repeater satellite—A satellite which stores information obtained from a ground terminal at one location and, upon interrogation by a terminal at a different location, transmits the stored message.

delayed sweep—1. In a cathode-ray tube, a type of sweep which is not allowed to begin for a while after being triggered by the initiating pulse. 2. A sweep that has been delayed either by a predetermined period or by a period determined by an additional independent variable.

delay equalizer—1. A device which adds delay at certain frequencies to a circuit in a way to reduce the delay distortion. 2. A corrective network which is designed to make the phase delay or envelope delay of a circuit or system substantially constant over a desired frequency range.

delay/frequency distortion—That form of distortion which occurs when the envelope delay of a circuit or system is not constant

Mercury type.

Prism type.

Delay lines.

over the frequency range required for transmissions.

delay line—1. A real or artificial transmission line or equivalent device designed to delay a signal or wave for a predetermined length of time. 2. A specially constructed cable used in the luminance channel of a color receiver to delay the luminance signal.

delay-line memory—*See* Delay-Line Storage.

delay-line register—An acoustic or electric delay line in an electronic computer, usually one or an integral number of words in length, together with input, output, and circulation circuits.

delay-line storage—Also called delay-line memory. In an electronic computer, a storage or memory device consisting of a delay line and a means for regenerating and reinserting information into it.

delay multivibrator—A monostable multivibrator that produces an output pulse a predetermined time after it is triggered by an input pulse.

delay relay—Also called time-delay relay. A relay in which there is a delay between the time it is energized or de-energized and the contacts open or close.

delay time—The amount of time one signal is behind (lags) another.

delay timer—A term sometimes used to designate a timer which is primarily used for energizing (or de-energizing) a load at the end of a timed period. (*See* Time Delay Relay—preferred meaning.)

delay unit—The unit of a radar system in which pulses may be delayed a controllable amount.

deletion record—In a computer, a new record to replace or remove an existing record in a master file.

delimiter—1. In a computer, a character that limits a string of characters and therefore cannot be a member of the string. 2. Also called separator. A flag that separates and organizes items of data.

Dellinger effect—*See* Radio Fadeout.

delta—1. The Greek letter delta (Δ) represents any quantity which is much smaller than any other quantity of the same units appearing in the same problem. 2. In a magnetic cell, the difference between the partial-select outputs of the same cell in a one state and in a zero state.

delta circuit—A three-phase circuit in which the windings of the system are connected in the form of a closed ring, and the instantaneous voltages around the ring equal zero. There is no common or neutral wire, so the system is used only for three-wire systems or generators.

delta connection—In a three-phase system, the terminal connections. So called because they are triangular like the Greek letter delta.

delta match—*See* Y Match.

delta matched antenna—Also called Y antenna. A single-wire antenna (usually one half-wavelength long) to which the leads of an open-wire transmission line are connected in the shape of a Y. The flared part of the Y matches the transmission line to the antenna. The top of the Y is not cut, giving the matching section its triangular shape of the Greek letter *delta*, hence the name.

delta matching transformer—An impedance device used to match the impedance of an open-wire transmission line to an antenna. The two ends of the transmission line are fanned out so that the impedance of the line gradually increases. The ends of the transmission line are attached to the antenna at points of equal impedance, symmetrically located with respect to the center of the antenna.

delta modulation—A means of encoding analog signals in control and communication systems. The output of the delta encoder is a single weighed digital pulse train which may be decoded at the receiving end to reconstruct an original analog signal.

delta network—A set of three branches connected in series to form a mesh.

delta pulse code modulation—A modulation system that converts audio signals into corresponding trains of digital pulses to pro-

123

vide greater freedom from interference during transmission over wire or radio channels.

delta wave—A brain wave the frequency of which is below 9 hertz.

dem—Abbreviation for demodulator.

demagnetization—Partial or complete reduction of residual magnetism.

demagnetization curve—In the second quadrant of a hysteresis loop, the portion which lies between the residual induction point, B_r, and the coercive force point, H_e.

demagnetization effect—A decrease in internal magnetic field caused by uncompensated magnetic poles at the surface of a sample.

demagnetizer—A device for removing the magnetism which may build up in a recording or playback head.

demagnetizing force—A magnetizing force applied in such a direction that it reduces the residual induction in a magnetized body.

Dember effect—Also known as the photodiffusion effect. The production of a potential difference between two regions of a semiconductor specimen when one is illuminated. This phenomenon is related to the photoelectromagnetic effect, except there is no magnetic field. H. Dember discovered when an illuminated metal plate, producing electrons, is bombarded by other electrons from an outside source, the photoelectric emission increases because, in addition to photoelectrons, secondary electrons are also knocked out by bombardment.

demodulation — Also called detection. The operation on a previously modulated wave in such a way that it will have substantially the same characteristics as the original modulating wave.

demodulator—1. A device which operates on a carrier wave to recover the wave with which the carrier was originally modulated. 2. A facsimile device which detects an amplitude-modulated signal and produces the modulating frequency as a direct current of varying amplitude. This type of unit is used to provide a keying signal for a frequency-shift exciter unit for radio facsimile transmission. 3. A device which receives tones from a transmission circuit and converts them to electrical pulses, or bits, which may be accepted by a business machine.

*R MAY BE INCREASED IN VALUE TO REDUCE CIRCUIT LOADING

Demodulator probe.

demodulator probe—A probe designed for use with an oscilloscope, for displaying modulated high-frequency signals.

demountable tube — A high-power electron tube having a metal envelope with porcelain insulation. Can be taken apart for inspection and for renewal of electrodes.

demultiplexer—A device used to separate two or more signals that were previously combined by a compatible multiplexer and are transmitted over a single channel.

demultiplexing circuit — A circuit that is used to separate the signals that have been combined for transmission by multiplex.

denary band — A band having frequency limits with the ratio of $f_b/f_a = 10$.

dendrite — A semiconductor crystal with a heavily-branched, tree-like structure which grows from the nucleus as the metal becomes solidified.

dendritic growth—A technique of producing semiconductor crystals in long, uniform ribbons with optically flat surfaces.

dense binary code—A binary code in which all the possible states of the pattern are used.

densitometer—An instrument for measuring the optical density (photographic transmission, photographic reflection, visual transmission, and so forth) of a material.

density—1. A measure of the light-reflecting or -transmitting properties of an area. 2. The mass per unit volume. The specific gravity of a body is the ratio of a density to the density of a standard substance. Water and air are commonly used as the standard substances. 3. Amount per unit cross-sectional area (e.g., current, magnetic flux, or electrons in a beam).

density modulation—Modulation of an electron beam by varying the density of the electrons in the beam with time.

dentaphone—A device by which deaf persons can hear sounds via the teeth.

dependent linearity—Nonlinearity errors expressed as a deviation from a desired straight line of fixed slope and/or position.

depletion field-effect transistor (FET) — An active semiconductor device in which the main current is controlled by the depletion width of a P-N junction.

depletion layer—Also called barrier layer. In a semiconductor, the region in which the mobile-carrier charge density is insufficient to neutralize the net fixed charge density of donors and acceptors.

depletion-layer capacitance — Also called barrier capacitance. Capacitance of the depletion layer of a semiconductor. It is a function of the reverse voltage.

depletion-layer rectification — Also called barrier-layer rectification. The rectification that appears at the contact between dissimilar materials, such as a metal-to-semiconductor contact or a PN junction, as the energy levels on each side of the discontinuity are readjusted.

depletion-layer transistor—Any of several types of transistors which rely directly for their operation on the motion of carriers through depletion layers (for example, a spacistor).

depletion region—Also referred to as the space charge, barrier, or intrinsic region. In a semiconductor, the region containing the acceptor and donor ions the excess holes or electrons of which have been removed.

depolarization—The process of preserving the activity of a primary cell by the addition of a substance to the electrolyte. This substance combines chemically with the hydrogen gas as it forms, thus preventing excessive buildup of hydrogen bubbles.

depolarizer—A chemical used in some primary cells to prevent formation of hydrogen bubbles at the positive electrode.

deposition — The application, usually in a vacuum, of a material to a substrate by means of an electrical, chemical, screening, or vapor method.

depth finder—*See* Fathometer.

depth of cut—The depth to which the recording stylus penetrates the lacquer of a recording disc.

depth of heating—The depth at which effective dielectric heating can be confined below the surface of a material when the applicator electrodes are placed adjacent to only one surface.

depth of modulation—In a radio-guidance system obtaining directive information from the two spaced lobes of a directional antenna, the ratio of the difference in total field strength of the two lobes to the field strength of the greater lobe at a given point in space.

depth of penetration—The thickness of a layer extending inward from the surface of a conductor and having the same resistance to direct current as the whole conductor has to alternating current of a given frequency.

depth sounder—*See* Fathometer.

de-Q—To reduce the Q of a tuned circuit, as generally applied to carrier-current transmission systems.

derate—To reduce the voltage, current, or power rating of a device to improve its reliability or to permit operation at high ambient temperatures.

Derating curve.

derating—The reduction in rating of a device or component, especially the maximum power-dissipation rating at higher temperatures.

derating factor — The factor by which the

ratings of component parts are reduced to provide additional safety margins in critical applications or when the parts are subjected to extreme environmental conditions for which their normal ratings do not apply.

derivative action—*See* Rate Action.

derivative control — Automatic control in which the rate of correction is determined by the rate at which the error producing it changes.

derived center channel — A monophonic composite signal derived from the sum or difference of the left and right stereo channels, often fed to an extra speaker to fill in an aural "hole" between the left and right speakers. The signal from a voltage-derived center-channel output must be fed to an external power amplifier before it can drive a speaker. A power-derived center channel can drive a speaker directly.

desensitization — 1. The saturation of one component (an amplifier, for instance) by another so that the first cannot perform its proper function. 2. The reduction in receiver sensitivity due to the presence of a high-level off-channel signal overloading the radio-frequency amplifier or mixer stages, causing automatic gain control action.

design-center rating—Values of operating and environmental conditions which should not be exceeded under normal conditions in a bogey electron device.

design for maintainability—Those features and characteristics of design of an item that reduce requirements for tools, test equipment, facilities, spares, highly skilled personnel, etc., and improve the capability of the item to accept maintenance actions.

design-maximum rating—Values of operating and environmental conditions which should not be exceeded under the worst possible conditions in a bogey electron device.

design proof test—A test used to verify that a design specification meets the overall functional requirements of the finished product.

Desk-Fax — Trade name of Western Union Telegraph Co. for a small facsimile transceiver employed principally in short-line telegraph service.

desk-top computer — A computer that requires no formally prepared stored program entered in a special language. Most desk-top computers are operated like adding machines or mechanical calculators.

destination register—In a computer, a register into which data is being placed.

Destriau effect—Sustained emission of light by suitable phosphor powders embedded in an insulator and subjected only to the action of an alternating electric field.

destructive read-out — In a computer, the destruction of data during the process of sensing.

destructive test — Any test resulting in the destruction or drastic deterioration of the test specimen.

detail—A measure of the sharpness of a recorded facsimile copy or reproduced image. Generally related to the number of lines scanned per inch. Defined as the square root of the ratio between the number of scanning lines per unit length and the definition in the direction of the scanning line.

detail contrast—The ratio of the amplitude of the high-frequency components of a video signal to the amplitude of the reference low-frequency component.

detection—*See* Demodulation.

detectophone—An instrument for secretly listening in on a conversation. A high-sensitivity, nondirectional microphone is concealed in the room and connected to an amplifier and headphones or recorder remotely located. Sometimes the microphone feeds into a wired-wireless transmitter that broadcasts over power lines, to permit the listener to be farther away.

detector—1. A device for effecting the process of detection or demodulation. 2. A mixer or converter in a superheterodyne receiver; often referred to as a "first detector." 3. A device that produces an electrical output that is a measure of the radiation incident on the device. 4. A rectifier tube, crystal, or dry disc by which a modulation envelope on a carrier or the simple on-off state of a carrier may be made to drive a lower-frequency device.

detector balanced bias—A controlling circuit used in radar systems for anticlutter purposes.

detector circuit—That portion of a receiver which recovers the modulation signal from the r-f carrier wave.

detector probe—A probe containing a high-frequency rectifying element such as a crystal diode or a tube. Used with an oscilloscope, vacuum-tube voltmeter, or signal tracer for recovering the modulation from a carrier.

detent—1. A stop or other holding device, such as a pin, lever, etc., on a ratchet wheel. 2. Switch action typified by a gradual increase in force to a position at which there is an immediate and marked reduction in force.

detune—To change the inductance and/or capacitance of a tuned circuit and thereby cause it to be resonant at other than the desired frequency.

deuterium—Heavy hydrogen, so called because it weighs twice as much as ordinary hydrogen. The nucleus of heavy hydrogen is a deuteron.

deuteron—Also called deuton. The nucleus of an atom of heavy hydrogen (deuterium) containing one proton and one neutron. Deuterons are often used as atomic projectiles in atom smashers.

deviation—1. The difference between the actual and specified values of a quantity. 2. In frequency modulation, the difference between the instantaneous frequency during modulation and the carrier frequency. 3. A

departure from specification requirements for which approval is obtained from the consumer prior to occurrence of the departure from specification requirements.

deviation absorption—Absorption that occurs at frequencies near the critical frequency. Occurs in conjunction with the slowing up of radio waves near the critical frequency, upon reflection from the ionosphere.

deviation distortion—Distortion caused by inadequate bandwidth, amplitude-modulation rejection, or discriminator linearity in an f-m receiver.

deviation ratio—In frequency modulation, the ratio of the maximum change in carrier frequency to the highest modulating frequency.

deviation sensitivity—The smallest frequency deviation that produces a specified output power in f-m receivers.

device—1. A single discrete conventional electronic device such as a resistor or transistor, or a microelectronic circuit. 2. Also called item. Any subdivision of a system.

device complexity—The number of circuit elements within an integrated circuit.

Dewar flask—A container with double walls. The space between the walls is evacuated, and the surfaces bounding this space are silvered.

dew point—The temperature at which condensation first occurs when a vapor is cooled.

DF—Abbreviation for direction finder or dissipation factor.

DF antenna—Any antenna combination included in a direction finder for obtaining the phase or amplitude reference of the received signal. May be a single or orthogonal loop, an adcock, or spaced differentially-connected dipoles.

DF antenna system—One or more DF antennas and their combining circuits and feeder systems, together with the shielding and all electrical and mechanical items up to the receiver input terminals.

Diac—Two-lead alternating-current switch semiconductor.

diagnostic routine—An electronic-computer routine designed to locate a malfunction in the computer, a mistake in coding, or both.

diagnotor—In a computer, combined diagnostic and edit routine that questions unusual situations and makes note of the implied results.

diagram—1. Schematics, prints, charts, etc., or any other graphical representation, the purpose of which is to explain rather than to represent. 2. A schematic representation of a sequence of subroutines designed to solve a problem. 3. A coarser and less symbolic representation than a flowchart, frequently including descriptions in English words. 4. A schematic or logical drawing showing the electrical circuit or logical arrangements within a component.

dial—1. A means for indicating the value to

126

which a control knob has been set. 2. A calling device which generates the required number of pulses in a telephone set and thereby establishes contact with the party being called.

dial cable—*See* Dial Cord.

dial cord—Also called dial cable. A braided cord or flexible wire cable connected to a tuning knob so that turning the knob will move the pointer or dial which indicates the frequency to which a radio receiver is tuned. Also used for coupling two shafts together mechanically.

dial light—A small pilot lamp which illuminates the tuning dial of a radio receiver.

dial pulse—Interruption in the direct current flowing through the loop of a calling telephone, produced by the opening and closing of the dial pulse springs of a calling telephone in response to the dialing of a digit. The current in the calling-line loop is interrupted as many times as there are units in the digit dialed—i.e., dialing of the digit 7 generates seven dial pulses (interruptions) in current flowing through the loop of the calling telephone.

dial register—*See* Standard Register of a Motor Meter.

dial tone—A hum or other tone employed in a dial telephone system to indicate that the line is not busy and that the equipment is ready for dialing.

diamagnetic—Term applied to a substance with a negative magnetic susceptibility.

diamagnetic material—A material which is less magnetic than air, or in which the intensity of magnetization is negative. There is no known material in which this effect has more than a very feeble intensity. Bismuth is the leading example of materials of this class.

diamond antenna—Also called a rhombic antenna. A horizontal antenna having four conductors that form a diamond, or rhombus.

diamond lattice—The crystal structure of germanium and silicon (as well as a diamond).

diamond stylus—A phonograph pickup with a ground diamond as its point.

diapason—The unique fundamental tone color of organ music.

diaphragm—1. A flexible membrane used in various electroacoustic transducers for producing audio-frequency vibrations when actuated by electric impulses, or electric impulses when actuated by audio-frequency vibrations. (*Also see* Iris.) 2. In electrolytic cells, a porous or permeable membrane, usually flexible, separating the anode and cathode compartments. 3. In waveguide technique, a thin plate, or plates, placed transversely across the waveguide, not completely closing it, and usually introducing a reactance component.

diathermy—Therapeutic heating of tissues beneath the skin by applying an r-f current to some part of the body.

diathermy interference—A form of television interference caused by diathermy equipment, resulting in a horizontal herringbone pattern across the picture.

diathermy machine—A medical apparatus consisting of an r-f oscillator frequently followed by r-f amplifier stages, used to generate high-frequency currents that produce heat within some predetermined part of the body for therapeutic purposes.

dichroic mirror—A special mirror through which all light frequencies pass except those for the color which the mirror is designed to reflect.

dichroism—A property of an optical material which causes light of some wavelengths to be absorbed when the incident light has its electric-field vector in a particular orientation and not absorbed when the electric-field vector has other orientations.

dicing—The process of sawing a crystal wafer into blanks.

die—*See* Chip.

die bonding—A bonding process in which chips are soldered to the substrate.

dielectric—1. The insulating (nonconducting) medium between the two plates of a capacitor. Typical dielectrics are air, wax-impregnated paper, plastic, mica, and ceramic. A vacuum is the only perfect dielectric. 2. A medium capable of recovering, as electrical energy, all or part of the energy required to establish an electric field (voltage stress). The field, or voltage stress, is accompanied by displacement or charging currents.

dielectric absorption—Also called dielectric hysteresis or dielectric soak. A characteristic of dielectrics which determines the length of time a capacitor takes to deliver the total amount of its stored energy. It manifests itself as the reappearance of a potential on the electrodes after the capacitor has been discharged. Its magnitude depends on the charge and discharge time of the capacitor.

dielectric amplifier—An amplifier employing a device similar to an ordinary capacitor, but with a polycrystalline dielectric which exhibits a ferromagnetic effect.

dielectric antenna—An antenna in which a dielectric is the major component producing the required radiation pattern.

dielectric breakdown—An abrupt increase in the flow of electric current through a dielectric material as the applied electric field strength exceeds a critical value.

dielectric breakdown voltage—The voltage between two electrodes at which electric breakdown of the specimen occurs under prescribed test conditions. Also called electric breakdown voltage, breakdown voltage, or hi-pot.

dielectric capacity—The inductivity or specific inductive capacity of a substance, being its ability to convey the influence of an electrified body.

dielectric constant—The ratio of the capacitance of a capacitor with the given dielectric to the capacitance of a capacitor having air for its dielectric but otherwise identical. Also called permittivity, specific inductive capacity, or capacitivity.

dielectric current—The current flowing at any instant through the surface of an isotropic dielectric which is in a changing electric field.

dielectric dissipation—*See* Loss Tangent.

dielectric dissipation factor—The cotangent of the dielectric phase angle of a material.

dielectric fatigue—The property of some dielectrics in which the insulating quality decreases after a voltage has been applied for a considerable length of time.

dielectric guide—A waveguide made of a solid dielectric material through which the waves travel.

TOP OF PRESS

METAL PLATES   HIGH-FREQUENCY OSCILLATOR

BASE OF PRESS

Dielectric heating.

dielectric heating—A method of raising the temperature of a nominally insulating material by sandwiching it between two plates to which an r-f voltage is applied. The material acts as a dielectric, and its internal losses cause it to heat up.

dielectric hysteresis—*See* Dielectric Absorption.

dielectric isolation—The electrical isolation of monolithic integrated circuit elements from each other by dielectric material rather than by reverse biased P-N junctions.

dielectric lens—A lens used with microwave antennas; it is made of dielectric material so that it refracts radio waves similar to the way an optical lens refracts light waves.

dielectric loss—The power dissipated by a dielectric as the friction of its molecules opposes the molecular motion produced by an alternating electric field.

dielectric loss angle—The complement of the dielectric phase angle (i.e., the dielectric phase angle minus 90°).

dielectric loss factor—The product of the dielectric constant of a material times the tangent of the dielectric loss angle. Also called dielectric loss index.

dielectric loss index—*See* Dielectric Loss Factor.

dielectric matching plate—In waveguide technique, a dielectric plate used as an impedance transformer for matching purposes.

dielectric mirror—A highly frequency-selective, multilayer dielectric reflector acting by partial reflection of light at the interface between materials of unequal refractive indices.

dielectric phase angle—The angular difference in phase between the sinusoidal alternating voltage applied to a dielectric and the component of the resultant alternating current having the same period.

dielectric phase difference—*See* Dielectric Loss Angle.

dielectric polarization—*See* Polarization, 3.

dielectric power factor—The cosine of the dielectric phase angle.

dielectric rating—Standard test voltages and frequencies above which failure occurs between specified points in a relay structure.

dielectric soak—*See* Dielectric Absorption.

dielectric strength—The maximum voltage a dielectric can withstand without rupturing. Usually expressed as volts per mil. Also called: electric strength, breakdown strength, and electric field strength.

dielectric susceptibility—The ratio of the polarization in a dielectric to the electric intensity responsible for it.

dielectric tests—1. Tests which consist of the application of a voltage higher than the rated voltage for a specified time for the purpose of determining the adequacy against breakdown of insulating materials and spacings under normal conditions. 2. The testing of insulating materials by the application of a constantly increasing voltage until failure occurs.

dielectric waveguide—A waveguide constructed from a dielectric (nonconductive) substance.

difference amplifier—*See* Differential Amplifier.

difference channel—In a stereophonic sound system, an audio channel that handles the difference between the signals in the left and right channels.

difference detector—A detector circuit in which the output is a function of the difference between the peak or rms amplitudes of the input waveforms.

difference frequency—1. A signal representing, in essence, the difference between the left and right sound channels of a stereophonic sound system. 2. One of the output frequencies of a converter. It is the difference between the two input frequencies.

difference in depth modulation—In directive systems employing overlapping lobes with modulated signals, a ratio obtained by subtracting from the percentage of modulation of the larger signal the percentage of modulation of the smaller signal and dividing by 100.

difference of potential—The voltage or electrical pressure existing between two points. It will result in a flow of electrons whenever a circuit is established between the two points.

differential—1. A planetary gear system which adds or subtracts angular movements transmitted to two components and delivers the answer to a third. Widely used for adding and subtracting shaft movements in servo systems and for addition and subtraction in computing machines. 2. In electronics, the difference between two levels.

SPUR GEAR - FIXED TO SPIDER SHAFT
COLLAR (2)
BALL OR OIL-LESS BEARINGS AS DESIRED
SPIDER CROSS-ARM
JUNCTION BLOCK
SHAFT HANGER
SPIDER BEVEL GEAR BEARING MOUNTED ON CROSS-ARM
CLAMPING RING FOR MOUNTING SPUR GEAR TO END BEVEL GEAR (2)
END BEVEL GEARS BEARING MOUNTED ON SPIDER SHAFT (2)
SPIDER SHAFT
SHAFT HANGER
BALANCING BLOCK
SPUR GEAR - FIXED TO BEVEL GEAR (2)

Differential.

differential amplifier—An amplifier having two similar input circuits so connected that they respond to the difference between two voltages or currents, but effectively suppress like voltages or currents.

differential angle—The total angle from the operation to the releasing position in a mercury switch.

differential analyzer — 1. A mechanical or electrical device primarily designed and used to solve differential equations. 2. An analog computer designed primarily for solving or analyzing many types of differential equations.

differential capacitance — The derivative with respect to voltage of a capacitor charge characteristic at a given point on the curve.

differential capacitance characteristic — The function that relates differential capacitance to voltage.

differential capacitor—A variable capacitor having two similar sets of stator plates and one set of rotor plates. When the rotor is turned, the capacitance of one section is increased while the capacitance of the other section is decreased.

differential cooling—A lowering of temperature which takes place at a different rate at various points on an object or surface.

differential delay — The difference between the maximum and the minimum frequency delays occurring across a band.

differential discriminator—A discriminator that passes only pulses having amplitudes between two predetermined values, neither of which is zero.

differential duplex system—A duplex system in which the sent currents divide through two mutually inductive sections of the receiving apparatus. These sections are connected respectively to the line and to a balancing artificial line in opposite directions. Hence, there is substantially no net effect on the receiving apparatus. The received currents pass mainly through one section, or through the two sections in the same direction, and operate the apparatus.

differential flutter — Speed-change errors which occur at different magnitudes, fre-

quencies, or phases across the width of a magnetic tape.

differential gain—The ratio of the differential output signal of a differential amplifier divided by the differential input signal causing that output.

differential gain control—Also called gain-sensitivity control. A device for altering the gain of a radio receiver in accordance with an expected change of signal level, in order to reduce the amplitude differential between the signals at the receiver output.

differential galvanometer—A galvanometer having two similar but opposed coils, so that their currents tend to neutralize each other. A zero reading is obtained when the currents are equal.

differential gap—The difference between two target values, one of which applies to an upswing of conditions and the other to a downswing.

differential generator—A synchro differential generator driven by a servo system.

differential impedance — The internal impedance observed between the input terminals of an operational amplifier.

differential input—An input circuit that rejects voltages which are the same at both input terminals and amplifies the voltage difference between the two input terminals. May be either balanced or floating and may also be guarded.

differential-input amplifier — An amplifier in which the output is ideally a function only of the difference between the signals applied to its two inputs, both signals being measured with respect to a common "low" or "ground" reference point.

differential-input capacitance—The capacitance between the inverting and noninverting input terminals.

differential-input impedance — The impedance between the inverting and noninverting input terminals of a differential amplifier.

differential-input measurement — Also called floating input. A measurement in which the two inputs to a differential amplifier are connected to two points in a circuit under test and the amplifier displays the difference voltage between the points. In this type of measurement, each input of the amplifier acts as a reference for the other, and ground connections are used only for safety reasons.

differential-input resistance — The resistance between the inverting and noninverting input terminals of a differential amplifier.

differential-input voltage — The maximum voltage that can be applied across the input terminals of a differential amplifier without damaging the amplifier.

differential-input voltage range—The range of voltages that may be applied between input terminals without forcing the circuit to operate outside its specifications.

differential-input voltage rating — The maximum allowable signal that may be applied between the inverting and noninverting inputs of a differential amplifier without damaging the amplifier.

differential instrument—A galvanometer or other measuring instrument having two circuits or coils, usually identical, through which currents flow in opposite directions. The difference or differential effect of these currents actuates the indicating pointer.

differential microphone—*See* Double-Button Carbon Microphone.

differential-mode signal—A signal that is applied between the two ungrounded terminals of a balanced three-terminal system.

differential modulation—A type of modulation in which the choice of the significant condition for any signal element is dependent on the choice for the previous signal element.

differential permeability—The ratio of the positive increase of normal induction to the positive increase of magnetizing force when these increases are minute.

differential phase—The difference in phase shift through a television system for a small, high-frequency sine-wave signal at two stated levels of a low-frequency signal on which the first signal is superimposed.

differential phase-shift keying—A modulation scheme in which the information is conveyed by changes in carrier phase during one interval relative to the preceding interval.

differential pressure — The difference in pressure between two pressure sources.

differential pressure transducer — A pressure transducer that accepts simultaneously two independent pressure sources, and the output of which is proportional to the pressure difference between the sources.

differential protective relay — A protective device which functions on a percentage or phase angle or other quantitative difference of two currents or of some other electrical quantities.

differential relay — A relay with multiple windings that functions when the voltage, current, or power difference between the windings reaches a predetermined value. The power difference may result from the algebraic addition of the multiple inputs.

differential selsyn—A selsyn in which both the rotor and the stator have similar windings that are spread 120° apart. The position of the rotor corresponds to the algebraic sum of the fields produced by the stator and rotor.

differential synchro—*See* Synchro Differential Generator *and* Synchro Differential Motor.

differential transducer—A device capable of simultaneously measuring two separate stimuli and providing an output proportional to the difference between them.

Differential transformer.

differential transformer—Also called linear variable-differential transformer. 1. A transformer used to join two or more sources of signals to a common transmission line. 2. An electromechanical device which continuously translates displacement or position change into a linear a-c voltage.

differential voltage gain—The ratio of the change in output signal voltage at either terminal or a differential device to the change in signal voltage applied to either input terminal, all voltages measured to ground.

differential winding—A coil winding so arranged that its magnetic field opposes that of a nearby coil.

differential-wound field—A type of motor or generator field having both series and shunt coils connected so they oppose each other.

differentiating circuit—Also called differentiator.

differentiating network—*See* Differentiator.

differentiator—1. An analog computer device which produces an output proportional to the derivative of the one variable with respect to another, usually time. 2. A transducer or circuit the output waveform of

No amplification.

Amplification.

$$E_O = T \frac{dE_I}{dT} \quad (T = RC)$$

Formula.

Differentiator.

which is the time derivative of its input waveform. Such a transducer or circuit preceding a frequency modulator makes the combination a phase modulator, or following a phase detector makes the combination a frequency detector. Its ratio of output amplitude to input amplitude is proportional to the frequency, and its output phase leads its input phase by 90°. 3. A circuit which produces an output voltage substantially in proportion to the rate of change of the input voltage or current. Differentiating circuits employ time constants that are short compared to the duration of the pulse applied, thus differentiating the input pulse.

diffracted wave—A radio, sound, or light wave which has struck an object and been bent or deflected, other than by reflection or refraction.

diffraction—1. The bending of radio, sound, or light waves as they pass through an object or barrier, thereby producing a diffracted wave. 2. The phenomenon whereby waves traveling in straight paths bend around an obstacle.

diffused-alloy transistor—Also called drift transistor. A transistor in which the semiconductor wafer is subjected to gaseous diffusion to produce a nonuniform base region, after which alloy junctions are formed in the same manner as for an alloy-junction transistor. It may also have an intrinsic region to give a PNIP unit.

diffused-base transistor—Also called graded-base transistor. A type of transistor made by combining diffusion and alloy techniques. A nonuniform base region and the collector-to-base junction are formed by gaseous dissemination into a semiconductor wafer that constitutes the collector region. Then the emitter-to-base junction is formed by a conventional alloy process on the base side of the diffused wafer.

diffused device—A semiconductor device in which a base, usually of silicon, has successive layers of P and N characteristics diffused upon and into the base by means of a series of masks and around which P and N materials, usually phosphorus and boron, adhere to the base by gaseous diffusion in a high-temperature furnace. It is possible to build areas of resistance, capacitance, and "active" diodes and transistors into the base, creating an entire circuit. Performance is poor in the presence of radiation.

diffused-emitter-and-base transistor—Also called double-diffused transistor. A semiconductor wafer which has been subjected to gaseous dissemination of both N- and P-type impurities to form two PN junctions in the original semiconductor material.

diffused-emitter-and-collector transistor—A transistor in which both the emitter and collector are made by a dissemination process.

diffused junction—A junction formed by the dissemination of an impurity within a semiconductor crystal.

diffused-junction rectifier—A semiconductor diode in which the PN junction is produced by diffusion.

Diffused-junction silicon transistor wafer.

diffused-junction transistor—A transistor in which the emitter and collector electrodes have been formed by diffusion of an impurity into the semiconductor wafer without heating.

diffused-layer resistor—A resistor formed by including an appropriate pattern in the photomask to define diffusion areas.

diffused mesa transistor—A transistor in which the collector-base junction is formed by gaseous diffusion, and the emitter-base junction is formed either by gaseous diffusion or by an evaporated metal strip. The collector-base junction is then defined by etching away the undesired parts of the emitter and base regions, thus producing a mesa.

diffused planar transistor—A transistor made by two gaseous diffusions, but in which the collector-base junction is defined by oxide masking. Junctions are formed beneath this protective oxide layer with the result that the device has lower reverse currents and good d-c gain at low currents.

diffused sound—Sound which has uniform energy density, meaning the energy flux is equal in all parts of a given region.

diffused transistor—A transistor in which the emitter and collector junctions are both formed by diffusion.

diffused transmission—The total net transmission, by a medium or device, of light that is neither perfectly Lambertian nor parallel. Often used interchangeably with the term "gross transmission."

diffusion—1. The movement of carriers from a region of high concentration to regions of lower concentration. 2. Migration of atoms from one substance into another substance.

diffusion capacitance—The capacitance of a forward-biased PN junction.

diffusion constant—The quotient of diffusion-current density in a homogeneous semiconductor, divided by the charge-carrier concentration gradient. It is equal to the drift mobility times the average thermal energy per unit charge of carriers.

diffusion current—The current produced when charges move by diffusion.

diffusion length—In a homogeneous semiconductor, the average distance the minority carriers move between generation and recombination.

diffusion process—The method of producing junctions by disseminating acceptors or donors into a semiconductor at a high temperature.

diffusion transistor—A transistor relying on the dissemination of carriers, donors, or acceptors for carrying current.

digiralt — A system of high-resolution radar altimetry in which pulse-modulated radar and high-performance time-to-digital conversion techniques are combined.

digit—One of the symbols, 0, 1, 2, 3, 4, 5, 6, 7, 8, and 9, used in numbering in the scale of 10. One of these symbols, when used in a scale of numbering to the base n, expresses integral values ranging from 0 to $n-1$ inclusive.

digital — Using numbers expressed in digits and in a certain scale of notation to represent all the variables that occur in a problem.

digital circuit—A circuit which operates like a switch—i.e., it is either "on" or "off."

digital communications—A system of telecommunications employing a nominally discontinuous signal that changes in frequency, amplitude, or polarity.

Block diagram of digital computer.

digital computer—An electronic calculator that operates with numbers expressed directly as digits, as opposed to the directly measurable quantities (voltage, resistance, etc.) in an analog computer. In other words, the digital computer counts (as does an adding machine); the analog computer measures a quantity (as does a voltmeter).

digital data — Data represented in discrete, discontinuous form, as contrasted with analog data represented in continuous form. Digital data are usually represented by means of coded characters (e.g., numbers, signs, symbols, etc.).

digital data-handling system — The electronic equipment which receives digital data, operates on it in a suitable manner, records it in a suitable manner, records it on a suit-

able medium, and presents it directly to a computer or a display.

digital information display—The presentation of digital information in tabular form on the face of a digital information display tube.

digital output—An output signal which represents the size of a stimulus or input signal in the form of a series of discrete quantities which are coded to represent digits in a system of numerical notation. This type of output is to be distinguished from one which provides a continuous rather than a discrete output signal.

digital phase shifter—A device which provides a signal phase shift by the application of a control pulse. A reversal of phase shift requires a control pulse of opposite polarity.

digital readout indicator—An indicator that reads directly in numerical form, as opposed to an analog indicator needle and scale.

digital rotary transducer—A rotating device utilizing an optical sensor that produces a serial binary output as a result of shaft rotation.

digital signals — Discrete or discontinuous signals whose various states are discrete intervals apart.

digital-to-analog converter — A computing device that changes digital quantities into physical motion or into a voltage (i.e., a number output into turns of a potentiometer).

digital voltmeter—An indicator which provides a digital readout of measured voltage rather than a pointer indication.

digit compression — In a computer, any of several techniques used to pack digits.

digitize—To convert an analog measurement of a physical variable into a number expressed in digits in a scale or notation.

digitizer—A device which converts analog data into numbers expressed in digits in a system of notation.

digit selector — In a computer, a device for separating a card column into individual pulses that correspond to punched row positions.

digit-transfer bus—The main wire or wires used to transfer information (but not control signals) among the various registers in a digital computer.

diheptal base—Also called diheptal socket. A vacuum-tube base having 14 pins (such as the base of a cathode-ray tube).

diheptal socket—*See* Diheptal Base.

dimensional stability—The ability of a body to maintain precise shape and size.

dimmer—A control for varying the intensity of illumination of a pilot, scale, or dial light.

D-indicator—A radar indicator which combines Types B and C indicators. The signal appears as a bright spot, with azimuth angle as the horizontal coordinate and elevation angle as the vertical coordinate. Each horizontal trace is expanded vertically by a com-

Diheptal socket.

pressed time sweep to facilitate separation of the signal from noise and to give a rough range indication.

SILICON DIODE

Diode.

diode—A two-terminal device which will conduct electricity more easily in one direction than in the other.

diode amplifier—A parametric amplifier that uses a special diode in a cavity. Used to amplify signals at frequencies as high as 6,000 MHz.

diode assembly—A single structure of more than one diode.

diode characteristic—The composite electrode characteristic of a multielectrode tube, taken with all electrodes except the cathode connected together.

Diode detector.

diode detector—A diode used in a demodulation, or detection, circuit.

diode gate—An AND gate that uses diodes as switching elements.

diode laser—A PN junction semiconductor electron device which converts direct forward-bias electrical input (pump power) directly into coherent optical output power via

a process of stimulated emission in the region near the junction. Called laser diodes, injected lasers, coherent electroluminescence devices, semiconductor lasers.

diode limiter—A circuit employing a diode and used to prevent signal peaks from exceeding a predetermined value.

diode mixer—A diode which mixes incoming radio-frequency and local-oscillator signals to produce an intermediate frequency.

diode peak detector—A diode used in a circuit to indicate when audio peaks exceed a predetermined value.

diode-pentode — A vacuum tube having a diode and a pentode combined in the same envelope.

diode rectification—The conversion of an alternating current into a unidirectional current by means of a two-element device such as a crystal, vacuum tube, etc.

diode switch—A diode in which positive and negative biasing voltages (with respect to the cathode) are applied in succession to the anode in order to pass and block, respectively, other applied waveforms within certain voltage limits. In this way, the diode acts as a switch.

diode transistor logic — Abbreviated DTL. A logic circuit that uses diodes at the input to perform the electronic logic function that activates the circuits transistor output. In monolithic circuits, the DTL diodes are a positive level logic AND function or a negative level OR function. The output transistor acts as an inverter to result in the circuit becoming a positive NAND or a negative NOR function.

diode-triode—A vacuum tube having a diode and triode combined in the same envelope.

diopter—The unit of optical measurement which expresses the refractive power of a lens or prism.

dip—1. A drop in the plate current of a class-C amplifier as its tuned circuits are being adjusted to resonance. 2. The angle between the direction of the earth's magnetic field and the horizontal as measured in a vertical plane.

dip coating—1. A method of applying an insulating coating to a conductor by passing it through an applicator containing the insulating medium in liquid form. The insulation is then sized and passed through ovens to solidify. 2. The insulation so applied.

dip encapsulation — A type of conformal coating—An embedding process in which the insulating material is applied by immersion and without the use of an outer container. The coating conforms generally with the contour of the embedding part or assembly.

diplexer—A coupling unit which allows more than one transmitter to operate together on the same antenna.

diplex operation—The simultaneous transmission or reception of two messages from a single antenna or on a single carrier.

diplex radio transmission — Simultaneous

Diplexer circuit.

transmission of two signals by using a common carrier wave.

diplex reception—The simultaneous reception of two signals having some feature in common—i.e., a single receiving antenna or a single carrier frequency.

dipole—1. *See* Dipole Antenna. 2. A molecule which has an electric moment. For a molecule to be a dipole, the effective center of the positive charges must be at a different point from the center of the negative charges.

$2L = 1/2$ WAVELENGTH $\times$ .95

$$L \text{ (FT)} = \frac{234}{\text{FREQ. (MC)}}$$

Dipole antenna.

dipole antenna—Also called dipole. A straight radiator usually fed in the center. Maximum radiation is produced in the plane normal to its axis. The length specified is the overall length.

dipole disc feed—An antenna, consisting of a dipole near a disc, used to reflect energy to the disc.

dipping—The process of impregnating or coating insulating materials or windings by the simple method of immersion in the liquid insulating material. A step in the process of treating insulating materials or electrical components by immersion in a liquid insulation, followed by draining and curing to provide increased electrical and mechanical protection.

dip soldering—The process of soldering component leads, terminals, and hardware to the conductive pattern on the "bottom" of a printed-circuit board by dipping that side into molten solder or floating it on the surface.

direct-acting recording instrument—An instrument in which the marking device is mechanically connected to or directly operated by the primary detector.

direct capacitance—The capacitance between two conductors excluding stray capacitance that may exist between the two conductors and other conducting elements.

direct-coupled amplifier—A direct-current amplifier in which the plate of one stage is coupled to the grid of the next stage by a direct connection or a low-value resistor.

direct coupling—The association of two or more circuits by means of an inductance, a resistance, a wire or a combination of these so that both direct and alternating currents can be coupled.

direct current—Abbreviated dc. An essentially constant-value current that flows in only one direction.

direct-current amplifier—Also called d-c amplifier. An amplifier capable of boosting d-c voltages. Resistive coupling only is generally employed between stages, but sometimes will be combined with other forms.

direct-current erasing head—A head which uses direct current in magnetic recording to produce the magnetic field required for erasure. Direct-current erasing is achieved by subjecting the medium to a unidirectional field. Such a medium is therefore in a different magnetic state than one erased by alternating current.

direct-current generator—A rotating machine that changes mechanical into electrical energy in the form of direct current. This is accomplished by commutating bars on the armature. The bars make contact with stationary brushes from which the direct-current is taken.

direct-current restorer—The means by which a direct current or low-frequency component is reinserted after transmission. Used in a circuit incapable of transmitting slow variations, but capable of transmitting components of higher frequency.

direct-current transmission—Of television, that form of transmission in which a fixed setting of the controls makes any instantaneous value of signal correspond to the same value of brightness at all times.

direct digital control—Time sharing, or multiplexing, of a computer among many controlled loops.

direct-drive torque motor—A servoactuator which can be directly attached to the load it is to drive. It converts electrical signals directly into sufficient torque to maintain the desired accuracy in a positioning or speed control system.

direct electromotive force—A unidirectional electromotive force in which the changes in values are either zero or so small that they may be neglected.

direct grid bias—The d-c component of grid bias (voltage). Commonly called grid bias.

direct-insert subroutine—*See* Open Subroutine.

direction—The position of one point in space with respect to another.

directional antenna—An antenna which radiates radio waves more effectively in some directions than in others. (The term is usually applied to an antenna the directivity of which is larger than that of a half-wave dipole.)

directional beam—An electromagnetic wave that is concentrated in a given direction.

directional coupler—A junction consisting of two waveguides coupled together in such a manner that a traveling wave in either guide will induce a traveling wave in the same direction in the other guide.

directional filter — A filter used to separate the two frequency ranges in a carrier system where one range of frequencies is used for transmission in one direction and another range of frequencies for transmission in the opposite direction. Also called directional separation filter.

directional gain—*See* Directivity Index.

directional homing—The procedure of following a path in such a way that the target is maintained at a constant relative bearing.

directional hydrophone—A hydrophone having a response that varies significantly with the direction of incidence of sound.

directional lobe—*See* Lobe.

directional microphone—A microphone the response of which varies significantly with the direction of sound. (*Also see* Unidirectional, Bidirectional, *and* Semidirectional Microphone.)

directional pattern—Also called radiation pattern. A graphical representation of the radiation or reception of an antenna as a function of direction. Cross sections are frequently given as vertical and horizontal planes, and principal electric and magnetic polarization planes.

directional power relay — A device which functions on a desired value of power flow in a given direction, or upon reverse power resulting from arcback in the anode or cathode circuits of a power rectifier.

directional relay—A relay which functions in conformance with the direction of power, voltage, current, pulse rotation, etc. *Also see* Polarized Relay.

directional separation filter—*See* Directional Filter.

direction angle—The angle between the antenna base line and a line connecting the center of the base line with the target.

direction cosine — The cosine of the angle between the base line and the line from the center of the base line to the target.

direction finder — Abbreviated DF. Also called radio compass. Apparatus for receiving radio signals and taking their bearings in order to determine their point of origin.

direction finding—The principle and practice of determining a bearing by radio means, using a discriminating antenna system and a radio receiver so that the direc-

tion of an arriving wave, and ostensibly the direction or bearing of a distant transmitter, can be determined.

direction of lay—The lateral direction in which strands or the elements of a cable are wound over the top of the cable. Expressed as right- or left-hand lay, viewed as they recede from the observer.

direction of polarization—For a linearly polarized wave, the direction of the electrostatic field.

direction of propagation—At any point in a homogeneous, isotropic medium, the direction of the time-average energy flow. In a uniform waveguide, the direction of propagation is often taken along the axis. In a uniform lossless waveguide, the direction of propagation at every point is parallel to the axis and in the direction of time-average energy flow.

direction rectifier — A rectifier which supplies a direct-current voltage, the magnitude and polarity of which are determined by the magnitude and relative polarity of an alternating-current selsyn error voltage.

directive gain—In a given direction, 4π times the ratio of the radiation intensity to the total power radiated by the antenna.

directivity diagram of an antenna — The graphical representation of the gain of an antenna in the different directions of space.

directivity factor—1. In acoustics, the directivity factor is equivalent to directivity, as applied to an antenna. 2. Of a transducer used for sound emission, the ratio of the intensity of the radiated sound at a remote point in a free field on the principal axis to the average intensity of the sound transmitted through a sphere passing through the remote point and concentric with the transducer. 3. Of a transducer used for sound reception, the ratio of the square of the electromotive force produced in response to sound waves arriving in a direction parallel to the principal axis of the transducer to the mean square of the electromotive force that would be produced if sound waves having the same frequency and mean square pressure were arriving at the transducer simul-

Direction finder.

taneously from all directions with random phase. The frequency should be specified in both cases.

directivity index — Also called directional gain. A measure of the directional properties of a' transducer. It is the ratio, in decibels, of the average intensity or response over the whole sphere surrounding the projector or hydrophone to the intensity or response on the acoustic axis.

directivity of a directional coupler—Ratio of the power measured at the forward-wave sampling terminals with only a forward wave present in the transmission line, to the power measured at the same terminals when the forward wave reverses direction. This ratio is usually expressed in db and would be infinite for a perfect coupler.

directivity of an antenna—The ratio of the maximum field intensity to the average field intensity at a given distance, implying a maximum value.

directivity signal—A spurious signal present in the output of any coupler because its directivity is not infinite.

direct light—Light from a luminous object such as the sun or an incandescent lamp, as opposed to reflected light.

directly grounded—*See* Solidly Grounded.

directly heated cathode — A wire, or filament, designed to emit the electrons that flow from cathode to plate. This is done by passing a current through the filament; the current heats the filament to the point where electrons are emitted. In an indirectly-heated cathode, the hot filament raises the temperature of a sleeve around the filament; the sleeve then becomes the electron emitter.

director—1. A parasitic antenna element located in the general direction of the major lobe of radiation for the purpose of increasing the radiation in that direction. 2. Equipment in common-carrier telegraph-message switching systems, used to make cross-office selection and connection from an input-line to an output-line equipment in accordance with addresses in the message. 3. A telephone switch which translates the digits dialed into the directing digits actually used to switch the call. 4. Electromechanical equipment which is used to track a moving target in azimuth and angular height, and which, with the addition of other necessary information from an outside source such as a radar set or a range finder, continuously computes firing data and transmits them to the guns.

direct pickup — Transmission of television images without resorting to an intermediate magnetic or photographic recording.

direct piezoelectricity—A name sometimes given to the piezoelectric effect in which an electric charge is developed on a crystal by the application of mechanical stress.

direct-radiator speaker—A speaker in which the radiating element acts directly on the air instead of relying on any other element such as a horn.

direct recording—The production of a visible record without subsequent processing, in response to received signals.

direct-recording magnetic tape—A method of recording using a high-frequency bias in which the electrical input signal is applied to the recording head without alteration.

direct resistance-coupled amplifier — An amplifier in which the plate of one stage is connected either directly or through a resistor to the control grid of the next stage, with the plate-load resistor being common to both stages. Used to amplify small changes in direct current.

direct scanning—In this method, the entire subject is illuminated continuously but the television camera views only one portion of it at a time.

direct sound wave—A wave in an enclosure emitted from a source prior to the time it has undergone its first reflection from a boundary of the enclosure. Frequently a sound wave is said to be direct if it contains reflections that have occurred from surfaces within about 0.05 second after the sound was first emitted.

direct voltage—Also called d-c voltage. A voltage that forces electrons to move through a circuit in the same direction and thereby produce a direct current.

direct wave—A wave that is propagated directly through space, as opposed to one that is reflected from the sky or ground.

direct Wiedemann effect — *See* Wiedemann Effect.

direct-wire circuit—A supervised protective signaling circuit usually consisting of one metallic conductor and a ground return and having signal-receiving equipment responsive to either an increase or a decrease in current.

direct writing recorder — A strip-chart recorder which produces a readable record without further processing.

disc—1. A phonograph record. 2. The blank used in a recorder.

disc capacitor—A small disc-shaped capacitor with a ceramic dielectric, generally used for bypassing or for temperature compensation in tuned circuits.

disc files—A type of storage medium consisting of numbers of discs that rotate; each disc has a special coating for retaining stored information.

disc generator—A capacitive-charge type of voltage generator.

discharge—1. In a storage battery, the conversion of chemical energy into electric energy. 2. The release of energy stored in a capacitor when a circuit is connected between its terminals.

discharge breakdown—Breakdown of a material as a result of degradation due to gas discharges.

discharge key—A device for switching a capacitor suddenly from a charging circuit to a load through which it can discharge.

Direct waves.

discharge lamp—A lamp containing a low-pressure gas or vapor which ionizes and emits light when an electric discharge is passed through it. Fluorescent materials are sometimes used on the inside of the glass envelope to increase the illumination, as in an ordinary fluorescent lamp.

discharge rate — The amount of current a battery will deliver over a given period of time. A slower discharge rate generally results in more efficient use of a battery.

discharge tube—A tube containing a low-pressure gas which passes a current whenever sufficient voltage is applied.

discone antenna—A special form of biconical antenna in which the vertex angle of one cone is 180°.

disconnect—1. To break an electric circuit. 2. To remove the power from an electrical device (colloquially, "to unplug the device"). 3. Also called release. To disengage the apparatus used in a connection and to restore it to its ready condition when not in use.

disconnecting means—A device whereby the current-carrying conductors of a circuit can be disconnected from their source of supply.

disconnect switch (motor circuit switch)—A switch intended for use in a motor branch circuit. It is rated in horsepower, and is capable of interrupting the maximum operating overload current of a motor of the same rating at the rated voltage.

disc pack—A set of magnetic discs that can be removed from a disc storage as one unit.

disc recorder—A recording device in which the sounds are mechanically impressed onto a disc—as opposed to a tape recorder, which impresses the sound magnetically on a tape.

discrete component — A component which has been fabricated prior to its installation (e.g., resistors, capacitors, diodes, and transistors).

discrete part—A separately packaged single circuit element supplying one fundamental property as a lumped characteristic in a given application. Examples: resistor, transistor, diode.

discrete sampling—The lengthening of individual samples so that the sampling process does not deteriorate the intelligence frequency response of the channel.

discrete thin-film component — An individually packaged electronic component having one or more thin films serving as resistive, conductive, and/or insulating elements. Resistors and potentiometers having thin-film metallic resistance elements are examples.

discrimination—1. The difference between losses at specified frequencies, with the system or transducer terminated in specified impedances. 2. In a frequency-modulated system, the detection or demodulation of the imposed variations in the frequency of the carriers. 3. In a tuned circuit, the degree of rejection of unwanted signals.

discriminator—1. A device in which amplitude variations are derived in response to frequency or phase variations. 2. Part of a receiver circuit which removes the desired signal from an incoming frequency-modulated carrier wave by changing modulations in terms of frequency variations into amplitude variations. 3. A facsimile auxiliary device between the radio receiver and the recorder which converts an audio-frequency shift facsimile signal to an amplitude-modulated facsimile signal. 4. A circuit, the output voltage of which varies in amplitude and polarity according to the frequency of the applied signal. It is used as a detector in a frequency-modulated receiver.

discriminator transformer — A transformer used in f-m receivers to convert frequency changes directly to a-f signals.

discriminator tuning unit—A device which tunes the discriminator to a particular subcarrier.

disc-seal tube—Also called lighthouse tube or megatron. An electron tube with disc-shaped electrodes arranged in closely spaced parallel layers, to give a low interelectrode capacitance along with a high power output in the uhf region.

disc storage—1. A storage device that uses magnetic recording on flat rotating discs. 2. The storage of data on the surface of magnetic discs.

dish—A microwave antenna, usually shaped like a parabola, which reflects the radio energy leaving or entering the system.

Dish antenna.

dislocation—In a crystal, a region in which the atoms are not arranged in the perfect crystal-lattice structure.

dispatcher—In a digital computer, the section which transfers the "words" to their proper destinations.

Dispersion by a prism.

dispersion—1. Separation of a wave into its component frequencies. 2. Scattering of a microwave beam as it strikes an obstruction. 3. The property of an optical material which causes some wavelengths of light to be transmited through the material at different velocities, and the velocity is a function of the wavelength. (This causes each wavelength of light to have a different refractive index.) 4. In a magnetostrictive delay line, the variation of a delay as a function of frequency. 5. The frequency difference that can be analyzed in one sweep by a spectrum analyzer. Dispersion can be considered as that frequency width over which sampling can be performed, and is always equal to or less than the frequency range.

dispersive medium—A medium in which the phase velocity of a wave is related to the frequency.

displacement—The vector quantity representing change of position of a particle.

displacement current—A current which exists in addition to ordinary conduction current in a-c circuits. It is proportional to the rate of change of the electric field. The current at right angles to the direction of propagation determined by the rate at which the field energy changes.

displacement of porches—The difference in level between the front and back porch of a television signal.

displacement transducer—A device which converts mechanical energy into electrical energy, usually by the movement of a rod or an armature. The amount of output voltage is determined by the amount the rod or armature is moved.

display—Visual presentation of a received signal on a cathode-ray tube.

display loss—*See* Visibility Factor.

display modes—Each display mode, such as vector, increment, character, point, vector continue, or short vector specifies the manner in which points are to be displayed on the screen.

display primaries—Also called receiver primaries. The red, green, and blue colors produced by a color television receiver and mixed in proper proportions to produce other colors.

display unit—A device used to provide a visual representation of data.

display window—The width of the portion of the frequency spectrum presented on panoramic presentation, expressed in frequency units, usually megahertz.

disruptive discharge—The sudden, large current through an insulating medium when electrostatic stress ruptures the medium and thus destroys its insulating ability.

dissector—In optical character recognition, a mechanical or electronic transducer that sequentially detects the level of light in different areas of a completely illuminated sample space.

dissector tube—A camera tube having a continuous photocathode on which a photo-electric-emission pattern is formed. Scanning is done by moving the electron optical image of the pattern over an aperture. (*Also see* Image Dissector.)

dissipation—Loss of electrical energy as heat.

dissipation constant—A constant of proportionality between the power dissipated and the resultant temperature rise in a thermistor at a specified temperature.

dissipation factor—Symbolized by D. Ratio between the permittivity and conductivity of a dielectric. The reciprocal of the dissipation factor is the storage factor, sometimes called the quality factor. Abbreviated DF.

dissonance—The formation of maxima and minima by the superposition of two sets of interference fringes from light of two different wavelengths.

dissymmetrical transducer—Also called dissymmetrical network. A transducer with unequal input and output image impedances.

dissymmetrical network—*See* Dissymmetrical Transducer.

distance mark—Also called range mark. A mark which indicates, on a cathode-ray screen, the distance from the radar set to a target.

distance-measuring equipment — Abbreviated DME. A radio navigational aid for determining the distance from a transponder beacon by measuring the time of transmission to and from it.

distance protection—The effect of a device operative within a predetermined electrical distance on the protected circuit to cause and maintain an interruption of power in a faulty circuit.

distance relay—1. A protective relay, the operation of which is a function of the distance between the relay and the point of fault. 2. A device which functions when the circuit admittance, impedance, or reactance increases or decreases beyond predetermined limits.

distance resolution—The ability of a radar to differentiate targets solely by distance measurement. Generally expressed as the minimum distance the targets can be separated and still be distinguishable.

distortion — An undesired change in the waveform of the original signal, resulting in unfaithful reproduction of audio or video signals. Distortion is classified as nonlinear, frequency, or phase, depending on how the waveform is affected.

distortion factor of a wave—The ratio of the effective value of the residue after the elimination of the fundamental to the effective value of the original wave.

distortion meter — An instrument which measures the deviation of a complex wave from a pure sine wave.

distortion tolerance — Of a telegraph receiver, the maximum signal distortion which can be tolerated without error in reception.

distress frequency—A frequency reserved for distress calls, by international agreement. It is 500 kHz for ships at sea and aircraft over the sea.

distributed—Spread out over an electrically significant length, area, or time.

distributed capacitance — Also called self-capacitance. Any capacitance not concentrated within a capacitor, such as the capacitance between the turns in a coil or choke, or between adjacent conductors of a circuit.

distributed constants—Constants such as resistance, inductance, or capacitance that exist along the entire length or area of a circuit,

instead of being concentrated within circuit components.

distributed inductance — The inductance along the entire length of a conductor, as distinguished from the inductance concentrated within a coil.

distributed network—An electrical-electronic device which for proper operation depends on physical size in comparison to a wavelength and physical configuration.

distributed parameter network—A network in which the parameters of resistance, capacitance, and inductance cannot be taken as being concentrated at any one point in space. Rather, the network must be described in terms of its magnetic and electric fields and the quantities related to the distributed constants of the network.

distributed pole—A motor has distributed poles when its stator or field windings are distributed in a series of slots located within the arc of the pole.

distributing amplifier—An amplifier, either radio-frequency or audio-frequency, having one input and two or more isolated outputs.

distributing cable—*See* Distribution Cable.

distributing frame—A structure for terminating permanent wires of a central office, private branch exchange, or private exchange, and for permitting the easy change of connections between them by means of cross-connecting wires.

distributing terminal assembly — A frame situated between each pair of selector bays to provide terminal facilities for the selector bank wiring and facilities for cross connection to trunks running to succeeding switches.

distribution—Also called frequency distribution. The number of occurrences of the particular values of a variable as a function of those values.

distribution amplifier—A power amplifier designed to energize a speech, music, or antenna distribution system. Its output impedance is sufficiently low that changes in the load do not appreciably affect the output voltage.

distribution cable—1. Also called distributing cable. A cable extended from a feeder cable for the purpose of providing service to a specific area. 2. In a system, the transmission cable from the distribution amplifier to the drop cable.

distribution center—In an alternating-current power system, the point at which control and rotating equipment is installed.

distribution coefficients — Equal - powered tristimulus values of monochromatic radiations.

distribution switchboard—A power switchboard used for the distribution of electrical energy at the voltage common for each distribution within a building.

distributor—1. *See* Memory Register. 2. The electronic circuitry which acts as an intermediate link between the accumulator and drum storage.

disturbance — An irregular phenomenon which interferes with the interchange of intelligence during transmission of a signal.

disturbed-one output—A "one" output of a magnetic core to which partial-write pulses have been applied since that core was last selected for writing.

disturbed-zero output—A "zero" output of a magnetic core to which partial-write pulses have been applied since that core was last selected for reading.

dither — An oscillation introduced for the purpose of overcoming the effects of friction, hysteresis, or clogging.

dithering — The application of intermittent or periodic acceleration forces sufficient to minimize the effect of static friction with a transducer, without introducing other errors.

divergence loss—The part of the transmission loss that is caused by the spreading of sound energy.

diverging lens—A lens that is thinner in the center than at the edges. Such a lens causes light passing through to spread out, or diverge.

diversity—A form of transmission using several modes, usually in space or in time, to compensate for fading or outages in any one of the modes. In the space diversity system, the same signal is sent simultaneously over several different transmission paths, which are separated enough so that independent propagation conditions can be expected. With time diversity, the same path may be used, but the signal is transmitted more than once, at different times. There are other forms of diversity, using different frequencies or different polarizations to provide the separate transmission modes.

diversity gain—The gain in reception as a result of the use of two or more receiving antennas.

diversity reception—A method of minimizing the effects of fading during reception of a radio signal. This is done by combining and/or selecting two or more sources of received-signal energy which carry the same intelligence but differ in strength or signal-to-noise ratio in order to produce a usable signal.

diverter pole generator — A compound-wound direct-current generator with the series winding of the diverter pole opposing the flux generated by the shunt-wound main pole; provides a close voltage regulation.

divided-carrier modulation—The process by which two signals are added so that they can modulate two carriers of the same frequency but 90° out of phase. The resultant signal will have the same frequency as the carriers, but its amplitude and phase will vary in step with the variations in amplitude of the two modulating signals.

divider—*See* Frequency Divider.

dividing network—Also called speaker dividing network and crossover network. A frequency-selective network which divides the audio-frequency spectrum into two or more parts to be fed to separate devices such as amplifiers or speakers.

D layer—The lowest ionospheric layer. Its intensity is proportional to the height of the sun and is greatest at noon. Waves below approximately 3 MHz are absorbed by the D layer when it is present. High-angle radiation may penetrate the D layer and be reflected by the E layer.

Doherty amplifier—A radio-frequency linear power amplifier divided into two sections, the inputs and outputs of which are connected by quarter-wave (90°) networks. As long as the input-signal voltage is less than

Doherty amplifier.

Diversity reception.

half the maximum amplitude, section No. 2 is inoperative and section No. 1 delivers all the power to the load. The load presents twice the optimum impedance required for maximum output. At one-half the maximum input, section No. 1 is operating at peak efficiency but is beginning to saturate. Above this level, section No. 2 comes into operation and decreases the impedance presented to section No. 1. As a result, section No. 2 delivers more and more power to the load until, at maximum signal input, both sections are operating at peak efficiency and each section is delivering one-half the total output power.

dolly—A wheeled platform on which a television camera or other apparatus is mounted to give it wider mobility.

domain—In magnetic theory, that region of a magnetic material in which the spontaneous magnetization is all in one direction. In conventional magnetic-tape coatings, this corresponds to one oxide particle.

domestic induction heater—A home cooking utensil which is heated by induced currents within it. The unit contains a primary inductor, with the utensil itself acting as the secondary.

dominant mode—Also called fundamental mode or principal mode. In waveguide transmission, the mode with the lowest cutoff frequency. Designations for this mode are $TE_{0,1}$ and $TE_{1,1}$ for rectangular and circular wave guides, respectively.

dominant wave—The guided wave which has the lowest cutoff frequency. It is the only wave which will carry energy when the excitation frequency is between the lowest and the next higher cutoff.

dominant wavelength of a color—The predominant wavelength of light in a color.

donor—Also called donor impurity. An impurity atom which tends to give up an electron and thereby affects the electrical conductivity of a crystal. Used to produce N-type semiconductors.

donor impurity—See Donor.

donut—See Land.

doorknob tube—So called because of its shape. It is a vacuum tube designed for uhf transmiter circuits. It has a low electron-transit time and low interlectrode capacitance because of the close spacing and small size, respectively, of its electrodes.

dopant—An impurity added to a semiconductor to improve its electrical conductivity.

doped junction—A semiconductor junction produced by the addition of an impurity to the melt during crystal growth.

doping—Adding impurities to change the resistivity of semiconductors in order to make N- or P-types.

doping agent—An impurity element added to semiconductor materials used in crystal diodes and transistors. Common doping agents for germanium and silicon include aluminum, antimony, arsenic, gallium, and indium.

doping compensation—The addition of donor impurities to a P-type semiconductor or of acceptor impurities to an N-type semiconductor.

Doppler cabinet—A speaker cabinet in which either the speaker or a baffle board is rotated or moved to change the length of the sound path cyclically and thereby produce a vibrato effect mechanically.

Doppler effect—The observed change of frequency of a wave caused by a time rate of change of the effective distance traveled by the wave between the source and the point of observation. As the distance between a source of constant vibration and an observer diminishes or increases, the received frequencies are greater or less.

Doppler radar—A radar unit that measures the velocity of a moving object by the shift in carrier frequency of the returned signal. The shift is proportionate to the velocity of the object as it approaches or recedes.

Doppler ranging (doran)—A c-w trajectory-measuring system which utilizes the Doppler shift to measure the distance between a transmitter, missile, transponder, and several receiving stations. From these measurements trajectory data are computed. In contrast to a similar system, doran circumvents the necessity of continuously recording the Doppler signal by performing the distance measurements with four different frequencies simultaneously.

Doppler shift—The change in frequency of a wave reaching an observer or a system, caused by a change in distance or range between the source and the observer or the system during the interval of reception. It is due to the Doppler effect.

dosage meter—See Dosimeter *and* Intensitometer.

dosimeter—Also called intensitometer or dosage meter. An instrument that measures the amount of exposure to nuclear or X-ray radiation utilizing the ability of such radiation to produce ionization of a gas.

dot—See Button.

dot cycle—One cycle of a periodic alternation between two signaling conditions, each condition having unit duration. Thus, two-condition signaling consists of a dot, or marking element, followed by a spacing element.

dot encapsulation—A packaging process in which cylindrical components are inserted into a perforated wafer to form a solid block with interconnecting conductors on both surfaces joining the components.

dot generator—An instrument used in servicing color television receivers. It produces a pattern of white dots so that convergence adjustments can be made on the picture tube.

dot pattern—Small dots of light produced on the screen of a color picture tube by the signal from a dot generator. If overall beam convergence has been obtained, the three color-dot patterns will merge into one white-dot pattern.

dot sequential

Expanded view of dosage indicator.

Dosage scale.

Dosimeter viewer.

Pocket dosimeter.

dot sequential—Pertaining to the association of the primary colors in sequence with successive picture elements of a color television system. (Examples: dot-sequential pickup, dot-sequential display, dot-sequential system, dot-sequential transmission.)

double armature—An armature having two windings and commutators but only one core.

double-base diode—*See* Unijunction Transistor.

double-base junction transistor — Also called tetrode junction transistor. Essentially a junction triode transistor with two base connections on opposite sides of the central region of the transistor.

double-beam cathode-ray tube—A cathode-ray tube having two electron beams capable of producing on the screen two independent traces that may overlap. The beams may be produced by splitting the beam of one gun or by using two guns.

double-bounce calibration — A method of calibration used to determine the zero set error by using round-trip echoes. The correct range is the difference between the first and second echoes.

double-break contacts—A set of contacts in which one contact is normally closed and makes simultaneous connection with two other contacts.

double-break switch—A switch which opens the connected circuit at two points.

double bridge—*See* Kelvin Bridge.

double-button carbon microphone — Also called differential microphone. A microphone with two carbon-resistance elements or buttons, one on each side of a central diaphragm. They are connected in parallel to the current source in order to give twice the resistance change obtainable with a single button.

double-checkerboard pattern — *See* Worst-Case Noise Pattern.

double-current generator — A machine which supplies both direct and alternating current from the same armature winding.

double-diffused epitaxial mesa transistor —*See* Epitaxial-Growth Mesa Transistor.

double-diffused transistor—A transistor in which two PN junctions are formed in the semiconductor wafer by gaseous diffusion of both P-type and N-type impurities. An intrinsic region can also be formed.

double diode — Also called duodiode. A vacuum tube or semiconductor having two diodes in the same envelope.

double-diode limiter—A type of limiter used to remove all the positive signals from a combination of positive and negative pulses or to remove all the negative signals from such a combination of positive and negative pulses.

double-doped transistor — A transistor formed by growing a crystal and successively adding P- and N-type impurities to the melt while the crystal is being grown.

double emitter follower — *See* Darlington Amplifier.

double image—A television picture consisting of two overlapping images due to reception of the signal over two paths that differ in length so signals arrive at slightly different times.

double-junction photosensitive semiconductor—A semiconductor in which the current flow is controlled by light energy. It consists of three layers of a semiconductor material with electrodes connected to the ends of each.

double-length number—Also called double-precision number. An electronic computer number having twice the normal number of digits.

double local oscillator—An oscillator mixing system which generates two r-f signals accurately spaced a few hundred hertz apart and mixes these signals to give the difference frequency which is used as the reference. This equipment is used in an interferometer system to obtain a detectable signal containing the phase information of an antenna pair, and the reference signal to allow removal of the phase data for use.

double-make contacts—A set of contacts in which one contact is normally open and makes simultaneous connection with two other independent contacts when closed.

double moding — Changing from one frequency to another abruptly and at irregular intervals.

double modulation—The process of modulation in which a carrier wave of one frequency is first modulated by a signal wave, and the resultant wave is then made to modulate a second carrier wave of another frequency.

double pole—A term applied to a contact arrangement to denote that it includes two separate contact forms (i.e., two single-pole contact assemblies).

Double-pole, double-throw switch.

double-pole, double-throw switch—Abbreviated dpdt. A switch that has six terminals and is used to connect one pair of terminals to either of the other two pairs.

Double-pole, single-throw switch.

double-pole, single-throw switch—Abbreviated dpst. A switch that has four terminals and is used to connect or disconnect two pairs of terminals simultaneously.

double-pole switch—A switch that operates simultaneously in two separate electric circuits or in both lines of a single circuit.

double-precision arithmetic—The use of two computer words to represent a number. This is done where it is necessary to obtain greater accuracy than a single word of computer storage will provide.

double-precision number — *See* Double-Length Number.

double-pulsing station — A Loran station that receives two pairs of pulses and emits pulses at two pulse rates.

double pumping—A technique of pumping a laser for a relatively long time to store energy in subthreshold-level excited states, followed immediately by a very brief second pumping in which the threshold condition is exceeded in some region. This triggers laser oscillation throughout the entire active

region and produces peak output powers several times larger than normally seen.

double screen—A three-layer screen consisting of a two-layer screen with the additional second long-persistence coating having a different color and different persistence from the first.

double sideband—Amplitude-modulated intelligence which is transmitted at frequencies both above and below the carrier frequency by the audio-frequency value of the intelligence.

double-sideband transmitter — One which transmits not only the carrier frequency, but also the two sidebands resulting from modulation of carrier.

double-spot tuning—Superheterodyne reception of a given station at two different local-oscillator frequencies. The local oscillator is adjusted either above or below the incoming signal frequency by the intermediate-frequency value.

double-stream amplifier — A microwave traveling-wave amplifier in which amplification occurs through interaction of two electron beams having different average velocities.

double-stub tuner—An impedance-matching device consisting of two stubs, usually fixed three-eighths of a wavelength apart, in parallel with the main transmission lines.

double superheterodyne reception — Also called triple detection. The method of reception in which two frequency converters are employed before final detection.

double-surface transistor—A point-contact transistor, the emitter and collector whiskers of which are in contact with opposite sides of the base.

doublet—The output voltage waveform of a delay line under linear operating conditions when the input to the line is a current step function.

doublet antenna—An antenna consisting of two elevated conductors substantially in the same straight line and of substantially equal length, with the power delivered at the center.

double throw—A term applied to a contact arrangement to denote that each contact form included is a breakmate.

double-throw circuit breaker — A circuit breaker by means of which a change in the circuit connections can be obtained by closing either of two sets of contacts.

double-throw switch—A switch which alternately completes a circuit at either of its two extreme positions. It is both normally open and normally closed.

double-track recorder—See Dual-Track Recorder.

double triode—*See* Duotriode.

doublet trigger—A trigger signal consisting of two pulses spaced by a fixed amount for coding.

double-tuned amplifier — An amplifier in which each stage utilizes coupled circuits

143

having two frequencies of resonance for the purpose of obtaining wider bands than are possible with single tuning.

double-tuned circuit—A circuit in which two circuit elements are available for tuning.

Double-V antenna.

double-V antenna—Also called fan antenna. A modified single dipole which has a higher input impedance and broader bandwidth than an ordinary dipole.

double-winding synchronous generator—A synchronous generator which has two similar windings in phase with one another, mounted on the same magnetic structure but not connected electrically, designed to supply power to two independent external circuits.

doubly-balanced modulator—A modulator circuit in which two Class-A amplifiers are supplied with modulating and carrier signals of equal amplitudes and opposite polarities. Carrier suppression takes place because the two amplifiers share a common plate circuit and only the sidebands appear at the output.

down lead—The wire that connects an antenna to a transmitter or receiver.

down time—The length of time a device is not usable because of a malfunction.

downward modulation — Modulation in which the instantaneous amplitude of the modulated wave is never greater than that of the unmodulated carrier.

dpdt—Abbreviation for double-pole, double-throw switch.

dpst—Abbreviation for double-pole, single-throw switch.

drag angle—A stylus cutting angle of less than 90° to the surface of the record. So called because the stylus drags over the surface instead of digging in. It is the opposite of dig-in angle.

drag cup—A nonmagnetic metal rotated in a magnetic field to generate a torque or voltage proportional to its speed.

drag-cup motor—A small, high-speed, two-phase, alternating-current electric motor having a two-pole, two-phase stator. The

rotating element consists only of an extremely light metal cup attached to a shaft rotating on ball bearings. Reversal is accomplished by reversing the connections to one phase. Used in applications requiring quick starting, stopping, and reversal characteristics.

drag magnet—*See* Retarding Magnet.

drain—1. The current taken from a voltage source. 2. In a field-effect transistor, the element that corresponds to the plate of a vacuum tube.

drainage equipment — Equipment used to protect connected circuits from transients produced by the operation of protection equipment.

drain wire—A metallic conductor frequently used in contact with foil-type signal-cable shielding to provide a low-resistance ground return at any point along the shield.

D-region—The region of the ionosphere up to about 90 kilometers above the earth's surface. It is below the E-region.

dress—The exact placement of leads and components in a circuit to minimize or eliminate undesirable feedback and other troubles.

drift—1. Movement of carriers in a semiconductor as voltage is applied. 2. A change in either absolute level or slope of an input-output characteristic. 3. *See* Flutter. 4. *See* Degradation. 5. An undesired change in one of the output parameters of a power supply (voltage, current, frequency, etc.) over a period of time. The change is unrelated to all other variables such as load, line, and environment. Drift is measured over a period of time by keeping all variables (such as line, load, and environment) constant. Specifications usually apply only after a warm-up period. 6. The angular displacement of an aircraft by the wind, generally expressed in degrees. 7. In a d-c amplifier, the change in output with constant input, usually measured in terms of the d-c input signal required to restore normal output; may be called out as microvolts or millivolts per hour. 8. A change in output attributable to any cause.

drift mobility—The average drift velocity of carriers in a semiconductor per unit electric field. In general, the mobilities of electrons and holes are not the same.

drift space — In an electron tube, a region substantially free of alternating fields from external sources, in which relative repositioning of the electrons depends on their velocity distributions and the space-charge forces.

drift speed—Average speed at which electrons or ions progress through a medium.

drift transistor—A type of transistor manufactured with a variable-conductivity base region. Such a base sets up an electric field which speeds up the carriers, thus reducing the transit time and improving high-frequency operation.

drift velocity—Net velocity of charged particles in the direction of the applied field.

drip loop—A loop formed in a transmission line at a point where it enters a building. Condensation of moisture and water that may form on the line will drip off at the loop and thus will not enter the building.

drip-proof motor—A motor in which the ventilating openings are such that foreign matter falling on the motor at any angle not exceeding 15° from the vertical cannot enter the motor either directly or indirectly.

driptight enclosure—An enclosure that is intended to prevent accidental contact with the enclosed apparatus and, in addition, is so constructed as to exclude falling moisture or dirt.

drive—*See* Excitation.

drive belt—A belt used to transmit power from a motor to a driven device.

drive circuit—A circuit, usually a printed-circuit card or an encapsulated module, that converts an input pulse to the appropriate winding excitation sequence to produce one step of the motor shaft.

drive control—*See* Horizontal-Drive Control.

driven element—An antenna element connected directly to the transmission line.

driven sweep—A sweep signal triggered by an incoming signal only.

drive pin—In disc recording, a pin similar to the center pin but located at one side of it and used to prevent a disc record from slipping on the turntable.

drive pulse—A pulsed magnetomotive force applied to a magnetic cell from one or more sources.

driver—1. An electronic circuit which supplies input to another electric circuit. 2. A stage of amplification which precedes the power output stage. 3. In a radar transmitter, a circuit which produces a pulse to be delivered to the control grid of the modulator tube. 4. A unit or stage driving another unit or stage.

driver element—An antenna array element that receives power directly from the transmitter.

driver stage—The amplifier stage preceding the power-output stage.

driving-point admittance—The complex ratio of the alternating current to the applied alternating voltage for an electron tube, network, or other transducer.

driving-point impedance—At any pair of terminals in a network, the driving-point impedance is the ratio of an applied potential difference to the resultant current at these terminals, all terminals being terminated in any specified manner.

driving power—The power supplied to the grid circuit of a tube where the grid swings positive and draws current for part of each cycle of the input signal.

driving-range potential—The voltage difference between the potential of the electrochemically more active anode and the less active protected metal or cathode. One example of driving potential is the electromotive force in a cathodic protection system that causes current between the protected structure (cathode) and the anode. The driving potential decreases as the electrodes become polarized.

driving signal—Television signals that time the scanning at the pickup point. Two kinds of driving signals are usually available from a central sync generator, one composed of pulses at the line frequency and the other of pulses at the field frequency.

driving spring—The spring driving the wipers of a stepping relay.

drone cone—An undriven speaker cone mounted in a bass-reflex enclosure.

droop—The decrease in mean pulse amplitude, expressed as a percentage of the 100% amplitude, at a specified time following the initial attainment of 100% amplitude.

drop bar—A protective device used to ground a high-voltage capacitor when opening a door.

drop bracket transposition—Reversal of the relative positions of two parallel wire conductors while depressing one, so that the crossover is in a vertical plane.

drop cable—In a catv system, the transmission cable from the distribution cable to a dwelling.

drop channel—A type of operation in which one or more channels of a multichannel system are terminated (dropped) at some intermediate point between the end terminals of the system.

drop indicator—An indicator for signaling, consisting of a hinged flap normally held up by a catch. The catch is released by an electromagnet, allowing the flap to drop when a signal is received.

dropout—1. Separate and distinct variations in signal level during reproduction of recorded data, the result of which causes an error in data reduction. 2. Any discrete variation in signal level during the reproduction of magnetic-tape recorded data which results in a data-reduction error.

dropouts—Also called keys. Special images inserted at certain points in the array on a photomask used in the production of monolithic circuits.

drop-out value—The maximum value of current, voltage, or power which will de-energize a previously energized relay. (*Also see* Hold Current *and* Pickup Value.)

dropping resistor—A resistor used to decrease a given voltage by an amount equal to the potential drop across the resistor.

drop repeater—A microwave repeater station equipped for local termination of one or more circuits.

drop wire—A wire suitable for extending an open wire or cable pair from a pole or cable terminal to a building.

drum memory—A rotating cylinder or disc coated with magnetic material so that information can be stored in the form of magnetic spots.

drum recorder—A facsimile recorder in which the record sheet is mounted on a rotating cylinder.

drum speed—The number of revolutions per minute made by the transmitting or receiving drum of a facsimile transmitter or recorder.

drum switch—A switch in which the electrical contacts are made on pins, segments, or surfaces on the periphery of a rotating cylinder or sector, or by the operation of a rotating cam.

drum transmitter—A facsimile transmitter in which the copy is mounted on a rotating cylinder.

drum-type controller—1. A multicircuit timing device, with or without a motor, using a cylindrical carriage into which pins are inserted to program events. 2. A multicircuit timing device intended to be driven from an external rotary power source.

drunkometer—A device measuring the degree of alcoholic intoxication by analyzing the subject's breath.

dry—A condition in which the electrolyte in a cell is immobilized. The electrolyte may be either in the form of a gel or paste or absorbed in the separator material.

dry battery—Two or more dry cells arranged in series, parallel, or series-parallel within a single housing to provide desired voltage and current values.

dry cell—A voltage-generating cell having an immobilized electrolyte. The commonest form has a positive electrode of carbon and a negative electrode of zinc in an electrolyte of sal ammoniac paste.

dry circuit—A circuit in which the open-circuit voltage is .03V or less and the current 200ma or less. (The voltage is most important because at such a low level it is not able to break through most oxides, sulfides, or other films which can build up on contacting surfaces.)

CAP
SEPARATOR
CARBON
MIX
ZINC
INSULATOR

Dry cell.

dry contacts—Contacts which neither break nor make a circuit.

dry-disc rectifier—A rectifier consisting of discs of metal and other materials in contact under pressure. Examples are the copper-oxide and the selenium rectifier.

dry-electrolytic capacitor—An electrolytic capacitor with a paste rather than liquid electrolyte. By eliminating the danger of leakage, the paste electrolyte permits the capacitor to be used in any position.

dry flashover voltage—The voltage at which the air surrounding a clean, dry insulator or shell completely breaks down between electrodes.

dry-reed relay—A relay that consists of one or more capsules containing contact mechanisms that are generally surrounded by an electromagnetic coil for actuation. The capsule consists of a glass tube with a flattened ferromagnetic reed sealed in each end. These reeds, which are separated by an air gap, extend into the tube so as to overlap. When placed in a magnetic field, they are brought together and close a circuit.

dry shelf life—The length of time that a cell can stand without electrolyte before it deteriorates to a point where a specified output cannot be obtained.

dry-type force-air-cooled transformer (class AFA)—A transformer which is not immersed in oil and which derives its cooling by the forced circulation of air.

dry-type self-cooled/forced-air-cooled transformer (class AA/FA)—A transformer which is not immersed in oil, and which has a self-cooled rating with cooling obtained by the forced circulation of air.

dry-type self-cooled transformer (class AA)—A transformer which is cooled by the natural circulation of air and which is not immersed in oil.

dry-type transformer—A transformer which is cooled by the circulation of air and which is not immersed in oil.

dsc—Abbreviation for double silk-covered.

D-scope—A radar display similar to a C-scope except that the blips extend vertically to give a rough estimate of the distance.

"D" service—FAA service pertaining to radio broadcast of meteorological information, advisory messages, and notices to airmen.

DT-cut crystal—A crystal cut to vibrate below 500 kHz.

dual-beam oscilloscope—An oscilloscope in which the cathode-ray tube produces two separate electron beams that may be individually or jointly controlled.

dual capacitor—Two capacitors within a single housing.

dual-channel amplifier—An amplifier which has two channels independent of each other, but similar in design, construction, and output.

dual-diversity receiver—A radio receiver that receives signals from two different receiving antennas and uses whichever signal is the stronger at each instant to offset fading. In one arrangement, two identical radio-frequency systems, each with its own antenna, feed a common audio-frequency channel. In another arrangement, a single receiver is changed over from one antenna to the other by electronic switching at a rate fast enough to prevent loss of intelligibility.

dual-emitter transistor—A passivated PNP silicon planer epitaxial transistor with two emitters; used as a low-level chopper.

dual-frequency induction heater—A type of induction heater in which work coils operating at two different frequencies induce energy, either simultaneously or successively, to material within the heater.

dual-groove record—*See* Cook System.

dual meter—A meter constructed so that two aspects of a circuit may be read simultaneously.

dual modulation—The use of two different types of modulation, each conveying separate intelligence, to modulate a common carrier or subcarrier wave.

dual pickup—*See* Turnover Pickup.

dual trace—A mode of operation in which a single beam in a cathode-ray tube is shared by two signal channels. *Also see* Alternate Mode *and* Chopped Mode.

dual-track recorder—Sometimes called a half-track recorder. Its recording head covers only half the width of the tape, making it possible to record on one half of the tape and then, by turning the reels over, to record on the unused half.

dubbing—In radio broadcasting, the addition of sound to a prerecorded tape or disc.

duct—1. A protective pipe through which conductors or cables are run. 2. In microwave transmission, atmospheric conditions may cause radio waves to follow a narrower path than usual. The narrower path is called a duct. The presence of ducting sometimes causes unusual transmission because the transmission waves do not follow the intended path.

ducting—The trapping of an electromagnetic wave, in a waveguide action, between two layers of the earth's atmosphere, or between a layer of the atmosphere and the earth's surface.

dummy antenna—*See* Artificial Antenna.

dummy instruction—An artificial instruction or address inserted in a list of instructions to a computer solely to fulfill prescribed conditions (such as word length or block length) without affecting the operation.

dummy load—*See* Artificial Load.

dump—1. Also called power dump. To withdraw all power from a computer, either accidentally or intentionally. 2. To transfer all or part of the contents of one section of a digital-computer memory into another section.

dump check—Checking a computer by adding all digits as they are dumped (transferred) to verify the sum to make sure no errors exist as the digits are retransferred.

dumping resistor—A resistor whose function is to discharge a capacitor or network for safety purposes.

duodecal socket—A vacuum-tube socket having 12 pins. Used for cathode-ray tubes.

duodecimal—1. Pertaining to a characteristic or property involving a selection, choice, or condition in which there are 12 possibilities. 2. Pertaining to the numbering system with a radix of 12.

duodiode—Also called dual diode. A vacuum tube or semiconductor having two diodes within the same envelope.

duodiode-pentode—An electron tube containing two diodes and a pentode in the same envelope.

duodiode-triode—An electron tube containing two diodes and a triode in the same envelope.

duolateral coil—*See* Honeycomb Coil.

duopole—An all-pass section with two poles and two zeros.

duotriode—An electron tube containing two triodes in the same envelope. Also called double triode.

duplex—1. The method of operation of a communication circuit in which each end can simultaneously transmit and receive. (Ordinary telephones are duplex. When used on a radio circuit, duplex operation requires two frequencies.) 2. Two-in-one, as two conductors with a common overall insulation or two telegraph transmission channels over one wire.

duplex artificial line—A balancing network simulating the impedance of the real line and distant terminal apparatus; it is employed in a duplex circuit for the purpose of making the receiving device unresponsive to outgoing signal currents.

duplex cable—A cable composed of two insulated stranded conductors twisted together. They may or may not have a common insulating covering.

duplex channel—A communication channel providing simultaneous transmission in both directions.

duplexer—A radar device which, by using the transmitted pulse, automatically switches the antenna from receive to transmit at the proper time.

duplexing assembly (radar)—*See* TR Switch.

duplex operation—Simultaneous operation of transmitting and receiving apparatus at two locations.

duplex system—A system with two distinct and separate sets of facilities, each of which is capable of assuming the system function while the other assumes a standby status. Usually both sets are identical in nature.

duplex tube—A combination of two vacuum tubes in one envelope.

duplication check—A computer check in which the same operation or program is checked twice to make sure the same result is obtained both times.

duration control—A control for adjusting

Duodecal socket.

the time duration of reduced gain in a sensitivity-time control circuit.

during cycle—The interval while a timer is operating for its present time period.

dust core—A pulverized iron core consisting of extremely fine iron particles mixed with a binding material for use in radio-frequency coils.

dust-ignitionproof motor—A totally enclosed motor, the enclosure of which is designed and constructed in a manner that will exclude ignitable amounts of dust or amounts which might affect the performance rating, and will not permit arcs, sparks, or heat otherwise generated or liberated inside the enclosure to cause ignition of exterior accumulations or atmospheric suspensions of a specific dust on or in the vicinity of the enclosure.

duty cycle—The amount of time a device operates, as opposed to its idle time. Applied to a device that normally runs intermittently rather than continuously.

duty cyclometer—A test meter which gives a direct reading of duty cycle.

duty factor—1. In a carrier composed of regularly recurring pulses, the product of their duration and repetition frequency. 2. Ratio of average to peak power.

duty ratio—In a pulsed system, such as radar, the ratio of average to peak power.

DX—1. Abbreviation for distance. 2. Reception of distant stations.

DX hound—An amateur who specializes in making distant contacts.

dynamic acceleration—Acceleration in a constantly changing magnitude and direction, either simple or complex motion usually called vibration. Also measured in gravity units.

dynamic braking—A system of braking of an electric drive in which the motor is used as a generator, and the kinetic energy of the motor and driven machinery is employed as the actuating means of exerting a retarding force.

dynamic characteristics—Relationship between the instantaneous plate voltage and plate current of a vacuum tube as the voltage applied to the grid is varied.

dynamic check—A check used to ascertain the correct performance of some or all components of equipment or a system under dynamic or operating conditions.

dynamic contact resistance—In a relay, a change in contact electrical resistance due to a variation in contact pressure on mechanically closed contacts.

dynamic convergence—The condition where the three beams of a color picture tube come together at the aperture mask as they are reflected both vertically and horizontally. (*Also see* Vertical Dynamic Convergence *and* Horizontal Dynamic Convergence.)

dynamic decay—In a storage tube, decay caused by an action such as that of ion charging.

dynamic demonstrator—A three-dimensional schematic diagram in which the components of the radio, television receiver, etc., are mounted directly on the diagram.

dynamic deviation—The difference between the ideal output value and the actual output value of a device or circuit when the reference input is changing at a specified constant rate and all other transients have expired.

dynamic equilibrium of an electromagnetic system—1. The tendency of any electromagnetic system to change its configuration so that the flux of magnetic induction will be maximum. 2. The tendency of any two current-carrying circuits to maintain the flux of magnetic induction linking the two at maximum.

dynamic error—An error in a time-varying signal resulting from inadequate dynamic response of a transducer.

dynamic focus—The application of an a-c voltage to the focus electrode of a color picture tube to compensate for the defocusing caused by the flatness of the screen.

dynamic magnetic field—A field the intensity of which is changing and the lines of force of which are expanding or contracting. Such change can be periodic or random. Unlike the static field, the dynamic field can transfer energy from one point to another without relative motion between the points.

dynamic microphone—*See* Moving-Coil Microphone.

dynamic mutual-conductance tube tester—*See* Transconductance Tube Tester.

dynamic noise suppressor—An audio filter the bandpass of which is adjusted automatically to the signal level. At low signal levels filtering is highest, and at high signal levels all filter action is removed.

dynamic output impedance—*See* Output Impedance.

dynamic pickup—*See* Moving-Coil Pickup.

dynamic plate impedance—The internal resistance to the flow of alternating current between the cathode and plate of a tube.

dynamic plate resistance—*See* A-C Plate Resistance.

dynamic printout—In a computer, a printout of data which occurs as one sequential operation during the machine run.

dynamic range—1. The difference, in decibels, between the overload level and the minimum acceptable signal level in a system or transducer. 2. The ratio of the specified maximum signal-level capability of a system or component to its noise or resolution level, usually expressed in decibels.

dynamic regulator—A transmission regulator in which the adjusting mechanism is in self-equilibrium at only one or a few settings and requires control power to maintain it at any other setting.

dynamic reproducer—*See* Moving-Coil Pickup.

dynamic resistance—Incremental resistance

measured over a relatively small portion of the operating characteristic of a device.

dynamic run—Also called dynamic test. The test performed on an instrument to obtain the overall behavior and to establish or corroborate specifications such as frequency response, natural frequency of the device, etc.

dynamic sequential control—A method of operation in which a digital computer can alter instructions or their sequence, as the computation proceeds.

dynamic speaker—*See* Moving-Coil Speaker.

dynamic storage—Stored computer data which remain in motion on the sensing device (i.e., acoustic delay line, magnetic drum, etc.), as opposed to static storage.

dynamic subroutine—In digital-computer programming, a subroutine which involves parameters (such as decimal point position) from which a properly coded subroutine is derived. The computer itself adjusts or generates the subroutine according to the parametric values chosen.

dynamic test—*See* Dynamic Run.

dynamic transfer-characteristic curve—A curve showing the variation in output current as the input current changes.

Dynamo.

dynamo—1. Normally called a generator. A machine that converts mechanical energy into electrical energy by electromagnetic induction. 2. In precise terminology, a generator of direct current—as opposed to an alternator, which generates alternating current.

dynamoelectric—Pertaining to the relationship between mechanical force and electrical energy or vice versa.

dynamometer—1. An instrument in which the force between a fixed and a moving coil provides a measure of current, voltage, or power. 2. Equipment designed to measure the power output of a rotating machine by determining the friction absorbed by a hand brake opposing the rotation.

dynamotor—Also called a rotary converter or synchronous inverter. A rotating device for changing a d-c voltage to another value. It is a combination electric motor and d-c generator with two or more armature windings and a common set of field poles. One armature winding receives the direct current and rotates (thus operating as a motor), while the others generate the required voltage (and thus operate as dynamos or generators).

dynaquad—A germanium PNPN semiconductor switching device which is base-controlled and has three terminals. Its operation is similar to that of a flip-flop circuit or latching relay.

dynatron—*See* Tetrode.

dynatron oscillator—A negative-resistance oscillator with negative resistance derived between the plate and cathode of a screen-grid tube operating such that secondary electrons produced at the plate are attracted to the higher-potential screen grid.

dyne—The force that produces an acceleration of one centimeter per second per second on a one-gram mass.

dyne per square centimeter—The unit of sound pressure. One dyne per square centimeter was originally called a bar in acoustics, but the full expression is used in this field now because the bar is defined differently in other applications. Also called microbar.

dynistor—A nonlinear semiconductor having the characteristics of a small current flow as voltage is applied. As the applied voltage is increased a point is reached at which the current flow suddenly increases radically and will continue at this rate even though the applied voltage is reduced.

dynode—An electrode having the primary function of supplying secondary-electron emission in an electron tube.

Dynode.

E

E—1. Symbol for voltage or emitter. 2. Abbreviation for illumination.

E and M leads—In a signaling system, the output and input leads, respectively.

early-failure period—The period of equipment life, starting immediately after final assembly, during which equipment failures initially occur at a higher than normal rate due to the presence of defective parts and abnormal operating procedures. Also called debugging period, burn-in period, or infant-mortality period.

early-warning radar—A radar which usually scans the sky in all directions, in order to detect approaching enemy planes and/or missiles at distances far enough away that interceptor planes can be in the air to meet their approach before they are near their target.

earphone—Also called receiver. An electro-acoustic transducer intended to be placed in or over the ear.

earth—Term used in Great Britain for ground.

earthed—A British term meaning grounded.

earth inductor—*See* Generating Magnetometer.

earth oblateness—The slight departure from a perfect spherical shape of the shape of the earth and the form of its gravity field.

E-bend—*See* E-Plane Bend.

ebiconductivity—Conductivity induced as the result of electron bombardment.

ebmd—Abbreviation for electron-beam mode discharge.

ec—Abbreviation for enamel covered.

eccentric circle—*See* Eccentric Groove.

eccentric groove—Also called eccentric circle. An off-center locked groove for actuating the trip mechanism of an automatic record changer at the end of a recording.

eccentricity—In disc recording, the displacement of the center of the recording-groove spiral with respect to the record center hole.

Eccles-Jordan circuit—A flip-flop circuit consisting of a two-stage, resistance-coupled electron-tube amplifier. Its output is coupled back to its input, two separate conditions of stability being achieved by alternately biasing the two stages beyond cutoff.

ECCM (electronic counter-countermeasures)—Retaliatory tactics used to reduce the effectiveness of electronic countermeasures.

ECDC (abbreviation for ElectroChemical Diffused-Collector transistor)—A PNP transistor in which all the mass of P material is etched off and replaced with metal, which acts as a heat sink. It is suitable for high-current, high-speed core driver and computer-memory applications.

echelon—One of a series of levels of accuracy of calibration, the highest of which is represented by an accepted national standard. There may be auxiliary levels between two successive echelons.

echo—1. In radar, that portion of the energy reflected to the receiver from a target. 2. A wave which has been reflected or otherwise returned with sufficient magnitude and delay to be distinguishable from the directly transmitted wave. 3. In facsimile, a multiple reproduction on the record sheet caused by the arrival of the same original facsimile signal at different times over transmission paths of different lengths. 4. In a radio system, an electronic condition which causes a signal such as a voice signal to be reflected from some point or points in the circuit back to the point of origination of the signal. 5. A delayed repetition (sometimes several rapid repetitions) of the original sound or signal.

echo area—Equivalent echoing area of a radar target (i.e., the relative amount of radar energy the target will reflect).

echo attenuation—In a four-wire (or two-wire) circuit equipped with repeater or multiplex equipment in which the two directions of transmission can be separated from each other, the attenuation of the echo currents (which return to the input of the circuit under consideration) is determined by the ratio of the transmitted power P1 to the echo power received P2.

echo box—Also called phantom target. A device for checking the over-all performance of a radar system. It comprises a resonant cavity which receives a portion of the pulse energy from the transmitter and retransmits it to the receiver as a slowly decaying transient. The time required for this transient response to decay below the minimum detectable level on the radar indicator is known as the ring time and is indicative of the over-all performance of the radar set.

echo chamber—A reverberant room or enclosure used for adding hollow effects or actual echoes to radio or television programs.

echo check—A method of checking the accuracy of transmission of data in which the received data are returned to the sending end for comparison with the original data.

echo depth sounder—*See* Fathometer.

echo depth sounding—A system of determining the ocean depth by producing a sound just below the water's surface and measuring the amount of time before the echo is reflected from the floor of the ocean.

echo intensifier—A device, located at the target, that is used to increase the amplitude of the reflected energy to an abnormal level.

echo matching—Rotating an antenna to a position in which the pulse indications of an echo-splitting radar are equal.

echo ranging—Determination of both direction and distance of an underwater object from a vessel by ultrasonic radiation.

echo sounder—A sounding device used by ships to determine the depth of water. (*Also see* Echo Depth Sounding.)

echo splitting—In certain radar equipment, the echo return is split and appears as a double indication on the screen of the radar indicator. This splitting is accomplished by special electronic circuits associated with the antenna lobe switching mechanism. When the two echo indications are of equal height, the target bearing is read from a calibrated scale.

echo suppressor—1. A voice-operated device that is connected to a two-way telephone circuit to attenuate echo currents in one direction caused by telephone currents in the other direction. 2. In navigation, a circuit which desensitizes the equipment for a fixed period after the reception of one pulse, for the purpose of rejecting delayed pulses arriving from indirect reflection.

echo talker—A portion of the transmitted signal returned from a distant point to the transmitting source with sufficient time delay to be received as interference.

ECM (electronic countermeasures)—Methods of jamming or otherwise hindering the operation of enemy electronic equipment.

ECO—Abbreviation for electron-coupled oscillator.

E-core.

E-core—The laminated configuration resembling the capital letter *E* in some transformers and inductive transducers.

eddy-current heating—Synonym for induction heating.

eddy-current loss—The core loss which results when a varying induction produces electromotive forces which cause a current to circulate within a magnetic material.

eddy currents—Also called Foucault currents. Those currents induced in the body of a conducting mass by a variation in magnetic flux.

edge effect—1. *See* Following or Leading White *and* Following or Leading Black. 2. Nonuniformity of electric fields between two parallel plates caused by an outward bulging of electric flux lines at the edges of the plates.

edging—Undesired coloring around the edges of different-colored objects in a color television picture.

Edison base—Standard screw-thread base used for ordinary electric lamps.

Edison distribution system—A three-wire direct-current distribution system, usually 120 to 240 volts, for combined light and power service from a single set of mains.

Edison effect—Also called Richardson effect. The phenomenon wherein electrons emitted from a heated element within a vacuum tube will flow to a second element that is connected to a positive potential.

Edison storage cell—A storage cell having negative plates of iron oxide and positive plates of nickel oxide immersed in an alkaline solution. An open-circuit voltage of 1.2 volts per cell is produced.

E-display—In radar, a rectangular display in which targets appear as blips with distance indicated by the horizontal coordinate and elevation by the vertical coordinate.

EDP—Abbreviation for electronic data processing.

EDP center—*See* Electronic Data Processing Center.

EDPM—Abbreviation for electronic data-processing machine.

eeg—Abbreviation for electroencephalograph.

effective acoustic center—The point from which the spherically divergent sound waves from an acoustic generator appear to diverge. Also called apparent source.

effective actuation time—The sum of the initial actuation time and the contact chatter intervals of a relay following such actuation.

effective ampere—That alternating current which, when flowing through a standard resistance, produces heat at the same average rate as 1 ampere of direct current flowing in the same resistance.

effective antenna length—The length which, when multiplied by the maximum current, will give the same product as the length and uniform current of an elementary electric dipole at the same location, and the same radio field intensity in the direction of maximum radiation.

effective area—The effective area of an antenna in any specified direction is equal to the square of the wavelength multiplied by the power gain (or directive gain) in that direction, divided by 4π.

effective bandwidth—For a bandpass filter, the width of an assumed rectangular bandpass filter having the same transfer ratio at a reference frequency and passing the same mean-square value of a hypothetical current and voltage having even distribution of energy over all frequencies.

effective capacitance—The total capacitance existing between any two given points of an electric circuit.

effective conductivity—The conductance between the opposite parallel faces of a portion of a material having unit length and unit cross section.

effective current—That value of alternating current which will give the same heating effect as the corresponding value of direct current. For sine-wave alternating currents, the effective value is 0.707 times the peak value.

effective cutoff—*See* Effective Cutoff Frequency.

151

effective cutoff frequency—Also called effective cutoff. The frequency at which the insertion loss of an electric structure between specified terminating impedances exceeds the loss at some reference point in the transmission band.

effective field intensity—Root-mean-square value of the inverse distance fields one mile from the transmitting antenna in all directions horizontally.

effective height—The height of the antenna center of radiation above the effective ground level.

effectively grounded—Grounded through a ground connection of sufficiently low impedance (inherent and/or intentionally added) so that fault grounds which may occur cannot build up voltages that are dangerous to connected equipment.

effective parallel resistance—The resistance leakage considered to be in parallel with a pure dielectric.

effective percentage modulation—For a single, sinusoidal input component, the ratio between the peak value of the fundamental component of the envelope and the direct-current component in the modulated conditions, expressed in percent.

effective radiated power—Antenna input times gain, expressed in watts. If specified for a particular direction, it is the antenna power gain in that direction only.

effective radius of the earth—A value used in place of the geometrical radius to correct the atmospheric refraction when the index of refraction in the atmosphere changes linearly with height. Under conditions of standard refraction, the effective radius is one and one-third the geometrical radius.

effective resistance—1. The average rate of dissipation of electric energy during a cycle divided by the square of the effective current. 2. The equivalent pure d-c resistance which, when substituted for the winding of a motor being checked, will draw the same power. It is also equivalent to the impedance of a circuit having a capacitor connected in parallel with the winding and the capacitor adjusted to unity power factor for the circuit.

effective series resistance—A dropping resistance considered to be in series with an assumed pure capacitance.

effective sound pressure—The root-mean-square value of the instantaneous sound pressure at one point over a complete cycle. The unit is the dyne per square centimeter.

effective speed—The speed (less than rated) which can be sustained over a significant period of time and which reflects slowing effects of control codes, timing codes, error detection, retransmission, tabbing, hand keying, etc.

effective speed of transmission—The average rate over some specified time interval at which information is processed by a transmission facility. Usually expressed as average characters or average bits per unit time. Also called average rate of transmission.

effective thermal resistance—Of a semiconductor device, the effective temperature rise per unit power dissipation of a designated junction above the temperature of a stated external reference point under conditions of thermal equilibrium.

effective value—Also called the rms (root mean square) value. The value of alternating current that will produce the same amount of heat in a resistance as the corresponding value of direct current. The effective value is 0.707 times the peak value.

effective wavelength—The wavelength corresponding to the effective propagation velocity and the observed frequency.

efficiency—1. Ratio of the useful output of a physical quantity which may be stored, transferred, or transformed by a device, to the total input of the device. 2. The ratio of the output power to the input power of a regulated power supply, expressed in percent. In the absence of statements to the contrary, it is assumed to be taken at nominal input and output levels and full load conditions.

efficiency of a source of light—The ratio of the total luminous flux to the total power consumed. In the case of an electric lamp, it is expressed in lumens per watt.

efficiency of rectification—Ratio of direct-current power output to alternating-current power input of a rectifier.

EGO—Acronym for Eccentric orbit Geophysical Observatory.

ehf—Abbreviation for extremely high frequency.

E-H tee—A waveguide junction composed of a combination of E and H plane tee junctions which intersect the main guide at a common point.

E-H tuner—An E-H tee having two arms terminated in adjustable plungers. It is used for impedance transformation.

EIA—Abbreviation for Electronic Industries Association.

Einthoven string galvanometer—A moving-coil type of galvanometer in which the coil is a single wire suspended between the poles of a powerful electromagnet.

E-I pick-off—An assembly of transformerlike laminations, the output coils of which develop a voltage proportional to the displacement of a magnetic element from the neutral position for limited rotary as well as angular travel.

ekg—Abbreviation for electrocardiograph.

elastance—Symbolized by S. In a capacitor, the ratio of potential difference between its electrodes to the charge in the capacitor. It is the reciprocal of capacitance. The unit of measure is the daraf.

$$S \text{ (daraf)} = \frac{V}{Q}$$

elastic collision—Collision resulting in no

molecular excitation when the conservation of momentum and kinetic energy governs the energy transfer.

elastic limit—The maximum stress a solid can endure and still return to its unstrained state when the stress is removed.

elastic wave—A pure acoustic wave; a moving lattice distortion without a magnetic component.

elastivity—The resistance of an electrostatic field. It is the reciprocal of permittivity.

E-layer—One of the regular ionospheric layers with an average height of about 100 kilometers. This layer occurs during daylight hours, and its ionization is dependent on the sun's angle. The principal layer corresponds roughly to what was formerly called the Kennelly-Heaviside layer.

E-layer.

electra—A specific radionavigational aid that provides a number (usually 24) of equisignal zones. Electra is similar to sonne except that in sonne the equisignal zones as a group are periodically rotated in bearing.

electralloy—A nonmagnetic alloy frequently used in radio chassis.

electret—A permanently polarized piece of dielectric material produced by heating the material and placing it in a strong electric field during cooling. Some barium titanate ceramics can be polarized in this way, and so can carnauba waxes. The electric field of an electret corresponds somewhat to the magnetic field of a permanent magnet.

electric—Pertaining to, consisting of, containing, producing, derived from, or produced or operated by, electricity. Used interchangeably with electrical.

electrical—*See* Electric.

electrical angle—A means of specifying a particular instant in an a-c cycle. One complete cycle is considered equal to 360°; hence a half-cycle is 180° and a quarter-cycle is 90°. If one voltage reaches a peak value a quarter of a cycle after another, the electrical angle (phase difference) between the two voltages is 90°.

electrical bail—A switch action in which, upon actuation of one station, the switch changes the contact position, electrically locks the switch in that position, and releases any station previously actuated.

electrical bias—An electrically produced force tending to move the armature of a relay toward a given position.

electrical boresight—The tracking axis as determined by an electrical indication, such as the null direction of a conical scanning or monopulse antenna system or the beam maximum direction of a highly directive antenna.

electrical center—The point approximately midway between the ends of an inductor or resistor. This point divides the inductor or resistor into two equal electrical values (e.g., voltage, resistance, inductance, or number of turns).

electrical degree—A unit of time measurement applied to alternating current.

electrical discharge machining—Machining in which metal is removed by a controlled electrical spark in a dielectric.

electrical distance—The distance between two points, expressed as the length of time an electromagnetic wave in free space takes to travel between them.

electrical element—The concept in uncombined form of any of the individual building blocks from which electronic circuits are synthesized. Examples of basic electrical elements are insulation, conductance, resistance, capacitance, and inductance.

electrical erosion—The loss of contact material due to action of an electrical discharge.

electrical forming—The application of electric energy to a semiconductor device in order to permanently modify the electrical characteristics.

electrical gearing—A term used to describe the action of a system in which the output shaft rotates at a different speed from the input shaft, the ratio being established by electrical means.

electrical glass insulation—Insulating materials made from glass fibers of varying diameters, lengths, compositions, etc., including yarns, rovings, slivers, cords, and sheets or mats, bounded or treated only as necessary to their manufacture.

electrical inertia—Inductance that opposes any change in current flow through an inductor.

electrical initiation—Any source of electrical power used to start a function or sequence.

electrical interlocks—Switches mounted on contactors or other devices and operated by rods or levers. These interlocks open or close, depending on the open or closed position of the contactor or device with which they are associated, and are used to govern succeeding operations of the same or allied devices.

electrical length—Length expressed in wavelengths, radians, or degrees. Distance in wavelengths × 2π = radians; distance in wavelengths × 360 = degrees.

electrical load—A device (e.g., a speaker) comprising resistive and/or reactive components into which an amplifier, generator, etc., delivers power.

electrically operated rheostat—A rheostat used to vary the resistance of a circuit in response to some means of electrical control.

electrically operated valve—A solenoid- or motor-operated valve used in vacuum, air, gas, oil, water, or similar lines.

electrically variable inductor—An inductor in which the inductance can be controlled by a current or a voltage. It is usually made in the form of a saturable reactor with two windings. One is called the signal, or tuned winding, corresponding to the a-c or load winding of a power-handling saturable reactor; the other is the control winding and corresponds to the d-c winding of the saturable reactor.

electrical noise—Unwanted electrical energy other than cross talk in a transmission system.

electrical radian—57.296°, or ½π (1/6.28) of a cycle of alternating current or voltage.

electrical reset — A term applied to a relay to indicate that it is capable of being electrically reset after an operation.

electrical resistivity—The resistance of a material to passage of an electric current through it. Expressed as ohms (units of resistance) per mil foot or as microhms (millionths of an ohm) per centimeter cubed (cm³) at a specified temperature.

electrical resolver—Special type of synchro having a single winding on the stator and two windings the axes of which are 90° apart on the rotor.

electrical sheet—Iron or steel sheets from which laminations for electric motors are punched.

electrical system — The organized arrangement of all electrical and electromechanical components and devices in a way that will properly control the particular machine tool or industrial equipment.

electrical twinning—See Twinning.

electrical zero—A standard synchro position at which electrical outputs have defined amplitudes and time phase.

electric arc—A discharge of energy through a gas.

electric bell — An audible signaling device consisting of one or more gongs and an electromagnetically actuated striking mechanism.

electric brazing—A brazing (alloying) process in which the heat is furnished by an electric current.

electric breakdown voltage — See Dielectric Breakdown Voltage.

electric breeze or wind—The emission of electrons from a sharp point of a conductor which carries a high negative potential.

electric charge—Electric energy stored on the surface of an object.

electric chronograph—A highly accurate apparatus for measuring and recording time intervals.

electric circuit—A continuous path consisting of wires and/or circuit elements over or through which an electric current can flow. If the path is broken at any point, current can no longer flow and there is no circuit.

electric contact—A separable junction between two conductors which is designed to make, carry, or break (in any sequence or singly) an electric circuit.

electric controller—A device which governs the amount of electric power delivered to an apparatus.

electric delay line—A delay line using properties of lumped or distributed capacitive and inductive elements. Can be used as a storage medium by recirculating the information-carrying signal.

electric dipole—Also called a doublet. A simple antenna comprising a pair of oppositely charged conductors capable of radiating an electromagnetic wave in response to the movement of an electric charge from one conductor to the other.

electric-discharge lamp—A sealed glass enclosure containing a metallic vapor or an inert gas through which electricity is passed to produce a bright glow.

electric displacement — See Electric-Flux Density.

electric-displacement density—See Electric-Flux Density.

electric eye—1. The layman's term for a photoelectric cell. 2. The cathode-ray, tuning-indicator tube used in some radio receivers.

electric field—The region about a charged body. Its intensity at any point is the force which would be exerted on a unit positive charge at that point.

electric-field intensity—A measure of the force exerted at a point by a unit charge at that point.

electric-field strength — The magnitude of the electric field in an electromagnetic wave. Usually stated in volts per meter. (*Also see* Dielectric Strength.)

electric-field vector—At a point in an electric field, the force on a stationary positive charge per unit charge. May be measured in either newtons per coulomb or volts per meter. This term is sometimes called the electric-field intensity, but such use of the word "intensity" is deprecated in favor of "field strength," since intensity denotes power in optics and radiation.

electric-filament lamp—A glass bulb either evacuated or filled with an inert gas and having a resistance element electrically heated to, and maintained at, the temperature necessary to produce incandescence.

electric filter—See Electric-Wave Filter.

electric-flux density — Also called electric-displacement density or electric displacement. At a point, the vector equal in magnitude to the maximum charge per unit area which would appear on one face of a thin metal plate introduced in the electric field at that point. The vector is normal to the plate from the negative to the positive face.

electric furnace—A furnace in which electric arcs provide the source of heat.

electric generator—A machine that transforms mechanical power into electrical power.

electric governor-controlled series-wound motor—A series-wound motor having an electric speed governor connected in series with the motor circuit. The governor is usually built into the motor.

electric hygrometer—An instrument for indicating humidity by electric means. Its operation depends on the relationship between the electric conductance and moisture content of a film of hygroscopic material.

electric hysteresis—Internal friction in a dielectric material when subjected to a varying electric field (e.g., the paper or mica dielectric of a capacitor in an a-c circuit). The resultant heat generated can eventually break down the dielectric and cause the capacitor to fail.

electrician—A person engaged in designing, making, or repairing electric instruments or machinery. Also, one who sets up an electrical installation.

electric image—The electrical counterpart of an object; i.e., the fictitious distribution of the same amount of electricity that is actually distributed on a nearby object.

electricity—The property of certain particles to possess a force field which is neither gravitational nor nuclear. The type of force field associated with electrons is defined as negative and that associated with protons and positrons as positive. The fundamental unit is the charge of an electron: 1.60203×10^{-19} coulomb. Electricity can be further classified as static electricity or dynamic electricity. Static electricity in its strictest sense refers to charges at rest, as opposed to dynamic electricity, or charges in motion. Static electricity is sometimes used as a synonym for triboelectricity or frictional electricity.

electric light—Light produced by an electric lamp.

electric lines of force—In an electric field, curves the tangents of which at any point give the direction of the fields at that point.

electric meter—A device that measures and registers the amount of electricity consumed over a certain period of time.

electric mirror—*See* Dynode.

electric moment—For two charges of equal magnitude but opposite polarities, a vector equal in magnitude to the product of the magnitude of either charge by the distance between the centers of the two charges. The direction of the vector is from the negative to the positive charge.

electric motor — A device which converts electrical energy into rotating mechanical energy.

electric network—A combination of any number of electric elements, having either lumped or distributed impedances, or both.

electric oscillations — The back-and-forth flow of electric charges whenever a circuit containing inductance and capacitance is electrically disturbed.

electric potential—A measure of the work required to bring a unit positive charge from an infinite distance or from one point to another (the difference of potential between two points).

electric precipitation—The collecting of dust or other fine particles floating in the air. This is done by inducing a charge in the particles, which are then attracted to highly oppositely charged collector plates.

electric probe—A rod inserted into an electric field during a test to detect d-c, audio, or r-f energy.

electric reset—A qualifying term indicating that the contacts of a relay must be reset electrically to their original positions following an operation.

electric shield—A housing, usually aluminum or copper, placed around a circuit to provide a low-resistance path to ground for high frequency radiations and thereby prevent interaction between circuits.

electric strain gage—A device which detects the change in shape of a structural member under load and causes a corresponding change in the flow of current through the device.

electric strength—The maximum electric charge a dielectric material can withstand without rupturing. (*Also see* Dielectric Strength.)

electric stroboscope—An instrument for observing or for measuring the speed of rotating or vibrating objects by electrically producing periodic changes in the intensity of light used to illuminate the object.

electric tachometer — A tachometer (rpm indicator) that utilizes voltage or electrical impulses.

electric telemeter—A system consisting of a meter which measures a quantity, a transmitter which sends the information to a distant station, and a receiver which indicates or records the quantity measured.

electric transcription — In broadcasting, a disc recording of a message or a complete program.

electric transducer — A device actuated by electric waves from one system and supplying power, also in the form of electric waves, to a second system.

electric tuning—A system by which a radio receiver is tuned to a station by pushing a button (instead of, say, turning a knob).

electric vector—A component of the electromagnetic field associated with electromagnetic radiation. The component is of the nature of an electric field. The electric vector is supposed to coexist with, but act at right angles to, the magnetic vector.

electric wave—Another term for the electromagnetic wave produced by the back-and-forth movement of electric charges in a conductor.

electric-wave filter — Also called electric filter. A device that separates electric waves of different frequencies.

electrification—1. The process of establishing an excess of positive or negative charges in a material. 2. The process of applying a voltage to a component or device.

electroacoustic—Pertaining to a device (e.g., a speaker and a microphone) which involves both electric current and sound-frequency pressures.

electroacoustic transducer—A device that receives excitations from an electric system and delivers an output to an acoustic system, or vice versa. A speaker is an example of the first, and a microphone is an example of the second.

electroanalysis—The process of determining the quantity of an element or compound in an electrolyte solution by depositing the element or compound on an electrode by electrolysis.

electrobiology—The science concerned with electrical phenomena of living creatures.

electrobioscopy—The application of a voltage to produce muscular contractions.

electrocardiogram — Essentially an electromyogram of the heart muscle. All muscular activity in the body is characterized by the discharge of polarized cells, the aggregate current from which causes a voltage drop that can be measured on the skin. A changing emf will appear between electrodes connected to the arms, legs, and chest, which rises and falls with heart action such that the period of the resulting waveform is the time between heartbeats. Various positive and negative peaks within one cycle of this waveform have been lettered P, Q, R, S, and T, a notation which aids in subsequent analysis and diagnosis.

electrocardiograph—A medical instrument for detecting irregularities in the action of a human heart. It measures the changes in voltage occurring in the human body with each heartbeat. Abbreviated ekg.

electrochemical deterioration—A process in which autocatalytic electrochemical reactions produce an increase in conductivity and in turn ultimate thermal failure.

electrochemical equivalent—The weight of an element, compound, radical, or ion involved in a specified electrochemical reaction during passage of a specified quantity of electricity such as a coulomb.

electrochemical junction transistor — A junction transistor produced by etching an N-type germanium wafer on opposite sides with jets of a salt solution such as indium chloride.

electrochemical recording — A recording made by passing a signal-controlled current through a sensitized sheet of paper. The paper reacts to the current and thereby produces a visual record.

electrochemical transducer—A device which uses a chemical change to measure the input parameter, and the output of which is a varying electrical signal proportional to the measurand.

electrochemistry—That branch of science concerned with reciprocal transformations of chemical and electrical energy. This includes electrolysis, electroplating, the charge and discharge of batteries, etc.

electrocoagulation—The process of solidifying tissue by means of a high frequency electrical current.

electrocution—Killing by means of an electric current.

electrode—1. In an electronic tube, the conducting element that does one or more of the following: emits or collects electrons or ions, or controls their movement by means of an electric field on it. 2. In semiconductors, the element that does one or more of the following: emits or collects electrons or holes, or controls their movements by means of an electric field on it. 3. In electroplating, the metal being plated. 4. A conductor by means of which a current passes into or out of a fluid or an organic material such as human skin; often one terminal of a lead. 5. A metallic conductor such as in an electrolytic cell, where conduction by electrons is changed to conduction by ions or other charged particles.

electrode admittance—The alternating component of the electrode current divided by that of the electrode voltage (all other electrode voltages maintained constant).

electrode capacitance—The capacitance between one electrode and all the other electrodes connected together.

electrode characteristic—The relationship, usually shown by a graph, between the electrode voltage and current, all other electrode voltages being maintained constant.

electrode conductance—The quotient of the in-phase component of the electrode alternating current divided by the electrode alternating voltage, all other electrode voltages being maintained constant. This is a variational and not a total conductance.

electrode current—Current passing into or out of an electrode.

electrode dark current—In phototubes, the component of electrode current that flows in the absence of ionizing radiation and optical photons. Also called dark current.

electrode dissipation—The power which an electrode dissipates as heat when bombarded by electrons and/or ions and radiation from nearby electrodes.

electrode drop—The voltage drop produced in an electrode by its resistance.

electrode impedance—The reciprocal of electrode admittance.

electrodeless discharge — A luminous discharge produced by means of a high-frequency electric field in a gas-filled glass tube that has no internal electrodes.

electrodeposition—Also called electrolytic deposition. The process of depositing a substance on an electrode by electrolysis, as in electroplating, electroforming, electrorefining, or electrotinning.

electrode potential—The instantaneous voltage on an electrode. Its value is usually given with respect to the cathode of a vacuum tube.

electrode reactance—The imaginary component of electrode impedance.

electrode resistance—The reciprocal of electrode conductance. It is the effective parallel resistance, not the real component of electrode impedance.

electrode voltage—The voltage between an electrode and the cathode or a specified point of a filamentary cathode. The terms "grid voltage," "anode voltage," "plate voltage," etc., designate the voltage between these electrodes and the cathode. Unless otherwise stated, electrode voltages are measured at the available terminals.

electrodialytic process — A process for producing fresh water by using a combination of electric current and two types of chemically treated membranes.

electrodynamic—Pertaining to electric current, electricity in motion, and the actions and effects of magnetism and induction.

electrodynamic braking—A method of stopping a tape-deck motor gently by the application of a predetermined voltage to the motors.

electrodynamic instrument—An instrument which depends for its operation on the reaction between the current in one or more moving coils and the current in one or more fixed coils.

electrodynamics—The science dealing with the various phenomena of electricity in motion, including interactions of currents with each other, with their associated magnetic fields, and with other magnetic fields.

electrodynamic speaker—A speaker consisting of an electromagnet called the field coil, through which a direct current flows.

electrodynamometer—An instrument for detecting or measuring an electric current by determining the mechanical reactions between two parts of the same circuit.

electroencephalogram — A waveform obtained by plotting brain voltages (available between two points on the scalp) against time. An electroencephalogram is not necessarily a periodic function, although it can be—particularly if the patient is unconscious. These voltages are of extremely low level and require recording apparatus which display excellent noise rejection.

electroencephalograph (eeg) — An instrument for measuring and recording the rhythmically varying potentials produced by the brain by the use of electrodes applied to the scalp.

electroencephaloscope — An instrument for detecting brain potentials at many different sections of the brain and displaying them on a cathode-ray tube.

electroforming—1. Also called electrodeposition and electroplating. Making a metal object by using electrolysis to deposit a metal

on an electrode. 2. Creating a PN junction by passing a current through point contacts on a semiconductor.

electrographic recording—Also called electrostatography. The producing of a visible record by using a gaseous discharge between two or more electrodes to form electrostatically charged patterns on an insulator. (*Also see* Electrostatic Electography.)

electrokinetics—The branch of physics concerned with electricity in motion.

electroluminescence — Luminescence resulting from a high-frequency discharge through a gas or from application of an alternating current to a layer of phosphor.

electroluminescent lamp—A lamp in the shape of a panel which is decorative as well as illuminative. It consists primarily of a capacitor having a ceramic dielectric with electroluminescent phosphor. The amount of illumination is determined by the voltage across the layer and by the frequency applied to it.

Electroluminescent lamp.

electrolysis—1. The process of changing the chemical composition of a material (called the electrolyte) by sending an electric current through it. 2. The decay of an underground structure by chemical action due to stray electrical currents.

electrolyte—1. A substance in which the conduction of electricity is accompanied by chemical action. 2. The paste which forms the conducting medium between the electrodes of a dry cell, storage cell, or electrolytic capacitor. 3. A substance which, when dissolved in a suitable liquid (often water), dissociates into ions, thus rendering the liquid electrically conducting.

electrolytic—Pertaining to or made by electrolysis; deposited by electrolysis; pertaining to or containing an electrolyte.

electrolytic capacitor—A capacitor consisting of two conducting electrodes, with the anode having a metal oxide film formed on it. The film acts as the dielectric or insulating medium. It is repairable in the presence of an operating electrolyte, usually an acid or salt. Generally used for filtering, bypassing, coupling, or decoupling.

Electrolytic capacitor.

electrolytic cell—In a battery, the container, two electrodes, and the electrolyte.

electrolytic conduction—The flow of current between electrodes immersed in an electrolyte. It is caused by the movement of ions from one electrode to the other when a voltage is applied between them.

electrolytic conductivity — Also called specific conductance. A measure of the ability of a solution to carry an electric current. Defined as the reciprocal of the resistance in ohms of a 1-cm cube of the liquid at a specified temperature. The units of specific conductance are the reciprocal ohm-cm (or mho/cm) and one millionth of this, micromho/cm. (High-quality condensed steam and distilled or demineralized water have specific conductances at room temperatures as low as or lower than 1 micromho/cm).

electrolytic corrosion—*See* Corrosion.

electrolytic deposition — *See* Electrodeposition.

electrolytic dissociation—The breaking up of molecules into ions in a solution.

electrolytic interrupter—A device which is tilted to change the current through it.

electrolytic iron—Iron obtained by an electrolytic process. The iron possesses good magnetic qualities and is exceptionally free of impurities.

electrolytic potential—The difference in potential between an electrode and the immediately adjacent electrolyte, expressed in terms of some standard electrode difference.

electrolytic recording—A form of facsimile recording in which ionization causes a chemically moistened paper to undergo a change.

electrolytic rectifier — A rectifier consisting of metal electrodes in an electrolyte, in which rectification of alternating current is accompanied by electrolytic action. A polarization film formed on one of the electrodes permits current in one direction but not in the other.

electrolytic refining—The refining or purifying of metals by electrolysis.

electrolytic switch — A switch having two electrodes projecting into a chamber containing a precisely measured quantity of a conductive electrolyte, leaving an air bubble of predetermined width. When the switch is tilted from true horizontal, the bubble shifts position and changes the amount of electrolyte in contact with the electrodes, thereby changing the amount of current passed by the switch. Used as a leveling switch in gyro systems.

electrolyzer—An electrolytic cell that produces alkalies, metals, chlorine, or other allied products.

Electromagnet.

electromagnet—A temporary magnet consisting of a solenoid with an iron core. A magnetic field exists only while current flows through the solenoid.

electromagnetic—Having both magnetic and electric properties.

electromagnetic cathode-ray tube—A cathode-ray tube which uses electromagnetic deflection to deflect the electron beam.

electromagnetic communications — The electromagnetic wave conductor is space itself. The electromagnetic frequencies available today for communications fall into two categories: frequencies which form "wireless" communications (such as visual light of fairly high frequency), and frequencies man uses for wireless communications (such as radio, short wave, and microwave transmitting, of relatively lower frequencies). In communicating by radio, short wave, and microwave frequencies, translators similar in principle to those used in electrical communications are needed, although the equipment requirement increases.

electromagnetic coupling—The mutual relationship between two separate but adjacent wires when the magnetic field of one induces a voltage in the other.

electromagnetic crack detector—An instrument for detecting hidden cracks in iron or steel objects by magnetic means.

Electromagnetic deflection coil.

electromagnetic deflection—The deflection of an electron stream by means of a magnetic field. In a television receiver, the magnetic field for deflecting the electron beam horizontally and vertically is produced by two pairs of coils, called the deflection yoke, around the neck of the picture tube.

electromagnetic deflection coil — A coil, around the neck of a cathode ray tube, for deflecting the electron beam.

electromagnetic delay line—A delay line the operation of which is based on the time of propagation of electromagnetic waves through distributed or lumped capacitance and inductance.

electromagnetic energy — Forms of radiant energy such as radio waves, heat waves, light waves, X-rays, gamma rays, and cosmic rays.

electromagnetic environment—The r-f field or fields existing in an area or desired in an area to be shielded.

electromagnetic field—1. The field of influence produced around a conductor by the current flowing through it. 2. A rapidly moving electric field and its associated magnetic field. The latter is perpendicular to both the electric lines of force and their direction.

electromagnetic focusing—In a television picture tube, the focusing produced by a coil mounted on the neck. Direct current through the coil produces magnetic field lines parallel to the tube axis.

electromagnetic horn—A horn-shaped structure that provides highly directional radiation of radio waves in the 100-megahertz or higher frequency range.

electromagnetic induction — The voltage produced in a coil as the number of magnetic lines of force (flux linkages) passing through the coil changes.

electromagnetic interference—Electromagnetic phenomena which, either directly or indirectly, can contribute to a degradation in performance of an electronic receiver or system. (The phrases "radio interference," "radio-frequency interference," and "noise" have been employed at various times in the same context.)

electromagnetic lens—An electron lens in which the electron beams are focused electromagnetically.

electromagnetic mirror—A surface or region capable of reflecting radio waves, such as one of the ionized layers in the upper atmosphere.

electromagnetic oscillograph — An oscillograph in which a mechanical motion is derived from electromagnetic forces to produce a record.

electromagnetic radiation — That form of energy which is characterized by transversely oscillating electric and magnetic fields and which propagates at velocity "c" in free space. At a sufficient distance from the source, the electric-field vector and the magnetic-field vector are at right angles to each other, forming a right-handed (coordinate) system. In an ionized medium, a longitudinal component may be present.

electromagnetic relay—An electromagnetically operated switch composed of one or more coils and armatures. Whenever current flows through the coil, its magnetic field attracts the armature and completes a circuit.

electromagnetic repulsion — The repelling action between like poles of electromagnets.

electromagnetics — In physics, the branch concerned with the relationships between electric currents and their associated magnetic fields.

electromagnetic spectrum—A chart or graph showing the relationship between all known electromagnetic waveforms classified by wavelengths.

electromagnetic theory of light—The theory which states that electromagnetic and light waves have identical properties.

electromagnetic transduction — 1. Conversion of the measurand into the output induced in a conductor by a change in magnetic flux. 2. A wave produced by the oscillation of an electric charge. 3. A wave in which there are both electric and magnetic displacements. 4. A transverse wave associated with the transmission of electromagnetic energy.

10^{22} CYCLES	COSMIC RAYS
10^{21} CYCLES	
10^{20} CYCLES	GAMMA RAYS
10^{19} CYCLES	
10^{18} CYCLES	X-RAYS
10^{17} CYCLES	
10^{16} CYCLES	ULTRAVIOLET
10^{15} CYCLES	VISIBLE LIGHT
10^{14} CYCLES	
10^{13} CYCLES	INFRARED
10^{12} CYCLES	DEVELOPMENTAL
10^{11} CYCLES	
10^{10} CYCLES	RADAR
10^{9} CYCLES	UHF TELEVISION
10^{8} CYCLES	TELEVISION CHANNELS 7 TO 13
	FREQUENCY MODULATION
10^{7} CYCLES	TELEVISION CHANNELS 2 TO 6
	SHORT WAVE RADIO
10^{6} CYCLES	LORAN
10^{5} CYCLES	COMMERCIAL RADIO BROADCASTING
	ULTRASONIC REGION
10^{4} CYCLES	
10^{3} CYCLES	SOUND WAVE REGION
10^{2} CYCLES	
10 CYCLES	SUBSONIC REGION
0 CYCLES	

Electromagnetic radiation spectrum chart.

electromagnetic-type microphones—Microphones in which the voltages are varied by an electromagnet (namely, ribbon or velocity, dynamic or moving-coil, and reluctance or moving-vane microphones).

electromagnetic unit—Abbreviated emu. A unit of electricity based primarily on the magnetic effect of an electric current. The fundamental centimeter-gram-second unit is the abampere. Now considered obsolete.

electromagnetic vibrator—A mechanical device for interrupting the flow of direct current and thereby making it a pulsating current. This is done where a circuit requires an alternating current to operate. A reed within the vibrator is alternately attracted to two electromagnets.

electromagnetic wave—The radiant energy produced by oscillation of an electric charge. It includes radio, infrared, visible and ultraviolet light waves, and X-, gamma, and cosmic rays.

electromagnetism — The magnetic field around a wire or other conductor when, and only when, current passes through it.

electromechanical—Any device using electrical energy to produce mechanical movement.

electromechanical bell—A bell with a prewound spring-driven clapper which is tripped electrically to ring the bell.

electromechanical breakdown—A mechanical runaway that occurs when the mechanical restoring force fails to balance the electrical compressive force.

electromechanical chopper — *See* Contact Modulator.

electromechanical frequency meter — A

meter which uses the resonant properties of mechanical devices to indicate frequency.

electromechanical recorder—A device which transforms electrical signals into equivalent mechanical motion which is transferred to a medium by cutting, embossing, or writing.

electromechanical timer—Usually refers to a motor-driven timer, with or without an electrically operated clutch. Can also apply to pneumatic and thermal timers, or slow pull-in or drop-out relays.

electromechanical transducer — A device that transforms electrical energy into mechanical energy or vice versa. A speaker is an example of the first, and a microphone of the second.

electromechanics—That branch of electrical engineering concerned with machines producing or operated by electric currents.

electrometallurgy—That branch of science concerned with the application of electrochemistry to the extraction or treatment of metals.

electrometer—1. An electrostatic instrument that measures a potential difference or an electric charge by the mechanical force exerted between electrically charged surfaces. 2. A d-c vacuum-tube voltmeter with an extremely high input resistance, usually around 10^{10} megohms, as opposed to 10 megohms or less for a conventional type.

electrometer amplifier—An amplifier circuit having sufficiently low-current drift and other noise components, sufficiently low amplifier input-current offsets, and adequate power and current sensitivities to be usable for measuring current variations of considerably less than 10^{-12}A.

electrometer tube—A vacuum tube having a very low control-electrode conductance, to facilitate the measurement of extremely small direct currents and voltages.

electromotive force—Abbreviated emf. The force which causes electricity to flow when there is a difference of potential between two points. The unit of measurement is the volt.

electromotive series—A list of metals arranged in decreasing order of their tendency to pass into ionic form by losing electrons.

electromyogram—Classically, a waveform of the contraction of a muscle as a result of electrical stimulation. Usually the stimulation comes from the nervous system (normal muscular activity). The record of potential difference between two points on the surface of the skin resulting from the activity or action potential of a muscle.

electromyograph — An instrument for measuring and recording potentials generated by muscles.

electromyography—An electronic method of measuring and recording the electrical activity of muscles.

electron—Also called negatron. One of the natural elementary constituents of matter; it carries a negative electric charge of one electronic unit and has approximately 1/1840th the mass of a hydrogen atom or 9.107×10^{-28} gram. Electrons surround the positively charged nucleus and determine the chemical properties of the atom. Positive electrons, or positrons, also exist.

electron attachment—Process by which an electron is attached to a neutral molecule to form a negative ion. Often characterized by the attachment coefficient η, which is the number of attachments per centimeter of drift. Also characterized by the ratio $h = \sigma_a/\theta$, where σ_a is the attachment cross section and θ the total cross section.

electron avalanche — The chain reaction started when one free electron collides with one or more orbiting electrons and frees them. The free electrons then free others in the same manner, and so on.

electron beam—A narrow stream of electrons moving in the same direction under the influence of an electric or magnetic field.

electron-beam generator—A velocity-modulated generator, such as a klystron tube, used to generate extremely high frequencies.

electron-beam instrument — Also called a cathode-ray instrument. An instrument in which a beam of electrons is deflected by an electric or magnetic field (or both). Usually the beam is made to strike a fluorescent screen so the deflection can be observed.

electron-beam machining — A process in which controlled electron beams are used to weld or shape a piece of material.

electron-beam magnetometer — An instrument that measures the intensity and direction of magnetic forces by the immersion of an electron beam into the magnetic field.

electron-beam mode discharge—A form of discharge produced by a perforated-wall hollow cathode operating under conditions of pressure, voltage, and geometry usually associated with the abnormal glow discharge.

electron-beam tube—An electron tube which depends for its operation on the formation and control of one or more electron beams.

electron-beam welding—The process of using a focused beam of electrons to heat materials to the fusion point.

electron charge — Also called elementary charge. The charge of a single electron. Its value is 1.60203×10^{-19} coulomb. The fundamental unit of electrical charge.

electron-coupled oscillator — Abbreviated ECO. A circuit using a multigrid tube in which the cathode and two grids operate as a conventional oscillator and the electron stream couples the plate-circuit load to the oscillator.

electron coupling—In vacuum (principally multigrid) tubes, the transfer of energy between electrodes as electrons leave one and go to the other.

electron drift—The movement of electrons in a definite direction through a conductor, as opposed to the haphazard transfer of energy from one electron to another by collision.

electronegative—Having an electric polarity that is negative.

electron emission—The freeing of electrons into space from the surface of a body under the influence of heat, light, impact, chemical disintegration, or a potential difference.

electron flow—The movement of electrons from a negative to a positive point in a metal or other conductor, or from a negative to a positive electrode through a liquid, gas, or vacuum.

a - CATHODE
b - GRID
c - PREACCELERATOR
d - FOCUSING
e - ACCELERATOR

Electron gun.

electron gun — 1. An electrode structure which produces and may control focus and may deflect and converge one or more electron beams. 2. The portion of a cathode-ray tube or camera tube which emits a beam of controlled electrons.

electronic—1. Pertaining to that branch of science which deals with the motion, emission, and behavior of currents of free electrons, especially in vacuum, gas, or phototubes and special conductors or semiconductors. This is contrasted with electric, which pertains to the flow of large currents in metal conductors. 2. Of or pertaining to devices, circuits, or systems using the principle of electron flow through a conductor—for example, *electronic* control, equipment, instrument, circuit.

electronic autopilot — An arrangement of gyroscopes, electronic amplifiers, and servomotors for detecting deviations in the flight of an aircraft and applying the required corrections directly to its control cables.

electronic "bug"—A keying system which converts the Morse signals from a hand key into correctly proportioned and spaced dots and dashes.

electronic camouflage — Use of electronic means, or exploitation of electronic characteristics, to reduce, submerge, or eliminate the radar-echoing properties of a target.

electronic circuit—A circuit containing one or more electron tubes, transistors, magnetic amplifiers, etc.

electronic commutator — A type of switch which provides a continuous switching or sampling of a number of circuits by means of a radial-beam electronic tube or electronic switching circuit.

electronic control — Also called electronic regulation. The control of a machine or condition by electronic devices.

electronic counter—An instrument capable of counting up to several million electrical pulses per second.

electronic countermeasures—Reducing the effectiveness of enemy equipment employing or affected by electromagnetic radiations. This is done by using appropriate electronic devices.

electronic countermeasures control—1. Collection and sorting of large quantities of data for the purpose of measuring and defining radar signals. 2. Examination of the data received in order to determine selection and switching of countermeasure devices with little or no time delay.

electronic coupling—The method of coupling electrical energy from one circuit to another through the electron stream in a vacuum tube.

electronic data-processing center—A place in which is kept automatically operated equipment, including computers, designed to simplify the interpretation and use of data gathered by instrumentation installations or information-collection agencies. Abbreviated EDP center.

electronic data-processing machine—Abbreviated EDPM. A machine or its device and attachments used primarily in or with an electronic data-processing system.

electronic data-processing system — Any machine or group of automatically intercommunicating machines capable of entering, receiving, sorting, classifying, computing and/or recording alphabetical or numerical accounting or statistical data (or all three) without intermediate use of tabulating cards.

electronic deception—Radiation or reradiation of electromagnetic waves to mislead the enemy in the interpretation of data received by his electronic equipment.

electronic differential analyzer—A form of analog computer using interconnected electronic integrators to solve differential equations.

electronic digital computer — A machine which uses electronic circuitry in the main computing element to perform arithmetic and logical operations on digital data (i.e., data represented by numbers or alphabetic symbols) automatically, by means of an internally stored program of machine instruction. Such devices are distinguished from calculators, on which the sequence of instructions is externally stored and is impressed manually (desk calculators) or from tape or cards (card-programmed calculators).

electronic efficiency — The ratio of (a) the power at the desired frequency delivered by the electron stream to the oscillator or amplifier circuit to (b) the direct power supplied to the stream.

electronic flash—Also called strobe. The firing of special light-producing, high-voltage, gas-filled glass tubes with a high instantaneous surge of current furnished by

Electronic flash unit.

a capacitor or bank of capacitors which have been charged from a high-voltage source (usually 450 volts or higher).

electronic flash tube—*See* Flash Tube.

electronic frequency synthesizer—A device which generates two or more selectable frequencies from one or more fixed-frequency sources.

electronic heating — Also called high-frequency heating. A method of heating a material by inducing a high-frequency current in it or having the material act as the dielectric between two plates charged with a high-frequency current.

electronic industries — Industrial organizations engaged in the manufacture, design, development, and/or substantial assembly of electronic equipment, systems, assemblies, or the components thereof.

Electronic Industries Association (EIA)—A trade association of the electronics industry. Some of its functions are the formulation of technical standards, dissemination of marketing data, and the maintenance of contact with government agencies in matters relating to the electronics industry.

electronic instrument — Any instrument which depends for its operation on the action of either one or more electron devices.

electronic intelligence — The technical and intelligence information derived from foreign noncommunications electromagnetic radiations emanating from other than nuclear detonations or radioactive sources.

electronic keying — A method of keying whereby the dots and dashes are produced solely by electronic means.

electronic line scanning—Facsimile scanning in which a spot on a cathode-ray tube moves across the copy electronically while the record sheet or subject copy is moved mechanically in a perpendicular direction.

electronic microphone—A device which depends for its operation on the generation of a voltage by the motion of one of the electrodes in a special electron tube.

electronic mine detector—*See* Mine Detector.

electronic multimeter—A device employing the characteristics of an electron-tube circuit for the measurement of electrical quantities, at least one of which is voltage or current, on a single calibrated scale.

electronic music—The electronic generation

and processing of audio signals or the electronic processing of natural sound, and the manipulation and arrangement of these signals via tape recorders into a finished musical composition.

electronic organ—The electronic counterpart of the pipe organ. All tones and tone variations such as vibrato, tremolo, etc., are produced by electronic circuits instead of by pipes.

electronic packaging—The coating or surrounding of an electronic assembly with a dielectric compound.

electronic photometer—An electronic instrument for measuring intensity of light, brightness of paints, turbidity of solutions, etc. It comprises a phototube, an electronic direct-current amplifier, and an indicating instrument.

electronic power supply—A circuit which transforms electrical input energy, alternating or direct current—into output energy—alternating or direct current. (Sources operating on rotating machine principles, or deriving electrical power from other energy forms such as batteries and solar cells, are excluded.) Supplies covered by this definition fall into one of four groups: 1. A-c in, d-c out—most common supplies. 2. A-c in, a-c out—line regulators, variable frequency supplies. 3. D-c in, d-c out—converters. 4. D-c in, a-c out—inverters.

electronic products—Materials, parts, components, subassemblies, and equipment which employ the principles of electronics in performing their major functions. These products may be used as instruments and controls in communications, detection, amplification, computation, inspection, testing, measurement, operation, recording, analysis, and other functions employing electronic principles.

electronic profilometer—An electronic instrument for measuring surface roughness. The diamond-point stylus of a permanent-magnet dynamic pickup is moved over the surface being examined. The resultant variations in voltage are amplified, rectified, and measured with a meter calibrated to read directly in micro-inches of deviation from smoothness.

electronic reconnaissance—Search for electromagnetic radiations to determine their existence, source, and pertinent characteristics for electronic warfare purposes.

electronic rectifier—A rectifier using electron tubes or equivalent semiconductor elements as rectifying elements.

electronic regulation—*See* Electronic Control.

electronic relay—An electronic circuit that provides the functional equivalent of a relay, but has no moving parts.

electronics—1. The field of science and engineering concerned with the behavior of electrons in devices and the utilization of such devices. 2. Of or pertaining to the field of electronics, such as electronics engineer, course, laboratory, committee.

electronic stethoscope—An electronic amplifier of sounds within a body. Its selective controls permit tuning for low heart tones or high pulmonary tones. It has an auxiliary output for recording or viewing audio patterns.

electronic stimulator—A device for applying electronic pulses or signals to activate muscles, or to identify nerves, or for muscular therapy, etc.

electronic switch—1. A circuit element causing a start and stop action or a switching action electronically, usually at high speeds. 2. A test instrument for presenting two waveshapes on a single-gun cathode-ray tube.

electronic thermal conductivity—The part of the thermal conductivity due to the transfer of thermal energy by means of electrons and holes.

electronic timer—1. A synchronizer, pulse generator, modulator, or keyer that originates a series of continuous control pulses at an unvarying repetition rate known as the pulse-recurrence frequency. 2. A timer using electronic circuits (either tube or transistor type) to control a time period, in place of a motor or other means.

electronic tube relay—A relay that employs electronic tubes as components.

electronic tuning—1. Altering the frequency of a reflex klystron oscillator by changing the repeller voltage. 2. Frequency changing in a transmitter or receiver by changing a control voltage rather than circuit components.

electronic voltmeter—Also called vacuum-tube voltmeter. A voltmeter which utilizes the rectifying and amplifying properties of electron tubes and their circuits to secure such characteristics as high input impedance, wide frequency range, peak-to-peak indications, etc.

electronic volt-ohmmeter—A device employing the characteristics of an electron-tube circuit for the measurement of voltage and resistance on a single calibrated scale.

electronic warfare—Military usage of electronics to reduce an enemy's effective use of radiated electromagnetic energy and to insure our own effective use.

electronic waveform synthesizer—An instrument using electron devices to generate an electrical signal of a desired waveform.

electron image tube—A cathode-ray tube having a photoemissive mosaic upon which an optical image is projected, and an electron gun to scan the mosaic and convert the optical image into corresponding electrical current.

electron lens—The convergence of the electrons into a narrow beam in a cathode-ray tube by deflecting them electromagnetically or electrostatically. So called because its action is analogous to that of an optical lens.

electron microscope—An instrument which

uses an electron beam to penetrate thin samples of a material. It is possible to magnify images of the material on a screen or film up to 350,000 times.

electron multiplier — A vacuum tube in which electrons liberated from a photosensitive cathode are attracted successively to a series of electrodes called dynodes. In doing so, each electron liberates others by secondary emission and thereby greatly increases the number of electrons flowing in the tube.

electron-multiplier section — A section of an electron tube in which an electron current is amplified by one or more successive dynode stages.

electron optics — The branch of electronics concerned with the behavior of the electron beam under the influence of electrostatic and electromagnetic forces.

electron-pair bond — A valence bond formed by two electrons, one from each of two adjacent atoms.

electron paramagnetic resonance — A condition in which a paramagnetic solid subjected to two magnetic fields, one of which is fixed and the other normal to the first and varying at the resonance frequency, emits electromagnetic radiation associated with changes in the magnetic quantum number of the electrons.

electron-ray tube — Also called a "magic eye." A tube which indicates visibly on a fluorescent target the effects of changes in control-grid voltage applied to the tube. Used as a tuning indicator in receivers.

CATHODE LIGHT SHIELD FLUORESCENT COATING RAY-CONTROL ELECTRODE TARGET TRIODE PLATE TRIODE GRID CATHODE

Electron-ray tube.

electron scanning — The moving of an electron beam back and forth and/or up and down by deflecting the beam electromagnetically or electrostatically.

electron spin — The twirling motion of an electron, independent of any orbital motion.

electron telescope — An apparatus for seeing through haze and fog. An infrared image is formed optically on the photoemissive mosaic of an electron-image tube and then made visible by the tube.

electron transit time — The time required for electrons to travel between two electrodes in a vacuum tube. This time is extremely important in tubes designed for ultrahigh frequencies.

electron tube — An electron device in which the electrons move through a vacuum or gaseous medium within a gas-tight envelope.

electron unit — The unit of charge (negative or positive) equal to the charge on an electron.

electron volt — Abbreviated ev or eV. The amount of kinetic energy gained by an electron when it is accelerated through an electric potential difference of 1 volt. It is equivalent to 1.603×10^{-12} erg. It is a unit of energy or work, not of voltage.

electron-wave tube — An electron tube in which streams of electrons having different velocities interact and cause a progressive change in signal modulation along their length.

electro-optical transistor — A transistor capable of responding in nanoseconds to both light and electrical signals.

electropad — The part of an electrocardiograph body electrode that makes contact with the skin.

electrophonic effect — The sensation of hearing produced when an alternating current of suitable frequency and magnitude from an external source is passed through an animal or human body.

electrophoresis — The movement of particles or ions in solution caused by applying an electric field, as reported by O. Lodge in 1886.

electrophoresis apparatus — An apparatus for causing migration of charged particles (ions) in solution in an electric field. Types include paper, cascading electrodes, high voltage, gel, and thin layer.

electrophoresis scanner — An instrument for reading bands on paper strips or gel, for the purpose of measuring particle movement due to electrophoresis.

electrophorus — An early type of static-electricity generator.

electrophotographic process — The process in which images are formed by various electrical and photographic means. Examples are processes employing selenium-coated drums or zinc-oxide–coated paper.

electrophotometer — An instrument using a photoelectric sensor for colorimetric determinations.

electroplaques — Individual electricity-producing cells in eels and other electric fishes connected in series-parallel arrays, like miniature elements of a battery. They are usually thin waferlike cells, the two surfaces of which differ markedly.

electroplate — To deposit a metal on the surface of certain materials by electrolysis.

electroplating — The electrodeposition of an adherent metal coating on a conductive object for protection, decoration, or other purposes. The object to be plated is placed in an electrolyte and connected to one terminal of a d-c voltage source. The metal to be deposited is similarly immersed and connected to the other terminal. Ions of the metal pro-

Electrostatic deflection.

vide transfer to the metal as they make up the current between the electrodes.

electropolishing—The process of producing a smooth, lustrous surface on a metal by making it the anode in an electrolytic solution and preferentially dissolving the minute protuberances.

electrorefining—*See* Electroplating.

electroretinograph—An instrument for measuring the electrical response of the human retina to light stimulation.

electroscope—An electrostatic instrument for measuring a potential difference or an electric charge by means of the mechanical force exerted between electrically charged surfaces.

Electroscope.

electrosensitive recording—The passage of electric current into a sheet of sensitive paper to produce a permanent record.

electroshock—A state of shock produced by passing an electric current through the brain. It is useful in the treatment of certain mental disorders.

electrospinograph — A device for detecting and recording electric signals of the spinal cord.

electrostatic—Pertaining to static electricity—i.e., electricity, or an electric charge, at rest.

electrostatic actuator—An apparatus comprising an auxiliary external electrode which permits known electrostatic forces to be applied to the diaphragm of a microphone for the purpose of obtaining a primary calibration.

electrostatic capacitor — Two conducting electrodes separated by an insulating material such as air, ceramic, mica, gas, paper, plastic film, or glass. These are generally high-impedance devices.

electrostatic charge — An electric charge stored in a capacitor or on the surface of an insulated object.

electrostatic component — The portion of radiation due to electrostatic fields.

electrostatic-convergence principle — The principle of electron-beam convergence through use of an electrostatic field.

electrostatic coupling—Method of coupling by which charges on one surface influence those on another through capacitive action.

electrostatic deflection—The method of deflecting an electron beam by passing it between charged plates mounted inside a cathode-ray tube.

electrostatic electrography—The branch of electrostatography which produces a visible record by employing an insulating medium to form latent electrostatic patterns without the aid of electromagnetic radiation.

electrostatic electrophotography — That branch of electrostatography which produces a visible record by employing a photoresponsive medium to form latent electrostatic images with the aid of electromagnetic radiation.

electrostatic energy—The energy contained in electricity at rest, such as in the charge of a capacitor.

electrostatic field—The vector force field set up in the vicinity of nonmoving electrical charges. The strength of this static field at a point is defined as the force per unit charge on a stationary positive test charge, provided the test charge is so small that it does not disturb the original charge distribution.

electrostatic flux—The electrostatic lines of force existing between bodies at different potentials.

electrostatic focusing—The focusing of an electron beam by the action of an electric field.

electrostatic galvanometer — Galvanometer

165

operated by the effects of two electric charges on each other.

electrostatic generator—A device for the production of electric charges by electrostatic action.

electrostatic induction—1. The process of charging an object electrically by bringing it near a charged object. 2. Capacitive induction of interfering signals over an air gap separating an instrument (e.g., from its wiring or housing).

electrostatic instrument — An instrument which depends for its operation on the attraction and repulsion between electrically charged bodies.

electrostatic memory—Also called electrostatic storage. A memory device in which information is retained by an electrostatic charge. A special type of cathode-ray tube is usually employed, together with associated circuitry.

electrostatic memory tube—Also called storage tube. An electron tube in which information is retained by electric charges.

electrostatic microphone—Also called capacitor or condenser microphone. A microphone which depends for its operation on variations in its electrostatic capacitance.

electrostatic precipitation—The process of removing smoke, dust, and other particles from the air by charging them so that they can be attracted to and collected by a properly polarized electrode.

electrostatic process — A reproduction method in which image formation depends on electrical rather than chemical changes induced by light.

electrostatic recording—Recording by means of a signal-controlled electrostatic field.

electrostatic relay—A relay in which two or more conductors that are separated by insulating material move because of the mutual attraction or repulsion produced by electric charges applied to the conductors.

electrostatics—The branch of physics concerned with electricity at rest.

electrostatic separator — An apparatus in which a finely pulverized mixture of the materials to be separated is passed through the powerful electrostatic field between two electrodes.

electrostatic series—See Triboelectric Series.

electrostatic shield—A shield which prevents electrostatic coupling between circuits, but permits electromagnetic coupling.

electrostatic speaker—Also called capacitor or condenser speaker. A speaker in which the mechanical forces are produced by the action of electrostatic fields.

electrostatic storage — The storage of changeable information in the form of charged or uncharged areas usually on the screen of a cathode-ray tube.

electrostatic transducer—A transducer that consists of a capacitor, at least one plate of which can be set into vibration. Its operation depends on the interaction between its

electric field and a change in its electrostatic capacity.

electrostatic tweeter — A speaker with a movable flat metal diaphragm and a nonmovable metal electrode capable of reproducing high audio frequencies. The diaphragm is driven by the varying high voltages applied across it and the electrode.

electrostatic unit—An electric unit based primarily on the dynamic interaction of electric charges. Defined as a charge which, if concentrated on a small sphere, would repel with a force of one dyne a similar charge one centimeter away in a vacuum.

electrostatic voltmeter — A voltmeter depending for its action on electrostatic forces. Its scale is usually graduated in volts or kilovolts.

electrostatography—The process of recording and reproducing visible patterns by the formation and utilization of latent electrostatic charge patterns.

electrostriction—A mechanical deformation caused by the application of an electric field to any dielectric material. The deformation is proportional to the square of the applied field. This phenomenon results from the induced dipole movement caused by the applied field, resulting in the mechanical distortion.

electrostrictive effect—The elastic deformation of a dielectric by an electrostatic field.

electrostrictive relay—A relay the operation of which is produced by an electrostrictive-dielectric actuator.

electrotape — An electronic distance-measuring device.

electrotherapeutics—See Electrotherapy.

electrotherapy—Also known as electrotherapeutics. The medical science or use of electricity to treat a disease or ailment.

electrotherapy apparatus — Equipment for applying electric current to the body for massage or heat treatment.

electrothermal—The heating effect of electric current, or the electric current produced by heat.

electrothermal expansion element—An actuating element consisting of a wire strip or

Electrostatic speaker.

other shape and having a high coefficient of thermal expansion.

electrothermal recorder—A recorder in which heat produces the image on the recording medium in response to the received signals.

electrothermal recording—*See* Electrothermal Recorder.

electrothermic instrument—An instrument which depends for its operation on the heating effect of a current. Examples are the thermocouple, bolometric, hot-wire, and hot-strip instruments.

electrothermics—The branch of science concerned with the direct transformation of electric energy into heat.

electrowinning—The process by which metals are recovered from a solution by electrolysis.

element—1. One of the 104 known chemical substances that cannot be divided into simpler substances by chemical means. A substance the atoms of which all have the same atomic number (e.g., hydrogen, lead, uranium). 2. In a computer, the portion or subassembly which constitutes the means of accomplishing one particular function, such as the arithmetic element. 3. Any electrical device (such as an inductor, resistor, capacitor generator, line, or electron tube) with terminals at which it may be connected directly to other electrical devices. 4. The dot or dash of an International Morse character. 5. A radiator, either active or parasitic, that is part of an antenna. 6. The smallest portion of a televised picture that still retains the characteristics of the picture. 7. A portion of a part that cannot be renewed without destruction of the part. 8. A constituent of a microcircuit or integrated circuit that contributes directly to its operation.

elemental area—*See* Picture Element.

elemental semiconductor—A semiconductor containing only one element in the undoped state.

elementary charge—A natural unit or quantum into which both positive and negative charges appear to be subdivided. It is the charge on a single electron and has a value of about 4.77×10^{-10} electrostatic units.

element error rate—The ratio of the number of elements incorrectly received to the total number of elements sent.

elevation—The angular position perpendicular to the earth's surface.

elevation-position indicator—A radar display which simultaneously shows angular elevation and slant range of detected objects.

elevator leveling control—A positioning control used to align the platform of an elevator with the floor level of the building. Metal vanes are mounted in the elevator shaft at each floor level, and an oscillator is mounted on the elevator car. When the elevator is properly leveled, the metal vane is between the plate and the grid coils of the oscillator. A relay connected in the oscillator circuit now energizes. The contacts of

this relay are connected in the motor-control circuit of the elevator so that the elevator stops in alignment with the floor level.

elf—Abbreviation for extremely low frequency.

eliminator—Also called a battery eliminator. A device operated from an a-c or d-c power line and used for supplying direct current and voltage to a battery-operated circuit.

elliptically polarized wave—An electromagnetic wave the electric intensity vector of which describes an ellipse at one point.

elliptical polarization—Polarization in which the wave vector rotates in an elliptical orbit about a point.

e/m—The ratio of the electric charge to the mass for particles such as electrons and positive rays. For slow-moving electrons, the value of e/m is 1.77×10^4 coulombs per gram. The value decreases with increasing velocity, however, because of an increase in effective mass.

embedding—A general term for all methods of surrounding or enclosing components and assemblies with a substantial thickness of electrically insulating solid or foam material that substantially fills the voids or interstices between parts.

embedment—The complete encasement of a part or assembly to some uniform external shape. A relatively large volume of a complete package consists of the embedment material.

embossed-foil printed circuits—A printed circuit formed by indenting the desired pattern of metal foil into an insulating base, and then mechanically removing the remaining unwanted raised portion.

Embossed-groove recording.

embossed-groove recording—A method of recording sounds on discs or film strips by embossing sound grooves with a blunt stylus rather than by cutting into them with a sharp stylus. Embossing throws the material up in furrows on each side of the sound groove without actually removing any of the material in the disc or strip.

embossing stylus—A recording stylus with a rounded tip which forms a groove in the recording medium by merely displacing the material instead of removing it completely.

emergency communication—The transmission or reception of distress, alarm, urgent, or safety signals or messages relating to the safety of life or property, or the occasional operation of equipment to determine whether it is in working condition.

emergency radio channel—Any radio frequency reserved for emergency use, particularly for distress signals.

emergency service—The radio-communication service carrier used for emergency purposes.

emf—Abbreviation for electromotive force.

emission—1. The waves radiated into space by a transmitter. 2. The ejection of electrons from the surface of a material (under the influence of heat, for example).

emission characteristic — The relationship between the emission and the factor controlling it, such as temperature, voltage, or current of the filament or heater. This relationship is usually shown on a graph.

emission current—The current produced in the plate circuit of a tube when all the electrons emitted by the cathode pass to the plate.

emission efficiency—The rating of a hot cathode. Expressed in milliamperes per watt.

emission spectrum—The spectrum showing the radiation emitted by a substance, such as the light emitted by a metal when placed in an electric arc, or the light emitted by an incandescent filament.

emission types—The classification of modes of radio transmission adopted by international agreement. The a-m designations are:
Type A0. Unmodulated continuous-wave transmission.
Type A1. Telegraphy or pure continuous waves.
Type A2. Modulated telegraphy.
Type A3. Telephony.
Type A4. Facsimile.
Type A5. Television.

emission-type tube tester — Also called an English-reading tube tester. A tube tester for checking the electron emission from the filament or cathode. The indicating meter is generally calibrated to read "Good" or "Bad." The tester connects all elements such as the plate and screen, suppressor, and control grids together and uses them as an anode.

emission velocity—The initial velocity at which electrons emerge from the surface of a cathode, ranging from zero up to a few volts (attained by very few electrons). This effect accounts for the existence of virtual cathodes, and also for the shape of the cutoff region of plate current.

emissivity—The ratio of the radiant energy emitted by a radiation source to the radiant energy of a perfect (black-body) radiator having the same area and at the same temperature and conditions.

emitron — A cathode-ray tube developed in England.

emitron camera—A British television camera tube resembling an iconoscope.

emittance—The power per unit area radiated by a source of energy.

emitter—1. An electrode within a transistor from which carriers are usually minority carriers; when they are majority carriers, the emitter is referred to as a majority emitter. 2. Of a transistor, a region from which charge carriers that are minority carriers in the base are injected into the base. 3. A device used on a punched-card machine to give timed pulses at regular intervals during the machine cycle.

emitter bias—The bias voltage applied to the emitter of a transistor.

emitter current—The direct current flowing in the emitter circuit of a transistor.

emitter follower—A common-collector transistor amplifier similar in operation to a vacuum-tube cathode follower.

emitter-follower amplifier — See Common-Collector Amplifier.

emitter junction—A semiconductor junction normally biased in the low-resistance direction so that minority carriers are injected into the interelectrode region.

emitter (junction transistor)—In a double-junction (PNP or NPN) transistor, the end semiconductor material that is forward-biased with respect to the base and emits a flow of carriers into the interelectrode region. Roughly comparable to the cathode of a tube.

emitter resistance—The resistance in series with the emitter lead in the common-T equivalent circuit of a transistor.

emitter semiconductor — A junction normally biased in the low-resistance direction to inject minority carriers into an interelectrode region.

emitter voltage—The voltage between the emitter terminal and a reference point.

empire cloth—A cotton or linen cloth coated with varnish and used as insulation on coils and other parts of electrical equipment.

empirical—Based on actual measurement, observation, or experience, as opposed to theoretical determination.

emu—Abbreviation for electromagnetic unit.

enable—To permit a circuit to be activated by the removal of a suppression signal.

enabling gate—A circuit which determines the start and length of a generated pulse.

enabling pulse—A pulse which opens a normally closed electric gate, or otherwise permits an operation for which a pulse is a necessary condition.

enameled wire—Wire coated with a layer of baked-enamel insulation.

encapsulating material—A composition primarily adapted for use on or around an electrical device to provide protection from the surrounding environment.

encapsulation—A protective coating of cured plastic placed around delicate electronic components and assemblies. It is identical to potting, except the cured plastic is removed from the mold. The plastic therefore determines the color and surface hardness of the finished part. The molds may be made of any suitable material.

enclosed relay — A relay in which both the coil and the contacts are protected from the environment.

enclosure—A housing for any electrical or electronic device, normally a speaker.

encode—Also called encipher; the inverse of decode. Conversion of signals to coded form. A circuit that generally converts signals from decimal to binary form.

encoder—1. An electromechanical device that can be attached to a shaft to produce a series of pulses to indicate shaft position; when the output is differentiated, the device is an accurate tachometer. (It is fundamentally oriented to digital rather than analog techniques.) An encoder contains a disc with a printed pattern; as the disc rotates, it makes and breaks a circuit. The more make-and-break cycles per revolution, the better the resolution. 2. A digital-to-analog converter.

end-around shift—In a computer, the movement of characters from one end of the register to the other end of the same register.

end bell—An accessory which is similar to a cable clamp and attaches to the back of a plug or receptacle. It serves as an adapter for the rear of connectors. Some angular end bells have built-in cable clamps. Angular end bells up to 90° are available.

end bracket—*See* End Shield.

end effect—The capacitive effect at the ends of a half-wave antenna. To compensate for this effect, a dipole is cut slightly shorter than a half wave.

end-fire array—A linear or cylindrical antenna having its direction of maximum radiation parallel to the long axis of the array.

end instrument—A device connected to one terminal of a loop and capable of converting usable intelligence into electrical signals, or vice versa. Includes all generating, signal-converting, and loop-terminating devices at the transmitting and/or receiving location.

end item—A combination of products, parts, and/or materials that is ready for its intended use.

end mark—In a computer, a code or signal used to indicate the termination of a unit of information.

endodyne reception—A British term applying to reception of unmodulated code signals. A vacuum-tube circuit having a local oscillator whose frequency is slightly different from that of the carrier signal. Thus a beat signal in the audio range is produced.

end-of-file mark—In a computer, a code instruction indicating that the last record of a file has been read.

end-on armature—Of a relay, an armature which moves in the direction of the core axis, with the pole face at the end of the core and perpendicular to this axis.

end-on directional antenna—A directional antenna which radiates chiefly toward the line on which the antenna elements are arranged.

endoradiosonde—Also called radio pill. A device for detecting and transmitting physiological data from the gastrointestinal tract or other inaccessible body cavities.

endothermic—A term describing a chemical reaction in which heat is absorbed.

end point—The shaft positions immediately before the first and after the last measurable change(s) in output ratio after wiper continuity has been established, as the shaft of a precision potentiometer moves in a specified direction.

end-point sensitivity—The algebraic difference in electrical output between the maximum and minimum value of the measurand over which an instrument is calibrated.

end-point voltage—The terminal voltage of a cell below which equipment connected to it will not operate or should not be operated.

end resistance—The resistance of a precision potentiometer measured between the wiper terminal and an end terminal, with the shaft positioned at the corresponding end point.

end-resistance offset—In potentiometers, the residual resistance between a terminal and the moving contact, at a position corresponding to full rotation against that terminal.

end scale value—The value of the actuating electrical quantity that corresponds to end scale indication of an instrument. When zero is not at the end or at the electrical center of the scale, the higher value is taken. Certain instruments such as power-factor meters, ohmmeters, etc., are necessarily excepted from this definition.

end setting—In a potentiometer, the minimum resistance that is measured between one end of a potentiometer and the wiper, with the wiper mechanically positioned at that end.

end shield—1. Frequently called end bracket or end bell. In a motor housing, the part that supports the bearing and also guards the electrical and rotating parts inside the motor. 2. In a magnetron, the shield that confines the space charge to the interaction space.

end spaces—In a multicavity magnetron, the two cavities at either end of the anode block which terminate all the anode-block cavity resonators.

end use—The way the ultimate consumer uses a device.

energize—To apply the rated voltage to a circuit or device, such as to the coil of a relay, in order to activate it.

energized—Also called alive, hot, and live. Electrically connected to a voltage source.

energy—The capacity for performing work. A particle or piece of matter may have energy because it is moving or because of its position in relation to other particles or pieces of matter. A rolling ball is an example of the first; a ball at rest at the top of an incline, an example of the second.

energy conversion—The change of energy from one form to another, e.g., from chemical energy to electrical energy.

energy conversion devices—Devices including primary and secondary cells; fuel cells;

photovoltaic systems; electrochemical energy converters; radiation conversion devices; thermionic converters; converters using solar, ionic, or nuclear energy sources; devices for creating a plasma in an interaction space between an emitter and a collector; electrostatic generators for creating an electrical output; organic and inorganic ion exchange and membrane devices; electron-volt energy devices; devices for direct conversion of fuel to electricity; and electrical-energy storage-unit devices capable of delivering a power output.

energy density — The ratio of the energy available from a cell to the weight or volume of the cell.

energy gap—The energy range between the bottom of the conduction band and the top of the valence band of a semiconductor.

energy-level diagram—A line drawing that shows the increase or decrease in electrical power as current intensities rise and fall along a channel of signal communications.

energy-measuring equipment — Equipment used to measure energy in electrical, electronic, acoustical, or mechanical systems.

energy of a charge — Represented by $E = \frac{1}{2}QV$, given in ergs, when the charge Q and the potential V are in electrostatic units.

energy-product curve—A curve obtained by plotting the product of the value of magnetic induction B and demagnetizing force H for each point of the demagnetization curve of a permanent magnetic material. Usually shown together with the demagnetization curve.

energy redistribution—A method of finding the duration of an irregularly shaped pulse by considering it as a power curve. The area under the curve can be represented by an equivalent rectangle of the same area and peak amplitude. The original-pulse duration is equal to the rectangle width.

energy state—The position and speed of an electron relative to the position and speed of other electrons in the same atom or adjoining atoms.

engineering—A profession in which a knowledge of the natural sciences is applied with judgment to develop ways of utilizing the materials and forces of nature.

English-reading tube tester—See Emission-Type Tube Tester.

enhanced carrier demodulation—An amplitude-demodulation system in which a synchronized local carrier of the proper phase is added to the demodulator. This has the effect of materially reducing the distortion produced in the demodulation process.

entropy—1. A measure of the unavailable energy in a thermodynamic system. 2. The unavailable information in a set of documents. 3. An inactive or static condition (total entropy).

entry—Each statement in a computer programming system.

envelope—1. The glass or metal housing of a vacuum tube. 2. The curve passing through the peaks of a graph and showing the waveform of a modulated radio-frequency carrier signal.

envelope delay—The time which elapses as a transmitted wave passes any two points of a transmission circuit. Such delay is determined primarily by the constants of the circuit and is measurable in milliseconds or microseconds.

envelope-delay distortion — The distortion that occurs during transmission when the phase shift of a circuit or system is not constant over the frequency range.

environmental conditions—External conditions of heat, shock, vibration, pressure, moisture, etc.

environmentally sealed—Provided with gaskets, seals, potting, or other means to keep out contamination which might reduce performance.

environmental testing—The testing of a system or component under controlled environmental conditions, each of which tends to affect its operation or life.

environmentproof switch—A switch which is completely sealed to insure constant operating characteristics. Sealing normally includes an "O" ring on the actuator shaft and fused glass-to-metal terminal seals or complete potting and an elastomer plunger-case seal.

episcotister—A device consisting of alternate opaque and transparent discs which rotate at a speed which interrupts light beams at an audio-frequency rate. It modulates the light beam used to excite a photoelectric element.

epitaxial—Pertaining to a single crystal layer on a crystalline substrate, oriented the same as the substrate. In certain semiconductor processes, an epitaxial layer is grown on a silicon substrate during the fabrication of transistors and integrated circuits.

epitaxial device — A device constructed in such a manner that the crystalline structure of successive layers is oriented in the same direction as that of the original base material.

epitaxial film—1. A film of single-crystal semiconductor material that has been deposited onto a single-crystal substrate. 2. Any deposited film, provided the orientation of its crystal is the same as that of the substrate material.

epitaxial growth — A chemical reaction in which silicon is precipitated from a gaseous solution, and grows on the surface of a silicon wafer present in the gaseous solution.

epitaxial-growth mesa transistor—A transistor made by overlaying a thin mesa crystal over another mesa crystal.

epitaxial growth process—The process of growing a semiconductor material by depositing it in vaporized form on a semiconductor seed crystal. The deposited layer continues the single-crystal structure of the seed.

epitaxial layer—A grown or deposited crystal layer with the same crystal orientation as the parent material and, in the case of semiconductor circuits, is also the same basic material as the original substrate.

epitaxial planar transistor—A transistor in which a thin collector region is epitaxially deposited on a low-resistivity substrate, and the base and emitter regions are produced by gaseous diffusion with the edges of the junction under a protective oxide mask.

epitaxial process—The process of growing from the vapor phase a single-crystal semiconductor material with controlled resistivity and thickness.

epitaxial transistor—A transistor with one or more epitaxial layers.

epitaxy—The controlled growth of a layer of semiconductor material in a suitable substrate.

E plane—The plane of an antenna containing the electric field. The principal E plane also contains the direction of maximum radiation.

E-plane bend—Also called E-bend. The smooth change in direction of the axis of a waveguide. The axis remains parallel to the direction of polarization throughout the change.

E-plane T-junction—Also called series T-junction. A waveguide T-junction in which the structure changes in the plane of the electric field.

epoxy resin—An insulating plastic used for encapsulating or embedding electronic equipment.

epsilon—The greek letter E, or ϵ, frequently used to represent 2.71828, which is the base of the natural system of logarithms.

equal-energy source—A light source having a constant emission rate of energy per unit of wavelength throughout the visible spectrum.

equal-energy white—The light produced by a source which radiates equal energy at all visible wavelengths.

equalization—The process of reducing the frequency and/or phase distortion of a circuit by the introduction of networks to compensate for the difference in attenuation and/or time delay at the various frequencies in the transmission band.

equalizer—1. A passive device designed to compensate for an undesired amplitude-frequency and/or phase frequency characteristic of a system or component. 2. A network having an attenuation complementary to that of a telephone line and inserted for the purpose of correcting frequency distortion caused by the line. 3. A network which improves the frequency response of a radio system. Usually a combination of resistors, inductors, and capacitors. 4. A series of connections made in paralleled, cumulatively

compound direct-current generators to give the system stability.

equalizer circuit breaker—A breaker which serves to control or to make and break the equalizer or the current-balancing connections for a machine field, or for regulating equipment, in a multiple-unit installation.

equalizing current—A current circulated between two parallel-connected compound generators to equalize their output.

equalizing network—A network connected to a line to correct or control its transmission frequency characteristics.

equalizing pulses—A series of pulses (usually six) occurring at twice the line frequency before and after the serrated vertical tv synchronizing pulse. Their purpose is to cause vertical retrace to occur at the correct instant for proper interlace.

equal-loudness contours—See Fletcher-Munson Curves.

equation solver—A computer, usually of the analog type, designed to solve systems of linear simultaneous (nondifferential) equations or to find the roots of polynomials.

equiphase surface—In a wave any surface over which the field vectors at the same instant are either in phase or 180° out of phase.

equiphase zone—In radionavigation, the region in space within which the difference in phase between two radio signals is indistinguishable.

equipment—An item having a complete function apart from being a substructure of a system. Sometimes called a set.

equipment life—The arithmetic mean of the cumulative operating times of identical pieces of equipment beginning with the time of acceptance by the ultimate consumer and ending when the equipment is no longer serviceable.

equipotential—A conductor having all parts at a single potential. The cathode of a heater-type tube is equipotential, whereas the filament is not because its voltage varies from one end to the other.

equipotential cathode—See Indirectly Heated Cathode.

equipotential line—An imaginary line in space having the same potential at all points.

equipotential surface—A surface or plane passing through all points having the same potential in a field of flow.

equisignal localizer—Also called tone localizer. A type of localizer in which lateral guidance is obtained by comparing the amplitudes of two modulation frequencies.

equisignal radio-range beacon—A radio-range beacon used for aircraft guidance. It transmits two distinctive signals, which are received with equal intensity only in certain directions called equisignal sectors.

equisignal surface—The surface formed around an antenna by all points which have a constant field strength (usually measured in volts per meter) during transmission.

equisignal zone—In radionavigation, the region in space within which the difference in amplitude between two radio signals is indistinguishable.

equivalence—A logic operator having the property that if P is a statement, Q is a statement, R is a statement, etc., then the equivalence of P,Q,R . . . is true if and only if all statements are true or all statements are false.

equivalent absorption—The rate at which a surface will absorb sound energy, expressed in sabins. Defined as the area of a perfect absorption surface that will absorb the same sound energy as the given object under the same conditions.

equivalent binary digits — The number of binary digits equivalent to a given number of decimal digits or other characters.

equivalent circuit—An arrangement of common circuit elements with electrical characteristics, equivalent to those of a more complicated circuit or device.

equivalent circuit of a piezoelectric crystal unit—The electric circuit which has the same impedance as the unit in the frequency region of resonance. It is usually represented by an inductance, capacitance, and resistance in series, shunted by the direct capacitance between the terminals of the crystal unit.

equivalent component density — In circuits where discrete components are not readily identifiable, the volume of the circuit divided by the number of discrete components necessary to perform the same function.

equivalent conductance—The normal conductance of an ATR tube in its mount, measured at its resonance frequency.

equivalent dark-current input — The incident luminous flux required to give an output current equal to the dark current.

equivalent differential input capacitance—The equivalent capacitance looking into the inverting or noninverting inputs of a differential amplifier with the opposite input grounded. *Also see* Equivalent Differential Input Impedance.

equivalent differential input impedance—The equivalent impedance looking into the inverting or noninverting input, with the opposite input grounded and the operational amplifier operated in the linear amplification region.

equivalent differential input resistance—The equivalent resistance looking into the inverting or noninverting input of a differential amplifier with the opposite input grounded. *Also see* Equivalent Differential Input Impedance.

equivalent diode—An imaginary diode consisting of the cathode of a triode or multigrid tube and a virtual anode to which is applied a composite controlling voltage of such a value that the cathode current would be the same as the current in the triode or multigrid tube.

equivalent four-wire system—A transmission system using frequency division to obtain full-duplex operation over only one pair of wires.

equivalent grid voltage—The grid voltage plus plate voltage, divided by the mu of the tube.

equivalent input offset current—The difference between the two currents flowing into the inverting and noninverting inputs of a differential amplifier when the output voltage is zero.

equivalent input offset voltage — The amount of voltage required at the input to bring the output to zero. Usually this voltage is adjustable to zero by using either a built-in or an external variable resistor (balance control).

equivalent input wideband noise voltage —The output noise voltage of a differential amplifier with the input shorted, divided by the d-c voltage gain of the amplifier. This voltage is measured with a true rms voltmeter and is limited to the combined bandwidth of the amplifier and meter.

equivalent height—The virtual height of an ionized layer of the ionosphere.

equivalent loudness—The intensity level of a sound relative to some arbitrary reference intensity, such as a 1000-hertz pure tone which is judged by the listeners to be equivalent in loudness.

equivalent network—A network which may replace another network without substantial change in the operation of the system.

equivalent noise input—In a photosensitive device, the value of incident luminous flux which produces an rms output current equal to the rms noise current within a specified bandwidth when the flux is modulated in a stated manner.

equivalent noise pressure—*See* Transducer Equivalent Noise Pressure.

equivalent noise resistance—A measure of the residual noise output of a potentiometer while the slider is being actuated. (The residual noise consists of active components in the form of self-generated voltages arising in the slider contact interface, and passive components in the form of ohmic contact resistance at the point of slider contact.)

equivalent noise temperature—The absolute temperature at which a perfect resistor with the same resistance as the component would generate the same noise as the component at room temperature.

equivalent permeability—The relative permeability which a component would have under specified conditions if it had the same reluctance as a component of the same shape and size but different materials.

equivalent plate voltage—The plate voltage plus mu times the grid voltage.

equivalent resistance—The concentrated or lumped resistance that would cause the same power loss as the actual small resistances distributed throughout a circuit.

equivalent series resistance — In a circuit, the square root of the difference between the impedance squared and the reactance squared.

equivocation—In a computer, the conditional information contained in an input symbol given an output symbol, averaged over all input-output pairs.

erasable storage — Storage media in a computer which holds information that can be changed.

erase—To replace all the binary digits in a storage device by binary zeros. In a binary computer, erasing is equivalent to clearing, while in a coded decimal computer where the pulse code for decimal zero may contain binary ones, clearing leaves decimal zero while erasing leaves all-zero pulse codes in all storage locations.

erase oscillator—In a magnetic recorder an oscillator that provides the high-frequency signal necessary for erasing a magnetic tape.

erasing head—A device for obliterating any previous recordings. It may also be used to precondition magnetic media for recording purposes.

erasing speed—In charge-storage tubes, the rate of erasing successive storage elements.

erasure—A process by which a signal recorded on a tape is removed and the tape made ready for rerecording. This may be accomplished by a-c erasure, where the tape is demagnetized by an alternating field which is reduced in amplitude from an initially high value, or by d-c erasure, where the tape is saturated by applying a primarily unidirectional field.

E-region — The region of the ionosphere about 50 to 100 miles above the earth's surface.

$E_r - E_y$—The resultant color television signal when E_y is subtracted from the original full red signal.

erg — The absolute centimeter-gram-second unit of energy and work. The work done when a force of one dyne is applied through a distance of one centimeter.

error—1. In mathematics, the difference between the true value and a calculated or observed value. A quantity (equal in absolute magnitude to the error) added to a calculated or observed value to obtain the true value is called a correction. 2. In a computer or data-processing system, any incorrect step, process, or result. In addition to the mathematical usage in the computer field, the term also commonly refers to machine malfunctions, or "machine errors," and to human mistakes, or "human errors."

error-correcting code — A code in which each acceptable expression conforms to specific rules of construction that also define one or more equivalent nonacceptable expressions, so that if certain errors occur, in an acceptable expression the result will be one of its equivalents and thus the error can be corrected.

error-correction routine—A series of computer instructions programmed to correct a detected error condition.

error detecting and feedback system—A system employing an error-detecting code and so arranged that a signal detected as being in error automatically initiates a request for retransmission of the signal detected as being in error.

error-detecting code—In a digital computer, a system of coding characters such that any single error produces a forbidden or impossible code combination.

error detector — That portion of an automatic control system that determines when the regulated quantity has deviated outside the dead zone.

error-rate damping—A damping method in which a signal proportional to the rate of change of error is added to the error signal for anticipatory purposes.

error signal—In an automatic control device, a signal whose magnitude and sign are used to correct the alignment between the controlling and the controlled elements.

error tape — A special tape developed and used for writing out errors in order to correct them by study and analysis after printing.

error voltage—A voltage which is present in a servo system when the input and output shafts are not in correspondence. The error voltage, which actuates the servo system, is proportional to the angular displacement between the two shafts.

Esaki diode—*See* Tunnel Diode.

E-scape—A radar display in which targets appear as blips, with distance indicated by the horizontal coordinate and elevation by the vertical coordinate.

escapement—A mechanical stepping device that stores energy over a predetermined time interval and delivers this stored energy at the end of said time interval to advance or move a camshaft a predetermined number of degrees.

escape velocity—The speed which a particle or larger body must attain in order to escape from the gravitational field of a planet or star.

escutcheon — A backing plate around an opening. Commonly, the ornamental metal, wood, plastic, or other framework around a radio tuning dial, control knob, or other panel-mounted part in a radio receiver or television receiver, audio-frequency amplifier, etc.

Estiatron—A special type of electrostatically focused traveling-wave tube.

etchant — In the preparation of a printed-circuit board, a solution used to remove the unwanted portion of the conductive material by means of a chemical reaction.

etched printed circuit—A type of printed circuit formed by chemically or electrolytically (or both) removing the unwanted portion of a layer of material bonded to a base.

ELECTRON GUN   ATTENUATOR   BIFILAR HELICES   COLLECTOR

INPUT COUPLER   COLLECTOR COOLING FINS

Estiatron.

etching to frequency — Finishing a crystal blank to its final frequency by etching it in hydrofluoric acid.

ether—A hypothetical medium that pervades all space (including vacuum) and all matter and is assumed to be the vehicle for propagation of electromagnetic radiations.

E transformer—A special form of differential transformer employing an E-shaped core. The secondaries of the transformer are wound on the outer legs of the E, and the primary is on the center leg.

Ettingshausen effect—Analogous to the Hall effect. The different temperatures found on opposite edges of a metal strip which is perpendicular to a magnetic field and through which an electric current flows longitudinally.

eureka—The ground transponder of secondary radar system rebecca-eureka.

ev or eV—Abbreviation for electron volt.

evaporation of electrons — The cooling which occurs on the surface of a cathode during emission. It is analogous to the cooling of a liquid or solid as it evaporates.

E-vector—A vector representing the electric field of an electromagnetic wave. In free space it is perpendicular to the direction of propagation.

even harmonic—Any harmonic that is an even multiple (2, 4, 6, etc.) of the fundamental frequency.

E-wave — Designation for TM (transverse magnetic) wave, one of the two classes of electromagnetic waves that can be sent through waveguides.

exalted-carrier receiver — A receiver that counteracts selective fading by maintaining the carrier at a high level at all times.

exalted-carrier reception—A method of receiving either amplitude- or phase-modulated signals in which the carrier is separated from the sidebands, filtered and amplified, and then recombined with the sidebands at a higher level prior to demodulation.

except gate—A gate in which the specified combination of pulses producing an output pulse is the presence of a pulse on one or more input lines and the absence of a pulse on one or more other input lines.

excess conduction — Conduction by excess electrons in a semiconductor.

excess electron—An electron introduced into a semiconductor by a donor impurity and available to promote conduction. An excess electron is not required to complete the bond structure of the semiconductor.

excess fifty—In a computer, a representation in which a number (N) is denoted by the equivalent of (N + 50).

excess meter—An electricity meter which measures and registers the integral, with respect to time, of those portions of the active power in excess of the predetermined value.

excess minority carriers—In a semiconductor, the number of minority carriers that exceed the normal equilibrium number.

excess modified index of refraction—*See* Refractive Modulus.

excess noise — Noise resulting from the passage of current through a semiconductor material. Also called current noise, bulk noise, and 1/f noise.

excess sound pressure—The total instantaneous pressure at a point in a medium containing sound waves, minus the static pressure when no sound waves are present. The unit is the dyne per square centimeter.

excess-three code—A number code in which the decimal digit N is represented by the four-bit binary equivalent of n + 3. (*Also see* Binary-Coded Decimal.)

exchange — To remove the contents of one storage unit of a computer and place it in a second, at the same time placing the contents of the second storage unit into the first.

exchange register—*See* Memory Register.

excitation—1. Also called stimulus. An external force or other input applied to a system to cause it to respond in some specified way. 2. Also called drive. A signal voltage applied to the control electrode of an electron tube. 3. In electric or electromagnetic equipment, supplying with a potential, a charge, or a magnetic field. 4. The addition of energy to a system so as to transfer the system from its ground state to an excited state.

excitation anode—An auxiliary anode of a pool-cathode tube, used to maintain a cathode spot when the output current is zero.

excitation current—The resultant current in the shunt field of a motor when voltage is applied across the field.

excitation energy — The external electrical energy required for proper operation of a transducer.

excitation purity—Also called purity. The ratio between the distance from the reference point to the point representing the sample and the distance along the same straight line from the reference point to the spectrum locus or to the purple boundary, both distances being measured (in the

174

same direction from the reference point) on the CIE chromaticity diagram.

excitation voltage—The voltage required for excitation of a circuit.

excited-field speaker—A speaker in which the steady magnetic field is produced by an electromagnet.

exciter—1. In a directional transmitting antenna system, the part connected directly to the source of power such as to the transmitter. 2. A crystal or self-excited oscillator that generates the carrier frequency of a transmitter. 3. A small, auxiliary generator that provides field current for an a-c generator.

exciter lamp—1. A high-intensity incandescent lamp having a concentrated filament. It is used in making variable-area, sound-on-film recording and in reproducing all types of sound tracks on film, as well as in some mechanical television systems. 2. A light source used in a facsimile transmitter to illuminate the subject copy being scanned.

exciter or d-c generator relay— A device which forces the d-c machine-field excitation to build up during starting, or which functions when the machine voltage has built up to a given value.

exciting current—1. The current which flows in the primary of a transformer when the secondary is open-circuited. This current produces a flux that generates a back emf equal to the applied voltage. 2. Also called magnetizing current. The current that passes through the field windings of a generator.

exciting current of a transformer— Also called no-load current. The current used in any winding to excite the transformer when all other windings are open-circuited, usually expressed in percent of the rated current of the windings in which it is measured.

exciton—A bound electron-hole pair in an insulator or a semiconductor. It may move through the crystal transporting excitation energy, but does not contribute to electric conductivity since it is neutral.

excitron—A single-anode pool tube with means for maintaining a continuous cathode spot.

exclusion principle— The principle which states that if particles are considered to occupy quantum states, then only one particle of a given kind can occupy any one state. Particles differ in kind due to their direction of spin, momentum, orbit, etc.

exclusive OR—A logic element with two inputs and one output. The output is true if either of the two inputs is true, but *not* if both are true.

excursion—A single movement away from the mean position in an oscillating or alternating motion.

execution—The performance of an operation or instruction.

executive routine—In digital-computer programming, a routine designed to process and control other routines.

exhaustion—The removal of gases from a space, such as the bulb of a vacuum tube, by means of vacuum pumps.

exit—In a computer, the means of halting a repeated cycle of operation in a program.

exosphere— The outermost region of the earth's atmosphere, where the atoms and molecules move in dynamic orbits under the influence of the gravitational field.

exothermic— A chemical reaction in which heat is produced.

expand—To spread out part or all the trace of a cathode-ray display.

expanded scale meter—A meter in which the ratio of deflection per unit of applied energy becomes greater as the energy approaches a specified value.

expanded scope—A magnified portion of a cathode-ray–tube presentation.

expanded sweep—A preselected portion of a sweep, during which time the electron beam is speeded up in a cathode-ray tube.

expander—A transducer which produces a larger range of output voltages for a given amplitude range of input voltages. One important type expands the volume range of speech signals by employing their envelope.

expansion—A process in which the effective gain applied to a signal is increased for larger signals and decreased for smaller signals.

experimental model— An equipment model that demonstrates the technical soundness of a basic idea but does not necessarily have the same form or parts as the final design.

experimental station—Any station (except amateur) utilizing electromagnetic waves between 10 kHz and 3000 GHz in experiments, with a view toward the development of a science or technique.

exploring coil—*See* Magnetic Test Coil.

explosion-proof motor— A motor designed and constructed so as to withstand an internal explosion of a specified gas or vapor and to prevent the ignition of the specified gas or vapor surrounding the motor by sparks, flashes, or explosions of the specified gas or vapor inside the motor casing.

explosive atmosphere—The condition where air is mixed with dust, metal particles, or inflammable gas in such proportion that it is capable of igniting or exploding.

exponential—Pertaining to exponents or to an expression having exponents. A quantity that varies in an exponential manner increases by the square or some other power of a factor, instead of linearly.

exponential curve—A curve representing the variation of an exponential function.

exponential damping—Damping which follows an exponential law.

exponential decay— The decay of signal strength, radiation, charge, or some other quantity at an exponential rate.

exponential horn—A horn the cross-sectional area of which increases exponentially with axial distance.

exponential quantity—A single quantity which increases or decreases at the same rate as the quantity itself (e.g., the discharge current of a capacitor through a non-inductive resistor).

exponential sweep—An electron-beam sweep which starts rapidly and slows down exponentially.

exponential transmission line—A two-conductor transmission line the characteristic impedances of which vary exponentially with the electrical length of the line.

exponential waveform—A waveform which is characterized by smooth curves but which possesses pulse properties because it contains numerous constituent frequencies. The exponential waveform undergoes a rate of amplitude change which is either inversely or directly proportional to the instantaneous amplitude.

THIN TRANSLUCENT METAL COLLECTING SURFACE
SELENIUM ALLOY
IRON DISK
LIGHT
SOFT IRON CORE
MOVING COIL
BAFFLE TO REGULATE ANGLE OF VIEW

Exposure meter.

exposure meter—In photography, an instrument which measures scene brightness and indicates proper lens opening and exposure time.

SWELL PEDAL

WHEEL ON VOLUME CONTROL SHAFT

Expression control.

expression control—In an organ the control which regulates the over-all volume. Usually operated with the right foot.

extended-cutoff tube—*See* Remote-Cutoff Tube.

extended octaves—In an organ, tones above or below the notes on the regular keyboard which can be sounded only when certain couplers are on.

extended play—Abbreviated ep. A 45-rpm record on a seven-inch disc. It provides eight minutes of playing time, instead of the five minutes of a standard 45-rpm disc.

external armature—A ring-shaped armature that rotates around the field magnets of a generator or motor.

external circuit—All wires and other conductors which are outside the source.

external control devices—All control devices mounted external to the control panel.

external critical damping resistance—The value of resistance that must be placed in series or in parallel with a galvanometer in order to produce the critically damped condition.

external feedback—In a magnetic amplifier, the ampere-turns of auxiliary windings which assist in equalizing the load winding ampere-turns, thereby reducing the control ampere-turns required for control. External feedback may be degenerative to reduce the gain and improve the stability of an amplifier.

externally adjustable timer—A time delay which can be adjusted by varying the resistance of the timer resistor externally, usually by means of a screwdriver.

externally caused contact chatter—That chatter resulting from shock or vibration imposed on the relay by external action.

externally caused failure—A failure caused by an environment outside the design limitations, such as excessive loads, voltages, etc., resulting from operator error, accident, or failure of another part.

externally quenched counter tube—A radiation counter tube that requires an external circuit to prevent it from reigniting.

external memory—A storage unit outside the computer (e.g., a magnetic tape).

external Q—In a microwave tube, the reciprocal of the difference between the reciprocal of the loaded Q and the reciprocal of the unloaded Q.

external storage—Storage facilities separate from the computer itself but holding information in a form acceptable to the computer, e.g., magnetic tapes, magnetic wires, punched cards, etc.

extinction potential—The lowest value to which the plate voltage of a gaseous tube can be reduced without cutting off the flow of plate current.

extra-class license—The highest classification of United States amateur license. Requirements include a code sending and receiving ability of 20 words per minute, a knowledge of advanced theory, and the holding of a general- or conditional-class license for two years.

extract—To remove from a set of items of information all those items that meet some arbitrary criterion.

extract instruction—In a digital computer, the instruction to form a new word by placing selected segments of given words side by side.

extractor—*See* Filter.

extraneous response—Any undesired response of a receiver, recorder, or other susceptible device, due to the desired signals, undesired signals, or any combination or interaction among them.

extraordinary wave component—The magnetoionic wave component in which the electric vector rotates in the opposite sense from that for the ordinary wave component.

extrapolate — To estimate the value of a function for variables lying outside the range in which values of the function are known (e.g., to extend the graphs of the function beyond the plotted points).

extremely high frequency — Abbreviated ehf. The frequency band extending from 30 to 300 GHz.

extremely low frequency—A frequency below 300 hertz. Abbreviated elf.

extrinsic base resistance-collector capacitance product—The product of the base resistance and collector capacitance of a transistor. It is expressed in units of time, since it is an RC time constant and affects the high-frequency operation of a transistor.

extrinsic conductance—The conductance resulting from impurities or external causes.

extrinsic properties—The properties of a semiconductor, modified by impurities or imperfections within the crystal.

extrinsic semiconductor — A semiconductor the electrical properties of which depend on its impurities.

eyelet—A tubular metal piece having one end (and possibly the second) headed or rolled over at a right angle.

F

f — 1. Abbreviation for farad, femto (10^{-15}). 2. Symbol for focal length, frequency.

F—1. Symbol for filament, fuse. 2. Abbreviation for Fahrenheit.

F − — *See* A−.

F + — *See* A+.

fa—Abbreviation for femtoampere (10^{-15} ampere).

fabrication holes—*See* Pilot Holes.

fabrication tolerance — In the construction or assembly of an equipment or portion of an equipment, the maximum variation in the characteristics of a part which, considering the defined variations of the other parts in the equipment, will permit the equipment to operate within specified performance limits.

Fabry-Perot interferometer — A resonant cavity bounded by two end mirrors separated so as to produce interference for certain allowed optical frequencies. The enhancements and cancellations produced by the internal reflections are, in fact, optical standing waves. The structure can be used as a laser cavity, mode filter, or frequency selector.

face—1. A plane surface on a crystal which stands in a particular and invariable relation to the axes and planes of reference and to other faces. 2. Front, or viewing, surface of a cathode-ray tube. 3. The portion of a meter bearing the scale markings.

face bonding—A method of attaching active devices to thin-film passive networks. The semiconductor chips are provided with small mounting pads turned face down and bonded directly to the end of the thin-film conductors on the passive substrate.

faced crystal—A single or twinned mass of quartz bounded in part or entirely by the original crystal growth faces.

face-parallel cut — A Y-cut for a quartz crystal.

face-perpendicular cut — An X-cut for a quartz crystal.

facom—A long-distance measuring or radio-navigational system which derives information of distances by comparing the phases of received and locally generated signals. It is a base-line system operating in the low-frequency band and will work under adverse propagation and noise conditions at ranges of up to 3000 miles from the signal source.

facsimile—A process or the result of a process by which fixed graphic material including pictures or images is scanned and the information converted into electrical signal waves, which are used either locally or remotely to produce in record form a likeness (facsimile) of the subject copy.

facsimile broadcast station — A station licensed to transmit images of still objects for reception by the general public.

facsimile posting—The process of transferring, by a duplicating process, a printed line on a report to a ledger or other recorded sheet. These may be posted from a transaction listing previously prepared on an accounting machine. A data-processing function.

facsimile receiver—An apparatus that translates the facsimile signal into a reproduced image.

facsimile recorder—Apparatus which reproduces on paper the image transmitted by a facsimile system.

facsimile signal—The signal resulting from the scanning in a facsimile system.

facsimile-signal level—An expression of the maximum signal power or voltage created by the scanning of the subject copy as measured at any point in a facsimile system. According to whether the system employs positive or negative modulation, this will correspond to picture white or black, respectively. It may be expressed in decibels with respect to some standard value, such as 1 milliwatt or 1 volt.

facsimile system—An integrated assembly of the elements used for facsimile transmission and reception.

facsimile transmission—The transmission of signal waves produced by the scanning of a

Facsimile transmitter.

picture on a revolving drum by a photo-electric cell for reproduction in permanent form at the receiver.

facsimile transmitter—An apparatus employed to convert the subject copy into suitable facsimile signals. Usually, the copy is wrapped around a revolving drum and scanned by a photoelectric cell, which converts the darks and lights into corresponding signal amplitudes.

fade—The gradual lowering in amplitude of a signal.

fade in—To increase the signal strength gradually in a sound or television channel.

fade out—1. The gradual decrease in signal strength in a sound or television channel. 2. The cessation or near cessation of radiowave propagation through parts of the ionosphere due to a sudden atmospheric disturbance.

fader—A multiple-unit control used in radio for gradual changeover from one microphone or audio channel to another; in television, from one camera to another; and in motion-picture projection, from one projector to another.

fading—The variation of radio field strength caused by a gradual change in the transmission medium.

fading margin—The number of decibels of attenuation which can be added to a specified radio-frequency propagation path before the signal-to-noise ratio of the channel falls below a specified minimum.

Fahnestock clip—A spring-type terminal to which a temporary connection can readily be made.

Fahrenheit temperature scale—A temperature scale in which the freezing point of water is defined as 32° and the boiling point as 212° under normal atmospheric pressure (760 mm of mercury).

fail hardover—Failure which results in a steady-state maximum system output with no input signal.

fail-safe circuit—A circuit that has an output state which indicates that either a circuit input or the circuit itself has failed. Finds application in complex systems where self-healing subsystems exist. When a subsystem failure is detected, a back-up subsystem is automatically inserted in its place.

fail-safe control—A system of remote control for preventing improper operation of the controlled function in event of circuit failure.

fail-safe operation—An electrical system so designed that the failure of any component in the system will prevent unsafe operation of the controlled equipment.

fail soft—An active failure which can be compensated for by the system or one where the operator can safely assume control.

failure—The inability of a system, subsystem, component, or part to function in the required or specified manner.

failure indicator—The observed characteristic that shows that an item is defective.

failure mechanism—*See* Failure Mode.

failure mode—The manner in which a failure occurs, including the operating condition of the equipment or part at the time of the failure. Also called failure mechanism.

failure rate—Also called hazard. The probability of failure, normally expressed in per cent per 1000 hours, of the items still operating.

fall-in—In a synchronous motor, the point at which synchronous speed is reached.

fallouts—*See* Transistor Seconds.

fall time—1. The length of time during which a pulse is decreasing from 90% to 10% of its maximum amplitude. 2. A measure of the time required for a circuit to change its output from a high level (1) to a low level (0).

false course—In navigation normally providing one or more course lines, a spurious additional course-line indication due to undesired reflections or maladjusted equipment.

false-echo device—A device for producing an echo different from that normally observed.

fan antenna—*See* Double-V Antenna.

fan beam—A field pattern having an elliptically shaped cross section in which the ratio of major to minor axes usually exceeds 3 to 1.

fan-in—The number of inputs that can be connected to a logic circuit.

fan-in circuit—A circuit that has many inputs feeding to a common point.

fan marker—A radio signal having a vertically directed fan beam which tells the pilot the location of his aircraft while flying along a radio range.

fanned-beam antenna—A unidirectional antenna so designed that transverse cross sections of the major lobe are almost elliptical.

fan-out—The number of parallel loads within a given logic family that can be driven from one output mode of a logic circuit.

fan-out circuit—A circuit that has a single output point which feeds many branches.

farad—The capacitance of a capacitor in which a charge of 1 coulomb produces a change of 1 volt in the potential difference between its terminals. The farad is the unit of capacitance in the mksa systems.

faraday—1. A unit equal to the number of coulombs (96,500) required for an electrochemical reaction involving one electrochemical equivalent. 2. In an electrolytic process, 1-gram equivalent weight of matter is chemically altered at each electrode for 1 faraday of electricity passed through the electrolyte.

Faraday cage—*See* Faraday Shield.

Faraday dark space—The relatively nonluminous region between the negative glow and the positive column in a glow-discharge–cold-cathode tube. (*Also see* Glow Discharge.)

Faraday effect—The rotation of the plane of polarization of radio waves as they pass through the ionosphere in the earth's magnetic field. This effect produces a decoupling loss between linearly polarized antennas.

Faraday rotation—The rotation of the plane of polarization of radiation when it passes through a plasma containing a magnetic field having a component in the direction of propagation.

Faraday screen—*See* Faraday Shield.

Faraday shield—Also called Faraday screen or Faraday cage. A network of parallel wires connected to a common conductor at one end to provide electrostatic shielding without affecting electromagnetic waves. The common conductor is usually grounded.

Faraday's laws—1. The mass of a substance liberated in an electrolytic cell is proportionate to the quantity of electricity passing through the cell. 2. When the same quantity of electricity is passed through different electrolytic cells, the masses of the substances liberated are proportional to their chemical equivalents. 3. Also called the law of electromagnetic induction. 4. When a magnetic field cuts a conductor, or when a conductor cuts a magnetic field, an electric current will flow through the conductor if a closed path is provided over which the current can circulate.

faradic current—An intermittent and nonsymmetrical alternating current like that obtained from the secondary winding of an induction coil.

faradmeter—An instrument for measuring electric capacitance.

far-end cross talk—Cross talk which travels along the disturbed circuit in the same direction as the signals in that circuit. To determine the far-end cross talk between two pairs, 1, and 2, signals are transmitted on pair 1 at station A and the cross-talk level is measured on pair 2 at station B.

far field—The space beyond the near field of an antenna in which radiation is essentially confined to a fixed pattern and power density along the axis of the pattern falls off inversely with the square of the distance.

far-field region—That region of the field of an antenna where the angular field distribution is essentially independent of the distance from the antenna.

Farnsworth image-dissector tube—A special cathode-ray tube for use in television cameras.

fast-access storage—In a computer memory or storage, the section from which information may be obtained most rapidly.

fastener—A device used to secure a conductor (or other object) to the structure which supports it.

fast forward—The provision on a tape recorder permitting tape to be run rapidly through the recorder in the play direction, usually for search or selection purposes.

fast-forward control—A tape-recorder control which permits running the tape through the machine rapidly in the forward direction.

fast groove—Also called fast spiral. In disc recording, an unmodulated spiral groove having a much greater pitch than the recorded grooves.

fast-operate–fast-release relay—A high-speed relay designed specifically for both short-operate and short-release times.

fast-operate relay—A high-speed relay designed specifically for short-operate but not short-release time.

fast-operate–slow-release relay—A relay designed specifically for short-operate and long-release times.

fast-release relay—A high-speed relay designed specifically for short-release but not short-operate time.

fast spiral—*See* Fast Groove.

fast time constant—An antijamming device used in radar video-amplifier circuits. It differentiates incoming pulses so that only the leading edges of the pulse are used.

fathometer—Also called depth finder, depth sounder, acoustic depth finder, echo depth sounder, or sonic depth sounder. A direct-reading device for determining the depth of water in fathoms or other units by reflecting sonic or ultrasonic waves from the ocean bottom. Also used to locate underwater bodies, such as schools of fish or sunken objects.

Fathometer.

fatigue—The weakening of a material under repeated stress.

fault—A defect in a wire circuit due to unintentional grounding, a break in the line, or a crossing or shorting of the wires.

fault current—The current that may flow in any part of a circuit or amplifier under specified abnormal conditions.

fault electrode current—The peak current that flows through an electrode during a fault, such as an arc back or a load short circuit.

fault finder—A test set for locating troubles in a telephone system.

fault indicator—Equipment that provides an instantaneous alarm, both visual and audible, of failures detected in the various components of its assorted equipment.

Faure plate—A storage-battery plate consisting of a conductive lead grid filled with active paste material.

fax—Abbreviation for facsimile.

fc—Abbreviation for footcandle.

FCC—Abbreviation for Federal Communications Commission.

F-display—Also called F-scan or F-scope. In radar, a rectangular display in which a target appears as a centralized blip when the radar antenna is aimed at it. Horizontal and vertical aiming errors are indicated by the horizontal and vertical displacement of the blip.

fdm—Abbreviation for frequency-division multiplex.

Federal Communications Commission—Abbreviated FCC. A board of seven commissioners appointed by the President under the Communications Act of 1934, having the power to regulate all interstate and foreign electrical communication systems originating in the United States.

feedback—1. In a transmission system or a section of it, the returning of a fraction of the output to the input. 2. In a magnetic amplifier, a circuit connection by which an additional magnetomotive force (which is a function of the output quantity) is used to influence the operating condition. 3. Part of a closed-loop system which brings back information about the condition under control, for comparison with the target value.

feedback amplifier—An amplifier that uses a passive network to return a portion of the output signal to modify the performance of the amplifier.

feedback attenuation—In the feedback loop of an operational amplifier, an attenuation factor by which the output voltage is attenuated to produce the input error voltage.

feedback control—A type of system control obtained when a portion of the output signal is operated upon and fed back to the input in order to obtain a desired effect.

feedback control loop—A closed transmission path which includes an active transducer and consists of a forward path, a feedback path, and one or more mixing points arranged to maintain a prescribed relationship between the loop input and output signals.

feedback control signal—That portion of the output signal which is returned to the input in order to achieve a desired effect, such as fast response.

feedback control system—A control system comprising one or more feedback control loops; it combines the functions of the controlled signals and commands, tending to maintain prescribed relationship between the two.

feedback cutter—An electromechanical transducer which performs like a disc cutter except it is equipped with an auxiliary feedback coil in the magnetic field. Signals exciting the cutter are induced into the feedback coil, the output of which is fed back in turn to the input of the cutter amplifier. The result is a substantially uniform frequency response.

feedback oscillator—An oscillating circuit, including an amplifier, in which the output is coupled in phase with the input. The oscillation is maintained at a frequency determined by the parameters of the amplifier and the feedback circuits, such as LC, RC, and other frequency-selective elements.

feedback path—In a feedback control loop, the transmission path from the loop output signal to the loop feedback signal.

feedback regulator—A feedback control system which tends to maintain a prescribed relationship between certain system signals and other predetermined quantities.

feedback transfer function—In a feedback control loop, the transfer function of the feedback path.

feedback winding—In a saturable reactor, the control winding to which a feedback connection is made.

feeder—A conductor or group of conductors

connecting two generating stations, two substations, a generating station and a substation or feeding point, a substation and a feeding point, or a transmitter and antenna.

feeder cable—1. A communication cable extending from the central office along a primary route (main feeder cable), or from a main feeder cable along a secondary route (branch feeder cable) and providing connections to one or more distribution cables. 2. Also called trunk cable. In a catv system, the transmission cable from the head end (signal pickup) to the trunk amplifier.

feed holes—A series of small holes in perforated paper tape which convey no information, but are solely for the purpose of engaging the feed pawls or sprocket which transports the tape over the sensing pins of various reading devices.

feed pitch—The distance between the centers of adjacent feed holes in a tape.

feed reel—On a tape recorder, the reel which supplies the magnetic tape to the recording or playback head.

feedthrough—1. The accidental or unintentional transfer of a signal from one track to another on a multitrack tape. 2. The use of special connectors to pass conductors through bulkheads or panels. Contacts can be male on one side and female on the other, or they can be male on both sides or female on both sides. Feedthrough connectors differ from rack-and-panel types in that connection can be made on both sides of the panel.

feedthrough capacitor—A feedthrough insulator that provides a desired value of capacitance between the feedthrough conductor and the metal chassis or panel through which the conductor is passing. Used chiefly for bypass purposes in uhf.

feedthrough insulator—A type of insulator which permits wire or cable to be fed through walls, etc., with minimum current leakage.

feed-thru connection—*See* Thru-hole Connection.

female—The recessed portion of a device into which another part fits.

femto—Prefix meaning 10^{-15}. Abbreviated f.

femtoampere—A unit of current equal to 10^{-15} ampere. Abbreviated fa.

femtovolt—A unit of voltage equal to 10^{-15} volt. Abbreviated fv.

Fermi level—The value of electron energy at which the Fermi distribution function is one half.

ferreed—An electromechanical switch that combines the rapid switching of bistable magnetic material with metallic contacts to produce output indications that persist as long as desired without further application of power.

ferret reconnaissance—A form of reconnaissance which detects, locates, and analyzes enemy radars. It is a passive technique that listens for signals transmitted by enemy radars and thus cannot be jammed. The maximum effective range is limited only by the radio horizon. Ferret systems flown at altitudes of a few miles can accurately locate and analyze radars 300 miles away. Ferret is the only all-weather reconnaissance technique, and no camouflage system works against a properly designed ferret.

ferri—Prefix indicating a material having a net dipole moment.

ferric oxide (Fe_2O_3)—A red, iron oxide coating for magnetic recording tapes.

ferrimagnetic amplifier—A microwave amplifier utilizing ferrite material in the coupling inductors and transformers.

ferrimagnetic materials—Those materials in which spontaneous magnetic polarization occurs in nonequivalent sublattices; the polarization in one sublattice is aligned antiparallel to the other.

ferristor—A two-winding ferroresonant magnetic amplifier that operates on a high carrier frequency.

ferrite—Also called ferrospinel. A powdered, compressed, and sintered magnetic material having high resistivity, consisting chiefly of ferric oxide combined with one or more other metals. The high resistance makes eddy-current losses extremely low at high frequencies. Examples of ferrite compositions include nickel ferrite, nickel-cobalt ferrite, manganese-magnesium ferrite, yttrium-ion garnet, and single-crystal yttrium-ion garnet.

ferrite circulator—A nonreciprocal microwave network which transmits power from one terminal to another in sequence. Can replace a conventional duplexer, provide isolation of transmitter from receiver, eliminate the requirement for an ATR, and isolate the transmitter from antenna reflections.

ferrite core—A core made from iron and other oxides and usually shaped like a doughnut. It is used in circuits and magnetic memories and can be magnetized and demagnetized very rapidly.

Ferrite cores.

ferrite isolator—A device either in a waveguide or coax which allows power to pass through in one direction with very little loss, while the r-f power in the reverse direction is absorbed. It is useful for maintaining signal source stability and eliminating long-line and frequency-pulling effects in all types of low-power microwave signal sources.

ferrite-rod antenna—Also called ferrod or loopstick antenna. An antenna used in place of a loop antenna in a radio receiver. It consists of a coil wound around a ferrite rod.

ferrites—Chemical compounds of iron oxide and other metallic oxides combined with ceramic material. They have ferromagnetic properties but are poor conductors of electricity. Hence they are useful where ordinary ferromagnetic materials (which are good electrical conductors) would cause too great a loss of electrical energy.

ferrod—*See* Ferrite-Rod Antenna.

ferrodynamic instrument — An electrodynamic instrument in which the measuring forces are materially increased by the presence of ferromagnetic material.

ferroelectric—Pertaining to a phenomenon exhibited by certain materials in which the material is polarized in one direction or the other, or reversed in direction by the application of a positive or negative electric field of magnitude greater than a certain amount. The material retains the electric polarization unless it is disturbed. The polarization can be sensed by the fact that a change in the field induces an electromotive force which can cause a current.

ferroelectric converter—A device which generates high voltage when heat is applied to it. Its operation is based on the change in the dielectric constant or the permittivity of certain materials such as barium titanate when heated. This change reaches maximum at the Curie point.

ferroelectric crystal—A crystal which can be polarized in the opposite direction by applying an electric field weaker than the breakdown strength of the material.

ferroelectricity—A property of a crystal having a spontaneously reversible polarization.

ferroelectric materials—Those materials in which the electric polarization is produced by cooperation action between groups or domains of collectively oriented molecules.

ferroelectrics—Pyroelectric materials the direction of polarization of which can be reversed by application of an electric field.

ferromagnetic—Pertaining to a phenomenon exhibited by certain materials in which the material is polarized in one direction or the other, or reversed in direction by the application of a positive or negative magnetic field of magnitude greater than a certain amount. The material retains the magnetic polarization unless it is disturbed. The polarization can be sensed by the fact that a change in

the field induces an electromotive force, which can cause a current.

ferromagnetic amplifier—A parametric amplifier based on the nonlinear behavior of ferromagnetic resonance at high r-f power levels. In one version, microwave pumping power is supplied to a garnet or other ferromagnetic crystal mounted in a cavity containing a strip line. A permanent magnet provides sufficient field strength to produce gyromagnetic resonance in the garnet at the pumping frequency. The input signal is applied to the crystal through the strip line, and the amplified output signal is extracted from the other end of the strip line. Sometimes incorrectly called a garnet maser, but the operating principle differs from that of the maser.

ferromagnetic material—A material having a specific permeability greater than unity, the amount depending on the magnetizing force. A ferromagnetic material usually has relatively high values of specific permeability and it exhibits hysteresis. The principal ferromagnetic materials are iron, nickel, cobalt, and certain of their alloys.

ferromagnetic oxide parts — Parts, consisting primarily of oxides which display ferromagnetic properties.

ferromagnetism — A high degree of magnetism in ferrites and similar compounds. The magnetic moments of neighboring ions tend not to align parallel with each other. The moments are of different magnitudes, and the resultant magnetization can be large.

ferromanganese—An alloy of iron and manganese.

ferrometer—An instrument for making permeability and hysteresis tests of iron and steel.

ferroresonance — Resonance associated with circuits in which at least one of the circuit elements is nonlinear and contains iron.

ferroresonant circuit—A resonant circuit in which one of its elements is a saturable reactor.

ferrospinel—A ceramic-like material containing iron and other elements combined with oxygen. A poor conductor of electricity, it is used in transformers, antenna loops, and television deflecting yokes.

ferrous — Composed of and/or containing iron. A ferrous metal exhibits magnetic characteristics, as opposed to a nonferrous metal such as aluminum which does not.

ferrule resistor—A resistor having ferrule terminals for mounting in standard fuse clips.

FET—Abbreviation for (unipolar) field effect transistor.

fetal electrocardiograph — An instrument for detecting and recording fetal ecg.

fetal heart monitor — An instrument that combines fetal ecg with an oscilloscope display and/or alarm.

fetal phonocardiograph — An instrument which provides continuous instantaneous recording of beat-to-beat changes in the fetal heart rate.

fetch—That portion of a computer cycle during which the location of the next instruction is determined. The instruction is taken from memory and modified if necessary, and it is then entered into the control register.

"f" factor — The slope of the straight line from which the nonlinearity of a displacement transducer is calculated in microvolts output per volt excitation per unit stimulus.

fiber—A tough insulating material, generally of paper and cellulose, compressed into rods, sheets, or tubes.

fiber needle—A playback point or phonograph needle made from fiber. Being softer than a metal or diamond needle, it is less scratchy; however, it has an extremely short life.

fiber-optic bundles—Assemblies of optical fibers.

fiber optics—Also called optical fibers or optical fiber bundles. An assemblage of transparent glass fibers all bundled together parallel to one another. The length of each fiber is much greater than its diameter. This bundle of fibers has the ability to transmit a picture from one of its surfaces to the other around curves and into otherwise inaccessible places with an extremely low loss of definition and light, by a process of total reflection.

fiber optics probe—A flexible probe made up of a bundle of fine glass fibers optically aligned to transmit an image.

fiber optics scrambler—Similar to a fiberscope except that the middle section of loose fiber is deliberately disoriented as much as possible, then potted and sawed. Each half is then capable of coding a picture, which can be decoded by the other half.

fiberscope—Optical glass fibers, when systematically arranged in a bundle, transmit a full color image that remains undisturbed when the bundle is bent. By mounting an objective lens on one end of the bundle, and an eyepiece at the other, the assembly becomes a flexible fiberscope that can be used to view objects that would be inaccessible for direct viewings.

fidelity—1. The accuracy with which a system or portion of a system reproduces at its output the essential characteristics of the signal impressed on its input. 2. A measure of the exactness with which sound is duplicated or reproduced.

field—1. One half of a television image. With present U. S. standards, pictures are transmitted in two fields of 262½ lines each, which are interlaced to form 30 complete frames, or images, per second. 2. A general term referring to the region under the influence of some physical agency such as electricity, magnetism, or a combination produced by an electrically charged object, electrons in motion, or a magnet. 3. A group of characters in a computer which is treated as

a single unit of information. 4. In each of a number of punch cards, a column or columns regularly used for a standard item of information.

field application relay—A device which automatically controls the application of the field excitation to an a-c motor at some predetermined point in the slip cycle.

field circuit breaker—A device which functions to apply, or to remove, the field excitation of a machine.

field coil—A coil of insulated wire wound around an iron core. Current flowing in the coil produces a magnetic field.

field density—*See* Magnetic Induction.

field-discharge protection — A control function or device to limit the induced voltage in the field when the field current attempts to change suddenly.

field distortion — Distortion between the north and south poles of a generator due to the counterelectromotive force in the armature winding.

field-effect tetrode—A semiconductor device consisting basically of a thin N region adjacent to a similarly thin P region. Two contacts are made to the N side and two to the P side so that currents can be passed through each thin region parallel to the single junction. The two currents remain separate because reverse bias is maintained on the junction. A current in either side affects the resistance of the other side and hence the current in the other side.

Field-effect transistor.

field-effect transistor—A transistor with a circuit application similar to that of a vacuum tube. The main conduction path is through a bar of N-type silicon, with control through depletion layers on each side of the N-type bar.

field-effect tube—A triode with its grid replaced by a nonintercepting control gate. A high positive voltage is applied to this gate in order to draw sufficient current from the cathode. The result is a strong concentration of the electric field at the gap between the gate and the cathode, producing an electron beam passing through the gate to the anode.

field emission—Also called cold emission. The liberation of electrons from a solid or liquid by application of a strong electric field at the surface.

field-enhanced photoelectric emission—Increased photoelectric emission resulting from

1-5/8 INCH
DIAMETER

EMITTER

GATE

COLLECTOR

MAGNETIC
FIELD

7-1/4
INCHES

Field-effect tube.

the action of a strong electric field on the emitter.

field-enhanced secondary emission — Increased secondary emission resulting from the action of a strong electric field on the emitter.

field forcing—The effect of a control function or device which temporarily overexcites or underexcites the field of an electrical machine in order to increase the rate of change of flux.

field-free emission current — Also called zero-field emission. The electron current emitted by a cathode when the electric field at the surface of the cathode is zero.

field frequency—Also called field-repetition rate. In television, the frame frequency multiplied by the number of fields contained in one frame. In the United States the field frequency is 60 per second, or twice the frame frequency.

field intensity—*See* Field Strength.

field loss relay — *See* Motor Field Failure Relay.

field magnet—An electromagnet or perma-

nent magnet which produces a strong magnetic field in a speaker, microphone, phonograph pickup, generator, motor, or other electrical device.

field-neutralizing coil—A coil encircling the faceplate of a color picture tube. The current through it produces a magnetic field which offsets any effects of the earth's and other stray magnetic fields on the electron beams.

field-neutralizing magnet—Also called rim magnet. A permanent magnet mounted near the edge of the faceplate of a color picture tube to prevent stray magnetic fields from affecting the path of the electron beams.

field of view—The solid angle from which objects can be acceptably viewed, photographed, or otherwise detected.

field period—The time required to transmit one television field. In the United States, it is 1/60th of a second.

field pickup—Also called a remote or nemo. A radio or television program originating outside the studio.

field relay — A device that functions on a given or abnormally low value or failure of machine field current, or on an excessive value of the reactive component of armature current in an a-c machine, indicating abnormally low field excitation.

field-repetition rate—*See* Field Frequency.

field resistor—A component in which the resistance element is a thin layer of conductive material on an insulated form. The conductive material does not contain either binding or insulating material.

field rheostat—A variable resistance connected to the field coils of a motor or generator and used for varying the field current.

field ring—The part which supports the field of a dc or series-wound motor housing. The motor end shields are attached to the ends of the field ring.

field selection—In a computer, the isolation of a particular data field with one computer word without isolating the word.

field sequential—Pertaining to the association of individual primary colors with successive fields in a color-television system (e.g., field-sequential pickup, display, system, transmission).

field-sequential color television—A color-television system in which the individual primary colors (red, blue, and green) are produced in successive fields.

field-simultaneous system — A color-television system in which a complete full-color field is presented simultaneously as a unit. The eyes then see a succession of full-color images rather than a succession of primary-color fields.

field strength—1. Also called field intensity. The value of the vector at a point in the region occupied by a vector field. In radio, it is the effective value of the electric-field intensity in microvolts or millivolts per meter produced at a point by radio waves from a particular station. Unless otherwise specified, the measurement is assumed to be in the direction of maximum field intensity. 2. The amount of magnetic flux produced at a particular point by an electromagnetic or permanent magnet.

field-strength meter—A calibrated measuring instrument for determining the strength of radiated energy (field strength) being received from a transmitter.

field telephone—A durable, portable telephone designed for use in the field.

field wire—A flexible insulated wire used in field-telephone and -telegraph systems.

figure of merit—1. The property or characteristic which makes a tube, coil, or other electronic device suitable for a particular application. It is a quality to look for in choosing a piece of equipment. 2. In a magnetic amplifier, the ratio of the power gain to the time constant. 3. For a thermoelectric material, the quotient of the square of the absolute Seebeck coefficient (α) divided by the product of the electrical resistivity (ρ) and the thermal conductivity.

Filaments (indirectly-heated).

filament—1. Also known as a filamentary cathode. The cathode of a thermionic tube, usually a wire or ribbon, which is heated by passing a current through it. 2. In tubes employing a separate cathode, the heating element.

filamentary transistor—A conductivity-modulation transistor which is much longer than it is wide.

filament battery—The source of energy for heating the filament of a vacuum tube.

filament circuit—The complete circuit through which filament current flows.

filament current—The current supplied to a filament to heat it.

filament emission—The liberation of electrons when the filament in a vacuum tube is heated.

filament power supply—The source of power for the filament or heater of a vacuum tube.

filament resistance—The resistance (in ohms) of the filament of a vacuum tube or incandescent lamp.

filament rheostat—A variable resistance placed in series with the filament of a vacuum tube to regulate the filament current.

filament sag—The bending of a filament when it heats up and expands.

filament saturation—Also called temperature saturation. The condition whereby a further increase in filament voltage will no longer increase the plate current at a given value of plate voltage.

filament transformer—A transformer used exclusively to supply filament voltage and current for the vacuum tubes.

filament voltage—The voltage value which must be applied to the filament of a vacuum tube to obtain the rated filament current.

filament winding—A secondary winding provided on a power transformer to furnish alternating filament voltage for one or more vacuum tubes.

file—1. A collection of related records—e.g., in inventory control, one line of an invoice containing data on the material, the quantity, and the price forms an item; a complete invoice forms a record; and the complete set of such records forms a file. 2. To insert an item into such a set.

file gap—A space or interval of time, the purpose of which is to indicate or signal the end of a file.

file maintenance—The processing of a computer file in order to bring it up to date.

filler—1. In mechanical recording, the inert material of a record compound (as distinguished from the binder). 2. Nonconducting component cabled with insulated conductors to impart roundness, flexibility, tensile strength, or a combination of all three, to the cable.

film badge—A type of dosimeter consisting of a badge containing a sensitized film which, when developed, gives an indication of the total dose of ionizing radiation to which the badge has been subjected.

film integrated circuit—An integrated circuit the elements of which are films formed *in situ* upon an insulating substrate. (*Also see* Integrated Circuit.) To further define the nature of a film integrated circuit, additional modifiers may be prefixed. Examples are: thin-film integrated circuit; thick-film integrated circuit.

film pickup—A film projector combined with a television camera for telecasting scenes from a motion-picture film.

film reader—A computer input device which scans opaque and transparent patterns on photographic film and relays the corresponding information to the computer.

film recorder—A device that receives information from a computer and records it on photographic film.

film reproducer—An instrument which reproduces a recording on film.

film resistor—A fixed resistor the resistance element of which is a thin layer of conductive material on an insulated form. Some sort of mechanical protection is placed over this layer.

film scanning—The process of converting

movie film into corresponding electrical signals that can be transmitted by a television system.

(A) T-section filter.

(B) Pi-section filter.

(C) Ladder-section filter.

Filters (wave filters).

filter—1. A selective network of resistors, inductors, or capacitors which offers comparatively little opposition to certain frequencies or to direct current, while blocking or attenuating other frequencies. 2. Also called a wave filter. A tuned circuit designed to pass a-c signals of a specified frequency. 3. A pattern of characters used to control the selection or elimination of portions of another pattern of characters. 4. A device or program that separates data, signals, or materials in accordance with specified criteria. 5. Also called extractor or mask. A machine word that specifies which parts of another machine word are to be operated on.

filter attenuation band—Also called a filter stop band. A frequency band in which the attenuation constant is not zero if dissipation is neglected. In other words, a frequency band of attenuation.

filter capacitor—A capacitor used in a filter circuit. The term is usually reserved for electrolytic capacitors in a power-supply filter circuit.

filter center—In an aircraft control and warning system, a location at which information from observation posts is filtered for further dissemination to air-direction centers.

filter choke — Normally, an iron-core coil which allows direct current to pass while opposing the passage of pulsating or alternating current.

filter-impedance compensator—An impedance compensator which is connected across the common terminals of electric-wave filters, when the latter are used in parallel, in order to compensate for the effects of the filters on each other.

filter passband — *See* Filter-Transmission Band.

filter slot—A choke, in the form of a slot,

designed to suppress unwanted modes in a waveguide.

filter stop band — *See* Filter Attenuation Band.

filter-transmission band — Also called filter passband. A frequency band in which the attenuation constant is zero if dissipation is neglected. In other words, a frequency band of free transmission.

final actuation time—The time of termination of the chatter of a relay following contact actuation.

final amplifier—The stage which feeds the antenna in a transmitter.

final wrap — The outer layer of insulation around a coil, covering the saddle and splice insulation.

finder — In a telephone switching system, a name applied to the switch or relay group that selects the path which the call is to follow through the system.

fine-chrominance primary—Also called the I-signal. In the color television system presently standardized for broadcasting in the United States, the chrominance primary associated with the greater transmission bandwidth.

fine-tuning control—A receiver control which varies the frequency of the local oscillator over a small range to compensate for drift and permit fine adjustment to the carrier frequency of a station.

finished blank—A crystal product after completion of all processes. It may also include the electrodes adherent to the crystal blank.

finishing — The process of repeated hand lapping and electrical testing by which a finished crystal blank is brought up to specifications.

finishing rate—Expressed in amperes, the rate of charge to which the charging current of a battery is reduced near the end of the charge to prevent excessive gassing and temperature rise.

finish lead—The lead connected to the finish, or outer end, of a coil.

finite—Having fixed and definite limits.

fins—Radial sheets or discs of metal attached to metal parts of a power tube or other component for the purpose of dissipating heat.

fire-control equipment — Equipment that takes in target indications from optical or radar devices and, after calculating the motion of the target and firing vehicle, properties of air, etc., puts out directions of bearing, elevation, and timing for aiming and firing the guns.

fire-control radar—Radar employed for directing gunfire against the targets it observes.

fired tube (TR, ATR, and pre-TR tubes)— The condition of a tube while a radiofrequency glow discharge exists at the resonant gap, resonant window, or both.

firing—1. In any gas- or vapor-filled tube, the ionization of the gas and the start of current flow. 2. The excitation of a device during a brief pulse. 3. In a magnetic amplifier, the transition from the unsaturated to the saturated state of the saturable reactor during the conducting or gating alternation. 4. An adjective modifying phase or time, to designate when firing occurs.

firing angle—1. The electrical angle of the plate-supply voltage at which an ionization of a gaseous tube occurs. 2. In a magnetic amplifier, the point on a sine-wave control voltage at which the control ampere-turns are sufficient to saturate the cure. This is the point where the secondary winding (load) impedance drops to zero, and almost all of the supply voltage appears across the load.

firing point—The point at which the gas or vapor in a tube ionizes and current begins to flow.

firing potential—The controlled potential at which conduction through a gas-filled tube begins.

first audio stage—The first stage in an audio amplifier.

first detector—Now called the mixer. In a superheterodyne receiver, the stage where the local-oscillator signal is combined with the modulated incoming radio-frequency signal to produce the modulated intermediate-frequency signal.

first Fresnel zone—In optics and radio communications, the circular portion of a wave front intersecting the line between an emitter and a more distant point where the resultant disturbance is being observed. The center intersects the front with the direct ray, and the radius is such that the shortest path from the emitter through the periphery to the receiving point is one-half wave longer than the ray.

fishbone antenna—An antenna consisting of a series of coplanar elements arranged in collinear pairs and loosely coupled to a balanced transmission line.

fishpaper—A tough fiber used in sheet form for insulating transformer windings from the core, field coils from field poles, or conductors from the armature.

fission—Also called atomic fission or nuclear fission. The splitting of an atomic nucleus into two parts. Fission reactions occur only with heavy elements such as uranium and plutonium and are accompanied by large amounts of radioactivity and heat.

fissionable—Capable of undergoing fission.

fission products—The elements which result from atomic fission. They may consist of more than forty different radioactive elements such as arsenic, silver, cadmium, iodine, barium, tin, cerium, and others.

fitting—An accessory, such as a locknut or bushing, to a wiring system. Its function is primarily mechanical rather than electrical.

fix—A position determined without reference to any former position.

fixed bias—A constant value of bias voltage.

fixed capacitor—A capacitor designed with a definite capacitance that cannot be adjusted.

fixed crystal—A crystal detector with a non-adjustable contact position.

fixed-cycle operation—1. A type of computer performance whereby a fixed amount of time is allocated to an operation. 2. Synchronous or clock-type arrangement in a computer in which events occur as a function of measured time.

fixed echo—A stationary echo indication on a radar ppi display, indicating a fixed target.

fixed-frequency iff—A class of iff (identification friend or foe) equipment which responds immediately to every interrogation, thus permitting the response to be displayed on plan-position indicators.

fixed-frequency transmitter—A transmitter designed for operation on a single carrier frequency.

fixed-point system—A system of notation in which a number is represented by a single set of digits and the position of the radix point is not numerically expressed. (Also see Floating-Point System.)

fixed-program computer — See Wired-Program Computer.

fixed resistor—A resistor designed to introduce only a predetermined amount of resistance into an electrical circuit and not adjustable.

fixed screen—Application of a potential to a screen grid which is unaffected by other operating conditions within the tube.

fixed service—Any service communicating by radio between fixed points, except broadcasting and special services.

fixed station—1. A station in the fixed service. (A fixed station may, as a secondary service, transmit to mobile stations on its normal frequencies.) 2. A permanent station which communicates with other fixed stations.

fixed transmitter — A transmitter operated from a permanent location.

fixed-voltage winding—The motor winding which is excited by a fixed voltage.

fl—Abbreviation for footlambert.

flag—A large sheet of metal or fabric for shielding television camera lenses from light.

flame-failure control—A system which automatically stops the fuel supply to a furnace if the pilot burner accidentally goes out.

flame microphone—A microphone in which the action of sound waves on a flame changes the resistance between two electrodes in the flame.

flame resistance — The characteristic of a material that prevents it from flaming when the source of heat is removed.

flame-resistant—See Flame-Retardant.

flame-retardant—Retarding ignition and the spread of flames, either inherently or because of special treatment. Also called flame-resistant.

flammability — The ability of a material to support combustion.

flammable—Term applied to material which readily ignites and burns when exposed to flames or elevated temperatures. Also called combustible.

flange—Also called waveguide flange. A fitting used at the end of a waveguide to a microwave component or to another waveguide.

flange connector—A mechanical joint employing plane flanges bolted together in a waveguide.

flange coupling — A connection utilizing flanges not in mechanical contact between two parts of a waveguide, yet introducing no discontinuity in the flow of energy along the guide.

flanking effect—The effect on filter characteristics of connecting additional filters in parallel.

flap attenuator — A form of waveguide attenuator in which a variable amount of loss is introduced by insertion of a sheet of resistive material, usually through a nonradiating slot.

flare—An enlarged and distorted radar-screen target indication due to excessive brightness.

flare angle—The continuous change in cross section of a wave guide.

flare factor—A number expressing the degree of outward curvature of a speaker horn.

flash—Sometimes called hit. Momentary interference to a television picture, lasting approximately one field or less and of sufficient magnitude to totally distort the picture information. In general, this term is used only when the impairment is so short that the basic impairment cannot be recognized.

flashback voltage—The inverse peak voltage at which ionization takes place in a gas tube.

flasher — A device, generally a thermal or motor-driven switch, that rapidly and automatically lights and extinguishes electric lamps.

flasher relay—A self-interrupting relay.

flashing — The application of a high-frequency electromagnetic field to an electron tube through the envelope to flash its getter during evacuation.

flashing of a dynamo — The flashing or sparking which is likely to take place at the brushes of a commutator.

flash magnetization — Magnetization of a ferromagnetic object by an abrupt current impulse.

flashover — A disruptive discharge through air, around or over the surface of insulation, or between parts of different potential or polarity produced by the application of voltage, wherein the breakdown path becomes sufficiently ionized to maintain an electric arc.

flashover voltage—1. The highest value attained by any voltage impulse which caused a flashover. 2. The voltage at which insulation fails by discharge between electrodes across the insulation surface.

flash pulsing—Transmission of short bursts of radiation at irregular intervals by a mechanically controlled keyer.

flash test—A method of testing insulation by momentarily applying a voltage much higher than the working voltage.

Flash tube.

flash tube—Also called electronic flash tube and photoflash tube. A gas-discharge tube for producing high-intensity, short-duration flashes of light. It consists of a glass tube bent in a U, a helix, or a combination of the two and filled with a rare gas. The tube has an anode, a cold cathode, and a trigger electrode. It is flashed by applying a high-voltage pulse to the trigger electrode.

flash welding—Welding in which an arc is first struck between the pieces to be welded. After the ends are thus heated, the weld is completed by bringing them together under pressure and cutting off the current.

flat fading—That type of fading in which all components of the received radio signal fluctuate in the same proportion simultaneously.

flat, flexible cable—*See* Tape Cable.

flat frequency response—The response of a system in a constant-amplitude function which varies in frequency. The response is flat if it varies within specified limits of amplitude, usually specified in decibels from a reference quantity.

flat leakage power (TR and pre-TR tubes)—The peak radio-frequency power transmitted through the tube after establishment of a steady-state radio-frequency discharge.

flat line—A radio-frequency transmission line or part of a line having a low standing-wave ratio.

flat pack—A flat, rectangular integrated-circuit or hybrid-circuit package with coplanar leads.

flat response—Ability of a sound system to reproduce all tones, from the lowest to the highest, in the proper proportion.

flat top—The horizontal portion of an antenna.

flat-top antenna—An antenna having two or more lengths of wire parallel to each other and to the ground.

flat-top response—Response characteristic in which a definite band of frequencies is transmitted uniformly.

flat-type armature — Of a relay, an armature which rotates about an axis perpendicular to that of the core, with the pole face on a side surface of the core.

flat-type relay — A relay having a flat-type armature.

flaw—In a material, any discontinuity that would be harmful to proper functioning of the material.

flaw detection—The process of using sonic or ultrasonic waves to locate imperfections in a solid material. This is done by transmitting the waves through the material and listening for reflections or variations in transmission when they strike an imperfection in the material.

F layer—An ionized layer in the F region, existing in the night hemisphere and in the weakly illuminated portion of the day hemisphere.

F₁ layer — One of the regular ionospheric layers at an average height of about 225 kilometers, which occurs during the daylight hours.

F₂ layer—The most useful of the ionospheric layers for radio-wave propagation. It is the most highly ionized and highest of the layers, having an average night height of 225 kilometers and a midday height of about 400 kilometers.

Fleming's rule—Also called the right-hand or left-hand rule. If the thumb and the first and second fingers are extended at right angles to one another, with the thumb representing the direction of the wire motion, the first finger representing the direction of magnetic lines of force (from the north pole to the south pole), and the second finger representing the direction of the current, then the right hand will give the correct relationships for a conductor in the armature of a generator, and the left hand will give the correct relationships for a conductor in the armature of a motor. This rule is applied to the so-called conventional current flow, which is the opposite of electron flow.

Fleming valve—An early name for a diode, or two-electrode thermionic vacuum tube used as a detector.

Fletcher-Munson curves—Also called equal-loudness contours. A group of sensitivity curves showing the characteristics of the human ear for different intensity levels between the threshold of hearing and the threshold of feeling. The reference frequency is 1,000 Hz.

Flewelling circuit—An early radio circuit in which one tube served as a detector, amplifier, and local oscillator.

flexible coupling—1. A device for connecting two shafts end to end so that they can be rotated even though not exactly aligned. 2. Mechanical connection between two lengths of waveguide normally lying in a

Fletcher-Munson curves.

straight line and designed to allow a limited angular movement between axes.

flexible resistor—A wirewound resistor that looks like a flexible lead. It is made by winding *Nichrome* or any other type of resistance wire around asbestos or other heat-resistant cord. The wire is then covered with braided insulation, which is color coded to indicate the resistor value.

flexible shaft—A flexible core made up of layers of wire, which rotate inside a metal or rubber-covered flexible casing. The casing not only supports the core, but also acts as the bearing surface for the core.

flex life — A measure of the resistance of a conductor or other device to failure due to fatigue from repeated bending.

Flexode.

flexode—A flexible diode containing a junction that may be altered at will from a PN junction in one direction, to no junction at all, to a PN junction in the opposite direction. Thus the direction of easy current may be reversed without reversing the leads to the diode, and the resistance of the diode may be continuously varied from the back-resistance value to the forward-resistance value. It may be set to behave as a simple resistor, with the same value for both directions of current.

flicker—1. In television, the flickering produced in the picture when the field frequency is insufficient to completely synchronize the visual images. 2. In a regulated power supply, a phenomenon due primarily to sudden, minute changes of brief duration in the reference voltage or the input-stage junctions of the correction amplifier in the regulator. 3. Also called jitter or wobble. Noise in an amplifier, of higher frequency than drift, but lower than power-line or chopper-drive frequency noise.

flicker effect—Small variations in the plate current of a thermionic vacuum tube, believed to be due to random emission of positive ions by the cathode.

flicker photometer—A device for measuring the intensity of a light source. Illumination from the light source being measured and a standard light source are observed alternately in rapid succession. When the standard source is equal to the other, the flickering disappears.

flight control—Real-time calculations for the control of a vehicle in flight; includes stabilization, fuel monitoring, cruise control, etc.

flight path—A planned course for an airborne vehicle.

flight-path computer—A computer that includes all the functions of a course-line computer and also controls the altitude of an aircraft in accordance with a desired plan of flight.

flight-path deviation—The difference between the flight track of an aircraft and the actual flight path expressed in terms of either angular or linear measurement.

flight-path-deviation indicator—An instrument that provides a visual indication of deviation from a flight path.

flight track—The three-dimensional path in space actually traced by a vehicle.

Flinders bar—A bar of soft iron placed near a compass to correct errors due to variation of the vertical component of the earth's magnetism in different parts of the world.

flip-chip—An unencapsulated semiconductor device in which bead-type leads terminate on one face to permit flip (face-down) mounting of the device by contact of the leads to the required circuit interconnectors.

flip coil—A small coil used for measuring a magnetic field. When connected to a ballistic galvanometer or other instrument, it gives an indication whenever the magnetic field of the coil or its position in the field is suddenly reversed.

Flip-flop circuit.

flip-flop—Also called bistable multivibrator, Eccles-Jordan circuit, or trigger circuit. 1. A two-stage multivibrator circuit having two stable states. In one state, the first stage is conducting and the second is cut off. In the other state, the second stage is conducting and the first stage is cut off. A trigger signal changes the circuit from one state to the other, and the next trigger signal changes it back to the first state. For counting and scaling purposes, a flip-flop can be used to deliver one output pulse for each two input pulses. 2. A similar bistable device with an input which allows it to act as a single-stage binary counter.

flip-flop equipment—An electronic or electromechanical device which causes automatic alternation between two possible circuit paths. The same term is often applied to any mechanical operation which is analogous to the principles of the flip-flop.

flip-flop multivibrator—Also called start-stop multivibrator. A biased rectangular wave generator which operates for one cycle when a synchronizing trigger signal is applied.

flipover cartridge—A phonograph cartridge having separate needles for playing microgrove and standard records. It may be turned to bring the proper needle into playing position.

floated battery—A storage battery kept fully charged across the leads of a generator. The generator carries the normal load, and the battery assists during peaks.

floating—1. Keeping a storage battery connected in parallel with an electric supply to serve as a standby in case of supply failure and to assist in handling peak loads. 2. The condition of a device or circuit that is not grounded and not tied to any established potential.

floating address—*See* Symbolic Address.

floating-carrier modulation—*See* Controlled-Carrier Modulation.

floating charge—Continuous charging of a storage battery with a low current to keep the battery fully charged while idle or on light duty.

floating grid—A vacuum-tube grid that is not connected to any circuit. It assumes a negative potential with respect to the cathode.

floating input—1. An isolated input circuit not connected to ground at any point (the maximum permissible voltage to ground is limited by electrical design parameters of the circuit involved). It is understood that in a floating input circuit, both conductors are equally free from any reference potential, a qualification which limits the types of signal sources which can be operated floating. 2. *See* Differential Input Measurement.

floating junction—A semiconductor junction through which no net current flows.

floating neutral—A circuit in which the voltage to ground is free to vary with circuit conditions.

floating-point calculation—In a computer, a calculation taking into account the varying location of the decimal point (if base 10) or binary point (if base 2). The sign and coefficient of each number are specified separately.

floating-point routine—Coded instructions in proper sequence to direct a computer to

Select
USED BOOKS

Bought - Sold - Traded

In

Downtown Poulsbo

206/779-9773

P.O. Box 1823
Poulsbo, WA 98370

Megan Holmberg
Bookseller

BOOK STOP

779-9773

P.O. Box 1823, 18954-A Front Street N.E., Poulsbo, WA 98370

Date 6/11/86

Dict. 8 Ellec 450-7973
Tech Query

15?

1.09
12
1.09

perform a calculation with floating-point operation.

floating-point system—A system of numbering in which an added set of digits is used to denote the location of the radix point. (*Also see* Fixed-Point System.)

floating potential—The d-c voltage between an open-circuited terminal of a circuit and a reference point when a d-c voltage is applied to the other circuit terminals as specified.

float switch—A switch actuated by a float on the surface of a liquid.

flock—Finely divided felt used on phonograph turntables, underneath microphone stands, or wherever a nonscratching surface is desired.

flow—1. The passage of electrons (a current) through a conductor or through the space between electrodes. 2. A general term to indicate a sequence of events.

flowchart—*See* Flow Diagram.

flow diagram—Also called flowchart. A chart showing all the logical steps of a computer program. A program is coded by writing down the successive instructions that will cause the computer to perform the logical operations necessary for solving the problem, as represented on a flowchart.

flowed wax—A mechanical recording disc prepared by melting and flowing wax onto a metal base.

flowmeter—A device for measuring the rate of flow of liquids or gases.

flow soldering—Also called wave soldering. A method of soldering printed-circuit boards by moving them over a flowing wave of molten solder in a solder bath.

fluctuating current—A direct current that changes in value, but not at a steady rate.

fluctuation noise—*See* Random Noise.

fluctuation voltage—Small voltage variations in a thermionic tube due to thermal agitation, shot effect, flicker effect, etc.

fluid damping—Damping obtained through displacement of a viscous fluid and the accompanying dissipation of heat.

fluorescence—Emission of light when a material is excited by electrons, ultraviolet radiation, or X rays.

fluorescent—Having the property of giving off light when activated by electronic bombardment or a source of radiant energy.

fluorescent lamp—An electric discharge lamp in which a gas ionizes and produces radiation that activates the fluorescent material inside the glass tubing. The phosphors in the fluorescent material transform the radiant energy from the electric discharge into wavelengths giving more light (higher luminosity).

fluorescent material—A material that fluoresces readily when exposed to electron beams, X rays, or other radiation.

fluorescent screen—The coating, on the face of a cathode-ray or television picture tube, which glows under electron bombardment.

fluorometer—An instrument for measuring fluorescence.

fluoroscope—An instrument with a fluorescent screen suitably mounted with respect to an X-ray tube, used for immediate indirect viewing of internal organs of the body, or internal structures in apparatus or masses of metals, by means of X rays. A fluorescent image (really a kind of X-ray shadow picture) is produced.

fluoroscopy—The use in diagnosis, testing, etc., of a fluorescent screen activated by X rays.

flush receptacle—A receptacle recessed into a wall, with only the plate extending beyond the surface.

flush-type instrument—An instrument designed to be mounted with its face projecting only slightly from the front of the panel.

flutter—1. Also called wow and drift. The frequency deviations produced by irregular motion of the turntable during recording, duplication, or reproduction. The term "flutter" usually refers to relatively high cyclic deviations (for example, 10 hertz), and the term "wow" to relatively low ones (for example, a variation of once per revolution). The term "drift" usually refers to a random rate close to zero hertz. 2. In communications, (a) distortion due to variations in loss resulting from simultaneous transmission of a signal at another frequency, or (b) a similar effect due to phase distortion.

Flutter bridge.

flutter bridge—An instrument for measuring the irregularities in a constant-speed device such as a film, disc, or tape recorder.

flutter echo—1. A rapid succession of reflected pulses resulting from a single initial pulse. 2. A multiple echo in which the reflections occur in rapid succession. If periodic and audible, it is referred to as a musical echo.

flutter rate—The number of times per second the flutter varies.

flux—1. A material used to promote the joining of metals in soldering. Rosin is widely used in soldering electronic parts. 2. Number of particles crossing a unit area per unit time. The common unit of flux is particles/cm^2/sec. Integrated flux, after an exposure of time T, is equal to the total number of particles which have traversed a unit area during time T.

flux density—Also called induction density. The number of magnetic lines of force passing through a unit area.

fluxgate—A magnetic azimuth-sensitive element of the fluxgate-compass system activated by the earth's magnetic field.

fluxgate compass—A gyrostabilized, remote-indicating compass and azimuth-control system used with automatic pilots.

fluxgraph—A machine that automatically plots on paper the magnetic field strength at various points in the vicinity of a coil.

flux guide—In induction heating, a magnetic material used for guiding the electromagnetic flux to the desired location or for confining it to definite regions.

flux linkage—Magnetic lines of force which link a coil of wire. Whenever the flux linkage changes, an emf is generated in the coil.

fluxmeter—An instrument used with a test coil for measuring magnetic flux. It consists usually of a moving-coil galvanometer in which the torsional control is either negligible or compensated.

flyback—1. The shorter of the two time intervals comprising a sawtooth wave. 2. Also called retrace. As applied to a cathode-ray tube, the return of the spot to its starting point after having reached the end of its trace. This portion of the wave is usually not seen because of blanking circuits or the shortage of time.

flyback checker—An instrument used to check flyback or other transformers or inductors for open windings or shorted turns.

Flyback power supply.

flyback power supply—The power supply that generates the high d-c voltage required by the second anode of a picture tube. This voltage is produced during the flyback period, the current in the horizontal-deflecting coils reversing and inducing a sharp pulse in the primary of the transformer supplying the deflection circuit. This pulse is stepped up by an autotransformer and rectified. After suitable filtering, it becomes a very high d-c voltage.

flyback tester—An instrument that tests flyback transformers and sometimes also deflection yokes.

flyback time—The period during which the electron beam is returning from the end of a scanning line to begin the next line.

flyback transformer—Also called horizontal-output transformer. A transformer used in the horizontal-deflection circuit of a television receiver to provide the horizontal-scanning and accelerating-anode voltages for the cathode-ray tube. It also supplies the filament voltage for the high-voltage rectifier.

flycutter—An accessory used with a drill press to cut out large holes in metal or wood.

flying spot—A small, rapidly moving spot of light, usually generated by a cathode-ray tube, used to scan an image field for television transmission.

flying-spot scanner—1. Also called light-spot scanner. A television scanning device embodying a small beam which is moved over a scene or film and translates the highlights and shadows into electrical signals. 2. In optical character recognition, a device employing a moving sopt of light to scan a sample space, the intensity of the transmitted or reflected light being sensed by a photoelectric transducer.

flywheel effect—The maintaining of oscillations in a circuit in the intervals between pulses of excitation energy. The action is analogous to the rotation of a flywheel due to its stored mechanical energy.

flywheel synchronization—Automatic frequency control of a scanning circuit. The sweep oscillator responds to the average timing of the sync pulses, not to each pulse individually.

flywheel tuning—A tuning-dial mechanism which uses a heavy flywheel on the control shaft for added momentum, to obtain a smoother tuning action.

f-m—Abbreviation for frequency modulation.

fm/am—A system in which information subcarriers are frequency-modulated and are used to amplitude-modulate the carrier.

f-m broadcast band—The band of frequencies extending from 88 to 108 MHz, which include those assigned to noncommercial educational broadcasting.

f-m broadcast channel—A band of frequencies 200 kHz wide and designated by its center frequency. Channels for f-m broadcast stations begin at 88.1 MHz and continue in successive steps of 200 kHz to and including 107.9 MHz.

f-m broadcast station—A station employing frequency modulation in the f-m broadcast band and licensed primarily for the transmission of radio-telephone emissions intended to be received by the general public.

f-m discriminator—A device which converts frequency variations to proportional variations in the amplitude of an electrical signal. Discriminators may be of several basic types, such as pulse averaging, Foster-Seely, ratio detector, or phase-lock correlation detector.

f-m discriminator (subcarrier)—The same as an f-m discriminator except that it is used to convert subcarrier frequency variations into proportional voltage or current signals.

fm/pm—A system in which information subcarriers are frequency-modulated and used to phase-modulate the carrier.

f-m multiplex—*See* F-M Stereo.

f-m radar—*See* Frequency-Modulated Radar.

f-m recording (magnetic tape)—A method of recording in which the input signal modulates a voltage-controlled oscillator, the output of which is delivered to the recording head.

f-m stereo — Also called f-m multiplex. A means by which f-m radio stations are able to transmit stereophonic program material to specially designed receivers and which is at the same time compatible with monophonic equipment.

f-m stereophonic broadcast—The transmission of a stereophonic program by a single f-m broadcast stations utilizing the main channel and a subchannel to carry the signals required to produce the stereophonic effect.

focal length—Symbolized by *f*. The distance from the principal focus (focus of parallel rays of light) to the surface of a mirror or the optical center of a lens.

focometer—An instrument for measuring the focal length of a lens or an optical system.

focus—1. The convergence of light rays or an electron beam at a selected point. 2. The sharp definition of a scanning beam in television receivers or optical systems.

focus control—On a television receiver, a potentiometer control used for fine focusing of the electron beam. The control varies the first-anode voltage of an electrostatic tube or the focus-coil current of a magnetic tube.

focusing—The process of controlling the convergence and divergence of an electron or light beam.

focusing anode—One of the electrodes used to focus the electron beam in a cathode-ray

tube. As its potential changes, so does the electric field, thereby altering the path of the electrons.

focusing coil—The coil around the neck of a cathode-ray tube. It provides a magnetic field, parallel to the electron beam, for controlling the cross-sectional area of the beam on the screen.

focusing electrode—An electrode to which a potential is applied to control the cross-sectional area of the electron beam.

focusing magnet—A permanent magnet assembly that produces a magnetic field for focusing the electron beam in a cathode-ray tube.

fold-back characteristic—*See* Current Limiting.

folded cavity—An arrangement used for producing a cumulative effect in a klystron repeater. This is done by making the incoming wave act in several places on the electron stream from the cathode.

folded-dipole antenna—An antenna comprising two parallel, closely spaced dipole antennas. Both are connected together at their ends, and one is fed at its center.

Folded-dipole antenna.

folded heater—A strand of bent, coated wire inserted into a cathode sleeve.

folded horn—An acoustic horn which is

F-m stereophonic broadcast system.

curled to permit more efficient use of the space it occupies.

foldover — A distorted television picture, which appears to overlap horizontally or vertically. It is due to nonlinear horizontal- or vertical-sweep circuits.

follow current — That line current which tends to follow a lightning discharge through an arrester to ground.

follower—A circuit in which the output of a high-gain amplifier is fed directly back to its negative input. The input signal is reproduced without polarity reversal.

follower drive — Also called slave drive. A drive in which the reference input and operation are direct functions of a master drive.

follower with gain—A follower in which only a part of the output voltage is fed back in series opposition to the input signal. Hence, closed-loop gain greater than unity is obtained over the rated range of operation.

following blacks—Also called edge effect, trailing reversal, or trailing blacks. A picture condition in which the edge following a white object is overshaded toward black (i.e., the object appears to have a trailing black border).

following whites—Also called edge effect, trailing reversal, or trailing whites. A picture condition in which the edge following a black or dark gray object is shaded toward white (i.e., the object appears to have a trailing white border).

footcandle—Abbreviated fc. A unit of brilliance of a light. It is the luminance on a surface of one square foot on which a flux of one lumen is uniformly distributed, or the luminance at a surface one foot from a uniform source of one candlepower.

footlambert—A unit of luminance equal to $1/\pi$ candle per square foot, or to the uniform luminance of a perfect diffusing surface emitting or reflecting light at the rate of one lumen per square foot.

foot-pound—A unit of measurement equivalent to the work of raising one pound vertically a distance of one foot.

forbidden band—The energy band lying between the conduction and valence bands. The energy difference across it determines whether a solid acts as a conductor, semiconductor, or insulator.

forbidden energy gap — The energy range of a semiconductor between the bottom of the conduction band and the top of the valence band.

force—1. Any physical action capable of moving a body or modifying its motion. 2. In computer programming, manual intervention which directs the computer to execute a jump instruction.

force-balance transducer — A transducer in which the output from the sensing member is amplified and fed back to an element which causes a force-summing member to

return it to its rest position. The magnitude of the signal fed back determines the output of the device, like the error signal in a servo signal.

forced coding — See Minimum-Access Programming.

force differential — The difference between the operating force and the release force of a momentary contact switch.

forced oscillation — In a linear constant-parameter system, the response to an applied driving force, excluding the transient which results from energy at the time the driving force is applied.

force factor (of an electromechanical or electroacoustic transducer)—1. The complex quotient of the force required to block the mechanical or acoustic system, divided by the corresponding current in the electrical system. 2. The complex quotient of the resultant open-circuit voltage in the electric system, divided by the velocity in the mechanical or acoustic system.

force-summing device—In a transducer the element directly displaced by the applied stimulus.

fore pump—An auxiliary vacuum pump used as the first stage in evacuating vacuum systems.

fork oscillator—An oscillator in which a tuning fork is the frequency-determining element.

fork tines—The projecting ends of a tuning fork. When vibrated, they produce a constant frequency.

formant—1. The particular frequency region in which the energy of a vowel sound is concentrated most strongly. 2. In an organ, an electrical circuit, the purpose of which is to alter the tone quality of sound amplified by it. A formant filter is applied to the entire output from a manual, rather than to individual tones.

formant filter—A waveshaping network used in an organ to modify the signal from the tone generator so it will assume the waveshape of the desired tone.

form factor—1. Ratio of the effective value of a current to its average value. 2. Shape (diameter/length) of a coil. 3. Ratio of the effective value of a symmetrical alternating quantity to its half-period average value.

Formica—Trade name for a phenolic compound having good insulating qualities.

forming—The application of voltage to an electrolytic capacitor, electrolytic rectifier, or semiconductor device to produce a desired permanent change in electrical characteristics as a part of the manufacturing process.

form-wound coil—An armature coil that is formed or shaped over a fixture before being placed on the armature of a motor or generator. Any coil wound on a fixture or dummy form.

FORTRAN — A computer programming system which enables the programmer to state, in relatively simple language, the steps of a procedure to be carried out by the computer and to automatically obtain an efficient machine language program.

fortuitous telegraph distortion—Distortion other than bias or characteristic. It occurs when a signal pulse departs from the average combined effects of bias and characteristic distortion for one occurrence. Since fortuitous distortion varies from one signal to another it must be measured by a process of elimination over a long period. It is expressed in a percentage of unit pulse.

forty-five/forty-five—Also called the Westrex system. A system of disc recording in which signals originating from two microphones are impressed on each side of a groove. The two sides are cut 45° from the surface of the record.

forty-five record—A 7-inch record with a 1½-inch center hole. It is recorded at 45 rpm and played at the same speed.

forty-four–type repeater—Type of telephone repeater used in a four-wire system. It employs two amplifiers and no hybrid arrangements.

forward-acting regulator—A transmission regulator which makes an adjustment without affecting the quantity that caused the adjustment.

forward-backward counter—A counter having both an add and subtract input and thus capable of counting in either an increasing or a decreasing direction.

forward bias—An external voltage applied in the conducting direction of a PN junction. The positive terminal is connected to the P-type region, and the negative terminal to the N-type region.

forward coupler—A directional coupler used for sampling incident power.

forward current—The current which flows across a semiconductor junction when a forward-bias voltage is applied.

forward direction—The direction of easy current flow through a semiconductor device when a given voltage within the ratings of the device is applied. In a conventional rectifier or diode, the forward direction is from anode to cathode when the anode is at a positive voltage with respect to the cathode.

forward path—In a feedback control loop, the transmission path from the loop-actuating to the loop-output signal.

forward propagation ionospheric scatter—A radiocommunication technique using the scattering phenomenon exhibited by electromagnetic waves in the 30- to 100-megahertz region when passing through the ionosphere at an elevation of about 85 kilometers.

forward-propagation tropospheric scatter—A method of communication by means of ultrahigh frequency f-m radio. It provides reliable multichannel telephone, teletype, and data transmission without line-of-sight restrictions or the necessity of using wire or cables.

forward recovery time—In a semiconductor diode, the time required for the current or voltage to arrive at a specified condition after instantaneous switching from zero or a specified reverse voltage to a specified forward voltage.

forward resistance—The resistance measured at a specified forward voltage drop or forward current in a rectifier.

forward scatter—1. Propagation of electromagnetic waves at frequencies above the maximum usable high frequency through use of the scattering of a small portion of the transmitted energy when the signal passes from a nonionized medium into a layer of the ionosphere. 2. A term referring collectively to very-high-frequency forward propagation by ionospheric scatter and ultrahigh-frequency forward propagation by tropospheric scatter communication techniques.

forward scattering—The reflected radiation of energy from a target away from the illuminating radar.

forward short-circuit–current-amplification factor—In a transistor, the ratio of incremental values of output to input current when the output circuit is a-c short-circuited.

forward-transfer function—In a feedback control loop, the transfer function of the forward path.

forward voltage—Voltage of the polarity that produces the larger current.

forward voltage drop—The resultant voltage drop when current flows through a rectifier in the forward direction.

forward wave—In a traveling-wave tube, a wave with a group velocity in the same direction the electron stream moves.

Foster-Seeley discriminator—A type of frequency discriminator that converts a frequency-modulated signal into an audio signal. It requires a limiter to prevent random amplitude variations of the f-m signal from appearing in its output.

Foster-Seeley discriminator.

Foster's reactance theorem—The driving-point impedance of a finite two-terminal network composed of pure reactances is a reactance which is an odd rational function of frequency and which is completely determined, except for a constant factor, by assigning the resonant and antiresonant frequencies. In other words, the driving-point impedance consists of segments going from minus infinity to plus infinity (except that at zero, or infinite, frequency, a segment may start or stop at zero impedance). The frequencies at which the impedance is infinite are termed poles, and those at which it is zero are termed zeros.

Foucault currents—*See* Eddy Currents.

four-address code—An artificial language for describing or expressing the instructions carried out by a digital computer. In automatically sequenced computers, the instruction code is used for describing or expressing sequences of instructions. Each instruction word then contains a part specifying the operation to be performed, plus one or more addresses which identify a particular location in storage.

four-horn feed—A cluster of four rectangular horn antennas used as the radiating and receiving elements of parabolic or lens-type radar antennas. The four segments of the horn assembly define the four quadrants of information for direction to target sensing. Used on monopulse-type radar systems such as the AN/FPS-16.

Fourier series—A mathematical analysis that permits any complex waveform to be resolved into a fundamental, plus a finite number of terms involving its harmonics.

Four-layer diode.

four-layer diode—A semiconductor diode that has three junctions with connections made only to the two outer layers that form the junctions. A Shockley diode is an example.

four-layer transistor—A junction transistor that has four conductivity regions, but only three terminals. A thyristor is an example.

four-level system—A laser involving four electronic energy levels. The ground state (level 1) is pumped to level 4, from which the excited electrons make a downward transition to the upper laser level 3 (or metastable level 3). Then, stimulated transition to the lower laser level 2 occurs, followed by rapid decay to the ground state. The four-level system has the advantage that the pump level and ground state are isolated from the laser action.

four-pole network—*See* Two-Terminal–Pair Network.

four-track recording—Also called quarter-track. On quarter-inch-wide tape, the arrangement by which four different channels of sound may be recorded on adjacent tracks. These may be recorded as four separate and distinct tracks (monophonic), or two related (stereo) pairs of tracks. By convention, tracks 1 and 3 are recorded in the forward direction of a given reel, and tracks 2 and 4 are recorded in the reverse direction.

four-track tape—A tape with four wire recording strips which permit it to be played in both directions for stereo recordings, like a two-track monophonic tape. Thus, twice as much material can be recorded than on a two-track stereo tape.

four-wire circuit—A two-way circuit with two paths. Each path transmits the electric waves in one direction only. The transmission paths may or may not employ four wires.

four-wire repeater—A telephone repeater used in a four-wire circuit. It has two amplifiers; one amplifies the telephone currents in one side of the four-wire circuit, and the other in the other side.

four-wire terminating set—A hybrid arrangement involving termination of four-wire circuits on a two-wire basis for interconnection with two-wire circuits.

fox message—A standard message which is used for testing teletypewriter circuits and machines because it includes all the alphanumerics on a teletypewriter, as well as most of the function characteristics such as space, figures shift, letters shift, etc. It is: THE QUICK BROWN FOX JUMPED OVER A LAZY DOG'S BACK 1234567890————SENDING. The sending station's identification is inserted in the three space blanks which precede the word "sending."

fractional arithmetic units—Arithmetic units in a computer that is operated with the decimal point at the extreme left so that all numbers have a value less than 1.

fractional-horsepower motor—Any motor having a continuous rating of less than one horsepower.

Frahm frequency meter—A meter that measures the frequency of an alternating current. It consists of a row of steel reeds, each with a different natural frequency. All are excited by an electromagnet fed with the current to be measured. The reed that vibrates is the one with a frequency corresponding most nearly to that of the current.

frame—1. In television, the total area occupied by the picture. In the United States, each frame contains 525 horizontal scanning lines, and 30 complete frames are shown per second. 2. One cycle of a recurring number of pulses. 3. In pam and pdm, one complete commutator revolution or sweep. In pcm, a recurring group of words which includes a single synchronizing signal. 4. The array of binary digits across the width of magnetic or paper tape.

frame frequency—The number of times per second the picture area is completely scanned (30 per second in the United States television system).

frame grid—The grid of a vacuum tube consisting of a rigid welded frame on which tungsten wire is wound under tension, resulting in a firm precision structure that can be positioned accurately. It also allows the use of much finer grid wire, which reduces electron interception and power dissipation in the grid.

frame-grounding circuit — A conductor which is electrically bonded to the machine frame and/or to any conduction parts which are normally exposed to operating personnel. This circuit may further be connected to external grounds as may be required by applicable Underwriters code.

frame of reference—A set of points, lines, or planes used for defining space coordinates.

frame pulse synchronization—Synchronization of the local-channel rate oscillator by comparison and phase lock with the separate frame synchronizing pulses.

framer — A device for adjusting facsimile equipment so that the recorded elemental area bears the same relationship to the record sheet as the corresponding transmitted elemental area bears to the subject copy as the line progresses.

frame rate—*See* Frame Frequency.

frame roll—A momentary roll, or "flip-flop," of a television picture.

frame synchronization signal—In pam, a coded pulse or interval to indicate the start of the commutation frame period. In pcm, any signal used to identify a frame of data.

frame-synchronizing pulse—A recurrent signal that establishes each frame.

frame-synchronizing pulse separator — A circuit for separating frame-synchronizing pulses or intervals from commutated signals.

framing—1. Adjusting the picture to a desired position in the direction of line progression. 2. The process of selecting the bit groupings representing one or more characters from a continuous stream of bits.

framing bits—Also called sync bits. Noninformation-carrying bits used to make possible the separation of characters in a bit stream.

framing control—More often called centering control. A knob (or knobs) for centering and adjusting the height and width of a television picture.

framing magnet—More often called centering magnet. A magnet which centers the televised picture on the face of the tube.

Franklin antenna—An antenna which is several half-wavelengths long and has non-radiating phasing coils between half-wave sections.

Franklin oscillator — A two-terminal feedback oscillator using two tubes or transistors and having sufficient loop gain to permit extremely loose coupling to the resonant circuit.

Fraunhofer region—The region in which the energy from an antenna proceeds essentially as though coming from a source located in the vicinity of the antenna.

free electrons — Electrons which are not bound to a particular atom, but circulate among the atoms of a substance.

free energy—The available energy in a thermodynamic system.

free field—1. Theoretically, a field (wave or potential) which is free from boundaries in a homogeneous, isotropic medium. In practice, a field in which the effects of the boundaries are negligible over the region of interest. 2. A property of information-processing recording media which permits recording of information without regard to a preassigned or fixed field; e.g., information-retrieval-devices information may be dispersed in the record in any sequence or location.

free-field emission — Electron emission that occurs when the electric field at the surface of an emitter is zero.

free grid—A grid electrode that is left unconnected in a vacuum tube. Its potential exerts a control over the plate current.

free impedance—Also called normal impedance. The input impedance of a transducer when the load impedance is zero.

free magnetic pole—A magnetic pole so far from an opposite pole that it is free from the effect of the other pole.

free motional impedance—The complex remainder after the blocked impedance of a transducer has been subtracted from the free impedance.

free net—A net in which any station may communicate with any other station in the same net without first obtaining permission from the control station.

free oscillations—Commonly referred to as shock-excited oscillations. Oscillations that continue in a circuit or system after the applied force has been removed. The frequency of the oscillations is determined by the parameters of the system or circuit.

free-point tube tester—A tester instrument that permits transferring a tube from a circuit to a test panel at which either voltage or current measurement for any electrode of the tube is readily made by plugging a meter into appropriate jacks. Connections to the receiver are made by means of a cord and plug inserted into the socket from which the tube was removed.

free position—The initial position of the actuator of a momentary-contact switch when there is no external force (other than gravity) applied on the actuator, and the switch is in the specified position.

free progressive wave — Also called free wave. A wave free from boundary effects in a medium. In other words, there are no reflections from nearby surfaces. A free wave can only be approximated in practice.

free radicals—Atoms, ionized fragments of atoms, or molecules which combine and release enormous amounts of energy.

free reel—The reel which supplies the magnetic tape on a recorder.

free-rotor gyro — A gyro the rotor of which is supported by a gas-lubricated spherical bearing.

free-running frequency—The frequency at which a normally synchronized oscillator operates in the absence of a synchronizing signal.

free-running local synchronizer oscillator —A free-running oscillator circuit in the decommutator normally triggered by separated channel synchronizing pulses. It supplies substitute pulses for missing channel pulses.

free-running multivibrator — See Astable Multivibrator.

free-running sweep — A sweep operating without synchronizing pulses.

free sound field—A field in a medium free from discontinuities or boundaries. In practice it is a field in which the boundaries cause negligible effects over the region of interest.

free space—Empty space, or space with no free electrons or ions. It has approximately the electrical constants of air.

free-space field intensity—The radio-field intensity that would exist at a point in a uniform medium in the absence of waves reflected from the earth or other objects.

free-space loss—The theoretical radiation loss which would occur in radio transmission if all variable factors were disregarded.

free-space propagation—Electromagnetic radiation over a straight-line path in a vacuum or ideal atmosphere, sufficiently removed from all objects that affect the wave in any way.

free-space radar equation—The equation for determining the characteristic of a radar signal propagated between the radar set and a reflected target in free space.

free-space radiation pattern—The radiation pattern of an antenna in free space, where there is nothing to reflect, refract, or absorb the radiated waves.

free-space transmission — Electromagnetic radiation over a straight line in a vacuum or ideal atmosphere sufficiently removed from all objects that affect the wave.

free speed—The angular speed of an energized motor under no-load conditions. (Also see Angular Velocity.)

free wave—See Free Progressive Wave.

freewheeling circuit—A motor arrangement in which the field is shunted by a half-wave rectifier which discharges the energy stored in the field during the negative half cycles.

freeze-out—A short-time denial of a telephone circuit to a subscriber by a speech-interpolation system.

F-region — The region of the ionosphere above 100 miles.

freq—Abbreviation for frequency.

frequency—Symbolized by f. 1. The number of recurrences of a periodic phenomenon in a unit of time. Electrical frequency is specified as so many hertz. Radio frequencies are normally expressed in kilohertz at and below 30,000 kilohertz and in megahertz above this frequency. 2. Number of complete hertz of a wave motion (e.g., of an alternating current or sound wave).

frequency agility—The rapid and continual shifting of a radar frequency to avoid jamming by the enemy, reduce mutual interference with friendly sources, enhance echoes from targets, or provide necessary patterns of ecm (electronic countermeasures) or eccm (electronic counter-countermeasures) radiation.

frequency allocation — The assignment of available frequencies in the radio spectrum to specific stations, for specific purposes. This is done to yield maximum utilization of frequencies with minimum interference between stations. Allocations in the United States are made by the Federal Communications Commission.

frequency authorization—The document of power which legalizes the assignment of a frequency or a frequency band.

frequency band—A continuous and specific range of frequencies.

frequency band of emission—The frequency band required for a specific type of transmission and speed of signaling.

frequency bias—A constant frequency purposely added to the frequency of a signal.

frequency-change signaling — A telegraph signaling method in which one or more particular frequencies correspond to each desired signaling condition of a telegraph code. The transition from one set of frequencies to the other may be either a continuous or a discontinuous change in frequency or in phase.

frequency changer — See Frequency Converter.

frequency-changing circuit—A circuit comprising an oscillator and a mixer and delivering an output at one or more frequencies other than the input frequency.

frequency channel—A continuous portion of the appropriate frequency spectrum for a specified class of emission.

frequency compensation—A method of extending the higher or lower (or both) frequency ranges within which an amplifier has nearly uniform gain.

frequency constant—The number relating the natural vibration frequency of a piezoid (finished crystal blank) to its linear dimension.

frequency conversion—1. The process of converting a signal to some other frequency by combining it with another frequency. 2. Of a heterodyne receiving system, converting the carrier frequency of a received signal from its original value to the intermediate frequency value in a superheterodyne receiver.

frequency converter—Also called frequency changer. A circuit, device, or machine that changes an alternating current from one frequency to another, with or without a change in voltage or number of phases. In a superheterodyne receiver, the oscillator and mixer first-detector stages together serve as a frequency converter.

frequency correction — Compensation, by means of an attenuation equalizer, for unequal transmission of various frequencies in a line.

frequency cutoff—The frequency at which the current gain of a transistor drops 3 db below the low-frequency gain.

frequency demodulation—Removal of the intelligence from a modulated carrier.

frequency departure—The amount a carrier or center frequency deviates from its assigned value.

frequency deviation—In frequency modulation, the peak difference between the instantaneous frequency of the modulated wave and its carrier frequency.

Frequency-deviation meter.

frequency-deviation meter—An instrument that indicates the number of hertz a transmitter has drifted from its assigned carrier frequency.

frequency discrimination — A term applied to the operation of selecting a desired frequency or frequencies from a spectrum of frequencies.

frequency discriminator—A circuit that converts a frequency-modulated signal into an audio signal.

frequency distortion—1. The distortion that results when all frequencies in a complex wave are not amplified or attenuated equally. 2. The impairment of fidelity introduced by a transducer as a result of the unequal transfer of frequencies—e.g., unequal amplification of frequencies with the passband of an amplifier.

frequency distribution—The number of occurrences of particular values plotted against those values.

frequency diversity—*See* Frequency-Diversity Reception.

frequency-diversity reception—Also called frequency diversity. The form of diversity

reception which utilizes transmission at different frequencies.

frequency divider—A device delivering an output voltage which is an integral submultiple or proper fraction of the input frequency.

frequency-division multiplex — Abbreviated fdm. A device or process for transmitting two or more signals over a common path by sending each one over a different frequency band.

frequency doubler—An electronic stage having a resonant plate circuit tuned to the second harmonic of the input frequency. The output signal will then have twice the frequency of the input signal.

frequency-doubling transponder — A transponder that doubles the frequency of the interrogating signal before retransmission.

frequency drift—Any undesired change in the frequency of an oscillator, transmitter, or receiver.

frequency-exchange signaling — The method in which the change from one signaling condition to another is accompanied by a decay in amplitude of one or more frequencies and by a build-up in amplitude of one or more other frequencies.

frequency frogging — The interchanging of the frequency allocations of carrier channels to prevent singing, reduce cross talk, and correct for line slope. It is accomplished by having the modulators in a repeater translate a low-frequency group to a high-frequency group and vice versa.

frequency indicator—A device which shows when two alternating currents have the same phase or frequency.

frequency interlace—In television, the relationship of intermeshing between the frequency spectrum of an essentially periodic interfering signal and the spectrum of harmonics of the scanning frequencies. Such relationship minimizes the visibility of the interfering pattern by altering its appearance on successive scans.

frequency keying—A method of keying in which the carrier frequency is shifted between two predetermined frequencies.

frequency-measuring equipment — Equipment for indicating or measuring the frequency or pulse-repetition rate of an electrical signal.

frequency meter—An instrument for measuring the frequency of an alternating current.

frequency-modulated broadcast band—The band from 88.1 to 107.9 megahertz. It is divided into 100 channels, each 200 kilohertz in width, and set aside for frequency-modulated broadcasting.

frequency-modulated, carrier-current telephony—A form of telephony in which a frequency-modulated carrier signal is transmitted over power lines or other wires.

frequency-modulated cyclotron—A cyclotron in which the frequency of the accelerating electric field is modulated in order to hold the positively charged particles in synchronism with the accelerating field despite their much greater mass at very high speeds.

frequency-modulated output—A transducer output which is obtained in the form of a deviation from a center frequency, where the deviation is proportional to the applied stimulus.

frequency-modulated radar—Also called f-m radar. A form of radar in which the radiated wave is frequency-modulated. The range is measured by beating the returning wave with the one being radiated.

frequency-modulated transmitter—One in which the frequency of the wave is modulated.

frequency-modulated wave—A carrier wave whose frequency is varied by an amount proportionate to the amplitude of the modulating signal.

frequency modulation — Modulation of a sine-wave carrier so that its instantaneous frequency differs from the carrier frequency by an amount proportionate to the instantaneous amplitude of the modulating wave. Combinations of phase and frequency modulation also are commonly referred to as frequency modulation. (*Also see* Frequency-Modulated Wave.)

frequency-modulation deviation—The peak difference between the instantaneous frequency of a modulated wave and the carrier or reference frequency.

frequency modulation-frequency modulation—A system in which the frequency-modulated subcarriers are used to frequency modulate a second carrier.

frequency modulation-phase modulation—A system in which the frequency-modulated subcarriers are used to phase-modulate a second carrier.

frequency monitor—An instrument for indicating the amount a frequency deviates from its assigned value.

frequency multiplex—A technique for the transmission of two or more signals over a common path. Each signal is characterized by a distinctive reference frequency or band of frequencies.

frequency multiplier—A device for delivering an output wave whose frequency is a multiple of the input frequency (e.g., frequency doublers and triplers).

frequency offset—The amount by which a frequency lies above or below a reference frequency. For example, if a frequency measures 1.000 001 MHz when compared against a reference frequency of 1.000 000 MHz, then its fractional frequency offset is 1 Hz/1 MHz, or 1 part in 10^6.

frequency offset transponder—A transponder which changes the interrogating signal frequency by a fixed amount before retransmission.

frequency output (transducer)—An output in the form of frequency which is a function of the applied measurand (e.g., angular speed and flow rate).

frequency overlap—1. In a color tv system, that part of the frequency spectrum occupied by both the monochrome and chrominance signals. 2. That part of the frequency band which is shared as a result of interleaving.

frequency pulling—A change in oscillator frequency due to a change in the load impedance.

frequency pushing — A change in the frequency of an oscillator due to a change in anode current or voltage.

frequency range—1. In a transmission system, those frequencies at which the system is able to transmit power without attenuating it more than an arbitrary amount. 2. In a receiver, the frequency band over which the receiver is designed to operate, covering those frequencies the receiver will readily accept and amplify. 3. A designated portion of the frequency spectrum.

frequency record—A recording of various known frequencies at known amplitudes, usually for testing purposes.

frequency regulator—A regulator that maintains the frequency of the frequency-generating equipment at a predetermined value or varies it according to a predetermined plan.

frequency relay—A relay which functions at a predetermined value of frequency. It may be an overfrequency or underfrequency relay, or a combination of both.

frequency response—1. A measure of how effectively a circuit or device transmits the different frequencies applied to it. 2. The portion of the frequency spectrum which can be sensed by a device within specified limits of amplitude error.

frequency-response characteristic — The amount by which the gain or loss of a device varies with the frequency.

frequency-response curve—A graphical representation of the way a circuit responds to different frequencies within its operating range.

frequency-response equalization — Also called equalization or corrective equalization. The effect of all frequency-discriminative means employed in a transmission system to obtain the desired overall frequency response.

frequency run—A series of tests for determining the frequency-response characteristics of a transmission line, circuit, or device.

frequency selectivity—The degree to which a transducer is capable of differentiating between the desired signal and between signals or interference at other frequencies.

frequency-sensitive relay—A relay that operates only when energized with voltage, current, or power within specific frequency limits.

frequency separator — The circuit which separates the horizontal-scanning from the vertical-scanning synchronizing pulses in a television receiver.

frequency shift—A system of telegraph operation in which the space signal is 70 hertz lower than the mark signal.

frequency-shift converter—A device which limits the amplitude of the received frequency-shift signal and then changes it to an amplitude-modulated signal.

frequency-shift indicator—In automatic code transmission, a device which designates mark and space by shifting the carrier back and forth between two frequencies instead of keying it on and off.

frequency-shift keying—Abbreviated fsk. A form of frequency modulation in which the modulating wave shifts the output frequency between predetermined values and the output wave has no phase discontinuity.

frequency-shift telegraphy—Telegraphy by frequency modulation in which the telegraph signal shifts the frequency of the carrier between predetermined values. There is phase continuity during the shift from one frequency to the other.

frequency-shift transmission—A method of transmitting the mark and space elements of a telegraph code by shifting the carrier frequency slightly, usually about 800 Hz.

frequency splitting—One condition of magnetron operation in which rapid alternation occurs from one mode of operation to another. This results in a similar rapid change in oscillatory frequency and consequent loss of power at the desired frequency.

frequency stability—The ability of electronic equipment to maintain the desired operating frequency.

frequency stabilization—The controlling of the center or carrier frequency so that it does not differ more than a prescribed amount from the reference frequency.

frequency standard—A stable low-frequency oscillator used for frequency calibration. It can generate a fundamental frequency of 50 to 100 kilohertz with a high degree of accuracy. Harmonics of this fundamental are then used as reference points for checking throughout the radio spectrum at 50- or 100-kilohertz intervals.

frequency swing—The instantaneous departure of the emitted wave from the center frequency when its frequency is modulated.

frequency synthesizer—A frequency source of high accuracy generally characterized by the fact that the output frequency is composed of two components. The frequency steps, mostly decadic, are derived from the crystal-stabilized frequency standard and the variable frequency of a free-running oscillator which fills in between these steps. The simplest method of frequency synthesis is to derive standard frequencies from a crystal-controlled frequency by harmonic generation and frequency division.

frequency tolerance—The maximum permissible deviation with respect to the reference frequency of the corresponding characteristic frequency of an emission. Expressed in percent or in hertz.

frequency translation—The transfer *en bloc* of signals occupying a definite frequency band, such as a channel or group of channels, from one position in the frequency spectrum to another in such a way that the arithmetic frequency difference of the signals within the band is unaltered.

frequency tripler—An amplifier whose output circuit is resonant to the third harmonic of the input signal. The output frequency is three times the input frequency.

frequency-type telemeter—A telemeter which employs the frequency of a periodically recurring electric signal as the translating means.

frequency-wavelength relation—For radio waves, the frequency in hertz is equal to approximately 300,000,000 divided by the wavelength in meters. The wavelength in meters is equal to approximately 300,000,000 divided by frequency in hertz or 300 divided by frequency in megahertz.

Fresnel—A little-used unit of frequency equal to 1012 hertz.

Fresnel lens—A thin lens constructed to have the optical properties of a much thicker lens.

Fresnel loss—*See* Surface Reflection.

Fresnel region—The region between an antenna and the Fraunhofer region.

Fresnel zone—1. An area selected in the aperture of a radiating system so that radiation from all parts of the system reaches some point at which it is desired at a common phase within 180°. 2. A circular zone about the direct path between a transmitter and a receiver at each radius that the distance from a point on this circle to the receiving point has a path length that is some multiple of a half-wavelength longer than the direct path.

frictional electricity—Electric charges produced by rubbing one material against another.

frictional error—1. Applied to pickups, the difference in values measured in percent of full scale before and after tapping, with the measurand constant.

frictional loss—The loss of energy due to friction between moving parts.

frictional machine—Also called a static machine. A device for producing frictional electricity.

friction effects—The difference in resistance or output between readings obtained prior to and immediately after tapping an instrument while applying a constant stimulus. Particularly applicable to potentiometric transducers.

friction error—A change in a reading originally taken in the absence of vibration that occurs after a transducer is tapped or dithered to remove internal friction.

friction-free calibration (transducer)—Calibration under conditions minimizing the effect of static friction often obtained by dithering.

friction tape—A fibrous tape impregnated with a sticky, moisture-resistant compound which provides a protective covering or insulation.

fringe area—The area just beyond the limits of the reliable service area of a television transmitter. Signals are weak and erratic, requiring the use of high-gain directional receiving antennas and sensitive receivers for satisfactory reception.

fringe howl—A squeal or howl heard when some circuit in a receiver is on the verge of oscillation.

fritting—A type of contact erosion in which an electrical discharge makes a hole through the contact film and produces molten matter that is drawn through the hole by electrostatic forces and then solidifies and forms a conducting bridge.

Frohlich high-temperature breakdown theory—A thermal mechanism for breakdown in which electrons rather than ions carry the current. The necessary number of conduction electrons is produced by thermal excitation of the electrons in impurity and imperfection levels.

Frohlich low-temperature breakdown theory—Also called the high-energy criterion. Similar to the Von Hippel theory, except that an electron energy distribution is assumed. Only a few electrons on the high-energy tail of the distribution must gain the necessary critical energy.

front contact—A movable relay contact which closes a circuit when the associated device is operated.

front end—The section of a tuner or receiver which is used to select the desired station from either the a-m, f-m, or tv band, and to convert the r-f signal to i-f. To do its job properly, a front end requires a high-gain, low-noise r-f stage, a mixer, and an oscillator. The degrees to which a desired station can be received without interference and without adding noise is expressed by sensitivity, selectivity, and signal-to-noise ratio.

front-end rejection—A db expression of the relative ability of a receiver network to reject signals outside the tuned bandwidth.

front porch—In the composite television signal, that portion of the synchronizing signal (at the blanking or black level) preceding the horizontal-sync pulse at the end of each active horizontal line. The standard EIA signal is 1.27 microseconds in duration.

front projection—A system of picture enlargement using an opaque reflective screen. The projector and viewers are on the same side of the screen.

front-surface mirror—An optical mirror on which the reflecting surface is applied to the front of the mirror instead of the back.

front-to-back ratio—Also called front-to-rear ratio. 1. The ratio of power gain between the front and rear of a directional antenna. 2. Ratio of signal strength transmitted in a forward direction to that transmitted in a backward direction. For receiving antennas, the ratio of received-signal strength when the source is in the front of the antenna to the received-signal strength when the antenna is rotated 180°.

front-to-rear ratio—See Front-to-Back Ratio.

fruit—See Fruit Pulse.

fruit pulse—Also called fruit. Radar beacon system video display of a synchronous beacon return which results when several interrogator stations are located within the same general area. Each interrogator receives its own interrogated reply as well as many synchronous replies resulting from interrogation of the airborne transponders by other ground stations.

F-scan—See F-Display.

F-scope—See F-Display.

fsk—See Frequency-Shift Keying.

Fuel cell.

fuel cell—An electrochemical generator in which the chemical energy from the reaction of air (oxygen) and a conventional fuel is converted directly into electricity. A fuel cell differs from a battery in that it uses hydrocarbons (or some derivative such as hydrogen) for fuel, and it operates continuously as long as fuel and air are available.

full duplex—A method of operation of a communication circuit in which each end can simultaneously transmit and receive. When used on a radio circuit, duplex operation requires two frequencies.

full-duplex operation—Simultaneous operation in opposite directions in a telegraph system.

full excursion—The application of a measurand, in a controlled manner, over the entire range of a transducer.

fullhouse—A multichannel radio control system in which all controls work to allow the model to fly a complete flight pattern.

full load—The greatest load a piece of equipment is designed to carry under specified conditions.

full-pitch winding—A type of armature winding in which the number of slots between the sides of the coil equals the pole-pitch measure in the slots.

full scale—The total interval over which an instrument is intended to be operated. Also, the output from a transducer when the maximum rated stimulus is applied to the input.

full-scale cycle—The complete range of an instrument, from minimum reading to full scale and back to minimum reading.

full-scale output — The algebraic difference in electrical output between the maximum and minimum values of measurand over which an instrument is calibrated. When the sensitivity slope is given by any other line than the end-point sensitivity, full scale expresses the algebraic difference, for the span of the instrument, which is calculated from the slope of the straight line from which nonlinearity is determined.

full-scale sensitivity—*See* Full-Scale Output.

full-scale value of an instrument — The largest actuating electrical quantity which can be indicated on the scale; or, for an instrument having its zero between the ends of the scale, the sum of the values of the actuating electrical quantity corresponding to the two ends.

full-track recording — Defines the track width as essentially equal to the tape width. Applies to quarter-inch-wide (or less) tape only.

INPUT   OUTPUT +   INPUT   OUTPUT +

FULL—WAVE CENTER TAPPED

FULL—WAVE BRIDGE

Full-wave rectifier.

full-wave rectifier—A circuit electron tube or other device which uses both positive and negative alternations in an alternating current to produce direct current.

full-wave rectifier tube—A tube containing two sets of rectifying elements, to provide full-wave rectification.

full-wave vibrator — A vibrator having an armature that moves back and forth between two fixed contacts, so as to change the direction of the direct-current flow through a transformer at regular intervals and thereby permit voltage step-up by the transformer. Used in battery-operated power supplies for mobile and marine radio equipment.

function—1. A quantity the value of which depends on the value of one or more other quantities. 2. A specific purpose of an entity, or its characteristic action.

functional device—*See* Integrated Circuit.

functional electronic block — A fabricated device serving a complete electronic function, such as amplification, without other individual components or conducting wires except those required for input, power, and output.

functional interface—An interface between the operating characteristics of equipment such as electrical power and signal characteristics, signal timing, and environmental coupling.

functional parts—Discrete items defined by functional characteristics and dimensions

which are not repairable with the use of spare parts (e.g., resistors, capacitors, diodes, potted transformers, permanently sealed batteries, etc.).

function characteristic — The relationship between the output ratio and the shaft position of a precision potentiometer.

function codes—Codes which appear in tape or cards to operate machine functions, such as carriage returns, space, shift, skip, tabulate, etc.

function digit—A coded instruction used in a computer for setting a branch order to link subroutines into the main program.

function generator—A device capable of generating one or more desired waveforms.

functioning time — In a relay, the time that elapses between energization and operation or between de-energization and release.

functioning value—In a relay, the value of applied voltage, current, or power at which operation or release occurs.

function switch—1. A network or system having a number of inputs and outputs. When signals representing information expressed in a certain code are applied to the inputs, the output signals will represent the input information in a different code. 2. In adapters or control units, the switch which determines whether the system plays as a monophonic or stereophonic unit; it may parallel the speakers or cut out one or the other, switch amplifiers from one speaker to the other, reverse channels, etc.

function table — 1. A table of values for mathematical function. 2. A hardware device or a computer program which translates one representation of information into another.

function unit—A device which can store a functional relationship and release it continuously or sporadically.

fundamental — *See* Fundamental Frequency.

fundamental component—The fundamental frequency component in the harmonic analysis of a wave.

fundamental frequency—The principal component of a wave; i.e., the component with the lowest frequency or greatest amplitude. It is usually taken as a reference.

fundamental harmonic—The harmonic component with the lowest frequency.

fundamental mode—1. *See* Dominant Mode. 2. Of vibration, the mode having the lowest natural frequency.

fundamental piezoelectric crystal unit—A unit designed to use the lowest resonant frequency for a particular mode of vibration.

fundamental tone—1. In a periodic wave, the component corresponding to the fundamental frequency. 2. In a complex tone, the component tone of lowest pitch.

fundamental units—Units arbitrarily selected to serve as the basis of an absolute system of units.

fundamental wavelength — The wavelength corresponding to the fundamental frequency.

(A) Glass-tube.

(B) Clear-window.

(C) Grasshopper.

Fuses.

In an antenna, the lowest resonant frequency of the antenna alone, without inductance or capacitance.

fungusproof—To chemically treat a material, component, or unit to prevent the growth of fungus spores.

fuse—A protective device, usually a short piece of wire but sometimes a chemical compound, which melts and breaks the circuit when the current exceeds the rated value.

fuse alarm—A circuit which produces a visual and/or audible signal to indicate a blown fuse.

fuse block—An insulating base on which fuse clips or other contacts for holding fuses are mounted.

fuse box—An enclosed box containing fuse blocks and fuses.

fuse clips—Contacts on the fuse support for connecting the fuse holder into the circuit.

fused disconnect—Generally an air-break switch with a fusing unit in the blade. Used for opening and closing high-voltage circuits.

fused junction—*See* Alloyed Junction.

fused quartz—A glasslike insulating material having exceptional heat and acid resistance.

fused semiconductor—The junction formed by recrystallization on a base crystal from a liquid phase of one or more components and the semiconductor.

fuse filler—Material placed within the fuse tube to aid circuit interruption.

fuse holder—A device for supporting a fuse and providing connections for its terminals.

fuse link—In a fuse, the current-carrying portion which melts when the current exceeds a predetermined value.

Fusestat—Trade name for a time-delay fuse similar to a Fusetron. It has a sized base requiring a permanent socket adapter, which prevents insertion of a fuse or Fusetron of an incorrect rating.

Fusetron—A screw-plug fuse that permits up to 50% overload for short periods of time without blowing.

fuse tube—The insulated tube enclosing a fuse link.

fuse unit—An assembly comprised of a fuse link mounted in a fuse holder, which contains parts and materials essential to the operation of the fuse link.

fuse wire—A wire made from an alloy that melts at a relatively low temperature.

fusible resistor—A resistor designed to protect a circuit against overload by opening when the current drain exceeds the design limits.

fusible wire—A wire used in fire-alarm circuits. It is made of an alloy with a low melting point.

fusion—Also called atomic fusion or nuclear fusion. The merging of atomic nuclei, under extreme heat (millions of degrees), to form a heavier nucleus. The fusion of two nuclei of light atoms is accompanied by a tremendous release of energy.

fv—Abbreviation for femtovolt (10^{-15} volt).

Fuse holders.

G

G—1. Symbol for conductance, the grid of a vacuum tube, a generator, or ground. 2. Abbreviation for giga (10^9).

g—Also called G-force. Symbol for the acceleration of a free-falling body due to the earths gravitational pull. Equal to 32.17 feet per second per second.

G/A (ground-to-air)—Communication with airborne objects from the ground.

GA coil—A coil wound with air spaces between its turns and layers to reduce the capacitance.

gage—Also spelled gauge. An instrument or means for measuring or testing. By extension, the term is often used synonymously with transducer.

gage pressure—1. A differential pressure measurement using the ambient pressure as a reference. 2. A pressure in excess of a standard atmosphere at sea level (i.e., 14.7 pounds per square inch).

gage pressure transducer — A pressure transducer that uses ambient pressure as the reference pressure. The sensing element is normally vented to the ambient pressure.

gain—Also called transmission gain. 1. Any increase in power when a signal is transmitted from one point to another. Usually expressed in decibels. Widely used for denoting transducer gain. 2. The ratios of voltage, power, or current with respect to a standard or previous reading.

gain bandwidth product — The product of the closed-loop gain of an operational amplifier and its corresponding closed-loop bandwidth. This product is often constant in operational amplifiers.

gain control—A device for varying the gain of a system or component.

gain margin—The amount of gain change of an operational amplifier at 180° phase-shift angle frequency that would produce instability.

gain-sensitivity control — See Differential Gain Control.

gain stability—The extent to which the sensitivity of an instrument remains constant with time. (The property reported in specifications should be instability, which is the maximum change in sensitivity from the initial value over a stated period of time under stated conditions.)

gain-time control—See Sensitivity Time Control.

galena—A bluish-gray, crystalline form of lead sulphide often used as the crystal in a variable crystal detector.

galloping ghost — See Proportional Control.

galvanic—An early term for current resulting from chemical action, as distinguished from electrostatic phenomena.

galvanic anode—A source of emf for cathodic protection provided by a metal less noble than the one to be protected (i.e., magnesium, zinc, or aluminum as used for cathodic protection of steel).

galvanic cell—An electrolytic cell capable of producing electric energy by electrochemical action.

galvanic corrosion — Accelerated electrochemical corrosion produced when one metal is in electrical contact with another more noble metal, both being in the same corroding medium, or electrolyte, with a current between them. (Corrosion of this type usually results in a higher rate of solution of the less noble metal and protection of the more noble metal.)

galvanic current—An electrobiological term for unidirectional current such as ordinary direct current.

galvanic series—A list of metals and alloys arranged in the order of their relative potentials (ability to go into solution) in a given environment. The table of potentials is arranged with the anodic, or least noble, metals at one end and the cathodic, or more noble, metals at the other. (For marine use, the potentials listed are related to a sea-water environment.)

galvanizing—The coating of steel with zinc to retard corrosion.

galvanometer—An instrument for measuring an electric current. This is done by measuring the mechanical motion produced by the electromagnetic or electrodynamic forces set up by the current.

galvanometer constant—The factor by which a certain function of a galvanometer reading must be multiplied to obtain the current in ordinary units.

galvanometer lamp—The lamp that illuminates a movable mirror of the galvanometer in some spectrophotometers. The angle at which the light is reflected to the galvanometer scale depends on the amount of current through the galvanometer coil.

galvanometer recorder (for photographic recording)—A combination of a mirror and coil suspended in a magnetic field. A signal voltage, applied to the coil, causes a light beam from the mirror to be reflected across a slit in front of a moving photographic film.

galvanometer shunt—A resistor connected in parallel with a galvanometer to increase the range of the instrument. The resistor limits the current to a known fraction and thus prevents excess current from damaging the galvanometer.

gamma—A numerical indication of the degree of contrast in a televised image. It is obtained by making a plot of the log of the output magnitude (ordinate) against the log of the input magnitude (abscissa), measured from a point corresponding to some reference black level. Then, take a straight line which approximates this plot over the region of interest and take its slope.

gamma correction—Introduction of a non-linear output-input characteristic for the purpose of changing the effective value of gamma.

gamma ferric oxide—The magnetic constituent of practically all present-day tapes, in the form of a dispersion of fine acicular particles within the coating.

gamma radiation—The radiation of gamma rays.

gamma rays—The emission from certain radioactive substances. They are electromagnetic radiations similar to X-rays, but with a shorter wavelength.

gang—To mechanically couple two or more variable capacitors, switches, potentiometers, or other components together so they can be operated from a single control knob.

gang capacitor—Also called gang tuning capacitor. Two or more variable tuning capacitors mounted on the same shaft and controlled by a single knob, but each capacitor tuning a different circuit. Thus, more than one circuit can be tuned simultaneously by a single control.

gang control—Simultaneous control of several

Gang capacitor.

similar pieces of apparatus with one adjustment knob or other control.

ganged tuning—Simultaneous tuning of two or more circuits with a single mechanical control.

gang punch—To punch information that is identical or constant into all of a group of punch cards.

gang switch—A number of switches mechanically coupled for simultaneous operation, but electrically connected to different circuits. In one common form, two or more rotary switches are mounted on the same shaft and operated by a single control.

gang tuning capacitor—*See* Gang Capacitor.

gap—1. In a magnetic circuit, the portion that does not contain ferromagnetic material (e.g., an air space). 2. The space between two electrodes in a spark gap. 3. The distance between the poles of a recording head.

gap arrester—A type of lightning arrester comprising a number of air gaps in series between metal cylinders or cones.

gap coding—In navigation, a process of communicating by interrupting the transmission of an otherwise continuous signal so that the interruptions form a telegraphic message.

gap depth—The dimension of the gap in a recording head, measured perpendicular to the surface of the head.

gap filler—1. A lightweight radar set used to fill in gaps in the coverage pattern of an early-warning radar net. 2. An auxiliary radar antenna used to fill in gaps in the pattern of the main radar antenna.

gap filling—Electrical or mechanical re-arrangement of an antenna array, or the use of a supplementary array, to produce lobes where gaps previously occurred.

gap insulation—Insulation wound in a gap.

gap length—The dimension of the gap of a recording head, measured from one pole face to the other. In longitudinal recording, the gap length is the dimension of the gap in the direction of tape travel.

gap loss—The loss in output attributable to the finite gap length of the reproduce head. The loss increases as the wavelength decreases, amounting to approximately 4 db when the wavelength is equal to twice the gap length, and subsequently increases rapidly toward a complete extinction of output when the wavelength is approximately equal to 1.15 times the gap length.

gap motor—A spark-gap drive motor.

gap scatter—In a computer, the deviation from true vertical alignment of the gaps of the magnetic readout heads for the several parallel tracks.

gap width—The dimension of the gap, measured in the direction parallel to the head surface and pole faces. The gap width of the record head governs the track width. The gap widths of reproduce heads are sometimes made appreciably less than those of the record heads to minimize tracking errors.

garbage—In a computer, a slang term for unwanted and meaningless information carried along in storage. Sometimes called hash.

garble—Faulty transmission, reception, or encoding which renders the message incorrect or unreadable.

garnet maser—*See* Ferromagnetic Amplifier.

garter spring—In facsimile, the spring fastened around the drum to hold the record sheet or copy in place.

gas—One of the three states of matter. An aeriform fluid having neither independent shape nor volume, but tending to spread out and occupy the entire enclosure in which it is placed. Gases are formed by heating a liquid above its boiling point.

gas amplification—Ratio of the charge collected to the charge liberated by the initial ionizing of the gas in a radiation counter.

gas-amplification factor—Ratio of radiant or luminous sensitivities with and without ionization of the gas contained in a gas phototube.

gas cleanup—The tendency of many gas-filled tubes to lose their gas pressure and hence become inoperable. This occurs when the ions of gas are driven at high velocity into the metal parts or the glass envelope of the tube where they form stable compounds and are lost as far as the tube is concerned.

gas current—The current which flows in the grid circuit of a vacuum tube when gas ions within the tube are attracted by the grid.

gas detector—An instrument used to indicate the concentration of harmful gases in the air.

gas diode—A tube having a hot cathode and an anode in an envelope containing a small amount of an inert gas or vapor. When the anode is made sufficiently positive, the electrons flowing to it collide with gas atoms and ionize them. As a result, the anode current is much greater than that for a comparable vacuum diode.

gas-electric drive—A self-contained power-conversion system comprising an electric generator driven by a gasoline engine. The generator in turn supplies power to the driving motor or motors.

gaseous electronics—The field of study involving the conduction of electricity through gases and a study of all atomic-scale collision phenomena.

gaseous tube—An electronic tube into which a small amount of gas or vapor is introduced after the tube has been evacuated. Ionization of the gas molecules during operation of the tube affects its operating characteristics.

gaseous-tube generator—A power source comprising a gas-filled electron-tube oscillator and a power supply, plus associated controls.

gas-filled cable—A coaxial or other type of cable containing gas under pressure which serves as insulation and keeps out moisture.

gas-filled lamp—A tungsten-filament lamp containing nitrogen or an inert gas such as argon.

gas-filled radiation-counter tube—A gas tube used for the detection of radiation. It operates on the principle that radiation will ionize a gas.

gas-filled tube rectifier—A rectifier tube in which a unidirectional flow of electrons from a heated electrode ionizes the inert gas within the tube. In this way, rectification is accomplished.

gas focusing—Also called ionic focusing. The use of an inert gas to focus the electron beam in a cathode-ray tube. Beam electrons ionize the gas molecules, forming a core of positive ions along the beam path which tends to attract beam electrons, making the beam more compact.

gasket-sealed relay—A relay in an enclosure sealed with a gasket.

gas laser—A laser where the active medium is a discharge in a gas within a glass or quartz tube that has a Brewster window at each end. This gas can be excited by a high-frequency oscillator or by a direct current flowing between electrodes inside the tube to pump the medium so as to obtain a population inversion.

gas magnification—The increase in current through a phototube due to ionization of the gas within the tube.

gas maser—A maser in which the microwave electromagnetic radiation interacts with the molecules of a gas such as ammonia. Use is limited chiefly to highly stable oscillator applications, as in atomic clocks.

gas noise—Electrical noise produced by erratic motion of gas molecules in gas or partially evacuated vacuum tubes.

gas-phase laser—A continuous-wave device for general experimental work with coherent light. It employs a resonator made up of a fused-silica plasma tube 60 cm long having internal, multilayer, dielectric-coated confocal reflectors of optical-grade fused silica.

gas phototube—A phototube into which a quantity of gas has been introduced, usually to increase its sensitivity.

gas ratio—The ratio of the ion current in a tube to the electron current that produces it.

gassiness—The presence of unwanted gas in a vacuum tube, usually in relatively small amounts. It is caused by leakage from outside the tube or by evolution from its inside walls or elements.

gassing—1. Evolution of a gas from one or more electrodes during electrolysis. 2. The production of gas in a storage battery when the charging current is continued after the battery has been completely charged.

gassy tube—See Soft Tube.

gaston—A modulator that produces a random-noise modulation signal from a gas tube. It may be attached to any standard aircraft communications transmitter to provide a counterjamming modulation.

gas tube—A partially evacuated electron tube containing a small amount of gas. Ionization of the gas molecules is responsible for the current flow.

gas-tube relaxation oscillator—A relaxation oscillator in which the abrupt discharge is provided by the breakdown of the gas in the tube.

gas X-ray tube—An X-ray tube in which electron emission from the cathode is produced by bombarding it with positive ions.

gate—1. A circuit having two or more inputs and one output, the output depending upon the combination of logic signal at the inputs. There are four gates, called AND, OR, NAND, and NOR. The definitions assume postive logic is used. In computer work, a gate is often called an AND circuit. 2. A signal used to trigger the passage of other signals through a circuit. 3. An electrode in a field-effect transistor. 4. An output element of a cryotron.

gate circuit—A circuit that passes a signal only when a gating pulse is present.

gate-controlled switch—Also called gate turn-off switch. A three-junction, three-terminal, solid-state device, constructed very much like a silicon controlled rectifier except that it has a turn-off ability, which is controlled by a negative-current pulse applied to the gate.

gate current—Instantaneous current flowing between the gate and cathode of a silicon controlled rectifier.

gate current for firing—Gate current required to fire a silicon controlled rectifier when the anode is at +6 volts with respect to the cathode and with the device at stated temperature conditions.

gated-beam detector—A single-stage f-m detector using a gated-beam tube.

gated-beam tube—A five-element tube in which the electrons flow in a beam between the cathode and plate. A small increase in voltage on the limiter grid will cut off the plate current, and further increases will have a negligible effect on it.

gated buffer—A low-impedance inverting driver circuit that may be used as a line driver for pulse differentiation or in multivibrators.

gated flip-flop—One that has a steering circuit that prevents both flip-flop outputs from becoming "0" at the same time. Alternating-current input pulses must be used to prevent the flip-flop from oscillating. This situation can arise if both input lines are made high simultaneously.

gated sweep—Sweep in which the duration as well as the starting time is controlled to exclude undesired echoes from the indicator screen.

gated transistor—A transistor in which a gate electrode covers the emitter and collector junctions. This allows the application of an electric field at the surface of the base region.

gate electrode—The control electrode of a FET, MOST controlled rectifier, or triac.

gate generator—A circuit or device used to produce one or more gate pulses.

gate impedance—The impedance of a gate winding in a magnetic amplifier.

gate power dissipation—The power dissipated between the gate and cathode terminals of a silicon controlled rectifier.

gate-producing multivibrator—A rectangular-wave generator that produces a single positive or negative gate voltage only when triggered by a pulse.

gate pulse—A pulse that enables a gate circuit to pass a signal. The gate pulse generally has a longer duration than the signal to insure time coincidence.

gate signal—That signal generated by some form of delay circuit required in connection with beam switching, automatic following, the application of agc to a selected echo, and many other purposes.

gate trigger current—In a controlled rectifier, the minimum gate current, for a given anode-to-cathode voltage, required to switch the rectifier on.

gate trigger voltage—In a controlled rectifier, the gate voltage that produces the gate trigger current.

gate tube—A tube which does not operate unless two signal voltages, derived from two independent circuits, are applied simultaneously to two separate electrodes.

gate turn-off current—In a controlled rectifier, the minimum gate current, for a given collector current in the on state, required to cause the rectifier to switch off.

gate turn-off switch — See Gate-Controlled Switch.

gate turn-off voltage—In a controlled rectifier, the gate voltage required to produce the gate turn-off current.

gate voltage—1. The voltage across the gate-winding terminals of a magnetic amplifier. 2. The instantaneous voltage between gate and cathode of a silicon controlled rectifier with anode open.

gate winding—The reactor winding that produces the gating action in a magnetic amplifier.

gating—1. Selecting those portions of a wave which exist during certain intervals or which have certain magnitudes. 2. Applying a rectangular voltage to the grid or cathode of a cathode-ray tube, to sensitize it during the sweep time only. 3. Application of a specific waveform to perform electronic switching. *Also see* Blanking.

gating circuit—A circuit that operates as a selective switch and allows conduction only during selected time intervals or when the signal magnitude is within specified limits.

gating pulse—A pulse which modifies the operation of a gate circuit.

gauge—*See* Gage.

gauge pressure—*See* Gage Pressure.

gauss — The centimeter-gram-second electromagnetic unit of magnetic induction. One gauss represents one line of flux (one maxwell) per square centimeter.

Gaussian distribution — Also called normal distribution. A density function of a population which is bell-shaped and symmetrical and which is completely defined by two independent parameters, the mean and the standard deviation.

Gaussian noise — Unwanted electrical disturbances or perturbations described by a probability density function that follows a normal law of statistics.

Gaussian random vibration — *See* Random Vibration.

gaussmeter—An instrument that provides direct readings of magnetic field density (flux density) by virtue of the interaction with an internal magnetic field.

Gauss's theorem—The summation of the normal component of the electric displacement over any closed surface is equal to the electric charge within the surface.

GCA—Abbreviation for ground-controlled approach.

GCI—Abbreviation for ground-controlled interception.

GCT or Gct — Abbreviation for Greenwich civil time.

G-display — Also called G-scan or G-scope. In radar, a rectangular display in which a target appears as a laterally-centralized blip on which wings appear to grow as the target approaches. Horizontal and vertical aiming errors are indicated by horizontal and vertical displacement of the blip.

gear—An element shaped like a toothed wheel which engages one or more similar wheels. The energy transmitted can be stepped up or down by making the driven gears of different sizes.

geared synchro system—A system in which the transmitting and receiving synchros turn at a higher speed than the input and output shafts. Geared systems are generally used when a high degree of accuracy is required.

gearmotor—A train of gears and a motor used for reducing or increasing the speed of the driven object.

Geiger counter—Also called Geiger-Mueller or G-M counter. A radiation detector that uses a Geiger-Mueller counter tube, an amplifier, and an indicating device. The tube consists of a thin-walled gas-filled metal cylinder with a projecting electrode. Nuclear particles enter a window in the metal cylinder and temporarily ionize the gas, causing a brief pulse discharge. These pulses, which appear at the projecting electrode, are amplified and indicated visibly or audibly.

Geiger-Mueller counter—*See* Geiger Counter.

Geiger-Mueller counter tube—A radiation-counter tube designed to operate in the Geiger-Mueller region.

Geiger-Mueller region—Also called Geiger region. The voltage interval in which the pulse size is independent of the number of primary ions produced in the initial ionizing event.

Geiger-Mueller threshold—Also called Geiger threshold. The lowest voltage at which all pulses produced in the tube by any ionizing event are of the same size regardless of the size of the primary ionizing event. This threshold is the start of the Geiger region where the counting rate does not substantially change with applied voltage.

Geiger region—*See* Geiger-Mueller Region.

Geiger threshold—*See* Geiger-Mueller Threshold.

Geissler tube—A gas filled dual-electrode discharge tube that glows when electric current passes through the gas.

gel—A material composed of a solid held in a liquid.

genemotor—A type of dynamotor having two armature windings. One winding serves as the driving motor and operates from the vehicle battery. The other winding functions as a high-voltage d-c generator for operation of mobile equipment.

general-purpose computer—A computer designed to solve a wide variety of problems, the exact nature of which may have been unknown before the computer was designed.

general-purpose motor—A motor of 200 hp or less and 450 rpm or more, rated for continuous operation, having standard ratings, and suitable for use without restriction to a particular application.

general-purpose relay—A relay that is adaptable to a variety of applications.

general rate—The amount of time taken by the creation of electron-hole pairs in a semiconductor.

general routine—A computer routine designed to solve a general class of problems, but when appropriate parametric values are supplied, it specializes in a specific problem.

generated noise—1. In potentiometric transducers, the noise which is attributable to causes such as the generation of emf when dissimilar metals are rubbed against each other, or the emf resulting from the thermocouple effects at points where dissimilar metals are joined.

generating electric field meter—Also called a gradient meter. A device for measuring the potential gradient at the surface of a conductor. A flat conductor is alternately exposed and then shielded from the electric field to be measured. The resultant current in the conductor is then rectified and used as the measure.

generating magnetometer—Also called earth inductor. A magnetometer which measures an electric field by the amount of emf generated in a coil rotated in the field.

generating station—An installation that produces electric energy from chemical, mechanical, hydraulic, or some other form of energy.

generating voltmeter—Also called a rotary voltmeter. A device which measures voltage. A capacitor is connected across the voltage, and its capacitance is varied cyclically. The resultant current in the capacitor is then rectified and used as a measure.

generation rate—The time rate of creation of electron-hole pairs in a semiconductor.

generator—1. Symbolized by G. A rotating machine which converts mechanical energy into electrical energy. 2. An electronic device which converts d-c voltage to alternating current of the desired frequency and waveshape.

generator efficiency—1. In a generator, the ratio between the power required to drive the generator and the output power obtained from it. 2. In a thermoelectric couple, the ratio of the electrical power output to the thermal power input. It is an idealized efficiency assuming perfect thermal insulation of the thermoelectric arms.

generator voltage regulator—A regulator which maintains or varies the voltage of a synchronous generator, capacitor motor, or direct-current generator at or within a predetermined value.

geodesic—The shortest line between two points on a given surface.

geometric distortion—In television, any geometric dissimilarity between the original scene and reproduced image.

geometric mean—The square root of the product of two quantities.

george box—An amplitude-sensitive device employed in an i-f amplifier. It rejects jamming signals of insufficient amplitude to operate its circuits; however, jamming signals having sufficient amplitude are not affected.

Germanium diode.

germanium diode—A rectifier or detector made from a germanium crystal.

germanium (Ge)—A brittle, grayish-white metallic element having semiconductor properties. Widely used in transistors and crystal diodes. Its atomic number is 32.

germanium transistor—A transistor in which germanium is the semiconducting material.

Germanium (power) transistor.

German silver—Usually called nickel silver. A silverish alloy of copper, zinc, and nickel.

getter—An alkali metal introduced into a vacuum tube during manufacture. It is fired after the tube has been evacuated, to react chemically with and eliminate any remaining gases. The getter then remains inactive inside the tube. The silvery deposit sometimes seen on the inside of the glass envelope is due to getter firing.

G force—*See* g.

G/G (ground-to-ground) — Communication between two points on the ground.

ghost—*See* Ghost Image.

ghost image—Also called ghost. An undesired duplicate image offset somewhat from the desired image as viewed on a television screen. It is due to a reflected signal traveling over a longer path and, hence, arriving later than the desired signal. It may be eliminated by the use of a directional antenna array which receives signals over only one path.

ghost pulse—*See* Ghost Signal.

Ghost signal.

ghost signal—Also called ghost pulse. An unwanted signal on the screen of a radar indicator. Echoes which experience multiple reflections before reaching the receiver are an example.

giant grid—An extensive regional or national system of backbones and networks.

giant ties—*See* Interconnection.

Gibson girl—A portable, hand-operated transmitter used by pilots forced down at sea.

giga—A prefix meaning one billion, or 10^9.

gigacycle—One kilomegacycle, or one billion cycles. An obsolete term. The currently preferred term is gigahertz.

gigahertz—A term for 10^9 cycles per second. Used to replace the more cumbersome and obsolete term kilomegacycle. Abbreviated GHz.

gigawatt—Abbreviated GW. One thousand megawatts (10^9 watts).

gigohm—One thousand megohms (10^9 ohms).

gilbert—A cgs unit of the magnetomotive force required to produce one maxwell of magnetic flux in a magnetic circuit of unit reluctance. Magnetomotive force in gilberts $= 10/4\pi$ ampere-turns.

gilbert per centimeter—The practical cgs unit of magnetic intensity. Gilberts per centimeter are the same as oersteds.

Gill-Morrell oscillator—A retarding-field oscillator in which the oscillation frequency depends not only on the electron-transit time within the tube, but also on the associated circuit parameters.

gill selector—A slow-acting telegraph sender and calling key for selective signaling.

gimbal—A mechanical frame having two perpendicularly intersecting axes of rotation.

gimmick—A capacitance formed by twisting two insulated wires together or bringing two conductors into close proximity.

gimp—A slang name given to the extremely flexible wire used in telephone cords and similar equipment. This wire cannot be directly soldered to, as it is a metallic cloth-type material.

Giorgi system—*See* Mksa System of Units.

glass electrode — In electronic pH measurement, an electrode used for determining the potential of a solution with respect to a reference electrode. The calomel type is the most common.

glassiviation—A method of transistor passivation by a pyrolytic glass-deposition technique, whereby silicon semiconductor devices, complete with metal contact systems, are fully encapsulated in glass.

glass-plate capacitor—A high-voltage capacitor in which the metal plates are separated by sheets of glass for the dielectric. The complete assembly is generally immersed in oil.

glass-to-metal seal — An airtight seal between glass and metal parts of an electron tube, made by fusing together a special glass and special metal alloy having nearly the same temperature coefficients of expansion.

glass tube—A vacuum or gaseous tube that has a glass envelope.

glide path—The approach path used by an aircraft making an instrument landing.

glide-path localizer—In an aircraft instrument-landing system, the part which indicates the altitude of the plane and creates a glide path for a blind landing.

glide slope—A radio beam used by pilots to determine their altitude when landing.

glide-slope facility — A radio transmitting facility which provides the glide-slope signals.

G-line—A round wire coated with a dielectric and used to transmit microwave energy.

glint—Also called glitter. A distorted radar-signal echo, which varies in amplitude from pulse to pulse because the beam is being reflected from a rapidly moving object such as an airplane propeller.

glissando – A tone that changes smoothly from one pitch to another.

glitch – A form of low-frequency interference appearing as a narrow horizontal bar moving vertically through the television picture. This is also observed on an oscilloscope at the field or frame rate as an extraneous voltage pip moving along the signal at approximately the reference-black level.

glitter – See Glint.

glossmeter – A photoelectric instrument for determining the gloss factor of a surface (i.e., the ratio of light reflected in one direction to the light reflected in all directions).

glow discharge – A discharge of electricity through a gas in an electron tube. It is characterized by a cathode glow resulting from a space potential, much higher than the ionization potential of the gas in the vicinity of the cathode.

glow-discharge microphone – A microphone in which the sound waves cause corresponding variations in the current forming a glow discharge between two electrodes.

Glow-discharge tube.

glow-discharge tube – A gas tube that depends for its operation on the properties of a glow discharge.

glow-discharge voltage regulator – A gas tube used for voltage regulation. The resistance of the gas within the tube varies in step with the voltage applied across the tube.

glow lamp – A lamp containing a small amount of gas or vapor. Current between the two electrodes ionizes the gas and causes the lamp to glow but does not provide rectification. Neon gives a red-orange glow, mercury vapor a blue glow, and argon a purple glow.

glow potential – The voltage at which a glow discharge begins in a gas-filled electronic tube as the voltage is gradually increased.

glow switch – An electron tube used in some fluorescent-lamp circuits. It contains two bimetal strips which are closed when heated by the glow discharge.

glow-tube rectifier – Also called a point-plane rectifier. A cold-cathode gas-discharge tube which provides a unidirectional current flow.

glue-line heating – An arrangement of electrodes designed to heat a thin film of material having a high loss factor between alternate layers of materials having a low loss factor.

g_m – Symbol for the mutual conductance or transconductance of a vacuum tube.

G-M counter – Abbreviation for Geiger-Mueller counter.

GMT or Gmt – Abbreviation for Greenwich mean time.

gobo – A dark mat used to shield the lens of a television camera from stray lights.

gold-bonded diode – A semiconductor diode in which a preformed whisker of gold contacts an N-germanium substrate as the junction is formed by millisecond electrical pulses.

gold doping – A technique used to control the lifetime of minority carriers in a diffused-mesa transistor. Gold is diffused into the base and collector regions to reduce the storage time.

gold-leaf electroscope – An apparatus comprising two pieces of gold leaf joined at their upper ends and suspended inside a glass jar. When a charge is applied to the terminal connected to the leaves, they spread apart due to repulsion of the like charges on them.

Goldschmidt alternator – An early radio transmitter. It is a rotating machine employing oscillating circuits in connection with the field and the armature to introduce harmonics in the generated fundamental frequency. Interaction between the stator and rotor harmonics gives a cumulative effect and thereby provides very high radio frequencies.

goniometer – 1. In a radio-range system, a device for electrically shifting the directional characteristics of an antenna. 2. An electrical device for determining the azimuth of a received signal by combining the outputs of individual elements of an antenna array in certain phase relationships.

googol – In mathematics, the figure 1 followed by 100 zeros.

goto circuit – A circuit capable of sensing the direction of current. It can be used in majority logic circuits in which the output is either positive or negative, depending on whether the majority of its inputs is positive or negative.

governed series motor – A motor used with teletypewriter equipment. It has a governor for regulating the speed.

governor – 1. A motor attachment that automatically controls the speed at which the motor rotates. 2. The equipment which controls the gate or valve opening of a prime mover.

GPI – Abbreviation for ground-position indicator.

graded base transistor – See Diffused Base Transistor.

graded filter – A power-supply filter in which the output stage of a receiver or audio amplifier is connected at or near the filter input so that the maximum available d-c voltage will be obtained. The output stage has low gain; therefore, ripple is not too important.

graded-junction transistor—*See* Rate-Grown Transistor.

graded thermoelectric arm — A thermoelectric arm having a composition that changes continuously in the direction of the current.

gradient — The rate at which a variable quantity increases or decreases. For example, potential gradient is the difference of potential along a conductor or through a dielectric.

gradient meter — *See* Generating Electric Field Meter.

gradient microphone — A microphone in which the output rises and falls with the sound pressure. (*Also see* Pressure Microphone.)

gram—A unit of mass and weight in the metric system.

gramme ring—A ring-shaped iron armature around which the coils are wound. Each turn is tapped from the inside diameter of the ring to a commutator segment.

grandfather cycle—The period during which magnetic-tape records are retained before re-using so that records can be reconstructed in the event of loss of information stored on a magnetic tape.

granular carbon—Small particles of carbon used in carbon microphones.

granularity — A characteristic of the output data of a measuring instrument. The measure of granularity is the smallest increment of the output data when it is in a digital form. The smallest increment is also called least count.

graph—A pictorial presentation of the relationship between two or more variables.

Graphechon.

graphechon—An electron tube which utilizes camera-tube principles for storing and recovering electrical signals.

graphical analysis—The use of diagrams and other graphic methods to obtain operating data and answers to scientific or mathematical problems.

graphic instrument—*See* Recording Instrument.

graphite—A finely divided carbon used as a lubricant and in the construction of some carbon resistance elements. The most common use is in so-called lead pencils.

grass — The pattern produced by random noise on an A-scope; it appears as closely spaced, sharp, constantly moving pulses on the base line. *Also see* Random Noise.

graticule—A calibrated screen placed in front of a cathode-ray tube for measurement purposes.

grating—A device for spreading out light or other radiation. It consists of narrow parallel slits in a plate or narrow parallel reflecting surfaces made by ruling grooves on polished metal. The slits or grooves break up the waves as they emerge. (*Also see* Ultrasonic Space Grating *and* Ultrasonic Cross Grating.)

grating reflector—An antenna reflector consisting of an openwork metal structure that resembles a grating.

Gratz rectifier—An arrangement of two rectifiers per phase connected into a three-phase bridge circuit to provide full-wave rectification.

gravity—The force which tends to pull bodies toward the center of the earth, thereby giving them weight. (*Also see* g.)

gravity cell—A primary cell in which two electrolytes are kept separated by differences in specific gravity. It is a modification of the Daniell cell and is now obsolete.

gray body—A radiating body whose spectral emissivity remains the same at all wavelengths. It is in constant ratio of less than unity to the ratio of a black-body radiator at the same temperature.

Gray code—A positional binary number notation in which any two numbers whose difference is one are represented by expressions that are the same except in one place or column and differ by only one unit in that place or column.

gray scale—In a television system, a scale of brightness values ranging from maximum to minimum.

great manual — In an organ, the keyboard normally used for playing the accompaniment to the melody. Also called the accompaniment manual or lower manual.

green-gain control—A variable resistor used in the matrix of a three-gun color television receiver to adjust the intensity of the green primary signal.

green gun—The electron gun the beam of which, when properly adjusted, strikes only the green phosphor dots in the color picture tube.

green restorer—A d-c restorer used in the green channel of a three-gun color-television picture-tube circuit.

green video voltage—The signal voltage that controls the grid of the green gun in a three-gun picture tube.

Greenwich mean time—Abbreviated GMT or Gmt. The mean solar time at the meridian of Greenwich (zero longitude).

grid—1. An electrode having one or more openings for the passage of electrons or ions. (*Also see* Control Grid, Screen Grid, Shield

Grid, Space-Charge Grid, *and* Suppressor Grid.) 2. An interconnected system in which high-voltage, high-capacity backbone lines overlay and are connected with networks of lower voltages. 3. A two-dimensional network consisting of a set of equally spaced parallel lines superimposed upon another set of equally spaced parallel lines so that the lines of one set are perpendicular to the lines of the other, thereby forming square areas. The intersections of the lines provide the basis for an incremental location system.

grid battery—Sometimes called a C-battery. A source of energy for supplying a bias voltage to the grid of a vacuum tube.

grid bearing—A bearing made with the reference line to grid north.

grid bias—Also called C-bias. A constant potential applied between the grid and cathode of a vacuum tube to establish an operating point.

grid-bias cell—A small cell used in a vacuum tube circuit to make the grid more negative than the cathode. It provides a voltage, but cannot supply an appreciable amount of current.

grid blocking—Blocking of capacitance-coupled stages in an amplifier because of an accumulated charge of the coupling capacitor as the result of current flow during the reception of large signals.

grid cap—At the top of some vacuum tubes, the terminal which connects to the control grid.

grid capacitor—A capacitor in parallel with the grid resistor or in series with the grid lead of a tube.

grid-cathode capacitance — Capacitance between the grid and the cathode in a vacuum tube.

grid characteristic—The curve obtained by plotting grid-voltage values of a vacuum tube as abscissas against grid-current values as ordinates on a graph.

grid circuit—The circuit connected between the grid and cathode, and forming the input circuit of a vacuum tube.

grid-circuit tester — A tester designed to measure the grid resistance of vacuum tubes without discriminating between the type or polarity of impedance.

grid clip—A spring clip used for making a connection to the top-cap terminal of some vacuum tubes.

grid conductance—The in-phase component of the alternating grid current divided by the alternating grid voltage, all other electrode voltages being maintained constant.

grid-controlled mercury-arc rectifier — A mercury-arc rectifier employing one or more electrodes exclusively for controlling start of the discharge.

grid-controlled rectifier—A triode mercury-vapor rectifier tube in which the grid determines the instant at which plate current

starts to flow during each cycle, but does not determine how much current will flow.

grid-control tube — A mercury-vapor–filled thermionic vacuum tube with an external grid control.

grid current—The current which flows in the grid-to-cathode circuit of a vacuum tube. It is usually a complex current made up of several currents having a variety of polarities and impedances.

grid detection—Detection by rectification in the grid circuit of a vacuum tube.

Grid-dip meter.

grid-dip meter—A multiple-range oscillator incorporating a meter in the grid circuit to indicate grid current. The meter is so named because its reading dips (reads a lower grid current) whenever an external resonant circuit is tuned to the oscillator frequency.

grid dissipation—The power lost as heat at the grid of a tube.

grid-drive characteristic—The relationship between the electrical or light output of an electron tube and the control-electrode voltage measured from cutoff.

grid driving power—The average product of the instantaneous value of grid current and the alternating component of grid voltage over a complete cycle.

grid emission—Electron or ion emission from the grid of an electron tube.

grid-glow tube — A glow-discharge, cold-cathode tube in which one or more control electrodes initiate the anode current, but do not limit it except under certain conditions.

gridistor—A field-effect transistor which uses the principle of centripetal striction and has a multichannel structure, combining advantages of both field-effect transistors and minority-carrier injection transistors.

grid leak—A high resistance connected across the grid capacitor or between the grid and cathode. It provides a direct-current path, to limit the accumulation of a charge on the grid.

grid-leak capacitor—A small capacitor connected in a vacuum-tube grid circuit, together with a resistor, to produce grid bias.

grid-leak detector—A triode or multielectrode tube in which rectification occurs because of electron current through a high resistance in the grid circuit. The voltage associated with this flow appears in amplified form in the plate circuit.

grid limiting—The use of grid-current bias derived from the signal, through a large series grid resistor, in order to cut off the plate current and consequently level the output wave for all input signals above a critical value.

grid locking—Faulty tube operation in which excessive grid emission causes the grid potential to become continuously positive.

grid modulation—Modulation produced by application of the modulating voltage to the control grid of any tube in which the carrier is present. Modulation in which the grid voltage contains externally generated pulses is called grid-pulse modulation.

grid neutralization—A method of neutralizing an amplifier. A portion of the grid-to-cathode alternating-current voltage is shifted 180° and applied to the plate-to-cathode circuit through a neutralizing capacitor.

grid north—An arbitrary reference direction used with the grid system of navigation.

grid-pool tank—A grid-pool tube having a heavy metal envelope somewhat resembling a tank in appearance.

grid-pool tube—A gas discharge tube having a mercury-pool cathode, one or more anodes, and a control electrode or grid to control the start of current. *Also see* Excitron *and* Ignitron.

grid-pulse modulation—Modulation produced in an amplifier or oscillator by application of one or more pulses to a grid circuit.

grid pulsing—Method of controlling the operation of a radio-frequency oscillator. The oscillator-tube grid is biased so negatively that no oscillation occurs, even at full plate voltage, except when this negative bias is removed by application of a positive voltage pulse to the grid.

grid resistor—A general term that denotes any resistor in the grid circuit.

grid return—An external conducting path for the return of grid current to the cathode.

grid suppressor—A resistor, sometimes connected between the control grid and the external circuit of an amplifier, to prevent parasitic oscillations caused by stray-capacitance feedback.

grid swing—The total variation in grid-to-cathode voltage from the positive peak to the negative peak of the applied-signal voltage.

grid-to-cathode capacitance—The direct capacitance between the grid and cathode of a vacuum tube.

grid-to-plate capacitance—Designated C_{gp}. The direct capacitance between the grid and plate in a vacuum tube.

grid-to-plate transconductance—The mutual conductance, or ratio of plate-current to grid-voltage changes, in a vacuum tube.

grid voltage—The voltage between the grid and cathode of a tube.

grid-voltage supply—The means for supplying, to the grid of an electron tube, a potential which is usually negative with respect to the cathode.

grommet—An insulating washer, usually of rubber or plastic, inserted through a hole in a chassis or panel to prevent a wire from touching the sides.

groove—In mechanical recording, the track inscribed in the record by a cutting or embossing stylus, including undulations or modulations caused by vibration of the stylus. In stereo discs, its cross section is a right-angled triangle, with each side at a 45° angle to the surface of the record; information is cut on both sides of the groove.

groove angle—In disc recording, the angle between the two walls of an unmodulated groove in a radial plane perpendicular to the surface of the recording medium.

groove shape—In disc recording, the contour of the groove in a radial plane perpendicular to the surface of the recording medium.

groove speed—In disc recording, the linear speed of the groove with respect to the stylus.

ground—1. A metallic connection with the earth to establish ground potential. 2. The voltage reference point in a circuit. There may or may not be an actual connection to earth, but it is understood that a point in the circuit said to be at ground potential could be connected to earth without disturbing the operation of the circuit in any way.

ground absorption—The loss of energy during transmission because of the radio waves dissipated to ground.

ground bus—A conductor, usually large-diameter wire, that connects a number of points to one or more grounding electrodes.

ground check (base-line check)—1. A procedure followed prior to the release of a radiosonde in order to obtain the temperature and humidity correction for the radiosonde system. 2. Any instrumental check prior to the ground launch of an airborne experiment.

ground clamp—A clamp used for connecting a grounding conductor (ground wire) to a grounded object such as a water pipe.

ground clutter—The pattern produced on the screen of a radar indicator by undesired ground return.

ground conduit—A conduit used solely to contain one or more grounding conductors.

ground-controlled approach—Abbreviated GCA. A ground radar system providing information with which aircraft approaches can be directed by radio.

ground-controlled interception—Abbreviated GCI. A radar system used for directing an aircraft to intercept enemy aircraft.

ground current—*See* Earth Current.

ground dielectric constant—The dielectric constant of the earth at a given location.

ground distance—The great-circle component

Grounded-grid amplifier.

Ground clamps.

of distance from one point to another at mean sea level.

grounded—Connected to the earth, or to some conducting body in place of the earth.

grounded-base amplifier—*See* Common-Base Amplifier.

grounded cable bond—A cable bond used for grounding the armor and/or sheaths of cables.

grounded capacitance—In a system having several conductors, the capacitance between a given conductor and the other conductors when they are connected together and to ground.

grounded-cathode amplifier — The conventional amplifier circuit. It consists of a tube amplifier in which the cathode is at ground potential at the operating frequency. The input is applied between the control grid and ground, and the output load is between the plate and ground.

grounded circuit—A circuit in which one conductor or point (usually the neutral conductor or neutral point of transformer or generator windings) is intentionally grounded (earthed) either solidly or through a grounding device.

grounded-collector amplifier—*See* Common-Collector Amplifier.

grounded conductor—A conductor which is intentionally grounded, either directly or through a current-limiting device.

grounded-emitter amplifier—*See* Common-Emitter Amplifier.

grounded-grid amplifier — An electron-tube amplifier circuit in which the control grid is at ground potential at the operating frequency. The input is applied between the cathode and ground, and the output load is between the plate and ground. The grid-to-plate impedance of the tube is in parallel with the load, instead of acting as a feedback path.

grounded-grid triode—A type of triode designed for use in a grounded-grid circuit.

grounded-grid triode circuit—A circuit in which the input signal is applied to the cathode and the output is taken from the plate. The grid is at r-f ground and serves as a screen between the input and output circuits.

grounded-grid triode mixer — A triode in which the grid forms part of a grounded electrostatic screen between the anode and cathode. It is used as a mixer for centimeter wavelengths.

grounded outlet—An outlet equipped with a receptacle of the polarity type having, in addition to the current-carrying contacts, one ground contact which can be used for the connection of an equipment-grounding conductor.

grounded parts—Parts of a completed installation that are so connected that they are substantially at the same potential as the earth.

grounded-plate amplifier—Also called cathode follower. An electron-tube amplifier circuit in which the plate is at ground potential at the operating frequency. The input is applied between the control grid and ground, and the output load is between the cathode and ground.

grounded system—A system of conductors in which at least one conductor or point (usually the middle wire or neutral point of transformer or generator windings) is intentionally grounded, either solidly or through a current-limiting device.

ground gating—The conversion of pam signals at a telemetry ground station to 50% duty-cycle signals.

ground indication — An indication of the presence of a ground on one or more of the normally ungrounded conductors of a system.

grounding—1. Connecting to ground, or to a conductor which is grounded. 2. A means of referencing electrical circuits to the well-bonded equipotential surface.

grounding conductor — A conductor which, under normal conditions, carries no current, but serves to connect exposed metal surfaces to an earth ground, to prevent hazards in case of breakdown between current-carrying parts and the exposed surfaces. The conductor, if insulated, is colored green with or without a yellow stripe.

grounding connection—A connection used in establishing a ground.

grounding electrode—A conductor embedded in the earth and used for maintaining ground potential on conductors connected to it, or for dissipating into the earth any current conducted to it.

grounding plate — An electrically grounded metal plate on which a person stands in order to discharge any static electricity that may be picked up by his body.

grounding switch—A form of air switch for connecting a circuit or apparatus to ground.

grounding transformer—A transformer intended primarily for the purpose of providing a neutral point for grounding purposes.

ground insulation — The major insulation used between a winding and structural parts at ground potential.

ground loop—The generation of undesirable signals within a ground conductor due to circulation current within the conductor which originates from a second source of potential—frequently as a result of connecting two separate grounds to a signal circuit.

ground lug—A lug for connecting a grounding conductor to a grounding electrode.

ground noise—In recording and reproducing, the residual noise in the absence of a signal. It is usually caused by dissimilarities between the recording and reproducing media, but may also include amplifier noise such as from a tube or noise generated in resistive elements at the input of the reproducer amplifier system.

ground-noise margin—The voltage that may be applied at the ground connection of a logic circuit without causing the circuit to malfunction. It is usually measured by increasing the static ground voltage on a single gate until the logic fails to operate properly.

ground plane—Copper or brass sheet used in interference testing to simulate missile, aircraft, or vehicle frame or skin so that actual installation and grounding conditions may be approximated.

Ground-plane antenna.

ground-plane antenna—A vertical antenna combined with a turnstile element to lower the angle of radiation. It has a concentric base support and a center conductor that place the antenna at ground potential, even though located several wavelengths above ground.

ground plate—A plate of conductive material buried in the earth to serve as a grounding electrode.

ground-position indicator — Abbreviated GPI. A dead-reckoning computer, similar to an air-position indicator, with provision for taking drift into account.

ground potential—Zero potential with respect to ground or the earth.

ground protective relay — A device which functions on failure of the insulation of a machine, transformer, or other apparatus to ground, or on flashover of a d-c machine to ground.

Ground reflection.

ground-reflected wave—In a ground wave, the component reflected from the earth.

ground resistance — The opposition of the earth to the flow of current through it. Its value depends on the nature and moisture content of the soil. The material, composition, and physical dimensions of the connections to earth, and the electrolytic action present.

ground return—1. In radar, the echoes reflected from the earth's surface and fixed objects on it. 2. A lead from an electronic circuit, antenna, or power line to ground.

ground-return circuit—A circuit which has a conductor (or two or more in parallel) between two points and which is completed through ground or the earth.

ground rod—A steel or copper rod driven into the earth to make an electrical contact with it.

ground shift—The variation in signal amplitude at different grounding points because of a voltage drop along a ground line.

ground speed—In navigation, the speed of a vehicle with reference to ground.

ground-support equipment — All ground equipment that is part of a complete weapons system and that must be furnished to insure complete support of the weapon system.

ground-to-air communication — One-way communication from ground stations to aircraft.

ground wave—A radio wave which travels along the earth's surface rather than through the upper atmosphere.

ground wire—A conductor leading to an electric connection with the earth.

group frequency—The number of sets or groups of waves passing a given point in one second.

grouping—Nonuniform spacing between the grooves of a disc recording.

group loop—A source of interference when a system is grounded improperly at several points.

group modulation—The process by which a number of channels, already separately modulated to a specific frequency range, are again modulated to shift the group to another range.

group velocity—1. Of a traveling plane wave, the velocity of propagation of the envelope delay is approximately constant. It is equal to the reciprocal of the envelope delay per unit length. (Group velocity differs from phase velocity in a medium in which the phase velocity varies with the frequency.) 2. The velocity of propagation of a pulse or a group of waves.

Grove cell—A primary cell with a platinum electrode submerged in an electrolyte of nitric acid within a porous cup, surrounded by a zinc electrode in an electrolyte of sulphuric acid. This cell normally operates on a closed circuit.

growler—An electromagnetic device for locating short-circuited coils and for magnetizing or demagnetizing objects. So called because of the growling noise it makes when indicating a short circuit. It consists essentially of two field poles arranged as in a motor.

grown-diffused transistor — A transistor made by combining the diffusion and double-doped techniques. Suitable N- and P-type impurities are added simultaneously to the melt while the crystal is being grown. Subsequently, the base region is formed by diffusion as the crystal grows.

grown junction—The boundary between P- and N-type semiconducting materials. It is produced by varying the impurities during the growth of a crystal from the melt. Such junctions have strong rectifying properties, the forward current being obtained when P is positive to N.

grown-junction photocell — A photodiode made of a small bar of semiconductor material that has a PN junction at right angles to its length and an ohmic contact at each end of the bar.

grown-junction transistor—A transistor in which junctions are formed by adding impurities to the melt while the crystal is being grown.

G-scan—*See* G-Display.
G-scope—*See* G-Display.

guard band—1. Also called interference-guard band. A frequency band left vacant between two channels to safeguard against mutual interference. 2. The unused chip surface area which by virtue of physical spacing serves to isolate functional elements in a printed circuit or an integrated circuit. Also refers to the consideration given instrumentation precision in electrical testing.

guard circle—An inner concentric groove on disc records. It prevents the pickup from being thrown to the center of the record and possibly damaged.

guarded input—An input that has a third terminal which is maintained at a potential near the input-terminal potential for a single-ended input, or near the mean input potential for the differential input. It is used to shield the entire input circuit.

guarded motor — An open motor in which all openings given direct access to live or rotating parts (except smooth shafts) are limited in size by the structural parts or by screens, grilles, expanded metal, etc., to prevent accidental contact with such parts. Such openings shall not permit the passage of a cylindrical rod $1/2$ inch in diameter.

guard ring—A metal ring placed around a charged terminal or object to distribute the charge uniformly over the surface of the object.

guard shield—A shield surrounding the input circuit of an amplifier.

guard wire—A grounded wire used frequently where high-tension lines cross a thoroughfare. Should a line break, it will contact the guard wire and be grounded.

Gudden-Pohl effect—The momentary illumination produced when an electric field is applied to a phosphor previously excited by ultraviolet radiation.

guidance—Control of a missile or vehicle from within by a person, a preset or self-reacting automatic device, or a device that reacts to outside signals.

guidance system—A system which measures and evaluates flight information, correlates it with target data, and converts the resultant into the parameters necessary to achieve the desired flight path.

guided ballistic missile—A ballistic missile which is guided during the powered portion of the trajectory and follows a free ballistic path during the remainder.

guided missile—An unmanned vehicle moving above the surface of the earth, the trajectory or flight path of which is capable of being altered by an external or internal mechanism.

guided propagation — A type of radio-wave propagation in which radiated rays are bent excessively by refraction in the lower layers of the atmosphere. This bending creates an effect much as if a duct or a wave guide has been formed in the atmosphere to guide part of the radiated energy over distances far beyond the normal range.

guided wave—A wave in which the energy is concentrated near a boundary (or between substantially parallel boundaries) separating materials of different properties. The direction of propagation is parallel to the boundary.

guide wavelength—*See* Waveguide Wavelength.

Guillemin line—A special type of artificial transmission line or pulse-forming network used in radar sets to control the duration of the pulses. It generates a nearly square pulse for use in high-level pulse modulation.

guillotine capacitor—A translatory-motion tuning capacitor consisting of a pair of stators and a sliding plunger in place of a rotor.

gun-directing radar—Radar used for directing antiaircraft or similar artillery fire.

Gunn effect—Current oscillations that occur at an r-f rate when an electric field of about 3000 v/cm is applied to a short (0.005 inch or less) specimen of N-type gallium arsenide. This effect takes place because electrons under the influence of sufficiently high fields are transferred from high- to low-mobility valleys in the conduction band of GaAs.

Gyrator symbol.

gutta-percha—A natural vegetable gum, similar to rubber, used principally as insulation for wires and cables.

Guy wire.

guy wire—A wire used to brace the mast or tower of a transmitting or receiving antenna system.

gyrator—A two-port circuit element that exhibits a 180° differential, or nonreciprocal, phase shift. The gyrator circuit symbol indicates that an r-f signal transmitted from port 1 to port 2 will undergo a 180° phase shift (arrow direction) relative to an r-f signal transmitted in the reverse direction.

gyro—Abbreviation for gyroscope.

gyrofrequency—The natural frequency at which charged particles rotate around the lines of force of the earth's magnetic field. For electrons, it is 700 to 1,600 kilohertz; for ions, it is in the audio-frequency range.

gyromagnetic—The magnetic properties of rotating electric charges, such as electrons spinning within atoms.

gyropilot—*See* Autopilot.

gyroscope—A rotating device the axle of which will maintain a constant direction, even though the earth is turning under it. It consists of a wheel mounted so that its spinning axis is free to rotate around either of two other axes perpendicular to itself and to each other. When its axle is pointed north, it can be used as a gyrocompass. Abbreviated gyro.

gyroscopic action—An action that causes a mass to turn on an axis perpendicular to the applied torque and to the axis of spin.

gyrostabilized platform—*See* Stable Platform.

G—Y signal—In color television, the green-minus-luminance signal representing primary green minus the luminance, or Y— signal. It is combined with a luminance, or Y— signal outside or inside the picture tube to yield a primary green signal.

H

h—Abbreviation for henry.

H—1. A radar air-navigation system using an airborne interrogator to measure the distance from two ground responder beacons. (*Also see* Shoran.) 2. Symbol for heater or magnetic field strength.

hairpin pickup coil—A hairpin-shaped, single-turn coil for transferring uhf energy.

hairpin tuning bar—A sliding hairpin-shaped metal bar inserted between the two halves of a doublet antenna to vary its electrical length.

halation—Distortion seen as blurred images and caused by reflection of the image rays off the back of a fluorescent screen that is too thick.

half adder—A circuit that will accept two binary input signals and produce corresponding sum and carry outputs. So called because, above the first order, two half adders per order are required when adding two quantities.

half cell—An electrode, submerged in an electrolyte, for measuring single electrode potentials.

half cycle—The time interval required for the operating frequency to complete one half, or 180°, of its cycle.

half-duplex circuit—A circuit which permits one-direction electrical communications between stations. Technical arrangements may permit operation in either direction, but not simultaneously. Therefore, this term is qualified by one of the following suffixes: S/O for send only; R/O for receive only; S/R for send or receive. Abbreviated hdx.

half-duplex operation—A duplex telegraph system capable of operating in either direction, but not in both simultaneously.

half-duplex repeater—A duplex telegraph repeater provided with interlocking arrangements which restrict the transmission of signals to one direction at a time.

half life—The time interval used to measure

Half-wave rectifier.

the rate of decay of radioactive material. In the first half-life, the amount of radioactive material left unchanged is one-half the original amount; in the next half-life interval, half of the remaining amount, or one-fourth of the original amount remains. Thus, by determining the remaining radioactivity of a fossil and comparing it with the half-life of the material, scientists can estimate the age of the fossil. The half-life of various materials varies greatly—from millionths of a second to billions of years.

half-nut—A feed nut which engages half the circumference or less of a lead screw, so that it can be withdrawn from the lead screw to stop the lateral scanning movement.

half-power point—On an amplitude response characteristic or other curve of the magnitude of a network quantity versus frequency, distance, angle, or other variable, the point that corresponds to half the power of a neighboring point having maximum power.

half-power width of a radiation lobe—In a plane containing the direction of the maximum of the lobe, the full angle between the two directions in that plane in which the radiation intensity is one half the maximum value of the lobe.

half-shift register—A logic circuit that consists of a gated input storage element with or without an inverter.

half step—*See* Semitone.

half tap—A bridge that can be placed across conductors without disturbing their continuity.

half-time emitter — A device that produces synchronous pulses midway between the row pulses of a punched card.

half-tone characteristic — In facsimile, the fidelity of the recorded density shadings in comparison with the original transmitted subject copy. Also used to express the relationship between the facsimile signal and the subject or recorded copy.

half-track recorder — *See* Dual-Track Recorder.

half-track tape—Also called two-track tape. Quarter-inch magnetic tape on which half the width of the tape is used for one sound path. Such a tape provides stereo in one direction of tape travel, or monosound in both directions.

half wave—A wave with an electrical length of half a wavelength.

half-wave antenna—An antenna having an electrical length equal to half the wave-

length of the signal being transmitted or received.

half-wave dipole—A straight, ungrounded antenna measuring substantially one-half wavelength.

half-wave rectification—The production of a pulsating direct current by passing only half the input cycle of an alternating current. The other half is blocked by the rectifier.

half-wave rectifier—A rectifier utilizing only one half of each cycle to change alternating current into pulsating direct current.

half-wave transmission line — A piece of transmission line having an electrical length equal to half the wavelength of the signal being transmitted or received.

half-wave vibrator—A vibrator used mainly in battery-operated mobile power supplies. It has only one pair of contacts, and supplies an intermittent unidirectional current at its output (usually connected to a half-wave rectifier).

Hall constant—The constant of proportionality in the equation for a current-carrying conductor in a magnetic field. The constant is equal to the transverse electric field (Hall field) divided by the product of the current density and the magnetic field strength. The sign of the majority carrier can be inferred from the sign of the Hall constant.

Hall effect—When a metal strip is placed with its plane perpendicular to a magnetic field and an electric current flows longitudinally through the strip, a potential difference is developed across the strip at right angles to the current flow and to the magnetic field.

Hall generator—A thin wafer of semiconductor material used for measuring a-c power and magnetic field strength. Its output volt-

Hall generator.

age is proportional to the current passing through it times the magnetic field perpendicular to it.

Hall mobility—The product of conductivity and the Hall constant for a conductor or semiconductor. It is a measure of the mobility of the electrons or holes in a semiconductor.

halo—The undesirable ring of light around a spot on the fluorescent screen of a cathode-ray tube.

halogen—A general name applied to four chemical elements, flourine, chlorine, bromine, and iodine, that have similar chemical properties.

halogen quenching—A method of quenching the discharge in a counter tube by the introduction of a small quantity of one of the halogens.

ham—Also called amateur. Slang for a licensed radio operator who operates a station as a hobby rather than a business.

Hamming code—One of the error correction code systems used in data transmission.

hand capacitance—The capacitance introduced when one's hand is brought near a tuning capacitor or other insufficiently shielded part of a receiver.

Handie-Talkie—Trade name of the Motorola Communications Div. for a two-way radio small enough to be carried in one's hand.

hand receiver—An earphone held to the ear by hand.

hand reset—A relay in which the contacts must be reset manually to their original positions after normal conditions are resumed.

handset—A telephone-type receiver and transmitter mounted on a single frame.

handset telephone—*See* Hand Telephone Set.

hand telephone set—Also called a handset telephone. A telephone set having a handset and a mounting which supports the handset when not in use.

hangover—Also called tailing. The smeared or blurred bass notes reproduced by a poorly damped speaker or one mounted in an improperly vented enclosure.

hangup—A condition in which the central processor of a computer is trying to perform an illegal or forbidden operation or in which it is continually repeating the same routine.

hard copy—Typewritten or printed characters on paper produced by a computer at the same time information is copied or converted into machine language that is not easily read by a human.

hard-drawn copper wire—Copper wire that is not annealed after work hardening during drawing, thus providing increased tensile strength.

hard firing—A condition in which the gate signal of an scr is several times the d-c triggering current and in which the rise time of the gate current is short relative to the turn-on time.

hardline—The intelligence link between two objects, consisting of a wire or wires, as opposed to a radio or radar link.

hard magnetic materials—Magnetic materials that are not easily demagnetized.

hardness—Referring to X rays, the quality which determines their penetrating ability. The shorter the wavelength, the harder and hence more penetrating they are.

hardness tester—Equipment for determining the force required to penetrate the surface of a solid.

hard rubber—A material formerly widely used for insulation. It is formed by vulcanizing rubber at high temperature and pressure to give it the desired hardness.

hard solder—Solder composed principally of copper and zinc. It must be red-hot before it will melt. Hard soldering is practically equivalent to brazing.

hard tube—A high-vacuum electronic tube.

hardware—1. Slang for the individual components in a circuit. 2. Particular circuits or functions built into a system.

hard X-rays—Highly penetrating X-rays as distinguished from less penetrating, or soft, X-rays.

harmful interference—Any radiation or any induction which disrupts the proper functioning of an electromagnetic system.

harmonic—A sinusoidal wave having a frequency that is an integral multiple of the fundamental frequency. For example, a wave with twice the frequency of the fundamental is called the second harmonic.

harmonic analysis—1. A method of identifying and evaluating the harmonics that make up a complex waveform of voltage, current, or some other varying quantity. 2. The expression of a given function as a series of sine and cosine terms that are approximately equal to the given function, such as a Fourier series.

harmonic analyzer—Also called harmonic-wave analyzer. A mechanical or electronic device for measuring the amplitude and phase of the various harmonic components of a wave from its graph.

harmonic antenna—An antenna the electrical length of which is an integral multiple of a half wavelength.

harmonic attenuation—Elimination of a harmonic frequency by using a pi network and tuning its shunt resistances to zero for the frequency to be eliminated.

harmonic component—Of a periodic quantity, any one of the simple sinusoidal quantities of the Fourier series into which the periodic quantity may be resolved.

harmonic content—1. The degree of distortion in the output signal of an amplifier. 2. The components remaining after the fundamental frequency has been removed from a complex wave.

harmonic conversion transducer—A conversion transducer in which the useful output frequency is a multiple or submultiple of the input frequency.

harmonic detector—A voltmeter circuit that measures only a particular harmonic of the fundamental frequency.

harmonic distortion—1. The production of harmonic frequencies at the output by the nonlinearity of a transducer when a sinusoidal voltage is applied to the input. The amplitude of the distortion is usually a function of the amplitude of the input signal. 2. A condition that exists in the output of an amplifying circuit when harmonics, added during the process, alter the signal waveform.

harmonic filter—A combination of inductance and capacitance tuned to an undesired harmonic to suppress it.

harmonic generator—A vacuum tube or other generator operated so that it generates strong harmonics in the output.

harmonic interference—Interference between radio stations because harmonics of the carrier frequency are present in the output of one or more stations.

harmonic-leakage power (TR and Pre-TR tubes) — The total radio-frequency power transmitted, through the fired tube in its mount, at other than the fundamental frequencies generated by the transmitter.

harmonic motion—Back and forth motion, such as that of a pendulum, in which the distance on one side of equilibrium always equals the distance on the other side; the acceleration is toward the point of equilibrium and directly proportional to the distance from it. Graphically, harmonic motion is represented by a sine wave.

harmonic producer — A tuning-fork–controlled oscillator used to provide carrier frequencies for broad-band carrier systems. It is capable of producing odd and even harmonics of the fundamental tuning-fork frequency.

harmonic ringing—A system of selectively signaling several parties on a subscriber's line. The different rings are produced by currents which are harmonics of several fundamental frequencies.

harmonic series of sounds — A series in which each basic frequency in it is an integral multiple of a fundamental frequency.

harmonic telephone ringer—A ringer which responds only to alternating current within a very narrow frequency band. A number of such ringers, each responding to a different frequency, are used in one type of selective ringing.

harmonic-wave analyzer — See Harmonic Analyzer.

harness—Wires and cables arranged and tied together so they can be connected or disconnected as a unit.

hartley—In computers, a unit of information content equal to one decimal decision, or the designation of one of ten possible and equally likely values or states of anything used to store or convey information. One hartley equals $\log_2 10$ (3.323) bits.

Hartley oscillator—An oscillator in which a

Hartley oscillator.

parallel-tuned tank circuit is connected between the grid and plate of an electron tube or between the base and collector of a junction transistor, the inductive element of the tank having an intermediate tap at the cathode or emitter potential.

hash—1. Electrical noise generated within a receiver by a vibrator or a mercury-vapor rectifier. (*Also see* Grass, Garbage.) 2. A completely random interfering signal usually caused by arcing and occasionally by natural environmental disturbances.

hash total—In a computer, a total for checking purposes. It is determined by adding all the digits or all the numbers in a particular field in a batch of unit records, with no attention paid to the meaning or significance of the total.

Hay bridge.

Hay bridge—A four-arm, alternating-current bridge used for measuring inductance in terms of capacitance, resistance, and frequency. The arms adjacent to the unknown impedance are nonreactive resistors, and the opposite arm is comprised of a capacitor in series with a resistor (unlike the Maxwell bridge, where it is in parallel). Usually the bridge is balanced by adjustment of the resistor, which is also in series with the capacitor and one of the nonreactive arms. The balance depends upon the frequency.

hazard—See Failure Rate.

Hazeltine neutralizing circuit — An early form of neutralized radio-frequency amplifier circuit.

H-bend—Also called H-plane bend. In waveguide technique, a smooth change in the direction of the axis of the waveguide. Throughout the change, the axis remains perpendicular to the direction of polarization.

H-display—Also called H-scan. In radar, a B-display modified to indicate the angle of elevation. The target appears as two closely spaced blips which approximate a short, bright line that slopes in proportion to the sine of the angle of target elevation.

head—A device which reads, records, or erases information in a storage medium; e.g., a small electromagnet used to read, write, or erase information on a magnetic drum or tape.

head alignment — Positioning the record-playback head on a tape recorder so that its gap is perpendicular to the tape.

head amplifier—An audio-frequency amplifier mounted on or near the sound head of a motion-picture projector to amplify the extremely weak output of the phototube.

head demagnetizer—Device for eliminating any magnetism built up in a recording head.

header—1. The part of a sealed component or assembly that provides support and insulation for the leads passing through the walls. 2. A preformed part made of an insulating material and containing the input and output leads of a module or component. May be part of, or attached to, the case by an adhesive bond or embedment material. Forms a portion of the other case of the module or component.

head guy—A messenger cable and attachments placed so they pull toward the pole line.

heading—The direction of a ship, aircraft, or other object with reference to true, magnetic, compass, or grid north.

headlight—An aircraft radar antenna small enough to be housed in the wing, like an automobile headlight. The beam operates like a searchlight.

headphone—Also called a head receiver or phone. A device held against the ear and having a diaphragm which vibrates according to current variations. It reproduces the incoming electrical signals as sound. Thus, the headphone permits private listening to a receiver, amplifier, or other device.

head receiver—*See* Headphone.

headset—A headphone (or a pair of headphones) and its associated headband and connecting cord.

head stack—A group of two or more heads mounted in a single unit, used to provide multiple-track recording or reproduction.

head-to-tape contact—The degree to which the surface of the magnetic coating approaches the surface of the record or replay heads during normal operation of a recorder. Good head-to-tape contact minimizes separation loss and is essential in obtaining high resolution.

hearing aid—A small audio reproducing system for the hard of hearing. It consists of a microphone, amplifier, battery, and earphone and is used to increase the sound level normally received by the ear.

hearing loss—Also called deafness. The hearing loss of an ear at a specified frequency—i.e., the ratio, expressed in decibels, of its threshold of audibility to the normal threshold.

hearing loss for speech—The difference in decibels between the speech levels at which the average normal ear and the defective ear, respectively, reach the same intelligibility. It is often arbitrarily set at 50%.

heat aging—A test used to indicate the relative resistance of various insulating materials to heat degradation.

heat coil—A protective device that grounds or opens a circuit, or both, when the current rises above a predetermined value. A mechanical element moves when the fusible substance that holds it in place is heated above a certain point by current through the circuit.

heater—1. Also called filament. An element that supplies the heat to an indirectly heated cathode. 2. A resistor that converts electrical energy into heat.

heater biasing—Application of a d-c potential to the heater to eliminate diode conduction between it and some other element within the tube.

heater current—The current flowing through a heater in a vacuum tube.

heater voltage—The voltage between the terminals of a heater.

heater-voltage coefficient—In a klystron, the frequency change per volt of heater voltage change when the reflector voltage is adjusted for the peak of a reflector voltage mode.

heat-eye tube—A cathode-ray tube powered by a midget generator. It is used as an infra-red instrument that can "see" in the dark.

heat gradient—The difference in temperature between two parts of the same object.

heating effect of a current—Assuming a constant resistance, the amount of heat produced by the current through it. It is proportionate to the square of the current.

heating element—The wirewound resistor, terminals, and insulating supports used in electric cooking and heating devices.

heating pattern—In induction or dielectric

Headset.

heating, the distribution of temperature in a load or charge.

heating station—In induction or dielectric heating, the work coil or applicator and its associated production equipment.

heat loss—The loss due to conversion of part of the electric energy into heat.

heat of emission—Additional heat energy that must be supplied to an electron-emitting surface to keep its temperature constant.

heat of radioactivity—Heat generated by radioactive disintegration.

Heat sink.

heat sink—Any device that absorbs and draws off heat from a hot object, reradiating it into the surrounding atmosphere.

heat waves—Infrared radiation similar to radiowaves but of a higher frequency.

heat writer—A direct writer which records on thermally sensitive paper with a heated stylus.

Heaviside - Campbell mutual - inductance bridge—A Heaviside mutual-inductance bridge in which one inductive arm contains a separate inductor that is included in the bridge arm during the first of a pair of measurements and is short-circuited during the second. The balance is independent of frequency. (*Also see* Heaviside Mutual-Inductance Bridge.)

Heaviside layer—Also called the Kennelly-Heaviside layer. The region of the ionosphere that reflects radio waves back to earth.

Heaviside mutual-inductance bridge—An alternating-current bridge normally used for the comparison of self- and mutual-inductances. Each of the two adjacent arms contains self-inductance, and one or both of them have mutual inductance to the supply circuit. The other two arms normally are nonreactive resistors. The balance is independent of frequency.

heavy hydrogen—Another term for deuterium (H^2) or tritium (H^3).

hecto—A prefix meaning 100.

hectometric wave—An electromagnetic wave between the wavelength limits of 100 and 1000 meters corresponding to the frequency range 3 MHz to 300 MHz.

heelpiece—Part of a relay magnetic structure at the end of a coil, opposite the armature. It generally supports the armature and completes the magnetic path between it and the core of the coil.

Hefner lamp—A standard source that gives a luminous intensity of 0.9 candlepower.

height control—In a television receiver, the adjustment which determines the amplitude of the vertical-scanning pulses and hence the height of the picture.

height finder—A radar which measures the altitude of an airborne object.

height-position indicator—A radar display which simultaneously shows the angular-elevation slant range and height of objects.

height-range indicator—A cathode-ray tube from which altitude and range measurements of airborne objects may be viewed.

Heising modulation—*See* Constant-Current Modulation.

helical—Spiral-shaped.

helical antenna—Also called a helical-beam antenna. A spiral conductor wound around a circular or polygonal cross section. The axis of the spiral normally is mounted parallel to the ground and fed at the adjacent end. The radiation produced has approximately a circular polarization and is confined mainly to a single lobe located along the axis of the spiral.

helical-beam antenna—*See* Helical Antenna.

helical potentiometer—A precision potentiometer which requires several turns of the control knob to move the contact arm from one end of the spiral-wound resistance element to the other end.

helical scanning—1. Radar scanning in which the r-f beam describes a distorted spiral motion. The antenna rotates about the vertical axis while the elevation angle rises slowly from zero to 90°. 2. Method of facsimile scanning in which the elemental area sweeps across the copy in a spiral motion.

helionics—The conversion of solar heat to electric energy.

helix—A spiral.

helix recorder—A recorder in which helical scanning is used.

Helmholtz coil—A phase-shifting network used for determining the range in certain types of radar equipment. It consists of fixed and movable coils. The phase is kept constant at the input, but may be continually shifted from 0° to 360° at the output.

Heaviside-Campbell mutual-inductance bridge.

Helmholtz resonator—An acoustic enclosure with a small opening which causes the enclosure to resonate. The frequency at which it does depends on the geometry of the resonator.

hemimorphic—Terminated at the two ends by dissimilar sets of faces.

HEM wave—*See* Hybrid Electromagnetic Wave.

henry—Abbreviated h. The measure of inductance. In a closed circuit one henry of inductance is present, when a current variation of 1 ampere per second induces 1 volt.

heptode—A seven-electrode electron tube containing an anode, a cathode, a control electrode, and four grids.

hermaphroditic connector—A connector in which both mating contacts are exactly alike at their mating face.

hermetically sealed relay—A relay in a gastight enclosure which has been completely sealed by fusion or comparable means to ensure a low rate of gas leakage over a long period of time.

hermetic sealing—The evacuating and sealing of an enclosure to make it airtight.

herringbone pattern—Television interference seen as one or more horizontal bands of closely spaced V- or S-shaped lines.

hertz—Abbreviated Hz. A unit of frequency equal to one cycle per second.

Hertz antenna—An antenna system which does not depend for its operation on the presence of ground. Its resonant frequency is determined by its distributed capacitance, which varies according to its physical length.

Hertz effect—The ionization and spark discharge produced by ultraviolet radiation.

Hertzian oscillator—A type of oscillator for producing ultrahigh-frequency oscillations. It consists of two metal plates or other conductors separated by an air gap. The capacitor formed has such a small capacitance that ultrahigh-frequency oscillations can occur.

Hertzian waves—Electromagnetic waves of frequencies between 10 kHz and 30,000 GHz. A radio wave.

Hertz vector—A vector which specifies the electromagnetic field of a radio wave. Both the electric and the magnetic intensities can be specified in terms of it.

heterodyne—Also called beat. To mix two frequencies together in order to produce two other frequencies equal to the sum and difference of the first two. For example, heterodyning a 100-kHz and a 10-kHz signal will produce a 110-kHz (sum frequency) and a 90-kHz (difference frequency) signal.

heterodyne conversion transducer (converter)—A conversion transducer in which the output frequency is the sum or difference of the input frequency and an integral multiple of the frequency of another wave.

heterodyne detection—Detection (or conversion) by mixing two signals together to generate the intermediate frequency in a superheterodyne receiver or to make c-w signals audible.

heterodyne detector—A detector that converts an incoming r-f signal to an audible tone by heterodyning. It incorporates a local oscillator (called a beat-frequency oscillator).

heterodyne frequency—The sum or difference frequency produced by combining two other frequencies.

heterodyne frequency meter—*See* Heterodyne Wavemeter.

heterodyne oscillator—An oscillator which produces a desired frequency by combining two other frequencies (e.g., two radio frequencies to produce an audio frequency, or the incoming and local-oscillator frequencies to produce the intermediate frequency of a superheterodyne receiver).

heterodyne principle—*See* Heterodyne.

heterodyne reception—Also called beat reception. Reception by combining a received high-frequency wave with a locally generated wave in a nonlinear device to produce sum and difference frequencies at the output.

heterodyne-type frequency meter—An instrument for measuring frequency by producing a zero difference frequency (zero beat) between the signal under test and an internally generated signal.

heterodyne wavemeter—A wavemeter employing the heterodyne principle to compare the frequency being measured with a frequency being generated in a calibrated oscillator circuit.

heterodyne whistle—A steady squeal heard in a radio receiver when the signals from stations having nearly equal frequencies beat together.

heterodyning—*See* Heterodyne.

heterogeneity—A state or condition being unlike in nature, kind, or degree.

heterogeneous—Composed of different materials (opposite of homogeneous).

heterosphere—The portion of the upper atmosphere in which the relative proportions of oxygen, nitrogen, and other gases are unfixed and radiation particles and micrometeroids are mixed with the air particles.

heuristic program—A set of computer instructions that simulate the behavior of human operators in approaching similar problems.

hexadecimal number system—A number system having as its base the equivalent of the decimal number sixteen.

hexode—A six-electrode electron tube containing an anode, a cathode, a control electrode, and three grids.

hf—Abbreviation for high frequency.

HH beacon—A nondirectional radio homing beacon with a power output of 2,000 watts or more.

hierarchy—A series of items classified according to rank or order.

hi-fi—*See* High Fidelity.

high band—Television channels 7 - 13, covering a frequency range of 174-216 MHz.

high boost—*See* High-Frequency Compensation.

high-contrast image — A picture in which strong contrast between light and dark areas is visible. Intermediate values, however, may be missing.

high definition — Television or facsimile equivalent of high fidelity.

high-energy materials — Also called hard magnetic materials. Magnetic materials having a comparatively high energy product, e.g., materials used for permanent-magnets.

highest probable frequency — Abbreviated HPF. An arbitrarily chosen frequency value 15% above the F_2-layer MUF (maximum usable frequency) for the radio circuit. For the E-layer, the HPF is equal to the MUF.

high fidelity—Popularly called hi-fi. The characteristic which enables a system to reproduce sound as nearly like the original as possible.

high-fidelity receiver—A radio receiver capable of receiving and reproducing, without noticeable distortion, the original modulation impressed on the carrier waves.

high filter—An audio circuit designed to remove undesired high-frequency noise from the program material. Such noise includes record scratch, tape hiss, a-m whistles, etc.

high frequency—Abbreviated hf. The frequency band from 3 to 30 MHz (10 meters to 100 meters).

high-frequency alternator — An alternator capable of generating radio-frequency carrier waves.

high-frequency band—The band of frequencies extending from 3 to 30 MHz.

high-frequency bias—In a tape recorder, a sinusoidal voltage that is mixed with the signal being recorded to better the linearity and dynamic range of the recorded signal. In practice, the bias frequency is three to four times the highest information frequency to be recorded.

high-frequency broadcast station—A commercial station licensed for transmission to the general public and operated in the high-frequency broadcast band, using frequency modulation exclusively.

high-frequency carrier telegraphy—Carrier telegraphy with the carrier currents above the frequencies transmitted over a voice telephone channel.

high-frequency compensation—Also called high boost. An increase in the amplification of the high frequencies with respect to the low and middle frequencies within a given band of frequencies.

high-frequency heating — *See* Electronic Heating.

high-frequency induction heater or furnace—An induction heater or furnace using frequencies much higher than the standard 60-hertz.

high-frequency resistance—Also called r-f or a-c resistance. The total resistance offered by a device in a high-frequency a-c circuit.

This includes the d-c and all other resistances due to the effects of the alternating current.

high-frequency treatment—Therapeutic use of intermittent and isolated trains of heavily damped oscillations having a high frequency and voltage and a relatively low current.

high-frequency trimmer—A trimmer capacitor that is used to calibrate the high-frequency end of the tuning range in a super-heterodyne receiver.

high-frequency unit—*See* Tweeter.

high-frequency welding — *See* Radio-Frequency Welding.

high-level detector—A linear power detector with a voltage-current characteristic that may be treated as a straight line or two intersecting lines.

high-level firing time—The time required to establish a radio-frequency discharge in a switching tube after radio-frequency power is applied.

high-level modulation—A system in which the modulation is introduced at a point where the power level approximates the output power.

high-level, radio-frequency signal (TR, ATR, and pre-TR tubes) — A radio-frequency signal with sufficient power to fire the tube.

high-level vswr (switching tubes) — The voltage standing-wave ratio due to a fired tube in its mount, located between a generator and the matched termination in a wave guide.

highlight—The brightest portion of a reproduced image.

high-mu tube—A vacuum tube with a high amplification factor.

high-pass filter—A wave filter having a single transmission band extending from some critical, or cutoff, frequency other than zero, up to infinite frequency.

high-performance equipment — Equipment having sufficiently exacting characteristics to permit their use in trunk or link circuits.

high-potential test—A test for determining the breakdown point of insulating materials and spacings. It consists of applying a voltage higher than the rated voltage between two points or between two or more windings. However, it is not a test of conductor insulation.

high-power silicon rectifiers—A group of rectifiers with continuous ratings exceeding 50 average amperes per section in a single-phase, half-wave circuit.

high Q—Having a high ratio of reactance to effective resistance. The factor determining the efficiency of a reactive component.

high-rate discharge — The storage-battery discharge equivalent to the heaviest possible duty in service.

high-recombination-rate contact—A semiconductor - to - semiconductor or metal-to-semiconductor contact at which thermal equilibrium charge-carrier concentrations are maintained substantially independent of current density.

high-resistance joint—A faulty union of conductors or conductor and terminal. The result is less current flow and a drop in voltage at the union.

high-resistance voltmeter—A voltmeter having a resistance considerably higher than 1,000 ohms per volt. As a result, it draws very little current from the circuit being measured.

high-speed bus—*See* Memory Register.

high-speed carry—In a computer, a type of carry in which: 1. A carry into a column results in a carry out of that column, because the sum without carry in that column is 9. 2. Instead of a normal adding process, a special process is used which takes the carry at high speed to the actual column where it is added. Also called standing-on-nines carry.

high-speed d-c circuit breaker — A device which starts to reduce the current in the main circuit in 0.01 second or less, after the occurrence of the d-c overcurrent or the excessive rate of current rise.

high-speed relay—A relay designed specifically for short-operate or short-release time, or both.

high-speed telegraph transmission—Transmission of code at higher speeds than are possible with hand-operated keys.

high tension—Lethal voltages, on the order of thousands of volts.

high-tension magneto—A self-contained generator in which the required high potential is generated directly; no induction coil is needed.

high-vacuum phototube—A phototube that is highly evacuated so that its electrical characteristics are essentially unaffected by gaseous ionization. In a gas phototube, some gas is intentionally introduced.

high-vacuum rectifier—A vacuum-tube rectifier in which conduction is entirely by electrons emitted from the cathode.

high-vacuum tube—An electron tube that is highly evacuated so that its electrical characteristics are essentially unaffected by gaseous ionization.

high-velocity scanning—The scanning of a target with electrons of such velocity that the secondary-emission ratio is greater than unity.

high voltage — The accelerating potential that speeds up the electrons in a beam of a cathode-ray tube.

high-voltage probe—A probe with a high internal resistance, for measuring extremely high voltages. It is used with a voltmeter having an internal resistance of 20,000 ohms per volt or more.

hill-and-dale recording — *See* Vertical Recording.

hinge—A joint in a relay that permits movement of the armature relative to the stationary parts of the relay structure.

hinged-iron ammeter—A moving-iron am-

High-voltage probe.

meter in which the fixed portion of the magnetic circuit is placed around the conductor to measure the current through it.

HIPERNAS — Acronym for HIgh PERformance NAvigation System. A self-compensated, pure-inertial guidance system.

hi-pot—1. *See* Dielectric Breakdown Voltage. 2. Contraction of high potential. *Commonly* refers to a device used for testing insulation breakdown or leakage, with high voltages. High potting is the verb.

hiss—Random noise characterized by prolonged sibilant sounds in the audio-frequency range.

histogram—A graphical representation of a frequency distribution by a series of rectangles which have for one dimension a distance proportional to a definite range of frequencies, and for the other dimension a distance proportional to the number of frequencies appearing within the range.

hit—*See* Flash.

hit-on-the-fly printer—A mechanical printer in which the printing head is in continual motion.

hits — Momentary line disturbances which could result in mutilation of characters being transmitted.

H-lines—Imaginary lines that represent the direction and strength of magnetic flux on a diagram.

H-network.

H-network—A network composed of five impedance branches. Two are connected in series between an input terminal and an output terminal and two are connected between another input terminal and another output terminal. The fifth is connected from the junction points of the two branches.

hog horn—A microwave feed horn shaped so that the input energy from the waveguide approaches from the same direction as the horn opening.

hold—Opposite of clear. 1. To maintain storage elements in charge storage tubes at equilibrium potentials by electron bombardment. 2. In computers, to retain information contained in one storage device after copying it into a second storage device.

hold control—In a television receiver, the adjustment which controls the frequency of the vertical- or horizontal-scanning pulses and hence the stability of the picture.

hold current—Also called the electrical hold value. The minimum current which will keep the contact springs energized in a relay.

hold electrode—In a mercury switch, the electrode that remains in contact with the mercury pool while the circuit is being closed or opened.

holding anode—In a mercury-arc rectifier, a small auxiliary anode that maintains the ionization while the main anode current is zero.

holding beam—A diffused beam of electrons for regenerating the charges retained on the dielectric surface of an electrostatic memory or storage tube.

holding circuit—Also called a locking circuit. An alternate operating circuit which, when completed, maintains sufficient current in a relay winding to keep the relay energized after the initial current has ceased.

holding coil—A separate relay coil which keeps the relay energized after the original current has been removed.

holding current—That value of average forward current (with the gate open) below which a silicon-controlled rectifier returns to the forward blocking state after having been in forward conduction.

holding gun—In a storage tube, the source of electrons constituting the holding beam.

holding time—The total time a trunk or circuit is in use on a call, including both operator's and user's time.

hold mode—In integrators or other charge-storage circuits, a condition or time interval in which input (s) are removed and the circuit is commanded (or expected) to maintain a constant output.

hold-off voltage—The maximum voltage an electronic flash tube will stand without self-flashing. Normal hold-off voltage is reduced at the end of lamp life and in the presence of high temperatures or r-f fields.

hold time—In resistance welding, the time that is allowed for the weld to harden.

hole—In the electronic valence structure of a semiconductor, a mobile vacancy which acts like a positive electronic charge with a positive mass.

hole conduction—Conduction occurring in a semiconductor when electrons move into holes under the influence of an applied voltage and thereby create new holes. The apparent movement of such holes is toward the more negative terminal, and is hence equivalent to a flow of positive charges in that direction.

hole current—Conduction in a semiconductor when electrons move into holes, creating new holes. The holes appear to move toward the negative terminal, giving the equivalent of positive charges flowing to the terminal.

hole density—In a semiconductor, the density of holes in an otherwise full band.

hole injection—The production of mobile vacancies in an N-type semiconductor when a voltage is applied to a sharp metal point in contact with the surface of the material.

hole injector—A pointed metallic device for injecting holes into an N-type semiconductor.

hole-in-the-center effect—Also called hole-in-the-middle effect. The lower volume or absence of sound between the left and right speakers of a stereo system.

hole mobility—The ability of a hole to travel easily through a semiconductor.

hole site—The area on a computer punch card or paper tape where a hole may or may not be punched. It can be a form of binary storage in which a hole represents a 1 and the absence of a hole represents a 0.

hole storage factor (K'$_s$)—In a transistor, the excess stored charge (when the transistor is in saturation) per unit excess base current. Excess base current is defined as the amount of current supplied to the base in excess of the current required to just keep the transistor in saturation.

hole trap—A semiconductor impurity which can trap holes by releasing electrons into the conduction or valence bands.

Hollerith code—A code based on the punching of holes in cards at specified locations. From one to three punches may be made in each column of the card and up to 80 columns may be punched in each card. Each column corresponds to one character; the specific character is determined by the number and location of the punches in that column.

hollow-cathode tube—A gas discharge tube with a hollow cathode closed at one end. Almost all the radiation is from the cathode glow within the hollow cathode.

hollow core—A plain ferrite core having a center hole for mounting purposes.

home loop—An operation involving only those input and output units associated with the hole terminal.

homing—1. Approaching a desired point by maintaining some indicated navigational parameter constant (other than altitude). 2. In missile guidance, the use of radiation from a target to establish a collision course.

homing adapter—A device used with an aircraft radio receiver to produce aural and/or visual signals which indicate the direction of a transmitting radio station.

homing antenna—A type of directional-antenna array used for pinpointing a target.

homing beacon—A radio transmitter which emits a distinctive signal for determining bearing, course, or location.

homing device—1. An automatic device that moves or rotates in the correct direction without first having to go to the end of its travel in the opposite direction. 2. A radio device that guides an aircraft to an airport or transmitter site.

homing guidance—A missile-guidance system in which the missile steers itself toward a target by means of a self-contained mechanism (infrared detectors, radar, etc.). Activated by some distinguishing characterism of the target. Homing guidance may be active, semiactive, or passive.

homing relay—A stepping relay that returns to a specified starting position prior to each operating cycle.

homing station—A radionavigational aid incorporating direction-finding facilities.

homodyne reception—Also called zero-beat reception. A system of reception using a locally generated voltage at the carrier frequency.

homogeneity—The state or condition of being similar in nature, kind, or degree.

homogeneous—Of the same nature (the opposite of heterogeneous).

homologous field—A field in which the lines of force in a given plane all pass through one point (e.g., the electric field between two coaxial charged cylinders).

homopolar — Electrically symmetrical — i.e., having equally distributed charges.

homopolar generator—A d-c generator in which all the poles presented to the armature are of the same polarity, so that the armature conductor always cuts the magnetic lines of force in the same direction. A pure direct current can thus be produced without commutation.

homopolar magnet—A magnet with concentric pole pieces.

homosphere—That part of the atmosphere which is made up mostly of atoms and molecules found near the earth's surface, and retaining the same relative proportions of oxygen, nitrogen, and other gases throughout.

homotaxial—A term coined by RCA from "homogeneous" and "axial" to describe a single-diffused transistor with a base region of homogeneous resistivity silicon in the axial direction (emitter-to-collector).

honeycomb coil—Also called duolateral or lattice-wound coil. A coil with the turns wound crisscross to reduce the distributed capacitance.

hood—A shield placed over a cathode-ray tube to eliminate extraneous light and thus make the image on the screen appear more clearly.

hookswitch — A hook or plunger-operated switch used in a telephone set to open the circuit when the instrument is not in use.

hook transistor — A transistor having four alternating P-type and N-type layers, with one layer floating between the base layer and the collector layer. This arrangement gives high emitter-input current gains. The PNPN transistor has a P-type floating layer, while an NPNP transistor has an N-type floating layer.

hookup—1. Method of connection between the various units in a circuit. 2. The diagram of connections used.

hookup wire—The wire used in coupling circuits together. It may be solid or stranded, and is usually tinned and insulated No. 18 or 20 soft-drawn copper.

hop—An excursion of a radio wave from the earth to the ionosphere and back. It is usually expressed as single-, double-, and multihop. The number of hops is called the order of reflection.

hopoff—In a potentiometer, the sudden jump in resistance as the contact is rotated over the junction of two resistance slopes or over the junction of two resistance slopes or over resistance slope. The magnitude of the hopoff is dependent on the ratio of the slopes and on the junction blending characteristic.

horizon—An apparent or visible junction of earth and sky as seen on or above the earth. It bounds the part of the earth's surface that can be reached by the direct wave of a radio station. The distance to the horizon is affected by atmospheric refraction.

horizon distance—The space between the farthest visible point and the transmitter antenna. It is the distance over which ultrahigh-frequency transmission can be received under ordinary conditions with an unelevated receiving antenna.

horizontal—1. Perpendicular to the direction of gravity. 2. In the direction of or parallel to the horizon. 3. On a level.

horizontal axes—The three horizontal axes of crystallographic reference.

horizontal blanking—Cutting off the electron beam between successive active horizontal lines during retrace.

horizontal blanking pulse—A rectangular pedestal in the composite television signal. It occurs between active horizontal lines and cuts off the beam current of the picture tube during retrace.

horizontal centering control—In a television receiver or cathode-ray oscilloscope, the adjustment for moving the entire display back and forth.

horizontal-convergence control—In a color television receiver, the control which adjusts the amplitude of the horizontal dynamic convergence voltage.

horizontal-deflecting electrode—A pair of electrodes that move the electron beam from side to side on the screen of a cathode-ray tube employing electrostatic deflection.

horizontal-discharge tube—A vacuum tube used in the horizontal-deflection circuit to discharge a capacitor and thereby form the sawtooth scanning wave. (*Also see* Discharge Tube.)

horizontal-drive control—In an electromagnetically deflected television receiver, the control which adjusts the ratio of the pulse amplitude to the linear portion of the scanning-current wave.

horizontal dynamic convergence—Convergence of the three electron beams in a color picture tube at the aperture mask during scanning of a horizontal line.

horizontal frequency—*See* Line Frequency.

horizontal hold control—A synchronization control which varies the free-running frequency of the horizontal deflection oscillator so it will be in step with the scanning frequency at the transmitter.

horizontal hum bars — Broad, horizontal, moving or stationary bars, alternately dark and light, that extend over an entire television picture. They are caused by interference at approximately 60 Hz or a harmonic of 60 Hz.

horizontal-linearity control—In a television receiver, the control for adjusting the width at the left side of the screen.

horizontal line frequency—*See* Line Frequency.

horizontal lock—The circuit that maintains horizontal synchronization in a television receiver.

Horizontally polarized wave.

horizontally polarized wave — A linearly polarized wave with a horizontal electric-field vector.

horizontal-output transformer—*See* Flyback Transformer.

horizontal parabola control—*See* Phase Control.

horizontal polarization — Transmission in which the electrostatic field leaves the antenna in a horizontal plane. Elements of the transmitting and receiving antennas likewise are horizontal. Horizontal polarization is standard for television in the United States.

horizontal repetition rate—Also called horizontal scanning frequency. The number of horizontal lines per second (15,750 hertz in the United States).

horizontal resolution—The number of picture elements in a horizontal scanning line that can be distinguished.

horizontal retrace—The line that would be seen on the screen, while the spot is returning from right to left, if retrace blanking were not used.

horizontal ring-induction furnace—A furnace for melting metal. It comprises an open trough or melting channel, a primary inductor winding, and a magnetic core which links the melting channel to the primary winding.

horizontal-scanning frequency—*See* Horizontal-Repetition Rate.

horizontal sweep—Movement of the electron beam from left to right across the screen or the scene being televised.

horizontal-sync discriminator—A circuit employed in the flywheel method of synchronization to compare the phase of the horizontal-sync pulses with that of the horizontal-scanning oscillator.

horizontal-sync pulse — The rectangular pulses which occur above the pedestal level between each active horizontal line. They keep the horizontal scanning at the receiver in step with the horizontal scanning at the transmitter.

horn—Also called an acoustic horn. A tubular or rectangular enclosure for radiating or receiving acoustic waves. (*Also see* Horn Antenna.)

Horn antenna.

horn antenna—Also called a horn. A tubular or rectangular microwave antenna which is wider at the open end and through which radio waves are radiated into space.

horn arrester—A lightning arrester that has a spark gap with upward-projecting diversion horns of thick wire. When the arc is formed, it travels up the gap, and is extinguished upon reaching the widest part of the gap.

horn cutoff frequency—A frequency below which an exponential horn will not function correctly, because it fails to provide for proper expansion of the sound waves.

horn loading — A method of coupling a speaker diaphragm to the listening space by an expanding air column having a small throat and large mouth.

horn mouth—The wide end of a horn.

horn radiator—An open-ended, metallic device for concentrating energy from a waveguide and directing this energy into space.

horn speaker—A speaker in which a horn couples the radiating element to the medium.

horn throat—The narrow end of a horn.

horsepower — Abbreviated hp. A unit of power, or the capacity of a mechanism to do work. It is the equivalent of raising 33,000 pounds one foot in one minute, or 550 pounds one foot in one second. One horsepower equals 746 watts.

horseshoe magnet—A permanent magnet or electromagnet shaped like a horseshoe or U to bring the two poles close together.

hot—1. Connected, alive, energized; pertains to a terminal or any ungrounded conductor. 2. Not grounded.

hot-carrier diode — A semiconductor diode

Horseshoe magnet.

which uses the thermoelectric effect of radio-frequency heating in bulk semiconductor material to provide current carriers. Characterized by relatively high power and low internal noise generation.

hot carriers—In barrier diodes, carriers that have energies greater than those that are in thermal equilibrium with the metal. Thus, electrons that cross the junction from semiconductor to metal must be energetic enough to surmount the barrier. Therefore electrons that are energetic enough to cross the junction are called "hot electrons."

hot cathode—Also called thermionic cathode. A cathode which supplies electrons by thermionic emission. (As opposed to a cold cathode, which has no heater.)

hot-cathode tube — Also called thermionic tube. Any electron tube containing a hot cathode.

hot-cathode X-ray tube — A high-vacuum X-ray tube in which a hot rather than cold cathode is used.

hot electrons—*See* Hot Carriers.

hot spot—The point of maximum temperature on the outside of a device or component.

hot tin dip—A process of passing a bare wire through a bath of molten tin to provide a coating.

hot-wire ammeter—Also called thermal ammeter. An ammeter in which the expansion of a wire moves a pointer to indicate the amount of current being measured. The current flows through the wire and changes its length in proportion to I^2. Instability because of wire stretching, and the lack of ambient temperature compensation make the hot-wire ammeter commercially unsatisfactory.

Hot-wire ammeter.

hot-wire anemometer—An instrument that measures the velocity of wind or a gas by its cooling effect on an electrically heated wire.

hot-wire instrument—An electrothermic instrument operated by expansion of a wire heated by the current it is carrying.

hot-wire microphone — A microphone in which the cooling or heating effect of a sound wave changes the resistance of a hot wire and thus the current through it.

hot-wire relay—A form of linear-expansion time-delay relay in which the longitudinal expansion of a wire, when heated, provides the mechanical motion to open or close contacts. The time required to heat the wire constitutes the delay.

hot-wire transducer — A unilateral transducer in which the cooling or heating effect of a sound wave changes the resistance of a hot wire and thus the current.

housekeeping—In a computer routine, those operations, such as setting up constants and variables for use in the program, that contribute directly ot the proper operation of the computer but not to the solution of the problem.

howl—An undesirable prolonged wail produced in a speaker by electric or acoustic feedback.

howler—An electromechanical device which produces an audio-frequency tone.

hp—Abbreviation for horsepower.

H-pad—An attenuation network in which the elements are arranged in the form of the letter *H*.

h-parameters—*See* Hybrid Parameters.

h-particle—The positive hydrogen ion or proton resulting from bombardment of the hydrogen atom by alpha rays or fast-moving positive ions.

HPF—Abbreviation for highest probable frequency.

H plane — The plane in which the magnetic field of an antenna lies. It is perpendicular to the E plane. The principal H plane of an antenna is the H plane that also contains the direction of maximum radiation.

H-plane bend—*See* H-Bend.

H-plane T-junction—Also called shunt T-junction. A waveguide T-junction in which the structure changes in the plane of the magnetic field.

H-scan—*See* H-Display.

hub — On a control panel or plugboard, a socket or receptacle into which an electrical lead or plug wire may be connected for the purpose of carrying signals.

hue—Often used synonymously with the term "color," but does not include gray. It is the dominant wavelength — i.e., the one which distinguishes a color as red, yellow, etc. Varying saturations may have the same hue.

hue control—On a color television receiver, the operating control that changes the hue (color) of the picture.

hull potential — The voltage difference between a reference electrode and an immersed metallic hull, or the bonded underwater metallic appendages of a nonmetallic hull.

hum — In audio-frequency systems, a low-pitched droning noise consisting of several harmonically related frequencies. It results from an alternating-current power supply, ripple from a direct-current power supply, or induction from exposure to a power system. By extension, the term is applied in visual systems to interference from similar sources.

human engineering—The science and art of developing machines for human use, giving consideration to the abilities, limitations, habits, and preferences of the human operator.

hum-balancing pot—A potentiometer usually placed across the heater circuit. Its arm is grounded so that the heater voltage is balanced with respect to ground.

hum bar—A dark band extending across the picture. It is caused by excessive 60-hertz hum (or harmonics) in the signal applied to the picture-tube input.

hum bucking—The introduction of a small amount of voltage, at the power-line frequency, into a circuit to cancel unwanted power.

hum-bucking coil—A coil wound around the field coil of a dynamic speaker and connected in series opposition with the voice coil. In this way, any hum voltage induced in the field coil will be induced in the voice coil in the opposite direction and buck, or cancel, the effects of the hum.

humidity transducer—A layer of hygroscopic (moisture-absorbing) substance deposited between two metal electrodes. These electrodes establish electrical contact with the hygroscopic chemical, which serves as a resistance element. Since the chemical coating tends to absorb moisture from the surrounding air, its resistance decreases as the humidity increases. In this manner, humidity variations are converted to resistance variations.

humming—A sound produced by transformers having loose laminations or by magnetostriction effects in iron cores. The frequency of the sound is twice the power-line frequency.

hum modulation — Modulation of a radio-frequency or detected signal by using hum.

hunting—An undesirable oscillation of an automatic control system where the controlled variable swings on both sides of the predetermined reference value without settling on it.

hv or HV—Abbreviation for high voltage.

H-vector — A vector which represents the magnetic field of an electromagnetic wave. In free space, it is perpendicular to the E-vector and the direction of propagation.

H-wave—A mode in which electromagnetic energy can be transmitted in a waveguide. An H-wave has an electric field perpendicular to the length of the waveguide, and

a magnetic field parallel as well as perpendicular to the length.

hybrid—*See* Hybrid Junction.

hybrid balance—A measure of the degree of balance between two impedances connected to two conjugate sides of a hybrid set. It is given by the formula for return loss.

hybrid circuit—1. A circuit which combines the thin-film and semiconductor technologies. Generally, the passive components are made by thin-film techniques, and the active components by semiconductor techniques. The active devices are attached to the thin-film passive components by a suitable bonding process. 2. Also called two-wire–four-wire terminating set. In telephone transmission circuits, a circuit for interconnecting two-wire and four-wire circuits through a differential balance or bridge circuit in which the two sides of the four-wire circuit form conjugate arms.

hybrid coil—Also called bridge transformer. A single transformer which has, effectively, three windings and which is designed to be connected to four branches of a circuit so as to render these branches conjugate in pairs.

hybrid computer — A computer that results from the interconnection of an analog computer and a digital computer, plus conversion equipment, each contributing its special advantages to an assigned part of the solution of a class of complex problems.

hybrid electromagnetic wave — Abbreviated HEM wave. An electromagnetic wave having components of both electric- and magnetic-field vectors in the direction of propagation.

hybrid integrated circuit — 1. An arrangement that consists of one or more integrated circuits combined with one or more discrete component parts. 2. The combination of more than one type of integrated circuit into one integrated component.

hybrid junction—1. Also called hybrid-t or magic-t. A waveguide arrangement with four branches. When they are properly terminated, energy is transferred from any one branch into two of the remaining three branches. In common usage, this energy is divided equally between the two. 2. Also called bridge hybrid, and hybrid. A transformer, resistor, or waveguide circuit or device that has four pairs of terminals so arranged that a signal entering at one terminal pair will divide and emerge from the two adjacent terminal pairs, but will be unable to reach the opposite terminal pair.

hybrid microcircuit — A microcircuit in which thin-film or diffusion techniques are combined with separately attached semiconductor chips to form the circuit.

hybrid network — A nonhomogeneous communication network required to operate with signals of dissimilar characteristics (such as analog and digital modes).

hybrid parameters — Also called h-parameters. The resultant parameters of an equivalent transistor circuit when the input current and output voltage are selected as independent variables.

hybrid ring—Also called a "rat race." A hybrid junction commonly used as an equal power divider. It consists of a re-entrant line (waveguide) to which four side arms are connected. The line is of the proper electrical length to sustain standing waves.

hybrid set—Two or more transformers interconnected to form a network having four pairs of accessible terminals. Four impedances may be connected to the four terminals, so that the branches containing them may be made conjugate in pairs.

hybrid-t—*See* Hybrid Junction.

hybrid thin-film circuit — A microcircuit formed by attaching discrete components and semiconductor devices to networks of passive components and conductors that have been vacuum deposited on glazed ceramic, sapphire, or glass substrates.

hybrid transformer—*See* Hybrid Coil.

hydroacoustics—The generation of acoustic energy from the flow of fluids under pressure.

hydroacoustic transducer — A transducer that produces high-level acoustic energy from the flow of high-pressure fluid.

hydroelectric—The production of electricity by water power.

hydrogen electrode—A platinum electrode covered with platinum black, around which a stream of hydrogen is bubbled. The hydrogen electrode furnishes a standard against which other electrode potentials can be compared.

hydrogen lamp—A special light source, used in some spectrophotometers, which produces invisible light energy. It is used in finding the light-energy frequency of test solutions.

hydrogen thyratron — A thyratron containing hydrogen.

hydromagnetics — *See* Magnetohydrodynamics.

hydromagnetic waves—Waves in which the energy oscillates between the magnetic field energy and kinetic energy of the hydrodynamic motion, the reservoirs being the self-inductance of the conductive matter and the mass inertia of the moving fluid.

hydrometer—An instrument for measuring the specific gravity of a liquid such as the electrolyte of a storage battery. It contains a graduated float which indicates the specific gravity by the amount of liquid displaced.

hydrophone — An electroacoustic transducer which responds to waterborne sound waves and delivers essentially equivalent electric waves.

hydrostatic pressure—*See* Static Pressure.

hygrometer—An instrument that measures the relative humidity of the atmosphere.

hygroscopic—Readily absorbing and retaining moisture from the atmosphere. The opposite term is nonhygroscopic.

hygrostat—A device that closes a pair of contacts when the humidity reaches a prescribed level.

hyperacoustic zone—The region in the upper atmosphere, above about 60 miles, in which the distance between the air molecules is roughly equal to the wavelength of sound, so that sound is transmitted with less

Hyperbolic guidance.

efficiency than at lower levels. Sound waves cannot be propagated above this zone.

hyperbola — 1. A curve that is the focus of points having a constant difference of distance from two fixed points. 2. In hyperbolic guidance systems, a path along which the difference between the arrival times of pulses from two transmitters is constant. (*Also see* Hyperbolic Guidance System).

hyperbolic error — The error in an interferometer system arising from the assumption that the directions of the wavefronts incident at two antennas of a base line are parallel, whereby the equiphase path is a cone. Mathematically the equiphase path is a hyperbola.

hyperbolic grind — A shape of tape playback and record heads. It permits good head contact and better response at high frequencies.

hyperbolic guidance system — A method of guidance in which sets of ground stations transmit pulses from which a hyperbolic path can be derived to give range and course information for steering. (*Also see* Hyperbola.)

hyperbolic horn — A horn in which the equivalent cross-sectional radius increases according to a hyperbolic law.

hyperbolic navigation system — A method of radionavigation (e.g., loran) in which pulses transmitted by two ground stations are received by an aircraft or ship. The difference in arrival time from each station is a measure of the difference in distance between the aircraft or ship and each station. This distance is plotted on one of many hyperbolic curves on a map. A second reading from another pair of stations (or from the same master and a different slave) establishes another point on a different hyperbolic curve. The intersection of the two curves gives the position of the aircraft or ship.

hyperfrequency waves — Microwaves having wavelengths in the range from 1 centimeter to 1 meter.

hypersonic — Having five or more times the speed of sound.

hyspersyn motor — A synchronous motor which combines the desirable features of the induction, hysteresis, and d-c excited synchronous motor, resulting in high efficiency and power factor. It possesses the vigorous starting torque of an induction motor, the synchronizating torque of a hysteresis motor, and the stiffness of an externally d-c excited synchronous motor.

hysteresigraph — A device for experimentally presenting or recording the hysteresis loop of a magnetic specimen.

hysteresis — 1. The amount the magnetization of a ferrous substance lags the magnetizing force because of molecular friction. 2. A type of oscillator behavior where multiple values of the output power and/or frequency correspond to given values of an operating parameter. 3. The temporary change in the counting-rate–vs–voltage characteristic of a radiation-counter tube (caused by previous

operation). 4. The difference between the response of a unit or system to an increasing and a decreasing signal. 5. A form of non-linearity in which the response of a circuit of a particular set of input conditions depends, not only on the instantaneous values of those conditions, but also on the immediate past (recent history) of the input and output signal. Hysteretical behavior is characterized by inability to "retrace" exactly on the reverse swing a particular locus of input/output conditions.

hysteresis brake — *See* Hysteresis Clutch.

hysteresis clutch — Also called hysteresis brake. A proportional torque-control device which employs the hysteresis effect in a permanent-magnet rotor to develop its output torque. It is capable of synchronous driving or continuous slip, provided heat can be removed, with almost no torque variation at any slip differential. Its control-power requirement is small enough for vacuum-tube or transistorized drive.

hysteresiscope — An instrument used to obtain hysteresis loops on a cathode-ray oscilloscope screen without the need for specially prepared ring samples. It is used in the inspection of magnetic material.

hysteresis curve — A curve showing the relationship between a magnetizing force and the resultant magnetic flux.

hysteresis distortion — Distortion of waveforms in circuits containing magnetic components. It is due to the hysteresis of the magnetic cores.

hysteresis error — The difference in the reading obtained on a measuring instrument containing iron when the current is increased to a definite value and when the current is reduced from a higher value to the same definite value.

hysteresis heater — An induction device in which a charge (or a muffle around the charge) is heated by hysteresis losses due to the magnetic flux produced in the charge.

Hysteresis loop.

hysteresis loop—For a magnetic material, a curve showing two values of magnetic flux density—one when the magnetizing force is increasing and the other when it is decreasing—for each value of the magnetizing force.

hysteresis loss—The power expended in a magnetic material as a result of magnetic hysteresis.

hysteresis meter—An instrument for determining the hysteresis loss in a ferromagnetic material. It measures the torque produced when the test specimen is placed in a rotating magnetic field or is rotated in a stationary magnetic field.

hysteresis motor—A synchronous motor without salient poles or direct-current excitation. It is started by the hysteresis losses induced in its secondary by the revolving field.

hystoroscope—An instrument used to observe, measure, and record the magnetic characteristics of both easy and hard axes of magnetic materials.

Hz—Abbreviation for hertz — the new term used in place of cycles per second.

I

I—1. Symbol for current. 2. Abbreviation for luminous intensity.

IC—1. Abbreviation for internal connection. 2. Abbreviation for integrated circuit.

ICBM—Abbreviation for intercontinental ballistic missile.

I_{CBO}—The reverse current that occurs when a specific d-c voltage is applied in the non-conducting directon to the collector junction of a transistor while the emitter is open-circuited.

iconoscope—A camera tube in which a beam of high-velocity electrons scans a photoemissive mosaic capable of storing an electrical charge pattern.

icw—Abbreviation for interrupted continuous wave.

ideal bunching—A theoretical condition where bunching of the electrons in a velocity-modulated tube would give an infinitely large current peak during each cycle.

ideal capacitor—A capacitor having a single-valued transferred-charge characteristic.

ideal crystal—A crystal having no mosaic structure and capable of X-ray reflection in accordance with the Darwin-Ewald-Prins law.

ideal dielectric—A dielectric in which all the energy required to establish an electric field in the dielectric is returned to the source when the field is removed. (A perfect dielectric must have zero conductivity. Also, all absorption phenomena must be lacking. A vacuum is the only known perfect dielectric.)

ideal-noise diode—A diode that has an infinite internal impedance and in which the current exhibits full shot-noise fluctuations.

ideal transducer—Theoretically, any linear passive transducer which—if it dissipated no energy and, when connected to a source and load, presented its combined impedance to each—would transfer maximum power from source to load.

ideal transformer—A hypothetical transformer which would neither store nor dissipate energy. Its self-inductances would have a finite ratio and unity coefficient of coupling, and its self- and mutual impedances would be pure inductances of infinitely great value.

I demodulator—A demodulator circuit the inputs of which are the chrominance signal and the signal from the local 3.58-MHz oscillator. The output of this demodulator is a video signal representing color in the televised scene. The Q demodulator is similar except that its input from the local oscillator is shifted 90°.

identification—1. In radar, determining the identity of a displayed target (i.e., which one of the blips in the display represents the target). 2. In a computer, a code number or code name which uniquely identifies a record, block, file, or other unit of information.

identification beacon—A code beacon used for positively identifying a particular point on the earth's surface.

identification, friend or foe—A system using radar transmissions to which equipment carried by friendly forces automatically responds, for example, by emitting pulses, thereby distinguishing themselves from enemy forces. It is the primary method of determining the friendly or unfriendly character of aircraft and ships by other aircraft or ships and by ground forces employing radar-detection equipment and associated identification, friend or foe units. Abbreviated iff.

identify—In a computer, to attach a unique code or code name to a specific unit of information.

idiochromatic—Having photoelectric properties characteristic of the pure crystal itself and not due to foreign matter.

I-display—In radar, a display in which a target appears as a circle when the radar antenna is pointed directly at it. The radius of the circle is proportionate to the target distance. When the antenna is not pointing at the target, only a segment of the circle appears. Its length is inversely proportionate to the magnitude of the pointing error, and the segment points away from the direction of error.

idle characters—Control characters interchanged by a synchronized transmitter and receiver to maintain synchronization during a nondata period.

idler—A rubber-tired wheel that transfers

power from a phonograph motor to the turntable rim.

idler pulley—A pulley used only for tightening a belt or changing its direction. The shaft does not drive any other part.

idling current—Also called quiescent current. The zero-signal power supply current drawn by a circuit or by a complete amplifier.

IEC's – *See* Integrated Equipment Components.

IEEE—A professional organization of scientists and engineers whose purpose is the advancement of electrical engineering, electronics, and allied branches of engineering and science. (The IEEE resulted from the merger of the IRE and the AIEE.)

if—Abbreviation for intermediate frequency.

i-f amplifier – *See* Intermediate-Frequency Amplifier.

iff—*See* Identification, Friend or Foe.

IFRU—*See* Interference-Rejection Unit.

i-f strip—*See* Intermediate-Frequency Strip.

ignistor—A transistor and a matched zener diode integrated into one power package.

Ignition coil .

ignition coil—An iron-core transformer which converts a low direct voltage to the 20,000 volts or so required to produce an ignition spark in gasoline engines. It has an open core, a heavy primary winding connected to the battery or other source through a vibrating armature contact, and a secondary winding with many turns of fine wire.

ignition control—Control of the instant that static current begins to flow in the anode circuit of a gas tube.

ignition interference – Noise produced by sparks or other ignition discharges in a car, motor, or furnace ignition, or by equipment with loose contacts or connections.

ignition reserve—In a gasoline engine, the difference between the available voltage and the required ignition voltage.

ignition voltage – In a gasoline engine, the peak voltage required to produce a spark across the plug electrodes.

ignitor discharge—In switching tubes, a d-c glow discharge between the ignitor electrode and a suitably located electrode. It is used to facilitate radio-frequency ionization.

ignitor electrode—An electrode (which is partly immersed in the mercury-pool cathode of an ignitron) used to initiate conduction at the desired points in each cycle.

ignitor firing time—In switching tubes, the interval between application of a d-c voltage

to the ignitor electrode and start of current flow.

ignitor interaction—In a TR, pre-TR or attenuator tube, the difference between the insertion loss measured at a specified level of ignitor current and that measured at zero ignitor current.

ignitor leakage resistance—In a switching tube, the insulation resistance measured between the ignitor electrode terminal and the adjacent r-f electrode in the absence of an ignitor discharge.

ignitor oscillation—A relaxation type of oscillation in the ignitor circuit of a TR, pre-TR, or attenuator tube.

ignitor voltage drop—In switching tubes, the d-c voltage between the cathode and anode at a specified ignitor current.

ignitron – A type of mercury-pool rectifier which has only one anode. The arc is started for each cycle of operation by an ignitor which dips into the mercury pool. The mercury pool serves as the cathode of the rectifier. The ignitron is characterized by the ability to withstand tube currents several times as high as rated values for a few cycles.

Ignitron.

ignore—In a computer, a character code indicating that no action is to be taken.

IGY – Abbreviation for international geophysical year.

IHFM—Abbreviation for Institute of High-Fidelity Manufacturers, an association of manufacturers which publishes ratings and standards for high-fidelity equipment.

illegal character—A character which a computer system cannot properly use because the structure of the character does not agree with the machine logic. Such characters can be generated by machine failure or improper programming.

illuminance—The density of the luminous flux on a surface. It equals the flux divided by the area of the surface when uniformly illuminated.

illuminant-C—The reference white of color

television—i.e., light which most nearly matches average daylight.

illuminate—1. To expose to light. 2. In radar, to strike with a radar signal so that reflection returns the signal to the source for interpretation.

illumination—The density of luminous flux (amount of light) striking a surface.

illumination control—A photo-relay circuit that turns on artificial lighting when natural illumination decreases below a predetermined level.

illumination sensitivity—The output current of a photosensitive device divided by the incident illumination at constant electrode voltages.

illuminometer—A portable photometer for measuring the illumination on a surface.

ILS—Abbreviation for instrument landing system.

image—1. The instantaneous illusion of a picture on a flat surface. 2. The unused one of the two groups of sidebands generated in amplitude modulation.

image admittance—Reciprocal of image impedance.

image antenna—The imaginary counterpart of an actual antenna. For mathematical purposes it is assumed to be located below the ground and symmetrical with the actual antenna.

image-attenuation constant—The real part of the transfer constant.

image converter—A solid-state optoelectric device capable of changing the spectral characteristics of a radiant image. Examples of such changes are infrared-to-visible and X-ray-to-visible.

image-converter tube—*See* Image Tube.

Image dissector.

image dissector—A television camera tube in which the image is swept past an aperture in a series of 525 interlaced lines thirty times per second. Instead of a beam scanning the image, the entire image is scanned past the aperture, which "dissects" the image—hence, the name. (*Also see* Dissector Tube.)

image distortion—Failure of the reproduced image in a television receiver to resemble the original scene scanned by the camera.

image effect—An effect produced on the field of an antenna as the electromagnetic waves are reflected from the earth's surface.

image force—The force on a charge due to that charge or polarization which it induces on neighboring conductors or dielectrics.

image frequency—In heterodyne frequency converters, an undesired input frequency capable of producing the selected frequency by selecting one of the two sidebands produced by beating. The word "image" implies the mirrorlike symmetry of signal and image frequencies about the beating oscillator frequency or intermediate frequency, whichever is higher.

image-frequency rejection ratio—Of a superheterodyne receiver, the ratio of the response at the desired frequency to the response at the image frequency.

image iconoscope—An iconoscope in which greater sensitivity is obtained by separating the function of charge storage from that of photoelectric emission. An optical image is projected on a continuous photosensitive screen, and the electron emission from the back of this screen is focused electromagnetically onto a mosaic screen that is scanned by an electron beam as in the original emitron cathode-ray tube. The British term is super-emitron.

image impedance—The impedances which will simultaneously terminate all inputs and outputs of a transducer in such a way that at each of its inputs and outputs the impedances in both directions are equal.

image intensifier—A system for increasing the sensor response to a radiation pattern or image by interposing active elements between the sensor and the image, and supplying power to the active element. This is normally done by focusing the scene to be imaged on the photocathode of the tube, giving rise to a photoelectron pattern corresponding to the optical image. This pattern is accelerated and focused onto a phosphor which emits light to reproduce a visual image of the scene.

image interference—In a receiver, a response due to signals of a frequency removed from the desired signal by twice the intermediate frequency.

image-interference ratio—In a superheterodyne receiver, the effectiveness of the preselector in rejecting signals at the image frequency.

Image orthicon.

image orthicon—A camera tube in which a photoemitting surface produces an electron image and focuses it on one side of a separate storage target. The opposite side of the target is then scanned by low-velocity electrons to produce the output.

image phase constant—The imaginary part of the transfer constant.

image ratio—In a heterodyne receiver, the ratio of the image-frequency signal input to the desired signal input for identical amplitude outputs.

image rejection—The suppression of image-frequency signals in a superheterodyne receiver.

image response—The response of a heterodyne receiver to a signal that is separated by twice the intermediate frequency from the frequency to which the receiver is tuned. Unless there is some preselection, images will cause spurious unwanted responses when the spectrum occupied by a signal is greater than twice the frequency of the first i-f stage of the receiver.

image-transfer constant—*See* Transfer Constant.

image tube—Also called an image-converter tube. An electron tube which reproduces on its fluorescent screen an image of an irradiation pattern incident on its photosensitive surface.

immersion pyrometer — An instrument for determining molten-steel temperature and normally consisting of a platinum-platinum rhodium bimetal thermocouple junction and a recording device for transposing the millivoltage into degrees of temperature.

impact excitation—The starting of damped oscillations by a sudden surge, such as by a spark discharge.

impact predictor—A device which can determine, in real time, the point on the earth's surface where a ballistic missile will impact if thrust is instantaneously terminated.

impedance—The total opposition (i.e., resistance and reactance) a circuit offers to the flow of alternating current. It is measured in ohms, and its reciprocal is called admittance.

impedance angle — Angle of the impedance vector with respect to the resistance vector. Represents the phase angle between voltage and current.

impedance bridge — A device for measuring the combined resistance and reactance of a component part of a circuit.

impedance characteristic—A graph of impedance versus frequency of a circuit or component.

impedance coil—A coil in which its inductive reactance is used to hinder the flow of alternating current in or between circuits.

impedance compensator—An electric network used with a line or another network to give the impedance of the combination a certain characteristic over a desired frequency range.

impedance coupling—A method of coupling using an impedance as the coupling device, common to both the primary and secondary circuits. This type of coupling is usually limited to audio systems, where high gain and limited bandpass are required.

impedance drop—The vector sum of the resistance drop and the reactance drop. (For transformers, the resistance drop, the reactance drop, and the impedance drop are, respectively, the sum of the primary and secondary drops reduced to the same terms. They are usually expressed in percent of the secondary-terminal voltage.)

impedance irregularities—Breaks or abrupt changes which occur in an impedance-frequency curve when unlike sections of a transmission line are joined together or when there are irregularities on the line.

impedance matching—The connection across a source impedance of another impedance having the same magnitude and phase angle. If the source is a transmission line, reflection is thereby avoided.

impedance-matching transformer—A transformer used to match the impedance of a source and load.

impedance transformer—A transformer that transfers maximum energy from one circuit to another.

impedance triangle—A diagram consisting of a right triangle. The sides are proportional to the resistance and reactance in an a-c circuit, with the hypotenuse representing the impedance.

imperfect dielectric—A dielectric in which part of the energy required to establish its electric field is converted into heat instead of being returned to the electric system when the field is removed.

imperfection (of a crystalline solid)—Any deviation in structure from an ideal crystal (one which is perfectly periodic in structure and contains no foreign atoms).

implode—The inward bursting of a picture tube due to its high vacuum.

impregnated coils—Coils that have been permeated with an electric grade varnish or other protective material to protect them from mechanical vibration, handling, fungus, and moisture.

impregnation—The process of coating the insides of coils and closely packed electronic assemblies by dipping them into a liquid and letting it solidify.

impressed voltage—The voltage applied to a circuit or device.

improvement threshold—A characteristic of f-m radio receivers which determines the minimum r-f signal power required to overcome the inherent thermal noise. For increasing values of r-f power above this point, an improvement of signal-to-noise ratio is obtained.

impulse—A pulse that begins and ends within so short a time that it may be regarded mathematically as infinitesimal. The change produced in the medium, however, is generally of a finite amount. (*Also see* Pulse.)

impulse bandwidth — The area divided by the height of the voltage-response selectivity curve as a function of frequency. It is used in the calculation of broad-band interference.

impulse-driven clock—An electric clock in which the hands are moved forward at regular intervals by current impulses from a master clock.

impulse excitation—Also called shock excitation. A method of producing oscillatory current in which the duration of the impressed voltage is relatively short compared with that of the current produced.

impulse frequency—The number of pulse periods per second generated by the dial-pulse springs in a telephone as they rapidly open and close in response to the dialing of a digit.

impulse generator—1. Also called surge generator. An electric apparatus that produces high-voltage surges for testing insulators and for other purposes. 2. A device that generates a broad energy spectrum by means of a very narrow impulse. Usually generated by discharging a short coaxial or waveguide transmission line. The pulses are discrete and regularly spaced, and are generally variable at a repetition rate from a few pulses per second to a few thousand pulses per second. The output of an impulse generator is specified as the rms equivalent of the peak voltage in db above 1 microvolt per megahertz. 3. An oscillator circuit that generates electric impulses for synchronizing purposes in a television system.

impulse noise — Noise due to disturbances having abrupt changes and of short duration. (These noise impulses may or may not have systematic phase relationships. The noise is characterized by nonoverlapping transient disturbance. The same source may produce impulse noise in one system and random noise in a different system.)

impulse-noise generator — Equipment for generating repetitive pulses which provide random noise signals uniformly spread over a wide band of frequencies.

impulse ratio — The ratio of the flashover, sparkover, or breakdown voltage of an impulse to the crest value of the power-frequency flashover, sparkover, or breakdown voltage.

impulse relay—1. A relay that stores enough energy from a brief impulse to complete its operation after the impulse ends. 2. A relay that can distinguish between different types of impulses, operating on long or strong impulses, and not operating on short or weak ones. 3. An integrating relay.

impulse sealing—A heat-sealing technique in which a pulse of intense thermal energy is applied to the sealing area for a very short time, followed immediately by cooling. It is usually accomplished by using an r-f heated metal bar which is cored for water cooling, or is of such a mass that it will cool rapidly at ambient temperatures.

impulse separator — Normally called sync separator. In a television receiver, the circuit that separates the synchronizing impulses from the video information in the received signal.

impulse speed—The rate at which a telephone dial mechanism makes and breaks the circuit to transmit pulses.

impulse timer—A timing device electrically powered by a synchronous motor, featuring a mechanical stepping device which enables it to advance a predetermined number of degrees within a predetermined time interval, controlling a multiple number of circuits. Said circuits are controlled by individual cams which program their activity.

impulse train—*See* Pulse Train.

impulse transmission—The form of signaling used principally to reduce the effects of low-frequency interference. Impulses of either or both polarities are employed for transmission, to indicate the occurrence of transitions in the signals.

impulse-transmitting relay — A relay in which a set of contacts closes briefly when the relay changes from the energized to the de-energized position, or vice-versa.

impulse-type telemeter—A telemeter which employs the characteristics of intermittent electric signals, other than their frequency, as the translating means.

impurity—An atom that is foreign to the crystal in which it exists. Material added to a semiconductor crystal to produce excess electrons (a donor impurity) or excess holes (an acceptor impurity).

impurity density—The amount of impurity material diffused into a certain volume of semiconductor material used in manufacturing semiconductor devices.

impurity level—The energy level existing in a substance because of impurity atoms.

inaccuracy — 1. The difference between the input quantity applied to a measuring instrument and the output quantity indicated by that instrument. The inaccuracy of an instrument is equal to the sum of its instrument error and its uncertainty. 2. The term sometimes used to indicate the deviation from an indicated or recorded value or the measure of conformity to an accepted standard.

inactive leg—Within a transducer, an electrical element which does not change its electrical characteristics with the applied stimulus. Applied specifically to elements that complete a Wheatstone bridge in certain transducers.

in-band signaling—The transmission of signaling tones at some frequency or frequencies within the channel normally used for voice transmission.

incandescence—The state of a body with such a high temperature that it gives off light.

incandescent lamp — An electric lamp in which electric current flowing through a filament of resistance material heats the filament until it glows.

INCH—Acronym for INtegrated CHopper. It is a device designed to operate as a chopper, commutator, modulator, demodulator, or mixer, depending on circuit requirements.

inching—*See* Jogging.

incidence angle—The angle between an approaching light ray or emission and the perpendicular (normal) to the surface in the path of the ray.

incidental f-m—Also called residual f-m. The short-term jitter or undesired f-m deviation of a local oscillator. It limits resolution when it approaches the i-f bandwidth in magnitude.

incident field intensity—The field strength of a down-coming sky wave, not including the effects of earth reflections at the receiving location.

incident wave—In a medium of certain propagation characteristics, a wave which strikes a gap in the medium or strikes a medium having different propagation characteristics.

incipient failure — A degradation failure in its beginning stages.

inclination—The angle which a line, surface, or vector makes with the horizontal.

inclinometer—An instrument for measuring the magnetic inclination of the earth's magnetic field. It uses a magnetic needle that pivots vertically to indicate the inclination.

incoherent detection—Detection wherein the information contained in the phase of the carrier is discarded.

incoherent scattering — The disordered change in their direction of propagation when radio waves encounter matter.

incomplete sequencer relay — A device which returns the equipment to the normal, or off, position and locks it out if the normal starting, operating, or stopping sequence is not properly completed within a predetermined time.

Increductor.

increductor—A controllable inductor similar to a saturable reactor, except that it is capable of operating at high frequencies (e.g., up to 400 MHz).

increment—A small change in value.

incremental hysteresis loss — Losses in a magnetic material that has been subjected to a pulsating magnetizing force.

incremental induction—One half the algebraic difference between the maximum and minimum magnetic induction at a point in a material which has been subjected simultaneously to a polarizing and a varying magnetizing force.

incremental permeability — Ratio of the cyclic change in magnetic induction to the corresponding cyclic change in magnetizing force when the mean induction is other than zero.

incremental sensitivity—The smallest change that can be detected by a particular instrument in a quantity under observation.

incremental tuner—A television tuner in which antenna, r-f-amplifier and r-f-oscillator inductors are continuous or in small sections connected in series. Rotary switches, connected to taps on the inductors, provide the portion of total inductance required for a channel, or short-circuit all remaining inductance except that required for the channel.

independent failure—A failure which has no significant relationship to other failures in a given device and can occur without interaction with other component parts in the equipment.

independent load contacts—Contacts which can control electrical loads that must be isolated from the timer clutch solenoid and motor circuit.

independent variable—One of several voltages and currents chosen arbitrarily and considered to vary independently.

index counter—An odometer-type counter which shows the amount of tape that has been unreeled on a recorder. In this way, the operator is able to note the location of a particular selection on the tape.

indexing—In a computer, a technique of address modification that is often implemented by means of index registers.

indexing slots—*See* Polarizing Slots.

index of cooperation—In facsimile, the product of the diameter of the scanning drum multiplied by the number of scanning lines per inch.

index of modulation—The modulation factor.

index of refraction—Ratio of the speeds of light or other radiation in two different materials. This determines the amount the ray will be refracted or bent when passing from one material to the other, such as from air to water.

index register — In a computer, a register that holds a quantity which may be used for modifying addresses or for other purposes, as directed by the program.

indicating demand meter—A meter equipped with a scale over which a pointer is advanced to indicate maximum demand.

indicating fuse—A protective device placed in a telephone circuit to provide visual and audible indication of a fault in the line. It consists of a fuse, pilot lamp, relay, and buzzer. When a line fault blows the fuse, the lamp lights and the buzzer sounds.

indicating instrument—An instrument which visually indicates only the present value of the quantity being measured.

indicating lamp—A lamp which indicates the position of a device or the condition of a circuit.

indicating meter — A meter which gives a visual indication of only the present or short-time average value of the measured quantity.

Indicating meter.

indication—The display to the human senses of information concerning a quantity being measured.

indicator—An instrument that makes information available, but does not store it.

indicator gate—A rectangular voltage waveform applied to the grid or cathode circuit of an indicator cathode-ray tube to sensitize or desensitize the tube during the desired portion of the operating cycle.

indicator tube—An electron-beam tube which conveys useful information by the variation in cross section of the beam at a luminescent target.

indirect-acting recording instrument — An instrument in which the marking device is actuated by raising the level of measurement energy of the primary detector. This is done mechanically, electrically, electronically, photoelectrically, or by some other intermediate means.

indirect addressing—A method of computer cross reference in which one memory location indicates where the correct address of the main fact can be found.

indirect light—Light from an object which has no self-luminous properties. Instead, it reflects light from another source.

indirectly controlled variable — A variable that is related to and influenced by the directly controlled variable but is not directly measured for control.

indirectly heated cathode—Also called equipotential or unipotential cathode. A cathode which is heated by an independent heater.

indirectly heated thermistor—A thermistor which incorporates, as part of its composite structure, an electrical heater. A thermistor the body temperature of which in use is significantly higher than the temperature of its surrounding medium as a result of current passing through its heater.

indirect piezoelectricity — The production of a mechanical strain in a crystal by applying a voltage to it (as opposed to the more common piezoelectric effect of applying a strain to the crystal in order to produce a voltage).

indirect scanning — A television technique used in early mechanical systems, and today in the flying-spot scanning of films. A small beam of light is moved across the subject and then reflected to a battery of phototubes.

indirect wave—A wave reaching a given reception point by a path from the transmitting point other than the direct-line path between the two (e.g., a sky wave received after deflection from the ionosphere layers).

individual gap azimuth—In a magnetic-tape record or reproduce head stack, the angle of an individual gap relative to a line perpendicular to the precision milled mounting pads in a plane parallel to the surface of the tape.

indoor antenna—Any receiving antenna located inside a building but outside the receiver.

indoor transformer—A transformer which must be protected from the weather.

induced—Produced by the influence of an electric or magnetic field.

induced charge—An electrostatic charge produced in one object by the electric field surrounding a nearby object.

induced current—1. The current that flows in a conductor which is moved perpendicularly to a magnetic field, or which is subjected to a magnetic field of varying intensity. The former takes place in an induction-motor rotor; the latter, in the secondary winding of a transformer. 2. In induction heating, the current that flows in a conductor when a varying electromagnetic field is applied.

induced electromotive force — Represented by E and is proportional to the rate of change of magnetic flux through the circuit $(d\phi/dt)$.

induced environment — The temperatures, vibrations, shocks, accelerations, pressures, and other conditions imposed on a system due to the operation or handling of the system.

induced failure — A failure that is basically caused by a condition or phenomenon external to the item that fails.

induced voltage—The voltage produced in a conductor when the conductor is moved up and down through the magnetic field of a second conductor, or when the field varies in intensity and cuts across the first conductor. Even though there is no mechanical coupling between the two conductors, the one producing the field will produce a voltage in the other.

inductance—In a circuit, the property which opposes any change in the existing current. Inductance is present only when the current is changing.

inductance bridge—An instrument, similar to a Wheatstone bridge, for measuring an unknown inductance by comparing it with a known inductance.

inductance coil—*See* Inductor.

inductance-tube modulation—A method of modulation employed in frequency-modulated transmitters. An oscillator control tube acts as a variable inductance in parallel with the tank circuit of the radio-frequency oscillator tube. As a result, the oscillator frequency varies in step with the audio-frequency voltage applied to the grid of the oscillator control tube.

induction—1. The establishment of an electric charge of a magnetic field in a substance by the proximity of an electrified source, a magnet, or a magnetic field. 2. The setup of an electromotive force and current in a conductor by variation of the magnetic field affecting the conductor.

induction brazing—The electric brazing process in which heat is produced by an induced current.

induction coil—1. A device for changing direct current into high-voltage alternating current. Its primary coil contains relatively few turns of heavy wire; and its secondary coil, wound over the primary, contains many turns of fine wire. Interruption of the direct current in the primary by a vibrating-contact arrangement induces a high voltage in the secondary.

induction compass—A compass in which the indications are produced by the current generated in a coil revolving in the magnetic field of the earth.

induction-conduction heater—A heating device through which electric current is conducted but is restricted by induction to a preferred path.

induction density—*See* Flux Density.

induction factor—In an alternating current circuit, the ratio between that element of the current which does no work and the total strength of the current.

induction field—1. That portion of the electromagnetic field of a transmitting antenna which acts as if it were permanently associated with the antenna, and into which energy is alternately stored and removed. 2. The electromagnetic field of a coil carrying alternating current, responsible for the voltage induced by that coil in itself or in a nearby coil.

induction frequency converter—A slip-ring induction machine driven by an external source of mechanical power. Its primary circuits are connected to a source of electric energy having a fixed frequency. The energy delivered by its secondary circuits is proportionate in frequency to the relative speed of the primary magnetic field and the secondary member.

induction furnace—A furnace heated by electromagnetic induction.

induction hardening—The process of hardening the surface of a casting by heating it above the transformation range by electrical induction, followed by rapid cooling.

induction heating—The method of producing heat by subjecting a material to a variable electromagnetic field. Internal losses in the material then cause it to heat up.

induction instrument—An instrument operated by the reaction between the magnetic flux set up by one or more currents in fixed windings and the currents set up by electromagnetic induction in movable conductive parts.

induction motor—An alternating-current motor in which the primary winding (usually the stator) is connected to the power source and induces a current into a polyphase secondary or squirrel-cage secondary winding (usually the rotor).

induction-motor meter—A meter containing a rotor that moves in reaction to a magnetic field and the currents induced into it.

induction noise—The noise—other than thump, flutter, cross fire or cross talk—produced when two circuits are inductively coupled together.

induction-resistance welding—Welding in which electromagnetic induction alone causes the heating current to flow in the parts being welded.

induction-ring heater—A core-type induction heater adapted principally for heating round objects. The core is open or can be taken off to facilitate linking the charge.

induction speaker—A speaker in which the current that reacts with the steady magnetic field is induced into the moving member.

induction-voltage regulator—A device having a primary winding in shunt, and a secondary winding in series with a circuit for gradually adjusting the voltage or the phase relation of the circuit by changing the relative position of the exciting and series windings of the regulator.

inductive—Pertaining to inductance or to the inducing of a voltage through mutual or electrostatic induction.

inductive circuit—A circuit with more inductive than capacitive reactance.

inductive coupling—The association of two or more circuits solely by the mutual inductance between them.

inductive feedback—1. The transfer of energy from the plate circuit to the grid circuit of a vacuum tube by induction. 2. The transfer of energy from the output circuit to the input circuit of an amplifying device through an inductor or inductive coupling.

inductive interference—Interference produced in communication systems by induced voltages within the system.

inductive kick—The voltage, many times higher than the impressed voltage, produced by the collapsing field in a coil when the current through it is abruptly cut off.

inductive load—Also called lagging load. A

load that is predominantly inductive, so that the alternating load current lags behind the alternating voltage of the load.

inductively coupled circuit—A network with two meshes having only mutual inductance in common.

inductive microphone—*See* Inductor Microphone.

inductive neutralization—Also called shunt or coil neutralization. A method of neutralizing an amplifier, whereby the equal and opposite susceptance of an inductor cancels the feedback susceptance caused by inter-element capacitance.

inductive pickup—Signals generated in a circuit or conductor due to mutual inductance between it and a disturbing source.

inductive reactance—The opposition to the flow of alternating or pulsating current by the inductance of a circuit. It is measured in ohms, and its symbol is X_L. It is equal to 2π times the frequency in hertz times the inductance in henrys.

inductive transducer—A transducer in which changes in inductance convey the stimulus information.

inductive transduction—The conversion of the measurand into a change in the self-inductance of a single coil.

inductive tuning—A method of tuning a radio by moving a core into and out of a coil to vary the inductance.

inductive winding—A coil through which a varying current is sent to give it an inductance.

inductor—Also called inductance or retardation coil. A conductor used for introducing inductance into an electric circuit. The conductor is wound into a spiral, or coil, to increase its inductive intensity.

inductor microphone—Also called inductive microphone. A microphone in which the sound waves move a conductor back and forth, cutting magnetic lines of force and producing an electrical output of the same frequency and proportional to the amplitude of the sound waves.

inductor-type synchronous motor — A type of synchronous motor having field magnets that are fixed in magnetic position relative to the armature conductors, the torques being produced by forces between the stationary poles and salient rotor teeth. Such motors usually have permanent-magnet field excitation, are built in fractional-horsepower frames, and operate at low speeds (300 revolutions per minute or less).

inductosyn—An extremely precise transducer based upon the magnetic circuit of a conductor deposited on glass for stability, and operated at a relatively high frequency. Extremely accurate, but requires much auxiliary equipment (Farrand Controls Inc.).

industrial radio services — Radiocommunication services essential to, operated by, and for the sole use of those enterprises which require radiocommunications in order to function efficiently.

industrial television — Television used for remote viewing of manufacturing or assembling processes, usually over cables rather than through the air.

industrial timer—A timing device, impulse or constant-speed type, used in industrial applications other than the appliance industry.

industrial tube—A vacuum tube designed for industrial electronic equipment.

inelastic collision—Collision resulting in excitation of a molecule.

inertance—Acoustical equivalent of inductance.

inert gas—*See* Noble Gas.

inertia—The tendency of an object at rest to remain at rest, or of a moving object to continue moving in the same direction and at the same speed, unless disturbed by an outside force.

inertial guidance—The automatic guidance system used in missiles and satellites to make them follow a predetermined trajectory without assistance from the ground. Gyroscopes, accelerometers, and possibly a gyrostabilized platform are used.

inertial navigation—A guidance technique in which air-frame acceleration is first measured and then integrated twice with respect to time in order to determine the distance traveled. External aids such as radio and radar are not necessary. The acceleration or deceleration of the air frame is measured continuously with accelerometers oriented in some convenient frame of reference, usually corresponding to the earth's north-south, east-west coordinates.

inertia relay—A relay having added weights or other modifications that increase its moment of inertia and either slow it or cause it to continue in motion after the energizing force is removed.

inertia switch—A switch capable of sensing acceleration, shock, or vibration.

infant mortality—The occurrence of premature catastrophic-type failures at a rate substantially greater than that observed during life prior to wearout.

infant-mortality period — *See* Early-Failure Period.

inferential—The kind of instrumentation, especially its signal source, in which there is sampling of an entirely different quantity from the one of interest, upon assuming that they vary in perfect proportion. Linearity or a perfectly repeatable relationship between the two is inferred, for the sake of a more convenient signal-source arrangement.

infinite—Boundless; having no limits whatsoever.

infinite baffle—A speaker enclosure with no openings through which sound waves can travel from the front of the cone to the back.

infinite-impedance detector—A detector circuit in which the load is a resistor connected in parallel with an r-f bypass capacitor between the cathode and ground. Since the grid is always negative with respect to the cathode, the tube presents an infinite impedance to the input.

infinite line—A transmission line with the same characteristics as an ordinary line that is infinitely long.

infinite resolution—The capability of a device to provide continuous output over its entire range.

infinitesimal — Immeasurably small; approaching zero.

infinity—1. A hypothetical amount larger than any assignable amount. 2. A number larger than any number a computer can store in any register.

inflection point—The point where a curve changes direction.

information—In computing, the basic data and/or program entered into the system.

information channel—The transmission and intervening equipment involved in the transfer of information in a given direction between two terminals. An information channel includes the modulator and demodulator and any error-control equipment irrespective of its location, as well as the backward channel, when provided.

information gate — A circuit that permits information or data pulses from passing when the circuit is triggered by an external source.

information handling — The storing and processing of information and its transmission from the source to the user. Information handling excludes the creation and use of information.

information rate—In computers, the minimum number of binary digits per second required to specify the source messages.

information rate changer — A device that speeds up the playback of tape-recorded speech without pitch change or deterioration of characteristic resonances. This is accomplished by rotating the playback head in the direction of tape travel.

information retrieval — A method for cataloging vast amounts of data related to one field of interest so that any part or all of this data can be called out at any time with accuracy and speed.

infrared—A form of electromagnetic radiation similar to visible light and radio waves. It is generated by thermal agitation and radiated by everything with a temperature above absolute zero (−273°C). High temperatures increase the thermal agitation. Hence, the hotter the object, the greater the infrared radiation. Abbreviated IR.

infrared counter-countermeasures—Action taken to employ infrared radiation equipment and systems in spite of enemy measures to counter their use.

infrared countermeasures—Action taken to reduce the effectiveness of enemy equipment employing infrared radiation.

infrared detector — A transducer which is sensitive to invisible infrared radiation (wavelength between 0.75 and 1000 microns),

Infrared spectrum.

usually using a semiconductor, thermocouple bolometer, or pneumatic (pressure) device to detect the radiation.

infrared guidance—A system using infrared heat resources for reconnaissance of targets or for navigation.

infrared homing—A type of missile homing in which the guidance system tracks the target from the infrared radiation it emits.

infrared light—Light rays just below the red end of the visible spectrum.

infrared optics — Lenses, prisms, and other optical elements for use with infrared radiation (radiation with a wavelength between 0.75 and 1000 microns).

infrared radiation — Heat radiation with wavelengths slightly longer than those of visible red (i.e., 0.75 to 1000 microns).

infrared sources—Emitters of radiation with a wavelength between 0.75 and 1000 microns.

infrared waves—Also called black light. Invisible waves longer than the longest visible red light waves but shorter than radiofrequency waves.

infrared window—A region of relatively high transmission in the infrared-frequency range.

infrasonic—Pertaining to frequencies below the range of human hearing, hence below about 15 hertz. Formerly called subsonic.

infrasonic frequency—Also called subsonic

Infrared guidance.

frequency. A frequency below the audio range. Infrasonic vibrations can be felt but not heard.

inharmonic frequency—A frequency which is not a rational multiple of another frequency.

inherent delay—Delay between the insertion of information into a unit and presentation of the information at the output. Delay is usually inserted into the crt vertical amplifier of pulse analyzers to allow the leading edge of the signal triggering the sweep to be seen.

inherent interference—A type of electromagnetic interference generated within a receiver by thermal agitation, shot effect, and nonlinear impedance.

inherited error—In a computer, the error in the initial values, especially that error accumulated from prior steps in a step-by-step integration.

inhibit gate—A circuit that provides an output when the inputs differ and only for one of these combinations. This function can be implemented directly or by using any previous gate, plus an inverter.

inhibiting input—A computer gate input which, if in its prescribed state, prevents any output which might otherwise occur.

inhibition gate—A gate circuit used as a switch and placed in parallel with the circuit it is controlling.

inhibit pulse—A computer drive pulse that tends to prevent certain drive pulses from reversing the flux of a magnetic cell.

initial actuation time—The time of the first closing of a previously open contact of a relay or the first opening of a previously closed contact.

initial contact chatter—That chatter caused by vibration produced by opening or closing the contacts in a relay themselves, as by contact impact in closure.

initial differential capacitance—The differential capacitance of a nonlinear capacitor when the capacitor voltage is zero.

initial drain—The current supplied at nominal voltage by a cell or battery.

initial element—*See* Primary Detector.

initial erection—The mode of operation of a vertical gyro in which the gyro is being erected or slaved initially. The initial erection rate is usually relatively fast.

initial failure—The first failure that occurs in use.

initial inverse voltage—Of a rectifier tube, the peak-inverse anode voltage immediately following the conducting period.

initial ionizing event—Also called primary ionizing event. An ionizing event that initiates a tube count.

initializing—The preliminary steps in arranging those instructions and data in a computer memory that are not to be repeated.

initial permeability—Permeability at a field density approaching zero.

initial reversible capacitance—In a nonlinear capacitor, the reversible capacitance at a constant bias voltage of zero.

initial-velocity current—A current which flows between an electrode, such as the grid of a vacuum tube, and its cathode as a result of electrons thrown off from the cathode because of heat alone. Their velocity is sufficient to allow the electrons to reach the grid unaided by an accelerating field.

injected lasers—*See* Diode Laser.

injection grid—A vacuum-tube grid that controls the electron stream without causing interaction between the screen and control grids. In some superheterodyne receivers, the injection grid introduces the oscillator signal into the mixer stage.

injection laser—A semiconductor diode in which radiation is produced as electrons recombine with holes in the junction region. For coherent emission, the current density must exceed a certain threshold value, commonly about 10,000 amperes per square centimeter for gallium-arsenide diodes.

injector—An electrode on a spacistor.

ink-mist recording—Also called ink-vapor recording. In facsimile, electromechanical recording in which particles of an ink mist are deposited directly onto the record sheet.

ink recorder—The ink-filled pen or capillary tube that produces a graphic record.

ink recording—A type of mechanical facsimile recording in which an inked helix marks the record sheet.

ink-vapor recording—*See* Ink-Mist Recording.

inleads—Those portions of the electrodes of a device that pass through an envelope or housing.

in-line heads—*See* Stacked Heads.

in-line tuning—The method of tuning the intermediate-frequency strip of a superheterodyne receiver in which all the intermediate-frequency amplifier stages are made resonant to the same frequency.

inorganic electrolyte—A solution that conducts electricity due to the presence of ions of substances not of organic origin.

in phase—Two waves of the same frequency that pass through their maximum and minimum values of like polarity at the same instant, are said to be in phase.

in-phase portion of the chrominance signal—That portion of the chrominance signal having the same phase as, or exactly the opposite phase from, that of the subcarrier modulated by the I-signal. This portion of the chrominance signal may lead or lag the quadrature portion by 90 electrical degrees.

input—1. The current, voltage, power, or other driving force applied to a circuit or device. 2. The terminals or other places where current, voltage, power, or driving force may be applied to a circuit or device.

input admittance—1. The reciprocal of input impedance. 2. The admittance between the input terminals with the outputs shorted together.

input area—In a computer, the area of internal storage into which data from external storage is transferred.

input block—In a computer, a section of the internal storage reserved for receiving and processing input data.

input capacitance—The sum of the direct capacitances between the control grid and cathode (and any other electrodes operated at the alternating potential of the cathode). This is not the effective capacitance, which is a function of the impedances of the associated circuits.

input common-mode rejection ratio—1. The ratio of the change in input voltage to the corresponding change in output voltage, divided by the open-loop voltage gain. 2. The ratio of the full differential voltage gain to the common-mode voltage gain.

input equipment—The equipment that introduces information into a computer.

input error voltage—The error voltage appearing across the input terminals of an operational amplifier when a feedback loop is applied around the amplifier.

input extender—A high-speed diode array used in a logic circuit when increased fan-in capability is required.

input gap—Also called buncher gap. In a microwave tube, the gap where the initial velocity modulation of the electron stream occurs.

input impedance—The impedance a transducer presents to a source.

input impedance of a transmission line—The impedance between the input terminals with the generator disconnected.

input-output devices—Computer hardware by which data is entered into a computer or by which the finished computations are recorded for immediate or future use. Abbreviated I/O.

input-power rating—Also called coil rating. A statement of the allowable voltage, current, or power to the actuating element of a relay beyond which unsatisfactory performances will occur.

input recorder—Any device which makes a record of an input electrical signal.

input register—In a computer, the register of internal storage able to accept information from outside the computer at one speed and supply the information to the computer calculating unit at another, usually much greater, speed.

input resonator—The buncher resonator in a velocity-modulated tube. It modifies the velocity of the electrons in the beam.

input transformer—A transformer that transfers energy from an alternating-voltage source to the input of a circuit or device. It usually provides the correct impedance match, too.

input uncertainty—In an operational amplifier, the algebraic sum of all the factors, including environmental and time effects, that contribute to the nonideal behavior of the input circuit.

input unit—In a computer, the unit that takes information from outside the computer into the computer.

input voltage offset—The d-c potential difference between the two inputs of a differential amplifier when the potential between the output terminals is zero.

input winding—*See* Signal Winding.

inquiry station—In a computer, a direct method of reading data from or entering data into storage.

inquiry unit—A device used to extract a quick reply to a random question regarding information in a computer storage.

inrush current—In a solenoid or coil, the steady-state current drawn from the line with the armature in its maximum open position.

insert core—An iron core used generally for adjusting an inductor to a fixed frequency. It consists of a threaded metal insert molded or cemented into one or both ends of the core.

insert earphones—Small earphones which fit partially inside the ear.

insertion gain—The gain resulting from the insertion of a transducer in a transmission system is the ratio of the power delivered to that part of the system following the transducer to the power delivered to that same part before insertion. (If more than one component is involved in the input or output, the particular component used must be specified. This ratio is usually expressed in decibels.)

insertion loss—1. The difference between the power received at the load before and after the insertion of apparatus at some point in the line. 2. Ratio in decibels of the power received at the load before and after insertion of the apparatus.

insertion phase shift—The change in phase of an electric structure when inserted into a transmission system.

inside lead—*See* Start Lead.

inside spider—A flexible device placed inside a voice coil to center it with the pole pieces of a speaker.

inspection chamber—In a spectrophotometer, the part in which the solution to be tested is placed for analysis.

inspectoscope—An instrument for viewing quartz crystals, while they are immersed in oil, to determine mechanical faults, the approximate direction of the optical axis, and regions of optical twinning.

instability—The measure of the fluctuations or irregularities in the performance of a device, system, or parameter.

instantaneous automatic gain control—In radar, an automatic gain control which instantly responds to variations in the mean clutter level and thereby reduces it.

instantaneous automatic volume control—A fast-acting automatic volume-control circuit installed in some radar receivers as an anticlutter device.

instantaneous companding — Companding which varies the effective gain in response to instantaneous values of the signal wave.

instantaneous contacts—Contacts which are actuated immediately when a starting signal is applied to a timer.

instantaneous disc—A blank recording disc that can be played back on a phonograph immediately after being cut on a recorder.

instantaneous frequency—The rate at which the angle of a wave changes when the wave is a function of time. If the angle is measured in radians, the frequency in hertz is the rate of change of the angle divided by 2π.

instantaneous overcurrent relay — Also called rate-of-rise relay. A device which functions instantaneously on an excessive value of current, or on an excessive rate of current rise, thus indicating a fault in the apparatus of the circuit being protected.

instantaneous power—The power at the points where an electric circuit enters a region. It is equal to the rate at which the circuit is transmitting electrical energy into the region.

instantaneous power output—The rate at which energy is delivered to a load at a particular instant.

instantaneous recording—A recording intended for direct reproduction without further processing.

instantaneous sampling—The process of obtaining a sequence of instantaneous values of a wave. These values are called instantaneous samples.

instantaneous sound pressure—The total instantaneous pressure at a certain point, minus the static pressure at that point. The most common unit is the microbar.

instantaneous speech power—The rate at which the speaker is radiating sound energy at any given instant.

instantaneous value—The magnitude, at any particular instant, of a varying value.

instruction—Information which, when properly coded and introduced as a unit into a digital computer, causes the computer to perform one or more of its operations. An instruction commonly includes one or more addresses.

instructional constant — Also called pseudo instruction. In a computer, data stored in the program or instructional area which will be used only as a test constant.

instruction code—The list of symbols, names, and definitions of the instructions which are intelligible to a given computer or computing system.

instruction counter—*See* Control Counter.

instruction modification — A change in the operation-code portion of a computer instruction or command such that, if the routine containing the instruction or command is repeated, the computer will perform a different operation.

instruction register — In a computer, the register that temporarily stores the instruction currently being performed by the control unit of the computer.

instrument—A device capable of measuring, recording, and/or controlling.

instrument approach—A blind landing—i.e., solely by navigational instruments, without visual reference to the terrain.

instrument-approach system — In navigation, a system furnishing vertical and horizontal guidance to aircraft during descent. Touchdown requires some other guidance.

instrumentation—The introduction and use of devices of any kind into a process for the purpose of obtaining more precise data (improving quality) or for obtaining information not otherwise available. Typically accomplished by generating, transmitting, displaying, controlling, correlating, and recording signals.

instrument chopper—A vibrating switch used for modulating, demodulating, and switching d-c or low-frequency a-c information in instrumentation. It is driven synchronously from an a-c or pulsating d-c source. The driven switching circuit is designed for low-level (0- to 10-volt) signal information.

instrument error—The inaccuracy of an instrument.

instrument flight—A blind flight—i.e., one in which the pilot controls the path and altitude of the aircraft solely by instrument.

instrument lamp—A light that illuminates or irradiates an instrument.

instrument-landing station—A special radio station for aiding in landing aircraft.

instrument-landing system — Abbreviated

ILS. A radionavigation system intended to aid aircraft in landing. It provides lateral and vertical guidance, including distance from the landing point.

instrument multiplier—*See* Voltage-Range Multiplier.

instrument relay—A relay which operates on the principles employed in such electrical measuring instruments as the electrodynamometer, iron-vane, and D'Arsonval meters.

instrument shunt—An internal or external resistor connected in parallel with the circuit of an instrument to extend its current range.

instrument switch—A switch disconnecting an instrument or transferring it from one circuit or phase to another.

Instrument transformers.

instrument transformer — A transformer which reproduces, in its secondary circuit, the primary current (or voltage) with its phase relationship substantially preserved, suitable for utilization in measurement, control, or protective devices.

instrument-transformer correction factor —The factor by which a wattmeter reading must be multiplied to correct for the effect of the instrument-transformer ratio correction factor and phase angle.

insulated—Separated from other conducting surfaces by a nonconductive material offering a high, permanent resistance to the passage of current and disruptive discharge.

insulated carbon resistor—A carbon resistor encased in fiber, plastic, or other insulation.

insulated clip—A clip terminating in an insulated eye through which flexible cords or wires may be run and supported.

insulated enclosure—A special shielded enclosure design providing insulation against weather or providing maximum temperature stability. Usually prefabricated as an exterior building panel in modular construction.

insulated-substrate monolithic circuit—An intergrated circuit which may be either an all-diffused device or a compatible structure so constructed that the components within the silicon substrate are insulated from one another by a layer of silicon dioxide, instead of the reverse-biased PN junctions used for isolation in other techniques.

insulated wire—A conductor covered with a nonconductive material.

insulating material — A material on or

through which essentially no current will flow. It is used to confine the flow of current within a conductor or to eliminate the shock hazard of a bare conductor.

insulating tape — Tape that is wrapped around joints in insulated wires or cables. It is impregnated with an insulating material and covered with adhesive on one side.

insulating varnish—A varnish applied to coils and windings to improve their insulation (and, at times, their mechanical rigidity).

insulation—A nonconductive material that prevents the leakage of electricity from a conductor, provides mechanical spacing or support, or protects against accidental contact.

insulation rating — The dielectric-strength and insulation-resistance values required to ensure satisfactory performance.

insulation resistance—1. The ratio of the voltage applied between two electrodes in contact with a specific insulator to the total current between the electrodes. 2. The ratio of the direct-current voltage applied to the terminals of a capacitor and the resulting leakage current after the initial charging current has ceased. It includes both the volume and surface resistance. Industrial specifications usually call for a certain minimum value (several thousand megohms) determined with a specific voltage applied.

insulation system—All of the insulation materials used to insulate a particular electrical or electronic product.

insulator—1. A material of such extremely low conductivity that, in effect, no current flows through it. 2. A high-resistance device that supports or separates conductors to prevent a flow of current between them or to other objects.

insulator arcing ring—A circular or oval metal part placed at one or both ends of an insulator to prevent current from arcing over and damaging it and/or the conductor.

insulator arc-over—The flow of power current over an insulator in the form of an arc following a surface discharge.

insulazing—*See* Surface Insulation.

insulectrics — The science encompassing insulating materials in electrical insulation.

integer—A whole number, not fractional or mixed (e.g., 1, 2, 9, 100, etc.—not 1.1 or ½).

integral-cavity, reflex-klystron oscillator—A reflex-klystron oscillator in which tuning is accomplished by changing the physical dimensions of the resonant cavity. It is usually referred to as a diaphragm- or grid-gap-tuned klystron, since a flexible diaphragm is used to change the cavity dimension, i.e., the gap between the cavity grids.

integral circuit packages—Microcircuits assembled from discrete components and all circuits created essentially in an active or passive substrate.

integral-external–cavity reflex oscillator—A reflex-klystron oscillator in which a fixed

247

internal cavity is tightly coupled to a permanently attached external cavity. Tuning is achieved by varying a reactance probe in the external cavity.

integral-horsepower motor—A motor which is built into a frame and has a continuous rating of one horsepower.

integral resistor — An internal or external resistor preconnected to the electrical element and forming an integral part of the cup assembly to provide a desired electrical characteristic of a precision potentiometer.

integrated amplifier — An audio unit containing both a preamplifier and a power amplifier on one chassis.

integrated circuit—A combination of interconnected circuit elements inseparably associated on or within a continuous substrate. (*Also see* Monolithic Integrated Circuit, Multichip Integrated Circuit, Film Integrated Circuit *and* Hybrid Integrated Circuit.) To further define the nature of an integrated circuit, additional modifiers may be prefixed. Examples are: dielectric isolated monolithic integrated circuit, beamlead monolithic integrated circuit, or silicon chip-tantalum thin-film hybrid integrated circuit.

integrated-circuit array — Multiple integrated circuits formed on a common substrate and electrically interconnected during fabrication.

integrated component — A number of electrical elements comprising a single structure which cannot be divided without destroying its stated electronic function.

integrated data processing — A method of transforming disjointed and repetitive paperwork tasks into a correlated and mechanized production of information for any purpose.

integrated electronics—That portion of electronic art and technology in which the interdependence of material, device, circuit, and system-design considerations is especially significant; more specifically, that portion of the art dealing with integrated circuits.

integrated equipment components — Integrated-circuit chips which contain a complete logic function. Abbreviated IEC's.

integrated morphology — The structural characterization of an electronic component in which the identity of the current or signal modifying areas, patterns, or volumes has become lost in the integration of electronic materials, in contrast to an assembly of devices performing the same function.

integrating circuit—*See* Integrator.

integrating meter—A meter which adds up (integrates) the electrical energy used over a period of time. An ordinary electric watt-hour meter is an example.

integrating photometer — A photometer which, with a single reading, indicates the average candlepower from a source in all directions or at all angles in a single plane.

integrating relay—A relay that sums up the inputs of voltage or current supplied to it and opens or closes its contacts in response to the input so integrated.

integrating-sphere densitometer—A photoelectric instrument that measures the density of motion-picture film or its sound track.

integrator (in electronic computers)—1. A device with an output proportionate to the integral of the input signal. 2. In certain digital machines, a device that numerically approximates the mathematical process of integration. 3. Also called an integrating network or circuit. A transducer with an output waveform that is the time integral of its input waveform.

intelligence bandwidth—The total audio (or video)frequency bandwidths of one or more channels.

intelligence sample—Part of a signal taken as evidence of the quality of the whole.

intelligence signal—Any signal which conveys information (e.g., voice, music, code, or television).

intelligibility—*See* Articulation.

intensifier electrode—Also called post-accelerating electrode. In some types of electrostatic cathode-ray tubes, an electrode which permits additional acceleration of the electron beam after it has been deflected. This electrode permits greater intensity of the trace without materially reducing the deflection sensitivity of the tube.

intensifying screen — A thin fluorescent screen placed next to a photographic plate to increase the effect of radiation on the plate.

intensitometer—Also called a dosage meter or dosimeter. An instrument that estimates the amount of X-ray radiation, for determining the duration of exposure during X-ray pictures or therapy.

intensity—1. The strength of a quantity. 2. The relative strength, or amplitude, of electric, magnetic, or vibrational energy. 3. The brilliance of an image on the screen of a cathode-ray tube.

intensity control — Used with cathode-ray tubes to control the intensity of the electron beam and hence the amount of light generated by the fluorescent screen. Generally, the grid bias of the tube is regulated.

intensity level—Ratio of the intensity of the

$$E_O = \frac{1}{T}\int^T E_I dT$$

$$(T = RC)$$

No amplification.   Amplification.   Formula.

Integrating circuits.

sound to a reference intensity of a free plane wave of 1 microwatt per square centimeter under normal conditions. Commonly expressed in decibels.

intensity modulation — The process and/or effect of varying the electron-beam current in a cathode-ray tube, resulting in varying brightness or luminance of the trace. *Also see* Z-Axis Modulation.

intensity of radiation—The radiant energy emitted in a specified direction per unit time, per unit area of surface, per unit solid angle.

interaction—The effects two or more parts, components, etc., have on each other while each is performing a function.

interaction cross talk—Cross talk resulting from mutual coupling between two paths by means of a third path. For example, if a signal on pair 1 is coupled to pair 2, and then coupled from pair 2 to pair 3, where it is measured it is known as interaction cross talk.

interaction loss (of a transducer) — Expressed in decibels, it equals 20 times the logarithm (to the base *10*) of the scalar value of the reciprocal of the interaction factor.

interaction space—In an electronic tube, the region where the electrons interact with an alternating electromagnetic field.

interaxis error — The deviation from 90° perpendicularity of one set of resolver windings when excitation is applied to one of the other windings. For rotor interaxis error one stator winding is excited; for stator interaxis error one rotor winding is excited.

interbase current — In a junction tetrode transistor, the current that flows from one base connection to the other through the base region.

interblock space—*See* Inter-Record Gap.

intercarrier noise suppression—The means of suppressing the noise resulting from increased gain when a high-gain receiver with automatic volume control is tuned between stations. The suppression circuit automatically blocks the audio-frequency output of the receiver when there is no signal at the second detector.

intercarrier sound system—A television receiving system in which use of the picture carrier and the associated sound-channel carrier produces an intermediate frequency equal to the difference between the two carrier frequencies. This intermediate frequency is frequency-modulated in accordance with the sound signal.

intercellular massage—The ultrasonic stimulation of body cells. Sometimes called micromassage.

intercept receiver—Also called search receiver. A specially calibrated receiver which can be tuned over a wide frequency range in order to detect and measure enemy r-f signals.

intercept service—In a telephone system, a

service provided to subscribers whereby calls to disconnected stations or dead lines are either routed to an intercept operator for explanation or the calling party receives a distinctive tone signal to indicate that he has made such a call.

intercharacter space — In telegraphy, the space between characters of a word. It is equal to three unit lengths.

intercom—*See* Intercommunication System.

intercommunicating system — Also called intercom. A two-way communication system without a central switchboard, usually limited to a single vehicle, building, or plant area. Stations may or may not be equipped to originate a call, but can answer any call.

interconnecting wire—Wires used for connections between subassemblies, panels, chassis, and remotely mounted devices. Does not necessarily apply to the internal connections of these units.

interconnection—1. Also called tie line. A transmission line connecting two electric systems or networks and permitting energy to be transferred in either direction. Larger interconnections are often called interties, giant ties, or regional interconnections. 2. Also called intraconnection. The physical wiring between components (outside a module), between modules, between units, or between larger portions of a system or systems.

interconnection diagram—Diagram showing the identity of all units in a piece of electronic equipment and the connections between them.

interconnections (microelectronic)—Those conductors and connections which are not in continuous integral contact with the substrate or circuit elements of an integrated circuit.

interconnection system—The electrical and mechanical interconnection of any one or all of the six levels of interconnections generally common to electronic equipment. The six levels of interconnection are: intramodule, module to motherboard, intramotherboard, motherboard to back panel, backpanel wiring, and input/output.

interdigital magnetron—A magnetron with anode segments around the cathode. Alternate segments are connected together at one end, and remaining segments at the opposite end.

interelectrode capacitance—The capacitance between certain electrodes of an electron tube.

interelectrode coupling—Capacitive feedback from the plate of a tube to the grid. In triodes, this limits the maximum amplification possible without starting oscillation.

interelectrode leakage—The undesired current which flows between elements not normally connected in any way.

interelectrode transit time—The time required for an electron to travel between two electrodes.

interelement capacitance—The capacitance caused by the PN junctions between the regions of a transistor and measured between the external leads of the transistor.

interexchange channel—A channel connecting two different exchange areas.

interface—The junction or the points within or between systems or subsystems where matching or accommodation must be properly achieved in order to make their operation compatible with the successful operation of all other functional entities.

interface resistance—*See* Cathode Interface.

interfacial connection—In a printed-circuit board, a conductor that connects conductive patterns on opposite faces of the base.

interference — Any electrical or electromagnetic disturbance, phenomenon, signal, or emission, man-made or natural, which causes or can cause undesired response, malfunctioning, or degradation of the electrical performance of electrical and electronic equipment.

interference eliminator—A device designed for the purpose of reducing or eliminating interference.

interference fading — Fading produced by different wave components traveling slightly different paths in arriving at the receiver.

interference filter—A device added between a source of man-made interference and a radio receiver to attenuate or eliminate noise signals. It generally contains a combination of capacitance and inductance.

interference guard band—*See* Guard Band.

interference pattern—1. The resultant space distribution of pressure, particle velocity, or energy flux when progressive waves of the same frequency and kind are superimposed. 2. The pattern produced on a radar scope by interference signals.

interference-rejection unit — A tunable filter or wave trap capable of being adjusted to reject any frequency within the i-f passband of a receiver while allowing the remainder of the passband curve to remain intact. It is adjusted to reject an interference signal and thus constitutes a form of antijamming. Abbreviated IFRU.

interference spectrum—The frequency distribution of the jamming interference.

interferometer—An apparatus that shows interference between two or more wave trains coming from the same luminous area, and also compares wavelengths with observable displacements of reflectors or other parts.

interferometer homing—A homing guidance system in which the direction of the target is determined by comparing the phase of the echo signal as received at more than one antenna.

interior label—In a computer, a magnetically recorded sequence added to a tape to identify the contents.

interior-wiring-system ground—The ground connection to one of the current-carrying conductors of an interior wiring system.

interlace—1. In a computer, to assign successive storage location numbers to physically separated storage locations on a magnetic drum. This serves to reduce access time. 2. To transmit different interrogation modes on successive sweeps.

interlaced scanning—Also called line interlace. A system of scanning whereby the odd- and even-numbered lines of a picture are transmitted consecutively as two separate fields. These are superimposed to create one frame, or complete picture, at the receiver. The effect is to double the apparent number of pictures and thus reduce flicker.

Interlaced scanning.

interlace factor—A measure of the degree of interlace of normally interlaced fields.

interlacing—A method of scanning used in television, in which each picture is divided into two or more complete sets of interlacing lines to reduce flicker.

interleave — 1. In a computer, to insert segments of one program into another program so that the two programs can be executed essentially simultaneously. 2. *See* interlace.

interleaving—Placing between. For example, in the transmission of a composite color signal, the bands of energy of the chrominance signal are interleaved with, or placed between, those of the luminance signal.

interlock—A device actuated by the operation of some other device with which it is directly associated, to govern succeeding operations of the same or allied devices. Interlocks may be either electrical or mechanical.

interlocking—The forcing of a voltage of one frequency to be in step with a voltage of another frequency.

interlock relay—1. A relay in which one armature cannot move or its coil be energized unless the other armature is in a certain position. 2. *See* Checking Relay.

intermediate frequency—Abbreviated if. A frequency to which a signal wave is shifted locally as an intermediate step in transmission or reception.

intermediate-frequency amplifier—1. An amplifier tuned to a fixed frequency, or capable of single-control tuning over a range of frequencies, for the purpose of selecting one of the frequency components generated in a mixer circuit. 2. The section of a superheterodyne receiver which amplifies signals with high efficiency at a predetermined frequency called the intermediate frequency of the receiver.

intermediate-frequency harmonic interference—Interference caused in superheterodyne receivers by the radio-frequency circuit accepting harmonics of the intermediate-frequency signal.

intermediate-frequency interference ratio — *See* Intermediate-Frequency Response Ratio.

intermediate-frequency response ratio — Also called intermediate-frequency interference ratio. In a heterodyne receiver, the ratio of intermediate-frequency signal input at the antenna to the desired signal input for identical outputs.

intermediate-frequency strip—A subassembly containing the intermediate-frequency stages in a receiver.

intermediate-frequency transformer — A transformer designed for use in the intermediate-frequency amplifier of a superheterodyne receiver.

intermediate-frequency–transformer-lead color code — Transformer leads in many radio receivers are identified by the following standard EIA colors:

Blue—plate.   Green—grid or diode.
Red—B+.   Black—grid return.
Green-black—second diode (full-wave transformers only).

intermediate means—All system elements needed to perform distinct operations in the measurement sequence between the primary detector and the end device.

intermediate-range ballistic missile — A tactical missile or rocket weapon with a range of 200 to 1,500 miles.

intermediate repeater — A repeater used other than at the end of a trunk or line.

intermediate state—The partial superconductivity that occurs when a magnetic field of appropriate strength is applied to a sphere of material below its critical temperature (i.e., the temperature below which the material superconducts if no magnetic field were present).

intermediate subcarrier—A carrier used for modulating a carrier or another intermediate subcarrier. It also may have been modulated by one or more subcarriers.

intermediate switching region—In a relay, an area between low level (including dry circuit) and power switching (including full rated load) where the contact arc does not destroy deposits which are by-products of the switching function.

intermittent—Occurring at intervals.

intermittent current—A unidirectional current that is interrupted at intervals.

intermittent defect—A defect that depends on variable conditions in a circuit. Hence it is not present at all times.

intermittent duty—Operation for specified alternate intervals of load and no-load; load and rest; or load, no-load, and rest.

intermittent-duty rating—The output rating of a device operated for specified intervals, rather than continuously.

intermittent-duty relay — A relay which must be de-energized at intervals to avoid excessive temperature, or a relay that is energized at regular or irregular intervals, as in pulsing.

intermittent pulsing — The transmission of short bursts of radiation at irregular intervals.

intermittent reception—A defect where the receiver operates normally for a while, at regular or irregular intervals.

intermittent scanning—One or two 360° scans of an antenna beam at irregular intervals to make detection by intercept receivers more difficult.

intermittent-service area—An area still receiving the ground wave of a broadcast station, but subject to interference and fading.

intermodulation—1. In a nonlinear transducer element, the production of frequencies corresponding to the sums and differences of the fundamentals and harmonics of two or more frequencies transmitted through the transducer. 2. An error form that occurs in chopper-stabilized amplifiers when a beat component forms between the chopper drive frequency and normal signals which have frequencies near that of the chopper.

intermodulation distortion — Nonlinearity characterized by the appearance of frequencies in the output equal to the sums and differences of integral multiples of the component frequencies present in the input signal. (Harmonics are usually not included.)

intermodulation frequencies—The sum and difference frequencies generated in a nonlinear element.

intermodulation interference—The combination-frequency tones produced at the output by a nonlinear amplifier or network when two or more sinusoidal voltages are applied at the input. Generally expressed as the ratio of the root-mean-square voltage of one or more combination frequencies to that of one of the parent frequencies measured at the output.

intermodulation noise—Noise introduced in the channel of interest by signals being transmitted in other channels.

internal arithmetic—Any computations performed by the arithmetic unit of a computer, as distinguished from those performed by peripheral equipment.

internal calibration—Calibration by an internal voltage source (provided with the instrument) rather than an external standard.

internal connection—Abbreviated IC. In a vacuum tube, a base-pin connection designed not to be used for any circuit connections.

internal correction voltage — The voltage added to the composite controlling voltage of an electron tube. It is the voltage equivalent of those effects produced by initial electron velocity, contact potential, etc.

internal graticule—A graticule the rulings of which are a permanent part of the inner surface of the cathode-ray tube faceplate.

internal input impedance—The actual impedance at the input terminals of a device.

internally caused contact chatter — That chatter resulting from the operation or release of the relay. It may be classified as initial, armature-impact, armature-rebound, or armature-hesitation chatter.

internally stored program — A sequence of instructions (program) stored inside a computer in the same storage facilities as the computer data, as opposed to being stored externally on punched paper tape, pin boards, etc.

internal magnetic recording—Storage of information within the material itself, such as used in magnetic cores.

internal memory—Also called internal storage. The total memory or storage which is automatically accessible to a computer. It is an integral physical part of the computer and is directly controlled by it.

internal output impedance—The actual impedance at the output terminals of a device.

internal resistance—The inherent resistance of a battery, generator, or circuit component.

internal storage — 1. Storage facilities in a computer forming an integral physical part of and directly controlled by the computer. 2. The total storage automatically available to the computer.

international broadcast station—A station licensed for transmission of broadcast programs for international public reception. By international agreement, frequencies are allocated between 6,000 and 26,600 kHz.

international call sign—The identifying letters and numbers assigned to a radio station in accordance with the International Telecommunications Union. The first character, or the first two, identify the nationality of the station.

international communication service — A telecommunication service between offices or stations (including mobile) belonging to different countries.

international coulomb — The quantity of electricity passing any section of an electric circuit in one second when the current is one international ampere. One international coulomb equals 0.99985 absolute coulomb.

international farad—The capacitance of a capacitor when a charge of one international coulomb produces a potential difference of one international volt between the terminals. One international farad equals 0.99952 absolute farad.

international henry—The inductance which produces an electromotive force of one international volt when the current is changing at a rate of one international ampere per second. One international henry equals 1.00018 absolute henrys.

international joule—The energy required to transfer one international coulomb between two points having a potential difference of one international volt. One international joule equals 1.00018 absolute joules.

International Morse code—Also called Continental code. A system of dot-and-dash signals used chiefly for international radio and wire telegraphy. It differs from American Morse code in certain code combinations only.

international ohm—The resistance at 0°C. of a column of mercury of uniform cross section 106.300 centimeters in length and with a mass of 14.4521 grams. One international ohm equals 1.00048 absolute ohms.

International Radio Consultative Committee — Abbreviated CCIR. An international committee which studies technical operating and tariff questions pertaining to radio, broadcast television, and multichannel video transmissions and issues recommendations. It reports to the International Telecommunications Union.

international radio silence — Three-minute periods of radio silence, commencing 15 and 45 minutes after each hour, on a frequency of 500 kHz only. During this time all radio stations are supposed to listen on that frequency for distress signals of ships and aircraft.

international radium standard—A standard of radioactivity, consisting of 21.99 milligrams of pure radium chloride.

international system (of electrical and magnetic units)—A system for measuring electrical and magnetic quantities by using four fundamental quantities. Resistance and current are arbitrary values that correspond approximately to the absolute ohm and the absolute ampere. Length and time are arbitrarily called centimeter and second. The international system of electrical units was used between 1893 and 1947. By international agreement, it was discarded on January 1, 1948, in favor of the mksa (Giorgi) system.

International Telecommunications Union— The international counterpart of the Federal Communications Commission. It provides standardized communications procedures and practices, including frequency allocations and radio regulations, on a world-wide basis.

International Telegraph Consultative Committee — Abbreviated CCIT. An international committee responsible for studying technical operating and tariff questions pertaining to telegraph and facsimile and issuing recommendations. It reports to the International Telecommunications Union.

International Telephone Consultative Committee — Abbreviated CCIF. An international committee responsible for studying and issuing recommendations regarding technical operations and tariff questions pertaining to ordinary telephones; carrier telephones; and music, picture, television, and multichannel telegraph transmission over wire line. It reports to the International Telecommunications Union.

international temperature scale — A temperature scale adopted in 1948 by international agreement. Between the boiling point of oxygen (−182.97°C) and 630.5°C it is based upon the platinum resistance thermometer. From 630.5°C to 1063.0°C it is based on the platinum rhodium thermocouple, and above 1063.0°C on the optical pyrometer.

international volt—The voltage that will produce a current of one international ampere through a resistance of one international ohm. One international volt equals 1.00033 absolute volts.

international watt—The power expended when one international ampere flows between two points having a potential difference of one international volt. One international watt equals 1.00018 absolute watts.

interphase transformer — An autotransformer or a set of mutually coupled reactors used with three-phase rectifier transformers to modify current relationships in the rectifier system and thereby cause a greater number of rectifier tubes to carry current at any instant.

interphone system—An intercommunication system like that in an aircraft or other mobile unit.

interpolation—The process of finding a value between two known values on a chart or graph.

interpole—A small auxiliary pole placed between the main poles of a direct-current generator or motor to reduce sparking at the commutator.

interpreter — A punch-card machine which will read the information conveyed by holes punched in a card and print its translation in characters arranged in specified rows and columns on the card.

interpreter code — A computer code which an interpretive routine can use.

interpretive programming — The writing of computer programs in a "pretend" machine language, which the computer precisely converts into actual machine-language instructions before performing them.

interpretive routine—Computer routine designed to transfer each pseudocode and, using function digits, to set a branch order that links the appropriate subroutine into the main program.

interrecord gap — Also called interblock space. The space between records on magnetic tape caused by delays involved in starting and stopping the tape motion. This gap is used to signal that the end of a record has been reached.

interrogation—The triggering of one or more transponders by transmitting a radio signal or combination of signals.

interrogation signal—A pulsed or c-w signal emitted to initiate a reply signal from a transponder or responder.

interrogator—Also called challenger. A radio transmitter used to trigger a transponder.

interrogator-responser—A combined radio transmitter and receiver for interrogating a transponder and displaying the replies.

interrupt—In a computer, a break in the normal flow of a system or routine such that the flow can be resumed from that point at a later time. An interrupt is usually caused by a signal from an external source.

interrupted continuous waves—Continuous waves that are interrupted at an audio-frequency rate.

interrupter—A magnetically operated device used for rapidly and periodically opening and closing an electric circuit in doorbells and buzzers and in the primary circuit of a transformers supplied from a d-c source.

interrupter contacts — On a stepping relay, an additional set of contacts operated directly by the armature.

interrupting capacity—The highest current at which the device can interrupt at the rated voltage.

interrupting rating — Conditions under which the contact of a relay must interrupt with a prescribed duty cycle and contact life.

interrupting time—In a circuit breaker, the interval between the energizing of the trip coil and the interruption of the circuit, at the rated voltage.

interstage—Between stages.

interstage coupling — Coupling between stages.

interstage punching — A system in which only the odd-numbered rows are punched in the British standard card.

interstage transformer—A transformer that couples two stages together.

interstation noise suppression—Canceling of the noise which occurs when a high-gain radio receiver with automatic volume control is tuned between stations.

interties—*See* Interconnection.

interval calibration—*See* Step Calibration.

interval circuit—A circuit which is energized during timing only. This can be accomplished by using a timer with interval contacts; or by using a timer with delayed contacts in series with the start switch, or one with instantaneous contacts in series with delayed contacts.

interval contacts—In a timer, contacts which are actuated only for the duration of the present time interval.

interval timer—1. A device for measuring the time interval between two actions. 2. A timer which switches electrical circuits on or off for the duration of the preset time interval.

interword space—In telegraphy, the space between words or coded groups. It is equal to seven unit lengths.

intonation—The slight modification of pitch, or frequency, that makes a note sound flat or sharp compared with the natural frequency of the note played.

intraconnections (microelectronics)—Those conductors and connections which are in continuous integral contact with the substrate or circuit elements of an integrated circuit.

intrinsic-barrier diode—A PIN diode in which a thin region of intrinsic material separates the N-type and P-type region.

intrinsic-barrier transistor—A PNIP or NPIN transistor in which a thin region of intrinsic material separates the collector from the base.

intrinsic brightness—The luminous intensity measured in a given direction per unit of apparent (projected) area when viewed from that direction.

intrinsic coercive force—The magnetizing force that, when applied to a magnetic material in a direction opposite to that of the residual induction, reduces the intrinsic induction to zero.

intrinsic coercivity—The measurement (in oersteds) of the force required to reduce the intrinsic induction of the magnetized material to zero.

intrinsic concentration—In a semiconductor, the number of minority carriers that exceeds the normal equilibrium number.

intrinsic conduction—In an intrinsic semiconductor, the conduction associated with the directed movement of electron-hole pairs under the influence of an electric field.

intrinsic-contact potential difference—The true potential difference between two spotlessly clean metals in contact.

intrinsic electric strength—The characteristic electric strength of a material.

intrinsic induction—The excess magnetic induction produced in a magnetic material by a given magnetizing force, over the induction that would be produced by the same magnetizing force in a vacuum.

intrinsic-junction transistor—*See* Intrinsic-Region Transistor.

intrinsic layering—The method of separating two conductive semiconductor regions by a region of near-intrinsic semiconductor material.

intrinsic mobility—The mobility of electrons in an intrinsic semiconductor, or in a semiconductor having a very low concentration of impurities.

intrinsic noise—Noise that is due to the device or transmission path and is independent of modulation.

intrinsic permeability—Ratio of intrinsic normal induction to the corresponding magnetizing force.

intrinsic properties—The semiconductor properties which are characteristic of the pure, ideal crystal.

intrinsic Q—*See* Unloaded Q.

intrinsic region—*See* Depletion Region.

intrinsic-region transistor—Also called intrinsic-junction transistor. A four-layer transistor with an intrinsic region between the base and collector. Examples are NPIN, PNIP, NPIP, and PNIN transistors.

intrinsic semiconductor—1. A semiconductor in which some hole and electron pairs are created by thermal energy at room temperature, even though there are no impurities in it. 2. A semiconductor with substantially the same electrical properties as those of the ideal crystal.

intrinsic temperature range—The temperature range at which impurities or imperfections within the crystal do not modify the electrical properties of a semiconductor.

Invar—An alloy containing 63.8% iron, 36% nickel, and 0.2% carbon. Has a very low thermal coefficient of expansion. Used primarily as resistance wire in wirewound resistors.

inverse electrical characteristics—In a transistor, those characteristics obtained when the collector and emitter terminals are interchanged and the transistor is then tested in the normal manner.

inverse electrode current—The current flowing through an electrode in the opposite direction from that for which the tube was designed.

inverse feedback—Returning part of the output power of an amplifying device to its input circuit in order to cancel a portion of the input.

inverse-feedback filter—A tuned circuit at the output of a highly selective amplifier having negative feedback. The feedback output is zero for the resonant frequency, but increases rapidly as the frequency deviates.

inverse limiter—A transducer with a constant output for inputs of instantaneous values within a specified range. Above and below that range, the output is linear or some other prescribed function of the input.

inverse networks—Any two two-terminal networks in which the product of their impedances is independent of frequency within the range of interest.

inverse-parallel connection—*See* Back-to-Back Circuit.

inverse peak voltage—1. The peak instantaneous voltage across a rectifier tube during the nonconducting half-cycle. 2. The highest negative voltage reached between the plate and cathode of a rectifier tube.

inverse photoelectric effect—The transformation of the kinetic energy of a moving electron into radiant energy, as in the production of X-rays.

inverse piezoelectric effect—Contraction or expansion of a piezoelectric crystal under the influence of an electric field.

inverse ratio—The seesaw effect whereby one value increases as the other decreases or vice versa.

inverse-square law—The strength of a field, or the intensity of radiation, decreases in proportion to the square of the distance from its source.

inverse time—A qualifying term applied to a relay, indicating that its time of operation decreases as the magnitude of the operating quantity increases.

inverse voltage—The effective voltage across a rectifier tube during the half-cycle when current does not flow.

inverse Wiedeman effect—*See* Wiedeman Effect.

inversion—1. The bending of a radio wave because the upper part of the beam is slowed down as it travels through denser air. This may occur when a body of cold air moves in under a moisture-laden body of air. 2. The producing of inverted or scrambled speech by beating an audio-frequency signal with a fixed band of the resultant beat frequencies. The original low audio frequencies then become high frequencies and vice versa.

inverted amplifier—An amplifier stage containing two vacuum tubes. The control grids are grounded, and the driving excitation is applied between the cathodes. The grids then serve as a shield between the input and output circuits. Thus, the output-circuit capacitance is greatly reduced.

inverted-L antenna—An antenna consisting of one or more horizontal wires with a vertical wire connected at one end.

Inverted-L antenna.

inverted speech—*See* Scrambled Speech.

inverter—1. A circuit which takes in a positive signal and puts out a negative one, or vice versa. 2. A device that changes alternating current to direct current or vice versa. It frequently is used to change 6-volt or 12-volt direct current to 110-volt alternating current. 3. A device that accepts an input that is a function of the maximum voltage and changes it into an output that is a function of both the maximum voltage and time. 4. A circuit with one input and one output, and its function is to invert the input. When the input is high, the output is low, and vice versa. The inverter is sometimes called a NOT circuit, since it produces the reverse of the input.

inverting connection—The closed-loop connection of an operational amplifier when the forward gain is negative for d-c signals. A 180° phase shift.

inverting parametric device—A parametric device the operation of which depends essentially upon three frequencies—a harmonic of the pump frequency, and two signal frequencies—of which the higher signal frequency is the difference between the pump harmonic and the lower signal frequency.

I/O device—Abbreviation for input/output device. A card reader, magnetic tape unit, printer, or similar device that transmits data to or receives data from a computer or secondary storage device.

ion—An electrically charged atom or group of atoms. Positively charged ions have a deficiency of electrons, and negatively charged ions have surplus electrons.

ion charging—In a storage tube, spurious charging or discharging caused by ions striking the storage surface.

ion counter—A tubular chamber for measuring the ionization of air.

ionic focusing—Focusing the electron beam in a cathode-ray tube by varying the filament voltage and temperature to change the electrostatic focusing field automatically produced by the accumulation of positive ions in the tube.

ionic-heated cathode—A cathode that is heated primarily by bombardment with ions.

ionic-heated cathode tube—An electron tube containing an ionic-heated cathode.

ionization—1. A process by which electrons are detached from atoms or molecules, thus originating ions and free electrons. It can be done by high-energy radiation or by collisions. 2. The electrically charged particles produced by high-energy radiation (such as light or ultra-violet rays) or by the collision of particles during thermal agitation.

ionization chamber—An enclosure containing two or more electrodes between which an electric current may pass when the gas within is ionized. The current is a measure of the total number of ions produced in the gas by externally induced radiations.

ionization current—The current resulting from the movement of electric charges, under the influence of an applied electric field, in an ionized medium.

ionization energy—Sometimes called ionization potential. The minimum amount of energy (usually expressed in electron-volts) required to eject an electron from a molecule.

ionization gage—A gage that measures the degree of a vacuum in an electron tube by the amount of ionization current in the tube.

ionization-gage tube—An electron tube that measures low gas pressure by the amount of ionization current produced.

ionization potential—Also called critical potential. The minimum energy that will produce ionization in a substance. Expressed as volts acting on one electronic charge.

ionization pressure—An increase in the pressure in a gaseous discharge tube due to ionization of the gas.

ionization resistance—*See* Corona Resistance.

ionization time—The time interval between the initiation and the establishment of conduction in a gas tube at some stated voltage drop for the tube.

Ionization transducer.

ionization transducer—A transducer in which displacement of the force-summing member is sensed by the induced changes in differential ion conductivity.

ionization vacuum gage—A gage in which the operation depends on the positive ions produced in a gas by electrons as they accelerate between a hot cathode and another electrode in a vacuum. It ordinarily covers a pressure range of 10^{-4} to 10^{-10} mm of mercury.

ionize—To free an electron from an atom or molecule (e.g., by X-ray bombardment) and thus transform the atom or molecule into a positive ion. The freed electron attaches itself to another atom or molecule, which then becomes a negative ion.

ionized layers—Layers of increased ionization within the ionosphere. They are responsible for absorption and reflection of radio waves and are important for communication and for tracking satellites and other space vehicles.

ionizing event—Any interaction by which one or more ions are produced.

ionizing radiation—Electromagnetic radiation or particle radiation having sufficient energy to dislodge electrons from atoms or molecules, thereby producing ions.

ion migration—Movement of the ions produced in an electrolyte by application of an electric potential between electrodes.

ionophone—A high-frequency speaker in which the audio-frequency signal modulates an r-f supply to maintain an arc in the mouth of a quartz tube. The resultant modulated wave acts directly on the ionized air under pressure and thus creates sound waves.

ionosphere—The part of the earth's outer atmosphere where sufficient ions and electrons are present to affect the propagation of radio waves.

ionospheric disturbance—The variation in the state of ionization of the ionosphere beyond the normal observed random day-to-day variation from average value for the location, data, and time of day under consideration.

ionospheric error—Also called sky error. In navigation, the total systematic and random error resulting from reception of the navigational signal after it has been reflected from the ionosphere. It may be due to variations in the transmission path, uneven height of the ionosphere, or uneven propagation within the ionosphere.

ionospheric prediction—The forecasting of ionospheric conditions and the preparation of radio propagation data derived from it.

ionospheric scatter—*See* Forward Scatter.

ionospheric storm—An ionospheric disturbance associated with abnormal solar activity and characterized by wide variations from normal, including turbulence in the F-region and increases in absorption. Often the ionization density is decreased and the virtual height is increased. The effects are most marked in high magnetic latitudes.

ionospheric wave—Also called a sky wave. A radio wave that is propagated by way of the ionosphere.

ion sheath—A positive-ion film which forms on or near the grid of a gas tube and limits its control action.

ion spot—1. In camera or image tubes, the spurious signal resulting from bombardment of the target or photocathode by ions. 2. On a cathode-ray-tube screen, an area where the luminescence has been deteriorated by prolonged bombardment with negative ions.

ion trap—Also called a beam bender. An electron-gun structure and magnetic field which diverts negative ions to prevent their burning a spot in the screen, but permits electrons to flow toward the screen.

I_p—Symbol for the plate current of a vacuum tube.

I-phase carrier—Also called in-phase carrier. A carrier separated in phase by 57° from the color subcarrier.

ips—Abbreviation for inches per second.

IR—Abbreviation for interrogator-responser or infrared.

I^2R—Power in watts expressed in terms of the current (I) and resistance (R).

IRAC—Acronym for Interdepartmental Radio Advisory Committee. It is composed of representatives of eleven government agencies: The FCC; Army; Navy; Air Force; Maritime Commission; and the Treasury,

Ion trap.

State, Commerce, Agriculture, Interior, and Justice Departments.

IR compensation — A control device that compensates for voltage drop due to current flow.

IR drop—The voltage drop produced across a resistance (R) by the flow of current (I) through it.

IRE—Abbreviation for Institute of Radio Engineers, an organization now merged with AIEE. *See* IEEE.

i (intrinsic) region — In silicon, a pure region of the group-IV element (i.e., having neither excess holes or excess electrons, and therefore having very high resistivity).

iris—Also called diaphragm. In a waveguide, a conducting plate which is very thin (compared with the wavelength) and occupies part of the cross section of a waveguide.

I²R loss—The power lost in transformers, generators, connecting wires, and other parts of a circuit because of the current flow I through the resistance R of the conductors.

iron-constantan — A combination of metals used in thermocouples, thermocouple wires, and thermocouple lead wires. Constantan is an alloy of copper, nickel, manganese, and iron.

iron-core coil—A coil in which iron forms part or all of the magnetic circuit, linking its winding. In a choke coil, the core is usually built up of laminations of sheet iron.

iron-core transformer — A transformer in which iron forms part or all of the magnetic circuit, linking the transformer windings.

iron loss—*See* Core Loss.

iron-vane instrument—A measuring instrument in which the movable element is an iron vane.

irradiation—The application of X-rays, radium rays, or other radiation.

irregularity—A change from normal in the impedance characteristics.

I-scan—A radar display in which a target appears as a complete circle when the radar

antenna is correctly pointed at it, the radius of the circle being proportional to the target distance.

I-scope—*See* I-scan.

I-signal—Also called the fine-chrominance primary. A signal formed by the combination of an R—Y signal having a +.74 polarity and a B—Y signal having a —.27 polarity. One of the two signals used to modulate the chrominance subcarrier, the other being the Q signal.

ISM equipment—A Federal Communications Commission designation for industrial, scientific, and medical equipment capable of causing interference.

isobar—1. On meteorological maps, a line denoting places having the same atmospheric pressure at a given time. 2. One of a group of atoms or elements having the same atomic weights but different atomic numbers.

isochrone—On a map or chart, a line joining points associated with a constant time difference in the reception of radio signals.

isochrone determination—A radio location in which a position line is determined by the difference in transit times of signals along two paths.

isochronous circuits — Circuits having the same resonant frequency.

isoclinic line—*See* Aclinic Line.

isodynamic lines—On a magnetic map, lines passing through points of equal strength of the earth's magnetic field.

isoelectronic—Having the same number of electrons outside the nucleus of the atom.

isolated—Utterly cut off from; refers to that condition in which a conductor, circuit, or device is not only insulated from another (or others), but the two are mutually unable to engender current, emf, or magnetic flux in each other. As commonly used, insulation is associated predominantly with direct current, whereas isolation implies additionally a bulwark against a-c fields.

Iron-vane instrument (movable).

isolated amplifier—A differential amplifier in which the input-signal lines are conductively isolated from the output-signal lines and chassis ground.

257

isolating diode—A diode that passes signals in one direction through a circuit but blocks signals and voltages in the opposite direction.

isolating switch—A switch intended for isolating an electric circuit from the source of power. It has no interrupting rating and is intended to be operated only after the circuit has been opened by some other means.

isolation—1. Electrical or acoustical separation between two locations. 2. The technique for producing a high electrical resistance between an integrated-circuit component and the substrate in which it is formed.

isolation amplifier—An amplifier employed to minimize the effects of the following circuit on the preceding circuit.

isolation network—A network inserted into a circuit or transmission line to prevent interaction between circuits on each side of the insertion point.

isolation transformer—A transformer designed to provide magnetic coupling (flux coupling) between one or more pairs of isolated circuits, without introducing significant coupling of any other kind between them—i.e., without introducing either significant conductive (ohmic) or significant electrostatic (capacitive) coupling.

isolator ferrite—A microwave device which allows r-f energy to pass through in one direction with very little loss but absorbs r-f power in the other direction.

isolith—An integrated circuit of components formed on a single silicon slice, but with the various components interconnected by beam leads and with circuit parts isolated by removal of the silicon between them.

isomer—One of two or more substances composed of molecules having the same kinds of atoms in the same proportions but arranged differently. Hence, the physical and chemical properties are different. Isomers which do not have the same molecular weights are called polymers.

isostatic—Being subjected to equal pressure from every side.

isothermal region—The stratosphere considered as a region of uniform temperature.

isotones—A group of atoms the nuclei of which have the same number of neutrons.

isotope—A species of matter the atoms of which contain the same number of protons as some other species, but a different number of neutrons. The atomic numbers of isotopes are identical, but the mass numbers (atomic weights) differ.

isotropic—Having the same properties in all directions.

isotropic antenna—Also called unipole. A hypothetical antenna radiating or receiving equally in all directions. A pulsating sphere is a unipole for sound waves. In the case of electromagnetic waves, unipoles do not exist physically, but represent convenient reference antennas for expressing directive properties of actual antennas.

isotropic gain of an antenna—*See* Absolute Gain of an Antenna.

isotropic magnet—A magnetic material having no preferred axis of magnetic characteristics.

isotropic radiator—A radiator which sends out equal amounts of energy in all directions.

item—A general term denoting one of a number of similar units, assemblies, objects, etc.

iterative impedance—An impedance used to terminate one of two pairs so that the other pair of terminals will have the same input impedance.

iterative process—The calculating of a desired result by means of a repeating cycle of operations which comes closer and closer to the desired result.

iterative routine—A computer routine composed of repetitive computations, so that the output of every step becomes the input of the succeeding step.

ITU—Abbreviation for International Telecommunications Union, an international organization established to provide standardized communications procedures and practices, including frequency allocation and radio regulations on a world-wide basis. It is the international equivalent of the Federal Communications Commission.

ITV—Abbreviation for industrial television.

I-type—Intrinsic semiconductor.

J

J—Abbreviation for joule.

Jack.

jack—A socket to which the wires of a circuit are connected at one end, and into which a plug is inserted at the other end.

jacket—Pertaining to wire and cable, the outer sheath of which protects against environment and may also provide additional insulation.

jack panel—An assembly composed of a number of jacks mounted on a board or panel.

jackscrew—A screw attached to one-half of a two-piece, multiple-contact connector and used to draw both halves together and to separate them.

jaff—Slang for the combination of electronic and chaff jamming.

jag—In facsimile, distortion caused in the received copy by a momentary lapse in synchronism between the scanner and recorder.

jam—In punch-card machines, a condition in the card feed which interferes with the normal travel of the punch cards through the machine.

jammer—An electronic device for intentionally introducing unwanted signals into radar sets to render them ineffective.

jammer band — The radio-frequency band where the jammer output is concentrated. It is usually the band between the points where the intensity is 3 db down from maximum.

jammer finder — Also called burnthrough. Radar which attempts to obtain the range of the target by training a highly directional pencil beam on a jamming source.

jamming—The intentional transmission of radio signals in order to interfere with the reception of signals from another station.

jamming effectiveness—The jamming-to-signal ratio—i.e., the percentage of information incorrectly received in a test message.

JAN specification — Joint Army-Navy specification. The forerunner of present Military Specifications, which are generally superseded by the designation MIL.

J-antenna—A half-wave antenna fed at one end by a parallel-wire, quarter-wave section having the configuration of a *J*.

J-carrier system—A broad-band carrier system which provides 12 telephone channels and utilizes frequencies up to about 140 kilohertz by means of four-wire transmission on a single open-wire pair.

J-display.

J-display—Also called J-scan. In radar, a modified A-display in which the time base is a circle and the target signal appears as a radial deflection from it.

JEDEC—Acronym for Joint Electron Device Engineering Council.

JETEC — Acronym for Joint Electron Tube Engineering Council.

jewel bearing—A natural or synthetic jewel, usually sapphire, used as a bearing for a pivot or other moving parts of a delicate instrument.

jezebel—A system for the detection and classification of submarines.

jitter—1. Instability of a signal in either its amplitude, its phase, or both. The term is applied especially to signals reproduced on the screen of a cathode-ray tube. The term "tracking jitter" describes minor variations in the pointing of an automatic tracking radar. 2. In facsimile, raggedness in the received copy caused by erroneous displacement of recorded spots in the scanning direction. 3. An aberration of a repetitive display indicating instability of the signal or of the oscilloscope. May be random or periodic, and is usually associated with the time axis. 4. *See* Flicker *and* Fortuitous distortion.

jittered pulse recurrence frequency—The random variation of the pulse-repetition period. Provides a discrimination capability against repeater-type jammers.

jogging—Also called inching. Quick and repeated opening and closing of a motor starting circuit to produce slight movements of the motor.

Johnson noise—Also called thermal noise. The noise generated by any resistor at a temperature above absolute zero. It is proportionate to the absolute temperature and the bandwidth, according to the following formula:

$$N = KTB$$

where,

N is the noise power in watts,
K is Boltzmann's constant, or 1.38047×10^{-23}
T is the absolute temperature in degrees Kelvin,
B is the bandwidth in hertz.

joined actuator — A multipole breaker such that when one pole trips, all trip, but whereas the faulted pole is trip-free, the other poles may be kept maintained by a restraining actuator.

joint — A connection between two or more conductors.

joint use—The simultaneous use of pole, line, or plant facilities by two or more kinds of utilities.

Jones plug—A type of polarized connector designed in the form of a receptacle and having several contacts.

Josephson effect — The phenomenon described by Brian Josephson to explain the action of currents through and voltages across hairlike gaps in superconductors. On the basis of theoretical considerations, it is predicted that if two superconductors could be brought close enough together, a current could be made to flow across the gap between them. Under certain conditions, a voltage appears across the gap, and high-frequency radiation emanates from it. This predicted radiation would have a frequency precisely equal to 2eV/h, where V is the measured voltage across the gap.

joule—1. The work done by a force of 1 newton acting through a distance of 1 meter. The joule is the unit of work and energy in the MKSA system. 2. The energy

259

required to transport 1 coulomb between two points having a potential difference of 1 volt. The joule is 10^7 ergs. The kilowatt-hour is 3.6×10^6 joules.

Joule effect—In a circuit, electrical energy is converted into heat by an amount equal to I^2R. Half of this heat flows to the hot junction and the other half to the cold junction.

Joule heat—The thermal energy produced as a result of the Joule effect.

Joule's law of electric heating—The amount of heat produced in a conductor is proportional to the resistance of the conductor, the square of the current, and the time.

J-scan—*See* J-Display.

J-scope—Also called Class-J oscilloscope. A cathode-ray oscilloscope that presents a J-display.

J/S ratio—A ratio, normally expressed in db, of the total interference power to the signal-carrier power in the transmission medium at the receiver.

juice—Slang for electric current.

jump—To cause the next instruction to be selected from a specified storage location in a computer.

jumper—1. A short length of wire used to complete a circuit temporarily or to bypass a circuit. 2. A direct electrical connection, which is not a portion of the conductive pattern, between two points in a printed circuit.

junction—1. A connection between two or more conductors or two or more sections of a transmission line. 2. A contact between two dissimilar metals or materials (e.g., in a rectifier or thermocouple). 3. A region of transition between P- and N-type semiconductor material. The controllable resultant asymmetrical properties are exploited in semiconductor devices. There are diffused, alloy, grown, and electrochemical junctions.

junction barrier—The opposition to the diffusion of majority carriers across a PN junction due to the charge of the fixed donor and acceptor ions.

junction box—A box for joining different runs of raceway or cable, plus space for connecting and branching the enclosed conductors.

junction diode—A two-terminal device containing a single crystal of semiconducting

Junction-diode assembly.

material which ranges from P-type at one terminal to N-type at the other. It conducts current more easily in one direction than in the other and is a basic element of the junction transistor. When fabricated in a suitable geometrical form, it can be used as a solar cell.

junction filter—A combination of a high-pass and a low-pass filter which is used to separate frequency bands for transmission over separate paths. For example, junction filters are used to separate voice and carrier frequencies at the junction between open-wire and cable so that the carrier frequencies and voice frequencies can be sent over nonloaded and v-f loaded cable pairs, respectively.

junction point—*See* Node.

junction station—A microwave relay station that joins a microwave radio leg or legs to the main, or through, route.

junction transistor—A transistor having three alternate sections of P-type or N-type semiconductor material. (*Also see* PNP Transistor *and* NPN Transistor.)

junctor—In crossbar systems, a circuit extending between frames of a switching unit and terminated in a switching device on each frame.

just-operate value—Also called drop-out value. The measured functioning value at which a particular relay releases.

just-release value—The measured functioning value at which a particular relay releases.

just scale—A musical scale formed by three consecutive triads (those in which the highest note of one is the lowest note of the other), each having the ratio 4:5:6 or 10:12:15.

jute—Cordage fiber (such as hemp) saturated with tar and used as a protective layer over cable.

jute-protected cable—A cable having its sheath covered by a wrapping of tarred jute or other fiber.

K

k—Abbreviation for kilo.

K—1. Symbol for cathode or dielectric constant. 2. Abbreviation for Kelvin or kilo. 3. Abbreviation for luminosity factor.

ka—Abbreviation for kiloampere.

Karnaugh map—A truth table that is rearranged to show a geometrical pattern of functional relationships for gating configurations. Essential gating requirements can then be recognized in their simplest form.

K-band—A radio frequency band extending from 11 to 36 GHz and having wavelengths of 2.73 to 0.83 cm.

kc—Abbreviation for kilocycle. Now obsolete.

K-carrier system—A broad-band carrier system which provides 12 telephone channels and utilizes frequencies up to about 60 kHz by means of four-wire transmission on cable facilities.

K-display—Also called K-scan. Modification

of a type-A scan, used for aiming a double-lobe system in bearing or elevation. The entire range scale is displaced toward the antenna lobe in use. One signal appears as a double deflection from the range and relative scales. The relative amplitudes of these two pips indicate the amount of error in aiming the antenna.

keep-alive anode — An auxiliary electrode that maintains a d-c discharge in a mercury-pool tube. It has the disadvantage of reducing the peak inverse voltage rating.

keep-alive circuit — In a TR or anti-TR switch, a circuit for producing residual ionization in order to reduce the time for full ionization when the transmitter fires.

keep-alive voltage — A d-c voltage that maintains a small glow discharge within one of the gap electrodes of a TR tube. This allows the tube to ionize more rapidly when the transmitter fires thus preventing damage to the receiver.

keeper — A magnetic conductor placed over the ends of a permanent magnet to protect it against being demagnetized.

kel-f — Polymonochlorotrifluoroethylene — used as a high-temperature insulation (−55°C to +135°C).

Kelvin balance — An instrument for measuring current. This is done by sending it through a fixed and a movable coil attached to one arm of a balance. The resultant force between the coils is then compared with the force of gravity acting on a known weight at the other end of the balance arm.

Kelvin bridge.

Kelvin bridge — Also called a double or Thomson bridge. A seven-arm bridge for comparing the resistances of two 4-terminal resistors or networks. Their adjacent potential terminals are spanned by a pair of auxiliary resistance arms of known ratio, and they are connected in series by a conductor joining their adjacent current terminals.

Kelvin scale — Also called absolute scale. A temperature scale using the same divisions as the Celsius scale, but with the zero point established at absolute zero ($\cong$ −273°C), theoretically the lowest possible temperature.

Kendall effect — A spurious pattern or other distortion in a facsimile record. It is caused by unwanted modulation produced by transmission of a carrier signal. Such modulation appears as a rectified baseband that interferes with the lower sideband of the carrier.

Kennelly-Heaviside layer — *See* Heaviside Layer.

kenopliotron — A diode-triode vacuum tube within one envelope. The anode of the diode also serves as the cathode of the triode.

kenotron — Also called a valve tube. A term used primarily in industrial and X-ray fields for a hot-cathode vacuum tube.

keraunophone — A radio circuit device for audibly demonstrating the occurrence of distant lightning flashes.

kernel — A line within a current-carrying conductor along which the magnetic intensity due to the current is zero.

Kerr cell — A transparent enclosure used as a light valve in some mechanical television systems. It contains a transparent substance which exhibits electric double refraction. Hence, it can convert a varying voltage into corresponding variations in the intensity of a polarized light passing through the cell.

Kerr effect — 1. An electro-optical effect in which certain transparent substances become double refracting when subjected to an electric field perpendicular to a beam of light. 2. The conversion of plane into elliptically polarized light when reflected from the polished end of a magnet.

kev — Abbreviation for kilo-electron-volt.

key — 1. A hand-operated switching device for switching one or more parts of a circuit. It ordinarily consists of concealed spring contacts and an exposed handle or push button. 2. A projection which slides into a mating slot or groove so as to guide two parts being assembled and assure proper polarization.

keyboard computer — A computer whose input employs a keyboard, e.g., an electric typewriter.

keyboard perforator — A mechanism that punches a paper tape from which messages are automatically transmitted by a transmitter distributor. The keyboard is similar to that of a typewriter and can be operated by any trained typist after a few hours' instruction. As each key is depressed, the tape is punched with corresponding code symbols.

keyboard send/receive — A combination teletypewriter transmitter and receiver with transmission capability from a keyboard only.

key click — Undesired clicking noises caused by the opening and closing of the signaling key.

key-click filter — Also called a click filter. A filter that attenuates the surges produced each time the keying circuit of a transmitter is opened or closed.

keyed agc — Abbreviation for keyed automatic gain control.

keyed automatic gain control — Abbreviated keyed agc. A television automatic gain control in which the agc tube is kept cut off except when the peaks of the positive horizontal-sync pulse act on its grid. The agc voltage is therefore not affected by noise pulses occurring between the sync pulses.

keyed rainbow generator—A color television test instrument which displays the individual colors of the spectrum, separated by black bars, on the picture tube.

keyed rainbow signal—A 3.563795-MHz (3.56-MHz) continuous sine-wave signal from a color-bar generator that is pulsed on and off. This signal creates a series of different color bars on the screen of the color picture tube. A typical pulse rate (for 10 color bars) is 12 times per 1 horizontal line.

keyer—In telegraphy a device which breaks up the output of a transmitter or other device into the dots and dashes that are used in the code.

keyer adapter—A device that detects a modulated signal and produces a d-c output signal whose amplitude varies in accordance with the modulation. In radio facsimile transmission, it is used to provide the keying signal for a frequency-shift exciter unit.

keying—The forming of signals, such as those employed in telegraph transmission, by an abrupt modulation of the output of a direct- or an alternating-current source (e.g., by interrupting it or by suddenly changing its amplitude, frequency, or some other characteristic).

keying chirps—Sounds accompanying code signals when the transmitter is unstable and shifts slightly in frequency each time the sending key is closed.

keying frequency—In facsimile, the maximum number of times a second a black-line signal occurs while scanning the subject copy.

keying wave—Also called marking wave. The emission that takes place in telegraphic communication while the information portion of the code characters is being transmitted.

key pulse—A telephone signaling system in which numbered keys are depressed instead of a dial being turned.

key pulsing—A switchboard arrangement using a nonlocking keyset for the transmission of pulse signals corresponding to the key depressions.

key punch—A keyboard machine for manually punching information into paper tape or cards.

key station—The master station from where a network radio or television program originates.

Keystone distortion.

keystone distortion—1. In a tv receiver, distortion seen as a trapezoidal instead of rectangular raster. 2. The distortion produced when a plane target area not normal to the average direction of the beam is scanned rectilinearly with constant-amplitude sawtooth waves. 3. Camera-tube distortion in which the slope or length of a horizontal line trace or scan line is linearly related to its vertical displacement.

keystone shaped—Wider at the top than at the bottom, or vice versa.

keystoning — The keystone-shaped scanning pattern produced when the electron beam in the television camera tube is at an angle with the principal axis of the tube. (*Also see* Keystone Shaped.)

keyswitch—In an organ, the switch which is closed to allow a tone from the tone generator to sound when a key is depressed.

keyway—The mating slot or groove in which a key slides.

kHz—Abbreviation for kilohertz.

kickback—The voltage developed across an inductance by the sudden collapse of the magnetic field when the current through the inductance is cut off.

kickback power supply—*See* Flyback Power Supply.

kick-sorter — British term for pulse-height analyzer.

Kikuchi lines—A series of spectral lines obtained by the scattering of electrons, when an electron beam is directed against a crystalline solid. The pattern may be interpreted to yield information on the structure of the crystal and its mechanical perfection.

killer circuit—1. The vacuum tube or tubes and associated circuits in which are generated the blanking pulses used to temporarily disable a radar set. 2. In a transponder, a logic circuit that kills replies to side-lobe interrogations.

killer pulse—*See* Suppression Pulse.

kilo — Abbreviated k. A prefix representing 10^3, or 1,000.

kiloampere—1,000 amperes. Abbreviated ka.

kilobit—1,000 bits.

kilocycle (kc)—1,000 cycles. Generally interpreted as meaning 1,000 cycles per second. Obsolete term, replaced by kilohertz (kHz).

kilo-electron-volt—1,000 electron-volts. The energy acquired by an electron that has been accelerated through a voltage difference of 1,000 volts. Abbreviated kev.

kilogauss—1,000 gausses.

kilogram (unit of mass)—The mass of a particular cylinder of platinum-iridium alloy, called the international prototype kilogram, which is preserved in a vault at Sevres, France, by the International Bureau of Weights and Measures.

kilohertz—1,000 hertz. Abbreviated kHz.

kilohm—One thousand ohms. Abbreviated k or kohm.

kilohmmeter—A meter designed for measuring resistance in kilohms.

kilomega (kM)—Obsolete prefix for giga (G), representing 10^9, or 1,000,000,000.

kilomegacycle—Now called gigahertz. One billion cycles per second.

kilometer—One thousand meters, or approximately 3,280 feet.

kilometric waves—British term for electromagnetic waves between 1,000 and 10,000 meters in length.

kilosecond—1,000 seconds.

kilovar — One reactive kilovolt-ampere, or 1,000 reactive volt-amperes. Abbreviated kvar.

kilovar-hour — 1,000 reactive volt-ampere-hours.

kilovolt—1,000 volts. Abbreviated kv.

kilovolt-ampere—1,000 volt-amperes. Abbreviated kva.

kilovoltmeter — A voltmeter which reads thousands of volts.

kilowatt—1,000 watts. Abbreviated kw.

kilowatt-hour—The equivalent energy supplied by a power of 1,000 watts for one hour. Abbreviated kwhr.

kine—Slang term for kinescope recording.

kine-klydonograph—An instrument that records the current-time characteristics of a lightning stroke. The instrument records a series of Lichtenberg figures in a manner similar to the field gradient recorder.

kinescope — 1. In television receivers, the cathode-ray tube in which the electrical signals are translated into a visible picture on a luminescent screen. 2. A film recording made from a television program on a picture tube and used as a permanent record or for subsequent rebroadcasting.

kinescope recorder—A camera which photographs television images directly from the picture tube onto motion-picture film.

kinetic energy—Energy which a system possesses by virtue of its motion.

Kirchhoff's laws—1. The current flowing to a given point in a circuit is equal to the current flowing away from that point. 2. The algebraic sum of the voltage drops in any closed path in a circuit is equal to the algebraic sum of the electromotive forces in that path. (Laws 1 and 2 are also called Laws of electric networks.) 3. At a given temperature, the emissive power of a body is the same as its radiation-absorbing power for all surfaces.

kit — A prepared package of parts with instructions for assembly and/or wiring a component or chassis (also a small accessory item).

klydonograph—A field gradient recording instrument that registers voltages on photographic film in the form of Lichtenberg figures.

klystron—1. An electron tube used as an oscillator or amplifier in ultrahigh frequencies. The electron beam is velocity-modulated (periodically bunched) to accomplish the desired results. 2. A type of oscillator or amplifier used for the generation or reception of microwave frequencies.

Kinescope.

klystron control grid—An electrode which controls the emission, or beam current, of a klystron or other velocity-modulated tube.

Klydonograph gradient recorder.

klystron frequency multiplier—A two-cavity klystron that has the output cavity tuned to a multiple of the fundamental frequency.

klystron generator—A klystron tube used as a generator. Its cavity feeds energy directly into a waveguide.

Cutaway view of klystron tube.

klystron oscillator—An oscillator employing a klystron tube to generate radio-frequency power.

klystron repeater—A klystron tube operated as an amplifier and inserted directly into a waveguide in such a way that incoming waves velocity-modulate the electron stream emitted from a heated cathode. A second cavity converts the energy of the electron clusters into waves of a much higher amplitude and feeds them into the outgoing guide.

kM—Abbreviation for kilomega (an obsolete term).

kmc—Abbreviation for kilomegacycle. Now replaced by gigahertz.

knee—An abrupt change in direction between two relatively straight segments of a curve, such as the region of a magnetization curve near saturation or the top bend of a vacuum-tube characteristic curve.

knife switch—A form of air switch in which a moving element is sandwiched between two contact clips. The moving element is usually a hinged blade, although when it is not, it is removable.

knob—A round, polygonal, or pointer-shaped part which is fastened to one end of a control shaft so that the shaft can be turned more easily. The knob sometimes indicates the degree of rotation also.

knocker—A term used with some fire-control radars to indicate a subassembly comprising synchronizing and triggering circuits. It drives the r-f pulse-generating equipment in the transmitter, and also synchronizes the cycle of operation with the transmitted pulse in range units and indicators.

knockout—A removable portion in the side of a box or cabinet. During installation it can be readily taken out with a hammer, screwdriver, or pliers so the raceway, cables, or fittings can be attached.

knot—One nautical mile (6,080.20 feet, or 1.15 statute miles) per hour.

kohm—Abbreviation for kilohm.

kraft paper—Relatively heavy, high-strength sulfate paper used for electrical insulating material. (Capacitor tissue is kraft paper of normal thickness equal to 0.002 inch or less.)

K-scan—*See* K-Display.

K-series—A series of frequencies in the X-ray spectrum of an element.

KSR—Keyboard send-receive set—A combination transmitter and receiver with transmission capability from the keyboard only (teletypewriter term).

kurtosis—The degree of curvature of the peak of a probability curve.

kv—Abbreviation for kilovolt.

kva—Abbreviation for kilovolt-ampere.

kvar—Abbreviation for kilovar.

kw—Abbreviation for kilowatt.

kwhr—Abbreviation for kilowatt-hour.

kymograph—An instrument for recording wavelike oscillations of varying quantities for medical studies.

L

L—Symbol for coil or inductance.

label—A code name used to identify or classify a name, term, phrase, or document.

labile oscillator—A local oscillator the frequency of which is remote-controlled by a signal received from a radio or over a wire.

laboratory power supply—A regulated d-c source having (a) less than 10-kV output at up to 500 W. (b) Output adjustable over a wide range, usually down to zero. (c) Regulation on the order of ±0.01% static line and load.

labyrinth—Speaker enclosure with absorbing air chambers at the rear to eliminate acoustic standing waves.

lacquer disc—Also called cellulose-nitrate discs. A mechanical recording disc, usually made of metal, glass, or paper and coated with a lacquer compound often containing cellulose nitrate.

lacquer master—*See* Lacquer Original.

lacquer original—Also called lacquer master. An original recording made on a lacquer surface to be used as a master.

lacquer recording—Any recording made on a lacquer medium.

ladder attenuator—A series of symmetrical sections used in signal generators and other devices where voltages and currents must be reduced in known ratios. They are designed

Ladder attenuator.

so that the required ratio of voltage loss per section is obtained with image-impedance operation. The impedance between any junction point and common ground in a ladder attenuator is half the image impedance.

ladder network—Also called series-shunt network. A network composed of H-, L-, T-, or pi-networks connected in series.

LAFOT—Coded weather broadcasts issued by the U. S. Weather Bureau for the Great Lakes region. They are broadcast every six hours by Marine radiotelephone broadcasting stations on their assigned frequencies.

lag—1. The displacement in time, expressed in electrical degrees, between two waves of the same frequency. 2. The time between transmission and reception of a signal. 3. In a television camera tube, the persistence of the electrical-charge image for a time interval equal to a few frames.

lagged-demand meter—A meter in which there is a characteristic time lag, by either mechanical or thermal means, before maximum demand is indicated.

lagging current—The current flowing in a circuit that is mostly inductive. If the circuit contains only inductance, the current lags the applied voltage by 90°. Because of the characteristics of an inductance, the current does not change direction until after the corresponding voltage does.

lagging load—A predominantly inductive load—i.e., one in which the current lags the voltage.

lag-lead (lead-lag)—A circuit the response of which includes lag components and their derivatives.

lambda—Greek letter λ, used to designate wavelength measured in meters.

lambert—A unit of luminance equal to $1/\pi$ candle per square centimeter. It is equal to the uniform luminance of a perfectly diffusing surface emitting or reflecting light at the rate of one lumen per square centimeter.

Lambert's law of illumination—The illumination of a surface on which the light falls normally from a point source is inversely proportional to the square of the distance of the surface from the source. If the normal to the surface makes an angle with the direction of the rays, the illumination is proportional to the cosine of that angle.

laminated—Made of layers.

laminated contact—A switch contact made up of a number of laminations, each making contact with an opposite conducting surface.

laminated core—An iron core for a coil, transformer, armature, etc. It is built up from laminations to minimize the effect of eddy currents. The sheet iron or steel laminations are insulated from each other by surface oxides or by oxides and varnish.

laminated record—A mechanical recording medium composed of several layers of material (normally a thin face of material on each side of a core).

lamination—A single stamping of sheet material used in building up a laminated object such as the core of a power transformer.

Lamont's law—The permeability of steel at any flux density is proportional to the difference between the saturation value of the flux density and its value at the point in question. This law is only approximately accurate and is not true for the initial part of the magnetization curve.

lamp—A device for producing light.

lamp bank—An arrangement of incandescent lamps commonly used as a resistance load during electrical tests.

lamp cord—A twin conductor, either twisted or parallel, used for connecting floor lamps and other electric appliances to wall outlets.

lamp holder—A lamp socket.

Lampkin oscillator—A variation of the Hartley oscillator. Its distinguishing feature is that an approximate impedance match is effected between the tank and grid-cathode circuits.

lamp receptacle—A device that supports an electric lamp and connects it to a power line.

land—1. The surface between two adjacent grooves of a recording disc. 2. Also called boss, pad, terminal point, blivet, tab, spot, donut. In a printed-circuit board, the conductive area to which components or separate circuits are attached. It usually surrounds a hole through the conductive material and the base material.

Landau damping—The damping of a space-charge wave by electrons moving at the phase velocity of the wave.

landing beacon—The radio transmitter that produces a landing beam for aircraft. (*Also see* Landing Beam.)

landing beam—A highly directive radio signal projected upward from an airport to guide aircraft in making a landing during poor visibility.

landline—A telegraph or telephone line passing over land, as opposed to submarine cables.

landline facilities—Domestic communications common-carrier's facilities that are within the continental United States.

landmark beacon—Any beacon other than an airport or airway beacon.

land mobile service—A radio service in which communication is between base stations and land mobile stations or between land mobile stations.

land mobile station—A two-way mobile station that operates solely on land.

land return—Radiation reflected from nearby land masses and returned to a radar set as an echo.

lands—Bonding points used in the manufacture of microelectronic circuits.

land station—A permanent, or fixed station.

Langevin ion—An electrified particle produced in a gas by an accumulation of ions on dust particles or other nuclei.

Langmuir dark space—The nonluminous region surrounding a negatively charged probe inserted into the positive column of a glow or arc discharge.

language—A set of computer symbols, with rules for their combination. They form a code to express information with fewer symbols and rules than there are distinct expressible meanings.

language converter—A data-processing device designed to change one form of data, i.e., microfilm, strip chart, etc., into another (punch card, paper tape, etc.).

language translation—The transformation of information from one language to another.

L-antenna—An antenna consisting of an elevated horizontal wire to which a vertical lead is connected at one end.

lanyard—A device which is attached to certain quick-disconnect connectors and which permits uncoupling and separation of connector halves by a pull on a wire or cable.

lap dissolve—In motion pictures or television, simultaneous transition in which one scene is faded down and out while the next scene is faded up and in.

lapel microphone—A microphone worn on the user's clothing.

Laplace's law—The strength of the magnetic field at any given point due to any element of a current-carrying conductor is directly proportional to the strength of the current and the projected length of the element, and is inversely proportional to the square of the distance of the element from the point in question.

Laplace transform—A mathematical substitution the use of which permits the solution of a certain type of differential equation by algebraic means.

lapping—Bringing quartz crystal plates up to their final frequency by moving them over a flat plate over which a liquid abrasive has been poured.

lap winding—An armature winding in which opposite ends of each coil are connected to adjoining segments of the commutator so that the windings overlap.

lap wrap—Tape wrapped around an object in an overlapping condition.

large-scale integrated circuit—An integrated circuit which contains 100 gates or more on a single chip, resulting in an increase in the scope of the function performed by a single device.

large-signal characteristics—The characteristics of an amplifier when rated (full) output signals are produced.

large-signal, d-c current gain—The d-c output current of a transistor with the d-c output circuit shorted, divided by the d-c input current producing the d-c output current.

large-signal power gain—The ratio of the a-c output power to the a-c input power under specified large-signal conditions. Usually expressed in decibels (db).

large-signal, short-circuit, forward-current transfer ratio—In a transistor, the ratio under specified test conditions of a change in output current to the corresponding change in input current.

Larmor orbit—The path of circular motion of a charged particle in a uniform magnetic field. The motion of the particle is unimpeded in the direction of the magnetic field, but motion perpendicular to the direction of the field is always accompanied by a force perpendicular to the direction of motion and the field.

laryngaphone—Also called a throat microphone. A microphone applied to the throat of a speaker to pick up voice vibrations directly. It is very useful in noisy locations because it picks up only the speaker's voice—no outside noises.

Laser.

laser—A device for transforming incoherent light of various frequencies of vibration into a very narrow, intense beam of coherent light. The name is derived from the initial letters of "Light Amplification by Stimulated Emission of Radiation." In the emission of ordinary light the molecules or atoms of the source emit their radiation independently of each other, and consequently there is no definite phase relationship among the vibrations in the resultant beam. The light is incoherent. The laser, by means of an optical resonator, forces the atoms of the material of the resonator to radiate in phase. The emitted radiation is stimulated by the excitation of atoms to a higher energy level by means of energy supplied to the device.

In the microwave region, the corresponding device is called a maser, and hence the laser is also known as a light maser.

laser cavity—An optical resonant and hence mode-selecting low-loss structure in which laser action occurs through the build-up of electromagnetic field intensity upon multiple reflection.

laser diode—*See* Diode Laser.

laser ranger — A device similar to conventional radar but using high intensity light rather than microwaves.

laser welding — A method of welding in which material heating is accomplished by concentration of a beam of coherent light on the area until fusion of the materials takes place.

lasing—In a laser, the generation of visible or infrared light waves that have very nearly a single frequency, by pumping or exciting electrons into high-energy states.

latching relay — A relay with contacts that lock in either the energized or de-energized positions, or both, until reset either manually or electrically.

Latch-in relay.

latch-in relay—Also called locking relay. A relay with contacts which remain energized or de-energized until reset manually or electrically.

latch mode—A mode of operation for a storage circuit in which all encoder contact closures, even momentary ones, are latched "on."

latch-up—1. A condition in which the collector voltage in a given circuit does not return to the supply voltage when a transistor is switched from saturation to cutoff. Instead, the collector finds a stable operating point in the avalanche region of the collector characteristics. 2. An unintended stable circuit mode which will not revert to a previous intended circuit mode after removal of a stimulus such as a spurious signal or radiation. The effect is usually caused by parasitic circuit elements.

late contacts—In a relay, contacts that open or close after other contacts when the relay operates.

latency—1. The time required by a digital computer to deliver information from its memory. 2. In a serial-storage system, the access time minus the word time.

latent image—A stored image (e.g., the one contained in the charged mosaic capacitance in an iconoscope).

lateral chromatic aberration — Aberration which affects the sharpness of images off the axis. This occurs because different colors produce different magnifications.

lateral compliance—The force required to move the reproducing stylus from side to side as it follows the modulation on a laterally recorded record.

lateral-correction magnet—In a three-gun picture tube, an auxiliary component used for positioning the blue beam horizontally so that beam convergence will be obtained. It operates on the principle of magnetic convergence and is used in conjunction with a set of pole pieces mounted on the focus element of the blue gun.

lateral forced-air cooling—A method of heat transfer which employs a blower to produce side to side circulation of air through or across the heat dissipators.

lateral recording—A mechanical recording in which the groove modulation is perpendicular to the direction of motion of the recording medium and parallel to its surface.

lattice—1. In navigation, a pattern of identifiable intersection lines placed in fixed positions with respect to the transmitters that establish it. 2. The geometrical arrangement of atoms in a crystalline material.

lattice network—A network composed of four branches connected in series to form a mesh. Two nonadjacent junction points serve as input terminals, and the remaining two as output terminals.

lattice structure—In a crystal, a stable arrangement of atoms and their electron-pair bonds.

lattice-wound coil—*See* Honeycomb Coil.

launch complex—The entire launch, control, and support system required for launching rockets.

launching—The transferring of energy from a coaxial cable or shielded paired cable into a waveguide.

lavalier microphone — A small microphone suspended from the neck by a cord or wire. Used mainly in broadcasting and public-address applications, it frees the speaker's hands.

LAWEB—Weather bulletins issued every 6 hours. They are given in layman's language from ship and shore positions along the Great Lakes during the navigation season. Part 1 is from land stations, and Part 2 is from a ship four or more miles off shore with the ship's position given.

lawn mower—In facsimile, a term often used when referring to a helix-type recorder mechanism.

law of electric charges—Like charges repel; unlike charges attract. (*Also see* Coulomb's Law.)

law of electromagnetic induction—*See* Faraday's Laws.

law of electromagnetic systems—1. Any two circuits carrying currents tend to dispose themselves in such a way that the flux of magnetic induction linking the two will be a maximum. 2. Every electromagnetic system tends to change its configuration so that the flux of magnetic induction will be a maximum.

law of electrostatic attraction—*See* Coulomb's Law.

law of magnetism—Like poles repel; unlike poles attract.

law of normal distribution—The Gaussian law of the frequency distribution of any normal, repetitive function. It describes the probability of the occurrence of deviants from the average.

law of reflection—The angle of reflection is equal to the angle of incidence—i.e., the incident, reflected, and normal rays all lie in the same plane.

laws of electric networks—*See* Kirchhoff's Laws.

lay—Pertaining to wire and cable, the axial distance required for one cable conductor or conductor strand to complete one revolution about the axis around which it is cabled.

layer—The consecutive turns of a coil lying in a single plane.

layer-to-layer adhesion—The tendency for adjacent layers of recording tape in a roll to adhere, particularly after prolonged storage under conditions of high temperature and/or humidity.

layer-to-layer signal transfer — The magnetization of a layer of tape in a roll by the field from a nearby recorded layer. The magnitude of the induced signal tends to increase with storage time and temperature, and to decrease after the tape is unwound. These changes are a function of the magnetic instability of the oxide.

layer winding — A coil-winding method in which adjacent turns are placed side by side and touch each other. Additional layers may be wound over the first and are usually separated by sheets of insulation.

layout—1. Diagram indicating the positions of parts on a chassis or panel. 2. The actual positions of the parts themselves.

L-band—A radio-frequency band of 390 to 1,550 MHz and corresponding wavelengths of 77 to 19 cm.

LC product—Inductance (L) in henrys multiplied by capacitance (C) in farads.

L/C ratio—Inductance in henrys, divided by capacitance in farads.

LCS—Abbreviation for loudness-contour selector.

LCVD—*See* Least Voltage Coincidence Detection.

L-display—Also called L-scan. A radar display in which the target appears as two horizontal blips to the right and left of a central vertical time base.

lead—1. A wire to or from a circuit element. 2. To precede (the opposite of lag).

lead-acid cell—Also called lead cell. A cell in an ordinary storage battery. It consists of electrodes (plates) immersed in an electrolyte of dilute sulphuric acid. The electrodes contain certain lead oxides that change their composition as the cell is charged or discharged.

Lead-acid cell.

lead cell—*See* Lead-Acid Cell.

lead-covered cable—A cable with a lead sheath. The sheath offers protection from the weather and mechanical damage to wires contained.

leader cable—A navigational aid in which the path to be followed is defined by a magnetic field around a cable.

leader tape—Also called timing tape. Plain nonmagnetic tape for splicing to either end of magnetic tape to facilitate threading and preserve recorded material, or for splicing between recorded tapes to separate selections or provide pauses.

lead-in — The conductor that provides the path for r-f energy between the antenna and the radio/television receiver or transmitter.

leading blacks—Also called edge effect. In a television picture, the condition where the edge preceding a white object is overshaded toward black (i.e., the object appears to having a preceding, or leading, black border).

leading current—Current that reaches maximum before the voltage that produces it does. A leading current flows in any predominantly capacitive circuit.

leading edge—The major portion of the rise of a pulse.

leading-edge pulse time—The time required by a pulse to rise from its instantaneous amplitude to a stated fraction of its peak amplitude.

leading ghost—A twin image appearing to the left of the original in a televised picture.

leading load — A predominantly capacitive load—i.e., one in which the current leads the voltage.

lead-in groove—Also called a lead-in spiral. A blank spiral groove around the outside of the record. Its pitch is usually much greater than the other grooves and is used to quickly lead the needle into the beginning of the recorded groove.

leading whites—Also called edge effect. In a television picture, the condition where the edge preceding a black object is shaded toward white (i.e., the object appears to have a preceding, or leading, white border).

lead-in insulator — A tubular insulator through which cables or wires are brought inside a building.

lead-in spiral—*See* Lead-in Groove.

lead-in wires—Wires which carry current into a building (e.g., from an antenna).

lead network—A network, either a-c or d-c, designed to provide error-rate damping in the controlling device of a servo system.

lead-out groove — Also called a throw-out spiral. A blank spiral groove on the inside of a recording disc, next to the label. It is generally much deeper than the recording groove and is connected to either the locked or eccentric groove.

lead-over groove — Also called a crossover spiral. On disc records containing several selections, the groove in which the needle travels as it crosses from one selection to the next.

lead polarity of a transformer—Also called polarity. A designation of the relative instantaneous directions of currents in the leads of the transformer. Primary and secondary leads are said to have the same polarity when, at a given instant, the current enters the primary lead in question and leaves the secondary lead in question in the same direction as though the two leads formed a continuous circuit. The lead polarity of a single-phase distribution or power transformer may be either additive or subtractive. If one pair of adjacent leads from the two windings in question is connected together and voltage is applied to one of the windings, a. the lead polarity is additive if the voltage across the other two leads of the windings in question is greater than that of the higher-voltage winding alone. b. the lead polarity is subtractive if the voltage across the other two leads of the winding in question is less than that of the higher-voltage winding alone.

lead screw—1. In recording, a threaded rod which guides the cutter or reproducer across the surface of a disc. 2. In facsimile, a threaded shaft which moves the scanning mechanism or drum lengthwise.

leakage—1. Electrical loss from poor insulation. 2. Undesired flow of electricity over or through an insulator. 3. The portion not utilized most effectively in a magnetic field (e.g., at the end pieces of an electromagnet).

leakage coefficient—Ratio of total to useful flux produced in the neutral section of a magnet.

leakage current—1. An undesirable small value stray current which flows through (or across the surface of) an insulator or the dielectric of a capacitor. 2. A current which flows between two or more electrodes in a tube other than across the interelectrode space.

leakage flux—The flux which does not pass through the air gap, or useful part, of the magnetic circuit.

leakage inductance—A self-inductance due to the leakage flux generated in the winding of a transformer.

leakage power—In TR and pre-TR tubes, the radio-frequency power transmitted through a fired tube.

leakage radiation—Spurious radiation in a transmitting system — i.e., radiation from other than the system itself.

leakage reactance — The reactance represented by the difference in value between two mutually coupled inductances when their fields are aiding and then opposing.

leakage resistance—The normally high resistance of the path over which leakage current flows.

leakance—The reciprocal of insulation resistance.

leaky — Usually applied to a capacitor in which the resistance has dropped so far below normal that leakage current flows.

leaky waveguide—A waveguide with a narrow longitudinal slot, permitting a continuous energy leak.

leaky waveguide antenna—An antenna constructed from a long waveguide with radiating elements along its length. It has a very sharp pattern.

leapfrogging—The process of phasing, or delaying, the ranging pulse of a tracking radar in order to move, or shift (on the scope presentation), the tracking gate (at target blip) past the target blip from another radar.

"leapfrog" test—Slang for a program designed to uncover malfunctions in a digital computer.

least maximum deviation—A manner of expressing nonlinearity as a deviation from a straight line for which the deviations for proportional or normal linearity are minimized.

least mechanical equivalent of light—The radiant power that is contained in one lumen at the wavelength of maximum visibility. It is equal to 1.46 milliwatts at a wavelength of 555 millimicrons.

least voltage coincidence detection—A system that provides protection against interfering signals by blocking all signals except those having a pulse-repetition frequency the same as or some exact multiple of the radar-set pulse-repetition frequency. Abbreviated LCVD.

Lecher line—*See* Lecher Wire.

Lecher oscillator—A device for producing standing waves on two parallel wires called Lecher wires.

Lecher wire—Also called Lecher line. Two parallel wires on which standing waves are set up, usually for the measurement of wavelength.

Leclanche cell—An ordinary dry cell. It is a primary cell with a positive electrode of carbon and a negative electrode of zinc in an electrolyte of sal ammoniac and a depolarizer of manganese dioxide.

left-handed polarized wave — Also called counterclockwise-polarized wave. An elliptically polarized transverse-electromagnetic wave in which the electric intensity vector rotates counterclockwise (looking in the direction of propagation).

left-hand rule—*See* Fleming's Rule.

left-hand taper—The greater resistance in the counterclockwise half of the operating range of a rheostat or potentiometer than in the clockwise half (looking from the shaft end).

left (or right) signal—The electrical output of a microphone or combination of microphones placed so as to convey the intensity, time, and location of sound originating predominantly to the listener's left (or right) of the center of the performing area.

left (or right) stereophonic channel—The left (or right) signal as electrically reproduced in the reception of f-m stereophonic broadcasts.

leg—A section or branch of a component or system (e.g., one of the windings of a transformer).

legend—A table of symbols or other data placed on a map, chart, or diagram to assist the reader in interpreting it.

Lenard rays—Cathode rays that emerge from a special vacuum tube through a thin glass window or metallic foil.

Lenard tube—An electron tube in which the beam can be taken through a section of the wall of the evacuated enclosure.

length of a scanning line—1. The length of the path traced by the scanning or recording spot as it moves from line to line. 2. On drum-type equipment, the circumference of the drum. 3. The spot speed divided by the scanning-line frequency.

lens—1. An optical device which focuses light by refraction. 2. An electrical device which focuses microwaves by refraction or diffraction. 3. An acoustic device which concentrates sound waves by refraction. 4. An electronic optical device which focuses electrons.

lens disc—A television scanning disc having a number of openings arranged in a spiral, with a lens set into each opening.

lens speed—The amount of light a lens will pass. It is equal to the focal length divided by the diameter of the lens.

lens turret—On a camera, an arrangement which accommodates several lenses and can be rotated to facilitate their rapid interchange.

Lens turret.

Lenz's law—The current induced in a circuit due to a change in the magnetic flux through it or to its motion in a magnetic field is so directed as to oppose the change in flux or to exert a mechanical force opposing the motion. If a constant current flows in a primary circuit A and if by motion of A or the secondary circuit, B, a current is induced in B, the direction of the induced current will be such that, by its electromagnetic action on A, it tends to oppose the relative motion of the circuits.

Lepel discharger—A quenched spark gap used in early radio-telegraph transmitters employing shock excitation.

let-through current—The current that actually passes through a circuit breaker under short-circuit conditions.

level—The magnitude of a quantity in relation to an arbitrary reference value. Level normally is stated in the same units as the quantity being measured (e.g., volts, ohms, etc.). However, it may be expressed as the ratio to a reference value (e.g., db—as in blanking level, transmission level, etc.).

level above threshold—Also called sensation level. The pressure level of a sound in decibels above its threshold of audibility for the individual listener.

level compensator—1. An automatic gain control which minimizes the effect of amplitude variations in the received signal. 2. A device that automatically controls the gain in telegraph-receiving equipment.

level indicator—A sound-volume indicator.

lever switch—Commonly referred to as a key lever or lever key. A hand-operated switch for rapidly opening and closing a circuit.

Leyden jar—The original capacitor. It consists of metal foil sheets on the inside and outside of a glass jar. The foil serves as the plates and the glass as the dielectric.

lf—Abbreviation for low frequency—(i.e., between 30 and 300 kHz).

LFM—A vhf fan-type marker. It is low powered (5 watts) and has a range of only 10 miles or less.

Leyden jar.

library—In computer programming, a collection of standard and fully tested routines and subroutines by which problems and parts of problems may be solved.

Lichtenberg figure camera — Also called klydonograph or surge-voltage recorder. A device for indicating the polarity and approximate crest value of a voltage surge by the appearance and dimensions of the Lichtenberg figure produced on a photographic plate or film. The emulsion coating of the plate or film contacts a small electrode coupled to the circuit in which the surge occurs. The film is backed by an extended plane electrode.

lie detector — Also called a polygraph. An electronic instrument which measures the blood pressure, temperature, heart action, breathing, and skin moisture of the human body. Abrupt or violent changes in these variables indicate the subject is not telling the truth.

life—The expected number of full excursions over which a transducer would operate within the limits of the applicable specification.

life test—The test of a component or unit under the conditions which approximate, or stimulate by acceleration, a normal lifetime of use. The test is performed to determine

life expectancy or reliability throughout a predetermined life expectancy.

lifetime—The average time interval between the introduction and recombination of minority carriers in a semiconductor.

lifting magnet—A powerful electromagnet used on the end of a crane to lift iron and steel objects. They can be dropped instantly by merely cutting off the current.

light—1. Radiant energy within the wavelength limits perceptible by the average human eye (roughly, between 400 and 700 millimicrons). Although ultraviolet and infrared emissions will excite some types of photocells, they are usually not considered light. 2. In combination with other terms, a device used as a source of luminous energy (e.g., a pilot light).

light-activated silicon controlled rectifier —A silicon controlled rectifier with the ability to be triggered by current to the gate terminal, or by a light flashed on a light-sensitive part of the semiconductor pellet.

light-activated switch—A semiconductor diode which is triggered into conduction by light irradiation of a light-sensitive part of the semiconductor pellet.

light amplifier—A solid-state amplifier using photoconductive and electroluminescent films.

light-beam instrument — An instrument in which a beam of light is the indicator.

light-beam pickup—A phonograph pickup utilizing a beam of light as a coupling element of the transducer.

light chopper—A device for interrupting a light beam. It is frequently used to facilitate amplification of the output of a phototube on which the beam strikes.

light-dimming control—A circuit, often employing a saturable reactor, used to control the brightness of the lights in theaters, auditoriums, etc.

light-emitting diode — A PN junction that emits light when biased in the forward direction.

light flux—*See* Luminous Flux.

light gun—A photoelectric cell used by computer operators to take specific actions in assisting and directing computer operation. So called because of its gunlike case.

lighthouse tube—1. An ultrahigh-frequency

Light (spectrum).

Cutaway view of lighthouse tube.

electron tube shaped like a lighthouse and having disc-sealed planar elements. 2. *See* Disc-Seal Tube.

lighting outlet—An outlet for direct connection of a lamp holder, lighting fixture, or pendant cord terminating in a lamp holder.

light load—A fraction of the total load the device is designed to handle.

light microsecond—The unit for expressing electrical distance. It is the distance over which light travels in free space in one microsecond (i.e., about 983 feet, or 300 meters).

light modulation—Variation in the intensity of light, usually at audio frequencies, for communications or motion-picture sound purposes.

light modulator—The device for producing the sound track on a motion-picture film. It consists of a source of light, an appropriate optical system, and a means for varying the resulting light beam (such as a galvanometer or light valve).

light negative—Having a negative photoconductivity—i.e., decreasing in conductivity when subjected to light.

lightning arrester — A device containing spark gaps, which allow lightning currents to flow into the earth.

Lightning arrester.

lightning generator—A generator of high-voltage surges (e.g., for testing insulators).

lightning rod—A rod projecting above the highest point on a structure and connected to ground in such a way that it can carry a lightning discharge to ground.

lightning surge—A transient disturbance in an electric circuit caused by lightning.

lightning switch—A switch for connecting a radio antenna to ground during electrical storms.

light pen—A small photocell or photomultiplier in a pen-shaped housing, which is held against a cathode-ray screen so as to detect the very instant the electron beam goes through that particular location during its scanning sweep.

light pipe—An optical transmission element in which unfocused transmission and reflection are used to reduce photon losses.

light-positive — Having positive photoconductivity—i.e., increasing in conductivity when subjected to light.

light ray—A very thin beam of light.

light relay—A photoelectric device that opens or closes a relay when the intensity of a light beam changes.

light sensitive — Exhibiting a photoelectric effect when irradiated (e.g., photoelectric emission, photoconductivity, and photovoltaic action).

light-sensitive tube—A vacuum tube that changes its electrical characteristics with the amount of illumination.

Light-spot scanner.

light-spot scanner—Also called a flying-spot scanner. A television camera in which the source of illumination is a spot of light that scans the scene to be televised. The picture signal is generated in a phototube, which picks up light either transmitted through the scene or reflected from it.

light valve—A device the light transmission of which can be varied in accordance with an externally applied electrical quantity such as voltage, current, an electric or magnetic field, or an electron beam.

light-year—The distance traveled by light in one year, or about 5,880,000,000,000 miles.

limit bridge—A form of Wheatstone bridge used for rapid routine production testing. Conformity with tolerance limits, rather than exact value, is determined.

limited signal—In radar, a signal that is intentionally limited in amplitude by the dynamic range of the system.

limited space-charge accumulation—A mode of oscillation for gallium arsenide diodes.

limited stability—The property of a system which remains stable only as long as the input signal falls within a particular range.

Limiter action.

limiter—1. A device in which some characteristic of the output is automatically prevented from exceeding a predetermined value—e.g., a transducer in which the output amplitude is substantially linear (with regard to the input) up to a predetermined value and substantially constant thereafter. 2. A radio-receiver stage or circuit that limits the amplitude of the signals and hence keeps interfering noise low by removing excessive amplitude variations from the signals.

Limiter circuit.

limiting—The restricting of the amplitude of a signal so that interfering noise can be kept to a minimum.

limiting resolution—In television, a measure of the resolution usually expressed in terms of the maximum number of lines per picture height discriminated on a test chart.

limits—The minimum and maximum values specified for a quantity.

limit switch—A mechanically operated contact-making or -breaking device mounted in the path of a moving object and actuated by its passage.

line—1. In television, a single trace of the electron beam from left to right across the screen. The present United States standard is based on 525 lines to a complete picture. 2. A conductor of electrical energy. 3. The

path of the moving spot in a cathode-ray tube 4. A term used interchangeably for maxwell.

line advance—Also called line feed. The distance between the centers of the scanning lines.

line amplifier—An amplifier that supplies a program transmission line or system with a signal at a specified level.

linear—Having an output that varies in direct proportion to the input.

linear acceleration—The rate of change in linear velocity.

linear accelerator—A device for speeding up charged particles such as protons. It differs from other accelerators in that the particles move in a straight line instead of in circles or spirals.

linear accelerometer—A transducer for measuring linear accelerations.

linear actuator—An actuator which produces mechanical motion from electrical energy.

linear amplification—Vacuum-tube amplification in which the plate current changes in direct proportion to the applied grid voltage.

linear amplifier—An amplifier that develops an output directly proportionate in amplitude to that of the input signal.

linear array—An antenna array in which the elements are equally spaced and in a straight line.

linear circuit—A circuit the output of which is an amplifier version of its input or a predetermined variation of its input.

linear control—A rheostat or potentiometer having uniform distribution of graduated resistance along the entire length of its resistance element.

linear detection—Detection in which the output voltage is substantially proportionate to the input voltage over the useful range of the detector.

linear detector—A detector that produces an output signal directly proportionate in amplitude to the variations in amplitude (for a-m transmission) or frequency (for f-m transmission) of the r-f input.

linear differential transformer—A type of electromechanical transducer that converts physical motion into an output voltage, the phase and amplitude of which are proportional to position. *Also see* Linear Motion Transducer.

linear distortion—Amplitude distortion in which the output- and input-signal envelopes are not proportionate, but no alien frequencies are involved.

linear electrical parameters of a uniform line—Frequently called the linear electrical constants. The series resistance and inductance, and the shunt conductance and capacitance, per length of a line.

linear electron accelerator—An evacuated metal tube in which electrons are accelerated through a series of small gaps (usually cavity resonators in the high-frequency range). The gaps are so spaced that, at a specific excitation frequency, the electrons gain additional energy from the electric field as they pass through successive gaps.

linear feedback-control system — A feedback-control system in which the relationship between the pertinent measures of the system signals are linear.

linearity—1. The relationship existing between two quantities when a change in a second quantity is directly proportionate to a change in the first quantity. 2. Deviation from a straight-line response to an input signal. 3. The ability of a meter to provide equal angular deflections proportional to the applied current. Usually expressed as a percent of the full-scale deflection.

linearity control—A manual control for adjusting the scanning waveshapes in television receivers.

linearity error—The deviation of a calibration curve from a specified straight line.

linear logarithmic intermediate-frequency amplifier—An amplifier used to avoid overload or saturation as a protection against jamming in a radar receiver.

linearly polarized wave—At a point in a homogeneous isotropic medium, a transverse electromagnetic wave the electric field vector of which lies along a fixed line.

linear magnetostriction—Under stated conditions, the relative change of length of a ferromagnetic object in the direction of magnetization when the magnetization of the object is increased from zero to a specified value (usually saturation).

linear mobility — The synchronized incremental mobility of functionally transitional electrons in a semiconductor.

linear modulation—Modulation in which the amplitude of the modulation envelope (or the deviation from the resting frequency) is directly proportionate to the amplitude of the modulating wave at all audio frequencies.

linear modulator—A modulator in which the modulated characteristic of the output wave is substantially linear with respect to the modulating wave for a given carrier magnitude.

linear motion transducer—An instrumentation component that translates straight-line

Linear motion transducer.

(linear) mechanical motion into an a-c analog which is usable as a feedback signal for control or display. A transformer-type device in which a movable magnetic core is displaced axially by the moving component being monitored. When the core is moved in one direction from the center of its stroke, the output voltage is in phase with the excitation voltage, and when the core is moved in the opposite direction from the center, the output voltage is 180° out of phase. At the center, the output voltage is (virtually) zero. In either direction from the center, the voltage increases as a precise linear function of probe displacement. Thus the output signal has two basic analog components; phase relationship wth the excitation voltage, indicating the direction of travel; and voltage amplitude, indicating the length of travel.

linear polarization—The polarization of a wave radiated by an electric vector that does not rotate but that alternates so as to describe a line. Normally the vector is oriented either horizontally or vertically.

linear power amplifier—A power amplifier in which the output voltage is directly proportionate to the input voltage.

linear programming—In computers, a mathematical method of sharing a group of limited resources among a number of competing demands. All decisions are interlocking because they must be made under a common set of fixed limitations.

linear pulse amplifier—A pulse amplifier which maintains the peak amplitudes of the input and output pulses in proportion.

linear rectification—The production, in the rectified current or voltage, of variations that are proportionate to variations in the input-wave amplitude.

linear rectifier—A rectifier with the same output-current or -voltage waveshape as that of the impressed signal.

linear scan—A radar beam which traverses only one arc or circle.

linear scanning—Scanning in which a radar beam generates only one arc or circle.

linear sweep—In a television receiver, the spot sweeps across the screen at a uniform velocity. This is due to a periodic voltage which, when applied to the horizontal-deflection plates of the cathode-ray tube, increases linearly to maximum and then falls abruptly to zero.

linearsyn—A linear displacement pick-off of the differential-transformer type consisting of a coil assembly and a moveable magnetic core. Linear velocity units of high-coercive-force permanent magnetic cores which induce sizable d-c voltages while moving concentrically within shielded coils; the voltage varies linearly with the core velocity. (Sanborn Co.)

linear taper—A potentiometer which changes the resistance linearly as it is rotated through its range.

linear time base—In a cathode-ray tube, the

time base in which the spot moves at a constant speed along the time scale. This type of time base is produced by application of a sawtooth waveform to the horizontal-deflection plates of a cathode-ray tube.

linear transducer—A transducer for which the pertinent measures of all the waves concerned are related by a linear function (e.g., a linear algebraic differential, or integral equation).

linear variable-differential transformer—*See* Differential Transformer.

linear varying parameter network—A linear network in which one or more parameters vary with time.

linear velocity transducer—A transducer which produces an output signal proportionate to the velocity of single-axis translational motion between two objects.

line balance—1. The degree to which the conductors of a transmission line are alike in their electrical characteristics with respect to each other, other conductors, and ground. 2. Impedance equal to that of the line at all frequencies (e.g., in terminating a two-wire line).

line-balance converter—A device used at the end of a coaxial line to isolate the outer conductor from ground.

line circuit—In a telephone system, the relay equipment associated with each station connected to a dial or manual switchboard. The term is also applied to a circuit for interconnecting an individual telephone and a channel terminal.

line coordinate—In a matrix, a symbol (normally at the side) identifying a specific row of cells and, in conjunction with a column coordinate, a specific cell.

line cord—Also called a power cord. A two-wire cord terminating in a two-prong plug at the end that goes to the supply, and connected permanently into a radio receiver or other appliance at the other end.

line-cord resistor—An asbestos-enclosed, wire-wound resistance element incorporated into a line cord along with the two regular wires. It lowers the line voltage to the correct value for the series-connected tube filaments and pilot lamps of a universal a-c/d-c receiver.

line diffuser—A circuit used to produce small vertical oscillations of the spot on the screen of a television monitor or receiver to make the line structure of the image less noticeable to an observer close to the screen.

line drop—A voltage loss occurring between any two points in a power or transmission line. Such a loss, or drop, is due to the resistance, reactance, or leakage of the line. An example is the voltage drop between a power source and load when the line supplying the power has excessive resistance to the amount of current.

line-drop signal—A signal associated with a subscriber line on a manual switchboard.

line-drop voltmeter compensator—A device

using a voltmeter to enable it to indicate the voltage at some distant point in the circuit.

line equalizer—An inductance and/or capacitance inserted into a transmission line to correct its frequency-response characteristics.

line-equipment balancing network—A hybrid network designed to balance filters, composite sets, and other line equipment.

line feed—*See* Line Advance.

line filter—1. A device containing one or more inductors and capacitors. It is inserted between a transmitter, receiver, or appliance and the power line to block noise signals. In a radio receiver, it prevents power-line noise signals from entering the receiver. In other appliances, it prevents their own electrical noises from entering the power line. 2. A filter associated with a transmission line. In some applications, line filter may imply a filter used to separate the speech frequencies. In other applications, it may imply directional separation, etc.

line-filter balance—A network designed to maintain phantom-group balance when one side of the group is equipped with a carrier system. Since the network must balance the phantom group for voice frequencies only, its configuration is much simpler than the filter it balances.

line-focus tube—An X-ray tube in which the focal spot is roughly a line.

line frequency—1. Also called horizontal line frequency or horizontal frequency. In television, the number of times per second the scanning spot crosses a fixed vertical line in the picture in one direction, including vertical-return intervals. 2. The frequency of the supply voltage.

line-frequency regulation—The change in output (current, voltage, or power) of a regulated power supply for a specified change in line frequency.

line group—The frequency spectrum occupied by a group of carrier channels as they are applied to a transmission facility.

line hit—An electrical interference causing the introduction of spurious signals on a circuit.

line hydrophone—A directional hydrophone consisting of a single straightline element, an array of adjacent electroacoustic transducing elements in a straight line, or the acoustic equivalent of such an array.

line impedance—The impedance measured across the terminals of a transmission line.

line interlace—*See* Interlaced Scanning.

line leakage—Resistance existing through the insulation between the two wires of a telephone-line loop.

line lengthener—A device for altering the electrical length of a waveguide or transmission line, but not its physical length or other electrical characteristics.

line level—The intensity of the signal at a certain position on a transmission line.

line load—Usually a percentage of maximum

circuit capability to reflect actual use during a period of time (e.g., peak-hour line load).

line loop—An operation performed over a communication line from an input unit at one terminal to output units at a remote terminal.

line loop resistance—Also called loop resistance. The metallic resistance of the local loop.

line loss—The total of the various energy losses in a transmission line.

line microphone—A directional microphone consisting of a single straight-line element, an array of adjacent electro-acoustic transducing elements in a straight line, or the acoustical equivalent of such an array.

line noise—Noise originating in a transmission line.

line of force—In an electric or magnetic field, an imaginary line in the same direction as the field intensity at each point. Sometimes called a maxwell when used as a unit of magnetic flux.

line of propagation—The path over which a radio wave travels through space.

line of sight—1. The distance to the horizon from an elevated point, including the effects of atmospheric refraction. The line-of-sight distance for an antenna at zero height is zero. 2. A straight line between an observer or radar antenna and a target. 3. An unobstructed, or optical, path between two points. 4. The radio-propagation characteristic of a microwave.

line-of-sight coverage—The maximum distance for transmission above the highest usable frequency. Radio waves at those frequencies do not follow the curvature of the earth and are not reflected from the ionosphere, but go off into space and are lost.

line-of-sight stabilization—In shipboard or airborne radar, compensating for the roll and pitch by automatically changing the elevation of the antenna in order to keep the beam pointed at the horizon.

line of travel—The path followed by an electromagnetic wave from one point to another.

line oscillator—An oscillator in which the resonant circuit is a section of transmission line an integral number of quarter wavelengths in electrical length.

line pad—In radio broadcasting, a pad inserted between the final program amplifier and the transmitter to insure a constant load on the amplifier.

line printer—In computers, a high-speed printer which produces an entire line at one time. All characters of the alphabet are contained around the rim of a continuously ro-

tated disc, and there are as many discs as there are characters in the line. The computer momentarily stops the discs at the right characters for each line, and stamps out an impression in a fraction of a second.

line pulsing—A method of pulsing a transmitter by charging an artificial line over a relatively long period, and then discharging it through the transmitter tubes at a shorter interval determined by the line characteristics.

line regulation—The change in output (current, voltage, or power) of a regulated power supply for a specified change in line voltage. It may be stated as a percentage of the specified output and/or an absolute value.

line relay—A relay activated by the signals on a line.

line-sequential color-television system—A color-television system in which the individual lines of green, red, and blue are scanned in sequence rather than simultaneously.

line spectrum—The spectrum of a periodic, discrete signal consisting of one or more frequencies. For example, a square wave is characterized by a fundamental and odd-order harmonics.

line-stabilized oscillator—An oscillator in which the frequency is controlled by using one section of a line as a sharply selective circuit.

line stretcher—A section of rigid coaxial line with telescoping inner and outer conductors that permit the section to be conveniently lengthened or shortened.

line switching—Also called circuit switching. A communications switching system which completes a circuit from sender to receiver at the time of transmission, as opposed to message switching.

line transformer—A transformer inserted into a system for such purposes as isolation, impedance matching, or additional circuit derivation.

line triggering—Triggering from the power-line frequency.

line unit—An electric device used in sending, receiving, and controlling the impulses of a teletypewriter.

line voltage—The voltage level of the main power supply to the equipment.

line-voltage regulator—A device that counteracts variations in the power-line voltage and delivers a constant voltage to the connected load.

linguistic — Pertaining to language or its study, including its origin, structure, phonetics, etc.

Line of sight.

link—1. A transmitter-receiver system connecting two locations. 2. In a digital computer, the part of a subprogram that connects it with the main program. 3. An interconnection. 4. In automatic switching, a path between two units of switching apparatus within a central office.

linkage—1. A measure of the voltage that will be induced in a circuit by magnetic flux. It is equal to the flux times the number of turns linked by the flux. 2. A mechanical arrangment for transferring motion in a desired manner. It consists of solid pieces with movable joints. 3. In a computer, a technique used to provide interconnections for entry and exit of a closed subroutine to or from the main routine.

link circuit—A closed loop used for coupling purposes. It generally consists of two coils, each having a few turns of wire, connected by a twisted pair of wires or by other means, with each coil placed over, near, or in one of the two coils to be coupled.

link coupling—Inductive coupling between circuits. A coil in one circuit acts as the primary, and a coil in the second circuit as the secondary.

link fuse—An unprotected fuse consisting of a short, bare wire between two fastenings.

link neutralization—Neutralization of a tuned radio-frequency amplifier by means of an inductive coupling loop from the output to the input.

link transmitter—In broadcasting, a booster for a remote pickup or from studio to main transmitter.

lin-log receiver—A radar receiver in which the amplitude response is linear for small-amplitude signals and logarithmic for large ones.

lip microphone—A sensitive microphone which is placed in contact with the lip.

liquid-borne noise—Undesired sound characterized by fluctuations of pressure of a liquid about the static pressure as a mean.

liquid cooling—The use of a circulating liquid to cool components or equipment that heat up during operation.

liquid-filled capacitor—A capacitor in which a liquid impregnant occupies substantially all of the case volume not required by the capacitor element and its connections. Space may be allowed for the expansion of the liquid under temperature variations.

liquid fuse unit—A fuse unit in which the fuse link is immersed in a liquid or the arc is drawn into the liquid when the fuse link melts.

liquid-impregnated capacitor—A capacitor in which a liquid impregnant is dominantly contained within the foil and paper winding, but does not occupy substantially all of the case volume not required by the capacitor element and its connections.

liquid rheostat—A rheostat consisting of metal plates immersed in a conductive liquid. The resistance is changed by raising or lowering the plates or the liquid level to vary the area of the plates contacting the liquid.

liser—A microwave oscillator of very high spectrum purity. Its emission consists of right circularly polarized waves of two different cavity resonant frequencies.

1:1.   2:1.

1:5.   10:1.

5:3.   6:5.

Lissajous figure.

Lissajous figures—Patterns produced on the screen of a cathode-ray tube when sine-wave signal voltages of various amplitude and phase relationships are applied to the horizontal- and vertical-deflection circuits simultaneously.

Listening angle.

listening angle—The enclosed angle between the listener and the two speakers of a stereo reproducing system.

listening sonar—*See* Sonar.

lithium—An alkali metal used in the construction of photocells.

litz wire—Also called Litzendraht wire. A conductor composed of a number of fine, separately insulated strands which are woven together so that each strand successively takes up all possible positions in the cross section of the entire conductor. Litz wire gives reduced skin effect; hence, lower resistance to high-frequency currents.

live—A term applied to a circuit through which current is flowing. *Also see* Energized.

live cable test cap—A protective cap placed over the end of a cable to insulate the cable and seal its sheath.

live end—The end of a radio studio where the reflection of sound is greatest.

live room—A room with a minimum of sound-absorptive material such as drapes, upholstered furniture, rugs, etc. Because of the many reflecting surfaces, any sound produced in the room will have a long reverberation time.

L-network—A network composed of two impedance branches in series. The free ends are connected to one pair of terminals, and the junction point and one free end are connected to another pair.

load—1. The power consumed by a machine or circuit in performing its function. 2. A resistor or other impedance which can replace some circuit element. 3. The power delivered by a machine. 4. A device that absorbs power and converts it into the desired form. 5. The impedance to which energy is being supplied. 6. Also called work. The material heated by a dielectric or induction heater. 7. In a computer, to fill the internal storage with information obtained from auxiliary or external storage.

load and go—In a computer, an operation and compiling technique in which the pseudo language is converted directly to machine language and the program is then run without the creation of an output machine-language program.

load balance—*See* Load Division.

load circuit—The complete circuit required to transfer power from a source to a load (e.g., an electron tube).

load-circuit efficiency—In a load circuit, the ratio between its input power and the power it delivers to the load.

load-circuit power input—The power delivered to the load circuit. It is the product of the alternating components of the voltage across the load circuit and the current passing through it (both root-mean-square values), times their power factors.

load coil—Also called a work coil. In induction heaters a coil which, when energized with an alternating current, induces energy into the item being heated.

load curve—A curve of power versus time—i.e., the value of a specified load for each unit of the period covered.

load divider—A device for distributing power.

load division—Also called load balance. A control function that divides the load in a prescribed manner between two or more power sources supplying the same load.

loaded antenna—An antenna to which extra inductance or capacitance has been added to change its electrical (but not its physical) length.

Center-loaded antenna.

loaded applicator impedance—In dielectric heating, the complex impedance measured at the point of application with the load material properly positioned for heating and at the specified frequency.

loaded impedance—In a transducer, the impedance at the input when the output is connected to its normal load.

loaded line—A transmission line that has lumped elements (inductance or capacitance) added at uniformly spaced intervals. Loading is used to provide a given set of characteristics to a transmission line.

loaded motional impedance—*See* Motional Impedance.

loaded Q—Also called the working Q. The Q of an electric impedance when coupled or connected under working conditions.

load factor—The ratio of average power demand, over a stipulated period of time, to the peak or maximum demand for that same interval.

load impedance—The impedance which the load presents to a transducer.

loading—1. In communication practice, the insertion of reactance into a circuit to improve its transmission characteristics. 2. Placing some material at the front or rear of a speaker so as to change its acoustic impedance and thus alter its radiation pattern.

loading coil—An inductor inserted into a circuit to increase its inductance and thereby improve its transmission characteristics.

loading-coil spacing—The line distance between the successive loading coils of a line.

loading disc—A metal disc placed on top of a vertical antenna to increase its natural wavelength.

loading error—The error introduced when more than negligible current is drawn from the output of a device.

loading noise—Any unwanted signal caused by fluctuating contact resistance between the slider and the wire or film in a potentiometric transducer when current is drawn from the instrument.

loading routine—In a computer, a routine which, when in the memory, is able to read other information into the memory from cards, tape, etc.

load isolator—A waveguide or coaxial device (usually ferrite) which provides a good energy path from a signal source to a load, but provides a poor energy path for reflections from a mismatched load back to the signal source.

load life—The ability of a device to withstand its full power rating over an extended period of time, usually expressed in hours.

load line—1. A straight line drawn across a series of plate-current-plate-voltage characteristic curves on a graph to show how plate current changes with grid voltage when a specified plate-load resistance is used. 2. A line drawn on the collector characteristic curves of a transistor on which the operating point of the transistor moves as the collector current changes. Called a load line because the slope of the line depends on the value of the collector load resistance.

load matching—In induction and dielectric heaters, adjustment of the load-circuit impedance so that the desired energy will be transferred from the power source to the load.

load-matching network—An electrical impedance network inserted between the source and the load to provide for maximum transfer of energy.

load-matching switch—In induction and dielectric heaters, a switch used in the load-matching network to alter its characteristics and thereby compensate for a sudden change in the load characteristics (such as in passing through the Curie point).

load point — The physical beginning of a magnetic tape recording as determined by a reflective spot attached to the tape at that point.

load regulation — In a power supply, the change in output for a specified change in load conditions. It may be stated as a percentage of the specified output or as an absolute value.

loadstone—*See* Lodestone.

load-transfer switch—A switch for connecting either a generator or a power source to one load circuit or another.

lobe — Also called directional, radiation, or antenna lobe. One of the areas of greater transmission in the pattern of a directional antenna. Its size and shape are determined by plotting the signal strength in various directions. The area with the greatest signal strength is known as the major lobe, and all others are called minor lobes.

lobe frequency—The number of times a lobing pattern is repeated per second.

lobe half-power width—In a plane containing the direction of the maximum energy of the lobe, the angle between the two directions in that plane about the maximum in which the radiation intensity is one-half the maximum value of the lobe.

lobe penetration — The penetration of the radar coverage of a station which is not limited by the pulse-repetition frequency, scope limitations, or the screening angle at the azimuth of penetration.

lobe switching—A form of scanning in which the maximum radiation or reception is periodically switched to each of two or more directions in turn.

lobing—The formation of maxima and minima at various angles of the vertical-plane antenna pattern by the reflection of energy from the surface surrounding the radar antenna. These reflections reinforce the main beam at some angles and detract from it at other angles, producing finders of energy.

local action—In a battery, the loss of otherwise usable chemical energy by currents which flow within regardless of its connections to an external circuit.

local battery—A battery made of single dry cells located at the subscriber's station.

local channel—1. In private line services, that portion of a through channel wthin an exchange which is provided to connect the main station with an interexchange channel. 2. A standard broadcast channel in which several stations, with powers not in excess of 250 watts, may operate.

local control—Control of a radio transmitter control directly at the transmitter, as opposed to remote control.

localizer—A radio which provides signals for guiding aircraft onto the center line of a runway.

localizer on-course line—A vertical line passing through a localizer. Indications of opposite sense are received on either side of the line.

local oscillator—Also called beating oscillator. An oscillator used in a superheterodyne circuit to produce a sum or difference frequency equal to the intermediate frequency of the receiver. This is done by mixing its output with the received signal.

local-oscillator injection — An adjustment used to vary the magnitude of the local-oscillator signal that is coupled into the mixer.

local-oscillator radiation—Radiation of the fundamental or harmonics of the local oscillator of a superheterodyne receiver.

local-oscillator tube — The vacuum tube which provides the local-oscillator signal in a superheterodyne receiver.

local program—A program originating at and released through only one broadcast station.

locating lug—The selection of two elements at specified attenuation points or in specified attenuation ranges so the ratio of the outputs of the elements at these points, calculated as a power ratio, do not exceed a specified limit.

location—A unit-storage position in the main or secondary storage of a computer.

location counter—In the control section of a computer, a register which contains the address of the instruction currently being executed.

locked groove—Also called concentric groove. The blank and continuous groove in the center, near the label, of a disc record. It prevents the needle from traveling farther inward, onto the label.

locked-rotor current—In a motor, the steady-state current taken from the line while the rotor is locked and the rated voltage (and frequency in alternating-current motors) is applied to the motor.

locked-rotor torque—Also called static torque. The minimum torque a motor will develop at rest, for all angular positions of the rotor, when the rated voltage is applied at rated frequency.

lock-in—1. The term used when a sweep oscillator is in synchronism with the applied sync pulses. 2. The shifting and automatic holding of one or both of the frequencies of two oscillating systems which are coupled together, so that the two frequencies have the ratio of two integral numbers.

locking—1. Controlling the frequency of an oscillator by means of an applied signal of constant frequency. 2. Automatic following of a target by a radar antenna.

locking circuit—*See* Holding Circuit.

locking-in—In two oscillators which are coupled together, the shifting and automatic holding of one or both of their frequencies so that the two frequencies are in synchronism (i.e., have the ratio of two integral numbers).

locking-out relay—An electrically operated hand or electrically reset device which functions to shut down and hold an equipment out of service on the occurrence of abnormal conditions.

locking relay—*See* Latch-in Relay.

lock-on—1. The instant at which radar begins to track a target automatically. 2. Signifies that a tracking or target-seeking system is continuously and automatically tracking a target in one or more coordinates.

lock-on range—The range from a radar to its target at the instant when lock-on occurs.

lockout—*See* Receiver Lockout System.

lock-up relay—A relay that is locked in the energized position magnetically or electrically rather than mechanically.

loctal base—*See* Loktal Base.

lodar—Also called lorad. A direction finder which compensates for night effect by observing the distinguishable ground- and sky-wave loran signals on a cathode-ray oscilloscope and positioning a loop antenna to obtain a null indication of the more suitable components.

lodestone—Also spelled loadstone. A natural magnet consisting chiefly of a magnetic oxide of iron called magnetite.

Loftin-White circuit—A type of direct-coupled amplifier circuit.

log—1. A listing of radio stations and their frequency, power, location, and other pertinent data. 2. A record of the station with which a radio station has been in communication. Amateur radio operators, as well as all commercial operators, are required by law to keep a log. 3. At a broadcast station, a detailed record of all programs broadcast by the station. 4. At a broadcast transmitter, a record of the meter readings and other measurements required by law to be taken at regular intervals. 5. Abbreviation for logarithm.

logarithmic amplifier—An amplifier the output of which is a logarithmic (as opposed to linear) function of its input.

logarithmic curve—A curve on which one coordinate of any point varies in accordance with the logarithm of the other coordinate of the point.

logarithmic decrement—1. For an exponentially damped alternating current, the natural logarithm of the ratio of the first to the second of two successive amplitudes having the same polarity. 2. *See* Damping Ratio.

logarithmic horn—A horn the diameter of which varies logarithmically with the length.

logarithmic scale—A scale on which the various points are plotted according to the logarithm of the number with which the point is labeled.

logarithmic scale meter—A meter having deflections proportional to the logarithms of the applied energies.

Loftin-White amplifier.

logger—An instrument which automatically scans conditions (temperature, pressure, humidity) and records (logs) the findings on a chart.

logic — 1. The science dealing with the basic principles and applications of truth tables, switching, gating, etc. 2. *See* Logical Design. 3. Also called symbolic logic. A mathematical approach to the solution of complex situations by the use of symbols to define basic concepts. The three basic logic symbols are "and", "or", and "not." When used in Boolean algebra, these symbols are somewhat analogous to addition and multiplication.

logical choice — In a computer, the correct decision where alternatives or different possibilities are open.

logical design—1. The preplanning of a computer or data-processing system prior to its detailed engineering design. 2. The synthesizing of a network of logical elements to perform a specified function. 3. The result of 1 and 2 above, frequently called the logic of the system, machine, or network.

logical element—In a computer or data-processing system, the smallest building blocks which operators can represent in an appropriate system of symbolic logic. Typical logical elements are the AND gate and the "flip-flop."

logical operations—The operations in which logical quantities (yes-no decisions, quantities expressed as zeros and ones, etc.) make comparisons, decisions, and extractions.

logical threshold voltage—At the output of a logic device, the voltage level at which the following logic device switches states.

logic array—An integrated device in which 50 or more circuits are integral to a single silicon chip. In addition, the circuits are interconnected on the chip to form some electronic function at a higher level of organization than a single circuit. Logic arrays are constructed by the unit cell method in which a simple circuit (or function) is repeated many times on a slice. The interconnection pattern for converting groups of cells into large functions is determined after cell probe tests are completed. Each interconnection pattern may be unique to a single slice. In general, logic arrays are characterized by multiple levels of metallization to effect the large-scale function.

logic diagram—In logical design, a diagram representing the logical elements and their interconnections, but not necessarily their construction or engineering details.

logic symbol—A symbol used to represent a logical element on a graph.

log/linear preamplifier—A preamplifier the electrical output of which is proportional to the common logarithm of the input, but which can be switched to a different mode wherein the output is proportional to the input. Any amplifier the transfer characteristic or calibration curve of which can be

arbitrarily switched from the form y — log x to the form y — x (y equals the output and x equals the input).

log-periodic antenna—A type of directional antenna that achieves its wideband properties by geometric iteration. The radiating element and the spacing between elements have dimensions that increase logarithmically from one end of the array to the other so that the ratio of element length to element spacing remains constant.

log receiver—A receiver in which the output amplitude is proportionate to the logarithm of the input amplitude.

log scan — A spectrum display in which the frequency axis is calibrated logarithmically.

loktal base—Also spelled loctal. An eight-pin base for small vacuum tubes. It is designed so that it locks the tube firmly in a corresponding eight-hole socket. Unlike in other tubes, the pins are sealed directly into the glass envelope.

loktal tube—Also spelled loctal. A vacuum tube with a loktal base.

long base-line system—A system in which the distance separating ground stations approximates the distance to the target being tracked.

long-distance navigational aid—A navigational aid usable beyond radio line of sight.

longevity—The period of time during which the failure rate of a group of components is essentially constant.

longitudinal chromatic aberration—A lack of sharpness in the image because different colors come to a focus at different distances from the lens.

longitudinal coils—The coils that are used in transmission lines to suppress longitudinal currents.

longitudinal current—A current which flows in the same direction in both wires of a parallel pair. The earth is its return path.

longitudinal magnetization — In magnetic recording, magnetization of the recording medium in a direction essentially parallel to the line of travel.

longitudinal redundance—In a computer, a condition in which the bits in each track or row of a record do not total an even (or odd) number. The term is generally used to refer to records on magnetic tape, and a system can have either odd or even longitudinal parity.

longitudinal wave—A wave in which the direction of displacement and propagation are the same at each point.

long - persistence screen — A fluorescent screen in which the light intensity of its spots does not immediately die out after the beam has moved on.

long-play record—Abbreviated LP record. Also called a microgroove record. A 10- or 12-inch record or transcription with finely-cut grooves which give it a long playing time.

long-pull magnet — An electromagnet designed to exert a practically uniform pull, for an extended range of armature movement. It consists of a conical plunger moving up and down inside a hollow core.

long-range radar—A radar installation capable of detecting targets 200 or more miles away.

long-range navigation — A long-range electronic navigation system which uses the time divergence of pulse-type transmission from two or more fixed stations.

long shunt—A shunt field connected across the series field and the armature, instead of directly across the armature alone, of a motor or generator.

long-tailed pair—A two-tube circuit in which decreased plate current through one tube results in increased plate current through the other tube, and vice versa.

long-term stability (or long-term instability)—The slow changes in average frequency arising from changes in an oscillator. Statements of long-term stability for quartz oscillators often term this characteristic "aging rate" and specify it as "parts per day" (fractional frequency change over 24 hours). For cesium standards, this term commonly refers to the total fractional frequency drift for the life of the cesium beam tube.

long throw—A method of speaker design in which the woofer moves freely through long excursions, providing excellent low-frequency response with low distortion.

long wave—Wavelengths longer than about 1,000 meters. They correspond to frequencies below 300 kHz.

long-wire antenna—A linear antenna which is much longer than the operating wavelength. For this reason, it can provide a directional pattern.

lookthrough—1. In jamming, sporadic interruption of the emission for extremely short periods in order to monitor the victim signal. 2. When a set is being jammed, the monitoring of the desired signal during lulls in the jamming signals.

loom—A flexible nonmetallic tubing placed around insulated wire for protection.

loop—*See* Mesh *and* Antinodes.

loop actuating signal—The signal derived from mixing the loop-input and loop-feedback signals.

Loop antenna.

loop antenna—An antenna used in radio direction-finding apparatus and modern radio receivers. It consists of one or more loops of wire.

loopback test—A test in which signals are looped from a test center through a data set or loopback switch and back to the test for measurement. *Also see* Bussback.

loop control — The maintaining of a specified loop of material between two sections of a machine by automatically adjusting the speed of at least one of the driven sections.

loop difference signal—The output signal from a summing point of a feedback control loop. It is a specific type of loop actuating signal produced by a particular loop input signal applied to that summing point.

loop error—The desired value minus the actual value of the loop output signal.

loop error signal—The loop actuating signal, when it is the loop error.

loop feedback signal—The signal derived from the loop output signal and fed back to the mixing point for control purposes.

loop feeder—A feeder which follows along a circuit and distributes the voltage more evenly at different points.

loop gain—1. The total usable power gain of a carrier terminal or two-wire repeater. Because any closed system tends to sing (oscillate), its usable gain may be less than the sum of the enclosed amplifier gains. The maximum usable gain is determined by—and cannot exceed—the losses in the closed path. 2. The increase in gain observed when the feedback path of an amplifier is opened, but with all circuit loads intact. 3. In an operational amplifier circuit, the product of the transfer characteristics of all of the elements (active or passive) encountered in a complete trip around the loop, starting at any point and returning to that point.

looping — A computer operation in which a sequence of steps is repeated.

loop input signal—An external signal applied to a feedback control loop.

loop-mile—The length of wire in a mile of two-wire line.

loop output signal—The controlled signal extracted from a feedback control loop.

loop pulsing—Also called dial pulsing. The regular, momentary interruption of the direct-current path at the sending end of a transmission line.

loop resistance—*See* Line Loop Resistance.

loop return signal—The signal returned, via a feedback control loop, to a summing point in response to a loop input signal applied to that summing point. The loop return signal is a specified type of loop input signal and is subtracted from it.

loopstick antenna—*See* Ferrite-Rod Antenna.

loop test—A method of locating a fault in the insulation of a conductor when the conductor can be arranged to form part of a closed circuit.

loop transfer function—The transfer function of the transmission path. It is formed by opening and properly terminating a feedback loop. (*Also see* Transfer Function.)

loose coupler—An obsolete tuning system consisting of two coils, one inside the other. Coupling was varied over a wide range by sliding one coil over the other.

loose coupling — Also called weak coupling. A degree of coupling that is considerably less than critical coupling. Hence, there is very little transfer of energy.

Lorac—A trademark of Seismograph Service Corp. for a specific navigation system that determines a position fix by the intersection of lines of position. Each line is defined by the phase angle between two heterodyne beat-frequency waves. One wave is the beat frequency between two c-w signals from two widely spaced transmitters. The other is a reference wave of the same frequency and is obtained by deriving the heterodyne beat of the same two c-w signals at a fixed location and transmitting it, via a second radio-frequency channel, to the receiver being located.

lorad—*See* Lodar.

loran—A contraction of LOng-RAnge Navigation. A navigation aid sending out pulses at radio frequencies between 1,800 and 2,000 kHz. It defines lines of position which are based on the differences in travel time between radio waves from a master and a slave station. Airborne equipment utilizes a picture tube and measuring circuits to determine the time differences and relate them to time-difference lines drawn on a map. A navigation fix is established by the intersection of two or more lines of position.

loran-C — A hyperbolic navigation system that relies on the stability of electromagnetic propagational characteristics at a frequency of 100 kHz. Each loran-C station operates in a pulse mode in such a way that no two stations can be received simultaneously. During the transmission period of the master station, both slave stations remain silent. After a fixed delay time, slave X will transmit a similar pulse. After a second delay, slave Y will transmit a pulse.

loran line—A line of position on a loran chart where each line is the locus of points, the distances from two fixed stations of which differ by a constant amount.

loran station—A radionavigational land station transmitting synchronized pulses.

loran tables—Tables giving terrestrial coordinates (latitude and longitude) of loran lines of position and values of the sky-wave correction.

Lorentz force — The force exerted by an electric field and a magnetic field on a moving electric charge.

Lorentz force equation—An equation relating the force on a charged particle to its motion in an electromagnetic field.

lorhumb line—In navigation, a course line in a lattice; the derivation of one coordinate from the other is always equal to the ratio of the difference between coordinates at the beginning and ending of the course line.

loss—1. A decrease in power suffered by a signal as it is transmitted from one point to another. It is usually expressed in decibels. 2. Energy dissipated without accomplishing useful work.

loss angle—The complement of the phase angle of an insulating material.

losser—A circuit having less power in the output as compared to the power applied to the input. This term is particularly applicable to mixers; a crystal mixer is a losser.

losser circuit—A resonant circuit having sufficient high-frequency resistance to prevent sustained oscillation at the resonant frequency.

losser effect—Radiation resulting from the recombination of charge carriers injected in a PN or PIN junction biased in the forward direction.

Lossev effect—The resultant radiation when charge carriers recombine after being injected into a forward-biased PN or PIN junction.

loss factor—The characteristic which determines the rate at which heat is generated in an insulating material. It is equal to the dielectric constant times the power factor.

loss index—The product of the power factor times the dielectric constant of a material.

lossless line—A theoretically perfect line— i.e., one that has no loss and hence transmits all the energy fed to it.

loss modulation—*See* Absorption Modulation.

loss tangent — Also called dielectric dissipation factor. The decimal ratio of the irrecoverable to the recoverable part of the electrical energy introduced into an insulating material by the establishment of an electric field in the material.

lossy—Insulating material which dissipates more than the usual energy.

lossy attenuator—A length of waveguide made from some dissipative material and used to deliberately introduce transmission loss.

lossy line—1. A transmission line designed with high attenuation. 2. Cable used in test measurements which has a large attenuation per unit length.

lot — A group of similar components which have been either all manufactured in a continuous production run from homogeneous raw materials under constant process conditions or assembled from more than one production run and submitted for random sampling and acceptance testing. Specifically, a quantity of material all of which was manufactured under identical conditions, and assigned an identifying lot number.

lot tolerance percent defective—A process average that will be rejected 90% of the time. Abbreviated LTPD.

loudness—The intensive attribute of an auditory sensation, in terms of which sounds may be ordered on a scale extending from soft to loud. Loudness depends primarily upon the sound pressure of the stimulus, but it also depends upon the frequency and waveform of the stimulus.

loudness contour — A curve showing the sound pressure required at each frequency to produce a given loudness sensation to a typical listener.

loudness-contour selector — Abbreviated as LCS. A circuit that alters the frequency response of an amplifier so that the characteristics of the amplifier will more closely match the requirements of the human ear.

loudness control—Also called compensated volume control. A combined volume and tone control which boosts the bass frequencies at low volume to compensate for the inability of the ear to respond to them. Some loudness controls provide similar compensation at the treble frequencies.

loudness level—The sound-pressure level of a 1,000-Hz tone judged by a listener to be as loud as the sound under consideration. It is measured in decibels relative to .0002 microbar.

loudspeaker—*See* Speaker.

loudspeaker dividing network—*See* Dividing Network.

loudspeaker impedance—*See* Speaker Impedance.

loudspeaker system—*See* Speaker System.

loudspeaker voice coil—*See* Speaker Voice Coil.

louver—The grill of a speaker.

low-angle radiation—Radiation that proceeds at low angles above ground.

low band—Television channels 2 through 6 covering frequencies between 54 and 88 MHz.

low-capacitance contacts—A type of contact construction providing small capacitance between contacts.

Low-capacitance probe circuit.

low-capacitance probe—A probe with very low capacitance. It is connected between the input of an oscilloscope and the circuit under observation.

low-corner frequency — The frequency at which the output of a resolver is 3 db below the mid-frequency value and the phase shift is 45°.

low-definition television—A television system employing less than 200 scanning lines per frame.

low-energy circuit—Also called a dry circuit. A circuit application that functions at low voltage (i.e., approximately 10 volts or less) and low current (i.e., approximately 1 ma or less).

low-energy criterion — *See* Von Hippel Breakdown Theory.

low-energy material — *See* Soft Magnetic Material.

lower manual—*See* Accompaniment Manual.

lower sideband—The lower of two frequencies or groups of frequencies produced by the amplitude-modulation process.

lowest effective power—The minimum product of the antenna input power in kilowatts and the antenna gain required for satisfactory communication over a particular radio route.

lowest useful high frequency—In radio transmission, the lowest frequency effective at a specified time for ionospheric propagation of radio waves between any two points, excluding frequencies below several megahertz. It is determined by such factors as absorption, transmitter power, antenna gain, receiver characteristics, type of service, and noise conditions.

low filter—An audio circuit designed to remove low-frequency noises from the program material. Such noises include turntable rumble, tone-arm resonance, etc.

low frequency—Abbreviated lf. The band of frequencies extending from 30 to 300 kHz (1,000 to 10,000 meters).

low-frequency compensation—A technique for extending the low-frequency response of a broad-band amplifier.

low-frequency impedance corrector — An electric network designed to be connected to a basic network, or to a basic network and a building network, so that the combination will simulate, at low frequencies, the sending-end impedance, including the dissipation, of a line.

low-frequency induction heater or furnace —A heater or furnace in which the charge is heated by inducing a current at the power-line frequency through it.

low-frequency padder—In a radio receiver, a small adjustable capacitor connected in series with the oscillator tuning coil. During alignment it is adjusted to obtain correct calibration of the circuit at the low-frequency end of the tuning range.

low-level contacts — Contacts that control only the flow of relatively small currents in relatively low-voltage circuits—e.g., alternating currents and voltages encountered in voice or tone circuits, direct current on the order of microamperes, and voltages below the softening voltages on record for various contact materials (that is, 0.080 volt for gold, 0.25 volt for platinum, and the like). Also defined as the range of contact electrical loading where there can be no electrical (arc transfer) or thermal effects and where only mechanical forces can change the conditions of the contact interface.

low-level modulation—The modulation produced in a system when the power level at a certain point is lower than it is at the output.

low-level radio-frequency signal (TR, ATR, and pre-TR tubes)—A radio-frequency signal with insufficient power to fire the tube.

low-level signal—Very small amplitudes serving to convey information or other intelligence. Variations in signal amplitude are frequently expressed in microvolts.

low-loss insulator—An insulator with high radio-frequency resistance and hence slight absorption of energy.

low-loss line—A transmission line with relatively low losses.

Low-pass filter.

low-pass filter—A filter network which passes all frequencies below a specified frequency with little or no loss but discriminates strongly against higher frequencies.

low-print tape — Special magnetic recording tape significantly less susceptible to print-through (the transfer of signal from one layer to another), which results when tape is stored for long periods of time. These tapes are especially useful for speech "master recording" (making an original recording from which copies will be made) on professional-quality equipment.

low-rate discharge — The withdrawal of a small current from a cell or battery for long periods of time.

low tension—British term for low voltage. Generally refers to the heater or filament voltage.

low-velocity scanning—The scanning of a target with electrons having a velocity below the minimum required to give a secondary-emission ratio of unity.

low-voltage protection — *See* Undervoltage Protection.

L-pad—A volume control that has practically the same impedance at all settings. It consists essentially of an L-network in which both elements are adjusted simultaneously.

LP record—Abbreviation for long-play record.

L + R, L − R—The sum and difference signals of the two stereo channels; the L + R signals combines the signals of both channels in phase; the L − R signal combines them out of phase. By combining in suitable circuitry, L + R and L − R can be added to obtain 2 L, the signal from one channel; L − R can be subtracted from L + R to obtain 2 R, the signal from the other channel.

LTPD—Abbreviation for lot tolerance percent defective.

L-scan—*See* L-Display.

lug—A device soldered or crimped to the end of a wire lead to provide an eye or fork that can be placed under the head of a binding screw.

lumen—A unit of luminous flux equal to the flux (illumination) on a surface, all points of which are the same distance from a uniform source of one candle.

lumen-hour—A unit of the quantity of light delivered in one hour by a flux of one lumen.

luminaire—A complete lighting unit consisting of a light source, together with a globe, reflector, refractor, housing, socket, and other parts integral with the housing.

luminance—1. The luminous flux emitted, reflected, or transmitted from the source. Usual units are the lumen per steradian per square meter, candle per square foot; meter-lambert, millilambert, and foot-lambert. 2. In color television, the photometric quantity of light radiation.

luminance channel—In a color television system, any path intended to carry the luminance signal. The luminance channel may also carry other signals such as the carrier color, which may or may not be used.

luminance channel bandwidth—The bandwidth of the path intended to carry the luminance signal.

luminance flicker—The flicker resulting from fluctuation of the luminance only.

luminance primary—The one of three transmission primaries whose amount determines the luminance of a color.

luminance signal—Also called Y signal. The signal in which the amplitude varies with the luminance values of a televised scene. It is part of the composite color signal and is made up of 0.30 red, 0.59 green, and 0.11 blue. The luminance signal is capable of producing a complete monochrome picture.

luminescence—1. The absorption of energy by matter, and its subsequent emission as light. If the light is emitted within 10^{-8} second after the energy is absorbed, the process is known as fluorescence. If the emission takes longer, the process is called phosphorescence. 2. The emission of light of certain wavelengths or limited regions of the spectrum in excess of that due to incandescence and the emissivity of the surface. This property is not exhibited by all materials. 3. Light emission without heat.

luminescence threshold—Also called threshold of luminescence. The lowest radiation frequency that will excite a luminescent material.

luminescent—Any material which will give off light but not heat when energized by an external source such as a stream of electrons or radiant energy.

luminescent screen—A screen which becomes luminous in those spots excited by an electron beam. The screen of a cathode-ray tube is the best-known example.

luminosity—Ratio of luminous flux to the corresponding radiant flux at a particular wavelength. It is expressed in lumens per watt.

luminosity coefficients—The constant multipliers for the respective tristimulus values of any color. The sum of the three products is the luminance of the color.

luminosity curve — A distribution curve

showing luminous flux per element of wavelength as a function of wavelength.

luminosity factor—For radiation of a particular wavelength, the ratio of the luminous flux at that wavelength to the corresponding radiant flux. It is expressed in lumens per watt. Abbreviated K.

luminous—Emitting light (i.e., glowing).

luminous efficiency—The ratio of luminous flux to radiant flux. It is usually expressed in lumens per watt of radiant flux and should not be confused with the term "efficiency" when applied to a practical source of light. The latter is based on the power supplied to the source—not the radiant flux from the source. For energy radiated at a single wavelength, luminous efficiency is synonymous with luminosity.

luminous flux—Also called light flux. Time rate of flow of light (the total visible energy produced by a source per unit time). Usually measured in lumens.

luminous intensity—Light intensity in a specified direction. The standard unit is called the international candle. Originally an ordinary wax candle was selected as the standard, and even today it is rated as having a luminous intensity of approximately one candle.

luminous sensitivity—1. In a phototube, the output current divided by the incident luminous flux at a constant electrode voltage. (The term "output current" here does not include the dark current.) 2. The sensitivity of an object to light from a tungsten-filament lamp operating at a color temperature of 2870°K. This definition is permissible, since luminous sensitivity is not an absolute characteristic but depends on the spectral distribution of the incident flux.

lumped—Concentrated at a single point.

lumped-constant elements—Distinct electrical units smaller than a wavelength. They are calibrated and used, in conjunction with other electrical/electronic equipment, for controlling voltage and current.

lumped-constant – tuned heterodyne-frequency meter—A device for measuring frequency. Its operation depends on the use of a tuned electrical circuit consisting of lumped inductance and capacitance.

lumped impedance—Impedance concentrated in a component, as distinguished from impedance due to stray or distributed effects.

lumped inductance—Inductance concentrated in a component, as opposed to stray or distributed inductance.

lumped loading—Inserting uniformly spaced inductance coils along the line, since continuous loading is impractical.

lumped parameter—Any circuit parameter which—for purposes of analysis—can be considered to represent a single inductance, capacitance, resistance, etc., throughout the frequency range of interest.

lux—A practical unit of illumination in the metric system. It is equivalent to the meter-candle and is the illumination on a one square-meter area on which there is a uniformly distributed flux of one lumen, or the illumination produced at a surface one meter from a source of one candle.

Luxemburg effect—A nonlinear effect in the ionosphere. As a result, the modulation on a strong carrier wave will be transferred to another carrier passing through the same region.

luxmeter—A type of illumination photometer employing a variable aperture and the contrast principle.

M

m—Abbreviation for the prefix milli-.

M—1. Symbol for mutual inductance. 2. Abbreviation for the prefix mega or meg meaning one million.

ma—Abbreviation for milliampere.

Ma—Abbreviation for megampere.

machine-available time—In a computer, power-on time less maintenance time.

machine cycle—The shortest complete process or action that is repeated in order. The minimum length of time in which the foregoing can be performed.

machine hardware—Circuits contained in the five parts of the computer: input, output, control, storage, and arithmetic sections; any other circuit is "off-line."

machine language—Also called computer code. A set of symbols, characters, or signs and the rules for combining them to convey instructions or data to a computer.

machine run—In a computer, the performance of one or more machine routines which are linked to form one operating unit.

machine sensible—Information in a form such that it can be read by a specific machine.

machine thermal relay—A device which functions when the temperature of an a-c machine armature, or of the armature or other load-carrying winding or element of a d-c machine, or converter, power rectifier, or power transformer (including a power-rectifier transformer) exceeds a predetermined value.

machine word—A unit of information consisting of a standard number of characters which a computer regularly handles in each register.

macrocode—A coding system which assembles groups of computer instructions into single code words and which therefore requires interpretation or translation so that an automatic computer can follow it.

macroprogramming—In a computer, the writing of machine-procedure statements in terms of macrocode instructions.

macroscopic — Large enough to be observed by the unaided eye.

macrosonics—The utilization of high amplitude sound waves for performing functions such as cleaning, drilling, emulsification, etc.

madistor — A semiconductor device that makes use of the effects of a magnetic field on a plasma current. The strength of a magnetic field determines the conductivity of the madistor material. A small change in the magnetic field produces a larger change in the madistor current.

MADT transistor—A microalloy diffused-base transistor.

magamp—Abbreviation for magnetic amplifier.

magic eye—*See* Electron-Ray Tube.

magic-t—*See* Hybrid Junction.

magnaflux—A magnetic method of determining surface and subsurface defects in metals.

magnal base—An 11-pin base used on cathode-ray tubes.

Magnal socket.

magnal socket—An 11-pin socket used with cathode-ray tubes.

magnesium—An alkaline metal the compounds of which are sometimes used for cathodes.

magnesium anode — A bar of magnesium, buried in the earth, connected to an underground cable to prevent cable corrosion due to electrolysis.

magnesium cell—A primary cell the negative electrode of which is made of magnesium or one of its alloys.

magnesium-copper-sulphide rectifier — A dry disc rectifier consisting of magnesium in contact with copper sulphide.

magnesium-silver chloride cell—A reserve primary cell that becomes activated when water is added.

Magnesyn—Trade name for a device made by Bendix Aviation Corp. It is a portion of a repeater unit consisting of a two-pole permanent-manet rotor within a three-phase, two-pole, delta-connected stator. The rotor carries the indicating pointer and is free to rotate in any direction.

magnet—A body that has the property of attracting or repelling magnetic materials. In its natural form it is called a lodestone. It may also be produced by permanently magnetizing a piece of iron or steel. A temporary magnet—called an electromagnet—is produced by passing a current through a coil surrounding a piece of iron or steel; the

magnetism persists only while current is flowing. When suspended freely, a magnet will turn and align its poles with the north and south magnetic poles of the earth. (*Also See* Electromagnetism *and* Permanent Magnet.)

magnet brake—A friction brake controlled electromagnetically.

magnetic—Pertaining to magnetism.

magnetic aging—The normal change in the magnetic material resulting from gradual metallurgical change in the material. The term also applies when the metallurgical changes are accelerated by an increase or decrease in temperature. When used in reference to core loss, this term, unless otherwise modified, implies an increase in loss. When used in reference to permeability remanence, the term, in a positive sense, indicates a decrease in these quantities.

magnetic air gap—The air space, or non-magnetic portion, of a magnetic circuit.

magnetically damped—A form of damping achieved by moving a metal vane through a magnetic field. This motion induces currents in the vane which set up magnetic fields opposing those of the stationary magnets, thus tending to bring the pointer to rest. This type of damping is found in many quality moving-iron and dynamometer-type instruments.

Magnetic amplifiers.

magnetic amplifier—Abbreviated magamp. A variable-impedance device by which load power and voltage can be controlled. Amplification occurs since the control source requires much less power than is supplied to the load.

magnetic analysis — The separation of a stream of electrified particles by a magnetic field, in accordance with their mass, charge, or speed. This is the principle of the mass spectrograph.

magnetic anisotropy — The dependence of the magnetic properties of some materials on direction.

magnetic-armature speaker—Also called a magnetic-armature loudspeaker or magnetic speaker. A speaker comprising a ferromagnetic armature actuated by magnetic attraction.

magnetic azimuth—Azimuth measured from magnetic north.

magnetic bearing—The position in which an object is pointing with respect to the earth's magnetic north pole. It is expressed in degrees clockwise from that pole.

magnetic bias—A steady magnetic field applied to the magnetic circuit of a relay.

magnetic biasing—The superimposing of another magnetic field on the signal magnetic field of a tape while a magnetic recording is being made.

magnetic blowout—A magnet for establishing a field where an electrical circuit is broken. The field lengthens the arc and thus helps to extinguish it.

magnetic blow-out switch—A switch that contains a small permanent magnet which provides a means of switching high d-c loads. The magnet deflects the arc to quench it.

magnetic braking—Application of the brakes by magnetic force. The current for exciting the electromagnets is derived either from the traction motors acting as generators, or from an independent source.

magnetic bremsstrahlung—*See* Synchrotron Radiation.

magnetic cartridge—*See* Variable-Reluctance Pickup.

magnetic character—A character imprinted with ink having magnetic properties. These characters are unique in that they can be read directly by both humans and machines.

magnetic circuit—The path of the flux as it travels from the north pole, through the circuit components, and back to the north pole. In a generator, the magnetic-circuit components include the field yoke, field pole pieces, air gap, and armature core. The magnetic circuit may be compared to an electrical circuit, with magnetomotive force corresponding to voltage, flux lines to current, and reluctance to resistance.

magnetic circuit breaker—A circuit breaker that depends on the response of an electromagnetic coil for operation.

magnetic coated disc—A magnetic disc-recording medium consisting of a coat of magnetizable material over a nonmagnetic base.

magnetic coil—The winding of an electromagnet.

magnetic compass—A device for indicating direction. It consists of a magnetic needle which pivots freely and points toward the earth's north magnetic pole.

magnetic conduction current—The rate of flow of magnetism through a magnetized body.

magnetic contactor—A contactor actuated electromagnetically.

magnetic-convergence principle—The obtaining of beam convergence through the use of a magnetic field.

magnetic core—1. A configuration of magnetic material which is, or is intended to be, placed in a rigid special relationship to current-carrying conductors and the magnetic properties of which are essential to its use. For example, it may be used to concentrate an induced magnetic field as in a transformer induction coil, or armature, to retain a magnetic polarization for the purpose of storing data, or for its non-linear properties as in a logic element. It may be made of such material as iron, iron oxide, or ferrite in such shapes as wires, tapes, toroids, or thin film. 2. The ferrous material in the center of an electromagnet.

magnetic core storage—A type of computer storage which employs a core of magnetic material surrounded by a coil of wire. The core can be magnetized to represent a binary 1 or 0.

magnetic course—A course in which the reference line is magnetic north.

Magnetic cutter.

magnetic cutter—A cutter in which the mechanical displacement of the recording stylus is produced by the action of magnetic fields.

magnetic cycle—The sequence of changes in the magnetization of an object corresponding to one cycle of the alternating current producing the magnetization.

magnetic damping—The damping of a mechanical motion by means of the reaction between a magnetic field and the current generated in a conductor moving through that field. The resistance of this conductor converts excess kinetic energy to heat.

magnetic deflection—The moving of the electron beam by means of a magnetic field produced by a coil around the neck of the cathode-ray tube (i.e., a linear motion is produced when the current through the coil has a sawtooth waveform).

magnetic delay line—A computer delay line in which magnetic energy is propagated consisting in essence of a metallic medium

N

ELECTRON
BEAM

+

L ⊗ R

WALL OF
TUBE

ELECTRONS
MOVING
INTO PAGE

S

Magnetic deflection.

along which the velocity of propagation of magnetic energy is small when compared to the speed of light. The storage of information, which is usually in a binary form, is accomplished by recirculation of wave patterns.

magnetic density—The number of lines of magnetic force passing through a magnet or magnetic field per unit area of cross section.

magnetic detecting device—A device for detecting cracks in iron or steel. This is done by introducing magnetic particles, which are attracted to the opposing magnetic poles created at the break.

magnetic device—Any device actuated electromagnetically.

magnetic dip—Also called magnetic inclination. The angle of the magnetic field of the earth with the horizontal at a particular location.

magnetic dipole—A pair of equal-strength north and south magnetic poles spaced close together, and so small that its directive properties are independent of its size and shape. It is the magnetic equivalent of an electrical dipole.

magnetic direction indicator—Abbreviated MDI. An instrument that provides a compass indication, which it obtains electrically from a remote gyrostabilized magnetic compass (or its equivalent).

magnetic disc—A flat circular plate with a magnetic surface on which data can be stored by selective magnetization of portions of the flat surface.

magnetic disc storage—Storage of digital information on magnetic discs.

magnetic displacement—Magnetic flux density or magnetic induction.

magnetic drag—Undesired torque usually caused by useless eddy currents and residual magnetism.

magnetic drum—A storage device consisting of a rapidly rotating cylinder, the surface of which can be easily magnetized and which will retain the magnetization. Information is stored in the form of magnetized spots (or no spots) on the drum surface.

magnetic-drum receiving equipment—Radar developed for detection of targets beyond line of sight using ionospheric reflection and very low power. To distinguish radar signals from ground noise, a noise-free standard system is employed whereby the amplitude and characteristics are reproduced and preserved for comparison with returned signals. Fluctuations in the amplitude of the returned signals indicate the position and velocity of the target accurately to within 10 miles.

magnetic electron multiplier—One type of electron multiplier in which the paths of the emitted secondary electrons are controlled by an externally applied magnetic field.

magnetic field—An area where magnetic forces can be detected around a permanent, natural, or electromagnet.

magnetic field strength—See Magnetizing Force.

magnetic figures—A pattern showing the distribution of a magnetic field. It is made by sprinkling iron filings on a nonmagnetic surface in the field.

magnetic flip-flop—A bistable amplifier using one or more magnetic amplifiers. The two stable output levels are determined by appropriate changes in the control voltage or current.

magnetic flux—The magnetic induction in a material. An electromotive force will be induced in a conductor placed in a magnetic field whenever the magnitude of the flux changes.

magnetic flux density—See Magnetic Induction.

magnetic focusing—The focusing of an electron beam by the action of a magnetic field.

magnetic freezing—In a relay, sticking of the armature to the core due to residual magnetism.

magnetic gap—The nonmagnetic part of a magnetic circuit.

Magnetic field.

magnetic gate — A gate circuit used in a magnetic amplifier.

magnetic head—In magnetic recording, a transducer that converts electric variations into magnetic variations for storage on magnetic media, or for reconverting such stored energy into electric energy. Stored energy can also be erased by this method.

magnetic heading—The heading of an aircraft with reference to magnetic north.

magnetic hysteresis—In a magnetic material, the property by virtue of which the magnetic induction for a given magnetizing force depends on the previous conditions of magnetization.

magnetic hysteresis loss—The power expended in a magnetic material, as a result of magnetic hysteresis, when the magnetic induction is cyclic.

magnetic inclination—*See* Magnetic Dip.

magnetic induction—Also called magnetic flux density. The flux per unit area perpendicular to the direction of the flux. The cgs unit of induction is called the gauss (plural, gausses) and is defined by the equation:

$$B = \frac{d\phi}{dA}$$

magnetic ink—Visible ink containing magnetic particles. When printed on a document (e.g., a bank check), the ink can be read by a magnetic character sensor and also by humans.

magnetic integrated circuit—An integrated component in which magnetic elements perform all or a major portion of its intended function.

magnetic integrated circuitry—The physical realization of one or more magnetic elements inseparably associated to perform all or at least a major portion of its intended function.

magnetic-latch relay—*See* Polarized Double-Biased Relay.

magnetic leakage—Passage of magnetic flux outside the path along which it can do useful work.

magnetic lens—An apparatus that uses a nonuniform magnetic field to focus beams of rapidly moving electrons or ions in a cathode-ray or other tube.

magnetic line of force—In a magnetic field, an imaginary line which has the direction of the magnetic flux at every point.

magnetic materials — Materials that show magnetic properties. Ferromagnetic materials are more strongly magnetic than paramagnetic materials.

magnetic memory—A computer memory (or any portion) in which information is stored in the form of magnetism.

magnetic microphone — *See* Variable-Reluctance Microphone.

magnetic mine—An underwater mine that detonates when near the steel hull of a ship. This is accomplished by relays, which re-distribute the magnetic field in the mine when it is near the ship.

magnetic modulator—Also called a magnettor. A modulator employing a magnetic amplifier as the modulating element.

magnetic moment—Ratio of the maximum torque exerted on a magnet, to the magnetizing force of the field in which the magnet is situated.

magnetic needle — The magnetized needle used in a compass. When freely suspended, it will point to the earth's magnetic north and south poles.

magnetic north—The direction indicated by the north-seeking end of the needle in a magnetic compass.

magnetic phase modulator—A ferrite-core delay line in which the delay is varied by an external magnetic field.

magnetic pickup — *See* Variable-Reluctance Pickup.

magnetic-plated wire—A wire with a nonmagnetic core and a plated surface of ferromagnetic material.

Magnetic poles.

magnetic poles—Those portions of a magnet toward which the lines of flux converge. All magnets have two poles, called north and south or north-seeking and south-seeking, poles.

magnetic pole strength—The magnetic moment of a magnetized body divided by the distance between the poles.

magnetic potential difference—The line integral of magnetizing force between two points in a magnetic field.

magnetic-powder-coated tape — Also called coated tape. A tape consisting of a coating of uniformly dispersed powdered ferromagnetic material on a nonmagnetic base.

magnetic printing — Also called magnetic transfer, and cross talk. The permanent transfer of a recorded signal from a section of one magnetic recording medium to another section of the same or a different medium when they are brought near each other.

magnetic probe—A loop-type conductor for detecing presence of static, audio, or r-f magnetic fields.

magnetic radio bearing—*See* Radio Bearing.

magnetic recorder—Equipment incorporating an electromagnetic transducer and a means for moving a magnetic recording medium past the transducer. Electric signals are recorded in the medium as magnetic variations. (*Also see* Magnetic Recording.)

magnetic recording—Recording audio frequencies by magnetizing areas of a tape or wire. The magnetized tape or wire is played back by passing it through a reproducing head. Here the magnetized areas are reconverted into electrical energy, which headphones or speakers then change back into sound.

magnetic recording head—In magnetic recording, a magnetic head that transforms electric variations into magnetic variations for storage on a magnetic medium such as tape or discs.

magnetic recording medium—A wire, tape, cylinder, disc, or other magnetizable material which retains the magnetic variations imparted to it during magnetic recording.

magnetic reproducer — Equipment which picks up the magnetic variations on magnetic recording media and converts them into electrical variations.

magnetic reproducing head—In magnetic recording, the head that converts the magnetic variations into electric variations.

WIRE WINDING

MAGNETIC MATERIAL
CONDUCTOR
GLASS ROAD

Magnetic rod.

magnetic rod—A square-loop switching and storage element for digital systems. It consists of a silver-coated glass rod upon which a thin layer of iron and nickel is deposited. Conductors are wound around the rod for the drive, sense, enable, and inhibit currents.

magnetics—The branch of science concerned with the laws of magnetic phenomena.

magnetic saturation—In an iron core, the point where application of a further increase in magnetizing force will produce little or no increase in the magnetic lines of force.

magnetic separator—An apparatus for separating powdered magnetic ores from nonmagnetic ores, or iron filings and other small iron objects from nonmagnetic materials. An electromagnet is employed which deflects the magnetic materials from the path taken by the nonmagnetic materials.

magnetic shield—A sheet or core of iron enclosing instruments or radio parts to protect them from stray magnetic fields. The shield provides a convenient path for the magnetic lines of force and thus diverts them from the component being protected.

magnetic shift register—A register in which magnetic cores are used as binary storage elements. By means of pulses, the pattern of binary digital information can be shifted one position to the left or right in the register.

magnetic shunt—A piece of iron used during instrument calibration to divert a portion of the magnetic lines of force passing through an air gap in the instrument.

magnetic speaker — A speaker in which acoustic waves are produced by mechanical forces resulting from magnetic reaction.

magnetic starter—A starter actuated electromagnetically.

magnetic storage — Any storage system in a computer which makes use of the magnetic properties of materials to store information.

magnetic storm—A disturbance in the earth's magnetic field. It is associated with abnormal solar activity and is capable of disrupting both radio and wire transmission.

magnetic strain gage—Also spelled gauge. An instrument for measuring strain in rails or other structural members that bend only microscopically under a normal load. It does this by determining the change in reluctance of a magnetic circuit having a movable armature.

magnetic susceptibility—Ratio of the intensity of magnetization to the corresponding value of the magnetizing force.

magnetic tape—The recording media used in tape recorders. A paper or plastic tape on which a magnetic emulsion (usually ferric oxide) has been deposited. The most common width for home recorders is one-quarter inch. Some tapes are made of a magnetic material and hence need no magnetic-emulsion coating.

magnetic-tape core—A toroidal core made by winding a strip of thin magnetic-core material around a form. A toroidal winder is then used to wind coils around the core.

magnetic tape recorder — A recorder in which magnetic tape is the recording medium.

magnetic test coil—Also called search or exploring coil. A coil which is connected to a suitable device to measure a change in the magnetic flux linked with it. The flux linkage may be changed by either moving the coil or varying the magnitude of the flux.

magnetic thin film—A layer of magnetic material, usually less than 10,000 angstroms thick. In electronic computers, magnetic thin films may be used for logic or storage elements.

magnetic transducer — See Variable-Reluctance Transducer.

magnetic transfer — See Magnetic Printing.

magnetic transition temperature — Also called the Curie point. In a ferromagnetic material, the point where its transition to paramagnetic seems to be complete as its temperature is raised.

magnetic tubes of flux — Regions in space

the sides of which are everywhere tangent to the magnetic induction and the ends of which may meet to form closed rings.

magnetic units—Ampere-turn, gauss, gilbert, line of force, maxwell, oersted, and unit magnetic pole are examples of magnetic units—i.e., those used in measuring magnetic quantities.

magnetic-vane meter—Also called a moving-vane meter. A meter for measuring alternating current. It contains a metal vane which pivots inside a coil. Alternating current flows through the coil and sets up magnetic forces which rotate the vane and attached pointer in proportion to the value of the current.

magnetic variometer — An instrument for measuring the differences in a magnetic field with respect to space or time.

magnetism—A property possessed by certain materials by which these materials can exert mechanical force on neighboring masses of magnetic materials and can cause voltages to be inducted in conducting bodies moving relative to the magnetized bodies.

magnetite—A mineral which exists in a magnetized condition in its natural state. It consists chiefly of a magnetic oxide of iron.

magnetization curve—A curve plotted on a graph to show successive states during magnetization of a ferromagnetic material. A normal magnetization curve is a portion of a symmetrical hysteresis loop. A virgin magnetization curve shows what happens to the material the first time it is magnetized.

magnetization intensity—At any point in a magnetized body, the ratio between the magnetic moment of the element of volume surrounding the point, and an infinitesimal volume.

magnetize—To make magnetic.

magnetizing current—*See* Exciting Current.

magnetizing force — Also called magnetic field strength. The magnetomotive force per unit length at any given point in a magnetic circuit. In the cgs system the unit is the oersted. It is defined by the equation:

$$\frac{\text{Magnetomotive force in gilberts}}{\text{Length in centimeters}}$$

Magnet keeper.

magnet keeper—A bar of iron or steel placed across the poles of a horseshoe magnet when the magnet is not in use. The keeper prevents the magnet from becoming demag-

netized, by completing the magnetic circuit to keep the flux from leaking off.

magnet meter—Also called a magnet tester. An instrument for measuring the magnetic flux produced by a permanent magnet. It usually comprises a torque-coil or moving-magnet magnetometer with a particular arrangement of pole pieces.

magneto—1. An a-c generator for producing ringing signals. 2. An a-c generator for producing the ignition voltage in some gasoline engines.

magnetoelastic coupling — Energy transfer between elastic and spin-wave modes of propagation. The strength of the effect varies with the material used.

magnetoelastic energy—In a crystal, energy of interaction between elastic (or lattice) strains and applied magnetization. If a ferromagnetic crystal is placed in a magnetic field, or if a magnetic field is varied about the crystal, the lattice structure of the crystal is distorted (magnetostriction occurs) and changes the amount of potential energy in the lattice. The energy associated with this change is magnetoelastic.

magnetoelastic wave—A hybrid of spin and elastic waves.

magnetoelectric generator—An electric generator with permanent-magnet field poles.

magnetoelectric transducer — A transducer which measures the emf generated by the movement of a conductor relative to a magnetic field.

magnetofluiddynamics—*See* Magnetohydrodynamics.

magnetofluidmechanics—*See* Magnetohydrodynamics.

magnetogasdynamics — *See* Magnetohydrodynamics.

magnetograph—A magnetometer that provides a continuous record of the changes occurring in the earth's magnetic field.

magnetohydrodynamic gyroscope — A gyroscope in which a rotating magnetic field drives a conducting fluid (e.g., mercury) around the closed path formed between the inner surface of a magnetic sleeve and the outer surface of a concentric magnetic cylinder.

magnetohydrodynamic power generation—The generating of electric current by the motion of an ionized gas.

magnetohydrodynamics—Abbreviated MHD. The study of the interaction between magnetic fields and electrically conductive fluids and gases. Also called magnetofluiddynamics, magnetofluidmechanics, magnetogasdynamics, hydromagnetics.

magnetoionic duct—A duct along the geomagnetic lines of force which exhibit waveguide characteristics for radio-wave propagation between conjugate points on the earth's surface.

magnetoionic wave component—Either of the two elliptically polarized wave components into which a linearly polarized wave

Magnetohydrodynamic generator.

in the ionosphere is separated by the earth's magnetic field.

magnetometer—An instrument for measuring the intensity or direction (or both) of a magnetic field (or component) in a particular direction.

magnetomotive force—The force by which a magnetic field is produced, either by a current flowing through a coil of wire or by the proximity of a magnetized body. The amount of magnetism produced in the first method is proportional to the current through the coil and the number of turns in it. The cgs unit of magnetomotive force is called the gilbert. Magnetomotive force may also result from a magnetized body.

magnetoresistance—The change in electrical conductivity of a material when a magnetic field is applied. This change is quite pronounced in materials with a high carrier mobility.

magnetoresistor—A semiconductor device in which the electrical resistance is a function of the applied magnetic field.

Magnetoresistor.

magnetosphere—A 900-mile–thick belt in the upper atmosphere, composed primarily of helium gas.

magnetostatic field—A magnetic field that is neither moving nor changing direction. Such a field could be produced by a stationary

magnetic pole or by a constant current flowing in a stationary conductor.

magnetostriction—That property of certain ferromagnetic metals, such as nickel, iron, cobalt, and manganese alloys, which causes them to shrink or expand when placed in a magnetic field. Conversely, if subjected to compression or tension, the magnetic reluctance changes, thus making it possible for a magnetostrictive wire or rod to vary a magnetic field in which it may be placed. This is true for lateral as well as longitudinal strains.

magnetostriction microphone—A microphone in which the deformation of a magnetostrictive material generates the required voltages.

magnetostriction oscillator—An oscillator in which the frequency is determined by the characteristics of the magnetostrictive element that inductively couples the plate circuit to the grid circuit.

magnetostriction speaker—A speaker in which the mechanical displacement is derived from the deformation of a magnetostrictive material.

Magnetostriction transducer.

magnetostriction transducer—A transducer comprising an element of magnetostrictive material inside a coil, and a force-summing member attached to one end of the element. Current flows through the coil, and the magnetic field around it expands and contracts the element to move the member back and forth.

magnetostrictive delay line—A delay line made of nickel or certain other materials which become shorter when placed in a magnetic field.

magnetostrictive filter—A filter network which uses the magnetostrictive phenomena to form high-pass, low-pass, bandpass, or band-elimination filters. The impedance characteristic is the inverse of that of a crystal.

magnetostrictive relay—A relay that functions because of dimensional changes occurring in a magnetic material under the influence of a magnetic field.

magnetostrictive resonator—A ferromagnetic rod which can be excited magnetically so that it will resonate (vibrate) at one or more desired frequencies.

magneto telephone—A telephone equipped with a magneto (a hand-driven, two-pole, ringing-signal generator). Although obsolete

293

for home and business telephones, it is still used in many field applications.

Magnetron.

magnetron—An electron tube which produces an a-c power output. The tube is surrounded by an electromagnet, which controls the flow of electrons from cathode to anode.

magnetron effect—In a thermionic vacuum tube, the reduced electron emission due to the magnetic field of the filament current.

magnetron oscillator—An electron tube in which electrons are accelerated by a radial electric field between the cathode and one or more anodes and by an axial magnetic field that provides a high-energy electron stream to excite the tank circuits.

magnetron pulling—A shift in the frequency of a magnetron due to a change in the standing waves on the r-f lines.

magnetron pushing—The shift in frequency of a magnetron caused by faulty modulator operation.

magnetron rectifier—A gas-tube rectifier in which the electron stream is controlled by an optical element or instrument instead of by heated electrodes.

magnet steel—A special steel used in permanent magnets because of its high retentivity. In addition to steel, it also contains tungsten, cobalt, chromium, and manganese.

magnet strip—Sheet or foil aluminum (either bare or insulated) used as a conductor in electric windings. Copper is also used sometimes.

magnet tester—*See* Magnet Meter.

magnettor—*See* Magnetic Modulator.

magnet wire—An insulated copper wire used for winding the coils of electromagnets.

magnified sweep—In an oscilloscope, a sweep the time per division of which has been decreased by amplification of the sweep waveform rather than by changing the time constants used to generate it.

Magnistor—A saturable reactor for controlling electrical pulses or sine waves having frequencies of 100 kHz to 30 MHz and power levels ranging from microwatts to tens of watts.

magnitude—Size; the quantity assigned to one unit so that it may be compared with other units of the same class (i.e., the ratio of one quantity to another).

magnitude-controlled rectifier—A type of rectifier circuit in which a thyratron is used as the rectifying element. The load current is controlled by varying the bias on the grid of the thyratron.

mag-slip—A British term for synchro (i.e., a synchronous device such as the selsyn, autosyn, motortorque and generator).

main anode—The anode which conducts the load current.

main bang—The transmitted pulse of a radar system.

main control unit—Transmitter or receiver controls for energizing, adjustment, etc., of the transmitter or receiver, but not for operating it while on the air.

main exciter—An exciter which supplies energy for the field excitation of another exciter.

main frame—1. Also called central processing unit. The central processor of the computer system. It contains the main storage, arithmetic unit, and special register groups. 2. All of a computer exclusive of the input, output, peripheral, and, in some instances, storage units.

main gap—The conduction path between the principal cathode and anode.

main power—Power supplied to a complete system from a line.

mains—Interior wires extending from the service switch, generator bus, or converter bus to the main distribution center.

main storage—Usually the fastest storage device of a computer and the one from which instructions are executed.

main sweep—The longest-range scale available on some fire-control radars.

maintained contact switch—A switch which remains in a given condition until actuated to another condition, which is also maintained until further actuation.

maintained switch—A switch which remains at the operated circuit condition when the actuating force is removed. It returns to the normal circuit condition, or moves to another position, when actuated a second time.

maintainability—The probability of restoring a system to its specified operating conditions within a specified total down time, when maintenance action is initiated under stated conditions.

maintenance—All procedures necessary to keep an item in, or restoring it to, a serviceable condition, including servicing, repair, modification, modernization, overhaul, inspection, etc.

major-apex face—In a natural quartz crystal, any one of the three larger sloping faces extending to the apex (pointed) end. The other three are called the minor-apex faces.

major cycle—1. In a memory device which provides serial access to storage positions, the time interval between successive appearances of a given storage position. 2. A number of minor cycles.

major defects—Those defects usually responsible for the failure of a component to function in its intended manner.

major face—Any one of the three larger sides of a hexagonal quartz crystal.

major failure—A noncritical failure that can degrade the system performance due to cumulative tolerance buildup.

majority carrier—The predominant carrier in a semiconductor. Electrons are the majority carrier in N-type semiconductors, since there are more electrons than holes. Likewise, holes are the majority carrier in P-types, since they outnumber the electrons.

majority-carrier contact—An electrical contact across which the ratio of majority-carrier current to applied voltage is substantially independent of the voltage polarity but the ratio of minority-carrier current to applied voltage is not.

majority emitter—The transistor electrode from which the majority carriers flow into the interelectrode region.

major lobe—The antenna lobe in the direction of maximum energy radiation or reception.

major loop—A continuous network composed of all the forward elements and the primary feedback elements of a feedback control system.

make—The closing of a relay, key, or other contact.

make-before-break contacts—Double-throw contacts so arranged that the moving contact establishes a new circuit before disrupting the old one.

make-before-break switch—*See* Shorting Switch.

make-break contacts—Also called continuity-transfer contact. A contact form of a relay, in which one contact closes connection to another contact and then opens its prior connection to a third contact.

make-break electrode—In a mercury switch, that electrode which serves the function of making and breaking contact with the mercury pool to close or open the electrical circuit.

make contact—The contact which closes a circuit when a normally open device is operated. *Also see* Normally Open Contact.

male—Adapted so as to fit into a matching hollow part.

malfunction—*See* Error.

mandrel test—A test used to determine the flexibility of insulation. In it a wire, with or without previous stretch, is wrapped around a mandrel.

manganin—An alloy wire used in precision wirewound resistors because of its low temperature coefficient of resistance.

manipulated variable—A quantity or condition that is varied as a function of the actuating signal in order to control the value of the directly controlled variable.

man-made interference—A type of electromagnetic interference generated by electric motors, communication and broadcast transmitters, fluorescent lighting, and other electrical and electronic systems that radiate spurious signals.

man-made static—High-frequency noise signals created by sparking in an electric circuit. When picked up by radio receivers, it causes buzzing and crashing sounds from the speaker.

Manometer.

manometer—A gage for measuring the pressure of gases. It contains a column of incompressible liquid. The amount the liquid is displaced indicates the magnitude of the pressure causing the displacement.

manpack—Also called packset. A portable radio-transmitting/receiving device which can be carried easily in a harness by a man.

manual — 1. Hand operated. 2. In an organ, a group of keys played with the hand. In two-manual organs the upper manual, also referred to as the solo or swell manual, is normally used to play the melody. The lower manual, also referred to as the accompaniment manual or great manual, is normally used to play the accompaniment.

manual control—1. The opening or closing of switches by hand. 2. The direction of a computer by means of manually operated switches.

manual controller—An electric controller in which all but its basic functions are performed by hand.

manual direction finder—A radio compass that uses a rotatable loop which is operated manually.

manual preset timer—A manual start timer, the cycle of which is initiated by turning a pointer to the desired setting.

manual reset—A qualifying term used to indicate that a relay may be reset manually after an operation.

manual ringing—A method of ringing a telephone. The key must be held down for the ringing to continue. Nor does it stop when the receiver is lifted off the hook, unless the caller releases the key.

manual start timer — An interval time on which each cycle must be manually started at the timer.

manual switch—A switch which is actuated by an operator.

manual switchboard — A telephone switchboard in which the operator makes connections manually with plugs and jacks or with keys.

manual switching—A characteristic of a circuit breaker permitting manual opening and closing of the circuit by operation of the actuator.

manual telegraphy—Telegraphy in which an operator forms the individual characters of the alphabet in code.

manual telephone set—A set not equipped with a dial for securing the number to be called. Instead, lifting the receiver alerts the switchboard operator, who then connects the caller to the person being called.

manual telephone system — A system in which telephone connections between customers are ordinarily established manually by telephone operators, in accordance with orders given verbally by the calling parties.

manual tuning—Rotation by hand of a knob on a radio receiver to tune in a desired station.

manufacturing holes—*See* Pilot Holes.

Marconi antenna — An antenna system in which one end of the signal source is connected to a radiating element and the other end is connected to ground.

margin—1. The difference between an actual operating point and the point or conditon where a failure to operate properly will occur. 2. Also called range or printing range. In telegraphy, the interval between limits on a scale, usually arbitrary, in which printing is error-free.

marginal checking — Also called marginal testing. Preventive maintenance in which certain operating conditions (e.g., supply voltage or frequency) are varied from normal in order to locate defects before they become serious.

marginal relay—A relay with a small margin between its nonoperative current value (maximum current applicable without operation) and its operative value (minimum current that operates the relay).

marginal testing—*See* Marginal Checking.

marine broadcast station—A coastal station which regularly broadcasts the time and meteorological and hydrographic information.

marine radiobeacon station — A radionavigation land station, the emissions from which are used to determine the bearing or direction of a ship in relation to the marine radiobeacon station.

maritime mobile service—The radio service in which ships communicate with each other or with coastal and other land stations on specified frequencies.

maritime radionavigation service—A radio service intended to be used for the navigation of ships.

mark — 1. In telegraphy, the closed-circuit condition—i.e., the signal that closes the circuit at the receiver to produce a click of the key or to print a character on a teletypewriter. 2. The presence of signal. In telegraph communications a mark represents the closed condition or current flowing. A mark impulse is equivalent to a binary 1. 3. *See* Flag.

marker—Also called marker beacon. A radio navigational aid consisting of a transmitter that sends a signal to designate the small area around and above it.

marker antenna—The transmitting antenna for a marker beacon.

marker beacon—*See* Marker.

marker generator—An r-f generator that injects one or more pips of a specific frequency onto the response curve of a tuned circuit being displayed on the screen of a cathode-ray oscilloscope.

marker pip—The inverted V (Λ) or spot of light used as a frequency index mark in cathode-ray oscilloscopes for alignment of tv sets. It is produced by coupling a fixed-frequency oscillator to the output of a sweep-driven signal generator.

marker thread—A colored thread laid parallel and adjacent to the strands of an insulated conductor which identifies the wire manufacturer and often the specification under which the wire is constructed.

marking-and-spacing intervals — In telegraphy, the intervals corresponding to the closed and open positions, respectively, of the originating transmitting contacts.

marking pulse—The signal interval during which the selector unit of a teletypewriter is operated.

marking wave—Also called keying wave. In telegraphy, the emission while the active portions of the code characters are being transmitted.

mark sense—To mark a position on a punch card, using a special pencil that leaves an electrically conductive deposit for later conversion to machine punching.

mark sensing—A technique for detecting special pencil marks entered in special places on a card and automatically translating the marks into punched holes.

marshalling sequence — *See* Collating Sequence.

maser—Acronym for Microwave Amplification by Stimulated Emission of Radiation. A low-noise microwave amplifier in which a signal is boosted by changing the energy level of a gas or crystal (commonly, ammonia or ruby, respectively).

mask—1. A frame mounted in front of a television picture tube to limit the viewing area of the screen. 2. A device (usually a thin sheet of metal which contains an open pattern) used to shield selected portions of a base during a deposition process. 3. A device used to shield selected portions of a photosensitive material during photographic processing.

masking—The process by which a sound is made audible by the addition of a second sound called the masking sound. The unit of measurement is usually the decibel.

masking audiogram—A graphical representation of the amount of masking by a noise. It is plotted in decibels as a function of the frequency of the masked tone.

mask microphone—A microphone designed for use inside an oxygen or other respiratory mask.

Masonite—Trade name of The Masonite Corp. Fiberboard made from steam-exploded wood fiber. Its highly compressed forms are used for panels in electrical equipment.

mass—The quantity of matter in an object. It is equal to the weight of a body divided by the acceleration due to gravity.

mass data—A larger amount of data than can be stored in the central processing unit of a computer at any one time.

mass radiator—A spark radiator which generates a low-level, broad-band signal extending into and above the ehf band. Arcing occurs between fine metal particles suspended in a liquid dielectric.

mass spectrometer—An instrument that permits rapid analysis of chemical compounds. It consists of a vacuum tube into which a small amount of the gas to be studied is admitted. The gas is ionized by the electrons emitted from the cathode and speeded up by an accelerating grid. An electric field draws the ions out of the ionizing chamber. They are then sent through electric and magnetic fields that sort them according to their ratios of mass to charge.

mass spectrum—The spectrum obtained by deflecting a beam of electrons with an electric or magnetic field as they emerge from a tube containing a small quantity of the gas being investigated. The amount a particle is deflected depends on the ratio of its mass to its atomic charge. Hence, every element has a characteristic mass-spectrum line.

mast—The pole on which an antenna is mounted.

master—The mold from which other disc recordings are cast. It is made by electroforming from a disc recording, and is a "negative" of the disc (i.e., has ridges instead of grooves).

master brightness control—In a color television receiver, a variable resistor that adjusts the bias level on all three guns in the picture tube at the same time.

master clock—1. In a computer, the primary source of timing signals. 2. A very accurate timer with an absolute time reference, providing controlled power to drive slave or auxiliary timers and display units. May also provide correcting pulses for slave devices.

master contactor—A device which is generally controlled by a master element or equivalent, and the necessary permissive and protective devices, and which serve to make and break the necessary control circuits to place an equipment into operation under the desired conditions, and to take it out of operation under other or abnormal conditions.

master control—1. In a studio, a central point from which sound or television programs are switched to one or more transmitters. 2. An application-oriented routine usually applied to the highest level of a subroutine hierarchy.

master drawing—A drawing showing the dimensional limits or grid location applicable to any or all parts of a printed circuit including the base.

master drive—A drive that determines the reference input for one or more follower drives.

master element—The initiating device, such as a control switch, voltage relay, float switch, etc., which serves either directly or through such permissive devices as protective and time-delay relays to place an equipment in or out of operation.

master file—In a computer, a file of relatively more permanent information that is usually updated periodically.

master gain control—An amplifier control that permits adjusting the gain of two or more channels simultaneously.

master oscillator—In an amplifier, the oscillator that establishes the carrier frequency of the output.

master oscillator-power amplifier—Abbreviated MOPA. An oscillator followed by a radio-frequency buffer-amplifier stage.

master pattern—An accurately scaled pattern which is used to produce the printed circuit within the accuracy specified in the master drawing.

master reticle—A reticle plate properly aligned in a reticle frame and sealed in place. The master reticle is inserted into a photorepeater to make the final-sized photomask. Used in the production of monolithic circuits.

master routine—*See* Subroutine.

master slice—Silicon wafers containing 30 or more groups of components. The elements can be interconnected with paths of aluminum to form desired circuits. The wafer is then diced into single devices.

master stamper—A master from which phonograph records are pressed.

master station—The radio station to which the emissions of other stations of a synchronized group are referred.

master switch—The switch that dominates the operation of contactors, relays, or other electromagnetic devices.

master tv system—A combination of components for providing multiple tv sets operation from one antenna.

master wafer—A processed semiconductor wafer with unconnected active and passive circuit elements located in a standardized pattern. Different integrated circuits may be synthesized by using various interconnection paths.

MAT—Acronym for microalloy transistor.

match—The similarity or equality of one thing to another.

matched filter—An optimum filter for separating a waveform of known shape from random perturbing noise.

matched impedance—The condition that exists when two coupled circuits are adjusted so that the impedance of one circuit equals the impedance of the other.

matched load—A device used to terminate a transmission line or waveguide so that all the energy from the signal source will be absorbed.

matched power gain—That power gain which is obtained when the impedance of the load is matched to the effective output impedance of the amplifier to which the load is connected.

matched symmetrical transistor—A special case of the bidirectional transistor in which not only are the requirements for a symmetrical transistor met, but actual matching specifications are also given. *Also See* Symmetrical Transistor.

matched termination—A termination that does not reflect the waves along the waveguide or transmission line.

matched transmission line—A transmission line along which there is no wave reflection.

matched waveguide—A waveguide along which there is no reflected wave.

matching—Connecting two circuits or parts together with a coupling device in such a way that the maximum transfer of energy occurs between the two circuits, and the impedance of either circuit will be terminated in its image.

matching diaphragm—A window consisting of an aperture (slit) in a thin piece of metal, placed transversely across a waveguide; used as a matching device. The orientation of the slit (whether parallel to the long or short dimensions of the waveguide) determines whether it is respectively capacitive or inductive.

matching impedance—The impedance value that must be connected to the terminals of a signal-voltage source for proper matching.

matching plate—In waveguides, a diaphragm used for matching.

matching stub—A device placed on a radio-frequency transmission line to vary its electrical length and hence its impedance.

matching transformer—A transformer used for matching impedances.

mate—Joining of two connector halves, or of a cable to a connector.

material system—The designation of the number of basic metals (e.g., silver-antimony-telluride) making up thermoelectric materials.

mathematical check—A check making use of mathematical identities or other properties.

mathematical logic—Also called symbolic logic. Exact reasoning concerning nonnumerical relations by using symbols that are efficient in calculation.

matrix—1. A coding network or system in a computer. When signals representing a certain code are applied to the inputs, the output signals are in a different code. 2. In electronic computers, any logical network the configuration of which is a rectangular array of intersections of its input-output leads, with elements connected at some of these intersections. The network usually functions as an encoder or decoder. 3. A computer network or system in which only one input is excited at a time and produces a combination of outputs. 4. In a color tv circuit, the section that combines the I, Q, and Y signals and transforms them into individual red, green, and blue signals which are applied to the picture-tube grids.

matrixer—Also called matrix unit. A device which transforms the color coordinates, usually by electrical or optical means.

matrix life test—A test in which each test condition has two components. For example in transistor-matrix life testing each life-test condition is represented by an ambient temperature and a power dissipation. At each stress level of temperature, there are several dissipations; and at each stress level of dissipation, there are several temperatures. The test conditions are placed into blocks or groups.

matrix unit—*See* Matrixer.

matter—Any physical entity—i.e., having mass.

Matteucci effect—The ability of a twisted ferromagnetic wire to generate a voltage as its magnetization changes.

max—Abbreviation for maximum.

maxima/minima—In radar, regions of maximum and minimum return from the transmitted pulse caused by additive and subtractive combinations of the direct and reflected wave. A plot of these data is usually known as a null pattern or fade chart.

maximum—Abbreviated max. The highest value occurring during a stated period.

maximum average power output—In television, the maximum radio-frequency output power, averaged over the longest repetitive modulation cycle.

maximum deviation sensitivity—Under maximum system deviation, the smallest signal input for which the output distortion does not exceed a specified limit.

maximum frequency of oscillation—The highest frequency at which a transistor or vacuum tube will oscillate.

maximum keying frequency—In a facsimile system, the frequency (in hertz) equal to half the number of critical areas of the subject copy scanned per second.

maximum modulating frequency—In a facsimile system, the maximum scanning frequency process that can be transmitted without degrading the recorded copy.

maximum output—The highest average output power into a rated load, regardless of distortion.

maximum overshoot—The maximum amplitude deviation from the average of the steady-state values that exist immediately before and after the transient.

maximum peak plate current—The highest instantaneous plate current a tube can safely carry.

maximum percentage modulation — The highest percentage of modulation permitted in a transmitter without producing excessive harmonics in the modulating frequency.

maximum permeability—The highest permeability reached as induction or magnetization is increased.

maximum power transfer theorem — The maximum power that will be absorbed by one network from another joined to it at two terminals, when the impedance of the receiving network is varied, if the impedances (looking into the two networks at the junction) are conjugates of each other.

maximum record level—In direct recording, the amount of record-head current required to produce 3-percent third-harmonic distortion of the reproduced signal at the record-level set frequency. Such distortion must result from magnetic-tape saturation, not from electronic circuitry.

maximum response speed — The maximum pulse frequency that can be applied to a stepper motor at random and result in synchronized steps. The motor must not miss a step while operating within this range.

maximum retention time — The maximum time interval between writing into a storage element of a charge storage tube, and reading an acceptable output.

maximum sensitivity — The smallest signal input that produces a specified output.

maximum signal level — In an amplitude-modulated system, the level corresponding to copy black or copy white—whichever has the higher amplitude.

maximum sound pressure — For any given cycle of a periodic wave, the maximum absolute value of the instantaneous sound pressure. The most common unit is a microbar.

maximum storage time—In a storage tube, the length of time after writing during which an acceptable output can be read. *Also See* Maximum Usable Viewing Time.

maximum system deviation—In a frequency-modulation system, the greatest permissible deviation in frequency.

maximum undistorted output—Also called maximum useful output. The maximum power an amplifier can deliver without producing excessive harmonics.

maximum usable frequency — Abbreviated MUF. In radio transmission by ionospheric reflection, the highest frequencies that can be transmitted by reflection from regular ionized layers.

maximum usable viewing time—Also called maximum storage time. The length of time during which the visible output of a storage tube can be viewed, without rewriting, before a specified decay occurs.

maximum useful output—*See* Maximum Undistorted Output.

maximum writing rate—The maximum spot speed which produces a line of specified density on a photographic negative or on the screen of a cathode-ray tube.

maxwell—10^{-8} weber, the cgs unit of magnetic flux.

Maxwell bridge.

Maxwell bridge—A four-arm a-c bridge normally used for measuring inductance in terms of resistance and capacitance (or capacitance in terms of resistance and inductance). One arm has an inductor in series with a resistor, and the opposite arm has a capacitor in parallel with a resistor. The other two arms normally are nonreactive resistors. The balance is independent of frequency.

Maxwell inductance bridge—A four-arm a-c bridge for comparing inductances. Two adjacent arms have inductors, and the other two arms usually have nonreactive resistors. The balance is independent of frequency.

Maxwell mutual-inductance bridge—A four-arm a-c bridge for measuring mutual inductance in terms of self-inductance. Mutual inductance is present between the supply circuit and the arm which includes one coil of the mutual inductor. The other three arms normally are nonreactive resistors. The balance is independent of frequency.

Maxwell's equations — Fundamental equations, developed by J. C. Maxwell, for expressing radiation mathematically and describing the condition at any point under the influence of varying electric and magnetic fields.

Maxwell's law—A movable portion of a circuit will always travel in the direction that gives maximum flux linkages through the circuit.

Maxwell triangle—A graph that defines the chromaticity values of a color in terms of three coordinates.

Maxwell-turn—A unit of magnetic linkage equal to one magnetic line of force passing through one turn of a circuit.

mayday—International distress call for radio-telephone communication. It is derived from the French *m'aidez*, meaning "help me."

mc—Abbreviation for megacycle—an obsolete term superseded by MHz (megahertz).

MCM—*See* Monte Carlo Method.

McNally tube—A velocity-modulated vacuum tube that produces low-power uhf oscillations. It is used as a local oscillator in some radar receivers.

mcw—Abbreviation for modulated continuous wave.

m-derived filter—A filter derived by multiplying the values of a constant-K filter by a factor m, the value of which is less than unity.

m-derived L-section filter—A reactance network derived from the prototype L-section filter, so that the image-transfer coefficient and one image impedance are changed, but the other image impedance is left unchanged.

MDI — Abbreviation for magnetic direction indicator.

M-display—*See* M-Scan.

Meacham-bridge oscillator—A crystal oscillator in which the crystal forms one arm in a bridge so as to obtain effective multiplication of the actual Q of the crystal.

meaconing—The interception and rebroadcast of beacon signals. They are rebroadcast on the received frequency to confuse enemy navigation. As a result, aircraft or ground stations are given inaccurate bearings.

mean carrier frequency—The average carrier frequency of a transmitter (corresponding to the resting frequency in a frequency-modulated system).

mean charge — The arithmetic mean of the transferred charges corresponding to a given capacitor voltage, as determined from a specified alternating-charge characteristic curve.

mean charge characteristic — The function giving the relation of mean charge to capacitor voltage.

mean free path—1. The average distance which sound waves travel between successive reflections in an enclosure. 2. The average distance between collisions of atomic particles, which may be further specified according to type of collision (e.g., elastic, inelastic).

mean life — 1. Also called average life. In a semiconductor, the time taken by injected excess carriers to recombine with others of the opposite sign. 2. A measure of the probability that a part or equipment will function satisfactorily during its constant-failure-rate period. It is unrelated to longevity.

mean power of a radio transmitter—Power supplied to the antenna transmission line by a transmitter during normal operation, averaged over a time sufficiently long compared with the period of the lowest frequency encountered in the modulation. A time of 1/10 second during which the mean power is greatest will be selected normally.

mean pulse time—The arithmetic mean of the leading-edge and trailing-edge pulse times.

means of communications — The medium (i.e., electromagnetic or sound waves, visual, messenger) by which a message is conveyed from one person or place to another.

mean-time-between-failures — Abbreviated MTBF. The limit of the ratio of operating time in a device to the number of observed failures as the latter approaches infinity.

mean-time-to-failure — Abbreviated MTTF. In a piece of equipment, its measured operating time divided by its total number of failures during that time. Normally this measurement is made between the early-life and wearout failures.

mean-time-to-first-failure — Abbreviated MTTFF. A special case of MTBF, where T is the accumulated operating time to first failure of a number of devices (failures).

mean-time-to-repair — The total effective maintenance time during a given time interval divided by the total number of failures during the interval.

measurand—Also called stimulus. The physical quantity, force, property, or condition measured by an instrument.

measurement component—Those parts or subassemblies used primarily for the construction of measurement apparatus, excluding screws, nuts, insulated wire, or other stable materials.

measurement device—An assembly of one or more basic elements with other components needed to form a self-contained unit for performing one or more measurement operations. Included are the protecting, supporting, and connecting, as well as functioning parts.

measurement energy—The energy required to operate a measurement device or system. Normally it is obtained from the measurand or the primary detector.

measurement equipment — Any assemblage of measurement components, devices, apparatus, or systems.

measurement inverter—*See* Measuring Modulator.

measurement range of an instrument—The total range throughout which the instrument will provide an accurate measurement.

measurement voltage divider—Also called voltage-ratio or volt box. A combination of two or more resistors, capacitors, or other elements arranged in series so that the voltage across any one is a definite, known fraction of the voltage applied to the combination (provided the current drain at the tap point is negligible or taken into account). The term "volt box" is usually limited to resistance voltage dividers intended for extending the range of direct-current potentiometers.

measuring modulator—Also called measurement inverter or chopper. An intermediate means of modulating a direct-current or low-frequency alternating-current input in a measurement system to give a proportionate alternating-current output, usually as a preliminary to amplification.

mechanical bail — Switch action in which, upon actuation of one station, the switch changes the contact position, mechanically locks the switch in that position, and releases any station previously actuated.

mechanical bandspread — A vernier tuning dial or other mechanical means of lengthening the rotation of a control knob. This permits more precise tuning in crowded short-wave bands.

mechanical bias — A mechanical force tending to move the armature of a relay toward a given position.

mechanical compliance — The displacement of a mechanical element per unit of force, expressed in centimeters per dyne. It is the reciprocal of stiffness and is analogous to capacitance.

mechanical damping — Mechanical resistance, generally associated with the moving parts of a cutter or reproducer.

mechanical damping ring — A loose member mounted on a contact spring for the purpose of reducing contact chatter.

mechanical filter — See Mechanical Wave Filter.

mechanical impedance — The complex ratio of the effective force acting on a specified area of an acoustic medum or mechanical device to the resulting effective linear velocity through or of that area, respectively. The unit is the newton-sec/m or the mks mechanical ohm. (In the cgs system, the unit is the dyne-sec/cm or the mechanical ohm.)

mechanical joint — A joint made by clamping cables or other conductors together mechanically rather than by soldering them.

mechanical life — The maximum number of complete cycles through which a device may be actuated without electrical or mechanical failure.

mechanically timed relay — A relay that is mechanically timed by such means as a clockwork, escapement, bellows, or dashpot.

mechanical ohm — The magnitude of a mechanical resistance, reactance, or impedance for which a force of 1 dyne produces a linear velocity of 1 centimeter per second (dyne-sec/cm). When expressed in newton-sec/m it is called the mks mechanical ohm.

mechanical overtravel — The shaft travel of a precision potentiometer between each end point (or limit of theoretical electrical travel) and its adjacent corresponding limit of total mechanical travel.

mechanical phonograph — A phonograph the playback stylus of which drives the diaphragm of an acoustic pickup that radiates acoustic energy without any further amplification.

mechanical phonograph recorder — Also called mechanical recorder. Equipment that converts electric or acoustic signals into mechanical motion and cuts or embosses it into a medium.

mechanical reactance — The magnitude (size) of the imaginary component of mechanical impedance.

mechanical recorder — See Mechanical Phonograph Recorder.

mechanical recording head — See Cutter.

mechanical rectifier — A rectifier in which its action is done mechanically (e.g., by making and breaking the electrical circuit at the correct times with a rotating wheel or vibrating reed).

mechanical register — An electromechanical device which records or indicates a count.

mechanical reproducer — See Phonograph Pickup.

mechanical resistance — The real part of the mechanical impedance. The cgs unit is the mechanical ohm. The mks unit is the mks mechanical ohm.

mechanical scanning — An obsolete type of scanning in which a rotating device, such as a disc or mirror, breaks up a scene into a rapid succession of narrow lines for conversion into electrical impulses.

mechanical shock — Shock which occurs when the position of a system is significantly changed in a relatively short time in a nonperiodic manner. It is characterized by suddenness and large displacements which develop significant internal displacements within the system.

mechanical television system — A television system which uses mechanical scanning.

mechanical transducer — A device that transforms mechanical energy directly into acoustical energy.

mechanical transmission system — An assembly of gears, etc., for transmitting mechanical power.

mechanical tuning range — The frequency range of oscillation of a klystron that is obtainable by tuning mechanically while keeping the reflector voltage optimized for the peak of the reflector-voltage mode.

mechanical tuning rate — In a klystron, the frequency change per degree of rotation of the tuning apparatus while oscillation is maintained on the peak of the reflector-voltage mode.

mechanical wave filter — Also called mechanical filter. A filter that separates mechanical waves of different frequencies.

mechanical waveform synthesizer — A device which mechanically generates an electrical signal with the desired waveform.

mechanism of failure — See Failure Mode.

mechanized assembly — The joining together of elements by operators using semiautomatic equipment as contrasted to fully automatic assembly.

median — The middle, or average, value in a series (e.g., in the series 1, 2, 3, 4, and 5, the median is 3).

medical electronics — The branch of electronics concerned with its therapeutic or diagnostic applications in the field of medicine.

medium frequency — The band of frequencies between 300 kHz and 3000 kHz (3 MHz).

medium-power silicon rectifiers — Rectifiers with maximum continuous ratings of 1 to

50 average amperes per section in a single-phase, half-wave circuit.

meg—Abbreviation for megohm.

mega—Abbreviated M. Prefix denoting 10^6 (one million).

megabar—The absolute unit of pressure equal to one million bars.

megabit—A unit equal to one-million binary digits.

megacycle (mc)—One million cycles—Obsolete term replaced by megahertz. (MHz).

megahertz—One million hertz. Abbreviated MHz.

megampere—One million amperes. Abbreviated Ma.

megatron—A tube having a high power output at high frequencies, but very low interelectrode capacitances because its electrodes are arranged in parallel layers. *Also see* Disc-Seal Tube.

megavolt — One million volts. Abbreviated Mv.

megavolt-ampere — One million volt-amperes. Abbreviated Mva.

megawatt — One million watts. Abbreviated Mw.

megawatt-hour — One million watt-hours. Abbreviated Mwh.

megger—A high-range ohmmeter having a built-in, hand-driven generator as a direct voltage source, used for measuring insulation resistance values and other high resistances. Also used for continuity, ground, and short-circuit testing in general electrical power work.

megohm — Abbreviated meg. One million ohms.

megohm-farads—*See* Megohm-Microfarad.

megohm-microfarad—A term used to indicate the insulation resistance of capacitors. For larger high-voltage capacitors, megohm-farads are used.

megohm sensitivity—The resistance in megohms which must be placed in series with a galvanometer in order that an applied emf of 1 volt shall produce the standard deflection. If the resistance of the galvanometer coil itself is neglected, the number representing the megohm sensitivity is equal to the reciprocal of the number representing the current sensitivity.

Meissner effect—The sudden loss of magnetism in superconductors as they are cooled below the temperature required for superconductivity. As a result, they become diamagnetic—i.e., the self-induced magnetization opposes the applied magnetic field to such an extent that there is no longer a magnetic field.

Meissner oscillator—An oscillator in which the grid and plate circuits are inductively coupled through an independent tank circuit, which determines the frequency.

mel—A unit of pitch. A simple 1,000-hertz tone, 40 db above a listener's threshold, produces a pitch of 1,000 mels. The pitch of

any sound that is judged by the listener to be n times that of a 1-mel tone is n mels.

meltback process—The making of junctions by melting a correctly doped semiconductor and allowing it to refreeze.

meltback transistor — A grown transistor produced by melting the tip of a double-doped pellet. Junctions are formed when the tip recrystallizes.

melting channel—The restricted portion of the charge in a submerged horizontal ring induction furnace. The induced currents are concentrated here to effect high energy absorption and thereby melt the charge.

melt-quench transistor—A junction transistor made by quickly cooling a melted-back region.

memory—*See* Storage.

memory buffer register — In a computer, a register in which a word is stored as it comes from memory (reading) or just prior to its entering memory (writing).

memory capacity—*See* Storage Capacity.

memory cycle—In a computer, an operation consisting of reading from and writing into memory.

memory dump—In a computer, a process of writing the contents of memory consecutively in such a form that it can be examined for computer or program errors.

memory fill—In a computer, the placing of a pattern of characters in the memory registers not in use in a particular problem to stop the computer if the program, through error, seeks instructions taken from forbidden registers.

memory register—Also called high-speed bus, distributor, or exchange register. In some computers, a register used in all data and instruction transfers between the memory, the arithmetic unit, and the control register.

memory relay—A relay in which each of two or more coils may operate independent sets of contacts, and another set of contacts remains in a position determined by the coil last energized. The term is sometimes erroneously used for polarized relay.

memory timer—A timing device wherein the cycle duration is infinitely variable within the specified overall cycle time and having the ability, once the cycle is selected, to repeat this cycle any number of times by a simple mechanical actuation of the time shaft.

memory unit—That part of a digital computer in which information is stored in machine language, using electrical or magnetic techniques.

mercuric-oxide–cadmium cell — A primary-cell electrochemical system. Its primary advantage is its long shelf life in the fully charged condition and its operation at low temperatures, far below $0°C$. Nominal cell voltage is about 0.9 volt.

mercury—A silver-white metal that becomes a liquid above $-38.87°$ Centigrade. In addition to thermometers, it is used in switches and many electronic tubes. When it is vaporized, mercury ionizes readily and conducts electricity.

mercury arc — A cold-cathode arc through ionized mercury vapor. A very bright bluish-green glow is given off.

mercury-arc converter — A frequency converter using a mercury vapor tube.

mercury-arc rectifier — Also called mercury-vapor or simply mercury rectifier. A diode rectifier tube containing mercury vapor. The mercury vapor is ionized by the voltage across the tube, and a much greater current can flow. There is only a small voltage drop in the tube during conduction.

mercury barometer — An instrument for measuring atmospheric pressure.

mercury battery — A type of battery characterized by extremely uniform output throughout its life. Employs a zinc-powder anode; the cathode is mercuric-oxide powder and graphite powder.

Mercury cell.

mercury cell — A primary cell with a zinc anode and a mercuric-oxide cathode in a potassium-hydroxide electrolyte. This cell offers a higher capacity than the alkaline or zinc-carbon cells and a much flatter voltage-discharge characteristic.

mercury-contact relay — A relay in which the contacts are mercury.

mercury delay line — *See* Mercury Memory.

mercury displacement relay — A relay in which the displacement of mercury, such as caused by a solenoid-actuated plunger, results in a mercury-to-mercury electrical contact.

mercury-hydrogen spark-gap converter — A spark-gap generator in which the source of radio-frequency power is the oscillatory discharge of a capacitor through an inductor and a spark gap. The latter comprises a solid electrode and a pool of mercury in hydrogen.

mercury-jet scanning switch — A commutating switch in which a stream of mercury performs the switching between the common circuit and those to be sampled.

mercury memory — Also called mercury storage and mercury delay line. Delay lines us-

Mercury-jet scanning switch.

ing mercury as the medium for storage of a circulating train of waves or pulses.

mercury-motor meter — A motor meter in which a portion of the rotor is immersed in mercury, which directs the current through conducting portions of the rotor.

mercury-pool cathode — The cathode of a gas tube consisting of a pool of mercury. An arc spot on the pool emits electrons.

mercury rectifier — *See* Mercury-Arc Rectifier.

mercury relay — A relay in which the energized coil pulls a magnetic plunger into a tube containing mercury. The plunger moves the mercury in order to make connection between the contacts.

mercury storage — *See* Mercury Memory.

mercury switch — An electric switch comprising a large globule of mercury in a metal or glass tube. Tilting the tube causes the mercury to move toward or away from the electrodes to make or break the circuit.

mercury tank — In a computer, a container of mercury holding one or more delay lines for storing information.

mercury-vapor lamp — A glow lamp in which mercury vapor is ionized by the electric current, producing a bluish-green luminous discharge.

mercury-vapor rectifier — *See* Mercury-Arc Rectifier.

mercury-vapor tube — A tube containing mercury vapor, which when ionized allows conduction and produces a luminous glow.

mercury-wetted contact relay — A special form of reed relay. It consists of a glass-encapsulated reed, with its base mounted in a pool of mercury and the other end arranged so as to move between two sets of stationary contacts. By capillary action, the mercury flows up the reed to coat the movable and stationary contact surfaces, thus assuring mercury-to-mercury contact during make.

merge — To produce a single sequence of items ordered according to some rule (i.e., arranged in some orderly sequence), from two or more sequences previously ordered according to the same rule, without changing the size, structure, or total number of the items.

mesa isolation — A process for isolating IC's in which transistors, resistors, and other components are fabricated before isolation.

303

mesa transistor—A transistor that is produced by chemically etching away a transistor chip formed by either a double-diffused or diffused-alloy process. When the etching process is complete, the base and emitter regions appear as plateaus above the collector region. One result of the mesa construction is a reduction in the collector-base capacitance as a result of lowering the junction area.

mesh—Sometimes called a loop. A set of branches forming a closed path in a network—provided that if any branch is omitted, the remaining branches do not form a closed path.

mesh beat—*See* Moiré.

mesh current—The current assumed to exist over all cross sections of a closed path in a network. It may be the total current in a branch included in the path, or a partial current which, when combined with the others, forms the total current.

meson—A particle which weighs more than an electron but generally less than a proton. Mesons can be produced artificially as well as by cosmic radiation. They are so unstable that they disintegrate in millionths of a second.

message—1. An ordered selection of an agreed set of symbols for the purpose of communicating information. 2. The original modulating wave in a communication system.

metadyne—British term for amplidyne. A direct-current machine used for voltage regulation or transformation. It has more than two brushes for each pair of poles.

metal—A material that has high electrical and thermal conductivity at normal temperatures.

metal-base transistor—A transistor with a base of a thin metal film sandwiched between two N-type semiconductors, with the emitter doped more heavily than the base to give it a high electron-current–to–hole-current ratio.

metal detector—Also called metal locator. An electronic device for detecting concealed metal objects.

metal film resistor—An electronic component in which the resistive element is an extremely thin layer of metal alloy vacuum-deposited on a substrate.

metalized capacitor—A self-healing fixed capacitor. A thin film of metal is vacuum-deposited directly on the dielectric, which can be paper or plastic. When a breakdown

metalized resistor—A fixed resistor in which the resistance element is a thin film of metal deposited on the surface of a glass or ceramic substrate.

metalizing—Applying a thin coating of metal to a nonmetallic surface. This may be done by chemical deposition or by exposing the surface to vaporized metal in a vacuum chamber.

occurs, the metal film around it immediately burns away.

metallic circuit—A circuit in which the earth itself is not used as ground.

metallic insulator—A shorted quarter-wave section of transmission line. It acts as an electrical insulator at a quarter-wave length of the transmitted frequency.

metallic noise—Weighted noise current in a metallic circuit at a given point when the circuit is terminated at that point in the nominal characteristic impedance of the circuit.

metallic rectifier—A rectifier in which the asymmetrical junction between dissimilar solid conductors presents a high resistance to current flow in one direction and a low resistance in the opposite direction.

metallic-rectifier cell—An elementary rectifying device having only one positive electrode, negative electrode, and rectifying junction.

metallic-rectifier stack—A single structure made up of one or more metallic-rectifier cells.

metal locator—*See* Metal Detector.

metal master—*See* Original Master.

metal negative—*See* Original Master.

metal-oxide resistor—A type of film resistor in which the material deposited on the substrate is tin oxide, which provides good stability.

metal-oxide semiconductor—The technique of insulating a metalized electrode, the "gate" from a semiconductor substrate material using an oxide (or nitride) dielectric to form a unipolar device. Abbreviated MOS.

Metal-oxide semiconductor transistor.

metal-oxide semiconductor transistor (MOST)—An active semiconductor device in which conduction is controlled in a region between two electrodes by a voltage applied to an insulated electrode over the region.

metal-tank mercury-arc rectifier—A mercury-arc rectifier in which its anodes and mercury cathode are enclosed in a metal chamber.

metal tube—A vacuum tube with a metal envelope. The electrode leads pass through glass beads fused into the metal housing.

meteorological aids service—A radio service in which emissions consist of special signals intended solely for meteorological uses.

meteorological radar station—A station, operating in the meteorological aids service, that employs radar and is not intended for operation while in motion.

meter—1. Any measuring device; specifically, any electrical or electronic measuring instrument. 2. In the metric system of measurement, the unit of length equal to 39.37 inches, 3.281 feet, or 1.094 yards.

meter ampere—A measure of the strength of a radio transmitter. It is equal to the antenna height in meters times the maximum antenna current in amperes.

meter-candle—*See* Lux.

meter-correction factor — The factor by which a meter reading must be multiplied to compensate for meter errors in order to obtain the true reading.

meter display—A display in which one or more pointer instruments give the indications.

meter-kilogram–second-ampere system of units—*See* MKSA System of Units.

meter rating — A manufacturer's designation used to indicate the operating limitations of the meter. The full-scale marking on a meter scale does not necessarily correspond to the rating of the meter.

meter resistance—The resistance of a meter as measured at the terminals at a given reference temperature. When applied to rectifier-type meters, the frequency and waveshape of the applied energy, as well as the indicated value at which the measurement is to be made, must be specified.

meter-type relay—A meter movement in which the armature function is performed by a contact-bearing pointer.

metrechon—A storage tube used in scanning converters (e.g., in radar and industrial tv).

metric system — The decimal system of weights and measures, used extensively by scientists.

metric waves—British classification for wavelengths between 1 and 10 meters.

mev—Usually pronounced M-E-V. Abbreviation for million electron-volts. 1 mev equals 4.45×10^{-20} kilowatt hours, or 1.6020×10^{-6} erg.

MEW — Abbreviation for microwave early warning.

mf—1. Abbreviation for medium frequency. 2. Alternate abbreviation for microfarad.

mfd—Alternate abbreviation for microfarad.

mh—Abbreviation for millihenry.

MHD — Abbreviation for magnetohydrodynamics.

mho—The unit of conductance of a conductor when a potential difference of 1 volt between its ends maintains an unvarying current of 1 ampere. The mho is the unit of conductance in the mksa system. This term has now been replaced by siemens.

MHz—Abbreviation for megahertz.

mica—A transparent mineral which can be split into thin sheets. Because of its excellent insulating and heat-resisting qualities, it is used to separate the plates of capacitors and to insulate electrode elements in vacuum tubes.

mica capacitor—A fixed capacitor employing mica sheets as the dielectric material between adjacent plates. The complete units are usually encased in molded *Bakelite*.

micro—1. In the metric system, a prefix meaning one millionth (1/1,000,000). 2. A prefix meaning something very small.

microalloy diffused transistor — Abbreviated MADT. A microalloy transistor made by incorporating diffusion techniques. Prior to the electrochemical plating process, the semiconductor wafer is subjected to gaseous diffusion in order to provide a nonuniform base region.

microalloy transistor — A high-frequency transistor in which the emitter and collector are alloyed to a slight depth on opposite sides of the germanium base material by an electrochemical process. Abbreviated MAT.

microammeter—A meter, having a scale that reads in microamperes, for measuring extremely small currents.

microampere—One millionth of an ampere.

microbar—A unit of pressure commonly used in acoustics. One microbar is equal to one dyne per square centimeter. (Originally the term "bar" denoted 1 dyne per square centimeter. Therefore, to avoid confusion it is preferable to use microbar or "dynes per square centimeter" when speaking of sound pressures.)

micro B-display—A B-scope in which range and azimuth data are so expanded that only a small portion of the area under surveillance is presented, and, because of the degree of expansion, distortion of the presentation is negligible.

microcircuit—A packaged circuit made up of discrete components which are often indistinguishable to the naked eye, or of components fabricated with integrated-circuit techniques. *Also see* Microminiaturization.

microcircuitry — A small circuit having a high equivalent circuit element density which is considered as a single part and which is a combination of interconnection elements inseparably associated on or within a single substrate to perform an electronic circuit function. This excludes printed-wiring boards, circuit-card assemblies, and modules composed exclusively of discrete electronic parts.

microcircuit wafer — A microwafer carrying one or more circuit functions such as a flip-flop or gate. Integrated-circuit chips may be bonded to deposited conductors.

microcoding — In a computer, a system of coding that uses suboperations not ordinarily accessible in programming.

microcomponents—Those components smaller than existing components by several orders of magnitude.

microdensitometer—An instrument used in spectroscopy to measure lines in a spectrum by light-transmission measurement.

microelectronic circuit — Discrete electrical components assembled and connected in extremely small and compact form.

microelectronic device — An alternate term for "integrated circuit."

microelectronics — Also called microsystems electronics. The entire body of electronic art which is connected with or applied to the realization of electronic systems from extremely small electronic parts.

microelement — A resistor, capacitor, transistor, diode, inductor, transformer, or other electronic element or combination of elements mounted on a small ceramic wafer (0.01 inch thick and about 0.3 inch square). Individual microelements are stacked, interconnected, and potted to form micromodules.

microelement wafer — A microwafer carrying one or more components or a simple network. The network can consist, for example, of several thin-film resistors deposited directly on the wafer.

microfarad — One millionth of a farad. Abbreviated mfd, mf, or μf.

microfaradmeter — *See* Capacitance Meter.

microflash lamp — A lamp that emits radiation pulses having a duration of approximately one microsecond.

microgroove — In disc recording, the groove width of most long-play and 45-rpm records. Normally it is .001 inch, or about half as wide as the groove on a 78-rpm record.

microgroove record — *See* Long-Play Record.

microhenry — One millionth of a henry.

microhm — One millionth of an ohm.

microlock — A phase-lock-loop system for transmitting and receiving information. Because the system reduces bandwidth drastically, it is used as a radar beacon for tracking, or to provide telemetering data.

micrologic — A group of high-speed, low-power integrated logic building blocks primarily intended to be used in building the logic section of a digital computer.

micrologic elements — Semiconductor networks used in computer and other critical circuits.

micromassage — *See* Intercellular Massage.

micromho — One millionth of a mho.

micromicro — An obsolete prefix meaning one-millionth of a millionth, or 10^{-12}. Now called pico.

micromicrofarad — Abbreviated mmf or mmfd. One millionth of a microfarad, or one picofarad.

micromicrowatt — One picowatt, or 10^{-12} watt.

microminiature lamp — Any incandescent lamp, usually rated in the milliwatt range, that operates on 3 volts or less. Diameters range from 0.01 to 0.06 inches.

microminiaturization — 1. The producing of microminiature electronic circuits from individual miniature solid-state and other nonthermionic components. 2. A relative degree of miniaturization resulting in an equipment or assembly volume an order of magnitude

smaller than that existing in subminiature equipment. 3. The technique of packaging a microminiature part of an assembly composed of elements radically different in shape and form. Electronic parts are replaced by active and passive elements, through use of fabrication processes such as screening, vapor-deposition diffusion, and photoetching.

micromodule — A tiny ceramic wafer made from semiconductive and insulative materials. It is capable of functioning as either a transistor, resistor, capacitor, or other basic component.

micromodules — The packaging approach developed by the U.S. Army and RCA wherein individual components or combined components are fabricated on small square wafers and made into larger modules by stacking.

micron — 1. A unit of length equal to 10^{-6} meter. 2. A unit used in the measurement of very low pressures. It is equivalent to 0.001 mm (10^{-6} meter) of mercury at 32° F.

microphone — An electroacoustic transducer which responds to sound waves and delivers essentially equivalent electric waves.

microphone amplifier — Also called a microphone preamplifier. An audio-frequency amplifier that boosts the output of a microphone before the signal reaches the main audio-frequency amplifier.

microphone boom — A movable crane from which a microphone is suspended.

microphone button — The resistance element of a carbon microphone. It is button-shaped and filled with carbon particles.

microphone cable — A shielded cable for connecting a microphone to an amplifier.

microphone mixer — An audio mixer that feeds the output from two or more microphones into a single input to an audio amplifier. The output from each microphone is adjustable by individual controls on the mixer.

microphone preamplifier — *See* Microphone Amplifier.

microphone stand — A stand that holds a microphone the desired distance above the floor or a table.

microphone transformer — An iron-core transformer used for coupling certain microphones to an amplifier or transmission line.

microphonics — The mechanical translation, by a vacuum tube, of vibration or shock into an electrical signal.

microphonism — 1. The production of noise as a result of magnetic shock or vibration. 2. The quasiperiodic voltage output of a tube produced by mechanical resonance of its elements as a result of mechanical impulse excitation. 3. The periodic voltage output of a tube produced by mechanical resonances of its elements as a result of sustained mechanical excitation. 4. The output voltage of a tube action as an electrical transducer or mechanical energy.

microphonograph — A device which amplifies

and records weak sounds; used in training the deaf to speak.

microphonoscope—A binaural stethoscope using a membrane in the chest piece to accentuate the sound.

microphotograph—A small picture of a large subject. The microfilming of a check or other document produces a microphotograph.

microprogramming—In a computer, a technique in which the coder builds his own machine instructions from the basic, elemental instructions built into the hardware.

microradiometer—Also called a radio micrometer. A thermosensitive detector of radiant power. It consists of a thermopile supported on and connected directly to the moving coil of a galvanometer.

microsecond—One millionth of a second.

microstrip—A microwave transmission component utilizing a single conductor supported above ground.

microsyn—A precise and sensitive pick-off device for converting angular displacement within a small range to an electrical signal.

microsystems electronics—See Microelectronics.

microvolt—One millionth of a volt.

microvoltmeter—A highly sensitive voltmeter, which measures millionths of a volt.

microvolts/meter/mile—One method of stating the field strength of a radiated field. Radiation from industrial heating equipment, for example, must be suppressed so that the radiated field strength does not exceed 10 microvolts per meter at a distance of 1 mile from the source.

microvolts per meter—The potential difference in microvolts developed between an antenna system and ground, divided by the distance in meters between the two points.

microwafer—A basic microcircuit building block generally made of beryllia, alumina, or glass. Terminations on the edges are usually of gold on top of chromium, with a heavy nickel overlay for welding.

microwatt—One millionth of a watt.

microwave—A term applied to radio waves in the frequency range of 1,000 megahertz and upward. Generally defines operations in the region where distributed constant circuits enclosed by conducting boundaries are used instead of the conventional lumped-constant circuit components.

microwave discriminator—A tuned cavity which converts a frequency-modulated microwave signal into an audio or video signal.

microwave early warning—Abbreviated MEW. A high-power, long-range, early-warning radar. It has numerous indicators that give high resolution and large traffic-handling capacity.

microwave filter—A filter built into a microwave transmission line to pass desired frequencies but reject or absorb all other frequencies.

microwave frequencies—Frequencies of 890 MHz and above.

microwave oscillator—An oscillator that generates frequencies higher than about 300 megahertz (wavelengths shorter than about one meter).

microwave power transmission—A method of transmitting power through space from a microwave transmitting antenna to a remotely located receiving antenna.

microwave radio relay—The relaying of long-distance telephone calls and television broadcast programs by means of highly directional high-frequency radio waves that are received and sent on from one booster station to another.

microwave refractometer—A device for measuring the refractive index of the atmosphere at microwave frequencies, usually in the 3-cm region.

microwave region—The portion of the electromagnetic spectrum between the far infrared and conventional radio-frequency portion. Commonly regarded as extending from 1,000 (30 cm) to 300,000 (1 mm) megahertz.

microwave relay system—A series of ultra-high-frequency radio transmitters and receivers comprising a system for handling communications (usually multichannel).

microwaves—Radio frequencies with such short wavelengths that they exhibit some of the properties of light. Their frequency range is from 1,000 MHz and up. (Microwaves are preferred in point-to-point communications because they are easily concentrated into a beam.)

middle marker—In an instrument-landing system, a marker located on a localizer course line, about 3,500 feet from the approach end of the runway.

middle-side system—See M-S Stereo System.

migration—The movement of ions through a medium.

mike—Slang for microphone.

mil—One thousandth of an inch. Used in the United States for measuring wire diameter.

MIL—Abbreviation for military. Pertains to a nation's armed forces, including its army, navy, and air force. Specifically, the armed forces of the United States.

Miller bridge—A type of bridge circuit for measuring the amplification factor of vacuum tubes.

Miller effect—The increase in the effective grid-to-cathode capacitance of a vacuum tube because the plate induces a charge electrostatically on the grid through grid-to-plate capacitance.

Miller oscillator—A crystal-controlled oscillator in which the crystal oscillates at its parallel resonant frequency due to the connection of negative resistance across its plates.

milli—Abbreviated m. Prefix meaning one thousandth ($1/1000$, or 10^{-3}).

milliammeter—An electric current meter calibrated in milliamperes.

milliampere—Abbreviated ma. One one-thousandth (.001) of an ampere.

millihenry—Abbreviated mh. One one-thousandth (.001) of a henry.

millilambert—A unit of brightness equal to one one-thousandth (.001) of a lambert.

millimaxwell—One-thousandth of a maxwell.

millimeter waves—Electromagnetic radiation in the frequency range of 30 to 500 gigahertz with corresponding wavelengths of 10 millimeters to 0.6 millimeter.

millimicro—Obsolete prefix for nano, representing 10^{-9}.

millimicron—A unit of length equal to one ten-millionth of a centimeter (10^{-7} cm), or one one-thousandth of a micron.

milliohm—One one-thousandth (.001) of an ohm.

milliroentgen—A unit of radioactive dose equal to one one-thousandth of a roentgen.

millisecond—One-thousandth of a second. Abbreviated msec.

millitorr—One-thousandth of a torr.

millivolt—One-thousandth of a volt. Abbreviated mv.

millivoltmeter—A sensitive voltmeter calibrated in millivolts.

millivolts per meter—The potential difference in millivolts developed between an antenna system and ground, divided by the distance in meters between the two points.

milliwatt—One one-thousandth of a watt. The reference level used for db measurements.

mine detector—Also called electronic mine detector. An electronic device that indicates the presence of metallic or nonmetallic explosive mines under the ground or under water.

Miniature tube.

miniature tube—A small electron tube usually having a 7- or 9-pin base.

miniaturization—The process of reducing the minimum volume required by equipments or parts in order to perform their required functions.

minigroove—A recording having more lines per inch than the average 78-rpm phonograph record but not as many as the extended play, long playing, or microgroove records.

minimum-access programming—Also called minimum-latency programming, or forced coding. Programming a digital computer so information is obtained from the memory in the minimum waiting time.

minimum detectable signal—The signal level which just exceeds the threshold.

minimum discernible signal—Abbreviated MDS. In a receiver, the smallest input signal that will produce a discernible signal at the output. The smaller the signal required, the more sensitive the receiver.

minimum firing power—The lowest radio-frequency power that will initiate a radio-frequency discharge in a switching tube at a specified ignitor current.

minimum flashover voltage—The crest value of the lowest voltage impulse of a given waveshape and polarity which causes flashover.

minimum-latency programming—*See* Minimum-Access Programming.

minimum-phase network—A network for which the phase shift at each frequency equals the minimum value determined solely by the attenuation-frequency characteristic.

minimum reject number—A number that defines the maximum number of rejects allowed for each sample given for each LTPD. Abbreviated MRN.

minimum (reliable) current—As applied to relay contacts, the range at which there is insufficient energy under arcing conditions at a mating contact surface to insure good contacting for the kind of contact material, shape, and forces employed.

minimum resistance—The resistance of a precision potentiometer, measured between the wiper terminal and any terminal with the shaft positioned to give a minimum value.

minimum-signal level—In facsimile, the level corresponding to the copy white or copy black signal, whichever is the lower.

minimum starting voltage—The minimum voltage of rated frequency applied to the control-voltage winding of a servomotor necessary to start the rotor turning at no-load conditions with rated voltage and frequency on the fixed-voltage winding.

minitrack—A satellite tracking system which uses a miniature pulse-type telemeter and a precise directional antenna system, with phase-comparison tracking techniques.

minor apex face—In a quartz crystal, any one of the three smaller sloping faces near but not touching the apex (pointed end). The other three are called the major-apex faces.

minor bend—A rectangular waveguide bent so that one of its longitudinal axes is parallel to its narrow side throughout the length of the bend.

minor cycle—Also called word time. In a digital computer using serial transmission, the time required to transmit one word or the space between words.

minor face—One of the three smaller sides of a hexagonal quartz crystal.

minor failure—A failure which has no significant effect on the satisfactory performance of a system.

minority carrier—The less predominant carrier in a semiconductor. Electrons are the minority carrier in P-type semiconductors, since there are fewer electrons than holes. Likewise, holes are the minority carrier in

Minter stereo-disc playback.

N-types, since they are outnumbered by the electrons.

minority emitter—An electrode from which minority carriers flow into the inter-electrode region.

minor lobe—Any lobe except the major lobe.

minor loop—A continuous network composed of both forward and feedback elements, which is only part of the overall feedback control system.

Minter stereo system—A stereo recording technique for producing the right and left channels. The two program channels are combined additively and recorded with a monophonic cutter. A 25-kHz note is also recorded and is frequency-modulated by the two channels combined subtractively. The sum and difference signals are then matrixed (combined) to produce the right and left channels.

mirror galvanometer—A suspended-coil instrument which, instead of using a pointer to indicate the reading, employs a light beam reflected from a mirror attached to the moving coil.

mirror galvanometer oscillograph—An instrument that photographs the deflection of a light spot from a mirror attached to a moving coil. Used for recording small current variations.

mirror-reflection echoes — Multiple-reflection echoes produced when a radar beam is reflected from a large, flat surface (such as the side of an aircraft carrier) and strikes nearby targets.

misfire—Failure of a mercury-pool-cathode tube to establish an arc between the main anode and cathode during a scheduled conducting period.

mismatch—The difference in impedance between a load and its source.

mismatch factor—*See* Reflection Factor.

mismatch loss—The ratio between the power a device would absorb if it were perfectly matched to the source, and the power it actually does absorb.

mistake—*See* Error.

mistor—A magnetic-field sensing device the resistance of which increases with an increase in magnetic-field intensity.

mitte-seite stereo system—German for middle-side system. A technique of stereo pickup in which two directional microphones, placed close together and at right angles to each other, are oriented so that one picks up

sound from directly ahead, and the other from the two sides, with maximum intensity.

Mitte-seite stereo system.

mixed-base notation — A number system in which a single base, such as 10 in the decimal system, is replaced by two number bases, such as 2 and 5, used alternately.

mixed highs—In color television, the method of reproducing very fine picture detail by transmitting high-frequency components as part of the luminance signal for achromatic reproduction.

mixer—1. In a sound transmission, recording or reproducing system, a device having two or more inputs (usually adjustable) and a common output. The latter combines the separate input signals linearly in the desired proportion to produce an output signal. 2. Also called the first detector. In a superheterodyne receiver, the stage where the incoming signal is modulated with the signal from the local oscillator to produce the intermediate-frequency signal.

309

mixer tube—An electron tube which, when supplied with voltage or power from an external oscillator, performs the frequency-conversion function of a heterodyne-conversion transducer.

mixing—Combining two or more signals—e.g., the outputs of several microphones, or the received and local-oscillator signals in a superheterodyne receiver.

mixing amplifier—An amplifier which combines several signals, each with a different amplitude and waveshape, into a composite signal.

mixing point—In a block diagram of a feedback control loop, a symbol indicating that the output is a function of the inputs at any instant.

mksa electromagnetic system of units—Also called the Giorgi system. A system in which the fundamental units are the meter, kilogram, second, and ampere.

mm—Abbreviation for millimeter.

mmf—Abbreviation for micromicrofarad; replaced by picofarad.

mmfd—Abbreviation for micromicrofarad; replaced by picofarad.

mnemonic—A term describing something used to assist the human memory.

mnemonic code—Computer instructions written in a form easy for the programmer to remember (although they must later be converted into machine language).

mobile radio service—Radio service between a fixed location and one or more mobile radio stations, or between mobile stations.

mobile receiver—The radio receiver in an automobile, truck, or other vehicle.

mobile-relay station—A type of base station in which the base-station receiver automatically turns on the base-station transmitter which then retransmits all signals received by the base-station receiver. Such a station is used to extend the range of mobile units and requires two frequencies for operation.

mobile station—A radio station intended for use while in motion or during halts at unspecified points. Included are hand- and pack-carried units.

mobile telemetering—Electric telemetering between moving objects, where interconnecting wires cannot be used.

mobile transmitter—A radio transmitter installed and operated in a vessel, land vehicle, or aircraft.

mobility—Symbolized by the Greek letter *mu* (μ). The ease with which carriers move through a semiconductor when they are subjected to electric forces. In general, electrons and holes do not have the same mobility in a given semiconductor. Also, their mobility is higher in germanium than in silicon.

mod/demod—Abbreviated form of modulating and demodulating.

mode—1. One of several types of electromagnetic wave oscillations that may be sustained in a given resonant system. Each type of vibration is designed as a particular mode and has its own particular electric- and magnetic-field configurations. 2. One of several methods of exciting a resonant system. The term has also been used to describe the existence of a number of different input voltages which allow operation of a klystron at the same frequency. 3. A computer system of data representations (e.g., the binary mode). 4. The most frequent value in a series of measurements or operations.

mode coupling—The interaction or exchange of energy between similar modes.

mode filter—A waveguide filter designed to separate waves of the same frequency but of different transmission modes.

mode hopping—The random shifting of laser output energy from one mode to another for short durations, usually in the microsecond range. The modes are generally closely spaced.

mode jump—A change in the mode of magnetron operation from one pulse to the next. Each mode represents a different frequency and power level.

modem—Acronym for MOdulator DEModulator.

mode number—1. In a reflex klystron, the number of whole cycles that a mean-speed electron remains in the drift space. 2. The number of radians of phase shift resulting from going once around the anode of a magnetron divided by 2π.

mode of failure—*See* Failure Mode.

mode of resonance—A form of natural electromagnetic oscillation in a resonator. It is characterized by an unvarying field pattern.

mode (of transmission propagation)—1. A form of guided-wave propagation characterized by a particular field pattern that intersects the direction of propagation. The field pattern is independent of its position along the waveguide. For a uniconductor waveguide, it also is independent of frequency. 2. In a vibrating system, the state which corresponds to one of the resonant frequencies.

mode of vibration—1. The pattern formed by the movement of the individual particles in a vibrating body (e.g., a piezoelectric crystal). This pattern is determined by the stresses applied to the body, the properties of the body, and the boundary conditions. The three common modes of vibration are flexural, extensional, and shear. 2. In a vibrating system, its characteristic pattern (i.e., the motion of every particle) is a simple harmonic, all of the same frequency. More than one mode may exist concurrently in a multiple-degree-of-freedom system.

mode purity—The freedom of an ATR tube from undesirable mode conversion while the tube is in its mount.

mode separation—In an oscillator, the difference in frequency between resonator modes of oscillation.

mode shift—In a magnetron, the change in mode during a pulse.

mode skip—Failure of a magnetron to fire during each successive pulse.

mode transducer—Also called mode transformer. A device that transforms an electromagnetic wave from one mode of propagation to another.

mode transformer—*See* Mode Transducer.

modification — The physical alteration of a system, subsystem, etc., for the purpose of changing its designed capabilities or characteristics.

modified constant-voltage charge — The charging of a storage battery in which the voltage of the charging circuit is held substantially constant, but a fixed resistance is inserted in the battery circuit, producing a rising voltage characteristic at the battery terminals as the charge progresses.

modified index of refraction — Also called modified refractive index. In the troposphere, the index of refraction at any height increased by h/a, where h is the height above sea level and a is the mean geometrical radius of the earth. When the index of refraction in the troposphere is horizontally stratified, propagation over a hypothetical flat earth through an atmosphere with the modified index of refraction is substantially equivalent to propagation over a curved earth through the real atmosphere.

modified refractive index—*See* Modified Index of Refraction.

moding—A defect of magnetron oscillation in which the magnetron oscillates in one or more undesired modes.

modular—1. Made up of modules. 2. Dimensioned according to a prescribed set of size increments.

modulate—To vary the amplitude, frequency, or phase of a wave by impressing one wave on another wave of constant properties.

modulated amplifier—In a transmitter, the amplifier stage where the modulating signal is introduced and modulates the carrier.

modulated-beam photoelectric system—An intrusion-detector system which provides reliable beam ranges of several thousand feet. This is done by interrupting the light beam at the source with a rotating punched or slotted disc. In this way, the phototube output is converted to an a-c signal, which can then be easily amplified.

modulated carrier—A radio-frequency carrier in which the amplitude or frequency has been varied by, and in accordance with, the intelligence to be conveyed.

modulated continuous wave — Abbreviated mcw. A wave in which the carrier is modulated by a constant audio-frequency tone. In telegraphy service, the carrier is keyed to produce the modulation.

modulated light — Light whose intensity has been made to vary in accordance with variations in an audio-frequency or code signal.

modulated oscillator—An oscillator the output frequency of which is varied by an input signal.

modulated signal generator—A device which produces an output signal that may be changed in amplitude and/or frequency according to a desired pattern. It is calibrated in units of both power (or voltage) and frequency.

modulated stage—The radio-frequency stage to which the modulator is coupled and in which the continuous wave (carrier wave) is modulated, in accordance with the system of modulation and the characteristics of the modulating wave.

modulated wave—A carrier wave in which the amplitude, frequency, or phase varies in accordance with the intelligence signal being transmitted.

modulating amplifier using variable reactance—A very-high-frequency electron-beam parametric amplifier with bandpass characteristics that are independent of gain, and which is unconditionally stable.

modulating electrode — In a cathode-ray tube, an electrode to which a potential is applied to control the magnitude of the beam current.

modulating signal—*See* Modulating Wave.

modulating wave—Also called modulating signal, or simply signal. A wave which varies some characteristic (i.e., frequency, amplitude, phase) of the carrier.

modulation—The process of modifying some characteristic of a wave (called a carrier) so that it varies in step with the instantaneous value of another wave (called a modulating wave or signal). The carrier can be a direct current, an alternating current (provided its frequency is above the highest frequency component in the modulating wave), or a series of regularly repeating, uniform pulses called a pulse chain (provided their repetition rate is at least twice that of the highest frequency to be transmitted).

modulation capability—The maximum percentage of modulation possible without objectionable distortion.

modulation code—A code used to cause variations in a signal in accordance with a predetermined scheme; normally used to alter or modulate a carrier wave to transmit data.

modulation distortion—Distortion occurring in the radio-frequency amplifier tube of a receiver when the operating point is at the bend of the grid-voltage–plate-current characteristic curve. As a result, the plate-current changes are greater on positive than on negative half-cycles. The effect is equivalent to an increase in the percentage of modulation.

modulation envelope — A curve, drawn through the peaks of a graph, showing how the waveform of a modulated carrier represents the waveform of the intelligence carried by the signal. The modulation envelope is the intelligence waveform.

modulation factor—In an amplitude-modulated wave, the ratio of half the difference

311

Modulation envelope.

between the maximum and minimum amplitudes to the average amplitude. This ratio is multiplied by 100 to obtain the percentage of modulation.

modulation frequency — That signal which causes the output frequency of an oscillator to be modulated.

modulation index—In frequency modulation with a sinusoidal modulating wave, the ratio of the frequency deviation to the frequency of the modulating wave.

modulation meter—Also called modulation monitor. An instrument for measuring the degree of modulation (modulation factor) of a modulated wave train. It is usually expressed in percent.

modulation monitor—*See* Modulation Meter.

modulation noise—Also called noise behind the signal. The noise caused by the signal, but not including the signal.

modulation percentage — The modulation factor multiplied by 100.

modulation plan — The arrangement by which the individual channels or groups of channels are modulated to a final frequency allocation.

modulation ratio—For an electrically modulated source, the number obtained by dividing the percentage of radiation modulation by the percentage of current modulation.

modulation rise—An increase in the modulation percentage. It is caused by a nonlinear tuned amplifier, usually the last intermediate-frequency stage of a receiver.

modulator—1. A device that effects the process of modulation. 2. In radar, a device for generating a succession of short energy pulses which cause a transmitter tube to oscillate during each pulse. 3. An electrode in a spacistor.

modulator crystal—A crystal which is used to modulate a polarized light beam by the use of Pockel's effect. Useful as a modulator in laser systems.

modulator driver—A transmitter circuit that produces a pulse to be delivered to the control grid of the modulator stage.

modulator glow tube—A cold-cathode recorder tube used for facsimile and sound-on-film recording. It provides a modulated, high-intensity, point-of-light source.

modulator stage—The last stage in which the modulated radio-frequency wave is amplified.

module—A unit in a packaging scheme displaying regularity and separable repetition. It may or may not be separable from other modules after initial assembly. Usually all major dimensions are in accordance with a prescribed series of dimensions.

modulus—An integer designating the number of states through which a counter sequences during each cycle. Abbreviated mod.

moiré—A wavy or satiny effect produced by the convergence of lines. Usually appears as a curving of the lines in the horizontal wedges of the test pattern and is most pronounced near the center, where the lines forming the wedges converge. A moiré pattern is a natural optical effect when converging lines in the picture are nearly parallel to the scanning lines. To a degree this effect is sometimes due to the characteristics of color picture tubes and of image-orthicon pickup tubes (in the latter, termed "mesh beat").

moisture absorption—The amount of moisture (in percentage) that an insulation will absorb. The figure should be as low as possible when the insulation is to be used in a moist environment.

moisture repellent—Having properties such that moisture will not penetrate.

moisture resistance—The ability of a material not to absorb moisture, either from the air or from being immersed in water.

moisture resistant — Having characteristics such that exposure to a moist atmosphere will not readily lead to a malfunction.

mol—Abbreviation for molecular weight.

mold—In disc recording, a metal part derived from a master by electroforming. It is a positive of the recording (i.e., it has grooves similar to those of a recording and can thus be played).

molded capacitor—A capacitor that has been encased in a molded plastic insulation.

molecular circuitry—*See* Morphological Circuitry.

molecular circuits — *See* Monolithic Integrated Circuits.

molecular electronics—Abbreviated moletronics. The science of making a single block of matter perform the function of a complete circuit. This is done by merging the function with a material, using solid-state functional blocks.

molecular technique—A practical method of causing a single piece of material or a crystal to provide a complete circuit function.

molecular weight—The sum of the weights of all the atoms in a molecule, expressed relative to the arbitrary weight of atomic oxygen ($O = 16$). Abbreviated mol.

molecule—In any substance, the smallest particle that still retains the physical and chemical characteristics of that substance. A molecule consists of one or more atoms of one or more elements. Sometimes two entirely different substances may have similar chemical elements, but their atoms will be arranged in a different order.

moletronics — Acronym for molecular electronics.

molybdenum—A metallic element (chemical

symbol, *Mo;* atomic number, 42; atomic weight, 95.95) sometimes used for the grid and plate electrodes of vacuum tubes.

momentary-contact switch — A mercury switch designed to make contact for only a brief transitory interval while the mercury moves from one extreme position to another.

momentary switch—A switch which returns to its normal circuit condition when the actuating force is removed.

monaural—*See* Monophonic.

monaural recorder — Literally, a tape recorder intended for listening with one ear only; however, in popular usage refers to single-channel recorders, as distinguished from multichannel (stereophonic, binaural, etc.) types. More correctly but less universally called monophonic recorder.

monitor—1. "To listen . . ." to a communication service, without disturbing it, to determine its freedom from trouble or interference. 2. A device (e.g., a receiver, oscilloscope, teleprinter, etc.) used for checking signals.

monitor head—On some tape recorders an additional playback head which permits listening to the recorded material while it is being made.

monitoring—Observing the characteristics of transmitted signals as they are being transmitted.

monitoring amplifier — A power amplifier used primarily for evaluation and supervision of a program.

monitoring radio receiver—A radio receiver for checking the operation of a transmitting station.

monkey chatter—So called because of the garbled speech or music heard along with the desired program. This interference occurs when the side frequencies of an adjacent-channel station beat with the signal from the desired station.

monobrid—A method of manufacturing an integrated circuit by using more than one monolithic chip within the same package.

monobrid circuit—An integrated circuit using a combination of monolithic and multichip techniques by means of which a number of monolithic circuits or a monolithic device in combination with separate diffused or thin-film components are interconnected in a single package.

monochromatic—1. Pertaining to or consisting of a single color. 2. Radiation of a single wavelength.

monochromatic emissivity—*See* Total Emissivity.

monochromatic sensitivity—The response of a device to light of a given color only.

monochromator—An instrument used to isolate narrow portions of the spectrum by making use of the dispersion of light into its component colors.

monochrome—Also called black-and-white in referring to television. Having only one chromaticity—usually achromatic, or black and white and all shades of gray.

monochrome channel—In a color television system, any path intended to carry the monochrome signal (although it may carry other signals also).

monochrome channel bandwidth — The bandwidth of the path that carries the monochrome signal.

monochrome signal — 1. In a monochrome television transmission, the signal wave that controls the luminance values in the picture. 2. In a color-television transmission signal wave, the portion with major control of luminance—whether displayed in color or monochrome.

monochrome television—Also called black-and-white television. Television in which the final reproduced picture is monochrome. That is, it has only shades of gray between black and white.

monochrome transmission — Also called black-and-white transmission. In television, the transmission of a signal wave for controlling the luminance—but not the chromaticity—values in the picture.

monoclinic—A crystal structure in which two of the three axes are perpendicular to the third, but not to each other.

monoergic—A type of emission in which the particles or radiations are produced with a small energy spread (i.e., a "line spectrum").

monogroove stereo—Also called single-groove stereo. A stereo recording in which both channels are contained in one groove.

monolithic—1. Existing as one large, undifferentiated whole. 2. Formed within a single body of material.

monolithic circuit—A circuit consisting of a semiconductor substrate into which all of the parts are fabricated by diffusion and epitaxial processes.

monolithic integrated circuit — An integrated circuit the elements of which are formed *in situ* upon or within a semiconductor substrate with at least one of the elements formed within the substrate. (*Also see* Integrated Circuit.) To further define the nature of a monolithic integrated circuit, additional modifiers may be prefixed. Examples are: PN junction isolated monolithic integrated circuit, dielectric isolated monolithic integrated circuit, or beam-lead monolithic integrated circuit.

monophonic—Also called by the older term "monaural." Pertaining to audio information on one channel (e.g., as opposed to binaural or stereophonic). Monophonic and monaural are usually, although not necessarily, associated with a one-speaker system.

monophonic recorder — *See* Monaural Recorder.

monopinch — Antijam application of the monopulse technique in which the error signal is used to provide discrimination against jamming signals.

monopole — A stub antenna fed against a ground plane.

monopulse—A method of determining azimuth and elevation angles simultaneously. The antenna system is not mechanically lobed in this method.

monopulse radar — Radar using a receiving antenna system having two or more partially overlapping lobes in the radiation pattern. Sum and difference channels in the receiver compare the amplitudes or phases of the antenna outputs.

monopulse tracking—A form of telemetry tracking which compares the phases of the carrier received simultaneously at four points on a plane (two elevation and two azimuth references) and positions the antenna so that all four signals are in phase, or equidistant from the source of radiation. A variation of the monopulse tracking technique is the scan-coded or single-channel monopulse tracking system.

monorange speaker—A speaker that provides the full spectrum of audio frequencies.

monoscope — Also called phasmajector or monotron. An electron-beam tube in which the picture signal is generated by scanning an electrode, parts of which have different secondary-emission characteristics.

monostable — The term used to describe a circuit with one stable state and one quasi-stable state. The circuit requires an external trigger to perform one cycle.

monostable multivibrator—Also called one-shot multivibrator, single-shot multivibrator, or start-stop multivibrator. A circuit having only one stable state, from which it can be triggered to change the state, but only for a predetermined interval, after which it returns to the original state.

monostatic reflectivity — The characteristic of a reflector which reflects energy only along the line of the incident ray (e.g., a corner reflector).

monotron—*See* Monoscope.

Monte Carlo method—Abbreviated MCM. 1. A computer technique in which a number of possible models under study are mathematically constructed from constituents selected at random from representative populations. 2. Any procedure that involves statistical sampling techniques in order to obtain an approximate solution of a mathematical or physical problem.

MOPA—Acronym for master oscillator-power amplifier.

morphological circuitry—Also called molecular circuitry. A circuit made from a material in which the molecular structure has been arranged to perform a certain electrical function.

Morse code—A system of dot-and-dash signals developed by Samuel F. B. Morse and now used chiefly in wire telegraphy.

Morse sounder—A telegraph receiving instrument that produces a sound at the beginning and end of each dot and dash. From these sounds, a trained operator can interpret the message.

Morse telegraphy—Telegraphy in which the

Morse code or its derivative is used—specifically, the International (also called Continental) or American Morse code.

MOS—Abbreviation for metal-oxide semiconductor.

mosaic—The light-sensitive surface of an iconoscope or other television camera tube. In one form, it consists of millions of tiny silver globules on a sheet of ruby mica. Each globule is treated with cesium vapor to make it sensitive to light.

mosaic detector—A device in which a number of active elements are arranged in an array. It is generally used as an imaging device.

MOS monolithic IC—A single-chip IC, consisting largely of interconnected unipolar active-device elements or MOS field-effect devices. This class of circuits results in higher equivalent parts density.

MOST—Abbreviation for metal-oxide semiconductor transistor.

mother—In disc recording, a mold electroformed from the master.

motherboard—A relatively large piece of insulating material on which components, modules, or other electronic subassemblies are mounted and interconnections made by welding, soldering, or other means, using point-to-point or matrix wire, or circuitry fabricated integrally with the board.

mother crystal—The quartz crystal found in nature. It has the characteristic geometric design of a crystal (i.e., flat faces at definite angles to each other), but all or some of the faces may be worn because of abrasion with stones or other objects.

motional impedance—Also called loaded motional impedance. The complex remainder after the blocked impedance of a transducer has been subtracted from the loaded impedance.

motion frequency — The natural frequency of a servo system; the frequency at which a given servo tends to oscillate.

motion-picture pickup—A television camera or technique for televising scenes directly from motion-picture film.

motor—A device that moves an object. Specifically, a machine that converts electric energy into mechanical energy.

motor board — Also called tape-transport mechanism. The platform or assembly of a tape recorder on which the motor (or motors), reels, heads, and controls are mounted. It includes parts of the recorder other than the amplifier, preamplifier, speaker, and case.

motorboating—1. Interference heard as the characteristic "putt-putt" made by a motorboat. It is due to self-oscillation, usually pulsating, in an amplifier below or at a low audio frequency. 2. A generally periodic, relatively low-frequency pulse disturbance of the output voltage of a regulated power supply, frequently line- or load-dependent, unstable, and significantly large, as in the case of oscillations.

motor circuit switch—*See* Disconnect Switch.

motor converter—A device for converting an alternating current to a pulsating direct current. It consists of an induction motor to which an a-c supply is connected. The armature of the induction motor is linked mechanically to the armature of a synchronous converter, which is connected to a d-c circuit.

motor-driven relay—A relay in which the contacts are actuated by the rotation of a motor shaft.

motor effect—The repulsion force exerted between adjacent conductors carrying currents in the opposite direction.

motor-field control—The method of controlling the speed of a motor by changing the magnitude of its field current.

motor-field failure relay (field loss relay)—A relay which functions to disconnect the motor armature from the line in the event of loss of field excitation.

motor-field induction heater—An induction heater in which the inducing winding typifies that of a rotary or linear induction motor.

motor-generator set—A motor-generator combination for converting one kind of electric power to another (e.g., alternating current to direct current). The two are mounted on a common base and their shafts are coupled together.

motor junction (conduit) box—An enclosure on a motor for the purpose of terminating a conduit run and joining the motor to power conductors.

motor meter—A meter comprising a rotor, one or more stators, and a retarding element which makes the speed of the rotor proportionate to the quantity being measured (e.g., power or current). A register, connected to the rotor by suitable gearing, counts the revolutions of the rotor in terms of the total.

motor-operated sequence switch—A multicontact switch which fixes the operating sequence (or the major devices) during starting and stopping, or during other sequential switching operations.

motor-run capacitor—A capacitor which is left in the auxiliary motor winding, and which is in parallel with the main winding, to obtain a higher power factor and efficiency.

motor-start capacitor—A capacitor which is in the circuit only during the starting period of a motor. The capacitor and its auxiliary winding are disconnected automatically by a centrifugal switch or other device when the motor reaches a predetermined speed, after which the motor runs as an induction motor.

mount—The flange or other means by which a switching tube, or a tube and cavity, are connected to a waveguide.

mount structure—The essential elements of a vacuum tube except the envelope.

mouth of a horn—The end having the larger cross section.

M-out-of-N code—A type of fixed-weight binary code in which M of the N digits are always in the same state.

movable contact—The one of a pair of contacts that is moved directly by the actuating system.

movement differential—The distance or angle from the operating position to the releasing position of a momentary contact switch.

moving-coil galvanometer—A galvanometer in which the moving element is a suspended or pivoted coil.

moving-coil meter—A meter in which a coil pivots between permanent magnets.

moving-coil microphone—Also called a dynamic microphone. A moving-conductor microphone in which the diaphragm is attached to a coil positioned in a fixed magnetic field. The sound waves strike the diaphragm moving it, and hence the coil, back and forth. An audio-frequency current is induced in the moving coil in the magnetic field and coupled to the amplifier.

Moving-coil pickup.

moving-coil pickup—Also dynamic pickup or reproducer. A phonograph pickup in which a conductor or coil produces an electric output as it moves back and forth in a magnetic field.

moving-coil speaker—Also called a dynamic speaker. A speaker in which the moving diaphragm is attached to a coil, which is conductively connected to the source of electric energy and placed in a constant magnetic field. The current through the coil interacts with the magnetic field, causing the coil and diaphragm to move back and forth in step with the current variations through the coil.

moving-conductor microphone—A microphone which produces its electric output from the motion of a conductor in a magnetic field.

moving-conductor speaker—A speaker in which a conductor is moved back and forth in a steady magnetic field. The cone is moved by the reaction between the magnetic field and the current in the conductor.

moving element—The parts of a meter that change position as a result of a variation in the electrical quantity being measured by the meter.

moving-iron instrument—An instrument in which the current in one or more fixed coils acts on one or more pieces of soft iron or magnetically similar material, at least one of which is movable. The various forms of this instrument (plunger, vane, repulsion, attraction, repulsion-attraction) are distinguished chiefly by their mechanical construction. Otherwise, the action is the same.

moving-magnet instrument—An instrument in which a movable permanent magnet aligns itself in the field produced by another permanent magnet and an adjacent coil or coils carrying current, or by two or more current-carrying coils.

moving-magnet magnetometer — A magnetometer in which the torques act on one or more permanent magnets, which can turn in the field to be measured. Some types use auxiliary magnets (gaussian magnetometer); others use electric coils (sine or tangent galvanometer).

moving-target indicator—Abbreviated MTI. A device which limits the display of radar information primarily to moving targets.

moving-vane meter — See Magnetic-Vane Meter.

mr/m — Abbreviation for milliroentgens per minute.

MRN — Abbreviation for minimum reject number.

ms—Abbreviation for milliseconds.

M-scan—Also called M-display. An A-scan radar display in which the target distance is determined by moving a pedestal signal along the base line until it coincides with the horizontal position of the target-signal deflection.

msec—Abbreviation for millisecond.

M-S stereo system — See Mitte-Seite Stereo System.

MTBF—Abbreviation for mean-time-between-failures.

MTI—Abbreviation for moving-target indicator.

MTTF — Abbreviation for mean-time-to-failure.

MTTFF—Abbreviation for mean-time-to-first-failure.

M-type backward-wave oscillator—A cross-field injected-beam oscillator. The electrons in this device interact with an r-f wave traveling backward or opposite to the electron beam. It is efficient, broad-band, and can be voltage-tuned. It is also insensitive to load variations.

mu—Generally written as the Greek letter μ. 1. Symbol for amplification factor. 2. Symbol for permeability. 3. Abbreviation for prefix micro-. 4. Abbreviation for micron.

μ—Abbreviation for the prefix "micro-."

μa—Abbreviation for microampere.

μh—Abbreviation for microhenry.

μmho—Abbreviation for micromho.

μohm—Abbreviation for micro-ohm.

μsec—Abbreviation for microsecond.

μv—Abbreviation for microvolt.

μw—Abbreviation for microwatt.

mu-circuit—In a feedback amplifier, the cir-

cuit which amplifies the vector sum of the input signal and the feedback portion of the output signal in order to generate the output signal.

muf—Abbreviation for maximum usable frequency.

mu factor—Ratio of the changes between two electrode voltages, assuming the current and all other electrode voltages are maintained constant—i.e., it is a measure of the relative effect which the voltages on two electrodes have on the current in the circuit of a specified electrode.

Muller tube—A thermionic vacuum tube having an auxiliary cathode or grid connected internally to the main cathode through a high-value resistor.

multiaddress — Pertaining to computer instructions which specify two or more addresses.

multianode tank—See Multianode Tube.

multianode tube — Also called multianode tank. An electron tube having two or more main anodes and a single cathode.

multiband antenna—An antenna usable at more than one frequency band.

multicasting—Broadcasting a stereo program by using two f-m stations. Two f-m receivers are required.

multicavity magnetron — A magnetron in which the circuit has more than one cavity.

multicellular horn—A cluster of horns with juxtaposed mouths, which control the directional pattern of the radiated energy.

multichannel radio transmitter — A radio transmitter having two or more complete radio-frequency portions capable of operating on different frequencies, either individually or simultaneously.

multichannel R/C—A radio-control installation that employs tuned reeds to supply several control functions. The basic carrier frequency remains the same, but different tones make possible a number of control channels.

multichip circuit—A microcircuit in which discrete, miniature active electronic elements (transistors and/or diode chips) and thin-film or diffused passive components or component clusters are interconnected by thermocompression bonds, alloying, soldering, welding, chemical deposition, or metalization.

multichip integrated circuit—An integrated circuit the elements of which are formed on or within two or more semiconductor chips that are separately attached to a substrate. Also see Integrated Circuit.

multicoupler—A device for connecting several receivers to one antenna and properly matching their impedances.

multielectrode tube—An electron tube containing more than three electrodes associated with a single electron stream.

multielement parasitic array—An array of dipoles and parasitic reflectors arranged to produce a beam of desired directivity.

multiemitter transistor — A transistor that

has more than one emitter. Used mainly in logic circuits.

multifrequency transmitter—A radio transmitter capable of operating on two or more selectable frequencies, one at a time, using preset adjustments of a single radio-frequency portion.

multifunction array radar — An electronic scanning radar which will perform target detection and identification, tracking, discrimination, and some interceptor missile tracking on a large number of targets simultaneously and as a single unit.

multigun tube—A cathode-ray tube having more than one electron gun. Used in color television receivers and multiple-presentation oscilloscopes.

multihop propagation — The bouncing of radio waves from the ionosphere to increase their range.

multilayer circuit—Three or more conductive patterns interspersed with layers of insulating base and laminated into sandwiches, with interconnection between layers provided by plate-through holes.

multilayer interconnection pattern — A technique used for the interconnection of arrays performing large complicated electronic functions. This technique involves the use of alternating films of insulating and conducting materials as a precondition for the realization of multiple interconnection planes.

multimeter—*See* Circuit Analyzer.

multimode operation—The operation of a laser sufficiently above threshold so as to stimulate more than one mode. If the modes are not degenerate, the output pattern will contain measurable power at more than one frequency.

multimoding—The simultaneous generation of many frequencies instead of one discrete frequency.

multipath cancellation—In effect, complete cancellation of signals because of the relative amplitude and phase differences of the components arriving over separate paths.

multipath delay—A form of phase distortion occurring most often in high-frequency layer-refracted or reflected signals, and also in vhf scattered signals. The existence of more than one signal path between transmitter and receiver causes the signal components to reach the receiver at slightly different times, causing echos or ghosting.

multipath effect—The arrival of radio waves at slightly different times because all components do not travel the same distance.

multipath reception—Reception in which the radio signal from the transmitter travels to a receiver antenna by more than one route, usually because it is reflected from obstacles. The result is seen as ghosts in a tv picture.

multipath transmission—The phenomenon where the signals reach the receiving antenna from two or more paths and usually

have both amplitude and phase differences. It may cause jitter in facsimile (in Europe it is called echo).

multiple—1. A group of terminals arranged in parallel to make a circuit or group of circuits accessible at any of several points to which a connection can be made. 2. To render a circuit accessible as in (1) above by connecting it in parallel with several terminals.

multiple access—The use of a communication satellite by more than one pair of ground stations at a time. Ideally it lets many independent ground stations use an active repeater without interfering with each other.

multiple accumulating registers — In a computer, additional internal storage capacity which can contain loading, storing, adding, subtracting, and comparing factors up to four computer words in length.

multiple-address code—A computer instruction code that includes more than one address.

multiple-address instruction—In a computer, an instruction that contains more than one address.

multiple break—In an electrical circuit, an interruption at more than one point.

multiple-break contacts—A contact arrangement such that a circuit is opened in two or more places.

multiple-chip circuit—*See* Hybrid Integrated Circuit.

multiple-contact switch—A switch in which the movable contact can be set to any one of several fixed contacts.

multiple course—One of a number of lines of position defined by a navigational system. Any one of these lines may be selected as a course line.

multiple-length number—In a computer, a quantity or expression that occupies two or more registers.

multiple modulation—Also called compound modulation. A succession of modulation processes in which the modulated wave from one process becomes the modulating wave for the next.

multiple pileup—Also called multiple stack. An arrangement of contact springs composed of two or more pile-ups.

multiple programming — In computer programming, simultaneous execution of two or more arithmetical or logical operations.

multiple-purpose tester—A single test instrument having several ranges, for measuring voltage, current, and resistance.

multiple-reflection echoes—Returned echoes that have been reflected from an object in the radar beam. Such echoes give a false bearing and range.

multiple sound track—Two or more sound tracks printed side by side on the same medium, containing the same or different material, but meant to be played at the same time (e.g., those used for stereophonic recording).

multiple stack—*See* Multiple Pile-up.

multiple tube counts—Spurious counts induced in a radiation counter by previous tube counts.

multiple-tuned antenna — A low-frequency antenna with one horizontal section and several tuned vertical sections.

multiple-twin quad — Quad cable in which the four conductors are arranged in two twisted pairs, and the two pairs twisted together.

multiple-unit semiconductor device — A semiconductor device having two or more sets of electrodes associated with independent carrier systems. It is implied that the device has two or more output functions which are independently derived from separate inputs (e.g., a duotriode transistor).

multiple-unit steerable antenna — An antenna unit composed of a number of stationary antennas, the major composite lobe of which is electrically steerable.

multiple-unit tube—Also called a duodiode, duotriode, diode-pentode, duodiode-triode, duodiode-pentode and triode-pentode. An electron tube containing two or more groups of electrodes associated with independent electron streams within one envelope.

multiplex—*See* Multiplexing.

multiplex adapter—A circuit incorporated in an f-m tuner or receiver to permit two-channel, or stereophonic, reception from a station transmitting multiplex broadcasts. The other audio channel is produced by demodulating the transmitted subcarrier.

multiplex code transmission—The simultaneous transmission of two or more code messages in either or both directions over the same transmission path.

multiplexer—A device which simultaneously transmits two or more signals over a common carrier wave.

multiplexing—The process of combining several measurements for transmission over a signal wire or link. There are two widely used methods of multiplexing. Time-division multiplexing utilizes the principle of time sharing among measurement channels. The second method of multiplexing also utilizes the principle of frequency sharing among measurement channels; it is called frequency-division multiplexing, where the data from each channel are used to modulate sinusoidal signals called "subcarriers" so that the resultant signal representing each channel contains only frequencies in a restricted, narrow frequency range.

multiplex operation—Simultaneous transmission of two or more messages in either or both directions over the same transmission path.

multiplex printing telegraphy—The form of printing telegraphy that uses a line circuit to transmit one character (or one or more pulses of a character) for each of two or more independent channels.

multiplex radio transmission—The simul-

taneous transmission of two or more signals over a common carrier wave.

multiplex stereo—A system of broadcasting both channels of a stereo program on a single carrier. This is commonly done by modulating an ultrasonic subcarrier—either with the signals of one of the stereo channels, or by a difference signal composed of the two channels combined out of phase, or subtractively.

multiplex telegraphy—Telegraphy employing multiplex code transmission.

multiplex transmission—*See* Multiplexing.

multiple x-y recorder—A recorder that plots a number of independent charts simultaneously, each showing the relation of two variables, neither of which is time.

multiplication point—A mixing point the output of which is obtained by multiplication of its inputs.

multiplier—1. A device in which the output is the product of the signal magnitudes represented by one of the two or more input signals. 2. A series resistor placed in a voltmeter to increase the voltage range.

multiplier phototube—Also called photomultiplier tube. A phototube with one or more dynodes between its photocathode and the output electrode.

multiplier-quotient register — In a computer, a register in which is placed the multiplier for multiplication and in which is developed the quotient for division.

multiplier resistor—*See* Multiplier.

multiplying factor—The number by which the reading of a meter must be multiplied to obtain the true value.

multipoint circuit—A circuit interconnecting several locations, wherein information transmitted is available at all locations simultaneously.

multipolar—Having more than one pair of magnetic poles.

multiposition relay — A relay having more than one operate or nonoperate position, e.g., a stepping relay.

multiprocessor—A computer having multiple arithmetic and logic units that can be used simultaneously.

multirate meter—A meter which registers at different rates or on different dials at different hours of the day.

multi-r-f-channel transmitter—A radio transmitter having two or more complete radio-frequency portions that may be operated on different frequencies either individually or simultaneously.

multisegment magnetron — A magnetron with an anode divided into more than two segments, usually by parallel slots.

multispeed motor—A motor which can be operated at any one of two or more definite speeds, each practically independent of the load.

multistage tube—An X-ray tube in which the cathode rays are accelerated by multiple ring-shaped anodes, each at a progressively higher potential.

multistate noise—Noise consisting of erratic switching that is generated within a device at various sharply defined levels of applied current.

multitrack magnetic system—A magnetic-recording system in which its medium has two or more tracks.

multitrack recording system—A recording system in which the medium has two or more recording paths, which may carry the same or different material but are played at the same time.

multiturn potentiometer—A potentiometer that must be rotated more than one turn for the slider to travel the complete length of the resistive element.

multiunit tube—An electron tube containing within one glass or metal envelope, two or more groups of electrodes, each associated with separate electron streams.

multivibrator—A relaxation oscillator in which the in-phase feedback voltage is obtained from two electron tubes or transistors. Typically, their outputs are coupled through resistive-capacitive elements. The time constants of the coupling elements determine the fundamental frequency, which may be further controlled by an external voltage. When such a circuit is normally in a non-oscillating state and a trigger signal is required to start a cycle of operation, it is called a one-shot, flip-flop, or start-stop multivibrator.

multivoltage control—A method of controlling the voltage of an armature by successive impression of a number of substantially fixed voltages on the armature. The voltages are usually obtained from multicommutator generators common to a group of motors.

Mumetal—A metallic alloy with high permeability and a low hysteresis loss. It is excellent for magnetic shielding.

Mumetal shield—A cone-shaped covering made of Mumetal. Placed over the flared portion of a picture tube, it acts as a shield to prevent outside magnetic fields from af-

fecting the alignment of the electron beams in the tube.

Munsell system—A color-specification system used principally in photography and color printing. It is based on sample cards containing the hue scale in five principal and five intermediate hues, and the brilliance scale in ten steps ranging from black to white. These represent visual, not physical, intervals.

Munsell value—In the Munsell system of object-color specification, the dimension which indicates the apparent luminous transmittance or reflectance of the object on a scale having approximately equal perceptual steps under the usual conditions of observation.

Murray loop test—A method of localizing a fault in a cable. This is done by replacing two arms of a Wheatstone bridge with a loop formed by the cable under test and a good cable connected to the far end of the defective cable.

MUSA antenna—Acronym for Multiple-Unit Steerable Antenna. It consists of several stationary antennas, the composite major lobe of which is electrically steerable.

mush winding—A type of winding in an a-c machine. The conductors are placed one by one in prepared slots and the end connections are separately insulated.

musical cushion—A musical selection added at the end of a program which is running short or over. By playing it slowly or cutting out portions, the program director can make the program come out on time.

musical echo—*See* Flutter Echo.

musical quality—*See* Timbre.

music power—The short-term power available from an amplifier for the reproduction of program material. The music power output exceeds the rms power rating to a greater or lesser extent. Its measurement is standardized by the Institute of High Fidelity (IHF) and represents a practical means of stating the actual capabilities of an amplifier for the reproduction of program material.

Multivibrator (asymmetrical).

must operate valve—A specified functioning value at which all relays meeting the specification must release.

must-release value—The specified operating value at which all relays that meet a certain specification must release.

muting—Muffling or deadening a sound.

muting circuit—1. A circuit which cuts off the receiver output when the r-f carrier reaching the first detector is at or below a predetermined intensity. 2. A circuit for making a receiver insensitive while its associated transmitter is on.

muting switch—A switch used with automatic tuning systems to silence the receiver while it is being tuned.

mutual capacitance—Capacitance between two conductors with all other conductors connected together and to a grounded shield. (Does not apply to a shielded single conductor.)

mutual conductance—See Transconductance.

mutual-conductance meter—See Transconductance Meter.

mutual-conductance tube tester—See Transconductance Tube Tester.

mutual impedance—Between any two pairs of network terminals (all other terminals being open), the ratio of the open-circuit potential at either one of the two pairs, to the current applied to the other pair of network terminals.

mutual inductance—The property that exists between two current-carrying conductors when the magnetic lines of force from one link with those of the other. It determines, for a given rate of change of current in one circuit, the electromotive force induced in the other.

mutual induction—The production of a voltage in one circuit by a changing current in a neighboring circuit, even though no apparent connection exists between the two circuits.

mutual inductor—An inductor for changing the mutual inductance between two circuits.

mutual information—See Transinformation.

mutual interference—Man-made interference from two or more electrical or electronic systems which affects these systems on a reciprocal basis.

mv—Abbreviation for millivolt.

Mv—Abbreviation for megavolt.

Mva—Abbreviation for megavolt-ampere.

Mw—Abbreviation for megawatt.

Mwh—Abbreviation for megawatt-hour.

Mycalex—Trade name of the Mycalex Corp. for mica bonded with glass. It has a low power factor at high frequencies, and is a good insulator at all frequencies.

Mylar—Trade name of E. I. duPont de Nemours and Co., Inc., for a highly durable, transparent plastic film of outstanding strength. It is used as a base for magnetic tape and as a dielectric in capacitors.

Mylar capacitor—A capacitor in which Mylar film, either alone or in combination with paper, is the dielectric.

myoelectric signals—Complex pulse potentials of 10 to 1,000 microvolts with durations between 1 and 10 milliseconds. As generated by a muscular effort, recorded from the body surface.

myograph—A recorder of forces of muscular contraction. *Also see* Electromyograph.

myokinesimeter—An apparatus for measuring the response of a muscle to stimulation by electric current.

myophone—An instrument for making audible the sound of a muscle when it is contracting.

myriametric waves—Very-low frequency band; 3 kHz to 30 kHz.

N

n—Abbreviation for the prefix "nano" (10^{-9}).

N—Symbol for number of turns, or the north-seeking pole of a magnet.

na—Abbreviation for nanoampere.

NAB—Abbreviation for National Association of Broadcasters.

NAB curve—The standard playback equalization curve set by the National Association of Broadcasters.

nail-head bond—An alternate term for ball bond.

nano—Abbreviated n. Prefix meaning one-billionth (10^{-9}).

nanoampere—One-thousandth of a microampere $(10^{-9}$ ampere$)$. Abbreviated na.

nanocircuit—An integrated microelectronic circuit in which each component is fabricated on a separate chip or substrate so that independent optimization for performance can be achieved.

nanofarad—One-billionth of a farad, equal to 10^{-9} farad, 0.001 microfarad, and 1000 picofarads. Abbreviated nf.

nanohenry—One-thousandth of a microhenry, equal to 10^{-9} henry and 1000 picohenrys. Abbreviated nh.

nanosecond—One-billionth of a second $(10^{-9}$ second$)$. Light travels approximately 1 foot in 1 nanosecond. Abbreviated nsec.

nanovolt—One-thousandth of a microvolt $(10^{-9}$ volt$)$. Abbreviated nv.

nanovoltmeter—A voltmeter sufficiently sensitive to give readings in thousandths of microvolts.

Naperian logarithm—Also called hyperbolic or natural logarithm. A logarithm to the base 2.71828.

napier—*See* Neper.

narrow band—A band whose width is greater than 1% of the center frequency and less than one-third octave.

narrow-band amplifier — An amplifier designed for optimum operation over a narrow band of frequencies.

narrow-band axis—In phasor representation of the chrominance signal, the direction of the coarse-chrominance primary of a color tv system.

narrow-band fm—Abbreviation for narrow-band frequency modulation.

narrow-band f-m adapter—An attachment which converts an a-m communications receiver to f-m.

narrow-band frequency modulation — Abbreviated NBFM. Frequency modulation which occupies only a small portion of the conventional f-m bandwidth. Used mainly for two-way voice communication by police, fire, taxicabs, and amateurs. The FCC limits the deviation to 3 kHz for amateurs and 15 kHz for all others.

narrow-band interference—Sharply tunable interference, having a spectrum that is small compared with the bandwidth of the measuring instrument. (Sine-wave carriers—both modulated and unmodulated—are good examples.)

narrow-sector recorder — A radio direction finder with which atmospherics are received from a limited sector related to the position of the antenna. The antenna is usually rotated continuously, and the bearings of the atmospherics recorded automatically.

NARTB—Abbreviation for National Association of Radio and Television Broadcasters.

n-ary code—A code in which each element can be any one of n distinct kinds or values.

n-ary pulse-code modulation — A type of pulse-code modulation in which the code for each element of information can consist of any one of n distinct kinds or values.

NASA — Acronym for National Aeronautics and Space Administration. The federal agency charged with all scientific space missions.

National Association of Broadcasters—Abbreviated NAB. An association of radio and television broadcasters.

National Association of Radio and Television Broadcasters—Abbreviated NARTB. A name used for a number of years by an association of broadcasters. In 1958 the name was changed back to National Association of Broadcasters, an earlier title.

National Electrical Manufacturers Association—Abbreviated NEMA. An organization of manufacturers of electrical products.

National Electric Code — Regulations governing construction and installation of electrical wiring and apparatus in the United States. They were established by the American National Board of Fire Underwriters for safety purposes.

National Television System Committee—Abbreviated NTSC. A committee organized in 1940 and comprising all United States companies and organizations interested in television. Between 1940 and 1941, it formulated the black and white television standards and between 1950 and 1953, the color television standards that were approved by the Federal Communications Commission.

natural frequency — 1. The frequency at which a body will oscillate if disturbed from its equilibrium position. 2. The lowest resonant frequency of a circuit or component without adding inductance or capacitance.

natural frequency of an antenna—The lowest resonant frequency of an antenna with no added inductance or capacitance.

natural interference—A type of electromagnetic interference caused by atmosphere and galactic electrical disturbances and precipitation static.

natural logarithm—*See* Naperian Logarithm.

natural magnet—Magnetic ore (e.g., a lodestone) which exhibits the property of magnetism in its natural state.

natural period—The period of the free oscillation of a body or system. When the period varies with amplitude, the natural period is the period when the amplitude approaches zero.

natural radiation — *See* Background Radiation.

natural resonance—*See* Periodic Resonance.

natural wavelength—The wavelength corresponding to the natural frequency of an antenna or circuit.

Navaglobe—A long-distance navigational system of the continuous-wave, low-frequency type. Bearing information is provided by amplitude comparison.

navar—A coordinated series of radar air-navigation and traffic-control aids utilizing transmissions at wavelengths of 10 and 60 centimeters. In an aircraft, it provides distance and bearing from a given point, display of other aircraft in the vicinity, and commands from the ground. On the ground, it provides a display of all aircraft in the vicinity, as well as their altitudes and identities, plus means for transmitting certain commands.

navarho — A continuous-wave, low-frequency navigation system that provides simultaneous bearing and range information over long distances.

navigation—The process of directing an airplane or ship toward its destination by determining its position, direction, etc.

navigational parameter—In a navigational aid, a visual or aural output having a specific relationship to navigational coordinates.

navigation beacon—A light, radio, or radar beacon that provides navigational aid to ships and aircraft.

NBFM—Abbreviation for narrow-band frequency modulation.

NC—Abbreviation for no connection (in a

vacuum-tube base) or normally closed relays or other contacts.

N-conductor concentric cable — A cable composed of an insulated central conducting core with (N-1) tubular stranded conductors laid over it concentrically and separated by layers of insulation.

n-cube — Also called n-dimensional cube or n-variable cube. In switching theory, a term used to indicate two n-1 cubes having corresponding points connected.

n-dimensional cube—*See* n-cube.

N-display—Also called N-scan, or N-scope. A radar display similar to the K-display. The target appears as a pair of vertical deflections (blips) from the horizontal time base. Direction is indicated by the related amplitude of the vertical deflections. Target distance is determined by moving a pedestal signal (the control of which is calibrated in distance) along the base line until it coincides with the horizontal position of the vertical deflections.

near-end cross talk—In a disturbed telephone channel, cross talk propagated in the opposite direction from the current in the disturbing channel. The terminal where the near-end cross talk is present is ordinarily near, or coincides with, the energized terminal of the disturbing channel.

near field — 1. The acoustic radiation field close to the speaker or some other acoustic source. 2. The electromagnetic field within a distance of 1 wavelength from a transmitting antenna.

near infrared—Name applied to the spectral region primarily comprising wavelengths between 3 and 30 microns.

necessary bandwidth—For a given class of emission, the minimum value of the occupied bandwidth sufficient to ensure the transmission of information at the rate and the quality required for the system employed, under specified conditions. Emissions useful for the good functioning of the receiving equipment—for example, the emission corresponding to the carrier of reduced carrier systems—shall be included in the necessary bandwidth.

neck—The narrow tubular part of the envelope of a cathode-ray tube; it extends from the funnel to the base and houses the electron gun.

needle—1. A probe used on stacks of punched cards. 2. *See* Stylus.

needle chatter—*See* Needle Talk.

needle drag—*See* Stylus Drag.

needle gap—A spark gap having needle-point electrodes.

needle pressure—*See* Stylus Force.

needle scratch—*See* Surface Noise.

needle talk — Also called needle chatter. Sounds produced directly by the needle of a phonograph pickup.

needle test point—Sharp steel probes connected to test cords for making contacts with conductors.

neg—Abbreviation for negative.

negative—1. Abbreviated neg. Less than zero. 2. The opposite of positive (e.g., negative resistance, transmission, feedback, etc.). 3. A terminal or electrode having an excess of electrons. Electrons flow out of the negative terminal of a voltage source, toward a positive source.

negative acceleration—A relative term often used to indicate that, referenced to zero acceleration, a negative electrical output will be obtained from a linear accelerometer when its sensitive axis is oriented normal to the surface of the earth, and a given minus reference point along the sensitive axis is located upward from the center of the seismic mass.

negative bias—In a vacuum tube, the voltage which makes the control grid more negative than the cathode.

negative booster—A booster used with a ground-return system to reduce the difference of potential between two points to the grounded return. It is connected in series with a supplementary insulated feeder extending from the negative bus of the generating station or substation to a distant point on the grounded return.

negative charge—A condition in a circuit when the element in question retains more than its normal quantity of electrons.

negative conductor—A conductor connected to the negative terminal of a source of supply. Such a conductor is frequently used as an auxiliary return circuit in a system of electric traction.

negative electricity—A body that contains an excess of electrons (e.g., the electricity that predominates in a comb which has been run through one's hair).

negative electrode — The electrode from which the forward current flows.

negative electron—Also called negatron. An electron, distinguished from a positive electron or positron.

negative feedback—Also called degeneration, inverse feedback, or stabilized feedback. A process by which a part of the output signal of an amplifying circuit is fed back to the input circuit. The signal fed back is 180° out-of-phase with the input signal; therefore, the amplification is decreased, and distortion reduced.

negative-feedback amplifier — An amplifier in which negative feedback is employed to improve the stability or frequency response, or both.

negative ghost—A ghost which has the opposite shading from that of the original image (i.e., is black when the image is white, and vice versa).

negative glow—The luminous glow between the cathode and Faraday dark spaces in a glow-discharge, cold-cathode tube. (*Also see* Glow Discharge.)

negative-grid generator — A conventional oscillator circuit in which oscillation is produced by feedback from the plate circuit to a grid which is normally negative with respect to the cathode and which is designed to operate without drawing grid current at any time.

negative image—A televised picture in which the whites appear black and vice versa. It is due to the picture signal having a polarity opposite to that of a normal signal.

negative impedance—1. Also called negative resistance when there is no inductance or capacitance in the circuit. A characteristic of certain electrical devices or circuits—instead of increasing, the voltage decreases when the current is increased and vice versa. 2. In general, the driving-point impedance of a circuit in which a current increase produces a voltage decrease, and vice versa. For a negative admittance, a voltage increase produces a current decrease, and vice versa.

negative ion—An atom with more electrons than normal. Thus, it has a negative charge.

negative light modulation — In television, the process whereby a decrease in initial light intensity causes an increase in the transmitted power.

negative modulation—In an a-m television system, that modulation in which an increase in brightness corresponds to a decrease in transmitted power.

negative modulation factor—The maximum negative departure of the envelope of an a-m wave from its average value, expressed as a ratio. This rating is used whenever the modulation signal wave has unequal positive and negative peaks.

negative phase-sequence relay — A relay which functions in conformance with the negative phase-sequence component of the current, voltage, or power of the circuit.

negative picture phase—For a television signal, the condition in which an increase in brilliance makes the picture-signal voltage swing in a negative direction from the zero level.

negative plate—The grid and active material connected to the negative terminal of a storage battery. When the battery is discharging, electrons flow from this terminal, through the external circuit, to the positive terminal.

negative resistance—A resistance which exhibits the opposite characteristic from normal—i.e., when the voltage is increased across it, the current will decrease instead of increase.

negative-resistance magnetron—A magnetron operated so that it acts as a negative resistance.

negative-resistance oscillator—An oscillator produced by connecting a parallel-tuned resonant circuit to a two-terminal negative-resistance device (one in which an increase in voltage results in a decrease in current). Dynatron and transitron oscillators are examples.

negative-resistance region—That operating region in which an increase in applied voltage results in a current decrease.

negative-resistance repeater—A repeater in which gain is provided by a series or shunt negative resistance, or both.

negative temperature coefficient — The amount of reduction in the value of a quantity, such as capacitance or resistance, for each degree of increase in temperature. (*Also see* Temperature Coefficient.)

negative terminal—In a battery or other voltage source, the terminal having an excess of electrons. Electrons flow from it, through the external circuit, to the positive terminal.

negative-transconductance oscillator — An electron-tube oscillator the output of which is coupled back to the input without phase shift, the phase condition for oscillation being satisfied by the negative transconductance of the tube. A transitron oscillator is an example.

negative transmission—The modulation of the picture carrier by a picture signal with a polarity such that the sync pulses occur in the blacker-than-black region and a decrease in initial light intensity increases the transmitted power.

negatron—1. An electron. 2. A four-electrode vacuum tube having a negative-resistance characteristic. *Also see* Negative Electron.

NEMA—Abbreviation for National Electrical Manufacturers Association.

NEMA standards—Specifications adopted as standard by the National Electric Manufacturers Association.

nemo—*See* Field Pickup.

neon—An inert gas used in neon signs and in some electron tubes. It produces a bright red glow when ionized. Symbol, *Ne;* atomic number, 10; atomic weight, 20.183.

Neon bulb.

neon bulb—A glass envelope filled with neon gas and containing two or more insulated electrodes. The tube will not conduct until the potential difference between two electrodes reaches the firing, or ionization, potential, and will remain conductive until the voltage is reduced to the extinction level.

neon-bulb oscillator — A simple relaxation oscillator in which a capacitor charges to the ionization potential of the neon gas within a bulb. Ionization rapidly depletes the charge on the capacitor, and a new charge cycle begins.

VOLTAGE
ACROSS
CAPACITOR

DEIONIZATION

IONIZATION

TIME

FREQUENCY OF SAWTOOTH WAVES CAN BE VARIED BY VARYING RESISTOR R.

Neon-bulb oscillator.

neper—Also called napier. The fundamental division of a logarithmic scale for expressing the ratio between two currents, powers, or voltages. The number of nepers denoting such a ratio is the natural (Naperian) logarithm of the square root of this ratio. One neper equals 0.8686 bels, or 8.686 decibels. Expressed as a formula:

$$N = \log_\epsilon \sqrt{\frac{E_1}{E_2}}$$

where,
  N is the number of nepers denoting their ratio,
  E_1 and E_2 are the two voltages.

Nernst effect—The effect whereby a potential difference is developed across a heated metal strip placed perpendicular to a magnetic field.

Nernst-Ettinghausen effect—A thermomagnetic effect that occurs in certain pure crystals, where a temperature difference is produced in a direction perpendicular to an applied magnetic field and a longitudinal electric current.

Nernst lamp—An electric lamp consisting of a short, slender rod of zirconium oxide that is heated to incandescence by a current.

nesting—In a computer, the inclusion of a routine or block of data within a larger routine or block of data.

net—Organization of stations capable of direct communications on a common channel, often on a definite schedule.

net authentification—Identification used on a communications network to establish the authenticity of several stations.

net information content—A message of the essential information contained in a message. It is expressed as the minimum number of bits or hartleys required to transmit the message with specified accuracy over a noiseless medium.

net loss—The algebraic sum of the gains and losses between two terminals of a circuit. It is equal to the difference in the levels at these points.

net reactance—The difference between the capacitive and inductive reactance in an a-c circuit.

network—1. A combination of electrical elements. 2. An interconnected system of transmission lines that provides multiple connec-

tions between loads and sources of generation.

network analysis—The obtaining of the electrical properties of a network (e.g., its input and transfer impedances, responses, etc.) from its configuration, parameters, and driving forces.

network analyzer—1. A group of electric-circuit elements which can readily be connected to form models of electric networks. From corresponding measurements on the model, it is then possible to infer the electrical quantities at various points on the prototype system. 2. Also called network calculator. An analog device designed primarily for simulating electrical networks.

network calculator—An analog device designed primarily for simulating electric networks.

network constant—Any one of the resistance, inductance, mutual-inductance, or capacitance values in a circuit or network. When these values are constant, the network is said to be linear.

network filter—A transducer for separating waves on the basis of their frequency.

network master relay—A relay that closes and trips an alternating-current, low-voltage network protector.

network phasing relay—A relay which functions in conjunction with a master relay to limit closure of the network protector to a predetermined relationship between the voltage and the network voltage.

network relay—A form of relay (e.g., voltage, power, etc.) used in the protection and control of alternating-current, low-voltage networks.

network synthesis—The obtaining of a network from prescribed electrical properties such as input and transfer impedances, specified responses for a given driving force, etc.

network transfer function—A frequency-dependent function, the value of which is the ratio of the output to the input voltage.

network transformer—A transformer suitable for use in a vault to feed a variable-capacity system of interconnected secondaries.

Neuman's law—Mutual inductance is a constant for a given relative physical position of coils, and independent of the fact that the current flows in one or the other coil, and of frequency, current, and phase.

neuristor—A two-terminal active device with some of the properties of neurons (e.g., propagation that suffers no attenuation and has a uniform velocity, and a refractory period).

neuroelectricity—The minute electric voltage generated by the nervous system.

neuron — The basic building block of the human nervous system. A specialized body cell that can conduct and code an electrical pulse.

neutral — In a normal condition; hence, neither positive nor negative. A neutral object has its normal number of electrons—i.e., the same number of electrons as protons.

neutral circuit—A teletypewriter circuit in which current flows in only one direction. The circuit is closed during the marking condition and open during the spacing condition.

neutral conductor — That conductor of a polyphase circuit or of a single-phase three-wire circuit which is intended to have a potential such that the potential differences between it and each of the other conductors are approximately equal in magnitude and are also equally spaced in phase.

neutral ground—A ground connection to the neutral point or points of a circuit, transformer, rotating machine, or system.

neutralization — The nullifying of voltage feedback from the output to the input of an amplifier through the interelectrode impedance of the tube. Its principal use is in preventing oscillation in an amplifier. This is done by introducing, into the input, a voltage equal in magnitude but opposite in phase to the feedback through the interelectrode capacitance.

neutralize—In an amplifier stage, to balance out the feedback voltage due to grid-plate capacitance, thus preventing regeneration.

neutralizing capacitor—A capacitor, usually variable, employed in a radio receiving or transmitting circuit to feed a portion of the signal voltage from the plate circuit back to the grid circuit.

neutralizing circuit—In an amplifier circuit, the portion that provides an intentional feedback path from plate to grid. This is done to prevent regeneration.

neutralizing indicator—An auxiliary device (e.g., a lamp or detector coupled to the plate tank circuit of an amplifier) for indicating the degree of neutralization in an amplifier.

neutralizing tool—Also called a tuning wand. A small screwdriver or socket wrench, partly or entirely nonmetallic, for making neutralizing or aligning adjustments in electronic equipment. (*Also see* Alignment Tool.)

neutralizing voltage—The a-c voltage fed from the grid circuit to the plate circuit (or vice versa). It is deliberately made 180° out of phase with and equal in amplitude to the

a-c voltage similarly transferred through undesired paths (usually the grid-to-plate interelectrode capacitance).

neutral operation — The system whereby marking signals are formed by current impulses of one polarity, either positive or negative, and spacing signals are formed by reducing the current to zero or nearly zero.

neutral point—The point which has the same potential as the point of junction of a group of equal nonreactive resistances connected at their free ends to the appropriate main terminals or lines of the system.

neutral relay—Also called a nonpolarized relay. A relay in which the armature movement does not depend on the direction of the current in the controlling circuit.

neutrino—An atomic particle with essentially no mass and no charge postulated to explain the conservation of energy and momentum when a radioactive atom emits an electron.

neutrodyne — An amplifier circuit used in early tuned radio-frequency receivers. It was neutralized by the voltage fed back by a capacitor.

neutron—One of the three elementary particles (the electron and proton are the other two) of an atom. It has approximately the same mass as the hydrogen atom, but no electric charge. It is one of the constituents of the nucleus (the proton is the other one).

neutron flux—A term used to express the intensity of neutron radiation, usually in connection with the operation of a reactor.

newton—In the mksa system, the unit of force that will impart an acceleration of 1 meter per second per second to a mass of 1 kilogram.

nf—Abbreviation for nanofarad.

Nichrome—Trade name of Driver-Harris Co. for an alloy of nickel and chromium used extensively in wirewound resistors and heating elements.

nickel-cadmium cell—The most widely used rechargeable sealed cell, nickel-cadmium gives a flat voltage discharge characteristic,

Nickel-cadmium cell.

nominal cell voltage of 1.25 volts, and good low-temperature operation. A cell with a nickel and oxide positive electrode and a cadmium negative electrode. The plates are wrapped with a separator between them, and are immersed in a potassium-hydroxide electrolyte.

nickel-oxide film diode—A solid-state diode made of nickel-oxide film. It may be switched from off to on by applying a 300-volt low-current pulse for 10 μsec, and may be switched from on to off by applying a 30-volt high-current pulse for 10 μsec. In effect it works like a diode flip-flop.

nickel silver—See German Silver.

nif—Abbreviation for noise-improvement factor.

NI junction—A semiconductor junction between N-type and intrinsic materials.

Nipkow disc—A round plate used for scanning small elementary areas of an image in correct sequence for a mechanical television system. It has one or more spirals of holes around its outer edge, and successive openings are positioned so that rotation of the disc provides the scanning.

NIPO—Acronym for Negative Input, Positive Output.

nit—In a computer, a choice among events that are equally probable. One nit equals 1.44 bits.

Nixie tube—A glow tube which converts a combination of electrical impulses into a visual display. (Also see Numerical-Readout Tube.)

n-level logic—Pertaining to a collection of gates connected in such a way that not more than n gates appear in series. (Computer term).

N-N junction—In an N-type semiconducting material, a region of transition between two regions having different properties.

no-address instruction—An instruction specifying an operation which the computer can perform without having to refer to its storage or memory unit.

noble gas—Also called inert gas or rare gas. One of the chemically inert gases, including helium, neon, argon, krypton, and xenon.

noctovision—A television system employing invisible rays (usually infrared) for scanning purposes at the transmitter. Hence, no visible light is necessary.

nodal point—1. See Node. 2. Two points on the axis of a lens such that a ray entering the lens in the direction of one, leaves as if from the other and parallel to the original direction.

nodal-point keying—Keying an arc transmitter at a point that is essentially at ground potential in the antenna circuit.

node—1. Also called junction point, branch point, or vertex. A terminal of any branch of a network, or a terminal common to two or more branches. 2. Also called nodal point. In a standing wave, a point, line, or surface where some characteristic of the wave field has essentially zero amplitude. 3. The point, line, or surface in a standing-wave system where some characteristic of the wave field has essentially zero amplitude. The appropriate modifier should be used with the word "node" to signify the type that is intended (pressure node, velocity node, etc.).

nodules—Clusters of oxide particles which protrude above the surface of magnetic tape.

noise—1. Any unwanted disturbance within a dynamic electrical or mechanical system (e.g., undesired electromagnetic radiation in a transmission channel or device). 2. Any unwanted electrical disturbance or spurious signal which modifies the transmitting, indicating, or recording of desired data. 3. In a computer, extra bits or words which have no meaning and must be ignored or removed from the data at the time it is used. 4. Random electrical variations generated internally in electronic components.

noise analysis—Determination of the frequency components that make up the noise being studied.

noise analyzer—An instrument used for determining the amplitude versus frequency characteristics of noise.

noise bandwidth—The width of the equivalent rectangular power gain versus frequency response of a network. It is the width of the rectangle the area of which equals that of the actual power gain versus frequency response and the height of which equals the maximum available power gain at a reference frequency f_o. It does not include any spurious responses. Any responses other than those in the useful channel are accounted for by a degraded noise figure.

Nipkow's television system.

noise behind the signal — *See* Modulation Noise.

noise-canceling microphone — *See* Close-Talking Microphone.

noise clipper—A circuit that automatically or manually clips the noise from the output of a receiver.

noise-current generator—A current generator in which the output is a random function of time.

noise diode — A standard electrical-noise source consisting of a diode operated at saturation. The noise is due to random emission of electrons.

noise equivalent bandwidth — The useful bandwidth of a thermistor bolometer for various frequencies in the input radiation is ¼t (where t is the time constant of the bolometer).

noise equivalent power—The value of radiation which produces, in a detector, an rms signal-to-noise ratio of unity. It is usually measured with a black-body radiation source at 500 K and a bandwidth of 1 or 5 hertz. The modulation rate varies with the type of detector and is usually between 10 and 1,000 hertz.

noise factor—Also called noise figure. 1. For a given bandwidth, the ratio of total noise at the output, to the noise at the input. 2. A number expressing the amount by which a receiver falls short of equaling the theoretical optimum performance.

noise figure—*See* Noise Factor.

noise figure (of a network with a generator connected to its input terminal)—The ratio of the available signal–to–noise-power ratio at the signal-generator terminals (weighted by the network bandwidth) to the available signal–to–noise-power ratio at the output.

noise filter—A combination of electrical components which prevent extraneous signals from passing into or through an electronic circuit.

noise-improvement factor—In a receiver, the ratio of output signal-to-noise ratio to the input signal-to-noise ratio. (The term receiver is used in the broad sense and is taken to include pulse demodulators.) Abbreviated nif.

noise killer—An electric network inserted into a telegraph circuit (usually at the sending end) to reduce interference with other communication circuits.

noise level—1. The strength of extraneous audible sounds at a given location. 2. The strength of extraneous signals in a circuit. (Noise level is referred to a specified base and usually measured in decibels.)

noise limiter—A vacuum-tube circuit that cuts off all noise peaks stronger than the highest peak in the received signal. In this way, the effects of strong atmospheric or man-made interference are reduced.

noise-measuring set — *See* Circuit Noise Meter.

noise pulse—Also called noise spike. A spurious signal of short duration and of a magnitude considerably in excess of the average peak value of the ordinary system noise.

noise quieting — The ability, usually expressed, in decibels, of a receiver to reduce background noise in the presence of a desired signal.

noise ratio—The ratio of the available noise power at the output of a circuit divided by the noise power at the input.

noise-reducing antenna system — A receiving-antenna system so designed that only the antenna proper can pick up signals. It is placed high enough to be out of the noise-interference zone, and is connected to the receiver with a shielded cable or twisted transmission line that is incapable of picking up signals.

noise source—A device employed to generate random noise (e.g., photomultiplier and gaseous-discharge tubes).

noise spike—*See* Noise Pulse.

noise suppression—1. The ability of a radio receiver to materially reduce the noise output when no carrier is being received. 2. A means of reducing surface noise during reproduction of a phonograph record.

noise suppressor—1. A circuit which reduces high-frequency hiss or noise. It is utilized primarily with old phonograph records. 2. In a receiver circuit, the portion which reduces noise automatically when no carrier is being received.

noise temperature—At a pair of terminals and at a specific frequency, the temperature of a passive system having an available noise power per unit bandwidth equal to that of the actual terminals.

noise-voltage generator—A voltage generator the output of which is a random function of time.

noisy mode—In a computer, a floating-point arithmetic procedure associated with normalization. In this procedure digits other than zero are introduced in the low-order positions during the left shift.

no-load current—*See* Exciting Current of a Transformer.

no-load losses—The losses in a transformer when it is excited at the rated voltage and frequency, but is not supplying a load.

nominal band—In a facsimile-signal wave, the frequency band equal to the width between the zero and the maximum modulating frequency.

nominal bandwidth—1. The difference between the nominal upper and lower cutoff frequencies of a filter. It may be expressed in octaves, in hertz, or as a percentage of the passband center frequency. 2. The maximum band of frequencies, inclusive of guard bands, assigned to a channel.

nominal horsepower—The rated power of a motor, engine, etc.

nominal impedance—The impedance of a circuit under normal conditions. Usually it is specified at the center or the operating-frequency range.

nominal line pitch—The average separation between the centers of adjacent lines in a raster.

nominal line width—1. In television, the reciprocal of the number of lines per unit length in the direction of line progression. 2. In facsimile transmission, the average separation between centers of adjacent scanning or recording lines.

nominal power rating of a resistor—The power which a resistor can dissipate continuously at a specified ambient temperature and for a stipulated length of time without excessive resistance drift.

nominal value—The stated or specified value as opposed to the actual value.

nominal voltage — The voltage of a fully charged storage cell when delivering rated current.

nomograph—*See* Alignment Chart.

nonbridging—A contact transfer in which the movable contact leaves one contact before touching the next.

nonbridging contacts — A contact arrangement in which the opening of one set of contacts occurs before the closing of another set.

noncombustible—*See* Nonflammable.

nonconductor—An insulating material—i.e., one through which no electric current can flow.

noncorrosive flux—A flux that does not contain acid and other substances which might corrode the surfaces being soldered.

nondestructive readout—In a computer, the copying of information from a storage device without altering the physical representation of the information in the device.

nondeviated absorption—1. Absorption that occurs without any appreciable slowing up of waves. 2. Normal sky-wave absorption.

nondirectional—*See* Omnidirectional.

nondirectional antenna — *See* Omnidirectional Antenna.

nondirectional microphone—*See* Omnidirectional Microphone.

nondissipative stub—A lossless length of waveguide or transmission line coupled into the sides of a waveguide.

nonequivalence element — A logic element having an action that represents the Boolean connective exclusive OR.

nonerasable storage—In a computer, a storage medium which cannot be erased and re-used, e.g., punched cards or perforated paper tape.

nonferrous—Not made of or containing iron.

nonflammable — Also called noncombustible. Term applied to material which will not burn when exposed to flame or elevated temperatures, e.g., asbestos, ceramics, and structural metals.

nonhoming tuning system—A motor-driven automatic-tuning system in which the motor starts in the direction of the previous rotation. If this direction is incorrect for the new station, the motor reverses, after turning to the end of the dial, then proceeds to the desired station.

noninductive—Having practically no inductance.

noninductive capacitor — A capacitor in which the inductive effects at high frequencies are reduced to a minimum. Foil layers are offset during winding so that an entire layer of foil (projecting at either end) is connected together for contact-making purposes. A current then flows laterally rather than spirally around the capacitor, and the inductive effect is minimized.

noninductive circuit—A circuit in which the inductance is reduced to a minimum or negligible value.

noninductive load—A load that has no inductance. It may consist entirely of resistance or capacitance.

noninductive resistor—A wirewound resistor with little or no self-inductance.

noninductive winding—A winding in which the magnetic fields produced by its two parts cancel each other and thereby provide a noninductive resistance.

noninverting connection — The closed-loop connection of an operational amplifier when the forward gain is positive for a d-c signal ($0°$ phase shift).

noninverting parametric device — A parametric device the operation of which depends essentially upon three frequencies, a harmonic of the pump frequency and two signal frequencies, of which one is the sum of the other plus the pump harmonics. Such a device can never provide gain at either of the signal frequencies. It is said to be noninverting because, if either of the two signals is moved upward in frequency, the other will move upward in frequency.

nonionizing radiation—Radiation which does not produce ionization (e.g., infrared, ultraviolet, and visible light).

nonlinear—Having an output that does not rise or fall in direct proportion to the input.

nonlinear capacitor — A capacitor that has a nonlinear mean-charge characteristic or peak-charge characteristic or a reversible capacitance that varies with bias voltage.

nonlinear coil—A coil with an easily saturable core. Its impedance is high at low or zero current, and is low when enough current flows to saturate the core.

nonlinear distortion—1. Distortion that occurs when the output does not rise and fall directly in proportion to the input. The input and output values need not be of the same quantity—e.g., in a linear detector, these values are the signal voltage at the output and the modulation envelope at the input. 2. Distortion which occurs because the transmission properties of a system are dependent upon the instantaneous magnitude of the transmitted signal. NOTE: Non-linearity distortion gives rise to amplitude/

amplitude and harmonic distortion, intermodulation, and flutter.

nonlinear network—A network (circuit) not specifiable by linear differential equations with time as the independent variable.

nonloaded Q—Also called basic Q. The value of the Q of an electric impedance without external coupling or connection.

nonmagnetic—Material which is not attracted by a magnet and cannot be magnetized (e.g., paper, plastic, tin, glass). In a strict sense, having a permeability equal to that of air or 1.

nonmagnetic armature shim — Also called nonmagnetic armature stop. A nonmagnetic member separating the pole faces of the core and armature in the operated position, used to reduce and stabilize the pull from residual magnetism in release.

nonmagnetic steel—A steel alloy that contains about 12% manganese, and sometimes a small quantity of nickel. It is practically nonmagnetic at ordinary temperatures.

nonmetallic sheathed cable—Two or more rubber- or plastic-covered conductors assembled in an outer sheath of nonconducting fibrous material that has been treated to make it flame- and moisture-resistant.

nonphysical primary—A color primary represented by a point outside the area of the chromaticity diagram enclosed by the spectrum locus and the purple boundary.

nonplanar network—A network that cannot be drawn on a plane without crossing branches.

nonpolar crystals—Crystals having the property that each lattice point is identical.

OXIDE FILM

ANODE   ANODE

Nonpolarized electrolytic capacitor.

nonpolarized electrolytic capacitor — An electrolytic capacitor which can be connected without regard to polarity. This is possible because the dielectric film is formed on both electrodes.

nonpolarized relay—*See* Neutral Relay.

nonrenewable fuse unit—A fuse unit that cannot be readily restored for service after operation.

nonreset timer—A timer which cannot be reset by electrical means.

nonresonant line—A transmission line with a natural resonant frequency different from that of the transmitted signal.

nonreturn-to-zero—A method of writing information on a magnetic surface in which the current through the write-head winding does not return to zero after the write pulse.

nonsaturated color—A color that is not pure—i.e., one that has been mixed with white or its complementary color.

nonshorting switch—A switch in which contact is broken from one position before contact is made with the next. Classified as a "break before make" switch.

nonsinusoidal wave—Any wave that is not a sine wave. It therefore contains harmonics.

nonstorage camera tube—A television camera tube in which the picture signal is always in proportion to the intensity of the illumination on the corresponding area of the scene being televised.

nonsynchronous—Not related in frequency, speed, or phase to other quantities in a device or circuit.

nonsynchronous starting torque — The maximum load torque with which motors can start. However, the motor will not come to a synchronous speed.

nonsynchronous vibrator—A vibrator that interrupts a direct-current circuit at a frequency unrelated to the other circuit constants. It does not rectify the resulting stepped-up alternating voltage.

nontrip-free circuit breaker — A breaker that can be maintained closed by manual override action while a tripping condition persists.

nonuniform field—A field in which the scalar (or vector) at that instant does not have the same value at every point in a given region.

nonvolatile storage — Storage media which retain information in the absence of power and which will make the information available when power is restored.

no operation — In a computer, a specific instruction that causes the computer to perform no operation.

NOR element—A gate circuit having multiple inputs and one output that is energized only if all inputs are zero.

norm—1. The mean or average. 2. A customary condition or degree.

normal condition—The de-energized condition of a relay.

normal contact—A contact which in its normal position closes a circuit and permits current to flow.

normal distribution—The most common frequency distribution in statistics. The probability curve is bell-shaped, and the greatest probability occurs at the arithmetical average (i.e., at the top of the curve). The probability of occurrence of a particular value is shown by the areas between two abscissa values on the curve. *Also see* Gaussian Distribution.

normal electrode—A standard electrode used for measuring electrode potentials.

normal failure period—That period of time during which an essentially constant failure rate exists.

normal impedance—*See* Free Impedance.

normal induction—The limiting induction, either positive or negative, in a magnetic material that is under the influence of a magnetizing force that varies between two extremes.

normal induction curve—The curve obtained by plotting B (induction) against H (magnetizing force), starting from a totally demagnetized state.

normalization—The transforming of signals to a common basis—e.g., adjusting two signals, representing the same spoken word but differing in loudness, to the same loudness.

normalized admittance—The reciprocal of normalized impedance.

normalized impedance—An impedance divided by the characteristic impedance of a wave guide.

normalized plateau slope—The slope of the substantially straight portion of the counting-rate-versus-voltage characteristic of a radiation counter tube, divided by the quotient of the counting rate and the voltage at the Geiger-Mueller threshold.

normal linearity—A manner of expressing linearity as the deviation from a straight line in terms of a given percentage of the output at a certain stimulus value, usually the full-scale value.

normally closed—Symbolized by NC. Designation applied to the contacts of a switch or relay when they are connected so that the circuit will be completed when the switch is not activated or the relay coil is not energized.

normally closed contact—Also called break contact. A contact pair which is closed when the coil of a relay is not energized.

normally open—Symbolized by NO. Designation applied to the contacts of a switch or relay when they are connected so that the circuit will be broken when the switch is not activated or the relay coil is not energized.

normally open contact—A contact pair which is open when the coil of a relay is not energized.

normal mode—The expected or usual operating conditions, such as the voltage that occurs between the two input terminals of an amplifier.

normal mode of vibration—A characteristic distribution of vibration amplitudes among the parts of the system, each part of which is vibrating freely at the same frequency. Complex free vibrations are combinations of these simple vibration forms.

normal-mode voltage—1. The actual signal voltage developed by a transducer. 2. The difference voltage between two input-signal lines.

normal operating period—The time interval between debugging and wear-out.

normal permeability—Ratio of the normal induction to the corresponding magnetizing force. In the cgs system, the flux density in a vacuum is numerically equal to the magnetizing force.

normal position—The position of the relay contacts when the coil is not energized.

normal propagation—The phenomenon of passing radio waves through space when atmospheric and/or ionospheric conditions are such as to permit the passage with little or no difficulty.

normal record level—In direct recording, the amount of record-head current required to produce 1% third-harmonic distortion of the reproduced signal at the record-level set frequency. Such distortion must result from magnetic-tape saturation, not from electronic circuitry.

normal-stage punching—In a computer, a card-punching system in which only the even-numbered rows are punched on the British standard card.

north pole—In a magnet, the pole from where magnetic lines of force are considered to leave the magnet.

Norton's theorem—The current in any impedance Z_R, connected to two terminals of a network, is the same as though Z_R were connected to a constant-current generator the generated current of which is equal to the current that flows through the two terminals when these terminals are short-circuited, the constant-current generator being in shunt with an impedance equal to the impedance of the network, looking back from the terminals in question.

NOT AND circuit—An AND gating circuit which inverts the pulse phase.

notation—A manner of representing numbers. Some of the more important notation scales are:

Base	Name
2	binary
3	ternary
4	quaternary, tetral
5	quinary
10	decimal
12	duodecimal
16	hexadecimal, sexidecimal
32	duotricenary
2, 5	biquinary

notch antenna—An antenna that forms a pattern by means of a notch or slot in a radiating surface. Its characteristics are similar to those of a properly proportioned metal antenna and may be evaluated with similar techniques.

notch filter—An arrangement of electronic components designed to attenuate or reject a specific frequency band with sharp cutoff at either end.

notch gate—The early and late gate display on the range crt. It appears as a negative deflection of the range base line equal in width to the early and late gates.

notching—A term indicating that a predetermined number of separate impulses are required to complete operation of a relay.

notching circuit—A control circuit used in a cathode-ray oscilloscope to expand portions of the displayed image.

NOT circuit — In a computer, a circuit in which the output signal has a phase or polarity opposite from that of the input signal. *Also see* inverter.

note—1. The pitch, duration, or both of a tone sensation. 2. The sensation itself. 3. The vibration causing the sensation. 4. The general term when no distinction is desired between the symbol, the sensation, and the physical stimulus. 5. A single musical tone. The notes of the musical scale are referred to by letters running alphabetically from A to G for the white keys. The black keys may be called a sharp of the note below it or a flat of the note above it. Each note has a frequency exactly one-half that of the corresponding note in the next higher octave.

NOT gate—An inhibitory circuit equivalent to the logical operation of negation (mathematical complement). The output of the circuit is energized only when its single input is not energized and there will be no output if the input is energized.

noval base—A nine-pin glass base for a miniature electron tube. For orientation of the tube into its socket, the spacing between pins 1 and 9 is greater than between the other pins.

novice license—A class of amateur license issued only to those who have never held an FCC license of any kind. Its requirements are the easiest of all, but novice operation is limited. Transmitters must be crystal controlled, and the maximum permissible plate input power is 75 watts. Novice licensees are restricted to certain frequencies (3.70-3.75, 7.15-7.20, 21.10-21.25, and 145-147 MHz). A novice license is valid for two years only, and it is not renewable.

NPIN transistor—An intrinsic-region transistor with a P-type base and an N-type emitter and collector.

NPIP transistor—An intrinsic-region transistor in which the intrinsic region is located between two P-regions.

n-plus-one address instruction—In a computer, a multiple-address instruction in which one address serves to specify the location of the next instruction of the normal sequence to be executed.

NPN transistor—A junction transistor with a P-type base and an N-type collector and emitter.

NPNP transistor—A hook transistor with a P-type base, N-type emitter, and a hook collector.

npo body (negative positive zero)—A designation referring to a class of capacitors in the temperature-compensating series that have an essentially variant dielectric constant over a specified temperature range (commonly $+25°C$ to $+85°C$).

N-quadrant—One of the two quadrants where the N-signal is heard in an A-N radio range.

N-region—1. Also called N-zone. The region where the conduction-electron density in a semiconductor exceeds the hole density. 2. The region created by diffusing into a silicon crystal a group-V element which creates an excess electron condition.

N-scan—*See* N-Display.

N-scope—*See* N-Display.

nsec—Abbreviation for nanosecond (10^{-9} sec).

n-signal—A dash-dot signal heard in either a bisignal zone or an N-quadrant of a radio range.

n-terminal network—A network with n accessible terminals.

nth harmonic—A harmonic whose frequency is n times the frequency of the fundamental.

NTSC—National Television Systems Committee, named after an all-industry engineering group who developed U.S. color-television specifications. Now describes the American system of color telecasting.

NTSC signal—A 3.579545-MHz (3.58-MHz) signal, the phase of which is varied with the instantaneous hue of the televised color, and the amplitude of which is varied with the instantaneous saturation of the color—as specified by the National Television Systems Committee.

NTSC triangle—On a chromaticity diagram, a triangle which defines the gamut of color obtainable through the use of phosphors.

N-type conductivity—The conductivity associated with conduction electrons in a semiconductor.

N-type crystal rectifier—A crystal rectifier in which forward current flows when the semiconductor is more negative than the metal.

N-type semiconductor—An extrinsic semiconductor in which the conduction-electron density exceeds the hole density. By implication, the net ionized impurity concentration is a donor type.

nuclear battery—Also called an atomic battery. A battery which converts nuclear energy into electrical energy.

nuclear bombardment—The shooting of atomic particles at nuclei, usually in an attempt to split the atom in order to form a new element.

nuclear energy—Also called atomic energy or power. The energy released in a nuclear reaction when a neutron splits the nucleus of an atom into smaller pieces (fission), or when two nuclei are joined together under millions of degrees of heat (fusion).

nuclear fission—*See* Fission.

nuclear fusion—*See* Fusion.

nuclear magnetic resonance — The flipping over of a particle such as a proton as the result of the application of an alternating magnetic field at right angles to a steady magnetic field in which the particle is placed.

nuclear pile—*See* Nuclear Reactor.

nuclear reaction—The reaction, accompanied by a tremendous release of energy, when the nucleus of an atom is split into smaller pieces (fission) or when two or more nuclei are joined together under millions of degrees of heat (fusion).

nuclear reactor—Also called an atomic reactor, nuclear pile, or reactor. A device which can sustain nuclear fission in a self-supporting chain reaction.

nucleation — The occurrence in an existing phase or state of a new phase or state.

nucleonics—The application of nuclear science in physics, chemistry, astronomy, biology, industry, and other fields.

nucleus—The core of an atom. It contains most of the mass and has a positive charge equal to the number of protons it contains. Its diameter is about one ten-thousandth that of the atom. Except for the ordinary hydrogen atom, the nuclei of all other atoms consist of protons and neutrons tightly locked together.

null—1. A balanced condition which results in zero output from a device or system. 2. To oppose an output which differs from zero so that it is returned to zero. 3. The minimum output amplitude (ideally, zero) in direction-finding systems where the amplitude is determined by the direction from which the signal arrives or by the rotation in bearing of the system's response pattern. 4. In a computer, a lack of information as opposed to a zero or blank for the presence of no information.

null balance—A condition in which two or more signals are summed and produce a result that is essentially zero.

null detection—A method of making DF measurements. The antenna is turned to the point where the received signal is weakest. The true bearing of the signal is then found by noting the antenna direction and using a correction factor.

null detector—An apparatus that senses the complete balance, or zero-output condition, of a system or device.

null-frequency indicator—A device that indicates frequency by heterodyning two electrical signals together to give a zero-beat indication.

null indicator—A device that indicates when current, voltage, or power is zero.

null method—Also called zero method. A method of measurement in which the circuit is balanced, to bring the pointer of the indicating instrument to zero, before a reading is taken (e.g., in a Wheatstone bridge, or in a laboratory balance for weighing purposes).

null-spacing error—In a resolver, the difference between 180° and the angle between null positions of the output winding with respect to one input winding.

number—An abstract mathematical symbol for expressing a quantity. In this sense, the manner of representing the number is im-

material. Take 26, for example. This is its decimal form—but it could be expressed as binary 011010 and still mean the same. Some common numbering systems are: binary (base *2*), quinary (base *5*), octonary or octal (base *8*), and decimal (base *10*).

number of overshoots—The total number of times that the transient response goes to a minimum or maximum value that is outside a specified range.

number of scanning lines—The ratio of the scanning frequency to the frame frequency.

number system—Any system for the representation of numbers. (*Also see* Positional Notation.)

numerical control—Descriptive of systems in which digital computers are used for the control of operations, particularly of automatic machines (e.g., drilling or boring machines, wherein the operation control is applied at a discrete point in the operation or process). Contrasted with process control, in which control is applied continuously.

numerical control system—A system controlled by direct insertion of numerical data at some point. The system must automatically interpret at least some portion of the data.

numerical-readout tube—A gas-filled, cold-cathode, digital-indicator tube having a common anode and containing stacked metallic elements in the form of numerals. When a negative voltage is applied to one of them, the element then becomes the cathode of a simple gas-discharge diode.

numeric coding — A system of abbreviation used in the preparation of information for machine acceptance in which all information is reduced to numerical quantities, in contrast to alphabetic coding.

nutating feed—In a tracking radar, an oscillating antenna feed that produces an oscillating deflection of the beam without changing the plane of polarization.

nutation field — The time-variant, three-dimensional field pattern of a directional or beam-producing antenna having a nutating feed.

nuvistor—A small vacuum tube with a can-

INTERNAL VIEW
Nuvistor.

tilever-supported cylindrical electrode that eliminates the need for mica supports. Only metal and ceramic are used, and there is no getter.

nv—Abbreviation for nanovolt.

n-variable cube—See n-Cube.

nw—Abbreviation for nanowatt (10^{-9} watt).

Nyquist diagram—A plot, in rectangular coordinates, of the real and imaginary parts of factor $\mu\beta$ for frequencies from zero to infinity in a feedback amplifier—where μ is the amplification in the absence of feedback, and β is the fraction of the output voltage superimposed on the amplifier input.

Nyquist interval—The maximum separation in time which can be given to regularly spaced instantaneous samples of a wave of a given bandwidth for complete determination of the waveform of the signal. Numerically it is equal in seconds to one-half the bandwidth.

Nyquist rate—Of a channel, the maximum rate at which independent signal values can be transmitted over the specified channel without exceeding a specified amount of mutual interference.

N-zone—See N-Region.

O

OAO—Abbreviation for Orbiting Astronomical Observatory.

object program—A computer program which is the output of an automatic coding system. The object program may be a machine-language program ready for execution, or it may be in an intermediate language.

oblique-incidence transmission—Transmission of a radio wave by reflection from the ionosphere.

oboe—A radar navigation system consisting of two ground stations, which measure the distance to an airborne transponder beacon and relay this information to the aircraft.

obsolescence-free—Not likely to become outdated within a reasonable time. Frequently applied to tube testers and other test instruments which have provisions for accommodating new developments.

occlude—To absorb—e.g., some metals will occlude gases, which must be driven out before the metals can be used in the electrodes or supports of a vacuum tube.

occluded gas—Gas that has been absorbed by a material (e.g., by the electrodes, supports, leads, and insulation of a vacuum tube).

occupied bandwidth—The frequency bandwidth such that, below its lower and above its upper frequency limits, the mean powers radiated are each equal to 0.5% of the total mean power radiated by a given emission.

octal—See Positional Notation.

octal base—An eight-pin tube base (although unneeded pins are often omitted without changing the position of the remaining pins). An aligning key in the center of the base assures correct insertion of the tube into the socket.

octal digit—One of the symbols 0, 1, 2, 3, 4, 5, 6, and 7 when used in numbering in the scale of 8.

octal number system—A number system in which the equivalent of the decimal integer 8 is used as a base.

octave—The interval between two sounds having a basic frequency ratio of two—or, by extension, the interval between any two frequencies having a ratio of 2:1. The interval, in octaves, between any two frequencies is the logarithm to the base 2 (or 3.322 times the logarithm to the base 10) of the frequency ratio.

octave band—A band of frequencies the limits of which have the ratio 2 to 1.

octave-band pressure level—Also called octave pressure level. The pressure level of a sound for the frequency band corresponding to a specified octave.

octave pressure level—See Octave-Band Pressure Level.

octode—An eight-electrode electron tube containing an anode, a cathode, a control electrode, and five additional grids.

octonary—See Positional Notation.

odd-even check—An automatic computer check in which an extra digit is carried along with each word, to determine whether the total number of 1's in the word is odd or even, thus providing a check for proper operation.

odd harmonic—Any frequency that is an odd multiple of the fundamental frequency (e.g., 1, 3, 5, etc.).

odd-line interlace—The double-interlace system in which, since there are an odd number of lines per frame, each field contains a half line. In the 525-line television frame used in the United States, each field contains 262.5 lines.

odograph—Automatic electronic map tracer used in military vehicles for map making and land navigation. It automatically plots, on an existing map or on cross-sectional paper, the exact course taken by the vehicle. This is done by phototubes and thyratrons, which transfer the indication of a precision magnetic compass onto a plotting unit actuated by the speedometer drive cable. A pen then traces the course.

oersted—In the cgs electromagnetic system, the unit of magnetizing force equal to $1{,}000/4\pi$ ampere-turns per meter.

off-center display—A ppi display, the center of which does not correspond to the position of the radar antenna.

off-delay—A circuit that retains an output signal some definite time after the input signal is removed.

off-ground — The voltage above or below ground at which a device is operated.

off-limit contacts — Contacts on a stepping relay used to indicate that the wiper has reached the limiting position on its arc and must be returned to normal before the circuit can function again.

off-line operation — 1. Computer operation that is independent of the time base of the actual inputs. 2. In a computer system, operation of peripheral equipment independent from the central processor, e.g., the transcribing of card information to magnetic tape, or of magnetic tape to printed form.

off-normal contacts—Relay contacts that assume one condition when the relay is in its normal position and the reverse condition for any other position of the relay.

off-period—That portion of an operating cycle during which an electron tube or semiconductor is nonconducting.

offset—The measure of unbalance between halves of a symmetrical circuit. Generally caused by differences in transistor betas or in values of biasing resistors.

offset angle—In lateral-disc reproduction, the smaller of the two angles between the projections, into the plane of the disc, of the vibration axis of the pickup stylus and the line connecting the vertical pivot (assuming a horizontal disc) of the pickup arm with the stylus point.

offset current—A d-c error current appearing at either input terminal of a d-c amplifier.

offset stacker—In a computer, a card stacker having the ability to stack cards selectively under machine control so that they protrude from the balance of the stack, thus giving physical identification.

offset voltage—A d-c error voltage appearing in series with either input terminal of a d-c amplifier.

off-target jamming—Employment of a jammer away from the main units of the force. This is done to prevent the enemy from monitoring the jamming signals and using them to pinpoint the location of the force.

OGO—Abbreviation for Orbiting Geophysical Observatory.

ohm—Symbolized by the Greek letter *omega* (Ω). The unit of resistance. It is defined as the resistance, at 0°C., of a uniform column of mercury 106.300 cm long and weighing 14.4521 grams. One ohm is the value of resistance through which a potential difference of one volt will maintain a current of one ampere.

ohmic contact—1. Between two materials, a contact across which the potential difference is proportionate to the current passing through it . 2. A contact that has linear voltage-current characteristics through its entire operating range.

ohmic heating — The energy imparted to charged particles as they respond to an electric field and make collisions with other

particles. The name was chosen due to the similarity of this effect to the heat generated in an ohmic resistance due to the collisions of the charge carriers in their medium.

ohmic resistance—Resistance to direct current.

ohmic value—The resistance in ohms.

ohmmeter—A direct-reading instrument for measuring electric resistance. Its scale is usually graduated in ohms, megohms, or both. (If the scale is graduated in megohms, the instrument is called a megohmmeter; if the scale is calibrated in kilohms, the instrument is a kilohmmeter.)

ohmmeter zero adjustment — In an ohmmeter, a potentiometer or other means of compensating for the drop in battery voltage with age. Usually a knob is rotated until the meter pointer is at zero on the particular scale being used.

Ohm's law.

Ohm's law—The voltage across an element of a d-c circuit is equal to the current in amperes through the element, multiplied by the resistance of the element in ohms. Expressed mathematically as $E = I \times R$. The other two equations obtained by transposition are $I = E/R$ and $R = E/I$.

ohms per square — The resistance of any square area of thin-film resistive material as measured between two parallel sides.

ohms-per-volt—A sensitivity rating for voltage-measuring instruments (the higher the rating, the more sensitive the meter). On any particular range, it is obtained by dividing the resistance of the instrument (in ohms) by the full-scale voltage value of that range.

oil—A prefix used with a device which interrupts an electrical circuit; it indicates that the interruption occurs in oil.

oil circuit breaker—A circuit breaker in which the interruption occurs in oil to suppress the arc and prevent damage to the contacts.

oiled paper—Paper that has been treated with oil or varnish to improve its insulating qualities.

oil-filled cable — A cable having insulation impregnated with an oil which is fluid at all operating temperatures and provided with facilities such as longitudinal ducts or channels and with reservoirs, or their equivalent, by means of which positive oil pressure can be maintained within the cable at all times.

oil fuse cutout—An enclosed fuse cutout in which all or part of the fuse support is mounted in oil.

oil-immersed forced-oil-cooled transformer (class FOA or FOW)—A transformer having its core and coils immersed in oil and cooled by the forced circulation of its oil through an external heat exchanger. If the heat exchanger utilizes forced circulation of air, the transformer is class FOA; if it utilizes forced circulation of water, the transformer is class FOW.

oil-immersed self-cooled forced-air-cooled transformer (class OA/FA)—A transformer having its core and coils immersed in oil and having a self-cooled rating with cooling obtained by the natural circulation of air over the cooling surface and a forced-air-cooled rating with cooling obtained by the forced circulation of air over this same cooling surface.

oil-immersed self-cooled transformer (class OA)—A transformer having its core and coils immersed in oil, the cooling being effected by the natural circulation of air over the cooling surface. (Smooth tank surfaces are generally sufficient to cool small transformers, but for about 25 kva and larger, a supplementary heat-dissipating surface is provided in the form of external fins, tubes, or tubular radiators.)

oil-immersed transformer — A transformer the core and coils of which are immersed in oil.

oil-immersed water-cooled transformer (class OW)—A transformer having its core and coils immersed in oil, the cooling being effected by the natural circulation of oil over the water-cooled surface. The water-cooled surface is provided by water flowing through copper cooling coils immersed in the oil and located inside the main transformer tank, through which the oil flows by thermosiphon action.

oil switch—A switch in which the interruption of the circuit occurs in oil to suppress the arc and prevent damage to the contacts.

Omega—A long-range hyperbolic navigation system which transmits interrupted c-w signals from which phase differences are extracted. Transmissions occur from two or more locations on a single carrier frequency utilizing time-sharing techniques.

omnibearing—The bearing indicated by a navigational receiver on transmissions from an omnirange.

omnibearing converter — An electromechanical device which combines an omnirange signal with aircraft heading information to furnish electrical signals for operating the pointer of a radio magnetic indicator. (Also see Omnibearing Indicator.)

omnibearing indicator — An omnibearing converter to which a dial and pointer have been added.

omnibearing line—One of an infinite number of straight, imaginary lines radiating from the geographical location of a vhf omnirange.

omnibearing selector—Instrument capable of being set manually to any desired omnibearing or its reciprocal in order to control a coarse-line deviation indicator.

omnidirectional—Also called nondirectional. All-directional; not favoring any one direction.

omnidirectional antenna—Also called nondirectional antenna. An antenna producing essentially the same field strength in all horizontal directions and a directive vertical radiation pattern.

omnidirectional hydrophone—A hydrophone having a response that is essentially independent of the angle of arrival of the incident sound wave.

omnidirectional microphone — Also called nondirectional microphone. A microphone that responds to a sound wave from almost any angle of arrival.

omnidirectional radio range—Radio air-to-air navigation using a transmitter that radiates throughout 360° azimuth, providing aircraft with a direct indication of the bearing of the transmitter.

omnidirectional range — Also called omnirange. A radio facility providing bearing information to or from such facilities at all azimuths within its service area.

omnidirectional range station—In the aeronautical radionavigational service, a land station that provides a direct indication of the bearing (omnibearing) of that station from an aircraft.

omnigraph—An instrument that produces Morse-code messages for instruction purposes. It contains a buzzer circuit which is usually actuated by a perforated tape.

omnirange—See Omnidirectional Range.

on-call channels—Similar to allocated channels except that full-time exclusive use of the channel is not warranted.

on-course curvature—In navigation, the rate at which the indicated course changes with respect to the distance along the course path.

on-course signal—The monotone radio signal which indicates to the pilot that he is neither too far to the right nor to the left of the radio beam being followed.

on-delay—A circuit that produces an output signal some definite time after an input signal is applied.

on-demand system — A system from which the desired information or service is available at the time of request.

ondograph—An instrument for drawing alternating voltage waveform curves. It employs a capacitor which is momentarily charged to the amplitude at a particular point on the curve and then discharged through a recording galvanometer. This is repeated at intervals of about once every hundred cycles with the sample taken a little farther along on the waveform each time.

ondoscope—A glow-discharge tube used on an insulating rod to indicate the presence of high-frequency r-f near a transmitter. The radiation ionizes the gas in the tube, and the visible glow indicates the presence of r-f.

one-input terminal—Called the set terminal. The terminal which, when triggered, will put a flip-flop in the one (opposite of starting) condition.

one-many function switch—A function switch in which only one input is excited at a time and each input produces a combination of outputs.

one output—See One State.

one-output terminal—The terminal which produces an output of the correct polarity to trigger a following circuit when a flip-flop circuit is in the one condition.

one-shot—A circuit that produces an output signal of fixed duration when an input signal of any duration is applied.

one-shot multivibrator—See Monostable Multivibrator.

one state—Also called one output. In a magnetic cell, the positive value of the magnetic flux through a specified cross-sectional area, determined from an arbitrarily specified direction. (Also see Zero State).

one-third–octave band—A frequency band in which the ratio of the extreme frequencies is 1.2599.

one-to-partial-select ratio—In a computer, the ratio of a *1* output to a partial-select output.

one-to-zero ratio—In a computer, the ratio of a *1* output to the *0* output.

O-network.

O-network—A network composed of four impedance branches connected in series to form a closed circuit. Two adjacent junction points serve as input terminals, and the remaining two as output terminals.

one-way communication—Applied to certain radio-communication or intercommunications systems where a message is transmitted from one station to one or more receiving stations that have no transmitting apparatus.

one-way repeater—See Repeater.

on line—In a computer, having to do with the operation of input-output devices under direct control of the central processing unit.

on-line data reduction—The processing of information as rapidly as the information is received by the computing system or as rapidly as it is generated by the source.

on-line operation—An operation carried on within the main computer system (e.g., computing and writing results onto a magnetic tape, printed report, or paper tape).

on-off control—A simple control system in a switch in which the device being controlled is either fully on or fully off and no operating positions are available.

on-off keying—Keying in which the output of a source is alternately transmitted and suppressed to form signals.

on-off ratio—Ratio of the duration (on) of a pulse to the space (off) between successive pulses.

on-off switch—See Power Switch.

on period—That portion of an operating cycle during which an electron tube is conducting.

on the air—Transmitting.

opacimeter—Also called turbidimeter. A photoelectric instrument for measuring the turbidity (amount of sediment) of a liquid. It does this by determining the amount of light that passes through the liquid.

opacity—The degree of nontransparency of a substance—i.e., its ability to obstruct, by absorption, the transmission of radiant energy such as light. Opacity is the reciprocal of transmission.

open—A circuit interruption that results in an incomplete path for current flow (e.g., a broken wire, which opens the path of the current).

open-center display—A ppi display on which zero range corresponds to a ring around the center of the display.

open circuit—A circuit which does not provide a complete path for the flow of current. (Also see Open.)

open-circuit impedance—The driving-point impedance of a line or four-terminal network when the far end is open.

open-circuit jack—A jack that normally leaves its circuit open. The circuit can be closed only by inserting the plug into the jack.

Open-circuit jack.

open-circuit signaling—Signaling in which no current flows under normal (i.e., inoperative) conditions.

open-circuit voltage—The voltage at the terminals of a battery or other voltage source when no appreciable current is flowing.

open core—A core fitting inside a coil but having no external return path. The magnetic circuit thus has a long path through air.

open-delta connection — Two single-phase transformers connected so that they form only two sides of a delta, instead of the three sides with three transformers in a regular delta connection.

open-fuse cutout — An enclosed fuse cutout in which the fuse support and fuse holder are exposed.

open loop — Implies an operational amplifier without feedback.

open-loop bandwidth — Without feedback, the frequency limits at which the voltage gain of the device drops off 3 db below the gain at some lower reference frequency.

open-loop control system — A control system in which there is no self-correcting action, as there is in a closed-loop system.

open-loop differential voltage gain — See Differential Voltage Gain.

open-loop gain — The ratio of the (loaded) output of an amplifier without any feedback to its net input at any frequency. Usually implies voltage gain.

open-loop output impedance — The complex impedance seen looking into the output terminals of an operational amplifier with no external feedback and in the linear-amplification region. In closed-loop operation, the output impedance is equal to the open-loop impedance divided by the loop gain. If the open-loop impedance is not more than a few hundred ohms and the loop gain is high enough for good gain accuracy and stability, the closed-loop impedance will be on the order of an ohm or less, which can be neglected in most applications.

open-loop output resistance — The resistance looking into the output terminal of an operational amplifier operating without feedback and in the linear-amplification region.

open-loop voltage gain — The ratio of the change in voltage between the differential input terminals of an operational amplifier to the corresponding change in output voltage, with no feedback.

open magnetic circuit — A magnet that has no closed external ferromagnetic circuit and does not form a complete conducting circuit itself (e.g., a permanent magnet ring interrupted by an air gap).

open motor — A motor having ventilating openings which permit passage of external cooling air over and around the windings of the machine. When such motors have an internal fan to aid the movement of ventilating air, they may be referred to as self-ventilated.

open-phase protection — The effect of a device operating on the loss of current in one phase of a polyphase circuit to cause and maintain the interruption of power in the circuit.

open-phase relay — A relay which functions when one or more phases of a polyphase circuit open and sufficient current is flowing in the remaining phase or phases.

open plug — A plug designed to hold jack springs in their open position.

open relay — A relay not having an enclosure.

open routine — In a computer, a routine that it is possible to insert directly into a larger routine without a linkage or calling sequence.

open subroutine — Also called direct-insert subroutine. A subroutine inserted directly into a larger sequence of instructions. Such a subroutine is not entered by a jump instruction; hence, it must be recopied at each point where it is needed.

open-temperature pickup — A temperature transducer in which its sensing element is directly in contact with the medium whose temperature is being measured.

open wire — A conductor separately supported above the earth's surface.

open-wire circuit — A circuit made up of conductors separately supported on insulators.

open-wire loop — The branch line on a main open-wire line.

open-wire transmission line — A transmission line formed by two parallel wires. The distance between them, and their diameters, determine the surge impedance of the transmission line.

operand — A computer word on which an operation is to be performed.

operate current — The minimum current required to trip all the contact springs of a relay.

operate time — The time that elapses, after power is applied to a relay coil, until the contacts being checked have operated (i.e., first opened in a normally closed contact, or first closed in a normally open contact).

operate-time characteristic — The relation between the operate time of an electromagnetic relay and the operate power.

operating angle — The electrical angle (portion of a cycle) during which plate current flows in an amplifier or an electronic tube. Class-A amplifiers have an operating angle of 360°; Class-B, 180° to 360°; and Class-C, less than 180°.

operating cycle — The complete sequence of operations required in the normal functioning of an item of equipment.

operating frequency — The rated a-c frequency of the supply voltage at which a relay is designed to operate.

operating life — The minimum length of time over which the specified continuous and intermittent rating of a device, system, or transducer applies without change in performance beyond the specified tolerance.

operating-mode factor — A failure-rate modifier determined by the type of equipment environment, e.g., laboratroy computer, nose-cone compartment, etc.

operating overload — The overcurrent to which electric apparatus is subjected in the course of the normal operating conditions that it may encounter.

operating point — Also called the quiescent

337

point. On a grid-voltage–plate-current characteristic curve of a vacuum tube, the point which corresponds to the direct-voltage value being used for the grid and plate.

operating position—The operator-attended terminal of a communications channel. It is usually used in its singular sense (e.g., a radio-operator's position, a telephone-operator's position), even when there is more than one operating position.

operating power—The power actually reaching a transmitting antenna.

operating ratio—*See* Availability.

operating temperature—The temperature or range of temperatures at or over which a device is expected to operate within specified limits of error.

operating temperature range—The interval of temperatures in which a component device or system is intended to be used, specified by the limits of this interval.

operating time — The time period between turn-on and turn-off of a system, subsystem, component, or part during which the system, etc., functions as specified. Total operating time is the summation of all operating-time periods.

operating voltages—The direct voltages applied to the electrodes of a vacuum tube under operating conditions.

operation—A specific action which a computer will perform whenever an instruction calls for it (e.g., addition, division).

operational amplifier—An amplifier that performs various mathematical operations. Application of negative feedback around a high–d-c amplifier produces a circuit with a precise gain characteristic that depends on the feedback used. By the proper selection of feedback components, operational amplifier circuits can be used to add, subtract, average, integrate, and differentiate. An operational amplifier can have a single-input–single-output, differential-input–single-output, or differential-input–differential-output configuration.

operational differential amplifier—An operational amplifier which utilizes a differential amplifier in the first stage.

operational readiness—The probability that, at any point in time and under stated conditions, a system will be either operating satisfactorily or ready to be placed in operation.

operational reliability—*See* Achieved Reliability.

operation code (computer)—1. Also called the operation part of an instruction. The list of operation parts occurring in an instruction code, together with the names of the corresponding operations (e.g., "add," "unconditional transfer," "add and clear," etc.). 2. The part of a computer instruction word which specifies, in coded form, the operation to be performed.

operation decoder—In a computer, circuitry which interprets the operation-code portion of the machine instruction to be executed and sets other circuitry for its execution.

operation number—In a computer program, a number indicating the position of a given operation or its equivalent subroutine.

operation part—In a computer instruction, the part that specifies the kind of operation, but not the location of the operands. (*Also see* Instruction Code.)

operation register—In a computer, the register that stores the operation-code portion of an instruction.

operation time—The amount of time required by a current to reach a stated fraction of its final value after voltages have been applied simultaneously to all electrodes. The final value is conventionally taken as that reached after a specified length of time.

operator—Any person who operates, adjusts, and maintains equipment — specifically, a computer, radio transmitter, or other communications equipment.

opposition—The phase relationship between two periodic functions of the same period when the phase difference between them is half of a period.

optical ammeter—An electrothermic instrument for measuring the current in the filament of an incandescent lamp. It normally uses a photoelectric cell and indicating instrument to compare the illumination with that produced by a current of known magnitude in the same filament.

optical axis—The Z-axis of a crystal.

optical character recognition — An automatic means of direct reading and recognition of data in printed or hand-lettered form.

optical damping—A damping ratio slightly less than unity in which the overshoot is less than the specified uncertainty of the instrument.

optical maser—*See* Laser.

optical mode—In a crystal lattice, a mode of vibration that produces an oscillating dipole.

optical pattern—Also called Christmas-tree pattern. In mechanical recording, the pattern observed when the surface of the record is illuminated by a light beam of essentially parallel rays.

optical pyrometer—A temperature-measuring device comprising a comparison source of illumination, together with some convenient arrangement for matching this source—either in brightness or color—against the source whose temperature is to be measured. The comparison is usually made by the eye.

optical sound recorder—Also called a photographic sound recorder. Equipment for optically recording the electric signals derived from sound signals. A light modulator is incorporated, plus means for moving a light-sensitive medium relative to the modulator.

optical sound reproducer — Also called a photographic sound reproducer. Equipment for converting optical sound into electrical signals. It consists of a light source, an optical system, a photoelectric cell (or other light-sensitive device such as a photoconductive cell), and a mechanism for moving the medium (usually film) carrying the optical sound record.

Optical sound recorder.

optical spectrometer—An instrument with an entrance slit, a dispersing device, and one or more exit slits, with which measurements are made at selected wavelengths within the spectral range, or by scanning over the range. The quantity detected is a function of radiant power.

optical twinning—A defect occurring in natural quartz crystals. The right quartz and left quartz both occur in the same crystal. This generally results in small regions of unusable material, which are discarded when the crystal is cut up.

optics—The branch of science concerned with vision—i.e., the nature and propagation of electromagnetic radiation in the infrared, visible, and ultraviolet regions.

optimization—The continual adjustment of a process for the best obtainable set of conditions.

optimum bunching—The bunching condition required for maximum output in a velocity-modulation tube.

optimum coupling—*See* Critical Coupling.

optimum load—The value of load impedance which will transfer maximum power from the source to the load.

optimum plate load—The ideal plate-load impedance for a given tube and set of operating conditions.

optimum reliability—The value of reliability that yields a minimum total successful mission cost.

optimum working frequency—The frequency at which transmission by ionospheric reflection can be expected to be most effectively maintained between two specified points and at a certain time of day. (For propagation by way of the F_2 layer, the optimum working frequency is often taken as being 15% below the monthly median value of the F_2 maximum usable frequency for a specified path and time of day.)

optoelectronic integrated circuit—An integrated component that uses a combination of electroluminescence and photoconductivity in the performance of all or at least a major portion of its intended function.

optoelectronics—Technology dealing with the coupling of functional electronic blocks by light beams.

optoelectronic transistor—A transistor that has an electroluminescent emitter, a transparent base, and a photoelectric collector.

optophone—A photoelectric device that converts light energy into sound energy. Thus, a blind person by using a selenium cell and a circuit for connecting the resulting signals into sounds of corresponding pitch can "read" by ear.

orange peel—A term applied to the surface of a recording blank which resembles an orange peel. Such a surface has a high background noise.

orbit—1. The path of a body or particle under the influence of a gravitational or other force. For instance, the orbit of a celestial body is its path relative to another body around which it revolves. 2. To go around the earth or other body in an orbit.

orbital electron—An electron which is visualized as moving in an orbit around the nucleus of an atom or molecule—as opposed to a free electron.

OR circuit—*See* OR Gate.

order—In computer terminology, the synonym for instruction, command, and — loosely — operation part. These three usages, however, are losing favor because of the ambiguity between them and the more common meanings in mathematics and business.

ordering—In a computer, the process of sorting and sequencing.

orders of logic—A measure of the speed with which a signal can propagate through a logic network (commonly referred to as orders-of-logic capability).

order tone—A tone sent over trunks to indicate the trunk is ready to receive an order, and to the receiving operator that it is about to arrive.

ordinary wave—Sometimes called the O-wave. One of the two components into which the magnetic field of the earth divides a radio wave in the ionosphere. The other component is called the extraordinary wave, or X-wave.

ordinate—1. The vertical line, or one of the coordinates drawn parallel to it, on a graph. 2. The vertical scale on a graph.

organ—In a computer subassembly, the portion which accomplishes some operation or function (e.g., arithmetic organ).

OR gate—Also called an OR circuit. A gate that performs the function of logical "inclusive or." It produces an output whenever any one (or more) of its inputs is energized.

orient—To position or otherwise adjust with respect to some reference point (e.g., to orient an antenna for best reception).

oriented—In crystallography, a crystal in which the axes of its individual grains are aligned so that they have directional magnetic properties.

orifice—An opening or window—specifically, in a side or end wall of a waveguide or cavity resonator, an opening through which energy is transmitted.

339

original lacquer—An original disc recording made on a lacquer surface for the purpose of producing a master.

original master—Also called metal master or metal negative. In disc recording, the master produced by electroforming from the face of a wax or lacquer recording.

orthicon—Also called an orthiconoscope. A camera tube in which a beam of low-velocity electrons scans a photoemissive mosaic capable of storing an electrical-charge pattern. It is more sensitive than the iconoscope.

orthiconoscope—*See* Orthicon.

orthocode—An arrangement of black and white bars that resemble a piano keyboard and that can be read by an electric-eye device.

orthocore—A completely closed flux memory device designed to almost duplicate the geometry of the ferrite core memory, eliminate the wiring of memory cores, and provide a plurality of wires through the memory element. The concept involves the formation of a group of plastic rods around a suitable wiring array.

orthogonal axes—Axes which are perpendicular to each other. In an instrument, these axes usually coincide with its axes of symmetry.

osciducer—A transducer in which information pertaining to the stimulus is provided in the form of deviation from the center frequency of an oscillator.

oscillating current—An alternating current—specifically, one that changes according to some definite law.

oscillating quantity—A quantity which alternately increases and decreases in value, but always remains within finite limits—e.g., the discharge of current from a capacitor through an inductive resistance (provided the inductance is greater than the capacitance times the resistance squared).

oscillating transducer—A transducer in which information pertaining to the stimulus is provided in the form of deviation from the center frequency of an oscillator.

oscillation—1. The state of a physical quantity when, in the time interval under consideration, the value of the quantity is continually changing in such a manner that it passes through maxima and minima (e.g., oscillating pendulum, oscillating electric current, and oscillating electromotive force). 2. Fluctuations in a system or circuit, especially those consisting of the flow of electric currents alternately in opposite directions; also, the corresponding changes in voltages.

oscillator—1. An electronic device which generates alternating-current power at a frequency determined by the values of certain constants in its circuits. An oscillator may be considered an amplifier with positive feedback, with circuit parameters that restrict the oscillations of the device to a single frequency. 2. A nonrotating device capable of setting up and maintaining oscil-

lations at a frequency determined by the physical constants of the system, such as a vacuum-tube, sparks, or arc generator. 3. A circuit generally using a vacuum tube capable of converting direct current into alternating current of a frequency determined by the inductive and capacitive constant of the circuit. 4. A device used to generate and oscillate at radio frequencies.

Oscillator (shunt-fed Hartley).

oscillator circuit—*See* Oscillator.

oscillator coil—A radio-frequency transformer that provides the feedback required for oscillation in the oscillator circuit of a superheterodyne receiver or in other oscillator circuits.

oscillator harmonic interference—Interference caused in a superheterodyne receiver by the interaction of incoming signals with harmonics (usually the second harmonic) of the local oscillator.

oscillator-mixer-first detector—A single stage which, in a superheterodyne receiver, combines the functions of the local oscillator and the mixer-first detector. It usually employs a pentagrid converter tube.

oscillator padder—An adjustable capacitor placed in series with the oscillator tank circuit of a superheterodyne receiver. It is used to adjust the tracking between the oscillator and preselector at the low-frequency end of the tuning dial.

oscillator radiation—The amount of voltage available across the antenna terminals of a receiver, (or at a distance) traceable to any oscillators incorporated in the receiver.

oscillatory circuit—A circuit containing inductance and/or capacitance and resistance, so arranged or connected that a voltage impulse will produce a current which periodically reverses.

oscillatory current—A current which periodically reverses its direction of flow.

oscillatory discharge—Alternating current of gradually decreasing amplitude which, under certain conditions, flows through a circuit containing inductance, capacitance, and resistance when a voltage is applied. *Also see* Damped Wave.

oscillatory surge—A surge which includes both positive and negative polarity values.

oscillistor—A semiconductor bar which is subjected to a magnetic field and a direct current, and which generates oscillations believed to be due to diffusion of ions toward the surface of the semiconductor as a result of the magnetic field.

oscillogram—The recorded trace produced by an oscillograph.

oscillograph—An instrument primarily for producing a record of the instantaneous values of one or more rapidly varying electrical quantities as a function of time, or of another electrical or mechanical quantity.

oscillograph recorder—A form of mechanical oscillograph in which the waveform is traced on a moving strip of paper by a pen.

oscillograph tube—*See* Oscilloscope Tube.

oscillography—The art and practice of utilizing the oscillograph.

oscilloscope—An instrument primarily for making visible the instantaneous values of one or more rapidly varying electrical quantities as a function of time, or of another electrical or mechanical quantity. It does not inherently produce a permanent record.

oscilloscope differential amplifier—A device that amplifies and displays the voltage difference that exists at every instant between signals applied to its two inputs.

oscilloscope tube—Also called oscillograph tube. A cathode-ray tube that produces a visible pattern which is the graphical representation of electric signals. The pattern is seen as a spot or spots, which change position in accordance with the signals.

OSO—Abbreviation for Orbiting Solar Observatory.

O-type backward-wave oscillator—A wideband, voltage-tunable microwave oscillator that uses a fundamental or space harmonic with phase and group velocity of different signs.

outdoor antenna—A receiving antenna located on an elevated site outside a building.

outdoor transformer—A transformer of weatherproof construction.

outer marker—In an instrument-landing system, a marker located on a localizer course line at a recommended distance (normally about 4½ miles) from the approach end of the runway.

outlet—The point where current is taken from a wiring system.

outline drawing—A drawing showing approximate over-all shape, but no detail.

out of phase—Two or more waveforms that have the same shape, but do not pass through corresponding values at the same instant.

outphasing—In electronic organs, a term applied to a method sometimes used for producing certain voices. Special circuitry, placed between the keying-system output and the formant filters, either adds or subtracts harmonics or subharmonics of the tone-generator signal.

output—1. The current, voltage, power, or driving force delivered by a circuit or device. 2. The terminals or other places where the circuit or device may deliver the current,

voltage, power, or driving force. 3. Information transferred from the internal to the secondary or external storage of a computer.

output amplifier—A circuit that energizes high-power-level devices upon application of a low-power-level input signal.

output axis—The axis around which the spinning wheel of a gyroscope precesses after the wheel has received an input.

output block—In a computer, a portion of the internal storage reserved for holding data which is to be transferred out.

output capacitance—1. Of an n-terminal electron tube, the short-circuit transfer capacitance between the output terminal and all other terminals, except the input terminal, connected together. 2. The shunt capacitance at the output terminal of a device.

output capacitive loading—The maximum capacitance that can be placed on the output of an operational amplifier at unity gain without increasing the phase shift to the point of inducing oscillation. The limiting value increases in direct proportion to the closed-loop gain.

output capacity—The number of loads that can be driven by the output of a circuit.

output device—The part of a machine which translates the electrical impulses representing data processed by the machine into permanent results such as printed forms, punched cards, and magnetic writing on tape.

output equipment—Equipment that provides information in visible, audible, or printed form from a computer.

output gap—An interaction gap with which usable power can be extracted from an electron stream.

output impedance—1. The impedance measured at the output terminals of a transducer with the load disconnected and all impressed driving forces (including those connected to the input) taken as zero. 2. Also called dynamic output impedance. The impedance presented by power supply to the load. It is calculated from the ratio of the change in output voltage (at the prescribed terminals) to the change in load current causing the change. The impedance is specified from d-c to a stated maximum a-c.

output indicator—A meter or other device that indicates variations in the signal strength at the output circuits.

output limits—The maximum output signal available when an operational amplifier is operated in the saturation region.

output load current—The maximum current that the amplifier will deliver to, or accept from, a load. This rating includes the amount, however small, which is caused to flow in the feedback loop.

output meter—An alternating-current voltmeter that measures the signal strength at the output of a receiver or amplifier.

output-meter adapter—A device that can

be slipped over the plate prong of the output tube of a radio receiver to provide a conventional terminal to which an output meter can be connected during alignment.

output power—The power which a system or component delivers to its load.

output saturation voltage—The lowest voltage level to which the collector of the output transistor can be reduced without degrading circuit performances.

output stage—The final stage in any electronic equipment. In a radio receiver, it feeds the speaker directly or through an output transformer. In an audio-frequency amplifier, it feeds one or more speakers, the cutting head of a sound recorder, a transmission line, or any other load. In a transmitter, it feeds the antenna.

output transformer—A transformer used for coupling the plate circuit of one or more power tubes to a speaker or other load.

output tube—A power-amplifier tube designed for use in an output stage.

output voltage—The maximum output voltage which an amplifier will develop in the linear operating region (i.e., before the onset of saturation).

output winding—The winding of a saturable reactor, other than a feedback winding, through which power is delivered to the load.

outside lead—*See* Finish Lead.

overall electrical efficiency (induction- and dielectric-heating usage)—Ratio of the power absorbed by the load material, to the total power drawn from the supply lines.

overall thermoelectric generator efficiency—The ratio of electrical power output to thermal power input to the thermoelectric generator.

overall ultrasonic system efficiency—The acoustical power output at the point of application, divided by the electrical power input into the generator.

overbunching—The condition where the buncher voltage of a velocity-modulation tube is higher than required for optimum bunching of the electrons.

overcompounding—In a compound-wound generator, use of sufficient series turns to raise the voltage as the load increases, in order to compensate for the increased line drop. In a motor, overcompounding makes it run faster as the load increases.

overcoupled circuit—A tuned circuit in which the coupling is greater than the critical coupling. The result is a broad-band response characteristic.

overcurrent—In a circuit, the current which will cause an excessive or even dangerous rise in temperature in the conductor or its insulation.

overcurrent protective device—A device operative on excessive current which causes

and maintains the interruption of power in the circuit.

overcutting—In disc recording, the cutting through of one groove into an adjacent one when the level becomes excessive.

overdamping—1. Any periodic damping greater than the amount required for critical damping. 2. The absence of overshoot or oscillation as the output of a transducer reaches a final steady value in response to a step change in the measurand. 3. *See* Aperiodic Damping.

overdriven amplifier—An amplifier stage designed to distort the input-signal waveform by permitting the grid signal to drive it beyond cutoff or even into plate-current saturation.

overflow—1. The condition occurring whenever the result of an arithmetic operation exceeds the capacity of the number representation in a digital computer. 2. The carry digit arising from (1) above.

overflow position—In a computer, an extra register position in which the overflow digit is developed.

overhang—1. In terms of printed wiring, the inverted shelf of plating formed when conductor material is selectively removed from under the plating. The measurement between the base copper and the plating (generally refers to one side of the conductor only; thus, for a conductor width reduction, one must take two times the overhang). 2. The critical dimension by which the stylus overreaches the center spindle of a turntable when an offset tone arm is mounted for minimum tracking error.

overhead line—A conductor carried on elevated poles (e.g., telephone or telegraph wires).

overinsulation—In a coil, the insulating material placed over a wire which is brought from the center over the top or bottom wall.

overlap—The amount by which the effective height of the scanning facsimile spot exceeds the nominal width of the scanning line. When the spot is rectangular, overlap may be expressed as a percentage of the nominal width of the scanning line.

overlapping contacts—Combinations of two sets of contacts actuated by a common means, each set closing in one of two positions, and so arranged that the contacts of one set open after the contacts of the other set have been closed.

Overcoupled circuit.

overlap radar—Long-range radar which is located in one sector but also covers a portion of another sector.

overlay — In a computer, the technique of using the same blocks of internal storage for different routines during different stages of a problem, e.g., when one routine is no longer needed in internal storage, another routine can be placed in that storage location.

overlay transistor—A transistor containing a large number of emitters connected in parallel to provide maximum power amplification at extremely high frequencies.

overload—1. A load greater than that which an amplifier, other component, or a whole transmission system is designed to carry. It is characterized by waveform distortion or overheating. 2. In electronics, that quantity of power from an amplifier or other component or from a whole transmission system which is sufficient to produce unwanted waveform distortion.

overload capacity—The level of current, voltage, or power beyond which a device will be ruined. It is usually higher than the rated load capacity.

overload level—The level at which a system, component, etc., ceases to operate satisfactorily and produces signal distortion, overheating, damage, etc.

overload operating time — The length of time a system, component, etc., may be safely subjected to a specified overload current.

overload protection—A device which automatically disconnects the circuit whenever the current or voltage becomes excessive.

overload relay—A relay designed to operate when its coil current rises above a predetermined value.

OVERMODULATED WAVE

Overmodulation.

overmodulation — Modulation greater than 100%. Distortion occurs because the carrier is reduced to zero during certain portions of the modulating signal.

overpotential — Also called overvoltage. A voltage greater than the normal operating voltage of a device or circuit.

overpressure—Pressure greater than the full-scale rating of a pressure transducer.

overpunch—Also called zone punch. A hole punched in one of the three top rows of a punch card and which, in combination with a second hole in one of the nine lower rows, identifies an alphabetic or special character.

override—To manually or otherwise deliberately overrule an automatic control system or circuit and thereby render it ineffective.

overscanning—In a cathode-ray tube, the deflection of the electron beam beyond the normal limits of the screen.

overscan recovery—A characteristic of differential comparators that states the time required for the amplifier to recover to within some amount of voltage after a return to the screen of a crt.

Overshoot.

overshoot—1. The initial transient response, which exceeds the steady-state response, to a unidirectional change in input. 2. Amplitude of the first maximum excursion of a pulse beyond the 100% amplitude level expressed as a percentage of this 100% amplitude. 3. A transient rise beyond regulated output limits, ocurring when the a-c power input is turned on or off, and for line or load step changes.

overshoot distortion—*See* Overthrow Distortion.

overshoot of an instrument—The amount which the indicator travels beyond its final steady deflection when a new constant value of the measured quantity is suddenly applied to the instrument. The overtravel and deflection are determined in angular measure, and the overshoot is expressed as a percentage of the change in steady deflection.

overtemperature protection—A thermal relay or other protective device which turns off the power automatically in the event of the occurrence of an overtemperature condition.

over-the-horizon transmission—*See* Scatter Propagation.

overthrow distortion—Also called overshoot distortion. The distortion that occurs in a signal wave when the maximum amplitude of the signal wavefront exceeds the steady-state amplitude.

overtone—1. A physical component of a complex sound having a frequency higher than that of the basic frequency. 2. A component of a complex tone having a pitch higher than that of the fundamental pitch. The term "overtone" has frequently been used in place of "harmonic," the nth harmonic being called the $(n-1)$st overtone. There is, however, ambiguity sometimes in the numbering of components of a complex sound when the word "overtone" is employed. Moreover, the word "tone" has many different meanings, so that it is preferable to employ terms which do not involve "tone" wherever possible.

overtone-type piezoelectric crystal unit— Also called harmonic-mode crystal unit. A crystal designed to be operated at an overtone of its resonant frequency.

overvoltage—1. The amount by which the applied voltage in a radiation-counter tube exceeds the Geiger-Mueller threshold. 2. *See* Overpotential.

overvoltage relay—A relay designed to operate when its coil voltage rises above a predetermined value.

O-wave—*See* Ordinary Wave.

Owen bridge—A four-arm, alternating-current bridge for measuring self-inductance in terms of capacitance and resistance. One arm, adjacent to the unknown inductor, comprises a capacitor and resistor in series. The arm opposite the unknown consists of a second capacitor, and the fourth arm is a resistor. Usually the bridge is balanced by adjusting the resistor in series with the first capacitor, and also the resistor in series with the inductor. The balance is independent of frequency.

oxalizing—*See* Surface Insulation.

oxidation—Commonly known as rust when ferrous material is involved. The increase in oxygen or in an acid-forming element or radical in a compound.

OWEN BRIDGE

$$C_3 R_4 = C_1 R_2 \qquad L = C_1 R_3 R_2$$

Owen bridge.

oxide (in magnetic recording) — Microscopic particles of ferric oxide dispersed in a liquid binder and coated on a recording-tape backing. These oxides are magnetically hard—i.e., once magnetized, they remain so permanently unless exposed to a strong magnetic field.

oxide-coated cathode—A cathode that has been coated with oxides of alkaline-earth metals to improve its electron emission at moderate temperatures.

oximeter—An instrument that determines the degree of oxygenation of the blood (e.g., in the ear lobe). It uses a photoelectric cell.

ozone—An extremely reactive form of oxygen, normally occurring around electrical discharges and present in the atmosphere in small but active quantities. It is faintly blue and has the odor of weak chlorine. In sufficient concentrations, it can break down certain rubber insulations under tension (such as a bent cable).

P

P—Symbol for power, primary winding, permeance, or the plate of an electron tube.

p—Abbreviation for the prefix "pico-" (10^{-12}).

pa—Abbreviation for picoampere.

PABX — Abbreviation for Private Automatic Branch Exchange. Has the same usage as a PBX except that calls within the system are completed automatically by dialing. An attendant at an attendant's board is required to route and complete incoming calls from the central office. Stations within the system are connected to the central office by dialing directly, or they are made to go through the attendant as company policy dictates.

pacemaker—Also called pacer. An electronic device for controlling rhythms of the heart or for initiating cardiac beatings, in event of cardiac arest. Includes implanted induction type and external type.

pacer—*See* Pacemaker.

pack—In computer programming, to combine several fields of information into one machine word.

packaged magnetron—An integral structure comprising a magnetron, its magnetic circuit, and its output matching device.

packaging—The physical process of locating, connecting, and protecting devices, components, etc.

packaging density — 1. The number of devices or equivalent devices in a unit volume of a working system. 2. In a computer, the number of units of information per dimensional unit.

packing—Excessive crowding of carbon particles in a carbon microphone. The abnormal pressure of the particles lowers their resistance. As a result, the current increases excessively and fuses some of the particles together, further lowering the resistance and raising the current. Packing causes the sensitivity of the microphone to decrease.

packing density—In a digital computer, the number of units of desired information contained within a storage or recording medium.

packing factor — The number of pulses or bits of information that can be written on a given length of magnetic surface.

pack unit—A term applied to a compact, combination radio transmitter/receiver that can be carried or strapped on the back. Some pack units are popularly known as walkie-talkies.

Pad (definition 2).

pad—1. A transducer capable of reducing the amplitude of a wave without introducing appreciable distortion. 2. An assembly of resistors that presents the proper input and output impedances to the circuits with which it is connected, and thereby maintains a fixed value of energy loss. 3. A device inserted into a circuit to introduce transmission loss or to match impedances. 4. *See* Land, 2.

padder—A series capacitor inserted into the oscillator tuning circuit of a superheterodyne receiver to control the calibration at the low-frequency end of the tuning range.

Padder capacitor.

pad electrode—One of a pair of electrode plates between which a load is placed for dielectric heating.

paint—Vernacular for a target image on a radarscope.

pair—In electric transmission, two like conductors employed to form an electric circuit.

paired cable—A cable in which all of the conductors are arranged in the form of twisted pairs, none of which is arranged with others to form quads.

pairing—In television, the imperfect interlace of lines comprising the two fields of one frame of the picture. Instead of being equally spaced, the lines appear in groups of two—hence the name.

Palmer scan—A combination of circular and conical scans. The beam is swung around the horizon at the same time the conical scan is performed.

PAM—Abbreviation for pulse-amplitude modulation.

pam/fm—Frequency modulation of a carrier by subcarriers modulated by pulses which, in turn, are modulated by data.

pam/fm/fm—Frequency modulation of a carrier by subcarriers modulated by pulses which, in turn, are modulated by data.

pan—1. To move a television or movie camera slowly up and down or across a scene to secure a panoramic effect. 2. To move the camera up and down, or back and forth, in order to keep it trained on a moving object.

pancake coil—A coil shaped like a pancake, usually with the turns arranged in a flat spiral.

panel—1. An electrical switchboard or instrument board. 2. A mounting plate of metal or insulation for the controls and/or other parts of equipment.

panel layout—The general physical layout of an electrical control panel with all relays, disconnect switch, control transformer, terminal strip, etc.

panning—*See* Pan.

panoramic adapter — An attachment used with a search receiver to provide, on an oscilloscope screen, a visual presentation of the band of frequencies extending above and below the center frequency to which the search receiver is tuned.

Panoramic adapter.

panoramic presentation—A presentation of signals as intensity pips (vertical deflections) along a line. The horizontal distance along the line represents frequency.

panoramic radar — A nonscanning radar which transmits signals omnidirectionally over a wide beam.

panoramic receiver—A radio receiver that displays, on the screen of a cathode-ray tube, the presence and relative strength of all signals within a wide frequency range. Used in communications for monitoring a wide band, locating open channels quickly, indicating intermittent signals or interference, and monitoring a frequency-modulated transmitter.

panoramic sonic analyzer—A heterodyne-type instrument which separates the frequency components of a complex waveform and displays them on an oscillographic screen, indicating both frequency and magnitude.

pan-range—Intensity-modulated A-type indication with slow vertical sweep applied to video. Stationary targets give solid vertical deflection, and moving targets give broken vertical deflection.

pantography—A system for transmitting and automatically recording radar data from an indicator to a remote point.

A-B-C PARAFINED PAPER
D-E   METAL FOIL

Paper capacitor.

paper capacitor—A fixed capacitor consisting of two strips of metal foil separated by oiled or waxed paper or other insulating material, the whole rolled together into a compact roll. The foil strips can be staggered so that one strip projects from each end, or tabs can be added. The connecting wires are attached to the strips or tabs.

PAR—*See* Precision Approach Radar.

parabola—Locus of points equidistant from a fixed point and a straight line.

parabola controls—Sometimes called vertical-amplitude controls. The three controls in a color television receiver employing the magnetic-convergence principle. They are used for adjusting the amplitude of the parabolic voltages applied, at the vertical-scanning frequency, to the coils of the magnetic-convergence assembly.

parabolic antenna—An antenna with a radiating element and a parabolic reflector that concentrates the radiated power into a beam.

parabolic microphone—A microphone positioned at the focus of a parabolic sound reflector to give highly directional characteristics.

parabolic reflector—A metallic sheet formed so that its cross section is in the shape of a cylindrical parabola. The antenna elements are placed along the line that runs

through the focal point of the parabola, parallel to the leading edge of the reflecting sheet.

parabolic-reflector microphone—A microphone employing a parabolic reflector for improved directivity and sensitivity.

paraboloid—The surface which a parabola generates when rotated about its axis of symmetry.

paraboloidal reflector—A hollow concave reflector which is a portion of a paraboloid of revolution.

paraffin—A vegetable wax having insulating properties.

parallax—An optical illusion which makes an object appear displaced when viewed from a different angle. Thus, a meter pointer will seem to be at different positions on the scale, depending from which angle it is read. To eliminate such errors, the eye should be directly above the meter pointer.

Parallel-connected resistors.

parallel—1. Also called shunt. Connected to the same pair of terminals, so that the current can branch out over two or more paths. 2. In electronic computers, the simultaneous transmission of, storage of, or logical operations on a character or other subdivision of a word, using separate facilities for the various parts.

parallel arithmetic unit—In a computer, a unit in which separate equipment operates (usually simultaneously) on the digits in each column.

parallel circuit—A circuit in which all positive terminals are connected to a common point, and all negative terminals are connected to a second common point. The voltage is the same across each element in the circuit.

parallel connection—Also called shunt connection. Connection of two or more parts of a circuit to the same pair of terminals, so that current divides between the parts—as contrasted with a series connection, where the parts are connected end to end so that the same current flows through all.

parallel cut—A Y-cut in a crystal.

parallel digital computer—A computer in which the digits are handled in parallel. Mixed serial and parallel machines are frequently called serial or parallel according to the way arithmetic processes are performed. For example, a parallel digital computer handles decimal digits in parallel, although the bits which comprise a digit might be handled either serially or in parallel.

parallel feed—Also called shunt feed. Application of a d-c voltage to the plate or grid of a tube in parallel with an a-c circuit, so that the d-c and a-c components flow in separate paths.

parallel gap welding—A method of resistance welding in which both electrode tips are in close proximity to each other, being separated by a small gap or insulating material, approach the work from the same direction, and contact only one of the two materials being welded.

paralleling reactor—A reactor for correcting the division of load between parallel-connected transformers with unequal impedance voltages.

parallelogram distortion—In camera or image tubes, a form of distortion which amounts to a skewing of the reproduced image laterally across the crt face.

Parallelogram distortion.

parallel operation—1. Also called master/slave operation. The connecting of two or more power supplies so that their outputs are tied together, permitting the accumulated flow of current from all units to a common load. In regulated power supplies, interconnections other than the output terminals themselves may be required. For example, the amplifiers of all units but one may be made inoperable, and this single amplifier would control all regulating elements. Such operation is denoted. 2. Pertaining to the manipulation of information within the computer circuitry, in which the digits of a word are transmitted simultaneously on separate lines. Faster than serial operation, but requires more equipment.

parallel-plate oscillator—A push-pull, ultrahigh-frequency oscillator circuit that uses two parallel plates as the main frequency-determining elements.

parallel-plate waveguide—A pair of parallel conducting planes for propagating uniform cylindrical waves that have their axes normal to the plane.

parallel processing—In a computer, the processing of more than one program at a time through more than one active processor.

parallel recording—A technique in which the record heads in a head stack are energized simultaneously to record a specific set of bits.

parallel resonance—In a circuit comprising inductance and capacitance connected in parallel, the steady-state condition that exists when the current entering the circuit from the supply line is in phase with the voltage across the circuit.

parallel-resonant circuit—1. A resonant circuit in which the applied voltage is connected across a parallel circuit formed by a capacitor and an inductor. 2. An inductor and capacitor connected in parallel to furnish a high impedance at the frequency to which the circuit is resonant.

parallel-rod oscillator—An ultrahigh-frequency oscillator circuit in which the tank circuits are formed by parallel rods or wires.

parallel-rod tank circuit—A tank circuit consisting of two parallel rods connected at their far ends. This is done to provide the small values of inductance and capacitance in parallel required for ultrahigh-frequency circuits.

parallel-rod tuning—A tuning method sometimes used at ultrahigh frequencies. The transmitter, receiver, or oscillator is tuned by sliding a shorting bar back and forth on two parallel rods.

parallel-series circuit—Also called shunt-series circuit. Two or more parallel circuits connected together in series.

parallel storage—Computer storage where all bits, words, or characters are equally available.

Parallel-T network.

parallel-T network—Also called twin-T network. A network composed of separate T-networks (usually two), the terminals of which are connected in parallel.

parallel-T oscillator—An RC sine-wave oscillator which provides phase inversion at one discrete frequency and is so connected that positive feedback results only when phase inversion occurs.

parallel transfer—Data transfer where all characters of a word are transferred simultaneously over a set of lines.

parallel transmission—In a computer, the system of information transmission in which the characters of a word are transmitted (usually simultaneously) over separate lines, as contrasted with serial transmission.

parallel-wire line—A transmission line consisting of two wires a fixed distance apart.

parallel-wire resonator—A resonator circuit consisting of two parallel wires connected at one end to the oscillator tube or transistor. The other end is short circuited and can be adjusted for the desired frequency.

Paraloc—A phase-shift amplifier the positive feedback of which results in an oscillation that is frequency-modulated by the change in a sensed variable. The sensor is one arm of a resistance bridge.

paramagnetic—Having a magnetic permeability greater than that of a vacuum but less than that of ferromagnetic materials. Unlike the latter, the permeability of paramagnetic materials is independent of the magnetizing force.

paramagnetic material—A material having a permeability which is slightly greater than that of a vacuum and which is approximately independent of the magnetizing force.

paramagnetism—Magnetism that involves a permeability somewhat greater than unity.

parameter—1. A constant or element, the value of which characterizes the behavior of one or more variables associated with a given system. 2. A measured value which expresses performance.

parameter extraction—A technique that reduces the bandwidth required to transmit a given data sample by means of an information-describing irreversible transformation. These transformations are considered irreversible in that, while they provide useful descriptions of the input signal, they so distort the signal that it is impossible to reconstruct the original waveform.

parametric amplifier—A low-noise device for amplifying signals in the uhf and microwave regions of the electromagnetic spectrum. The essential element of the amplifier is a semiconductor crystal (varactor). By its very nature the diode contributes very little noise, unlike an amplifier utilizing electron tubes, where the random nature of the electron emission from the hot cathode produces large fluctuations in the current, called shot noise. Thus the signals to be amplified can be of extremely low levels.

parametric converter—An inverting or non-inverting parametric device used to convert an input signal at one frequency into an output signal at a different frequency.

parametric device—A device the operation of which depends essentially upon the time variation of a characteristic parameter usually understood to be a reactance.

parametric down-converter—A parametric converter in which the output signal is at a lower frequency than the input signal.

parametric excitation—A term referring to the method of exciting and maintaining oscillation in either an electrical or mechanical dynamic system, in which excitation results from a periodic variation in an energy storage element in a system such as a capacitor, inductor, or spring constant.

parametric frequency converter—A frequency converter that utilizes the variation of the reactance parameter of an energy-storage element for frequency conversion.

parametric modulator—A modulator that utilizes the variation in the reactance parameter of an energy-storage element to produce modulation.

parametric up-converter—A parametric converter in which the output signal is at a higher frequency than the input signal.

(A) Magnetic types.

(B) Capacitive types.

Parametrons.

parametron—A digital circuit element utilizing the principle of parametric excitation. It is essentially a resonant circuit with a nonlinear reactive element which oscillates at half the driving frequency. The oscillation can be made to represent a binary digit by the choice between two stationary phases π radians apart.

paramistor—A digital logic-circuit module containing several parametron elements.

paraphase amplifier—An amplifier which converts a single input signal into two out-of-phase signals for driving a push-pull stage.

parasite—Current in a circuit, due to some unintentional cause such as inequalities of temperature or of composition; particularly troublesome in electrical measurement.

parasitic—An undesired low- or high-frequency signal in an electronic circuit.

parasitic antenna—An antenna that is excited by radiation from other antennas rather than by electrical connection with them.

parasitic arrays—An antenna array containing one or more elements not connected to the transmission line.

parasitic component—In a monolithic integrated circuit, the capacitors and diodes which are formed between the planned circuit elements and the substrate during processing. The circuit design must allow for the functional effects of these parasitic components.

parasitic element—Also called passive element. An antenna element (i.e., reflector, director, etc.) not connected to the transmission line or to any driven element. A parasitic element affects the gain and directivity pattern of an antenna, and also acts on a driven element by absorbing and re-turning energy from it. In a dipole reflector combination, the reflector is the parasitic element.

parasitic oscillations—Also called parasitics. Unintended self-sustaining oscillations, or transient impulses.

parasitics—*See* Parasitic Oscillations.

parasitic suppressor—A parallel resistance, or a parallel combination of inductance and resistance, inserted into a grid or plate circuit to suppress parasitic oscillations.

pard—In an electronic power conversion unit, the Periodic And Random Deviation of the output d-c voltage, current, or power from its average value, with all external operational and environmental parameters maintained constant. The load impedance in particular must be held constant. Perturbations in the output which are induced by load impedance changes are dynamic load regulation or transient response. Pard may be defined as rms pard or peak-to-peak pard.

parent population—Prototype or initial group of the articles under consideration.

parity check—A computer checking method in which the total number of binary 1's (or 0's) is always even or always odd. Either an even-parity or odd-parity check can be made.

part—1. The smallest subdivision of a system. 2. An item which cannot ordinarily be disassembled without destruction.

part failure—A breakdown that cannot be repaired and which ends the life of a part.

part-failure rate—The number of occasions, during a specified time period, on which a given quantity of identical parts will not function properly.

partial—1. A physical component of a complex tone. 2. A component of a sound sensation that can be distinguished as a simple tone which cannot be further analyzed by the ear and which contributes to the character of the complex sound.

partial node—The place in a standing-wave system at which some characteristic of the wave field has a minimum amplitude other than zero.

partial-read pulse—In a computer, any one of the applied currents which cause selection of a core for reading.

partial-select output—In a computer, the voltage response of an unselected magnetic cell produced by the application of partial-read pulses or partial-write pulses.

partial-write pulse—In a computer, any one of the applied currents which cause a core to be selected for writing.

particle—An infinitesimal subdivision of matter—e.g., a molecule, atom, or electron.

particle accelerator—Any device for accelerating charged particles to high energies (e.g., cyclotron, betatron, Van de Graaff generator, linear accelerator, etc.).

particle velocity—The velocity of a given infinitesimal part of a sound wave. The most common unit is centimeter per second.

partitioning—Also called segmenting. In a computer, subdividing a large block into smaller, more conveniently handled subunits.

partition noise—A noise caused in an electron tube by random fluctuations as the electron stream divides between the electrodes. It is more pronounced in pentodes and tetrodes than in triodes.

part programmer—One who translates the physical operations for machining a part into a series of mathematical steps and then prepares the coded computer instructions for those steps.

parts density—The number of parts in a unit volume.

party line—A telephone line serving more than one subscriber, with discriminatory ringing for each.

Paschen's law—The sparking potential between two terminals in a gas is proportional to the pressure times the spark length. For a given voltage, this means the spark length is inversely proportionate to the pressure.

passband—The band of frequencies which will pass through a filter with essentially no attenuation.

passband ripple—In a filter, the difference, in db, between the minimum loss point and the maximum loss point in a specified bandwidth.

pass element—An automatic variable resistance device, either a vacuum tube or power transistor, in series with the source of d-c power. The pass element is driven by the amplifier error signal to increase its resistance when the output needs to be lowered or to decrease its resistance when the output must be raised. *Also see* Series Regulator.

passivation—The growth of an oxide layer on the surface of a semiconductor to provide electrical stability by isolating the transistor surface from electrical and chemical conditions in the environment. This reduces reverse-current leakage, increases breakdown voltages, and raises the power dissipation rating.

passive—An inert component which may control, but does not create or amplify energy.

passive communication satellite—A communication satellite which simply reflects a signal without amplification. In essence, it is a radio mirror. It requires a large reflecting surface and large, high-powered, complex ground stations. Abbreviated passive comsat.

passive component—A nonpowered component generally presenting some loss (expressed in db) to a system.

passive comsat—*See* Passive Communications Satellite.

passive decoder—A device that is set so that only one specific reply code will pass a decoder and give an output from one decoder for display.

passive detection—Detection of a target without revealing the position of the detector.

passive device—A device which exhibits no transistance. It has no gain or control and does not require any input other than a signal to perform its function. Examples of passive devices are conductors, resistors, and capacitors.

passive electric network—An electric network with no source of energy.

passive element—1. A parasitic element. 2. A circuit element with no source of energy (e.g., a resistor, capacitor, inductor, etc.).

passive film circuit—A thin- or thick-film circuit network consisting entirely of passive circuit elements and interconnections.

passive homing system—A guidance system based on the sensing of energy radiated by the target. (*Also see* Active Homing *and* Homing Guidance System.)

passive network—A network with no source of energy.

passive reflector—A reflector often used on microwave relay towers to change the direction of a microwave. This permits convenient location of transmitter, repeater, and receiver equipment on the ground rather than at the tops of towers.

passive sonar—*See* Sonar.

passive substrate—A substrate that may serve as a physical support and thermal sink for a thin-film integrated circuit but does not exhibit transistance. Examples of passive substrates are glass, ceramic, etc.

passive tracking system—Usually a system that tracks by reflected radiation from some external source, or by the jet emission of the vehicle (e.g., optical systems, use of commercial radio or television, reflection and infrared systems).

passive transducer—A transducer, the output waves of which are independent of any sources of power controlled by the actuating waves.

paste—In batteries, the medium in the form of a paste or jelly, containing an electrolyte. It is positioned adjacent to the negative electrode of a dry cell. In an electrolytic cell, the post serves as one of the conducting plates.

pa system—Abbreviation for public-address system.

patch—1. To connect circuits together temporarily with a special cord known as a patch cord. 2. In a computer, to make a change or correction in the coding at a particular location by inserting transfer instructions at that location and by adding elsewhere the new instructions and the replaced instructions. This procedure is usually used during checkout. 3. The section of coding so inserted.

patch board—A board or panel where circuits are terminated in jacks for patch cords.

patch cord—Sometimes called an attachment cord. A short cord with a plug or a pair of clips on one end, for conveniently connecting two pieces of sound equipment such as a phonograph and tape recorder, an amplifier and speaker, etc.

Patch cord.

patching—Connecting two lines or circuits together temporarily by means of a patch cord.

patching jack—A jack for interconnection of circuit elements.

path—In navigation, an imaginary line connecting a series of points in space and constituting a proposed or traveled route.

pattern—1. The means of specifying the character of a wave in a guide. This is done by showing the loops of force existing in the guide for that wave. The pattern identifies the order and mode of the wave and the cross-sectional shape of the guide. 2. A geometrical figure representing the directional qualities of an antenna array.

pattern recognition—In a computer, the examination of records for certain code-element combinations.

pause control—A feature of some tape recorders making it possible to temporarily stop the movement of the tape without switching the machine from the "play" or "record" position. (Essentially for a tape recorder used for dictation and generally helpful for editing purposes.)

PAX—Acronym for Private Automatic Exchange. An automatic system used exclusively for interoffice dial communications and having no trunks to the central office.

pay television—Also called subscription television. A system whereby viewers must insert coins or record cards into a decoding device in order to view a television program that has been deliberately scrambled to prevent unpaid viewing.

P-band—A radio-frequency band extending from 225 to 390 MHz and having a wavelength from 133.3 to 76.9 cm.

PBX — Abbreviation for Private Branch Exchange. A manual telephone system located on the premises of a business and requiring an attendant to complete all calls. It is usually owned by the telephone company and is equipped with trunks to a telephone-company central office.

pc—1. Abbreviation for picocoulomb. 2. Abbreviation for picocurie.

pcm—Abbreviation for pulse-code modulation.

pcm/fm—Frequency modulation of a carrier by pulse code modulated information.

pcm/fm/fm—Frequency modulation of a carrier by subcarrier(s) which is (are) frequency modulated by pulse code modulated information.

pcm level—The number by which identification of a given quantized-signal subrange may be made.

pcm/pm—Phase modulation of a carrier by pulse code modulated information.

P-display—*See* Plan-Position Indicator.

pdm—Abbreviation for pulse-duration modulation.

pdm/fm—Frequency modulation of a carrier by a subcarrier(s) which is (are) frequency modulated by pulses which are modulated in duration by information.

pdm/fm/fm—Frequency modulation of a carrier by subcarrier(s) which is (are) frequency modulated by pulses which are time duration modulated by information.

pdm/pm—Phase modulation of a carrier by pulses which are duration modulated by information.

peak—Also called crest. 1. A momentary high amplitude level. 2. The maximum instantaneous value of a quantity.

peak alternating gap voltage—In a microwave tube, the negative of the line integral of the peak alternating electric field, taken along a specified path across the gap.

peak amplitude—The maximum deviation (e.g., of a wave) from an average or mean position.

peak-anode current—The maximum instantaneous value of an anode current in an electron tube.

peak-cathode current (fault)—The highest instantaneous value of a nonrecurrent pulse of cathode current occurring under fault conditions.

peak-cathode current (steady-state)—The maximum instantaneous value of a periodically recurring cathode current.

peak-cathode current (surge)—The highest instantaneous value of a randomly recurring pulse of cathode current.

peak-charge characteristic — The function giving the relation of one half the peak-to-peak value of transferred charge in the steady state to one half the peak-to-peak

value of a specified symmetrical alternating voltage applied to a nonlinear capacitor.

peak current—The maximum current which flows during a complete cycle.

peak distortion—The largest total distortion of signals noted during a period of observation.

peak electrode current—The maximum instantaneous current that flows through an electrode.

peak-envelope power of a radio transmitter—The average power supplied to the antenna transmission line by a transmitter during one radio-frequency cycle at the highest crest of the modulation envelope, taken under conditions of normal operation.

peak flux density—The maximum flux density in a magnetic material.

peak forward anode voltage — The maximum instantaneous anode voltage in the direction the tube is designed to pass current.

peak forward-blocking voltage—The maximum instantaneous value of repetititve positive voltage that may be applied to the anode of an scr with its gate circuit open.

peak forward drop—The maximum instantaneous voltage drop measured when a tube or rectifier cell is conducting forward current, either continuously or during transient operation.

peaking—Adjusting a component so as to increase the response of a circuit at a desired frequency or band of frequencies.

peaking circuit—A circuit capable of converting an input wave into a peaked waveform.

peaking control—In a television receiver, a fixed or variable resistor-capacitor circuit which controls the negative shape of the pulses originating at the horizontal oscillator. This is done to assure a linear sweep.

peaking network—A type of interstage coupling network used to increase the amplification at the upper end of the frequency range. It consists of an inductance effectively in series (series peaking network) or shunt (shunt peaking network) with a parasitic capacitance.

peaking resistor—A resistor placed in series with the charging capacitor of the vertical sawtooth generator. By adding a negative peaking pulse to the sawtooth voltage, it creates the waveform required to produce a linear sawtooth current in the yoke.

peaking transformer—A transformer having a core designed to saturate at relatively low values of primary current.

peak inverse anode voltage—The maximum instantaneous anode voltage in the direction opposite from that in which the tube is designed to pass current.

peak inverse voltage—The peak a-c voltage which a rectifying cell or PN junction will withstand in the reverse direction.

peak level—The maximum instantaneous level that occurs during a specific time interval (i.e., in acoustics, the peak sound pressure level).

peak limiter—A device which automatically limits the magnitude of its output signal to approximate a preset maximum value by reducing its amplification when the instantaneous signal magnitude exceeds a preset value.

peak load—The maximum electrical power load consumed or produced in a stated period of time. It may be the maximum instantaneous load or the maximum average load over a designated interval of time.

peak magnetizing force — The upper or lower limiting value of a magnetizing force.

peak-or-valley readout memory—A circuit in which the output remains at the condition corresponding to the most positive (least negative) or vice versa input signal since the circuit was set to initial conditions, until reset to those conditions.

peak plate current—The maximum instantaneous current passing through the plate circuit of a tube.

peak power—1. The mean power supplied to the antenna of a radio transmitter during one radio-frequency cycle at the highest crest of the modulation envelope. 2. The maximum power of the pulse from a radar transmitter. Since the resting time of a radar transmitter is longer than its operating time, the average power output is much lower than the peak power.

peak power output—The output power averaged over the radio-frequency cycle and having the maximum peak value that can occur under any combination of signals transmitted.

peak pulse amplitude—The maximum absolute peak value of the pulse, excluding unwanted portions such as spikes.

peak pulse power—The maximum power of a pulse, excluding spikes.

peak response—The maximum response of a system to an input.

peaks—1. A momentarily high amplitude occurring in electronic equipment. 2. A momentarily high volume level during a radio program. It causes the volume indicator at the studio or transmitter to swing upward.

peak signal level—An expression of the maximum instantaneous signal power or voltage as measured at any point in a facsimile transmission system. This includes auxiliary signals.

peak sound pressure—The maximum absolute value of instantaneous sound pressure for any specified time interval. The most common unit is the microbar.

peak speech power—The maximum instantaneous speech power over the time interval considered.

peak to peak—The algebraic difference between the positive and negative maximum values of a waveform.

peak-to-peak amplitude—The amplitude of an alternating quantity, measured from positive peak to negative peak.

peak-to-peak voltmeter—A voltmeter which indicates the over-all difference between the positive and negative voltage peaks.

peak value—Also called crest value. The maximum instantaneous value of a varying current, voltage, or power. For a sine wave, it is equal to 1.414 times the effective value of the sine wave.

peak voltage—The maximum value present in a varying or alternating voltage. This value may be either positive or negative.

peak voltmeter—A voltmeter that reads peak values of an alternating voltage.

pea lamp—An incandescent lamp with a bulb about the size of a pea. Its small size makes it ideal for use by doctors, on instrument panels, and in small flashlights.

pedal clavier — In an organ, the pedal keyboard which supplies the bass accompaniment for the other manuals.

pedal keyboard—*See* Pedal Clavier.

pedestal—1. A substantially flat-topped pulse which elevates the base level for another wave. 2. The base of a radar antenna.

pedestal level—*See* Blanking Level.

pedestal pulse—A square-wave pulse or gate on which a video signal or sweep voltage may be superimposed.

peek-a-boo—In a computer, a method of determining the presence or absence of holes in identical locations on punched cards by placing one card on top of another. (*Also see* Batten System.)

peel-strength adhesion—*See* Bond Strength.

Peltier coefficient—The quotient of the rate of Peltier heat absorption by the junction of two dissimilar conductors divided by the current through the junction. The Peltier coefficient of a couple is the algebraic difference between either the relative or absolute Peltier coefficients of the two conductors making up the couple.

Peltier effect—The production or absorption of heat at the junction of two metals when current is passed through the junction. Heat generated by current in one direction will be absorbed when the current is reversed.

Peltier electromotive force—The component of voltage produced by a thermocouple after being heated by the Peltier effect at the junction of the different metals. It adds to the Thomson electromotive force to produce the total voltage of the thermocouple.

Peltier heat — The thermal energy absorbed or produced as a result of the Peltier effect.

pen centering—An electrical or mechanical adjustment by which an oscillograph pen is positioned to channel center.

pencil beam—A radar beam in which the energy is confined to a narrow cone.

pencil-beam antenna—A unidirectional antenna in which those cross sections of the major lobe perpendicular to the maximum radiation are approximately circular.

pencil tube—A small tube designed for operation in the ultrahigh-frequency band and used as an oscillator or r-f amplifier.

pendant—The type of plug and/or receptacle that is not mounted in a fixed position or attached to a panel or side of equipment.

pendant station—A push-button station suspended from overhead and connected by means of flexible cord or conduit, but supported by a separate cable.

pendulous accelerometer—A device which measures linear accelerations by means of a restrained unbalanced mass. Two pivots and jewels support the unbalanced gimbal, and the torsion bar functions as the spring.

penetrating frequency — See Critical Frequency.

Penning discharge—A type of discharge in which electrons are forced to oscillate between two opposed cathodes and are prevented from going to the surrounding anode by the presence of a magnetic field. It is sometimes referred to as a pig discharge because the device producing it was first used as an ionization gage called the Penning Ionization Gage.

Penning Ionization Gage—See Penning Discharge.

pen position—An electrical or mechanical adjustment by which an oscillograph pen is positioned to any desired amplitude grid mark on the chart to represent zero signal.

pent—Abbreviation for pentode.

Pentagrid converter.

pentagrid converter—A pentagrid tube used as a combination oscillator, mixer, and first detector in a superheterodyne receiver.

pentagrid mixer—A pentagrid tube used to mix the r-f and local-oscillator signals in a superheterodyne receiver.

pentagrid tube—An electron tube having five grids, plus an anode and a cathode.

pentatron—A five-electrode vacuum tube that provides push-pull amplification with a single tube. It has one cathode, two grids, and two anodes. In effect, it is two tubes in one.

pentode—A five-electrode electron tube containing an anode, a cathode, a control electrode, and two grids.

pentode field-effect transistor—A five-lead transistor with three gates. It can be connected like a pentode if each of the gates is supplied from an independent bias source.

percentage-differential relay—A differential relay which functions when the difference between two quantities of the same nature exceeds a fixed percentage of the smaller quantity. This term includes relays formerly known as ratio-balance relays, biased relays, and ratio differential relays.

percentage of meter accuracy—The ratio of the actual meter reading to the true reading, expressed as a percent.

percentage sync—Ratio of the amplitude of the synchronizing signal to the peak-to-peak amplitude of the picture signal between blanking and reference white level, expressed in percent.

percentage timers—A repeat-cycle nonreset timer with fixed cycle length, having a dial adjustment of the percentage of the cycle time for which the contacts are operated.

percent modulation meter—An instrument which indicates the modulation percentage of an amplitude-modulated signal, either on a meter or a cathode-ray tube.

percent of deafness—See Percent of Hearing Loss.

percent of harmonic distortion—A measure of the harmonic distortion in a system or component. Each harmonic frequency is equal to 100 times the ratio of the square root of the sum of the squares of the root-mean-square voltages (or currents), to the root-mean-square voltage (or current) of the fundamental.

percent of hearing—At a given frequency, 100 minus the percent of hearing loss at that frequency.

percent of hearing loss—Also called percent of deafness. At a given frequency, 100 times the ratio of the hearing loss in decibels, to the number of decibels between the normal threshold levels of audibility and feeling.

percent of modulation—1. In am, the ratio of half the difference between the maximum and minimum amplitudes of a wave to the average amplitude, expressed in percentage. 2. In f-m and tv audio transmission, the ratio of the actual frequency swing, to the frequency swing defined as 100% modulation, expressed in percentage. For f-m broadcast stations, a frequency swing of ±75 kHz is defined as 100% modulation. For television, it is ±25 kHz.

percent of ripple voltage—Ratio of the effective (root-mean-square) value of the ripple voltage to the average value of the total voltage, expressed in percent.

percent of syllabic articulation—See Syllable Articulation.

percent ripple (rms)—The ratio of the

effective (rms) value of the ripple voltage to the average value of the total voltage, expressed in percent. The new term is pard.

perceptron—A system capable of—either in theory or in practice—performing knowledgeable functions such as recognition, classification, and learning. These functions may exist as mathematical analyses, computer programs, or "hardware."

percussion—Musical sounds characterized by sudden or sharp transients. Organ percussion is achieved by causing the tone to start to decay the instant it is played rather than waiting until the key is released.

percussive welding — An electrical arc method of welding studs and cable ends to plates and terminals. The weld is accomplished by storing electrical energy in capacitors, then releasing it to produce a high current density at the stud or cable tip. This ionizes an area which in turn produces an arc that melts the tip and allows the stud to be pressed against the plate for a welded union.

perfect dielectric—Also called ideal dielectric. A dielectric in which all the energy required to establish the electric field in it is returned to the electric system when the field is removed. A perfect dielectric has zero conductivity and exhibits no absorption phenomena. A vacuum is the only known perfect dielectric.

perforated tape—See Punched Tape.

performance—Degree of effectiveness of operation.

performance characteristic—A characteristic measurable in terms of some useful denominator—e.g., gain, power output, etc.

period—The time required for one complete cycle of a regular, repeating series of events.

periodic—Repeating itself regularly in time and form.

periodic antenna—An antenna in which the input impedance varies as the frequency does (e.g., open-end wires and resonant antennas).

periodic current—Oscillating current, the values of which recur at equal time intervals.

periodic damping—Damping in which the pointer of an instrument oscillates about the final position before coming to rest. The point of change between periodic and aperiodic damping is called critical damping.

periodic duty—Intermittent duty where the load conditions recur at regular intervals.

periodic electromagnetic wave—A wave in which the electric field vector is repeated in detail—either at a fixed point, after a lapse of time known as the period; or at a fixed time, after the addition of a distance known as the wavelength.

periodicity—The variations in the insulation diameter of a transmission cable that result in reflections of a signal, when its wavelength or a multiple thereof is equal to the distance between two diameter variations.

periodic law—When chemical elements are arranged in the ascending or descending

order of their atomic number, their properties will occur in cycles.

periodic line—A line consisting of identical, similarly oriented sections, each section having nonuniform electrical properties throughout.

periodic pard—Pertains to that portion of the total pard, in an electronic power supply, the frequency of which is identical or harmonically related to the input frequency and/or intentionally internally generated signal frequencies. This phenomenon is frequently referred to as "ripple."

periodic pulse train—A pulse train made up of identical groups of pulses repeated at regular intervals.

periodic quantity—An oscillating quantity in which any value it attains is repeated at equal time intervals.

periodic rating—The load which can be carried for the alternate periods of load and rest specified in the rating without exceeding the specified heating limits.

periodic resonance—Also called natural resonance. Resonance in which the applied agency maintaining the oscillation has the same frequency as the natural period of oscillation of a system.

periodic time — See Period of an Underdamped Instrument.

periodic vibration — A vibration having a regularly recurring waveform, e.g., sinusoidal vibration.

periodic wave—A wave in which each point is displaced at regular time intervals.

period of an underdamped instrument — Also called periodic time. The time required, following an abrupt change in the measurand, for the pointer or other indicating means to make two consecutive transits in the same direction through the rest position.

peripheral control unit—An intermediary control device which links a peripheral unit to the central processor, or, in the case of offline operation, to another peripheral unit.

peripheral electron—Also called a valence electron. One of the outer electrons of an atom. Theoretically, it is responsible for visible light, thermal radiation, and chemical combination.

peripheral equipment—Units which work in conjunction with a computer but are not part of it (e.g., tape reader, analog-to-digital converter, typewriter, etc.).

permalloy — A high-permeability magnetic alloy composed mainly of iron and nickel.

permanent echo—A radar echo from a fixed target.

permanent-field synchronous motor — A type of synchronous motor in which the member carrying the secondary laminations and windings also carries permanent-magnet field poles that are shielded from the alternating magnetic flux by the laminations. It behaves as an induction motor when starting but runs at synchronous speed.

permanent magnet—A piece of hardened steel or other magnetic material which has been so strongly magnetized that it retains the magnetism indefinitely.

permanent-magnet centering — Vertical or horizontal shifting of a television picture by means of magnetic fields from permanent magnets mounted around the neck of the picture tube.

permanent-magnet focusing — Focusing of the electron beam in a television picture tube by means of one or more permanent magnets located around the neck.

permanent-magnet material — Ferromagnetic material which, once having been magnetized, resists external demagnetizing forces (i.e., requires a high coercive force to remove the magnetism).

permanent-magnet, moving-coil instrument—Also called D'Arsonval instrument. An instrument in which a reading is produced by the reaction between the current in a movable coil or coils and the field of a fixed permanent magnet.

permanent-magnet, moving-iron instrument—Also called polarized-vane instrument. An instrument in which a reading is produced by an iron vane as it aligns itself in the magnetic field produced by a permanent magnet and by the current in an adjacent coil of the instrument.

FRAME

RIM SUSPENSION

CONE

SPIDER

PERMANENT MAGNET

VOICE COIL

MAGNETIC GAP

LEADS TO VOICE COIL

Permanent-magnet speaker.

permanent-magnet speaker—A moving-conductor speaker in which the steady magnetic field is produced by a permanent magnet.

permanent magnistor—A saturable reactor which has the properties of memory and the ability to handle appreciable power.

permanent-memory computer—A computer in which the stored information remains intact, even after the power has been turned off.

permanent storage—A computer storage device which retains the stored data indefinitely.

permatron—A thermionic gas diode, the discharge of which is controlled by an external magnetic field. It is used mainly as a controlled rectifier and functions like a thyratron.

permeability—Symbolized by the Greek letter

mu (μ). The measure of how much better a given material is than air as a path for magnetic lines of force. (Air is assumed to have a permeability of 1.) It is equal to the magnetic induction (B) in gausses, divided by the magnetizing force (H) in oersteds.

permeability tuning—A method of tuning a circuit by moving a magnetic core into or out of a coil to vary its inductance.

permeameter—An apparatus for determining the magnetizing force and flux density in a test specimen. From these values, the normal induction curves or hysteresis loops can then be plotted and the magnetic permeability computed.

permeance — The reciprocal of reluctance. Through any cross section of a tubular portion of a magnetic circuit bounded by lines of force and by two equipotential surfaces, permeance is the ratio of the flux to the magnetic potential difference between the surfaces under consideration. In the cgs system, it is equal to the magnetic flux (in maxwells) divided by the magnetomotive force (in gilberts).

permissive control device—Generally a two-position, manually operated switch which in one position permits the closing of a circuit breaker or the placing of an equipment into operation, and in the other position prevents the circuit breaker or the equipment from being operated.

permittivity—*See* Dielectric Constant.

peroxide of lead—A lead compound that forms the principal part of the positive plate in a charged lead-acid cell.

perpendicular magnetization—In magnetic recording, magnetization that is perpendicular to the line of travel and parallel to the smallest cross-sectional dimension of the medium. Either single– or double–pole-piece magnetic heads may be used.

persistence—The length of time a phosphor dot glows on the screen of a cathode-ray tube before going out—i.e., the length of time it takes to decay from initial brightness (reached during fluorescence) until it can no longer be seen.

persistence characteristic (of a luminescent screen)—Also called the decay characteristic. The relationship (usually shown by a graph) between the time a luminescent screen is excited and the time it emits radiant power.

persistence of vision — The phenomenon whereby the eye retains an image for a short time after the field of vision has disappeared.

persistent current—A current that is magnetically induced and flows undiminished in a superconducting material or circuit.

persistor—A bimetallic circuit used for storage or readout in a computer. It is operated near absolute zero, and changes from a resistive to a superconductive state at a critical current value.

persistron—A device in which electroluminescence and photoconductivity are combined into a single panel capable of producing a steady or persistent display with pulsed signal input.

perveance—The space-charge-limited cathode current divided by the three-halves power of the anode voltage in a diode.

petticoat insulator—An insulator having an outward flaring lower part that is hollow to increase the length of the surface leakage path and keep part of the path dry at all times.

pf—Abbreviation for picofarad.

phanotron—A term used primarily in industrial electronics to mean a hot-cathode gas diode.

phantastron—An electronic circuit of the multivibrator type which is normally used in the monostable form. It is a stable trigger generator in this connection and is used in radar systems for gating functions and sweep-delay functions.

phantom channel—In a stereo system, an electrical combination of the left and right channels fed to a third, centrally located speaker.

phantom circuit—A superimposed circuit derived from two suitably arranged pairs of wires called side circuits. Each pair of wires is a circuit itself, and at the same time acts as one conductor of the phantom circuit.

phantom-circuit loading coil—A loading coil that introduces the desired amount of inductance into a phantom circuit and a minimum amount into the constituent side circuits.

phantom-circuit repeating coil—A repeating coil used at a terminal of a phantom circuit in the terminal circuit extending from the midpoints of the associated side-circuit repeating coils.

phantom coil—A coil originally used in a phantom circuit for impedance matching. Now, generally, any coil, side or phantom, in a phantom circuit. When the term is used, the meaning should be made clear.

phantom group—1. A group of four open-wire conductors suitable for the derivation of a phantom circuit. 2. Three circuits which are derived from simplexing two physical circuits to form a phantom circuit.

phantom repeating coil—A side-circuit repeating coil or a phantom-circuit repeating coil, when discrimination between these two types is not necessary.

phantom signals—Signals appearing on the screen of a cathode-ray tube indicator; their cause cannot readily be determined, and they may be due to circuit fault, interference, propagation and anomalies, jamming, etc.

phantom target—*See* Echo Box.

phase—1. The angular relationship between current and voltage in alternating-current circuits. 2. The number of separate voltage waves in a commercial alternating-current supply (e.g., single-phase, three-phase, etc.).

Symbolized by the Greek letter *phi* (ϕ). 3. In a periodic function or wave, the fraction of the period which has elapsed, measured from some fixed origin. If the time for one period is represented as 360° along a time axis, the phase position is called phase angle.

phase advancer—A phase modifier which supplies leading reactive volt-amperes to the system to which it is connected. Phase advancers may be either synchronous or non-synchronous.

phase angle—Of a periodic function, the angle obtained by multiplying the phase by 2π if the angle is to be expressed in radians, or 360 for degrees.

phase-angle correction factor—That factor by which the reading of a wattmeter or watt-hour meter operated from the secondary of a current or potential transformer, or both, must be multiplied to correct for the effective phase displacement of current and voltage due to the measuring apparatus.

phase-angle measuring relay—Also called out-of-step protective relay. A device which functions at a predetermined phase angle between two voltages or currents, or between voltage and current.

phase-angle meter—*See* Phase Meter.

phase angle of a current transformer—The angle between the primary-current vector and the secondary-current vector reversed. This angle is conveniently considered as positive when the reversed secondary-current vector leads the primary-current vector.

phase angle of a potential (voltage) transformer—The angle between the primary-voltage vector and the secondary-voltage vector reversed. This angle is conveniently considered as positive when the reversed secondary-voltage vector leads the primary-voltage vector.

phase balance—On a chopper, the phase-angle difference between positive and negative halves of the square wave; the difference in degrees between 180° and the measured angle between square-wave midpoints.

phase-balance current relay—*See* Reverse-Phase Current Relay.

phase-balance relay—A relay which functions by reason of a difference between two quantities associated with different phases of a polyphase circuit.

phase center (center of radiation)—Pertaining only to antenna types which have radiation characteristics such that while they are radiating energy, one can observe the antenna from a distance of many wavelengths and see the energy radiating from a point within the antenna array. The position of a point-source radiator which would replace the antenna and produce the same for field phase contour.

phase characteristic—A graph of phase shift versus frequency, assuming sinusoidal input and output.

phase-coefficient distortion—The difference

between the maximum transit time for frequencies within a specified band.

phase-comparison tracking system—A system which provides target-trajectory information by the use of c-w phase-comparison techniques.

phase-compensation network—A network used to provide closed-loop stability in an operational amplifier. No greater than 12db/octave rolloff of the open-loop gain is allowed.

phase conductor—Those conductors other than the neutral conductor of a polyphase circuit.

phase constant—The imaginary component of the propagation constant. For a traveling plane wave at a given frequency, the rate in radians per unit length, at which the phase lag of a field component (for the voltage or current) increases linearly in the direction of propagation.

phase control—Also called horizontal-parabola control. One of three controls for adjusting the phase of a voltage or current in a color television receiver employing the magnetic-convergence principle. Each control varies the phases of the sinusoidal voltages applied, at the horizontal-scanning frequency, to the coils of the magnetic-convergence assembly.

phase-controlled rectifier—A rectifier circuit in which the rectifying element is a thyratron having a variable-phase, sine-wave grid bias.

phase correction—The process of keeping synchronous telegraph mechanisms in substantially correct phase relationship.

phase corrector—A network designed to correct for phase distortion.

phased array—An antenna term used to describe an array of dipoles on a radar antenna in which the signal feeding each dipole is varied in such a way that antenna beams can be formed in space and scanned very rapidly in azimuth and elevation.

phase delay—1. In the transfer of a single frequency wave from one point to another in a system, the delay of part of the wave identifying its phase. 2. The insertion phase shift divided by the frequency (both in cycles). *Also see* Delay Distortion.

phase-delay distortion—The difference between the phase delay at one frequency and the phase delay at a reference frequency.

phase detector—1. A tv circuit in which a d-c correction voltage is derived to maintain a receiver oscillator in sync with some characteristic of the transmitted signal. 2. A circuit which detects both the magnitude and the sign of the phase angle between two sine-wave voltages or currents.

phase deviation—In phase modulation, the peak difference between the instantaneous angle of the modulated wave and the angle of the carrier.

phase difference—1. The time in electrical degrees by which one wave leads or lags

another. 2. Between two sinusoidal quantities that have the same period, the phase difference is the fraction of a period (one-half or less) through which the independent variable must be advanced or retarded so that the two quantities will coincide.

phase discriminator—A device in which amplitude variations are derived in response to phase variations.

phase distortion—*See* Phase-Frequency Distortion.

phase-distortion coefficient—In a transmission system, the difference between the maximum and minimum transit times for frequencies within a specified band.

phase equalizer—A circuit employed to neutralize the effect of phase-frequency distortion in a particular range of frequencies.

phase-frequency distortion—Also called phase distortion. Distortion that occurs when the phase shift is not directly proportionate to the frequency over the range required for transmission.

phase inversion—The condition whereby the output of a circuit produces a wave of the same shape and frequency but 180° out of phase with the input.

Phase inverter.

phase inverter—1. A stage that functions chiefly to change the phase of a signal by 180°, usually for feeding one side of a following push-pull amplifier. 2. *See* Vented Baffle.

phase localizer—An airfield runway localizer in which lateral guidance is obtained by comparing the phases of two signals.

phase lock—The technique of making the phase of an oscillator signal follow exactly the phase of a reference signal by comparing the phases between the two signals and using the resultant difference signal to adjust the frequency of the reference oscillator.

phase-locked loop—A narrow-band filter that continuously servos itself to the strongest signal frequency in the input spectrum. Phase-locked loops are used as highly selective, very narrow-band noise-rejection filters

357

when an ordinary fixed filter might not stay aligned with the incoming signal frequency. Phase-locked loops differ from ordinary passive filters in that they utilize active components (they have gain) and a feedback loop. The feedback property is used for both the filtering and the frequency-servoing action.

phase magnet—Also called trip magnet. A magnetically operated latch used to phase a facsimile transmitter or recorder.

phase margin—1. A safety factor in phase shift. When the loop gain is 1.0 or more and the phase shifts total 180°, instability will occur. The amount that the total phase shift is less than 180° is called the phase margin. 2. The additional amount of phase shift of the output signals in an operational amplifier at the open-loop unity-gain crossover frequency that would produce instability.

phase meter—Also called phase-angle meter. An instrument for measuring the difference in phase between two alternating quantities of the same frequency.

phase modifier—A device that supplies leading or lagging volt-amperes to the system to which it is connected.

phase-modulated transmitter—A transmitter, the output of which is a phase-modulated wave.

phase-modulated wave—A wave whose phase angle has been caused to deviate from its original (no-signal) angle by an amount proportional to the modulating signal amplitude.

phase modulation—Abbreviated pm. Modulation in which the angle of a sine-wave carrier deviates from the original (no signal) angle by an amount proportional to the instantaneous value of the modulating wave. Phase and frequency modulation in combination are commonly referred to as "frequency modulation."

phase modulator—A circuit which modulates the phase of a carrier signal.

phase multiplier—A device that multiplies the frequency of signals used for phase comparison so that phase differences may be measured to a higher degree of resolution.

phase noise—A measure of the random phase instability of a signal.

phase of a wave—See Angle of a Wave.

phase-propagation ratio—In wave propagation, the propagation ratio divided by the magnitude of the wave.

phaser—A device for adjusting facsimile equipment so that the recorded area bears the same relationship to the record sheet as the corresponding transmitted area bears to the subject copy in the direction of the scanning line.

phase-recovery time (TR and pre-TR tubes)—The time required for a fired tube to deionize to such a level that a specified phase shift is produced in the low-level

radio-frequency signal transmitted through the tube.

phase resonance—Also called velocity resonance. Resonance in which the angular phase difference between the fundamental components of the oscillation or vibration and the applied agency is 90°.

phase-response characteristic—The phase displacement versus frequency properties of a network or system.

phase reversal—A change of 180°, or one half of a cycle.

phase-reversal protection—In a polyphase circuit, the interruption of power whenever the phase sequence of the circuit is reversed.

phase-reversal switch—A switch used on a stereo amplifier or in a speaker system to shift the phase 180° on one channel.

phase-rotation relay—See Phase-Sequence Relay.

phase-sensitive amplifier—A servoamplifier the output signal polarity or phase of which is dependent upon the polarity or phase relationship between an error (input) voltage and a reference voltage.

phase-sequence indicator—A device that indicates the sequence in which the fundamental components of a polyphase set of potential differences, or currents, successively reach some particular value (e.g., their maximum positive value).

phase-sequence relay—Also called phase-rotation relay. A relay which functions according to the order in which the phase voltages successively reach their maximum positive values.

phase-sequence voltage relay—A device which functions upon a predetermined value of polyphase voltage in the desired phase sequence.

phase shift—1. The difference between corresponding points on input and output signals waveshapes (not affected by magnitude) expressed as degrees lead or lag. 2. A change in the phase of a periodic quantity.

phase-shift circuit—A network which shifts the phase of one voltage with respect to another voltage of the same frequency.

phase shifter—A device in which the output voltage (or current) may be adjusted to have some desired phase relationship with the input voltage (or current).

phase-shifting transformer—Also called a phasing transformer. A transformer connected across the phases of a polyphase circuit to provide voltages of the proper phase for energizing varmeters, varhour meters, or other instruments. (Also see Rotatable Phase-Adjusting Transformer.)

phase-shift keying—A form of phase modulation in which the modulating function shifts the instantaneous phase of the modulated wave between predetermined discrete values.

phase-shift microphone—A microphone, the

Phase-shift oscillator.

directional properties of which are provided by phase-shift networks.

phase-shift oscillator — An oscillator in which a network having a phase shift of an odd multiple of 180° (per stage) at the oscillation frequency is connected between the output and input of an amplifier. When the phase shift is obtained by resistance-capacitance elements, the circuit is called an RC phase-shift oscillator.

phase simulator—A precision test instrument which generates reference and data signals on the same frequency but precisely separated in phase. It is normally used to check out precision phase meters.

phase splitter—1. A device which produces, from a single input wave, two or more output waves that differ in phase from one another. 2. In color television, the stage which takes I and Q signals from demodulators, produces four signals, positive and negative I and Q, and feeds them to the matrix.

phase-tuned tube (TR tubes) — A fixed tuned broad-band TR tube in which the phase angle through it and the reflection it introduces are kept within limits.

phase undervoltage relay—A relay which is tripped by the reduction of one phase voltage in a polyphase circuit.

phase velocity—The velocity at which a point of constant phase is propagated in a progressive sinusoidal wave.

phase–versus–frequency response characteristic—A graph or other tabulation of the phase shifts occurring, in an electrical transducer, at several frequencies within a band.

phasing—1. Causing two systems or circuits to operate in phase or at some desired difference from the in-phase condition. 2. Adjusting a facsimile-picture position along the scanning line. 3. In stereo application, the establishment of the correct relative polarity in the connection between amplifier output and speakers so that one speaker tends to reinforce rather than cancel the output of the other (particularly evident at low frequencies).

phasing capacitor—A capacitor used in a crystal-filter circuit for neutralizing the capacity of the crystal holder.

phasing line—In facsimile, the portion of the scanning line set aside for the phasing signal.

phasing pulse—A short pulse or signal em-

ployed for phasing the recorder with the transmitter in a television or facsimile system.

phasing signal—In facsimile, a signal used for adjusting the position of the picture along the scanning line.

phasing transformer — *See* Phase-Shifting Transformer.

phasitron—A tube designed to produce a frequency-modulated audio signal, which is induced by a varying field from a magnet placed around the glass envelope of the tube.

phasmajector—*See* Monoscope.

phasor—An entity which includes the concepts of magnitude and direction in a reference plane.

phenolic material—Any one of several thermosetting plastic materials available which may be compounded with fillers and reinforcing agents to provide a broad range of physical, electrical, chemical, and molding properties.

Phillips gage—A vacuum gage in which gas pressure is determined by measuring the current in a glow discharge.

Phillips screw—A screw with an indented cross in its head, instead of the conventional slot. It must be removed or inserted with a special screwdriver, also called a Phillips.

phi polarization — In an electromagnetic wave, the state in which the E vector of the wave is tangential to the lines of latitude of some given spherical frame of reference.

pH meter—An instrument used with a probe to determine the alkalinity or acidity of a solution.

phon—The unit for measuring the apparent loudness level of a sound. Numerically equal to the sound-pressure level, in decibels relative to 0.0002 microbar, of a 1,000-hertz tone that is considered by listeners to be equivalent in loudness to the sound under consideration.

phone—*See* Headphone.

phone jack—Also called a telephone jack. A jack designed for use with phone plugs.

Phone jack.

Phone plug.

phonemes—The minimal set of shortest segments of speech which, if substituted one for another, convert one word to another.

phone plug—Also called telephone plug. A plug used with headphones, microphones, and other audio equipment.

phonetic alphabet—A list of standard words, one for each letter in the alphabet. It is used for distinguishing the letters in a spoken radio or telephone message. The list reads:

ALFA	NOVEMBER
BRAVO	OSCAR
CHARLIE	PAPA
DELTA	QUEBEC
ECHO	ROMEO
FOXTROT	SIERRA
GOLF	TANGO
HOTEL	UNIFORM
INDIA	VICTOR
JULIETT	WHISKEY
KILO	XRAY
LIMA	YANKEE
MIKE	ZULU

phonocardiogram—A graphic recording of the sounds produced by the heart and its associated parts (e.g., its mitral or aortic valves).

phonocardiograph—An instrument for recording sounds of the heart on a strip chart.

phonocatheter—A catheter-microphone combination that is inserted through the artery into the heart. It picks up inner cardiac sounds.

phonoelectrocardioscope—A dual-beam oscilloscope which displays both ecg signals and heart-sound signals.

phonograph—An instrument for reproducing sound. It consists of a turntable on which the grooved medium containing the impressed sound is placed, a needle that rides in the groove, and an electrical (formerly mechanical) amplifying system for taking the minute vibrations of the needle and converting them into electrical (formerly mechanical) impulses that drive a speaker.

phonograph oscillator—An r-f oscillator circuit, the output of which is modulated by a phonograph pickup and sent through space to a receiver. Thus, no wires to the receiver are needed.

phonograph pickup—Also called mechanical reproducer, pickup, or phono pickup. A mechanoelectric transducer which is actuated by modulations present in the groove of a recording medium and transforms this mechanical input into an electric output.

phono jack—A jack designed to accept a phono plug.

phonon—A lattice vibration with which a discrete amount (quantum) of energy is associated. Some thermal and electrical properties of the lattice are theoretically treated in terms of electron-phonon interactions.

phono pickup—*See* Phonograph Pickup.

Phono plug.

phono plug—A plug used at the end of a shielded conductor for feeding a-f signals to a mating phono jack on an audio preamplifier or amplifier.

phonoselectoscope — A stethoscopic device which suppresses low frequencies (characteristic of the normal heart function) to permit detection of higher-frequency sounds.

phosphor—A layer of luminescent material applied to the inner face of a cathode-ray tube. During bombardment by electrons it fluoresces, and after the bombardment, it phosphoresces.

phosphor-dot faceplate—The glass viewing screen on which the trios of color phosphor dots are mounted in a three-gun picture tube.

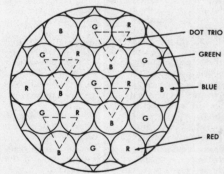

Phosphor dots.

phosphor dots—Minute particles of phosphor on the viewing screen of a picture tube. On a tricolor picture tube, the red, green, and blue phosphor dots are placed on the viewing screen in a pattern of dot triads—a phosphor dot of each color forming one-third of the triad.

phosphorescence — The emission of light from a substance after excitation has been removed. *Also see* Afterglow.

phosphors—Materials that emit visible or invisible (ultraviolet or infrared) radiation when irradiated with X-rays, cathode rays, and ultraviolet radiation, or when placed in an electric field. The quantity of visible light is proportional to the amount of excitation energy present. The emission is not due to incandescence and so is often called "cold light" to distinguish it from radiation due to heating, which occurs in an electric-light bulb. The conversion of electrical energy to light within these phosphors is called electroluminescence.

phosphor trio—In the phosphor screen of a tricolor kinescope, closely spaced triangular groups of three phosphor dots accurately deposited in interlaced positions.

photocathode—An electrode which releases electrons when exposed to light or other suitable radiation. Used in phototubes, television camera tubes, and other light-sensitive devices.

photocathode blue response — The photo-emission current resulting from a specified luminous flux from a tungsten lamp filament at a color temperature of 2,870° K when the flux is filtered by a specified blue filter.

photocathode luminous sensitivity — The quotient of photoelectric emission current from the photocathode divided by the incident luminous flux. The measurement is made under specified conditions of illumination, usually with radiation from a tungsten-filament lamp operated at a color temperature of 2,870° K. The cathode is usually illuminated by a collimated beam at normal incidence.

photocathode radiant sensitivity—The quotient of the photoelectric emission current from the photocathode divided by the incident radiant flux. It is usually measured at a given wavelength under specified conditions of irradiation with a collimated beam at normal incidence.

photocell—*See* Photoelectric Cell.

photoconductive cell—A photoelectric cell, the electrical resistance of which varies inversely with the intensity of light that strikes its active material.

photoconductive effect—The change of electrical conductivity of a material when exposed to varying amounts of radiation.

photoconductive material—Material having a high resistance in the dark, and a low resistance when exposed to the light.

photoconductivity — The greater electrical conductivity shown by some solids when illuminated. The incoming radiation transfers energy to an electron, which then takes on a new energy level (in the conduction band) and contributes to the electrical conductivity.

photoconductor—A passive, high-impedance device composed of thin single-crystal or polycrystalline films of compound semiconductor materials. When the sensitive surface is illuminated its resistance decreases and hence its conductivity increases.

photodielectric effect — The change in the dielectric constant and loss of a material when illuminated. The effect is observed only in phosphors that show photoconductivity during luminescence.

photodiffusion effect—*See* Dember Effect.

photodiode—A semiconductor diode in which the reverse current increases whenever light falls on the diode.

photoelasticity—Changes in the optical properties of transparent isotropic dielectrics subject to stress.

photoelectric—Pertaining to the electrical effects of light or other radiation—i.e., emission of electrons, generation of a voltage, or a change in electrical resistance upon exposure to light.

photoelectric absorption—Conversion of radiant energy into photoelectric emission.

photoelectric cathode—A cathode the primary function of which is photoelectric emission.

photoelectric cell—Also called a photocell. A light-sensitive cell which translates variations in light into corresponding variations in electrical signals.

photoelectric color comparator—*See* Color Comparator.

photoelectric colorimeter — A colorimeter which uses a photoelectric cell and a set of color filters to determine, by the output current for each filter, the chromaticity coordinates of light of a given sample.

photoelectric conductivity — The increased conductivity exhibited by certain crystals when struck by light (e.g., a selenium cell).

photoelectric constant — A quantity which, when multiplied by the frequency of the radiation causing the emission, gives (in centimeter-gram-second units) the voltage absorbed by the escaping photoelectron. The constant is equal to h/e, where h is Planck's constant and e is the electronic charge.

photoelectric control — The control of a circuit or piece of equipment in response to a change in incident light impinging on a photosensitive device.

photoelectric counter—A device that registers a count whenever an object breaks the light beam shining on its phototube or photocell. An amplifier then boosts the minute energy to register on a mechanical or other type of counter.

photoelectric current—The stream of electrons emitted from the cathode of a phototube under the influence of light.

photoelectric cutoff control—A photorelay circuit used in machines for cutting long strips of paper, cloth, metal, or other material accurately into predetermined lengths or at predetermined positions.

photoelectric effect—The transfer of energy from incident radiation to electrons in a substance. This phenomenon includes photoelectric emission of electrons from the surface of a metal, the photovoltaic effect, and photoconductivity.

photoelectric electron-multiplier tube — A vacuum phototube that employs secondary emissions to amplify the electron stream emitted from the illuminated photocathode.

photoelectric emission — Electron emission

due directly to the incidence of radiant energy on the emitter.

photoelectric flame-failure detector — An industrial electronic control employing a phototube and amplifier to actuate an electromagnetic or other valve that cuts off the fuel flow when the fuel-consuming flame is extinguished and light no longer falls on the phototube.

photoelectric inspection—Quality control of a product by means of a phototube, light-beam system, and associated electronic equipment.

photoelectric intrusion detector—A burglar-alarm system in which interruption of a light beam by an intruder reduces the illumination on a phototube and thereby closes an alarm circuit.

photoelectric liquid-level indicator—A level indicator in which the rising liquid interrupts the beam of light in a photoelectric control system.

photoelectric material—Any material that will emit electrons when illuminated in a vacuum (e.g., barium, caesium, lithium, potassium, rubidium, sodium, and strontium).

photoelectric phonograph pickup—A phonograph reproducing device consisting essentially of a light source, a jewel stylus to which a very thin mirror is attached, and a selenium cell that picks up light reflected from the mirror. Sidewise movements of the stylus in the record groove cause the amount of reflected light to vary, and accordingly the resistance of the selenium cell. The light source is fed by a radio-frequency oscillator rather than from the power line, to eliminate 60-hertz flicker from the light beam.

photoelectric photometer—A photometer which incorporates a phototube or photoelectric cell for measurements of light.

photoelectric pickup — A transducer that transforms a change in light into an electric signal.

photoelectric pyrometer—An instrument for measuring high temperatures from the intensity of the light given off by the heated object.

photoelectric reader—A device that reads information stored in the form of holes punched in paper tape or cards, by sensing light passed through the holes.

photoelectric recorder—An optical recording instrument employing a light source and phototube for the basic measuring element.

photoelectric register control — A photoelectric device used for controlling the position of a strip of paper, cloth, metal, etc., with respect to the machine through which it is being passed.

photoelectric relay—Also called light relay. A relay combined with a phototube (and amplifier if necessary), so arranged that changes in incident light on the phototube cause the relay contacts to open or close.

photoelectric scanner—A light source, lens system, and one or more phototubes in a

single, compact housing. It is mounted a few inches above a moving surface, where it actuates control equipment when the amount of light reflected from the surface changes.

photoelectric sensitivity—Also called photoelectric yield. The rate at which electrons are emitted from a metal per unit radiant flux at a given frequency.

photoelectric smoke detector—A photoelectric instrument used to measure the density of smoke and to sound an alarm when a predetermined smoke density is exceeded.

photoelectric sorter — An industrial-electronic control employing a light beam, phototube, and amplifier to sort objects according to color, size, shape, or other characteristics.

photoelectric threshold—The quantum energy just sufficient to release photoelectrons from a given surface. The corresponding frequency is the critical, or threshold, frequency.

photoelectric timer—An electronic instrument that automatically turns off an X-ray machine or other photographic device when the film reaches the correct exposure.

photoelectric transducer—A transducer that converts changes in light energy into electrical changes.

photoelectric tube—*See* Phototube.

photoelectric work function—The energy required to transfer electrons from a given metal to a vacuum or other adjacent medium during photoelectric emission. It is sometimes expressed as energy in ergs or joules per unit of emitted charge, and sometimes as energy per electron in electron volts.

photoelectric yield—*See* Photoelectric Sensitivity.

photoelectromagnetic effect — *See* Dember Effect.

photoelectromotive force — Electromotive force caused by photovoltaic action.

photoelectrons—The electrons emitted from a metal in the photoelectric effect.

photoemissive—Capable of emitting electrons when under the influence of light or other radiant energy.

Photoflash.

photoflash—A means of firing expendable flashbulbs with an instantaneous surge of current supplied by two or more 1½-volt, single-cell batteries, or by the discharge of

OXYGEN
FILLED
GLASS
ENVELOPE

METAL FOIL
OR WIRE

PRIMER COATED
ON THE FILAMENT
SUPPORT WIRES

FILAMENT

Photoflash bulb.

a capacitor which has been charged to full capacity by a medium-voltage battery.

photoflash bulb—An oxygen-filled glass bulb containing a metal foil or wire. A surge of current heats the metal to incandescence, and a brilliant flash of light is produced when the wire burns in the oxygen.

photoflash tube—*See* Flash Tube.

photoflood lamp—An incandescent lamp employing excess voltage to give brilliant illumination. Used in television and photography, it has a life of only a few hours.

photogalvanic cell—A cell which generates an electromotive force when light falls on either of the electrodes immersed in an electrolyte.

photogenerator—A semiconductor-junction device that emits light when pulsed.

photoglow tube—A gas-filled phototube used as a relay. This is done by making the operating voltage so high that ionization and a glow discharge occur, accompanied by considerable current flow, when certain illumination is reached.

photographic sound recorder—*See* Optical Sound Recorder.

photographic sound reproducer — *See* Optical Sound Reproducer.

photoionization—Ionization occurring in a gas as a result of visible light or ultraviolet radiation.

photo-island grid—A photosensitive surface in the storage-type Farnsworth dissector tube used with television cameras. It comprises a thin, finely perforated (about 400 holes per square inch) sheet of metal.

photojunction battery—A nuclear-type battery in which the radioactive material, promethium 147, irradiates a phosphor which converts nuclear energy into light. The light is then converted to electrical energy by a small silicon junction.

photoluminescence — Luminescence stimulated by visible light or ultraviolet radiation.

photomagnetic effect—The direct effect of light on the magnetic susceptibility of certain substances.

photomagnetoelectric effect — The production in a semiconductor of an electromotive force normal to both an applied magnetic field and to a photon flux of proper wavelength.

photometer—An instrument for measuring

the intensity of a light source or the amount of illumination, usually by comparison with a standard light source.

photometry—The techniques for measuring luminous flux and related quantities (e.g., luminous intensity, illuminance, luminance, luminosity, etc.).

photomultiplier pulse-height resolution — A measure of the smallest change in the number of electrons emitted during a pulse from the photocathode that can be discerned as a change in output-pulse height.

photomultiplier tube—*See* Multiplier Phototube.

photon—A quantum of electromagnetic energy. The equation is hv, where h is Planck's constant and v is the frequency associated with the photon.

photon-coupled isolator—A circuit-coupling device consisting of an infrared emitter diode-coupled to a photon detector over a short shielded light path, which provides extremely high circuit isolation.

photon coupling—Coupling between circuits by a beam of light.

photonegative—Having a negative photoconductivity—hence, decreasing in conductivity (increasing in resistance) under the action of light. Selenium sometimes exhibits this property.

photoparametric diode—A pill-sized device for simultaneously detecting and amplifying optical energy modulated at microwave frequencies.

photophone—A device for converting variations in light intensity into sound.

photopositive—Having a positive photoconductivity—hence, increasing in conductivity (decreasing in resistance) under the action of light. Selenium ordinarily has this property.

photorelay circuit—A form of on-off control actuated by a change of illumination.

photoresistive or photoconductive transduction—Conversion of the measurand into a change in the resistance of a semiconductor material (by changing the illumination incident on the material).

photoresistor — A semiconductor resistor which, when illuminated, drops in resistance.

photosensitive—Capable of emitting electrons when struck by light rays.

photosensitive field-effect transistor — A

363

special unipolar field-effect transistor (FET) structure that is positioned on a header to receive illumination transmitted through a lens in the top of the header can. It combines the circuit and device characteristics of a photodiode and a high-impedance low-noise amplifier.

photosensitive recording—Recording by the exposure of a photosensitive surface to a signal-controlled light beam or spot.

photosensitive semiconductor—A semiconductor material in which light energy controls the current-carrier movement.

photosphere—The outermost luminous layer of the gaseous body of the sun.

phototelegraphy—In facsimile, the process of sending photographs over a wire.

phototransistor—A thin wafer of germanium in which holes are generated by light absorption and produce a multiplied photocurrent by transistor action at the collector.

phototube—Also called photoelectric tube. An electron tube containing a photocathode. Its output depends on the total photoelectric emission from the irradiated area of the photocathode.

phototube bridge circuit—A circuit in which a phototube is one arm of a bridge circuit. With such a circuit, a balanced condition (no signal output) can be reached under either a black-signal or white-signal condition, depending on the impedance adjustments in the other arms.

phototube relay—An electrical relay in which the action of a beam of light on a phototube operates mechanical devices such as counters and safety controls.

photovaristor—A varistor in which the current-voltage relation may be modified by illumination. Cadmium sulphide and lead telluride exhibit such properties.

photovoltaic—Capable of generating a voltage when exposed to visible or other light radiation.

Photovoltaic cell.

photovoltaic cell — A self-generating semiconductor device which converts light energy into electrical energy when struck by light.

photovoltaic converter — A device for converting light to electric energy by means of the photovoltaic effect.

photovoltaic effect—The generation of a voltage (or an electric field) in a material

that is illuminated with radiation of a suitable wavelength.

photovoltaic transduction — Conversion of the measurand into a change in the voltage generated when a junction of dissimilar material is illuminated.

photox cell—A type of photovoltaic cell in which a voltage is generated between a copper base and a film of cuprous oxide during exposure to visible or other radiation.

photran—A triode PNPN-type switch of the reverse-blocking PNPN-type switch class. The photran provides optical triggering in addition to standard gate-terminal triggering.

photronic cell—A type of photovoltaic cell in which a voltage is generated in a layer of selenium during exposure to visible or other radiation.

pi—The Greek letter π. It designates the value 3.14159+, which is approximately the ratio of the circumference of a circle to its diameter.

pickoff—A device which produces a signal output, generally a voltage as a function of the angle between two gimbals, or between a gimbal and a base.

pickup—1. A device that converts a sound, scene, or other form of intelligence into corresponding electric signals (e.g., a microphone, television camera, or phonograph pickup). 2. The minimum current, voltage, power, or other value which will trip a relay. 3. Interference from a nearby circuit or system.

pickup arm—Also called tone arm. A pivoted arm for holding a pickup.

Pickup cartridge.

pickup cartridge—The removable portion of a pickup arm. It contains the electromechanical transducing elements and the reproducing stylus.

pickup current—Also called pull-in current. That current at which a magnetically operated device starts to operate.

pickup spectral characteristic—In television, the spectral response of the camera tube including the optical parts. It converts radiation into electric signals, which are measured at the output terminals of the pickup tube.

pickup value (voltage, current, or power)—The minimum value which will energize the contacts of a relay. (*Also see* Drop-out Value *and* Hold Current.)

pickup voltage—That voltage at which a magnetically operated device starts to operate.

pico—Prefix meaning 10^{-12}. (Formerly micromicro.) Abbreviated p.

picoammeter—A sensitive ammeter that indicates current values in picoamperes.

picoampere—One-millionth of a microampere (10^{-12} ampere). Abbreviated pa.

picocoulomb — One-millionth of a microcoulomb. (10^{-12} coulomb). Abbreviated pc.

picocurie—One-millionth of a microcurie (10^{-12} curie). Abbreviated pc.

picofarad—Abbreviated pf. 10^{-12} farad; formerly micromicrofarad. Called puff in England.

picosecond—A micromicrosecond (10^{-12} second). Abbreviated psec.

picowatt—One millionth of a microwatt (10^{-12} watt). Abbreviated pw. *Also see* Micromicrowatt.

pictorial wiring diagram—A wiring diagram containing actual sketches of components and clearly showing all connections between them.

picture black—Also called black signal. In facsimile, the signal produced at any point by the scanning of a selected area of subject copy having maximum density.

picture brightness—A measure of the brightness of the highlights in a television picture. usually measured in foot-lamberts.

picture carrier—Also called luminance carrier. The carrier frequency 1.25 MHz above the lower frequency limit of a standard NTSC television signal. In color television, this carrier is used for transmitting luminance information; and the chrominance subcarrier, which is 3.579545 MHz higher in frequency, transmits the color information.

picture element—1. In facsimile, that portion of the subject copy which is seen by the scanner at any instant. It can be considered a square area having dimensions equal to the width of the scanning line. 2. Also called elemental area, critical area, scanning spot, or recording spot. In television, any segment of a scanning line, the dimension of which along the line is exactly equal to the nominal line width. The area being explored at any instant in the scanning process.

picture frequency—The number of complete pictures scanned per second in a television system.

picture line standard—The total number of horizontal lines in a complete television

image. The standard in the United States is 525 lines.

picture monitor—A cathode-ray tube and its associated circuits arranged for viewing a television picture.

picture signal—In television, the signal resulting from the scanning process.

picture-signal amplitude—The difference between the white peak and the blanking level of a video signal.

picture-signal polarity—The polarity of the signal voltage which represents a dark area of a scene given with respect to the signal voltage representing a light area. Expressed as black negative or black positive.

picture size—The usable viewing area on the screen of a television receiver, measured in square inches.

picture synchronizing pulse—*See* Vertical Synchronizing Pulse.

picture transmission—Electric transmission of a shaded (halftone) picture.

picture transmitter—*See* Visual Transmitter.

picture tube—*See* Kinescope.

Picture-tube brightener.

picture-tube brightener—An accessory added to an aging picture tube to increase the image brightness and thereby extend its useful life. When the cathode emission is subnormal, the brightener raises the filament voltage and thereby increases the electron emission from the cathode.

Pierce oscillator.

Pierce oscillator—Basically a Colpitts oscillator in which a piezoelectric crystal is connected between the plate and grid. Voltage division is provided by the grid-to-cathode and plate-to-cathode capacitances of the circuit.

pie winding—A winding constructed from individual washer-shaped coils called pies.

piezodielectric—Pertaining to a change in dielectric constant under mechanical stress.

piezoelectric—The property of certain crystals, which: 1. Produce a voltage when subjected to a mechanical stress. 2. Undergo mechanical stress when subjected to a voltage.

piezoelectric accelerometer — Basically a crystalline material which, when force is applied, generates a charge. Through the incorporation of a mass in direct contact with the crystal, an acceleration transducer is produced.

piezoelectric axis—In a crystal, one of the directions in which tension or compression will develop a piezoelectric charge.

piezoelectric crystal—A piece of natural quartz or other crystalline material capable of demonstrating the piezoelectric effect. A quartz crystal, when ground to certain dimensions, will vibrate at a desired radio frequency when placed in an appropriate electric circuit.

piezoelectric crystal cut—The orientation of a piezoelectric crystal plate with respect to the axes of the crystal. It is usually designated by symbols—e.g., GT, AT, BT, CT, and DT identify certain quartz-crystal cuts having very low temperature coefficients.

piezoelectric crystal element—A piece of piezoelectric material cut and finished to a specified shape and orientation with respect to the crystallographic axes of the material.

piezoelectric crystal plate—A piece of piezoelectric material cut and finished to specified dimensions and orientation with respect to the crystallographic axes of the material and having two essentially parallel major surfaces.

piezoelectric crystal unit—A complete assembly comprising a piezoelectric crystal element mounted, housed, and adjusted to the desired frequency, with means for connecting it into an electric circuit. Such a device is commonly employed for frequency control or measurement, electric wave filtering, or interconversion of electric and elastic waves.

piezoelectric device—1. A substance which generates an electric voltage when bent, squeezed, or twisted. 2. Conversely, when a voltage is applied, it will twist, bend, expand, or contract.

piezoelectric effect—1. The mechanical deformity of certain natural and synthetic crystals under the influence of an electric field. This effect is used in high-precision oscillators and certain high-frequency filters. 2. The property of certain natural and synthetic crystals to produce a voltage when subjected to mechanical stress (compression,

expansion, twisting, etc.). 3. The production of a mechanical stress in a crystal by the application of a voltage.

piezoelectricity—The phenomenon whereby certain crystalline substances such as barium titanate generate electrical charges when subjected to mechanical deformation. The effect was first noticed by the Curie brothers in the 1880's as a result of extensive study of the symmetry of crystalline materials. The reverse effect also occurs.

piezoelectric material—A material which generates an electrical output when subjected to a mechanical stress. (The word is derived from the Greek *piezein*, meaning to squeeze or press.)

piezoelectric microphone — See Crystal Microphone.

piezoelectric oscillator—A crystal-oscillator circuit in which the frequency is controlled by a quartz crystal.

piezoelectric pickup—*See* Crystal Pickup.

piezoelectric pressure gage—An apparatus for measuring or recording very high pressures. The pressure is applied to quartz discs or other piezoelectric crystals. The resultant voltage, after amplification, is then measured or is recorded with an oscillograph.

piezoelectric speaker—*See* Crystal Speaker.

Piezoelectric transducer.

piezoelectric transducer — Also called ceramic or crystal transducer. A transducer that depends for its operation on the interaction between the electric charge and the deformation of certain asymmetric crystals having piezoelectric properties.

piezoelectric transduction—The conversion of the measurand into a change in the electrostatic charge or voltage generated by mechanically stressed crystals.

piezoid—The finished crystal product. It may include the electrodes making contact with the crystal blank.

piezoresistance — Resistance that changes with pressure.

pig discharge—*See* Penning discharge.

piggyback—*See* Voltage Corrector.

piggy-back control—*See* Cascade Control.

pigtail—Either a wire attached for terminating purposes to a shield, or a conductor extending from a small component.

pigtail splice—A splice made by tightly twisting the bared ends of parallel conductors together.

pile—A nuclear reactor. So called because early reactors were piles of graphite blocks and uranium slugs.

pileup—Also called stack. On a relay, a set of contact arms, assemblies, or springs fastened one on top of the other with layers of insulation separating them.

pillbox antenna—A cylindrical parabolic reflector enclosed by two plates perpendicular to the cylinder and spaced to permit propagation of only one mode in the desired direction of polarization. It is fed on the focal line.

pilot—1. In a transmission system, a signal wave, usually a single frequency, transmitted over the system to indicate or control its characteristics. 2. In a tape relay, instructions appearing in a routing line, relative to the transmission or handling of that message.

pilot cell—The storage-battery cell selected because its temperature, voltage, and specific gravity are assumed to be those of the entire battery.

pilot channel—A very narrow-band channel over which a single frequency, the pilot frequency, is transmitted to operate trouble alarms or automatic level regulators, or both.

pilot contacts—Contacts, the opening, closing, or transfer of which govern an operation of relays or similarly controlled devices.

pilot holes—Also called manufacturing holes or fabrication holes. Holes on a printed-circuit board used as guides during manufacturing operations. Mounting holes in a part are sometimes used as pilot holes.

pilot lamp—A light that indicates whether a circuit is energized.

pilot light—A light which, by means of position or color, indicates whether a control is functioning.

pilot regulator—A device for maintaining the receiving level of a carrier-derived circuit constant under varying attenuation conditions of the transmission line.

pilot spark—A low-power preliminary spark used in a gas-discharge tube to produce an ionized path for the large main spark discharge.

pilot subcarrier — A subcarrier used as a control signal in the reception of compatible f-m stereophonic broadcasts.

pilot wire—An auxiliary conductor used with remote measuring devices or for operating apparatus at a distance.

pilot-wire regulator—An automatic device for controlling adjustable gains or losses associated with transmission circuits to compensate for transmission changes caused by temperature variations, the control usually depending upon the resistance of a conductor or pilot wire having substantially the same temperature conditions as the conductors of the circuit being regulated.

pin—Also called a prong or base pin. A terminal on a connector, plug, or tube base.

pinch effect—1. The result of an electromechanical force that constricts, and sometimes momentarily ruptures, a molten conductor which is carrying a high-density current. 2. In the reproduction of lateral recordings, the pinching of the reproducing stylus tip twice each cycle. This is due to a decrease in the groove angle cut by the recording stylus during the swing from a negative to a positive peak. 3. The self-contraction of a plasma column carrying a large current due to the interaction of this current with the magnetic field it produces. The current required for such an effect is on the order of 10^5 amperes. If the current is in the form of a short pulse, a radially imploding shock wave is generated.

pinch-off—In a field-effect transistor, the reduction of source-to-drain current as much as possible.

pinch-off voltage—The gate voltage of a field-effect transistor that blocks the current for all source-drain voltages below the junction breakdown value. Pinch-off occurs when the depletion zone completely fills the area of the device.

pinch roller—*See* Pressure Roller.

pin connection—Connections made to the base of pins in a vacuum tube. They are identified by the following abbreviations: NC, no connection; IS, internal shield; IC, internal connection (not an electrode connection); P, plate; G, grid; SG, screen grid; SU, suppressor; K, cathode; H, heater; F, filament; RC, ray-control electrode; TA, target.

pin contact—A male-type contact, usually designed to mate with a socket or female contact. It is normally connected to the "dead" side of a circuit.

Pincushion distortion.

pincushion distortion—Distortion which results in a monotonic increase in radial magnification in the reproduced image away from the axis of symmetry of the electron optical system. The four sides of the raster are curved inward, leaving the corners extending outward.

pine-tree array—An array of dipole antennas aligned vertically (termed the radiating curtain), behind which and approximately a quarter wavelength away is a parallel array of dipole antennas forming the reflecting curtain.

Pi network.

pi network—A network composed of three branches, all connected in series with each other to form a mesh. The three junction points form an input terminal, an output terminal, and a common input and output terminal, respectively.

pinfeed platen—In a computer, a cylindrical platen having integral rings of pins that engage perforated holes in the paper, thus permitting feeding of the paper.

ping—A sonic or ultrasonic pulse of predetermined width.

ping-pong-ball effect—The bouncing of sound back and forth between the two sides of a stereophonic reproducing system.

pinhole detector—A photoelectric device that detects extremely small holes and other defects in moving sheets of material, and often actuates sorting equipment that automatically rejects defective sheets.

pinholes—Small holes, occurring as imperfections, which penetrate entirely through an applied material to the substrate (e.g., holes in semiconductor insulating oxides, screened resistors, thin-film elements, etc.).

pinion—Of two gears that mesh, the one with the fewer teeth.

pin jack—A single-conductor jack having a small opening into which a plug tipped with a metal pin can be inserted.

PINO—Acronym for Positive Input, Negative Output.

pinouts—The external wires or pins on a module (generally having a circuit function).

pip—*See* Blip.

piped program—A program transmitted over telephone wires, usually from one studio to another.

pip-matching display—A navigational display in which the received signal appears as a pair of blips. The desired quantity is measured by comparing the characteristics.

pi (π) point—The frequency at which the insertion phase shift of an electric structure is 180° or an integral multiple of 180°.

Pirani gage—A bolometric vacuum gage for measuring pressure. Its operation depends on the thermal conduction of the gas present. The pressure being measured is a function of the resistance of a heated fila-

ment, ordinarily over a range of 10^{-1} to 10^{-4} mm Hg.

piston—Also called a plunger. In high-frequency communications a conducting plate that can be moved along the inside of an enclosed transmission path to short out high-frequency currents.

piston action—The movement of a speaker cone or diaphragm when driven at the bass audio frequencies.

piston attenuator—An attenuator generally used at microwave frequencies, the amount of attenuation of which can be varied by moving an output coupling device along its longitudinal axis.

pistonphone—A small chamber equipped with a reciprocating piston of measurable displacement. In this way, a known sound pressure can be established in the chamber.

pitch—1. That attribute of auditory sensation by which sounds may be ordered on a scale extending from low to high (e.g., a musical scale). 2. The distance between two adjacent corresponding threads of a screw measured parallel to the axis. 3. The distance between the peaks of two successive grooves of a disc recording.

pits—Small holes occurring as imperfections which do not penetrate entirely through the printed element.

piv—Abbreviation for peak inverse voltage.

place—*See* Column.

planar—Lying essentially in a single plane.

planar devices—*See* Planar Process.

planar mask—A shadow or aperture mask which has no curvature; one which is perfectly flat.

planar module—A packaged module wherein the individual components are positioned and terminated flat or parallel with the plane of the substrate.

planar network—A network in which no branches cross when drawn on the same plane.

planar process—The technology used in fabricating semiconductor devices wherein all PN junctions terminate in the same geometric plane. An oxide is formed at the surface for the purpose of stabilizing the parameters (passivating).

Planar transistor.

planar transistor—A diffused transistor in which the emitter, base, and collector regions come to the same plane surface. Their junctions are protected by a material such as silicon oxide. The manufacturing process consists of an oxide-masking technique in which the silicon oxide is formed by adding oxygen or water vapor to the atmosphere of a diffusion furnace. The thickness of the oxide layer is a function of time, temperature, and the amount of oxidizing agent.

planchet—A small metal container or sample holder for radioactive materials undergoing radiation measurements in a proportional counter or scintillation detector.

Planckian locus—A line drawn through all points on a chromaticity diagram to represent light radiation from a reference black body at 2,000° to 10,000° Kelvin (K).

Planck's constant—Symbolized by h. The constant representing the ratio of the energy of any radiation quantum to its frequency. It has the dimension of action (energy × time) and a numerical value of 6.547×10^{-27} erg-second. Its significance was first recognized by the German physicist Max Planck in 1900.

plane earth—Earth that is considered to be a plane surface. Used in ground-wave calculations.

plane-earth attenuation—Attenuation of an electromagnetic wave over an imperfectly conducting plane earth in excess of that over a perfectly conducting plane.

plane-earth factor—Ratio of the electric field strength that would result from propagation over an imperfectly conducting plane earth, to that over a perfectly conducting plane.

plane of a loop—An infinite imaginary plane which passes through the center of a loop and is parallel to its wires.

plane of polarization—For a plane-polarized wave, the plane containing the electric field vector and the direction of propagation.

plane-polarized wave—At any point in a homogeneous isotropic medium, an electromagnetic wave with an electric field vector that at all times lies in a fixed plane containing the direction of propagation.

planetary electron—One of the electrons moving in an orbit or shell around the nucleus of an atom.

plane wave—A wave in which the wavefronts are everywhere parallel planes normal to the direction of propagation.

plan-position indicator—Abbreviated ppi. Also called P-display. A type of presentation on a radar indicator. The signal appears as a bright spot, with range indicated by the distance of the spot from the center of the screen, and the bearing by the radial angle of the spot.

plasma—1. A wholly or partially ionized gas in which the positive ions and negative electrons are roughly equal in number. Hence, the space charge is essentially zero. 2. The region in which gaseous conduction takes place between the cathode and anode of an electric arc.

plasma diode—A thermodynamic engine with electrons as the working fluid, the potential energy of which is converted to a useful output.

plasma engine—A reaction engine using electrically accelerated plasma as the propellant.

plasma frequency—A natural frequency for coherent electron motion in a plasma.

plasma jet—A high-temperature stream of electrons and positive ions produced by the magnetohydrodynamic effect of a strong electrical discharge.

plasma length—See Debye Length.

plasma oscillation—Electrostatic or space-charge oscillations in a plasma which are closely related to the plasma frequency. There is usually enough damping due to electron collisions to prevent self-generation of the oscillations. They can be excited, however, by such techniques as shooting a modulated electron beam through the plasma.

plasma thermocouple—An electronic device in which the heat from nuclear fission is converted directly into electric power.

plasmatron—A helium-filled current amplifier that combines the grid-control characteristics and linearity of a vacuum triode with the extremely low internal impedance of a thyratron.

plasticizer—A substance added to a plastic to produce softness and adhesiveness in the finished product.

PLAT—Acronym for Pilot Landing Aid Television. A system in which television cameras cover aircraft landings on a carrier from several angles, allowing the landing personnel to "talk" the pilot down with increased precision. Recordings can be made for future reference.

plate—1. Preferably called the anode. The principal electrode to which the electron stream is attracted in an electron tube. 2. One of the conductive electrodes in a capacitor. 3. One of the electrodes in a storage battery. 4. See Printed-Circuit Board.

plateau—In the counting rate-versus-voltage characteristic of a radiation counter tube, that portion in which the counting rate is substantially independent of the applied voltage.

plateau length—The applied-voltage range over which the plateau of a radiation counter tube extends.

plate bypass capacitor—A capacitor connected between the plate and cathode of a vacuum tube to bypass high-frequency currents and thus keep them out of the load. Also see Anode Bypass Capacitor.

plate characteristic—A graph showing how changes in plate voltage affect the plate current of a vacuum tube.

plate circuit—The complete external electrical circuit between the plate and cathode of an electron tube.

plate-circuit detector—A detector that functions by virtue of its nonlinear plate-current characteristic.

plate conductance—The in-phase component of the alternating plate current divided by

369

Plate characteristic curves.

the alternating plate voltage, all other electrode voltages being maintained constant.

plate current—Electron flow from the cathode to the plate inside an electron tube.

plate detection—The operation of a vacuum-tube detector at or near plate-current cutoff so that the input signal is rectified in the plate circuit.

plate dissipation—The amount of power lost as heat in the plate of a vacuum tube.

plated thru-hole — *See* Thru-Hole Connection.

plated-resist — A material electroplated on conductive areas to make them impervious to etching.

plate efficiency—Also called the anode efficiency. Ratio of load-circuit power (alternating current) to plate-power input (direct current).

plate impedance—Also called plate-load impedance. The total impedance between the anode and cathode, exclusive of the electron stream.

plate-input power—In the last stage of a transmitter, the direct plate voltage applied to the tubes times the total direct current flowing to their plates, measured without modulation.

plate keying—Keying done by interrupting the plate-supply circuit.

plate-load impedance—Also called the anode-load impedance. The total impedance between the anode and cathode of a vacuum tube, exclusive of the electron stream. *Also see* Plate Impedance.

plate modulation—Also called anode modulation. Modulation produced by applying the modulating voltage to the plate of any tube in which the carrier is present.

plate neutralization — Neutralizing an amplifier by shifting a portion of the plate-to-cathode a-c voltage 180° and applying it to the grid-to-cathode circuit through a capacitor.

plate neutralizer—*See* Anode Neutralization.

plate power input—Also called the anode power input. The d-c power (mean anode voltage times current) delivered to the plate (anode) of a vacuum tube.

plate power supply — *See* Anode Power Supply.

plate pulse modulation—Also called anode pulse modulation. Modulation produced in an amplifier or oscillator by applying externally generated pulses to the plate circuit.

plate resistance—The plate-voltage change divided by the resultant plate-current change in a vacuum tube, all other conditions being fixed.

plate saturation—Also called anode or voltage saturation. The point at which the plate current of a vacuum tube no longer increases as the plate voltage does.

plate supply—*See* Anode Supply.

plate-to-plate impedance—The load impedance between the two plates in a push-pull amplifier stage.

plate voltage—The d-c voltage between the plate and cathode of a vacuum tube.

plate winding—A transformer winding connected to the plate circuit of a vacuum tube.

plating resist—Any material which, when deposited on conductive areas, prevents the plating of the areas it covers.

platinotron—A cross-field vacuum tube used to generate and amplify microwave energy. It resembles the magnetron, except that it has no resonant circuit and has two external r-f connections instead of only one.

platinum—A heavy, almost white metal that resists practically all acids and is capable of withstanding high temperatures.

platinum contacts — Used where currents must be broken frequently (e.g., in induction coils and electric bells). Sparking does not damage platinum as much as it does other metals. Hence a cleaner contact is assured with minimum attention.

platter—A popular term for phonograph records and transcriptions.

playback—Reproduction of a recording.

playback head—A magnetic head used to pick up a signal from a magnetic tape.

playback loss—*See* Translation Loss.

plethysmogram—A graph of the changes in size or volume of an organ or of the amount of blood present or passing through a vessel. The transducer for a plethysmogram can be either a pressure transducer or a pair of surface electrodes.

pliodynatron—A four-element vacuum tube with an additional grid, which is maintained at a higher voltage than the plate to obtain negative-resistance characteristics.

pliotron—An industrial-electronic term for a hot-cathode vacuum tube having one or more grids.

plotter—A device that produces an inscribed visual display of the variation of a dependent variable as a function of one or more other variables.

plotting board—A device which plots one or more variables against one or more other variables.

Plug.

plug—1. The part of the two mating halves of a connector which is movable when not fastened to the other mating half. The plug is usually thought of as the male portion of the connector. This is not always the case; the plug comprises contacts, insert, shell, and any special sealing or holding accessories. 2. A connector free to move so as to be plugged into a receptacle. (*Also see* Connector.)

plugboard—In a computer, a removable board having many electric terminals into which connecting cords may be plugged in patterns varying for different programs. To change the program, one wired plugboard is replaced by another.

plugboard computer—A computer which has a punch-card input and output, and to which program instructions are delivered by means of interconnecting patch cords on a removable plugboard.

pluggable unit—A chassis which can be removed from or inserted into the rest of the equipment by merely plugging in or pulling out a plug.

plugging—A control function which provides braking by reversing the motor line-voltage polarity or phase sequence so that the motor develops a countertorque which exerts a retarding force.

plug-in—Any device to which connections can be completed through pins, plugs, jacks, sockets, receptacles, or other ready connectors.

plug-in coil—A coil that can be easily interchanged and used for varying the tuning range of a receiver or transmitter. It is wound around a form often resembling an elongated tube base, with the coil leads connected to pins on the base.

plug-in device—A component or group of components and their circuitry which can be easily installed or removed from the equipment. Electrical connections are made by mating contacts.

plug-in unit—A standard subassembly of components that can be readily plugged into or pulled out of a circuit as a unit.

plumbicon—A vidicon with a lead-oxide target; its major advantage is its lack of image retention. It is a tube with the simplicity of a vidicon, and the sensitivity and lag of a glass target image orthicon. The tube is used for live black-and-white and color broadcasting.

plumbing—Waveguides and accessory equipment for radio-frequency transmission.

plume—The hot gaseous material ejected briefly from a highly absorbent material after bombardment by an intense laser pulse. The plume emits broad-band white light and is the most prominent feature in most irradiation experiments.

plunger—*See* Piston.

plunger relay—A relay consisting of a movable core or plunger surrounded by a coil. Solenoid action causes the plunger or core to move and thus energize the relay whenever current flows through the coil.

plunger-type instrument—A moving-iron instrument for measuring current. It consists of a pointer attached to a plunger inside a coil. The current being measured flows through the coil and pulls the plunger down. How far it goes into the coil depends on the magnitude of the current.

plutonium—A heavy element which undergoes fission when bombarded by neutrons. It is a useful fuel in nuclear reactors. Its symbol is *Pu;* its atomic number, 94.

pm—Abbreviation for phase modulation or permanent magnet.

pm erasing head—A head which uses the fields of one or more permanent magnets for erasing.

pm speaker—Abbreviation for permanent-magnet speaker.

PN boundary—The surface where the donor and acceptor concentrations are equal in the transition region between P- and N-type materials.

pneumatic bellows—A gas-filled bellows sometimes used to provide delay time in plunger-type relays.

pneumatic speaker—A speaker in which the acoustic output is produced by controlled variation of an air stream.

pneumogram—A graphic recording of respiratory movements and/or forces.

PN hook transistor—Also called hook transistor or hook collector transistor. A junction transistor which secures increased current amplification by means of an extra PN junction.

PNIN—A transistor in which its intrinsic region is between two N-regions.

PNIP transistor—An intrinsic-region transistor with an N-type base and a P-type emitter and collector.

PN junction—The region of transition between P-type and N-type material in a single semiconductor crystal.

PNPN (four-layer) diode—A semiconductor device which may be regarded as a two-transistor structure with two separate emitters feeding a common collector. This combination constitutes a feedback loop which is unstable for loop gains greater than unity. The instability results in a current which increases until ohmic circuit resistances limit the maximum value. This gives rise to a negative-resistance region which may be utilized for switching or for waveform generation.

PNPN transistor—A hook transistor with an N-type base, P-type emitter, and a hook collector. The electrodes are connected to the four end layers of the N- and P-type semiconductor materials.

PNPN-type switch—A bistable semiconductor device made up of three or more junctions, at least one of which is able to switch between reverse and forward voltage polarity within a single quadrant of the anode-to-cathode voltage-current characteristic.

PNP transistor—A transistor consisting of two P-type regions separated by an N-type region. When a small forward bias is applied to the first junction and a large reverse bias to the second junction, the system behaves much like a vacuum-tube triode.

Pockel's effect—The alternation in the refractive properties of a transparent piezoelectric crystal by the application of an electric field. *Also see* Modulator Crystal.

Pockel's-effect modulation—A phenomenon that occurs when a transparent dielectric is a piezoelectric crystal. The crystal tends to strain whenever an electric field is applied, rotating the plane of polarization of the incident wave. Some 7500 V/m cause a 90-degree rotation of light.

POGO—Acronym for Polar Orbiting Geophysical Observatory.

poid—The curve traced by the center of a sphere when it rolls or slides over a surface having a sinusoidal profile.

point—Called the binary point in binary notation, and the decimal point in decimal notation. In positional notation, the character or location of an implied symbol which separates the integral part of a number from its fractional part.

point availability—The percent of time an equipment is available for use when an operator requires it.

point-based linearity—Nonlinearity expressed as the deviation from a straight line which passes through a given point or points.

point contact—A pressure contact between a semiconductor body and a metallic point.

point-contact diode—A diode which obtains its rectifying characteristic from a point contact.

point-contact transistor—A transistor having a base electrode and two or more point-contact electrodes.

point defect—An imperfection caused by the presence of an extra atom or the absence of an atom from its proper place in the crystal.

point effect—The phenomenon whereby a discharge will occur more readily at sharp points than elsewhere on an object or electrode.

pointer—Also called a needle. A slender rod that moves over the scale of a meter.

point impedance—Ratio of the maximum E-field to the maximum H-field observed at a given point in a waveguide or transmission line.

point-junction transistor—A transistor having a base electrode and both point-contact and junction electrodes.

point-plane rectifier—*See* Glow-tube Rectifier.

point source—A radiation source whose dimensions are small compared with the distance from which it is observed.

point-to-point radio communication—Radio communication between two fixed stations.

point-to-point wiring—A method of forming circuit paths by connecting the various devices, components, modules, etc., with individual pieces of wire or ribbon. May be soldered, welded, or attached by other means.

point transposition—Transposition, usually in an open-wire line, which is executed within a distance comparable to the wire separation, without material distortion of the normal wire configuration outside this distance.

Poisson's ratio—The ratio of the lateral strain to the longitudinal strain in a specimen subjected to a longitudinal stress.

polar—Pertaining to, measured from, or having a pole (e.g., the poles of the earth or a magnet).

polar circuit—A teletypewriter circuit in which current flows in one direction on a marking impulse and in the opposite direction during a spacing impulse.

polar coordinates—A system of coordinates in which a point is located by its distance

Point-contact transistor.

and direction (angle) from a fixed point on a reference line (called the polar axis).

polar crystals—Crystals having a lattice composed of alternate positive and negative ions.

Polar diagram of a speaker enclosure.

polar diagram—A diagram in which the magnitude of a quantity is shown by polar coordinates.

polar grid—A type of circular grid on which range and azimuth are represented from a central reference point.

polarity—1. A condition by which the direction of the flow of current can be determined in an electrical circuit (usually batteries and other direct-voltage sources). 2. Having two opposite charges, one positive and the other negative. 3. Having two opposite magnetic poles, one north and the other south.

polarity of picture signal—Stated as black negative or black positive. The particular potential state of a portion of the signal representing a dark area of a scene relative to the potential representing a light area.

polarization—1. The process of making light or other radiation vibrate perpendicular to the ray. The vibrations are straight lines, circles, or ellipses—giving plane, circular, or elliptical polarization, respectively. 2. The increased resistance of an electrolytic cell as the potential of an electrode changes during electrolysis. In dry cells, this shortens their useful life. 3. The slight displacement of the positive charge in each atom whenever a dielectric is placed into an electric field. 4. The magnetic orientation of molecules in a piece of iron or other magnetizable material placed in a magnetic field, whereby the tiny internal magnets tend to line up with the magnetic lines of force. 5. The direction of the electric vector in a linearly polarized wave radiated from an antenna. 6. A mechanical arrangement of inserts and shell configuration (referred to as clocking in some instances) which prohibits the mating of mismatched plugs and receptacles.

polarization diversity—A term that designates a method of transmission and reception used to minimize the effects of selective fading of the horizontal and vertical components of a radio signal. It is usually accomplished through the use of separate vertically and horizontally polarized receiving antennas.

polarization-diversity antenna—An antenna in which any of a number of types of polarization can be readily selected. The polarization can be horizontal, vertical, right-hand circular, left-hand circular, or any combination of these four.

polarization-diversity reception — Diversity reception which uses separate vertically and horizontally polarized receiving antennas.

polarization error—In navigation, the error arising from the transmission or reception of radiation having other than the intended polarization for the system.

polarization fading—Fading as the result of changes in the direction of polarization in one or more of the propagation paths of waves arriving at a receiving point. *Also see* Faraday Effect.

polarization in a dielectric—The slight displacement of the positive charge in each atom whenever a dielectric is placed into an electric field.

polarization modulation — A technique in which modulation is produced by changing the direction of polarization of circularly polarized layer energy.

polarization receiving factor—Ratio of the power received by an antenna from a given plane wave of arbitrary polarization, to the power received by the same antenna from a plane wave of the same power density and direction of propagation whose state of polarization has been adjusted for the maximum received power.

polarization unit vector (for a field vector)—A complex field vector at a point, divided by the magnitude of the vector.

polarize—To cause to be polarized.

polarized double-biased relay — Also called magnetic-latch relay. A relay whose operation depends on the polarity of the energizing current and which is magnetically biased, or latched, in either of two positions. Its coil symbol is usually marked + and DB.

polarized light—Light which has the electric-field vector of all the energy vibrating in the same plane. Looking into the end of a beam of polarized light, one would see the electric-field vectors as parallel or coincident lines.

polarized no-bias relay—A three-position or a center-stable polarized relay. Its coil symbol is usually + and NB.

polarized plug—A plug so constructed that it may be inserted in its receptacle only in a predetermined position.

polarized receptacle — A receptacle into which a polarized plug can be inserted only in a predetermined position.

polarized relay—Also called a polar relay. A relay in which the armature movement depends on the direction of the current. Its coil symbol is sometimes marked +.

polarized-vane instrument—*See* Permanent-Magnet, Moving-Iron Instrument.

polarizer—A substance which, when added to an electrolyte, increases the polarization.

polarizing slots—Also called indexing slots. One or more slots placed in the edge of a printed-circuit board to accommodate and align certain types of connectors.

polar radiation pattern—The characteristic lobed pattern of varying field strength of radiation from a source.

polar relay—A relay containing a permanent magnet that centers the armature. The direction of movement of the armature is governed by the direction of the current. *Also see* Polarized Relay.

pole—1. One end of a magnet. 2. One electrode of a battery. 3. An output terminal on a switch.

pole face—In a relay, the end of the magnetic core nearest the armature.

pole piece—One or more pieces of ferromagnetic material forming one end of a magnet and so shaped that the distribution of the magnetic flux in the adjacent medium is appreciably controlled.

pole shoe—The portion of a field pole facing the armature of the machine. It may be separable from the body of the pole.

poles of a network function—Those real or complex values of p, for which the network function is infinite.

pole-type transformer—A transformer suitable for mounting on a pole or similar structure.

police calls — Broadcasts (usually orders) issued by police radio stations.

poling—1. The adjustment of polarity. Specifically, in wire-line practice, it signifies the use of transpositions between transposition sections of open wire or between lengths of cable, to cause the residual cross-talk couplings in individual sections or lengths to oppose one another. 2. A step in the production of ceramic piezoelectric bodies which orients the axes of the crystallites in the preferred direction. In general, a process similar to magnetizing ferromagnetic materials.

Polish notation—A system for writing logical and arithmetic expressions without the use of parentheses. So called because it was originated by Polish logician, J. Lukasiewicz.

polycrystalline structure — The granular structure of crystals which have nonuniform shapes and arrangements.

polyergic—A type of emission in which the groups of energies or velocities are produced simultaneously (e.g., simulated micrometeoroids in varying charge states, separated by velocity where accelerated by the same potential).

polyester backing — A plastic-film backing added to magnetic tape to make it stronger and more resistant to changes in humidity

polyesters—A class of thermosetting synthetic resins having great strength and good resistance to moisture and chemicals.

polyethylene—Short for polymerized ethylene, a tough, white plastic insulator with low moisture absorption. It is often used as a dielectric.

polygraph—Also called a lie detector. A recorder of several signals simultaneously, such as blood pressure, respiratory motion, galvanic skin resistance, etc., commonly used for study of emotional reactions involving deception (lie detection).

polyphase—Having or utilizing several phases. Thus, a polyphase motor operates from a power line having several phases of alternating current.

polyphase circuit—A group of alternating-current circuits (usually interconnected) which enter (or leave) a delimited region at more than two points of entry. They are intended to be so energized that, in the steady state, the alternating potential differences between them all have exactly equal periods, but have differences in phase, and may have differences in waveform.

polyphase motor — An induction motor wound for operation on two- or three-phase alternating current.

polyphase synchronous generator—A generator with its a-c circuits so arranged that two or more symmetrical alternating electromotive forces with definite phase relationships to each other are produced at its terminals.

polyphase transformer—A transformer designed for use in polyphase circuits.

polyphase voltages—In an a-c electrical system, voltages having a definite phase relationship to each other.

polyplexer — Radar equipment that combines the functions of duplexing and lobe switching.

polyrod antenna — An end-fire, dielectric, microwave antenna made of tapered polystyrene rods.

polystyrene—A clear thermoplastic material having excellent dielectric properties, especially at ultrahigh frequencies.

polystyrene capacitor—A low-loss precision capacitor with a polystyrene dielectric.

polyvinyl chloride—A general-purpose thermoplastic used for insulations and jackets on components, wire, and cable.

pool cathode—A cathode at which the principal source of electron emission is a cathode spot on a metallic-pool electrode.

pool tube—A gas tube with a pool cathode.

popi (Post Office Position Indicator)—A British long-distance navigational system for providing bearing information. It is a continuous-wave, low-frequency system in which the phase difference between sequential transmissions on a single frequency is measured.

population—The entire group of items being studied, from which samples are drawn. Sometimes called universe.

porcelain—A glazed ceramic insulating material made from clay, quartz, and feldspar.

porcelain capacitor—A fixed electrostatic capacitor, the dielectric of which is a high grade of porcelain, molecularly fused to alternate layers of fine silver electrodes so as to form a monolithic capacitor.

port—1. A place of access to a system or circuit. Through it, energy can be selectively supplied or withdrawn or measurements can be made. Examples are the port in a waveguide or in a bass-reflex speaker enclosure. 2. A fluid connection to the servovalve (e.g., supply port, return port, control port). 3. Any two input or output signal terminals.

portable recorder—1. A sound recorder built into a case so that it can be easily carried from place to place. 2. Any tape recorder designed for easy mobility, but one which may require connection to a 110-volt a-c supply for operation. Also applied to self-powered units which do not require external power for operation.

portable standard meter—A portable meter used principally as a standard for testing other meters.

portable transmitter—A transmitter which can be readily carried on one's person and operated while in motion (e.g., Walkie-Talkies, Handy-Talkies, and similar personal transmitters). (*Also see* Transportable Transmitter.)

portamento—The continuous change of a tone from one pitch to another. (*Also see* Glissando.)

pos—Abbreviation for positive.

posistor—A thermally sensitive resistor which has a positive temperature characteristic of resistance.

position—The location of an object with respect to a specific reference point or points.

positional cross talk—In a multibeam cathode-ray tube, the deviation of an electron beam from its path under the influence of another electron beam within the tube.

positional notation—One of the schemes for representing numbers. It is characterized by the arrangement of digits in sequence, with successive digits forming coefficients of successive powers of an integer called the base of the number system.

position-changing mechanism—The mechanism used to move a removable circuit-breaker unit to and from the connected, disconnected, and test positions.

position feedback—A feedback signal which is proportional to the position or deflection of some object.

position of effective short—The distance between a specified reference plane and the apparent location of the short circuit of a fired switching tube in its mount.

position-type telemeter—*See* Ratio-type Telemeter.

positive—Any point to which electrons are attracted—as opposed to negative, from where they come.

positive bias—The condition in which the control grid of a vacuum tube is more positive than the cathode.

positive charge—An electrical charge with fewer electrons than normal.

positive column—The luminous glow, often striated, between the Faraday dark space and the anode in a glow-discharge, cold-cathode tube.

positive electricity—1. The electricity which predominates in a glass body after it has been electrified by rubbing with silk. 2. *See* Positive Charge.

positive electrode—The conductor that is connected to the positive terminal of a primary cell and serves as the anode when the cell is discharging. Electrons flow to it through the external circuit.

positive electron—*See* Positron.

positive feedback—Also see regeneration. The process by which the amplification is increased by having part of the power in the output circuit returned to the input circuit in order to reinforce the input power.

positive ghost—A television ghost-signal display with the same tonal variations as those of the image.

positive-going—Increasing toward a positive direction (e.g., a current or waveform).

positive grid—A grid with a more positive potential than the cathode in a vacuum tube.

positive-grid multivibrator—A multivibrator which has one or more grids connected to the plate-voltage supply, usually through a large resistance.

positive-grid oscillator—*See* Retarding-Field Oscillator.

positive-grid oscillator tube—Also called a Barkhausen tube. An oscillating triode in which the grid has a more positive quiescent voltage than either of the other electrodes.

positive ion—An atom which has lost one or more electrons and thus has an excess of protons, giving it a positive charge.

positive-ion emission—Thermionic emission of positive particles from the cathode of a vacuum tube. They either are made up of ions from the metal in the cathode, or are due to some impurity in it.

positive-ion sheath—A collection of positive ions on the control grid of a gas-filled triode tube. If too high a negative bias is applied to the grid, this positive sheath will block the plate current.

positive light modulation—Modulation in which the transmitted power increases as the light intensity does, and vice versa.

positive magnetostriction—Magnetostriction in which a material expands whenever a magnetic field is applied.

positive modulation—Also called positive picture modulation. In an a-m television system, modulation in which the brightness increases as the transmitted power does, and vice versa.

positive phase-sequence relay—A relay which is energized by the positive phase-sequence component of the current, voltage, or power of a circuit.

positive picture modulation—*See* Positive Modulation.

positive picture phase—The condition in which the picture-signal voltage goes positive above the zero level whenever a positive scene or picture increases in brilliance.

positive plate—1. A hollow lead grid filled with active material and connected to the positive terminal of a storage battery. When the battery is discharging, electrons flow toward it through the external circuit. 2. In a capacitor, the temporarily charged condition whereby one of the plates has fewer electrons.

positive ray—*See* Canal Ray.

positive temperature coefficient—The condition whereby the resistance, capacitance, length, or other characteristic of a substance increases as the temperature does.

positive terminal—In a battery or other voltage source, the terminal toward which electrons flow through the external circuit from the the negative terminal.

positive transmission—Transmission of television signals in such a way that the transmitted power increases whenever the initial light intensity does.

positron—Also called a positive electron. An unstable particle having the same weight as an electron but the opposite charge (positive rather than negative). Its existence was predicted years before it could be proved.

post—In a computer, to place a unit of information on a record.

post-accelerating electrode—*See* Intensifier Electrode.

post acceleration—Also called post-deflection acceleration. Acceleration of the beam electrons in a tube after they have been deflected.

post-conversion bandwidth—In a telemetry receiver, the bandwidth presented to the detector.

post-deflection accelerating electrode—*See* Post-Accelerating Electrode.

post-deflection acceleration—*See* Post-Acceleration.

post-edit—In a computer, to edit output data resulting from a previous computation.

post-emphasis—*See* De-emphasis.

post-equalization—*See* De-emphasis.

post-mortem—A diagnostic computer routine for locating a malfunction in the computer or an error in coding a problem. Should a problem tape come to a standstill, the computer will print out—either automatically or when called for—any information concerning the contents of all or part of the registers in the computer.

postregulator—A circuit that performs the functions of reference, comparison, and control in power supplies. So called because it follows the transformer, rectifier, and (usually) the ripple filter.

pot—Short for potentiometer.

potassium—An alkali metal having photosensitive characteristics, especially to blue light. It is used on the cathodes of phototubes whenever maximum response to blue light is desired.

pot core—A magnetic structure consisting of a rod and a sleeve arranged so that the rod fits inside a coil and the sleeve fits around the coil. The sleeve and rod are connected at one end by a plate. The open end (opposite the plate) is usually, by not necessarily, ground so that two pot cores or a pot core and a separate plate can be put together around a suitable coil to form a low-reluctance magnetic path and/or shield for the coil.

potential—The difference in voltage between two points of a circuit. Frequently one point is assumed to be ground, which has zero potential.

potential barrier—A semiconductor region through which electric charges attempting to pass will encounter opposition and may be turned back.

potential coil—The shunt coil in a measuring instrument or other device having series and shunt coils—i.e., the coil connected across the circuit and affected by changes in voltage.

potential difference—1. The algebraic difference between the individual potentials of two points. 2. A voltage existing between two points (e.g., the voltage drop across an impedance, from one end to another).

potential divider—*See* Voltage Divider.

potential drop—The difference in potential between the two ends of a resistance with a current flowing through it.

potential energy—Energy due to the position of one body with respect to another or to the relative parts of the same body.

potential galvanometer—A galvanometer with such a high resistance that it takes practically no current. It has been replaced by the vacuum-tube voltmeter.

potential gradient—1. The differences in value of the potential per unit length along a conductor or through a dielectric. 2. The rate of change of potential with distance. Units such as volts per meter or kilovolts per centimeter may be used.

potential transformer—Also called a voltage transformer. An instrument transformer, the primary winding of which is connected in parallel with the circuit whose voltage is to be measured or controlled.

potentiometer—1. An electromechanical device having a terminal connected to each end of the resistive element, and a third terminal connected to the wiper contact. The electrical input is divided as the contact moves over the element, thus making it possible to mechanically change the resistance. 2. A unit for measuring potential difference. It uses a calibrated voltage divider, a reference potential, and a null detector.

potentiometer circuit—A network arranged so that, when two or more electromotive

Potentiometer.

forces (or potential differences) are present in as many branches, the response of a suitable detecting device in any branch can be made zero by adjusting the electrical constants of the network.

potentiometer recorder — A null-balance type of recorder using a servo-operated voltage-balancing device; the sliding contact of a precision measuring potentiometer is adjusted automatically by a servomechanism so that the difference in voltage of the circuit becomes zero. Main feature is high sensitivity.

potentiometric transducer—A transducer in which displacement of a force-summing member is transmitted to the slider in a potentiometer, thus changing the ratio of output resistance to total resistance. Transduction is accomplished by changing the ratios of a voltage divider.

potentiometric transduction—The conversion of the measurand into a change in the position of a contact on a resistance element across which excitation is applied, the output usually being given as a voltage ratio.

pothead—An insulator for making a sealed joint between an underground cable and an overhead line.

Potier diagram—A vector diagram showing the voltage and current relationships in an a-c generator.

pot life—The period after the addition of a catalyst to a potting compound during which the potting operation must be completed.

potted circuit—A circuit which has been encapsulated in a nonconductive material.

potted line—A pulse-forming network immersed in oil and enclosed in a metal container.

Potter oscillator—A cathode-coupled multivibrator.

potting—An embedding process for parts that are assembled in a container or can into which the insulating material is poured, with the container remaining an integral part as the outer surface of the finished unit.

potting compound — A sealing material used to fill the case or enclosure in which a component is contained.

powdered-iron core—A core consisting of fine particles of magnetic material mixed with a suitable bonding material and pressed into shape.

power—The rate at which work is done. Units of power are: the watt, the joule, and the kilowatt.

power amplification—*See* Power Gain.

power amplifier—An amplifier intended for driving one or more speakers or other transducers.

power-amplifier stage — 1. An audio-frequency amplifier stage capable of handling considerable audio-frequency power without distortion. 2. A radio-frequency amplifier stage used in a transmitter primarily to increase the power of the carrier signal.

power attenuation—*See* Power Loss.

power cord—*See* Line Cord.

power density—The radiated field strength set up by a radiating source, expressed in microvolts per meter or in db above 1 $\mu v/m$.

power derating—Use of computed curves to determine the correct power rating of a device or component to be used above its reference ambient temperature.

power detection—Detection in which the power output of the detector is used for supplying a substantial amount of power directly to a device such as a speaker or recorder.

power detector—A vacuum tube detector operating with such a high plate voltage that strong input signals can be handled without appreciable distortion.

power dissipation—The dispersion of the heat generated within a device or component when a current flows through it. This is accomplished by convection to the air, radiation to the surroundings, or conduction.

power dissipation rating—The maximum average power that can be continuously dissipated under stated temperature conditions.

power dump—The removal of all power accidentally or intentionally. *Also see* Dump.

power factor—1. Ratio of the actual power of an alternating or pulsating current, as measured by a wattmeter, to the apparent power, as indicated by an ammeter and voltmeter. 2. Ratio of resistance to impedance—therefore, a measure of the loss in an inductor, capacitor, or insulator. 3. The cosine of the phase angle between the voltage applied to a load and the current passing through it. (Sometimes the cosine is multiplied by 100 and expressed as a percentage.)

power-factor correction—Adding capacitors to an inductive circuit in order to increase the power factor by making the total current more nearly in phase with the applied voltage.

power-factor meter—A direct-reading instrument for measuring power factor. Its scale is graduated directly in power factor.

power-factor regulator—A regulator which maintains the power factor of a line or apparatus at a predetermined value, or varies it according to a predetermined plan.

power-factor relay—A device which operates when the power factor in an a-c circuit becomes above or below a predetermined value.

power frequency—The frequency at which electric power is generated and distributed. Throughout most of the United States, this frequency is 60 Hz.

power gain—1. Also called power amplification. Of an amplifying device, the ratio of power delivered to a specified load impedance to the power absorbed by its input. 2. Of an antenna in a given direction, 4π times the ratio of the radiation intensity to the total power delivered to the antenna. (The term is also applied to receiving antennas.) 3. Of a transistor, the ratio of output power to signal input power. (Not to be confused with collector efficiency.)

power ground—1. The ground between units which is part of the circuit for the main source of power to, or from, these units. 2. The potential of the terminal or circuit point to which the output of a power supply and often an amplifier output load is returned (i.e., power-supply "zero").

power level—At any point in a transmission system, the difference between the measure of the steady-state power at that point, and the measure of an arbitrarily specified amount of power chosen as a reference.

power-level indicator — An a-c voltmeter calibrated to read the audio power level.

power line—Two or more wires conducting electric power from one location to another.

power loss—Also called power attenuation. Ratio of the power absorbed by the input circuit of a transducer, to the power delivered to a specified load under specified operating conditions.

power modulation factor—Ratio of the maximum positive departure of the envelope of an amplitude-modulation wave from its average value to its average value. This rating is used when the modulating signal wave has unequal positive and negative peaks.

power output—The power in watts delivered by a power amplifier to a load such as a speaker.

power pack—A unit for converting power from an alternating- or direct-current supply into alternating- or direct-current power at voltages suitable for supplying an electronic device.

power programmer—A device for controlling the output power of a radar automatically as a function of the target range.

power rating—The maximum power that can be dissipated in a component or device for a specified period.

power ratio—Ratio of the power output to the power input of a device. Usually expressed as the number of decibels loss or gain.

power-rectifier misfire relay—A device which functions if one or more of the power-rectifier anodes fails to fire.

power relay—A relay that functions at a predetermined value of power. It may be an overpower relay, an underpower relay, or a combination of both.

power response—The frequency-response capabilities of an amplifier running at or near its full rated power.

power supply—A unit that supplies electrical power to another unit. It changes ac to dc and maintains a constant voltage output within limits.

power switch—Often called an on-off switch. The switch that connects or disconnects a radio receiver, transmitter, or other equipment from its power line.

Power transformer.

power transformer—A transformer used for raising or lowering the supply voltage to the various values required by vacuum-tube plate, heater, and bias circuits.

power transistor—A transistor, usually an alloy-junction type, capable of handling high current and power.

power tube—An electron tube designed to handle more current and power than a voltage-amplifier tube.

power winding — A saturable-reactor winding to which the power to be controlled is supplied. Commonly, the output and power are furnished by the same winding, then termed the output winding.

Poynting's law—The transfer of energy can be expressed as the product of the values of the magnetic field and of the components of the electric field which are perpendicular to the magnetic field, and the flow of energy at any point is perpendicular to both fields.

Poynting's theorem—The rate of flow of electromagnetic energy into or out of a closed region is at any instant proportional to the surface integral of the vector product of the electric and magnetic intensities.

Poynting's vector—The vector product of the electric and magnetic intensities at one point and at a given instant in a wave.

ppi—Abbreviation for plan-position indicator.

ppi scope—A cathode-ray oscilloscope arranged to present a ppi display.

PP junction—A region of transition between two regions having different properties in a P-type semiconducting material.

ppm—1. Abbreviation for pulse-position modulation. 2. Abbreviation for parts per million.

ppm/am—Amplitude modulation of a carrier by pulses which are position modulated by data.

pps—Abbreviation for pulses per second.

practical system of electrical units—A system in which the units are multiples or submultiples of the units of the centimeter-gram-second electromagnetic system.

praetersonic—The higher region of the sonic spectrum.

preamplifier—An amplifier which primarily raises the output of a low-level source so that the signal may be further processed without appreciable degradation in the signal-to-noise ratio. A preamplifier may also include provision for equalizing and/or mixing.

preburning—Stabilizing tubes by operating their heaters continuously for a given number of hours. Cathode current may be drawn and the tubes vibrated at the same time.

precession—The effect resulting when a torque is applied to a rotating body, such as a gyroscope, causing it to wobble. The wobbling frequency is determined by the gravitational field strength and the mass of the body.

precipitation noise—Noise generated in an antenna circuit, generally in the form of a relaxation oscillation, caused by the periodic discharge of the antenna or conductors in the vicinity of the antenna into the atmosphere.

precipitation static—A type of interference experienced in a receiver during snow, rain, and dust storms. Often caused by the impact of dust particles against the antenna or the creation of induction fields by nearby corona discharges.

precipitator—Sometimes called a precipitron. An apparatus for removing small particles of smoke, dust, oil, mist, etc., from the air by electrostatic precipitation.

precipitron—*See* Precipitator.

precision—The quality of being sharply or exactly defined—i.e., the number of distinguishable alternatives from which a representation was selected. This is sometimes indicated by the number of significant digits the representation contains. (*Also see* Accuracy.)

precision approach radar—Abbreviated PAR. An airfield radar system aimed along the approach path of an aircraft and used for its guidance during approach.

precision comparator—A high-gain amplifier circuit the output of which changes decisively between two definite levels whenever the sum of the input voltages changes sign.

precision device—A device that operates within prescribed limits and will consistently repeat operations within those limits.

precision gate—A circuit that may be switched from closed to open circuit or vice versa without error (time, bias, impedance) in response to a command signal (voltage or current).

precision net—In a four-wire terminating set or similar device employing a hybrid coil, an artificial line designed and adjusted to provide an accurate balance for the loop and subscriber's set or line impedance.

precision potentiometer—A mechanical electrical transducer dependent upon the relative position of a moving contact (wiper) and a resistance element for its operation. It delivers a voltage output that is some specified function of the applied voltage and shaft position, to a high degree of accuracy.

precision snap-acting switch—An electromechanical switch having predetermined and accurately controlled characteristics and having a spring-loaded quick make-and-break contact action.

precision sweep—A delayed expanded radar sweep for high resolution and range accuracy.

preconduction current—The low value of plate current that flows in a thyratron or other grid-controlled gas tube prior to conduction.

precursor—Also called undershoot. The initial transient response to a unidirectional change in input. It precedes the main transition and is opposite in sense.

predetection recording—The recording of a telemetry receiver intermediate-frequency signals.

predictive control—A type of computer con-

APPLIED FORCE

AXIS OF PRECESSION

INNER GIMBAL

AXIS OF TORQUE

RESULTING TWIST

OUTER GIMBAL

AXIS OF SPIN

Precession of a gyroscope.

trol which allows a digital computer to include a dynamic control loop for repetitive comparison of pertinent factors.

predissociation—The dissociation that occurs in a molecule that has absorbed energy before it has had an opportunity to lose energy by radiation.

predistortion—*See* Pre-emphasis.

pre-emphasis—1. In a system, a process designed to emphasize the magnitude of some of the frequency components. Pre-emphasis is applied at the transmitting end (with de-emphasis at the receiving end) in order to improve the signal-to-noise ratio. 2. Also called pre-equalization or predistortion. In recording, an arbitrary change in the frequency response from its basic response (e.g., constant velocity or amplitude) in order to improve the signal-to-noise ratio or to reduce distortion. (*Also see* Accentuation.)

pre-emphasis network—A network inserted into a system to emphasize one range of frequencies.

pre-equalization—*See* Pre-emphasis.

preferred tube types—Tube types recommended to designers of electronic equipment, to minimize the number of tube types that must be stocked by the manufacturer or by service agencies.

preferred values—A series of resistor and capacitor values adopted by the EIA and military. In this system, the increase between any two steps is the same percentage as between all other steps. Increases may be in steps of 20%, 10%, or 5% each.

prefix multipliers—Prefixes which designate a greater or smaller unit than the original, by the factor indicated. These prefixes are:

Prefix	Symbol	Factor
tera	T	10^{12}
giga	G	10^{9}
mega	M	10^{6}
kilo	k	10^{3}
hecto	h	10^{2}
deka	da	10
deci	d	10^{-1}
centi	c	10^{-2}
milli	m	10^{-3}
micro	μ	10^{-6}
nano	n	10^{-9}
pico	p	10^{-12}
femto	f	10^{-15}
atto	a	10^{-18}

preform—Also called a biscuit. In disc recording, the small slab of record material used in the presses.

p+ region—The region created by diffusing into a silicon crystal a group-III element, which creates a deficiency of electrons or an excess of holes.

preliminary contacts—In a relay, contacts which open or close before other contacts when the relay is actuated.

prerecorded tape—*See* Recorded Tape.

preselection—1. The use of a preselector. 2. In buffered computers, a time-saving tech-

Pre- and post-emphasis curves.

nique in which a block of information is read into the computer memory ahead of time from whichever input tape will next be called on.

preselector—1. A device placed ahead of a frequency converter or other device to pass signals of desired frequencies but reduce all others. 2. In automatic switching, a device which makes its selection before seizing an idle trunk.

preselector stage—A radio-frequency amplifier stage in the input of a superheterodyne receiver.

presence—The quality of naturalness in sound reproduction. When the presence of a system is good, the illusion is that the sounds are being produced intimately at the speaker.

presence control—A potentiometer used in a three-way speaker system for controlling the volume of the middle-range speaker.

presentation—The form which the radar echo signals take on the screen, depending on the nature of the sweep circuit.

presenting—Displaying data in a form which human intelligence can comprehend and use.

preset guidance system—A guidance system in which the flight path is determined before the missile is launched and cannot be altered after launch.

preshoot—The initial transient response to a unidirectional change in input which precedes the main transmission and may be of the same or opposite polarity.

pressed stem—An obsolete method of vacuum-tube construction in which all support wires are formed into a flattened piece of glass tubing (actually a relic from the lampmaker's era). (*Also see* Button Stem.)

pressing—A disc recording produced in a record-molding press from a master or stamper.

press-to-talk switch—Also called a push-to-talk switch. A spring-loaded switch that must be held down as long as the operator talks. Releasing the switch deactivates the microphone. It is used on transmitter and dictating-machine microphones.

pressure—1. Force per unit area. Measured in pounds per square inch (psi), or by the height (in feet, inches, or centimeters) of a column of water or mercury which the force will support. 2. Absolute pressure is measured with respect to zero pressure. Gage pressure is measured with respect to atmospheric pressure.

pressure amplitude—For a sinusoidal sound wave, the maximum absolute value of the instantaneous sound pressure at a point during any given cycle. The unit is the dyne per square centimeter.

pressure connector—A conductor terminal applied under pressure to make the connection mechanically and electrically more secure.

pressure-gradient hydrophone — A type of hydrophone in which the electric output is essentially determined by a component of the gradient (space derivative) of the sound pressure.

pressure hydrophone—A type of hydrophone in which the electric output is essentially determined by the instantaneous sound pressure of the impressed sound wave.

pressure microphone — A microphone in which the electric output corresponds substantially to the instantaneous sound pressure of the impressed sound waves. It is a gradient microphone of zero order, and is nondirectional when its dimensions are smaller than a wavelength.

pressure pad—In single-motor tape recorders, a device which forces the tape into intimate contact with the head gap, usually by direct pressure at the head assembly. Felt or similar material, occasionally protected with self-lubricating plastic, is used to apply pressure uniformly and with a minimum of drag to the backing side of the tape.

COUNTERWEIGHT
PIVOT
PUSH ARM AND LINKAGE
WIPER ARM
BOURDON TUBE PRESSURE SENSING ELEMENT
POTENTIOMETER WINDING

Pressure potentiometer.

pressure potentiometer—A pressure transducer in which the electrical output is derived by moving a contact arm along a resistance element.

pressure roller—Also called pinch roller, puck, or capstan idler. A spring-loaded rubber-tired roller which holds the magnetic tape tightly against the capstan, permitting the latter to draw the tape off the stock reel and past the heads at a constant speed.

pressure-sensing element — In a pressure transducer, the part which converts the measured pressure into mechanical motion.

pressure spectrum level — The effective sound-pressure level for the sound energy contained within a band one hertz wide and centered at a specified frequency. Ordinarily

this level is not significant except for sound having a continuous distribution of energy within the frequency range under consideration.

pressure switch—A switch actuated by a change in the pressure of a gas or liquid.

pressure transducer—An instrument which converts a static or dynamic pressure input into the proportionate electrical output.

pressure-type capacitor—A fixed or variable capacitor used chiefly in transmitters. It is mounted inside a metal tank filled with nitrogen at a pressure that may be as great as 300 pounds per square inch. The high pressure permits a voltage rating several times that of air.

pressurization—The process by which the critical parts of equipment designed for high-altitude operation is surrounded with dry air or an inert gas under pressure (about five pounds per square inch at sea level). Thus, breakdowns from the impaired insulating properties of air at reduced pressure are prevented.

prestore—To store a quantity in an available or convenient location in a computer before it is required in a routine.

pretersonics—Sonic waves of frequencies higher than 500 MHz.

pretravel—The distance or angle through which the actuator moves from the actuator free position to the actuator operating position.

pretrigger—A timed pulse used to start a sequence of operation prior to the main trigger.

pre-TR tube—A gas-filled radio-frequency switching tube used to protect the TR tube from excessive power and the receiver from frequencies other than the fundamental.

preventive maintenance — Precautionary measures taken on a system to forestall failures rather than to eliminate them after they have occurred.

prf—Abbreviation for pulse-repetition frequency.

pri—Abbreviation for primary.

primaries—*See* Primary Colors.

primary—Abbreviated pri and symbolized by P. Also called a primary winding. A transformer winding that carries current and normally sets up a current in one or more secondary windings.

primary area—*See* Primary Service Area.

primary battery—A battery consisting of primary cells.

primary breakdown—Also called avalanche breakdown. The sustaining mode of a transistor—unlike second breakdown, not a failure mode. The transistor collector-to-emitter voltage is relatively constant for different collector supply voltages.

primary calibration—Calibration in which the transducer output is observed or recorded, while direct stimulus is applied under controlled conditions.

primary-carrier flow—Also called primary

flow. The current flow responsible for the major properties of a semiconductor device.

primary cell—A cell that produces electric current through an electrochemical reaction but is not rechargeable. Once discharged, it must be discarded.

primary circuit—The first, in electrical order, of two or more coupled circuits, wherein a change in current will induce a voltage in the other, or secondary, circuit.

primary colors—Also called primaries. A set of colors from which all other colors are derived; hence, any set of stimuli from which all colors may be produced by mixture. A primary color cannot be matched by any combination of other primaries. In color television, the primary colors are red, blue, and green.

primary current — The current flowing through the primary winding of a transformer. Changes in this current cause a voltage to be induced in the secondary winding of the transformer.

primary detector—Also called a sensing, primary, or initial element. The first system element or group of elements that respond quantitatively to the measurand and perform the initial measurement operation. A primary detector performs the initial conversion or control of measurement energy. It does not include those transformers, amplifiers, shunts, resistors, etc., used as auxiliary means.

primary electron—1. After a collision between two electrons, the one with the greater energy. The other is called the secondary electron. 2. The electron produced in a detector or counter tube after ionization.

primary element—See Primary Detector.

primary emission—Emission of electrons due to primary causes (e.g., heating of a cathode) rather than secondary effects (e.g., electron bombardment).

primary failure—A failure occurring under normal environmental conditions and having no significant relationship to a previous failure but whose occurrence imposes abnormal stress on some other part or parts which may then undergo a secondary failure.

primary fault—In an electric circuit, initial breakdown of the insulation of a conductor, usually followed by a flow of power current.

primary flow—See Primary-Carrier Flow.

primary frequency—The frequency assigned for normal use on a particular circuit or communications channel.

primary grid emission — See Thermionic Grid Emission.

primary ionizing event—See Initial Ionizing Event.

primary power cable—Power service cables connecting the outside power source to the main-office switch and metering equipment.

primary radar—See Radar.

primary radiation—Radiation direct from the source without interaction.

primary radiator — The antenna element

from which the radiated energy leaves the transmission system.

primary relay—A relay that produces the initial action in a sequence of operations.

primary service area—Also called the primary area. The area within which radio or tv reception is not normally subject to objectionable interference or fading.

primary skip zone—The area beyond the ground-wave range around a transmitter, but within the skip distance. Radio reception is possible in this zone by sporadic and zigzag reflections.

primary standard—A unit directly defined and established by some authority, and against which all secondary standards are calibrated.

primary storage — In a computer, the main internal storage.

primary voltage—The voltage applied to the terminals of the primary winding in a transformer.

primary winding—See Primary.

priming illumination—A small, steady illumination applied to a phototube or photoelectric cell to make it more sensitive to variations in the illumination being measured.

primitive period—The smallest increment of time during which a quantity repeats itself.

principal axis—A reference direction for angular coordinates, used in describing the directional characteristics of a transducer employed for sound emission or reception. It is usually an axis of structural symmetry or the direction of maximum response. If these two do not coincide, however, the reference direction must be described explicitly.

principal E-plane—The plane containing the direction of maximum radiation and in which the electric vector lies.

principal focus—For a lens or spherical mirror, the point of convergence of light coming from a source at an infinite distance.

principal H-plane—A plane containing the direction of maximum radiation; the electric vector is everywhere normal to the plane, and the magnetic vector lies in it.

principal mode—See Dominant Mode.

printed—Reproduced on a surface by some process (e.g., letterpress, lithography, silk screen, etching).

printed circuit—A circuit in which the interconnecting wires have been replaced by conductive strips printed, etched, etc., onto an insulating board. It may also include similarly formed components on the baseboard.

printed-circuit assembly — 1. A printed-circuit board to which separable components have been attached. 2. An assembly of one or more printed-circuit boards, which may include several components.

printed-circuit board—Also called a card, chassis, or plate. An insulating board onto which a circuit has been printed. (Also see Printed Circuit.)

Printed circuit.

printed-circuit switch — A special rotary switch which can be connected directly to a mating printed-circuit board without wires.

printed component—A type of printed circuit intended primarily for electrical and/or magnetic functions other than point-to-point connections or shielding (e.g., printed inductor, resistor, capacitor, transmission line, etc.).

printed contact — The portion of a printed circuit that connects the circuit to a plug-in receptacle and performs the function of a plug pin.

printed element—An element, such as a resistor, capacitor, or transmission line, that is formed on a circuit board by deposition, etching, etc.

printed wiring—A conductive pattern formed on the surface of an insulating baseboard by plating or etching.

printed-wiring substrate—A conductive pattern printed on a substrate.

printer—1. Also called a teleprinter and teletypewriter. A telegraph instrument with a signal-actuated mechanism for automatically typing received messages. It may have a keyboard similar to that of a typewriter for sending messages. The term "receiving-only" is applied to a printer with no keyboard. 2. A device that prints the output from a computer. It ranges from a conventional "single-stick" or "flying typebar" printer (as on a typewriter), to a high-speed unit that prints up to 1,000 lines per minute!

printer telegraph code—A five- or seven-unit code used for operation of a teleprinter, teletypewriter, or similar telegraph printer.

printing—The reproduction of a pattern on a surface by any of various processes, such as vapor deposition, photo etching, embossing, or diffusion.

printing demand meter—An integrated demand meter which prints on a paper tape the demand for each interval and indicates the time it occurred.

printing telegraphy—Telegraph operation in which the received signals are automatically recorded as printed characters.

print-through—The transfer of the magnetic field from layer to layer of tape on the take-up reel.

print wheel—In a wheel printer, the single element providing the character set at one printing position.

privacy system—In radio transmission, a system designed to make unauthorized reception difficult.

private-aircraft station—A mobile radio station on board an aircraft not operated as an air carrier.

probability distribution — A mathematical model showing a representation of the probabilities for all possible values of a given random variable.

probability of success—The likelihood that an article will function satisfactorily for a stated period of time when subjected to a specified environment.

probable error—The amount of error which, according to the laws of probability, is most likely to occur during a measurement.

Probe (high voltage).

probe—1. A resonant conductor which can be placed into a waveguide or cavity resonator to insert or withdraw electromagnetic energy. 2. A test lead which contains an active or passive network and is used with certain types of test equipment. 3. A rod placed into the slotted section of a transmission line to measure the standing-wave ratio or to inject or extract a signal.

probing (near field)—The determination of radio interference by obtaining the relative interference level in the immediate area of a source by the use of a small insensitive antenna in conjunction with a receiving device.

problem language—The language a computer programmer uses in stating the definition of a problem.

problem-oriented language—In a computer, a source language suited to the description of a specific class of problems.

procedure-oriented language—In a computer, a source language suited to describing procedural steps in machine computing.

process control—Automatic control of industrial processes in which continuous material or energy is produced.

Process-control system.

processing section—The portion of a computer that does the actual changing of input into output. This includes the arithmetic and logic sections.

processor—1. A generalized program to process a group of computer programs. 2. Electronic equipment which is used to reformat, convert, translate, edit, or pulse-shape signals or data to satisfy the requirements of other equipment such as a computer.

producer's reliability risk — The risk faced by the producer (usually set at 10%) that a product will be rejected by a reliability-acceptance test even though the product is actually equal to or better than a specified value of reliability.

production sampling tests—Those tests normally made by either the vendor or the purchaser on a portion of a production lot for the purpose of determining the general performance level.

production tests—Those tests normally made on 100% of the items in a production lot by the vendor and normally on a sampling basis by the purchaser.

product modulator—A modulator, the output of which is substantially equal to the carrier times the modulating wave.

profile chart—A vertical cross-sectional drawing of the microwave path between two stations. Terrain, obstructions, antenna-height requirements, etc., are indicated on the drawing.

program—1. A set of instructions arranged in proper sequence for directing a digital computer in performing a desired operation or operations (e.g., the solution of a mathematical problem or the collation of a set of data). 2. To prepare a program (as contrasted with "to code"). 3. A sequence of audio signals transmitted for entertainment or information.

program assembly—Also called a translator. A process which translates a symbolic program into a machine-language program before the working program is executed. It can also integrate several sections or different programs.

program circuit—A telephone circuit that has been equalized to handle a wider range of frequencies that ordinary speech signals require. In this way, musical programs can be transmitted over telephone wires.

program control—1. A control system which automatically holds or changes its target value on the basis of time, to follow a prescribed program for the process. 2. A system in which a computer is used to direct an operation or process and automatically to hold or to make changes in the operation or process on the basis of a prescribed sequence of events.

program counter—*See* Program Register.

program-distribution amplifier—A group of amplifiers fed by a bridging bus from a single source. Each amplifier then feeds a separate line or other service.

Program distribution amplifier.

program failure alarm—In broadcasting stations, a relay circuit that gives a visual and aural alarm when a program fails. A delay prevents the relay from giving a false alarm during the silence before and after station-identification or other short breaks.

program level—The measure of the program signal in an audio system. It is expressed in volume units (VU).

programmed check — A means of testing for the correctness of a computer program and machine functioning, either by running a similarly programmed sample problem with a known answer (including mathematical or logical checks) or by building a checking system into the actual program being run.

programmer—A person who prepares the sequences of instructions for a computer or other data-handling system. He may or may not convert them into detailed codes.

programming — 1. Definition of a computer problem resulting in a flow diagram. 2. Preparing a list of instructions for the computer to use in the solution of a problem. 3. Selecting various circuit patterns by interconnecting or "jumping" the appropriate contacts on one side of a connector plug. 4. The control of a power-supply parameter, such as output voltage, by means of a remotely located or internally located control element (usually resistance) or signal (voltage).

programming device—A device by which a series of mechanical or electrical operations or events may be present to be performed automatically in a predetermined sequence and at specified time intervals.

program parameter—In a subroutine of a computing or other data-handling system, an adjustable parameter which can be given different values on several occasions when the subroutine is used.

program register—Also called program counter, or control register. The computer control-unit register into which is stored the program instruction being executed, hence controlling the computer operation during the cycles required to execute that instruction.

program-sensitive error—In a computer, an error arising from unforeseen behavior of some circuits, discovered when a comparatively unusual combination of program steps occurs.

program signal—In audio systems and components, the complex electric wave—corresponding to speech, music, and associated sounds—destined for audible reproduction.

program step—An increment, usually one instruction, of a computer program.

program tape—In a computer, a magnetic or punched paper tape which contains the sequence of instructions for solving a problem.

program timer—1. A loosely used term sometimes referring to a complex multicircuit timing device in which the program is readily changed, such as tape-controlled timers, can timers, time switches, or to any other type of timer. 2. A multiple-circuit repeat-cycle timer which repeats a preset program continuously as long as power is applied.

progressive scanning—A rectilinear process in which adjacent lines are scanned in succession. In television, the scanning process in which the distance from center to center of successively scanned lines is equal to the nominal line width.

projection cathode-ray tube—A cathode-ray tube that produces an intense but relatively small image, which can be projected onto a large viewing screen by an optical system consisting of lenses or a combination of lenses and mirrors.

projection ppi—A unit in which the image of a 4-inch dark-trace cathode-ray tube is projected on a 24-inch horizontal plotting surface. The echoes appear as magenta-colored arcs on a white background. *Also see* Dark-Trace Tube.

Projection television.

projection television—A combination of lenses and mirrors for projecting an enlarged television picture onto a screen.

projector—1. A device used in an under-

water sound system to radiate sound pulses through the water from the bottom of a ship. 2. A horn designed to direct sound chiefly in one direction from a speaker.

promethium cell—A low-power cell containing a radioactive isotope called promethium 147, which emits beta particles that strike a phosphor. Two photocells then convert the light output from the phosphor into electrical energy.

prong—*See* Pin.

proof pressure — The maximum pressure which may be applied to the sensing element of a transducer without changing the transducer performance beyond specified tolerances.

propagation—1. In electrical practice, the travel of waves through or along a medium. 2. The traveling of a wave along a transmission path. 3. Also called wave propagation. The travel of electromagnetic waves or sound waves through a medium. Propagation does not refer to the flow of current in the ordinary sense.

propagation anomaly—An irregularity introduced into an electromagnetic or other sensing device by discontinuities in the propagation medium.

propagation constant — The transmission characteristic which indicates the effect of a line on a wave being transmitted along the line. It is a complex quantity having a real term called the attenuation constant and an imaginary term called the phase constant.

propagation delay—1. A measure of the time required for a change in logic level to propagate through a chain of circuit elements. 2. A measure of the time required for a logic signal to travel through a device or a series of devices forming a logic string. It occurs as the result of four types of circuit delays—storage, rise, fall, and turn-on delay—and is the time between when the input signal crosses the threshold-voltage point and when the responding voltage at the output crosses the same voltage point.

propagation error—For ranging systems, the algebraic sum of propagation-velocity error and curved-path error. Except at long ranges and low angles, the curved-path component of propagation error is generally negligible.

propagation factor—*See* Propagation Ratio.

propagation loss—The loss of energy suffered by a signal while passing between two points.

propagation ratio—Also called the propagation factor. For a wave that has been propagated from one point to another, the ratio of the complex electric-field strength at the second point to that at the first point.

propagation time—The time it takes for a signal to travel from point to point. In a communications channel, the velocity of signal propagation is less than that of radio. A signal delay of 20 msec per thousand miles is a reasonable maximum.

propagation time delay—The time required

for a wave to travel from one point to another along a transmission line. It varies according to the type of line.

propagation velocity—*See* Velocity of Propagation.

property sort — In a computer, a technique for the selection from a file of records meeting a certain criterion.

proportional band—The range of the controlled variable corresponding to the full range of operation of the final control element.

proportional control—1. A method of control in which the intensity of action varies linearly as the condition being regulated deviates from the conditions prescribed. 2. Also called galloping ghost. An advanced type of radio-control system in which the rudder (and sometimes the elevator) can move as much (or as little) as the operator wishes.

proportional counter tube—A sealed tube containing an inert gas such as argon, krypton, xenon, methyl bromide, etc. It is used like a Geiger-Muller counter and operated at about 100 volts in the proportional - region.

proportional linearity—A manner of expressing nonlinearity as the deviation from a straight line in terms of a given percentage of the transducer output at the stimulus point under consideration (i.e., as a percentage of the reading).

proportional region—In a radiation counter tube, the applied-voltage range in which the gas amplification is greater than unity and is independent of the charge liberated by the initial ionizing event.

protective cable—Small-gage quadded cable used in toll cables to serve as fuses, usually at building entrances.

protective device—Any device for keeping an undesirably large current, voltage, or power out of a given part of an electric circuit.

protective gap—A spark gap provided between a conductor and the earth by suitable electrodes. High-voltage surges due to lightning are thus permitted to pass harmlessly to earth through the gap.

protective relay—A relay, the principal function of which is to protect services from interruption or to prevent or limit damage to apparatus.

protective resistance—A resistance placed in series with a device (e.g., a gas tube) to limit the current to a safe value.

protector—1. A device to protect equipment or personnel from high voltage or current. 2. A device to protect a telephone circuit from the effects of lightning or other high voltages accidentally impressed on the line.

protector block—A rectangular piece of carbon, with an insulated metal insert, or porcelain with a carbon insert which, in combination with each other, makes one element of a protector. It forms a gap

which will break down and provide a path to ground for voltages over 350 volts.

protector tube—A glow-discharge, cold-cathode tube in which a low-voltage breakdown is employed between two or more electrodes to protect the circuit against overvoltage.

proton—An elementary particle with a positive charge equivalent to the negative charge of the electron, but with approximately 1,845 times the mass. The proton is the positive nucleus of the hydrogen atom.

prototype model—A working model, usually hand-assembled, and suitable for complete evaluation of mechanical and electrical form, design, and performance. Approved parts are employed throughout, so that it will be completely representative of the final, mass-produced equipment.

proximity detector—A sensing device which gives an indication when approaching or being approached by another object (e.g., a burglar alarm).

proximity effect—The redistribution of current brought about in a conductor by the presence of another current-carrying conductor.

proximity fuse—A fuse designed to detonate a projectile, bomb, mine, or charge when activated by an external influence in the vicinity of a target. The variable time fuse is one type of proximity fuse.

prr—Abbreviation for pulse-repetition rate.

psec—Abbreviation for picosecond (10^{-12} second).

pseudocode—An instruction that is not meant to be followed directly by a computer. Instead, it initiates the linking of a subroutine into the main program.

pseudoinstruction — *See* Instructional Constant.

pseudoprogram—A program that is written in a pseudocode and may include short coded logical routines.

pseudorandom—Having the property of being produced by a definite calculation process while simultaneously satisfying one or more of the standard tests for statistical-randomness.

pseudostereo—Devices and techniques for obtaining stereo qualities from one channel.

psophometric emf—The electromotive force (or voltage) generated by a source having an internal resistance of 600 ohms and no internal reactance, which, when connected across a standard receiver having 600 ohms of resistance and no reactance, produces the same sinusoidal current as an 800-hertz generator of the same impedance. *Also see* Psophometric Voltage.

psophometric voltage—The voltage which would appear across a 600-ohm resistance connected between any two points in a telephone circuit. (This value is one-half the psophometric emf since the latter is essentially the open-circuit potential necessary from a source to produce the psophometric voltage if the source has a 600-ohm internal resistance.)

ptm—Abbreviation for pulse-time modulation.

ptm-ptm-am—A system in which a number of pulse positions or pulse-time modulated subcarriers are used to amplitude-modulate the carrier.

P-type conductivity—The conductivity associated with the holes in a semiconductor.

P-type conductor—A positive-type conductor, one with electron holes as the principal carriers. This implies the presence of acceptors.

P-type crystal rectifier—A crystal rectifier in which forward current flows whenever the semiconductor is more positive than the metal.

P-type semiconductor—An extrinsic semiconductor in which the hole density exceeds the conduction-electron density. By implication, the net ionized impurity concentration is an acceptor type.

public-address system—Also called a p-a system. One or more microphones, an audio-frequency system, and one or more speakers used for picking up and amplifying sounds to a large audience, either indoors or out.

public radiocommunication services—Land mobile and fixed radio services, the stations of which are open to public correspondence.

public-safety radio service—Any radiocommunication service essential either to the discharge of nonfederal governmental functions relating to public-safety responsibilities or to the alleviation of an emergency endangering life or property. The radio transmitting facilities in this service may be fixed, land, or mobile stations.

puck—*See* Pressure Roller.

puff—British abbreviation for picofarad.

pull curves—The characteristics relating force to displacement in the actuating system of a relay.

pull-down resistor—A resistor connected across the output of a device or circuit to hold the output equal to or less than the 0 input level of the following digital device. Also used to lower the output impedance of a device.

pull-in current—*See* Pickup Current.

pull-in current (or voltage)—The maximum current (or voltage) required to operate a relay.

pulling—1. In an oscillator, the undesired change from the desired frequency. It is caused either by coupling from another source of frequency, or by the influence of the load impedance. 2. In television, partial loss of synchronization.

pulling figure—The difference between the maximum and minimum frequencies of an oscillator whenever the phase angle of the load-impedance reflection coefficient varies through 360°. The absolute value of this coefficient is constant and equal to .20.

pull-up torque—The minimum torque developed by an alternating-current motor during the period of acceleration from rest to the speed at which breakdown torque occurs. For motors which do not have a definite breakdown torque, the pull-up torque is the minimum torque developed up to rated speed.

pulsating current—A nonuniform electron flow, which varies periodically but does not reverse its direction.

pulsating direct current—A direct current that changes its value at regular or irregular intervals but flows in the same direction at all times.

pulsating quantity—A periodic quantity that can be considered the sum of a continuous component and an alternating component in the quantity.

pulsation welding—A form of resistance welding in which the power is alternately applied and removed.

pulse—1. The variation of a quantity having a normally constant value. This variation is characterized by a rise and a decay of a finite duration. 2. An abrupt change in voltage, either positive or negative, which conveys information to a circuit. (*Also see* Impulse.)

pulse amplifier—A wideband amplifier used to amplify square waves without appreciably changing their shape.

pulse amplitude—A general term for the magnitude of a pulse. For more specific designation, adjectives such as average, instantaneous, peak, rms (effective), etc., should also be used.

pulse-amplitude modulation—Modulation in which the modulating wave is caused to amplitude-modulate a pulse carrier. Abbreviated pam.

pulse analyzer—Equipment for analyzing pulses to determine their time, amplitude, duration, shape, etc.

pulse arc welding—A type of welding in which the material to be welded is positioned together, forming one electrode. The other electrode is positioned to form a gap with one of the workpieces. An arc is struck and the current heats the workpieces to the melting point at their interface. *Also see* Arc Percussive Welding.

pulse-average time—The duration of a pulse, measured between two points at 50% of the maximum amplitude on the leading and trailing edges.

pulse bandwidth—The smallest continuous frequency interval outside of which the amplitude of the spectrum does not exceed a prescribed fraction of the amplitude at a specified frequency.

pulse carrier—A carrier consisting of a series of pulses. Usually employed as a subcarrier.

pulse code—1. A pulse or series of pulses which, by means of waveform, pulse width, pulse time, pulse numbers, or pulse sequences, may be used to convey information. 2. Loosely, a code consisting of pulses—e.g., Morse, Baudot, binary.

E – PULSE VOLTAGE
a – RISE TIME
b – OVERSHOOT
c – DROOP
d – FALL TIME

e – BACKSWING
f – RETURN SWING
g – START OF FALL TIME
t – PULSE DURATION

Pulse.

pulse-code modulation — Abbreviated pcm. Pulsed modulation in which the signal is sampled periodically and each sample is quantized and transmitted as a digital binary code.

pulse code modulation-frequency modulation—A system in which pulse code modulated subcarriers are used to frequency-modulate a second carrier. Binary digits are formed by the absence or presence of a pulse in an assigned position.

pulse coder—A circuit which sets up pulses in an identifiable pattern.

pulse coding and correlation—A general technique concerning a variety of methods used to change the transmitted waveform and then decode upon its reception. Pulse compression is a special form of pulse coding and correlation.

pulse compression—A matched filter technique used to discriminate against signals which do not correspond to the transmitted signal.

pulse counter — A device that gives an indication or records of the total number of pulses that it has received during a given time interval.

pulsed Doppler system—A pulsed radar system which utilizes the Doppler effect to obtain information about the target (not including simple resolution from fixed targets).

pulse decay time—The amount of time required for the trailing edge of a pulse to decay from 90% to 10% of the peak pulse amplitude.

pulse delay time—The time interval between the leading edges of the input and output pulses, measured at 10% of their maximum amplitude.

pulse demoder—Also called a constant-delay discriminator. A circuit which responds only to pulse signals with a specified spacing between them.

pulse digit—A code element comprising the immediately associated train of pulses.

pulse-digit spacing—The time interval between the end of one pulse digit and the start of the next.

pulse discriminator—A device that responds only to pulses having a particular characteristic (e.g., duration, amplitude, period). One that responds to period is also called a time discriminator.

pulsed oscillator—1. An oscillator in which oscillations are sustained by either self-generated or external pulses. 2. An oscillator which generates a carrier-frequency pulse or a train of pulses.

pulsed-oscillator starting time—The interval between the leading-edge times of the pulse at the oscillator control terminals and the related output pulse.

pulse droop—Distortion characterized by a slanting of the top of an otherwise essentially flat-topped rectangular pulse.

Pulsed ruby laser.

pulsed ruby laser—A laser that uses ruby as the active material. The extremely high pumping power required is obtained by discharging a bank of energy storage capacitors through a special high-intensity flash tube.

pulse duration—Also called pulse length or width. The time interval between the points at which the instantaneous value on the leading and trailing edges bears a specified relationship to the peak pulse amplitude.

pulse-duration discriminator—A circuit in which the sense and magnitude of the output is a function of the deviation of the pulse length from a reference.

pulse-duration modulation — Abbreviated pdm. Also called by the less preferred terms "pulse-width modulation" and "pulse-length modulation." Pulse-time modulation in which the duration of a pulse is varied.

pulse - duration modulation – frequency modulation—Also called pulse-width modulation–frequency modulation. A system in which pulse-duration modulation subcarriers are used to frequency-modulate a second carrier.

pulse duty factor—Ratio of the average pulse duration to the average pulse spacing. Equivalent to the average pulse duration times the pulse-repetition rate.

pulse emission—Emission drawn for short periods; it may or may not follow a regular repetition rate.

pulse emitter load — The load seen by the collector of an inverter that drives the pulse input to a flip-flop, pulse amplifier, or delay.

pulse equalizer—A circuit that produces output pulses of uniform size and shape when driven by input pulses that vary in size and shape.

pulse fall time—That time during which the trailing edge of a pulse is decreasing from 90% to 10% of its maximum amplitude.

pulse-forming line—A combination of circuit components used to produce a square pulse of controlled duration.

Pulse-forming network.

pulse-forming network — A network which converts either an a-c or d-c charging source into an approximately rectangular wave output. By means of a high-speed switch, it alternately stores energy from the charging source and releases the energy through the load to which it is connected. This network supplies the accurately shaped pulse re-

quired by the magnetron or klystron oscillator of a radar modulator.

pulse-frequency modulation — Abbreviated pfm. More precisely called pulse-repetition-rate modulation. Pulse-time modulation in which the pulse repetition rate is varied.

pulse-frequency spectrum—*See* Pulse Spectrum.

pulse generator—A device for generating a controlled series of electrical pulses.

pulse group—*See* Pulse Train.

pulse-height analyzer — Also called kicksorter. An instrument that indicates the number or rate of occurrence of pulses within each of one or more specified amplitude ranges.

pulse-height discriminator — Also called a pulse-height selector. A circuit that selects and passes only those pulses which exceed a certain minimum amplitude.

pulse-height selector—*See* Pulse-Height Discriminator.

pulse-improvement threshold — In a constant-amplitude pulse-modulation system the condition existing when the peak pulse voltage is at least twice the peak noise voltage after selection and before any nonlinear process such as amplitude clipping and limiting. The ratio of peak to rms noise voltage is ordinarily assumed to be 4 to 1.

pulse interference eliminator—A device that removes pulse signals which are not precisely on the radar operating frequency.

pulse interleaving—A process in which pulses from two or more time-division multiplexers are systematically combined in time division for transmission over a common path.

pulse interrogation — The triggering of a transponder by a pulse or pulse mode. Interrogations by the latter may be employed to trigger one or more transponders.

pulse interval—*See* Pulse Spacing.

pulse-interval modulation—Pulse-time modulation in which the pulse spacing is varied. *Also see* Pulse-Spacing Modulation.

pulse jitter—A relatively slight variation of the pulse spacing in a pulse train. It may be random or systematic, depending on its origin, and is generally not coherent with any imposed pulse modulation.

pulse length—*See* Pulse Duration.

pulse-length modulation—*See* Pulse-Duration Modulation.

pulse load — The load presented to a pulse source.

pulse mode—1. A finite sequence of pulses, in a prearranged pattern, used for selecting and isolating a communication channel. 2. The prearranged pattern in (1) above.

pulse-mode multiplex—A process or device for selecting channels by means of pulse modes. In this way, two or more channels can use the same carrier frequency.

pulse moder—A device for producing a pulse mode. (*Also see* Pulse Demoder.)

pulse-modulated radar—Radar in which the radiation consists of a series of discrete pulses.

INTELLIGENCE

UNMODULATED PULSE-CHAIN CARRIER

AMPLITUDE-MODULATED CARRIER

WIDTH-MODULATED CARRIER

FREQUENCY-MODULATED CARRIER

PULSE-NUMBER-MODULATED CARRIER

PULSE-DISPLACEMENT-MODULATED CARRIER

Pulse modulation (definition 2).

pulse-modulated waves—Recurrent wave trains used extensively in radar. In general, their duration is shorter than the interval between them.

pulse modulation—1. Modulation of a carrier by pulses. 2. Modulation of a pulse carrier.

pulse modulator—A device which applies pulses to the element being modulated.

pulse operation—The method whereby the energy is delivered in pulses. Usually described in terms of the shape and the frequency of the pulses.

pulse oscillator—An oscillator in which the oscillations are sustained by self-generated or external pulses.

pulse packet—In radar, the volume of space occupied by the pulse energy.

pulse-position modulation—Abbreviated ppm. Pulse-time modulation in which the value of each instantaneous sample of the wave modulates the position in time of a pulse.

pulse-position modulator—A device which converts analog information to variations in pulse position.

pulser—A generator which produces extremely short, high-voltage pulses at definite recurrence rates for use in radar transmitters and similar pulsed systems.

pulse rate—*See* Pulse-Repetition Rate.

pulse ratio—Ratio of the length of any pulse to its total period.

pulse recovery—The time, usually in microseconds, required for electron flow in a diode to start or stop when voltage is suddenly applied or removed.

pulse-recurrence, counting-type frequency meter—A device for measuring frequency. It uses a direct-current ammeter calibrated in pulses per second.

pulse-recurrence time—The time elapsing between the start of one transmitted pulse and the next pulse. The reciprocal of the pulse-recurrence frequency.

pulse regeneration—The restoring of a series

of pulses to their original timing, form, and relative magnitude.

pulse repeater—Also called a transponder. A device that receives pulses from one circuit and transmits corresponding pulses at another frequency, waveshape, etc., into another circuit.

pulse-repetition frequency—The rate (usually given in hertz or pulses per second) at which pulses or pulse groups are transmitted from a radar set. Abbreviated prf.

pulse-repetition period—The reciprocal of the pulse-repetition frequency.

pulse-repetition rate—Abbreviated prr. Also called pulse rate. The average number of pulses per unit of time.

pulse-repetition-rate modulation—*See* Pulse-Frequency Modulation.

pulse reply—The transmission of a pulse or pulse mode by a transponder as the result of an interrogation.

pulse resolution—The minimum time separation, usually in microseconds or milliseconds, between input pulses that permits proper circuit or component response.

pulse rise time—The interval of time required for the leading edge of a pulse to rise from 10% to 90% of its peak amplitude, unless some other percentage is stated.

pulse sample-and-hold circuit—A circuit which holds the final amplitude of an integrated pulse until the final amplitude of the succeeding integrated pulse is reached. A less desirable sample-and-hold circuit resets after each hold period to a fixed level before integrating a succeeding pulse.

pulse scaler—A device capable of producing an output signal whenever a prescribed number of input pulses has been received. It frequently includes indicating devices that facilitate interpolation.

pulse selector—A circuit or device that selects the proper pulse from a sequence of (telemetering) pulses.

pulse separation—The interval between the trailing-edge pulse time of a pulse and the leading-edge pulse time of the succeeding pulse.

pulse shaper — Any transducer (including pulse regenerators) used for changing one or more characteristics of a pulse.

pulse shaping — Intentionally changing the shape of a pulse.

pulse spacing—The time interval from one pulse to the next—i.e., between the corresponding times of two consecutive pulses. (The term "pulse interval" is ambiguous—it may be taken to mean the duration of a pulse instead of the space or interval between pulses.)

pulse-spacing modulation—Formerly called pulse-interval modulation. A form of pulse-time modulation in which the pulse spacing is varied.

pulse spectrum—Also called pulse-frequency spectrum. The frequency distribution, in relative amplitude and phase, of the sinusoidal components of a pulse.

pulse spike — A relatively short duration pulse superimposed on the main pulse.

pulse-spike amplitude—The peak amplitude of a pulse spike.

pulse-storage time—The time interval from a point at 90% of the maximum amplitude on the trailing edge of the input pulse to the same 90% point on the trailing edge of the output pulse.

pulse stretcher—1. A circuit designed to extend the duration of a pulse—primarily so that its pulse modulation will be more readily discernible in an audio presentation. 2. In a computer, a circuit which generates a long pulse when triggered by a short pulse. The width of the output pulse is determined by the value of the coupling capacitor. The maximum width of the output pulse cannot exceed 50% of the clock rate.

pulse tilt—A distortion characterized in an otherwise essentially flat-topped rectangular pulse by either a decline or a rise of the pulse top.

pulse time—The time interval from a point at 90% of the maximum amplitude on the leading edge of a pulse, to the 90% point on the trailing edge.

pulse-time—modulated radiosonde — Also called time-interval radiosonde. A radiosonde which transmits the indications of the meterological sensing elements in the form of pulses spaced in time. The meterological data are evaluated from the intervals between the pulses.

pulse-time modulation — Abbreviated ptm. Modulation (e.g., pulse-duration and pulse-position) in which the values of instantaneous samples of the modulating wave are made to modulate the occurrence time of some characteristic of a pulse carrier.

pulse timer—A timer the time cycle of which is started with a continuous input voltage and application or removal of an additional positive input voltage pulse. At the end of the time-delay period, the contacts transfer.

pulse train—Also called pulse group or impulse train. A group or sequence of pulses of similar characteristics.

pulse-train frequency spectrum—*See* Pulse-train Spectrum.

pulse-train spectrum — Also called pulse-train frequency spectrum. The frequency distribution, in amplitude and in phase angle, of the sinusoidal components of the pulse train.

Pulse transformer.

pulse transformer—A transformer designed to pass pulse currents and voltages with the least possible change in waveshape, or to be used for generating pulses in a blocking oscillator.

pulse transmitter—1. A pulse-modulated transmitter in which the peak power-output capabilities are usually larger than the average power-output rating. 2. A transmitter used to generate and transmit pulses over a telemetering or pilot-wire circuit to the remote indicating or receiving device.

pulse valley—In a pulse, the portion between two specified maxima.

pulse width—*See* Pulse Duration.

pulse-width discriminator—A device that measures the pulse length of video signals and passes only those the time duration of which falls into some predetermined design tolerance.

pulse-width modulation—*See* Pulse-Duration Modulation.

pulse-width modulation–frequency modulation—*See* Pulse-Duration Modulation-Frequency Modulation.

pulsing transformer—A transformer designed to supply pulses of voltage or current.

pump—1. An external source used to increase the electron population of excited energy states. 2. Of a parametric device, the source of alternating-current power which causes the nonlinear reactor to behave as a time-varying reactance.

pumped tube—An electron tube (chiefly a pool-cathode) which is continuously connected to evacuating equipment during operation.

pumping—Of a laser, the application of radiation of appropriate frequency to invert the distribution of systems of electrons of the laser media so that the levels of higher energy states are more populated.

pumping frequency — The frequency at which pumping is provided in a maser, quadrupole amplifier, or other amplifier requiring high-frequency excitation.

pump oscillator—An alternating-current generator that supplies pumping energy for maser and parametric amplifiers. Operates at twice or some higher multiple of the signal frequency.

punched card—A heavy, stiff paper of constant size and shape, suitable for punching in a pattern that has meaning, and for being handled mechanically. The punched holes are sensed electrically by wire brushes, mechanically by metal fingers, or photoelectrically by photocells.

punch-card machine—*See* Key Punch.

punched tape—Also called tape or perforated tape. Paper tape punched in a coded pattern of holes, which convey information.

punch-through voltage—*See* Reach-Through Voltage.

puncture—A disruptive discharge of current through insulation, which breaks down under electrostatic stress and permits the flow of a sudden, large current through the opening. *Also see* Breakdown.

puncture voltage—1. The voltage at which an insulator or shell is electrically punctured when subjected to a gradually increasing voltage. 2. The voltage at which insulation fails by disruptive discharge through the insulation sample. It is assumed that the sample area is large enough to prevent flashover.

Pupin coil—An iron-core loading coil inserted into telephone lines at regular intervals to balance out the effect of capacitance between the lines.

pup jack—*See* Tip Jack.

pure tone—*See* Simple Tone.

purity—Physically complete saturation of a hue—i.e., uncontaminated by white and other colors. (*Also see* Excitation Purity.)

purity coil—A coil consisting of two current-carrying windings. In a color television receiver, they produce a magnetic field which directs the three electron beams so that each one will strike only the proper set of phosphor dots.

purity control—A variable resistor that controls the current through the purity coil mounted around the neck of a color picture tube.

purity magnet — Two adjustable magnetic rings used in place of a purity coil.

purple boundary—The straight line drawn between the ends of the spectrum locus on a chromaticity diagram.

pushback hookup wire—Tinned copper wire covered with loosely braided insulation, which can be pushed back with the fingers to expose enough bare wire for making a connection.

push-button control—Control of equipment by means of push-buttons, which in turn operate relays, etc.

push-button switch—A switch in which a button must be depressed each time the contacts are to be opened or closed.

push-button tuner—A series of interlocked push-button switches which connect into a circuit the correct tuning elements for the frequency corresponding to the depressed button.

pushdown list—A list of items in which the last item entered becomes the first item of the list and the relative position of each of the other items is pushed back one.

pushing figure—The change in oscillator frequency due to a specified change in plate current (excluding thermal effects).

push-pull amplifier—*See* Balanced Amplifier.

push-pull circuit—A circuit containing two like elements which operate in 180° phase relationship to produce additive output components of the desired wave and cancellation of certain unwanted products. Push-pull amplifiers and oscillators use such a circuit.

push-pull currents—Balanced currents.

push-pull doubler—An amplifier used for frequency doubling. It consists of two transistors or vacuum tubes; the latter have their grids (input) connected in push-pull and their plates (output) in push-push or parallel.

push-pull microphone—A microphone comprising two like elements actuated by the same sound waves and operated 180° out of phase.

push-pull oscillator—A balanced oscillator employing two similar tubes or transistors in phase opposition.

push-pull transformer—An audio-frequency transformer that has a center-tapped winding and is used in a push-pull amplifier circuit.

push-pull voltages—Balanced voltages.

push-push circuit—A circuit usually used as a frequency multiplier to emphasize even-order harmonics. Two similar transistors are employed, or two tubes with their grids connected in phase opposition and their plates in parallel to a common load.

push-push currents — Currents which are equal in magnitude and which flow in the same direction at every point in the two conductors of a balanced line.

push-push voltages — Voltages which are equal in magnitude and have the same polarity (relative to ground) at every point on the two conductors of a balanced line.

push rod—A shaft that connects a servo or other actuator with the part of the controlled device.

push-to-talk switch — *See* Press-to-Talk Switch.

pushup list — A list of items in which each item is entered at the end of the list and the previous items maintain their same relative position in the list.

pw—Abbreviation for picowatt.

pwm-fm—A system in which a number of pulse-width–modulated subcarriers are used to frequency-modulate the carrier.

pylon antenna — A vertical antenna constructed of one or more sheet-metal cylinders with a lengthwise slot. The gain depends on the number of sections.

pyramidal horn—An electromagnetic horn, the sides of which form a pyramid. The electromagnetic field in such a horn would be expressed basically in a family of spherical coordinates.

pyramid wave—A triangular wave, the sides of which are approximately equal in length.

pyrheliometer — A device for the measurement of infrared radiation.

pyroelectric effect—Also called pyroelectricity. The redistribution of the charge in a crystal that has been heated. The crystal is left with a net electric dipole moment—i.e., the centers of the positive and negative charges are separated.

pyroelectricity—*See* Pyroelectric Effect.

Pylon antenna.

pyroelectric material—A material which produces an electrical output when subjected to a change in temperature.

pyromagnetic—Pertaining to the effect of heat and magnetism on each other.

pyrometer—An instrument used to measure elevated temperatures (beyond the range of mercury thermometers) by electric means. These include immersion, optical, radiation, resistance, and thermoelectric pyrometers.

pyron detector—A crystal detector in which rectification occurs between iron pyrites and copper (or other metallic points).

Pythagorean scale—A musical scale in which the frequency intervals are represented by the ratios of integral powers of 2 and 3.

Q

Q—1. Symbol for quantity of electric charge. 2. A measure of the relationship between stored energy and rate of dissipation in certain electric elements, structures or materials. 3. In an inductor, the ratio of its reactance to its effective series resistance at a given frequency. 4. Also called quality factor or Q factor. In a capacitor, the ratio of its susceptance to its effective shunt conductance at a given frequency. 5. A measure of the sharpness of resonance or frequency selectivity of a mechanical or electrical system.

Q antenna—A dipole matched to its transmission line by stub matching.

Q band—A band of frequencies extending from 36 to 46 GHz, corresponding to wavelengths of 0.834 to 0.652 cm.

Q channel—The 0.5-MHz-wide band used in the American NTSC color-television system to transmit green-magenta color information.

QCW—A 3.58-MHz continuous-wave signal having Q phase. The term is generally limited to reference to the color-television receiver local oscillator and associated circuits.

QCW signal—*See* Quadrature-Phase Subcarrier Signal.

Q demodulator—A demodulator circuit the inputs of which are the chrominance signal and the signal from the local 3.58-MHz oscillator after it has been shifted 90°. This phase shift is necessary so that the local signal will be an accurate representation of the Q subcarrier that was suppressed at the transmitter. The output of the Q demodulator is a color-video signal representing colors in the televised scene.

Q-factor—*See* Q, 4.

Q-meter—Also called a quality-factor meter. An instrument for measuring the Q, or quality factor, of a circuit or circuit element.

Q-multiplier—A special filter which has a sharply-peaked response curve or a deep rejection notch at a particular frequency.

393

Q-phase—Also called quadrature carrier. A color-television signal carrier having a phase difference of 147° from the color subcarrier.

qrm—An obsolete term for any type of man-made interference.

qrs complex—That portion of the waveform in an electrocardiogram extending from point Q to point S; it includes the maximum amplitude shown in an ecg trace.

Q-signal — In color television, the signal formed by the combination of R—Y and B—Y color-difference signals having positive polarities of 0.48 and 0.41, respectively. It is one of the two signals used to modulate the chrominance subcarrier, the other being the I signal. (*Also see* Coarse-Chrominance Primary.)

Q-signals—Abbreviations used in radiocommunications.

QSL card—A card exchanged by radio amateurs to confirm radiocommunications with each other.

quad — 1. A structural unit employed in cables. A quad consists of four separately insulated conductors twisted together. These conductors may take the form of two twisted pairs. 2. A combination of four elements, either electronic components or complete circuits, in a series-parallel or parallel-series arrangement. 3. A (series-parallel) combination of four transistors.

quadded cable—A cable in which some or all of the conductors are in the form of quads.

quadding—Connecting transistors in a series-parallel configuration, to achieve greater reliability.

quadrant—1. A sector, arc, or angle of 90°. 2. An instrument for measuring or setting vertical angles.

quadrantal error—The error caused in magnetic-compass readings by the magnetic field of the steel hull of a ship, or by metal structures near the loop antenna of radio direction finders aboard a vessel or aircraft.

quadrant electrometer—An electrometer for measuring voltages and charges by means of electrostatic forces. A metal plate or needle is suspended horizontally inside a vertical metal cylinder that is divided into four insulated parts, each connected electrically to the one opposite it. The two pairs of quadrants are connected to the two terminals between which the potential difference is to be measured. The resultant electrostatic forces displace the suspended indicator a certain amount, depending on the voltage.

quadrature—The state or condition of two related periodic functions or two related points separated by a quarter of a cycle, or 90 electrical degrees.

quadrature amplifier—A stage used to supply two signals of the same frequency but with phase angles that differ by 90 electrical degrees.

quadrature carrier—*See* Q-phase.

quadrature component—1. The reactive current or voltage component due to inductive or capacitive reactance in a circuit. 2. A vector representing an alternating quantity which is in quadrature (at 90°) with some reference vector.

quadrature modulation—The modulation of two carrier components 90° apart in phase by separate modulating functions.

quadrature-phase subcarrier signal—That portion of the chrominance signal which leads or lags the in-phase portion by 90°. Abbreviated qcw signal.

quadrature portion—In the chrominance signal, the portion with the same or opposite phase from that of the subcarrier modulated by the Q-signal. This portion of the chrominance signal may lead or lag the in-phase portion by 90 electrical degrees.

quadrature sensitivity—Also called side sensitivity, lateral sensitivity, or cross-talk sensitivity. The sensitivity of a transducer to motion normal to the principal axis. Commonly expressed in percent of the sensitivity in the principal axis.

quadripole network—*See* Two-Terminal–Pair Network.

quadrupole—A combination of two dipoles that produces a force varying in inverse proportion to the fourth power of the distance from the generating charge.

quadrupole network — *See* Two-Terminal–Pair Network.

quality—The extent of conformance to specifications of a device or the proportion of satisfactory devices in a lot.

quality assurance — A planned, systematic pattern of actions necessary to provide suitable confidence that an item will perform satisfactorily in actual operation.

quality control—The control of variation of workmanship, processes, and materials in order to produce a consistent, uniform product.

quality engineering — An engineering program the purposes of which are to establish suitable quality tests and quality acceptance criteria and to interpret quality data.

quality factor—*See* Q, 4.

quality-factor meter—*See* Q-meter.

quantity—Any positive or negative number. It may be a whole number, a fraction, or a whole number and a fraction.

quantity of electricity — *See* Electrical Charge.

quantization — The process whereby the range of values of a wave is divided into a finite number of subranges, each represented by an assigned (quantized) value.

quantization distortion—Also called quantization noise. Inherent distortion introduced during quantization.

quantization error—The difference between the actual values of data and corresponding discrete values resulting from quantization.

quantization level—1. A particular subrange in quantization. 2. The symbol designating the subrange of (1) above.

quantization noise—*See* Quantization Distortion.

quantize—To convert a continuous variable, such as a waveform, into a series of levels or steps. There are no "in-between" values in such a quantized waveform. All values of signal are represented by the nearest standard value or code position.

quantized pulse modulation—Pulse modulation which involves quantization (e.g., pulse numbers or pulse code modulation).

quantizer—A device which decides in what particular digital subdivision an analog quantity will be placed.

quantizing—Expressing an analog value as the nearest one of a discrete set of prechosen values.

quantum—1. A discrete portion of energy of a definite amount. It was first associated with intra-atomic or intramolecular processes involving changes among the electrons, and the corresponding radiation. 2. If the magnitude of a quantity is always an integral multiple of a definite unit, then that unit is called the quantum of the quantity. 3. The angular increment of input-shaft rotation of an encoder, subtended by one code position.

quantum efficiency (of a phototube)—The average number of electrons photoelectrically emitted from the photocathode per incident photon of a given wavelength.

quantum mechanics—The study of atomic structure and other related problems in terms of quantities that can actually be measured.

quantum noise—A random variation or noise signal due to fluctuations in the average rate of incidence of quanta on a detector. The basic electromagnetic quantum of noise power is just 1 photon per electromagnetic mode.

quantum theory—The theory that an atom or molecule does not emit or absorb energy continuously. Rather, it does so in a series of steps, each step being the emission or absorption of an amount of energy called the quantum. The energy in each quantum is directly proportionate to the frequency.

quarter phase—*See* Two-Phase.

quarter-square multiplier—A circuit that achieves true four-quadrant multiplication

by taking advantage of the mathematical relationship that the product of two variables is equal to one-quarter of the difference of the squares of the sum and the difference of the variables.

quarter-wave antenna—An antenna, the electrical length of which is one-quarter the wavelength of the transmitted or received signal.

quarter-wave attenuator—Two energy-absorbing grids or other structures placed in a transmission line and separated by an odd number of quarter wavelengths. As a result, the wave reflected from the first grid annuls the wave reflected from the second grid.

quarter-wavelength—That distance which corresponds to an electrical length of a quarter of a wavelength of the frequency under consideration.

quarter-wave line—*See* Quarter-Wave Stub.

quarter-wave plate—A mica or other double-refracting crystal plate of such thickness that a phase difference of one-quarter cycle is introduced between the ordinary and extraordinary components of light passing through.

quarter-wave resonance—In a quarter-wave antenna, the condition in which its resonant frequency is equal to the frequency at which it is to be used.

quarter-wave stub—Also called a quarter-wave line or quarter-wave transmission line. A section of transmission line equal to one-quarter of a wavelength at the fundamental frequency. It is commonly used to suppress even harmonics. This is done by shorting the far end so that the open end presents a high impedance to the fundamental frequency and all odd harmonics, but not to the even-order harmonics.

quarter-wave support—A quarter-wave metallic stub, used in place of dielectric insulators between the inner and outer conductors of a coaxial transmission line.

quarter-wave termination—A waveguide termination consisting of a metal plate and a wire grating (or semiconducting film) spaced one-quarter wavelength apart. The plate is the terminating element. The wave reflected by the grating (or film) is cancelled by the wave reflected by the plate.

quarter-wave transformer—A one-quarter-

Quarter-wave supports.

wavelength section of transmission line used for impedance matching.

quarter-wave transmission line—*See* Quarter-Wave Stub.

quartz—A mineral occurring in hexagonal crystals in nature and having piezoelectric properties that are highly useful in radio and carrier communication. The crystals from which slabs are cut for oscillators are transparent and almost colorless. When excited electrically, they vibrate and maintain extremely accurate and stable frequencies.

quartz crystal—Also called a crystal. A thin slab cut from quartz and ground to the thickness at which it will vibrate at the desired frequency when supplied with energy. It is used to accurately control the frequency of an oscillator.

quartz delay line—A delay line in which fused quartz is the medium for delaying sound transmission or a train of waves.

quartz lamp—A mercury-vapor lamp having a transparent envelope made from quartz instead of glass. Quartz resists heat (permitting a higher current) and passes ultraviolet rays, which glass will absorb.

quartz plate—A crystalline-quartz section completely finished to specifications, with its two major faces essentially parallel.

quartz resonator—A piezoelectric resonator with a quartz plate.

quasi-linear feedback-control system—A feedback-control system in which the relationships between the pertinent measures of the system input and output signals are substantially linear despite the existence of nonlinear elements.

quasi-optical—Having properties similar to those of light waves. The propagation of waves in the television spectrum is said to be quasi-optical (i.e., cut off by the horizon).

quasi-rectangular wave—A wave nearly, but not, rectangular in shape.

quasi-single-sideband—Simulated single-sideband transmission done by transmitting parts of both sidebands.

quasi-steady-state vibration—A nearly periodic vibration in which the amplitude and phase relationships of the component sinusoids vary slowly with time.

quaternary signaling—The communications mode in which information is passed by the presence and absence, or plus and minus variations, of four discrete levels of one parameter of the signaling medium.

quenched spark—A spark consisting of only a few sharply defined oscillations, because the gap is deionized almost immediately after the initial spark has passed.

quenched spark gap—A spark gap with provision for producing a quenched spark. One form consists of many small gaps between electrodes that have a relatively large mass and thus are good radiators of heat. As a result, they cool the gaps rapidly and thereby stop conduction.

quenched spark-gap converter—A spark-gap

generator or other power source in which the oscillatory discharge of a capacitor through an inductor and a spark gap provides the radio-frequency power. The spark gap comprises one or more closely spaced gaps in series.

quench frequency—1. An a-c voltage applied to an electrode of a tube used as a superregenerative detector to alternately vary its sensitivity and thereby prevent sustained oscillations. The quench frequency is usually lower than the signal frequency to be received. 2. The number of times per second a circuit goes in and out of oscillation.

quenching—1. The terminating of a discharge in a radiation-counter tube by inhibiting the re-ignition. 2. A process of rapid cooling from an elevated temperature, in contact with liquids, gases, or solids.

quenching circuit—A circuit which inhibits multiple discharges from an ionizing event by suppressing or reversing the voltage applied to a counter tube.

quenching frequency—That frequency at which oscillations in a superregenerative receiver are suppressed (quenched).

quench oscillator—A superregenerative receiver circuit which produces the quench-frequency signal.

quick-break—A characteristic of a switch or circuit breaker, whereby it has a fast contact-opening speed that is independent of the operator.

Quick-break fuse.

quick-break fuse—A fuse that draws out the arc and rapidly breaks the circuit when its wire melts. Usually a spring or weight is used to quickly separate the broken ends.

quick-break switch—A switch that minimizes arcing by breaking a circuit rapidly, independent of the rate at which the switch handle is moved.

quick disconnect—A type of connector designed to facilitate rapid locking and unlocking of two contacts or connector halves.

quick-make—A characteristic of a switch or circuit breaker, whereby it has a fast contact-closing speed that is independent of the operator.

quick-make switch—A switch or circuit breaker which has a high contact-closing speed independent of the operator.

quick-stop control—On some tape recorders, and on all recorders used for dictation, a control with which the operator can stop the tape without taking the machine out of the play or record position.

quiescence—The state of a transistor amplifier with no signal applied.

quiescent—At rest—specifically, the condition of a circuit when no input signal is being applied to it.

quiescent-carrier modulation—A modulation system in which the carrier is suppressed during intervals when there is no modulation.

quiescent-carrier telephony—Telephony in which the carrier is suppressed whenever no modulating signals are to be transmitted.

quiescent current—*See* Idling Current.

quiescent period—The resting period—e.g., the period between pulses in pulse transmissions.

quiescent point—On the characteristic curve of an amplifier, the point representing the conditions existing when there is no input signal. (*Also see* Operating Point.)

quiescent push-pull—In a radio receiver, a push-pull output stage in which practically no current flows when no signal is being received. Thus, there is no noise while the radio is being tuned between stations.

quiescent state—The time during which a tube or other circuit element is not performing its active function in the circuit.

quiescent value—The voltage or current value of a vacuum-tube electrode when no signals are present.

quiet automatic volume control—*See* Delayed Automatic Volume Control.

quiet avc—*See* Delayed Automatic Volume Control.

quiet battery—Also called talking battery. A source of energy of special design, or with added filters, which is sufficiently quiet and free from interference that it may be used for speech transmission.

quieting—The decrease in noise voltage at the output of an f-m receiver in the presence of an unmodulated carrier.

quieting sensitivity—In an f-m receiver, the minimum input signal that will give a specified output signal-to-noise ratio.

quiet tuning—In a radio receiver, a form of tuning in which the output is silenced except when the receiver is tuned to the precise frequency of the incoming carrier wave.

R

R—Symbol for resistor, resistance, or reluctance.

r—Abbreviation for roentgen.

RACES—Acronym for Radio Amateur Civil Emergency Service.

raceway—Any channel designed and used solely for holding wires, cables, or bus bars.

rack—1. A bar with teeth, which engage a pinion, worm, etc., to provide straight-line motion. 2. A vertical frame on which equipment, relays, etc., are mounted.

rack and panel connector—A connector that is attached to a panel or side of equipment so that when these members are brought together, the connector is engaged.

rack and pinion—A toothed bar (rack) which engages a gear (pinion) to convert the back-and-forth motion of the rack into rotary motion, or the rotary motion of the pinion into back-and-forth motion.

racon—*See* Radar Beacon.

rad—The unit of absorbed radiation dose equivalent to an energy deposition of 100 ergs/gm—i.e., a measure of the energy which the ionizing radiation imparts to matter per unit mass of irradiated material.

radar—Acronym for RAdio Detecting And Ranging. 1. A system that measures distance (and usually the direction) to an object by determining the amount of time required by electromagnetic energy to travel to and return from an object. 2. Also called primary radar when the signals are returned by re-flection. 3. Also called secondary radar when the incident signal triggers a responder beacon and causes it to transmit a second signal.

radar altitude—Also called radio altitude. Absolute altitude measured by a radar altimeter.

radar and television aid to navigation—A device which converts a circular scan radar presentation to a horizontal scanned television presentation. It provides a continuous bright display with target trails for course and speed indications of moving targets.

REFLECTOR

HORN OUTPUT

WAVE GUIDE

Radar antenna.

radar antenna—Any of the many types of antennas used in radar.

radar attenuation—Ratio of the transmitted power to the reflected (received) power—

397

specifically, the ratio of the power which the transmitter delivers to the transmission line connected to the transmitting antenna, to the power reflected from the target and delivered to the transmission line connected to the receiving antenna.

radar beacon—Also called a racon. An automatic transmitter-receiver which receives signals from a radar transmitter, and retransmits coded signals that enable the radar operator to determine his position.

radar beam—The space where a target can be effectively detected and/or tracked in front of a radar. Its boundary is defined as the loci of points measured radially from the beam center at which the power has decreased to one-half.

radar calibration—Taking measurements on various parts of electronic equipment (e.g., radar, iff, communications) to determine its performance level.

radar camouflage—The use of coverings or surfaces on an object to considerably reduce the reflected radio energy and thus "conceal" the object from the radar beam.

radar clutter—The image produced on a radar indicator screen by sea or ground return. If not of particular interest, it tends to obscure the target indication.

radar-confusion reflectors—Metallic devices (e.g., chaff, corner reflectors) employed to return false signals in order to confuse enemy radar receivers. The use of radar-confusion reflectors is termed reflective jamming.

radar control area—The designated space within which aircraft approach, holding, stacking, and similar operations are performed under guidance of a surveillance-radar system.

radar countermeasures—Interception, jamming, deception, and evasion of enemy radar signals to obtain information about the enemy from his radar and to prevent him from obtaining accurate, usable information from his radar.

radar-coverage indicator—A device showing how far a radar station should track a given aircraft. It also provides a reference (detection) range for quality control. Aircraft size and altitude, screening angle, site elevation, type of radar, antenna radiation pattern, and antenna tilt are all taken into account.

radar cross section—That portion of the back-scattering cross section of a target associated with a specified polarization component of the scattered wave.

radar deception—Radiation or reradiation of radar signals in order to confuse or mislead an enemy operator when he interprets the data shown on his scope.

radar distribution switchboard—A switching panel for connecting video, trigger, and bearing from any 1 or 5 system, to any or all of 20 repeaters. Also contains order lights, bearing cutouts, alarms, test equipment, etc.

radar echo—1. The radio-frequency energy

received after it has been reflected from an object. 2. The deflection or change of intensity which a radar echo produces in the display of a cathode-ray tube.

radar equation—A mathematical expression relating the transmitted and received powers and antenna gains of a primary-radar system to the echo area and distance of the target.

radar fence—A network of radar warning stations which maintain constant watch against surprise attack (e.g., the DEW line).

radar homing—Missile guidance, the intelligence for which is provided by a radar aboard the missile.

radar horizon—The most distant point (from the radar antenna along a given azimuth) on the earth's surface illuminated by the radar on purely geometric conditions. The conditions are that the illumination occurs along a straight-line path, where the path is taken over an effective earth's radius of 4/3 its true radius and where the illuminating power of the radar is considered unlimited.

radar illumination—The subjection of an object (target) to electromagnetic radiation from a radar.

radar indicator—A cathode-ray tube with its associated equipment that provides a visual indication of the echo signals picked up by the radar set.

radar marker—A fixed facility which continuously emits a radar signal so that a bearing indication appears on a radar display.

radar nautical mile—The time interval of approximately 12.367 microseconds required for radio-frequency energy to travel one nautical mile and return, a total of two nautical miles.

radar paint—A radar-energy–absorbent material that can be applied to an object to reduce the possibility of detection.

radar-performance figure—Ratio of the pulse power of the radar transmitter, to the power of the minimum signal detectable by the receiver.

radar picket—Early-warning aircraft which flies at a distance from a ship or other force being protected, to increase the radar detection range.

radar pulse modulator—A modulator that turns an r-f energy source off and on in a precise, known manner. In essence, the modulator supplies the energy which causes an r-f source to oscillate or amplify, thus creating a burst or "pulse" or r-f energy.

radar range—The maximum range at which a radar can ordinarily detect objects.

radar receiver—The receiver which amplifies the returned radar signal and demodulates the r-f carrier before further amplifying the desired signal and delivering it—in a form suitable for presentation—to the indicator. Unlike a radio receiver, it is more sensitive, has a lower noise level, and is designed to pass a pulse signal.

radar-reflection interval — The length of time required for a radar pulse to reach a target and return.

radar relay—Equipment for relaying radar video and appropriate synchronizing signals to a remote location.

radar resolution—The ability of a radar to distinguish between the desired target and its surroundings.

radarscope—A cathode-ray tube serving as an oscilloscope, the face of which is the radar viewing screen.

radar selector switch—A manual or motor-driven switch which transfers a plan-position-indicator repeater from one system to another, switching video, trigger, and bearing data.

radar shadow—An area shielded from radar illumination by an intervening reflecting or absorbing medium. This region appears as an area that is void of targets on a radar display.

radar target—Any reflecting object of particular interest in the path of the radar beam (usually, but not necessarily, the object being tracked).

radar trace—The pattern produced on the screen of the cathode-ray tube in a radar unit.

radar transmitter—The transmitter portion of a radar system. The unit of the radar system in which the r-f power is generated and keyed.

radiac—Acronym for RAdioactive Detection, Identification, And Computation, a descriptive term referring to the detection, identification and measurement of nuclear radiation.

radiac instrument—*See* Radiac Set.

radiac meter—*See* Radiac Set.

radiac set—Also called radiac meter or radiac instrument. Equipment for detecting, identifying, and measuring the intensity of nuclear radiations.

radiac test equipment—Equipment for testing radiac sets.

radial—Pertaining to or placed like a radius (i.e., extending or moving outward from a central point, like the spokes of a wagon wheel).

radial-beam tube—A vacuum tube producing a flat, radial electron beam which can be rotated about the axis of the tube by an external magnetic field.

radial component—A component that acts along (parallel to) a radius—as contrasted to a tangential component, which acts at right angles (perpendicular) to a radius.

radial component of the electric field—The component of an electric field in the direction of the slant-range vector or the radius vector at which an antenna pattern is measured. The radial component of the electric field is relatively small in the far field and is normally neglected.

radial field—A field of force that is directed toward or away from a point in space.

radial field cathode-ray tube—A crt in which a fine-grained, curved, high-transmission metallic mesh is placed on the exit side of the deflection area. The mesh establishes a ground plane for the post-accelerating field so that the resulting equipotential surfaces are truly spherical, creating a radial electrostatic field.

radial grating—A conformal grating consisting of wires arranged radially in a circular frame, like the spokes of a wagon wheel. The radial grating is placed inside a circular waveguide to obstruct E waves of zero order, but not the corresponding H waves.

radial lead—A lead extending out the side of a component, rather than from the end. (The latter is called an axial lead.) Some resistors have radial leads.

radial transmission line—A pair of parallel conducting planes used for propagating uniform cylindrical waves whose axes are normal to the planes.

radian—In a circle, the angle included within an arc equal to the radius of the circle. Numerically it is equal to $57°$, $17'$, $44.8''$. A complete circle contains 2π radians. One radian equals 57.3 degrees, and 1 degree equals 0.01745 radian.

radiance—The apparent radiation of a surface. It is the same as luminance except radiance applies to all kinds of radiation instead of only light flux.

radian frequency—*See* Angular Velocity.

radian length—The distance, in a sinusoidal wave, between phases differing by an angle of one radian. It is equal to the wavelength divided by 2π.

radian per second—A unit of angular velocity.

radiant energy—Energy transmitted in the form of electromagnetic radiation (e.g., radio, heat, or light waves). It is measured in units of energy such as kilowatt-hours, ergs, joules, or calories.

radiant-energy detecting device—A device employing radiant energy to detect flaws in the surface and/or volume of solids.

radiant flux—Time rate of flow of radiant energy, expressed in watts or in ergs per second.

radiant heat—Infrared radiation from a body not hot enough to emit visible radiation.

radiant heater—An electric heating appliance with an exposed incandescent heating element.

radiant intensity — The energy emitted within a certain length of time, per unit solid angle about the direction considered.

radiant power—The rate of transfer of radiant energy.

radiant sensitivity—The output current of a phototube or camera tube divided by the incident radiant flux of a given wavelength at constant electrode voltages. The term "output current" as here used does not include the dark current.

radiant temperature—Energy traveling in the form of electromagnetic waves.

radiant transmittance—The ratio of transmitted radiant power to incident radiant power.

radiate—To emit rays from a center source—e.g., electromagnetic waves emanating from an antenna.

radiated—Energy transfer by propagation of electromagnetic fields.

radiated interference—Interference which is transmitted through the atmosphere according to the laws of electromagnetic wave propagation. (The term "radiates interference" is generally considered to include the transfer of interfering energy by inductive or capacitive coupling.)

radiated power—The total energy, in the form of Hertzian waves, radiated from an antenna.

radiating curtain—An array of dipoles in a vertical plane, positioned to reinforce each other. Usually placed one-quarter wavelength ahead of a reflecting curtain of corresponding half-wave reflecting antennas.

radiating element—Also called radiator. A basic subdivision of an antenna. It, by itself, is capable of radiating or receiving radio-frequency energy.

radiating guide—A waveguide designed to radiate energy into free space. The waves may emerge through slots or gaps in the guide, or through horns inserted into its wall.

radiation — The propagation of energy through space or through a material. It may be in the form of electromagnetic waves or corpuscular emissions. The former is usually classified according to frequency—e.g., Hertzian, infrared, (visible) light, ultraviolet, X-rays, gamma rays, etc. Corpuscular emissions are classified as alpha, beta, or cosmic.

radiation belt—*See* Van Allen Belt.

radiation counter—A device for counting radiation particles (alpha, beta, gamma neutrons, etc.) or photons of energy (X rays, etc.) usually using either scintillation or ionization resulting from the presence of the particle or photon to be measured.

radiation counter tube—*See* Counter Tube.

radiation-detector tube—A tube in which current passes between its electrodes whenever the tube is exposed to penetrating radiation. The amount of this current corresponds to the intensity of radiation.

radiation efficiency—In an antenna, the ratio of the radiated power to the total power supplied to the antenna at a given frequency.

radiation field — The electromagnetic field that breaks away from a transmitting antenna and radiates outward into space as electromagnetic waves.

radiation filter—A transparent body which transmits only selected wavelengths.

radiation intensity—In a given direction, the power radiated from an antenna per unit solid angle in that direction.

radiation lobe—*See* Lobe.

radiation loss—In a transmission system, the portion of the transmission loss due to radiation of the radio-frequency power.

radiation pattern—*See* Directional Pattern.

radiation potential—The voltage required to excite an atom or molecule and cause the emission of one of its characteristic radiation frequencies.

radiation pyrometer—Also called a radiation thermometer. A pyrometer which uses the radiant power from the object or source whose temperature is being measured. Within wide- or narrow-wavelength bands filling a definite solid angle, the radiant power impinges on a suitable detector—usually a thermocouple, thermopile, or a bolometer responsive to the heating effect of the radiant power, or a photosensitive device connected to a sensitive electric instrument.

radiation report—A formal report of radiation measurements made by an engineer skilled in interference control techniques. Usually required by the FCC prior to certification of industrial heating equipment.

radiation resistance—1. The power radiated by an antenna, divided by the square of the effective antenna current referred to a specified point. 2. The resistance which, if inserted in place of the antenna, would consume the same amount of power radiated by the antenna. 3. The characteristic of a material that enables it to retain useful properties during or after exposure to nuclear radiation.

radiation sickness—An illness resulting from exposure to radiation.

radiation survey meter—An instrument that measures instantaneous radiation.

Radiation pyrometer.

radiation temperature—The temperature to which an ideal black body must be heated so it will have the same emissive power as a given source of thermal radiation.

radiation thermometer—*See* Radiation Pyrometer.

radiative equilibrium — The constant-temperature condition that exists in a material when the radiant energy absorbed and emitted are equal.

radiator—Any device which emits radiation. (*Also see* Radiating Element.)

radio—1. Communication by electromagnetic waves transmitted through space. 2. A general term, principally an adjective, applied to the use of electromagnetic waves between 10 kHz and 3,000 GHz.

radioacoustic position finding—A method of determining distance through water. This is done by closing a circuit at the same instant a charge is exploded under water. The distance to the observing station can then be calculated from the difference in arrival times between the radio signal and the sound of the explosion.

radioacoustics—A study of the production, transmission, and reproduction of sounds carried from one place to another by radio-telephony.

radioactive — Pertaining to or exhibiting radioactivity.

radioactive isotope—*See* Radioisotope.

radioactive series—A succession of radioactive elements, each derived from the disintegration of the preceding element in the series. The final element, known as the end product, is not radioactive.

radioactivity—A property exhibited by certain elements, the atomic nuclei of which spontaneously disintegrate and gradually transmute the original element into stable isotopes of that element or into another element with different chemical properties. The process is accompanied by the emission of alpha particles, beta particles, gamma rays, positrons, or similar radiations.

radio altitude—*See* Radar Altitude.

radio approach aids—Equipment making use of radio to determine the position of an aircraft with considerable accuracy from the time it is in the vicinity of an airfield or carrier until it reaches a position from which a landing can be carried out.

radioastronomy—The branch of astronomy where the radio waves emitted by certain celestial bodies are used for obtaining data about them.

radio attenuation—For one-way propagation, the ratio of the power delivered by the transmitter to the transmission line connecting it with the transmitting antenna, to the power delivered to the receiver by the transmission line connecting it with the receiving antenna.

radio beacon—Also called a radiophone or, in air operations, an aerophare. A radio transmitter, usually nondirectional, which emits identifiable signals for direction finding.

radio-beacon station—In the radionavigation service, a station the emissions of which are intended to enable a mobile station to determine its bearing or direction in relation to the radio-beacon station.

radio beam—A radio wave in which most of the energy is confined within a relatively small angle and in at least one plane.

radio bearing—The angle between the apparent direction of a source of electromagnetic waves, and a reference direction determined at a radio direction-finding station. In a true radio bearing, this reference direction is true north. Likewise, in a magnetic radio bearing, it is magnetic north.

radio broadcast—A program of music, voice, and/or other sounds broadcast from a radio transmitter for reception by the general public.

radio broadcasting—*See* Radio Broadcast.

radio channel—A band of frequencies wide enough to be used for radiocommunication. The width of a channel depends on the type of transmission and on the tolerance for the frequency of emission.

radio circuit—A means for carrying out one radiocommunication at a time in either direction between two points.

radiocommunication—An over-all term for transmission by radio of writing, signs, signals, pictures, and sounds of all kinds.

radiocommunication circuit—A radio system for carrying out one communication at a time in either direction between two points.

radiocommunication guard—A communication station designated to listen for and record transmission and to handle traffic on a designated frequency for a certain unit or units.

radio compass—*See* Direction Finder.

radio control—Remote control of apparatus by radio waves (e.g., model airplanes, boats).

radio deception — Sending false dispatches, using deceptive headings or enemy call signs, etc., by radio to deceive the enemy.

radio detection—Also called radio warning. Determining the presence of an object by radiolocation, but not its precise position.

radio detection and ranging—1. Any of certain methods or systems of using beamed and reflected electromagnetic energy for detecting and locating objects; for measuring distance, velocity, or altitude; or for other purposes such as navigating, homing, bombing, missile tracking, mapping, etc. 2. In Federal Communications Commission regulations, a radiodetermination system based on the comparison of reference signals with radio signals reflected or retransmitted from the position to be determined.

radio direction finder—A radio receiver which pinpoints the line of travel of the received waves.

radio direction finding — Radiolocation in

401

which only the direction, not the precise location, of a source of radio emission is determined by means of a directive receiving antenna.

radio direction-finding station — A radiolocation station that determines only the direction of other stations, not their location, by monitoring their transmission.

radio doppler—A device for determining the radial component of the relative velocity of an object by observing the frequency change due to such velocity.

radioelectrocardiograph—A transmitter for broadcasting electrocardiograph signals from the subject to a remote receiver. It makes an ecg practical while the subject is exercising or during natural work or home activities.

radio engineering—The branch of engineering concerned with the generation, transmission, and reception of radio (and now, television) waves, and with the design, manufacture, and testing of associated equipment.

radio fadeout — Also called the Dellinger effect. The partial or complete absorption of substantially all radio waves normally reflected by the ionospheric layers in or above the E-region.

radio field intensity—Also called radio field strength. The maximum (unless otherwise stated) electric or magnetic field intensity at a given location associated with the passage of radio waves. It is commonly expressed as the electric field intensity in microvolts, millivolts, or volts per meter. For a sinusoidal wave, its root-mean-square value is commonly stated instead.

radio field strength—*See* Radio Field Intensity.

radio field-to-noise ratio—The ratio of the radio field intensity of the desired wave, to the noise field intensity at a given location.

radio fix—1. A method by which the position source of radio signals can be determined. Two or more radio direction finders monitor the transmissions and obtain cross bearings. The position can then be pinpointed by triangulation. 2. The method by which a ship, aircraft, etc., equipped with direction finding equipment can determine its own position. This it does by obtaining radio bearings from two or more transmitting stations of known location. The position can then be pinpointed by triangulation as in (1) above.

radio-fixing aids—Equipment making use of radio to assist a user in determining his geographical position.

radio frequency—Abbreviated r-f. Any frequency at which coherent electromagnetic radiation of energy is possible.

radio-frequency alternator—A rotating generator that produces radio-frequency power.

radio-frequency amplification — Amplification of a signal by a receiver before detection, or by a transmitter before radiation.

radio-frequency choke — An inductor used to impede the flow of radio-frequency currents. Its core is generally air or pulverized iron.

radio-frequency component—In a signal or wave, the portion consisting of the r-f alternations only—not its audio rate of change in amplitude or frequency.

radio-frequency converter—A power source for producing electrical power at frequencies of 10 kHz and above.

radio-frequency generator — In industrial and dielectric heaters, a power source comprising an electron-tube oscillator, an amplifier (if used), a power supply, and associated control equipment.

radio-frequency heating — The process of heating a substance by subjecting it to a high-frequency energy field. *Also see* Dielectric Heating.

radio-frequency interference—Any electrical signal capable of being propagated into and interfering with the proper operation of electrical or electronic equipment. The frequency range of such interference may be taken to include the entire electromagnetic spectrum.

radio-frequency oscillator—Abbreviated r-f oscillator. An oscillator that generates alternating current at radio frequencies.

radio-frequency pulse — A radio-frequency carrier which is amplitude-modulated by a pulse. Between pulses, the modulated carrier has zero amplitude. (The coherence of the carrier with itself is not implied.)

radio-frequency resistance—*See* Skin Effect.

radio-frequency signal generator—*See* Service Oscillator.

radio-frequency suppressor—A device that absorbs radiated energy which might interfere with radio reception.

radio-frequency transformer—Abbreviated r-f transformer. A transformer used with radio-frequency currents.

radio-frequency welding—Also called high-frequency welding. A method of welding thermoplastics using a radio-frequency field to apply the necessary heat.

radiogoniometer—In a radio direction finder, the part that determines the phase difference between the two received signals. The Bellini-Tose system has two loop antennas, both at right angles to each other and connected to two field coils in the radiogoniometer. Bearings are obtained by rotating a search coil inductively coupled to the field coils.

radiogram—A message sent via radio telegraphy.

radiograph—*See* Radiophoto.

radiography—Any nondestructive method of internal examination in which metal objects are exposed to a beam of X-ray or gamma radiation. Differences in thickness, density, or absorption caused by internal defects or inclusions are apparent in the shadow image, either on a fluorescent screen or on photographic film placed behind the object.

radio guard—A ship, aircraft, or radio station designated to listen for and record transmissions, and to handle traffic on a designated frequency for a certain unit or units.

radio guidance system—A guidance system using radio signals to direct aircraft in flight.

radio horizon—The boundary line beyond which direct rays of the radio waves cannot be propagated over the earth's surface. This distance is not a constant; rather, it is affected by atmospheric refraction of the waves.

radio inertial-guidance system—A command type of guidance system consisting essentially of: a. A radar tracking unit, comprising radar equipment on the ground, one or more transponders in the missile, and necessary communications links to the guidance station. b. A computer that accepts missile position and velocity information from the tracking system and furnishes to the command link appropriate signals to steer the missile. c. The command link, which consists of a transmitter on the ground and an antenna and receiver on the missile; actually the command link is built into the tracking unit. d. An inertial system for partial guidance in case of radio guidance failure.

radio intelligence—Interception and interpretation of enemy radio transmissions.

radio interference—Undesired conducted or radiated electrical disturbances, including transients, which can interfere with the operation of electrical or electronic equipment. These disturbances fall between 14 kHz and 10 GHz.

radioisotope—Also called a radioactive isotope. It is the isotope produced when an element is placed into a nuclear reactor and bombarded with neutrons. Radioisotopes are used as tracers in many areas of science and industry. Like all isotopes, they decay spontaneously with the emission of their radiation, at a definite rate measured by their half-lives.

radio jamming—Blocking communications by sending overpowering interference signals.

radio knife—A form of surgical knife that uses a high-frequency electric arc at its tip to cut tissue and, at the same time, also sterilizes the edges of the wound.

radio landing beam—A distribution of vertical, directional radio waves used for guiding aircraft into a landing.

radiolocation—Use of the constant-velocity or rectilinear-propagation characteristics of radio waves to detect an object or to determine its direction, position, or motion.

radiolocation service — A radio service in which radiolocation is used.

radiolocation station—A radio station in the radiolocation service.

radio log—A record of all messages sent and received, transmitter tests made, and other important information pertaining to the operation of a particular station.

radiology—The branch of physics concerned with X-rays, gamma rays, and other penetrating radiations.

radioluminescence—Luminescence produced by radiant energy (e.g., by X-rays, radioactive emissions, alpha particles, or electrons).

radiomagnetic indicator—Abbreviated RMI. A navigational instrument used by land vehicles. It presents a display combining the heading and the relative and magnetic bearings of the vehicle with the relative bearing of a radio station whose location is known.

radio marker beacon—In the aeronautical radionavigation service, a land station which provides a signal to designate a small area above the station.

radiometallography—X-ray examination of the crystalline structure and other characteristics of metals and alloys.

radiometeorograph—A meteorograph which, when carried into the stratosphere by an unmanned gas-filled rubber balloon, automatically reports atmospheric conditions by radio as it ascends into the stratosphere. The ultrahigh-frequency signals are transmitted so that they can be recorded and interpreted in terms of pressure, temperature, and humidity. *Also see* Radiosonde.

radiometer—An instrument for measuring the intensity of thermal (especially infrared) radiation.

radiomicrometer—*See* Microradiometer.

radionavigation—Navigational use of radiolocation for determining position or direction, or for providing a warning of obstructions.

radionavigation land station—A fixed station in the radionavigation service—i.e., one not intended for mobile operation.

radionavigation mobile station—A radionavigation station operated from a vehicle.

radionavigation service — A radiolocation service used for radionavigation.

radio net—A system of radio stations.

radio-noise field intensity—A measure of the field intensity of interfering electromagnetic waves at some point (e.g., a radio receiving station). In practice, the field intensity itself is not measured, but some proportionate quantity.

radiopaque—Not penetrable by X-rays or other radiation. (The opposite of radioparent.)

radioparent—Penetrable by X-rays or other radiation. (The opposite of radiopaque.)

radiophone—*See* Radiotelephone and Radio Beacon.

radiophoto — Also called radiophotography, radiophotograph, radiophotogram, or facsimile. The transmission of photographs and other illustrations by radio.

radiophotogram—*See* Radiophoto.

radiophotoluminescence — The property whereby the previous exposure of certain

Simple radiometer.

materials to nuclear radiation enables them to give off visible light when irradiated with ultraviolet light.

radio prospecting—The use of radio equipment to locate mineral or oil deposits.

radio proximity fuse—A radio device which detonates a missile by electromagnetic interaction within a predetermined distance from the target.

radio pulse—An intense, split-second burst of electromagnetic energy.

radio range—A radionavigational facility, the emissions of which provide radial lines of position by having special characteristics that are recognizable as bearing information and useful in lateral guidance of aircraft.

radio range beacon—A radionavigation land station in the aeronautical radionavigation service providing radio equisignal zones.

radio range finding—Determination of range by means of radio waves.

radio range leg—The space within which an aircraft will receive an on-course signal from a radio-range station.

radio-range monitor—An instrument that automatically monitors the signal from a radio-range beacon and warns attending personnel when the transmitter deviates from its specified current bearings. It also transmits a distinctive warning to approaching planes whenever trouble exists at the beacon.

radio-range station—A land station that operates in the aeronautical radionavigation service and provides radial equisignal zones.

radio receiver—A device for converting radio waves into signals perceptible to humans.

radio reception—Reception of radioed messages, programs, or other intelligence.

radio relay—*See* Radio Relay System.

radio-relay system—Also called radio relay. A radio transmission system in which the signals are received and retransmitted from point to point by intermediate radio stations.

radio set—A radio transmitter, radio receiver, or a combination of the two.

radio shielding—A metallic covering over all electric wiring and ignition apparatus which is grounded at frequent intervals for the purpose of eliminating electric interference with radiocommunications.

radio signal—A signal that is transmitted by radio.

radio silence—A period during which all or certain radio equipment capable of radiation is kept inoperative.

radiosonde—A balloonborne instrument for the simultaneous measurement and trans-

Radiosonde system.

mission of meteorological data. The instrument consists of transducers for the measurement of pressure, temperature, and humidity; a modulator for the conversion of the output of the transducers to a quantity which controls a property of the radio-frequency signal; a selector switch which determines the sequence in which the parameters are to be transmitted; and a transmitter which generates the radio-frequency carrier.

radiosonde recorder—An instrument which is located at the surface observing station and is used to record the data presented by a radiosonde aloft. The mechanism of the recorder depends upon the type of radiosonde system used.

radiosonde transmitter—The component of the radiosonde which includes the modulating blocking oscillator and the radio-frequency carrier oscillator.

radiosonobuoy—*See* Sonobuoy.

radio spectrum—The range of frequencies of electromagnetic radiation usable for radiocommunication. The radio spectrum may range from about 10 kHz to over 300 GHz. Corresponding wavelengths are 30 km to 1 mm.

radio station—An assemblage of equipment for radio transmission, reception, or both.

radio-station interference — Interference caused by reception of radio waves from other than the desired station.

radiotelegraph transmitter—A radio transmitter capable of handling code signals.

radiotelegraphy — Radiocommunication by means of the International Morse Code or some other, similarly coded signal.

radiotelephone—Also called radiophone. The complete radio transmitter, receiver, and associated equipment required at one station for radiotelephony.

radiotelephone distress signal—The spoken word MAYDAY (phonetic spelling of the French expression *m' aidez*, or "help me"). It corresponds to S O S in radiotelegraphy and is used by aircraft, ships, etc., needing help.

radiotelephone transmitter—A radio transmitter capable of handling audio-frequency modulation (e.g., voice and music).

radiotelephony—Two-way transmission and reception of sounds by radio.

radio telescope—A very sensitive radio receiver that is used in conjunction with a large and highly directional antenna to receive signals from radio stars.

radiotherapy—The treatment of diseases by the application of rays from radioactive substances (e.g., X-rays).

radiothermics—The application of heat generated by radio waves (e.g., in diathermy or electronic heating).

radio transmission—Transmission of signals by electromagnetic waves other than light or heat waves.

radio transmitter—A device capable of producing radio-frequency power and used for radio transmission.

radiotransparent—Permitting the passage of X-rays or similar radiation.

radio tube—A general term for any type of electron tube used in electronic equipment.

radiovision—An early name for television.

radio warning—*See* Radio Detection.

radio watch—Also called watch. The vigil maintained by an operator when on duty in the radio room of a vessel and listening for signals—especially on the international distress frequencies.

radio wave—Also called a Hertzian wave, or a wave. An electromagnetic wave produced by rapid reversals of current in a conductor. Such a wave travels through space at approximately the speed of light.

radio wavefront distortion—A change in the direction or advance of a radio wave.

radio-wave propagation—The transfer of energy by electromagnetic radiation at frequencies below approximately 3×10^{12} hertz.

radix—Also called the base. The total number of distinct marks or symbols used in a numbering system. For example, since the decimal numbering system uses ten symbols (0, 1, 2, 3, 4, 5, 6, 7, 8, 9), the radix is 10. In the binary numbering system the radix is 2, because there are only two marks or symbols (0, 1).

radix point—Also called base point, and binary point, decimal point, etc., depending on the numbering system. The index which separates the integral and fractional digits of the numbering system in which the quantity is represented.

radome—Also called a radar dome. The housing which protects a radar antenna from the elements, but does not block radio frequencies.

radux—A long-distance, low-frequency navigational system which provides hyperbolic lines of position. It is of the continuous-wave, phase-comparison type.

railing—Radar pulse jamming at high recurrence rates (50 to 150 kHz). On a radar indicator it results in an image resembling fence railing.

railings—The pattern produced on an A-scope by c-w modulated with a high-frequency signal. It appears as a series of vertical lines resembling target echoes along the baseline.

rainbow—The technique which applies pulse-to-pulse frequency changing to identifying and discriminating against decoys and chaff.

rainbow generator—A signal generator with which the entire color spectrum can be produced on the screen of a color television receiver. The colors merge together as in a rainbow. (*Also see* Keyed Rainbow Generator.)

ramark—Also called a radar marker. A fixed radar transmitter which emits a continuous signal that is used as a bearing indication on a radar display.

ramp input—A change, in an input signal, which varies at a constant rate.

Ramsauer effect—The absorption of slow-moving electrons by intervening matter.

random—Irregular; having no set pattern.

random access—Access to a computer storage under conditions whereby there is no rule for predetermining the position from where the next item of information is to be obtained.

random-access memory—A memory system for which the access time is independent of the location being addressed.

random-access programming — Programming a problem for a computer without regard to the access time to the information in the registers called for in the program.

random error—The inherent imprecision of a given process of measurement; the unpredictable component of repeated independent measurements on the same object under sensible uniform conditions, usually of an approximately normal (Gaussian) frequency distribution, other than systematic or erratic errors and mistakes, sometimes called short-period errors.

random experiment — An experiment that can be repeated a large number of times but may yield different results each time, even when performed under similar circumstances.

random failure—Also called chance failure. Any chance failure the occurrence of which at a given time is unpredictable.

random-function generator—A device which generates nonrepetitive signals which are distributed over a broad frequency range.

random-impulse generator—A generator of electrical impulses which occur at random rather than at specific intervals.

random interlace — A condition in which there is no fixed relationship between adjacent scanning lines and successive fields.

randomness — A condition of equal chance for the occurrence of any of the possible outcomes.

random noise—Also called fluctuation noise. Large numbers of random, overlapping transient disturbances. (*Also see* Broad-Band Electrical Noise.)

random-noise generator—A generator of a succession of random signals which are distributed over a wide frequency spectrum.

random number—1. A set of digits such that each successive digit is equally likely to be any of n digits to the base n of the number. 2. A number composed of digits selected from an orderless sequence of digits.

random-number generator — A special machine routine or hardware that produces a random number or series of random numbers in accordance with specified limitations.

random pard—Pertains to that portion of the total pard in an electronic power supply which is not periodic. This phenomenon is frequently referred to as noise.

random pulsing—Varying the repetition rate

of pulses by noise modulation or continuous frequency change.

random sample — A sample in which every item in the lot is equally likely to be selected in the sample.

random signals—Waveforms having at least one parameter (usually amplitude) that is a random function of time (e.g., thermal noise or shot noise).

random variable—1. Also called variate. The result of a random experiment. 2. A discrete or continuous variable which may assume any one of a number of values, each having the same probability of occurrence. 3. Also called stochastic variable. Any signal the amplitude or phase of which cannot be predicted by a study of previous values of the signal.

random velocity—The instantaneous velocity of a particle without regard to direction. It may be characterized by its distribution function or by its average, root-mean-square, or most probable value.

random vibration—A vibration generally composed of a broad, continuous spectrum of frequencies, the instantaneous magnitude of which cannot be specified to any given moment of time. (If random vibration has instantaneous magnitudes distributed according to the Gaussian distribution, it is called Gaussian random vibration.) *Also see* White Noise.

random winding—A coil winding in which the turns and layers are not regularly positioned or spaced but are positioned haphazardly.

range—1. The maximum useful distance of a radar or radio transmitter. 2. The difference between the maximum and the minimum value of a variable.

range-amplitude display—A radar display in which a time base provides the range scale from which echoes appear as deflections normal to the base.

range calibration—Adjustment of radar-range indications by use of known range targets or delayed signals so that, when on target, the radar set will indicate the correct range.

range coding—A method of coding a beacon response so that the response appears as a series of pulses on a radarscope. The coding provides identification.

range gate—A gate voltage used to select radar echoes from a very short-range interval.

range-height indicator—A radar display on which an echo appears as a bright spot on a rectangular field. The slant range is indicated along the X-axis, and the height above the horizontal plane (on a magnified scale) along the Y-axis. A cursor shows the height above the earth.

range mark—*See* Distance Mark.

range marker—A variable or movable discontinuity in the range time base of a radar display (in the case of a ppi, a ring). It is used for measuring the range of an echo or calibrating the range scale.

range of an instrument—*See* Total Range of an Instrument.

range ring—An accurate, adjustable ranging mark on a plan-position indicator corresponding to a range step on a type-M indicator.

range step—The vertical displacement on an M-indicator sweep to measure range.

range unit—A radar-system component used for control and indication (usually counters) of range measurements.

range zero—Alignment of the start of a sweep trace with zero range.

ranging oscillator—An oscillator circuit containing an LC resonant combination in the cathode circuit, usually used in radar equipment to provide range marks.

rapid memory—In a computer, that selection of the whole memory from which information may be obtained in the shortest possible time.

rare gas—*See* Noble Gas.

raster—1. On the screen of a cathode-ray tube, a predetermined pattern of scanning lines which provide substantially uniform coverage of an area. 2. The illuminated area produced by the scanning lines on a television picture tube when no signal is being received.

raster burn—In camera tubes, a change in the characteristics of the area that has been scanned. As a result, a spurious signal corresponding to that area will be produced when a larger or tilted raster is scanned.

ratchet relay—A stepping relay actuated by an armature-driven ratchet.

rate action—Also called derivative action. Corrective action, the rate of which is determined by how fast the error being corrected is increasing.

rate effect—The anode-voltage transients that cause PNPN devices to switch into high conduction.

rated operational voltage — The voltage on which a specific application rating of a device is based.

rated output—The output power, voltage, current, etc., at which a machine, device, or apparatus is designed to operate under normal conditions.

rated power output—The normal radio-frequency, power-output capability (peak or average) of a transmitter under optimum adjustment and operation conditions.

rated thermal current—In a contactor, that current at which the permissible temperature rise is reached.

rated voltage—The voltage at which a device or component is designed to operate under normal conditions.

rate generator — A proportional element which converts angular speed into a constant-frequency output voltage. (*Also see* Angular Velocity.)

rate grown junction—A grown junction, in a semiconductor, produced by varying the rate of crystal growth periodically so that N-type impurities alternately predominate.

rate-grown transistor—Also called graded-junction transistor. A variation of the double-doped transistor, in which N- and P-type impurities are added to the melt.

rate gyro—A particular kind of gyroscope used for measuring angular rates. A system of three rate gyros, each oriented to one of three mutually perpendicular axes — roll, pitch, and yaw—can control a missile or aircraft by detecting angular rates and then generating proportional corrective signals.

rate limit—*See* Slewing Rate.

rate limiting—Nonlinear behavior in an amplifier due to its limited ability to produce large, rapid changes in output voltage (slewing), restricting it to rates of change of voltage lower than might be predicted by observing the small signal frequency response.

ratemeter—An instrument for measuring the rate at which counts are received, usually in counts per minute.

rate of decay—The rate at which the sound-pressure level (velocity level, or sound-energy density level) is decreasing at a given point

Rate gyro.

and at a given time. The practical unit is the decibel per second.

rate-of-rise relay—*See* Instantaneous Overcurrent Relay.

rate of transmission—*See* Speed Of Transmission.

rate receiver—A device for receiving a signal giving the rate of speed of a launched missile.

rate signal—A signal proportional to the time derivative of a specified variable.

rating—A value which establishes either a limiting capability or a limiting condition for an electron device. It is determined for specified values of environment and operation, and may be stated in any suitable terms. (Limiting conditions may be either maxima or minima.)

rating system—The set of principles upon which ratings are established and by which the interpretation of the ratings is determined.

ratio—The value obtained by dividing one number by another. This value indicates their relationship to each other.

ratio arms—Two adjacent arms of a Wheatstone bridge, both having an adjustable resistance and so arranged that they can be set to have any of several fixed ratios to each other.

ratio calibration—1. The calibration of a dimensionless quantity that represents the ratio of one of its values to another. 2. A method by which potentiometric transducers may be calibrated, in which the value of the measurand is expressed in terms of decimal fractions representing the ratio of output resistance to total resistance.

ratio detector—An f-m detector which inherently discriminates against amplitude modulation. A pair of diodes are connected in such a manner that the audio output is proportionate to the ratio of the f-m voltages applied to them.

ratio meter—An instrument which measures electrically the quotient of two quantities. It generally has no mechanical control means such as springs. Instead, it operates by the balancing of electromagnetic forces, which are a function of the position of the moving element.

ratio of transformation—The ratio of the secondary voltage of a transformer to the primary voltage under no-load conditions, or the corresponding ratio of currents in a current transformer.

ratio squelch—*See* Squelch Circuit.

ratio-type telemeter—Also called a position-type telemeter. A telemeter in which the relative phase position between, or magnitude relation of, two or more electrical quantities is the translating means.

rat race—A magic tee modification for the acceptance of higher power. A circular loop of coaxial line closed upon itself and having four branching connections. *Also see* Hybrid Ring.

rat race—*See* Hybrid Ring.

raw data—Information that has not been processed or reduced.

raw tape—Also called virgin tape or blank tape. A term sometimes used to describe tape that has not been recorded.

ray-control electrode—An electrode that controls the position of the electron beam on the screen of a cathode-ray tuning-indicator tube.

raydist—A system using c-w transmission to provide hyperbolic lines of position through r-f phase comparison techniques. The system is used for surveying or ship positioning in a two-dimensional array. The frequency band is 1.7 to 2.5 MHz. Similar to lorac in principle.

Rayleigh disc—A special acoustic radiometer used for the fundamental measurement of particle velocity.

Rayleigh distribution—Frequency distribution for an infinite number of quantities of the same magnitude, but of random phase relationships. Sky-wave field intensities follow the Rayleigh distribution for intervals of one minute or less.

Rayleigh distribution (fading)—A statistical distribution describing the magnitude of a phaser composed of the sum of many component phasers randomly distributed in amplitude and phase. Fading of signals caused by cancellation and reinforcement of contributions received over separate paths often exhibits a Rayleigh distribution.

Rayleigh line—In scattered radiation, a spectrum line which has the same frequency as the corresponding incident radiation.

Ratio detector.

Rayleigh reciprocity theorem—The reciprocal relationship for an antenna when transmitting or receiving. The effective heights and the radiation resistance and pattern are alike, whether the antenna is transmitting or receiving.

Rayleigh scattering—Scattering of radiation by minute particles suspended in air (e.g., by dust).

Rayleigh wave—A surface wave associated with the free boundary of a solid. The wave is of maximum intensity at the surface, but diminishes quite rapidly as it proceeds into the solid.

ray path—An imaginary line, perpendicular to the wavefront, which describes the path along which the energy associated with a point on a wavefront moves.

Raysistor—Raytheon trade name for a four-terminal optoelectronic component designed for applications in a variety of control functions, providing comparatively noise-free control of a-c or d-c signals over a wide dynamic range, without transients or contact chatter, and with a high insulation and electrical isolation between the signal and control circuit. It consists of a light source and a photoresistive element assembled in a light-tight case.

RC—Symbol for resistance-capacitance, resistance-coupled, or ray-control electrode.

RC amplifier—Abbreviation for resistance-capacitance coupled amplifier.

RC circuit—A time-determining network of resistors and capacitors in which the time constant is defined as resistance times capacitance.

RC constant—The time constant of a resistor-capacitor circuit, equal in seconds to the resistance value in ohms multiplied by the capacitance value in farads.

RC coupling — *See* Resistance-Capacitance Coupling.

RC differentiator—*See* Resistance-Capacitance differentiator.

RC filter—*See* Resistance-Capacitance filter.

RC network—A circuit containing resistances and capacitances arranged in a particular manner to perform a specific function.

RC oscillator.

RC oscillator—An oscillator in which the frequency is determined by resistance-capacitance elements. *Also see* Resistance-Capacitance Oscillator.

RCTL—Abbreviation for resistor capacitor transistor logic.

rd—Abbreviation for rutherford.

rdf—Abbreviation for radio direction finder (or finding).

reach-through voltage — That value of reverse voltage for which the depletion layer in a reverse-biased PN junction spreads sufficiently to make electrical contact with another junction.

reacquisition time—The time required for a tracking radar to relock on the target after the radar's automatic tracking mechanism has been disengaged.

reactance—Symbolized by X. Opposition to the flow of alternating current. Capacitive reactance (X_C) is the opposition offered by capacitors, and inductive reactance (X_L) is the opposition offered by a coil or other inductance. Both reactances are measured in ohms.

reactance drop—The voltage drop in quadrature with the current.

reactance factor—In a conductor, the ratio of its a-c resistance to its ohmic resistance.

reactance frequency multiplier — A frequency multiplier the essential element of which is a nonlinear reactor, where the nonlinearity of the reactor is used to generate harmonics of a sinusoidal source.

reactance grounded—Grounded through a reactance.

reactance modulator—A modulator, the reactance of which can be varied in accordance with the instantaneous amplitude of the modulating electromotive force applied. It is normally an electron-tube circuit that usually modulates the phase or frequency.

reactance relay—A form of impedance relay, the operation of which is a function of the reactance of the circuit.

Reactance-tube modulator.

reactance tube—A stage connected in parallel with the tank circuit of an oscillator to produce a signal that will either lead or lag the signal produced by the tank circuit. The reactance tube is said to be inductive if this signal leads the one produced by the tank circuit, and is capacitive if the signal lags the tank-circuit signal. The resultant oscillator signal will be a combination of the two, and its phase or frequency can be advanced or retarded as the bias on the reactance tube is increased or decreased.

reactivation—Application of an above-normal voltage to a thoriated filament for a few seconds, to bring a fresh layer of thorium atoms to the filament surface and thereby improve electron emission.

reactive—Pertaining to either inductive or capacitive reactance. A reactive circuit has a higher reactance than resistance.

reactive attenuator—An attenuator that dissipates almost no energy.

reactive balance—1. The capacitive or inductive balance which is often required to null the output of certain transducers or systems when the excitation and/or the output is given in terms of alternating current. 2. The condition of an a-c circuit where the phase angle between the voltage and current is zero. 3. The amount of corrective capacitance or inductance required to null the output of certain transducers or systems having a-c excitation.

reactive factor—The ratio of reactive power to total power in a circuit.

reactive-factor meter—An instrument for measuring reactive factor.

reactive load—A load having reactance (i.e., a capacitive or inductive load), as opposed to a resistive load.

reactive near-field region—That region of the field of an antenna immediately surrounding the antenna wherein the reactive field predominates.

reactive power—Also called wattless power. The reactive voltage times the current, or the voltage times the reactive current, in an a-c circuit. Unit measurement is the var.

reactive volt-ampere—*See* Volt-Ampere Reactive.

reactive volt-ampere-hour meter—*See* Var-hour Meter.

reactive volt-ampere meter—*See* Varmeter.

reactor—A physical device used primarily to introduce reactance or susceptance into a branch. (*Also see* Nuclear Reactor.)

reactor-start motor—A form of split-phase motor designed for starting with a reactor in series with the main winding. The reactor is short-circuited (or otherwise made ineffective) and the auxiliary circuit is opened as soon as the motor attains a predetermined speed.

read—In a computer: 1. To copy, usually from one form of storage to another. 2. To sense the meaning of an arrangement of hardware representing information. 3. To extract information.

readability—The ability to be understood—specifically, the understandability of signals sent by any means of telecommunications.

read-around—*See* Read-around Ratio.

read-around ratio—Also called read-around. In electrostatic storage tubes, the number of successive times information can be recorded as an electrostatic charge on a single spot in the array without producing the necessity

for restoring the charge on surrounding spots.

reader—In a computer a device which converts information in one form of storage to information in another form of storage.

read head—In a computer, a device that converts digital information stored on a magnetic tape or on a drum into electrical signals usable by computer arithmetic.

reading access time—In a computer, the time before a word may be used during the reading cycle.

reading rate—In a computer, the number of characters, cards, etc. that can be sensed by an input unit in a given time.

readout—The manner in which a computer displays the processed information—e.g., digital visual display, punched tape, punched cards, automatic typewriter, etc.

readout device—In a computer, a device, consisting usually of physical equipment, that records the computer output either as a curve or as a set of printed numbers or letters.

readout equipment—The electronic apparatus that provides indications and/or recordings of transducer output.

read pulse—A pulse applied to one or more binary cells to determine whether a bit of information is stored there.

readthrough—The continuous recovery in an audio channel, of the target modulation, making possible rapid evaluation of the effectiveness of a jamming effort.

read-write head—The device that reads and writes information on tape, drum, or disc storage devices.

real power—The component of apparent power that represents true work in an a-c circuit. It is expressed in watts and is equal to the apparent power times the power factor.

real time—In solving a problem, a speed sufficient to give an answer within the actual time the problem must be solved.

real-time operation—Operations performed on a computer in time with a physical process so that the answers obtained are useful in controlling that process.

rear projection—A projection television system in which the picture is projected on a ground-glass screen to be viewed from the opposite side of that screen.

rebatron—A relativistic electron-bunching accelerator which produces a very tightly bunched beam with little velocity modulation, but high harmonic content. The beam can be used to excite structures which are large compared to a wavelength.

rebecca—An airborne interrogator-responsor of the British rebecca-eureka navigation system. It can also be used with a special ground beacon known as babs to provide low-approach facilities.

rebecca-eureka system—A British radar navigational system employing an airborne interrogator (rebecca) and a ground transponder beacon (eureka). It provides homing to an airfield from distances of up to 90 miles.

rebroadcast—The reception and the simultaneous or subsequent retransmission of a radio or television program by a broadcast station.

recalescent point—The temperature at which heat is suddenly liberated as the temperature of a heated metal drops.

receiver—1. Any device equipped for reception of incoming electrically transmitted signals. (*Also see* Earphone.) 2. An electromechanical device for converting electrical energy into sound waves.

receiver bandwidth—The spread in frequency between the half-power points on the response curve of a receiver.

receiver gating—Application of operating voltages to one or more stages of a receiver, only during the part of a cycle when reception is desired.

receiver incremental tuning—A control feature to permit receiver tuning (of a transceiver) up to 3 kHz to either side of the transmitter frequency.

receiver lockout system—In mobile communications, an arrangement of control circuits whereby only one receiver can feed the system at one time, to avoid distortion.

receiver noise figure—The ratio of noise voltage in a given receiver to that of a theoretically perfect receiver.

receiver primaries—*See* Display Primaries.

receiver radiation—Radiation of interfering electromagnetic signals by any oscillator of a receiver.

receiver sensitivity—The lower limit of useful signal input to the receiver. It is set by the signal-to-noise ratio at the output.

receiving amplifier—The amplifier used at the receiving end of a system to raise the level of the signal.

receiving antenna—A device for converting received space-propagated electromagnetic energy into electrical energy.

receiving circuit—An apparatus and connections used exclusively for the reception of messages at a radiotelephone or radiotelegraph station.

receiving equipment—The equipment (amplifiers, filters, oscillator, demodulator, etc.) associated with incoming signals.

receiving-loop loss—That part of the repetition equivalent assignable to the station set, subscriber line, and battery-supply circuit on the receiving end of a telephone line.

receiving perforator—In printing telegraph systems, an apparatus that punches a paper strip automatically, in accordance with the arriving signals. When the paper strip is later passed through a printing telegraph machine, the signals will be reproduced as printed messages, ready for delivery to the customer.

receptacle—Usually the fixed or stationary half of a two-piece multiple-contact connector. Also, the connector half usually mounted on a panel and containing socket contacts.

reception—Listening to, copying, recording, or viewing any form of emission.

rechargeable — Capable of being recharged. Usually used in reference to secondary cells or batteries.

rechargeable primary cell—A cell which is ordinarily used in "one-shot" service, but which is capable of a limited number of charge/discharge cycles (frequently five to ten). Applied to silver-zinc missile batteries.

reciprocal — The number *1* (unity) divided by a quantity—e.g., the reciprocal of 2 is $\frac{1}{2}$; of 4, $\frac{1}{4}$, etc.

reciprocal-energy theorem—If an electromotive force E_1 in one branch of a circuit produces a current I_2 in any other branch, and if an electromotive force E_2 inserted into this other branch produces a current I_1 in the first branch, then $I_1E_1 = I_2E_2$.

reciprocal impedance—Two impedances Z_1 and Z_2 are said to be reciprocal impedances with respect to an impedance Z (invariably a resistance) if they are so related as to satisfy the equation $Z_1Z_2 = Z^2$.

reciprocal transducer — A transducer that satisfies the principles of reciprocity—i.e., if the roles of excitation and response are interchanged, the ratio of excitation to response will remain the same.

reciprocation—The process of deriving a reciprocal impedance from a given impedance or finding a reciprocal network for a given network.

reciprocity theorem—In any system composed of linear bilateral impedances, if an electromotive force E is applied between any two terminals and the current I is measured in any branch, their ratio (called the "transfer impedance") will be equal to the ratio obtained if the positions of E and I are interchanged.

reclosing relay—Any voltage, current, power, etc., relay which recloses a circuit automatically.

recognition device — A device which can identify any number of a set of distinguishable entities.

recognition differential—For a specified listening system, the amount by which the signal level exceeds the noise level that is presented to the ear when a 50% probability of detection of the signal exists.

recombination—The simultaneous elimination of both an electron and a hole in a semiconductor.

recombination velocity (on a semiconductor surface) — The normal component of the electron (hole)-current density at the surface, divided by the excess electron (hole)-charge density at the surface.

reconditioned-carrier reception—Also called exalted-carrier reception. Reception in which the carrier is separated from the sidebands in order to eliminate amplitude variations and noise, and then is increased and added to the sideband in order to provide a relatively undistorted output. This method is frequently employed with a reduced-carrier single-sideband transmitter.

record—1. A unit of information comprised of smaller units (e.g., fields, characters, words). 2. A group of related facts or fields of information treated as a unit. 3. To preserve for later reproduction.

record changer—A device which will automatically play a number of phonograph records in succession.

record compensator—Also called a record equalizer. An electrical network that compensates for different frequency-response curves in various recording techniques.

recorded tape—Also called a prerecorded tape. A tape that contains music, dialogue, etc., and is sold to audiophiles and others for their listening pleasure.

recorded value—The value recorded by the marking device on a chart with reference to the division lines marked on the chart.

record equalizer—*See* Record Compensator.

recorder—Also called a recording instrument. An instrument that makes a permanent record of varying electrical impulses—e.g., a code recorder, which punches code messages into a paper tape; a sound recorder, which preserves music and voices on disc, film, tape, or wire; a facsimile recorder, which reproduces pictures and text on paper; and a video recorder, which records television pictures on film or tape.

record gap—In a computer, a space between records on a tape. It is usually produced by acceleration or deceleration of the tape during the write operation.

recording ammeter—An ammeter that provides a permanent recording of the value of either an alternating or a direct current.

recording blank—*See* Recording Disc.

recording channel—One of several independent recorders in a recording system, or independent recording tracks on a recording medium.

recording demand meter—Also called demand recorder. An instrument that records the average value of the load in a circuit during successive short periods.

recording disc—Also called a recording blank. A blank (unrecorded) disc made for recording purposes.

recording head—A magnetic head that transforms electrical variations into magnetic variations for storage on magnetic media. (*Also see* Cutter.)

recording instrument—Also called a recorder or graphic instrument. An instrument which makes a graphic record of the value of one or more quantities as a function of another variable (usually time).

recording lamp—A light source used in the variable-density system of sound recording on movie film. Its intensity varies in step with the variations of the audio-frequency signal sent through it.

Recording head.

recording level—The amplifier output required to provide a satisfactory recording.

recording loss—In mechanical recording, the loss that occurs in the recorded level because the amplitude executed by the recording stylus differs from the amplitude of the wave in the recording medium.

recording noise—Noise induced by the amplifier and other components of a recorder.

recording-reproducing head—A dual-purpose head used in magnetic recording.

recording spot—1. An instantaneous area acted on by the registering system of a facsimile recorder. 2. The elemental area at the facsimile recorder.

Recording stylus.

recording stylus—The tool which inscribes a groove into the recording medium.

recording voltmeter—A voltmeter that provides a permanent record of the value of either alternating or direct voltage.

record medium—In a facsimile recorder, the physical medium onto which the image of the subject copy is formed.

record player—A motor-driven turntable, pickup arm, and stylus, for converting the signals impressed onto a phonograph record into a corresponding a-f voltage. This voltage is then applied to an amplifier (usually contained within the record player cabinet) for amplification and conversion to sound waves.

record sheet—In a facsimile recorder, a sheet or medium upon which the image of the subject copy is recorded.

recovery time—1. The time required for a fired ATR tube in its mount to deionize to the level where its normalized conductance and susceptance are within the specified ranges. 2. The time required for the control electrode in a gas tube to regain control after the anode current has been interrupted. 3. In Geiger-Mueller counters, the minimum time from the start of a counted pulse to the instant a succeeding pulse can attain a specified percentage of the maximum amplitude of the counted pulse. 4. The time required for a fired TR or pre-TR tube to deionize to the level where the attenuation of a low-level radio-frequency signal transmitted through the tube drops to the specified value. 5. In a radar or its component, the time required—after the end of the transmitted pulse—for recovery to a specified relation between receiving sensitivity or received signal and the normal value. 6. The interval required, after a sudden decrease in input-signal amplitude to a system or component, for a specified percentage (usually 63%) of the ultimate change in amplification or attenuation to be attained. 7. In a thermal time-delay relay, the cooling time required from heater de-energization to re-energization such that the new time delay is 85% of that exhibited from a cold start. 8. In a power supply, the time required for recovery of the load voltage from a step change in load current or line voltage. Also called response time.

rectangular scanning—A two-dimensional sector scan in which a slow sector scan in one direction is superimposed perpendicularly onto a rapid sector scan.

rectangular wave—A periodic wave which alternately assumes one of two fixed values, the time of transition being negligible in comparison with the duration of each fixed value.

Rectangular waveguide.

rectangular waveguide—A waveguide with a rectangular cross section.

rectification—The conversion of alternating current into unidirectional or direct current.

rectification efficiency—Ratio of the direct-current power output to the alternating-current power input of a rectifier.

rectification factor—The change in average current of an electrode divided by the change in amplitude of the alternating sinusoidal voltage applied to the same electrode, the direct voltages of all electrodes being maintained constant.

rectifier—A device which, by virtue of its asymmetrical conduction characteristic, converts an alternating current into a unidirectional current.

rectifier instrument—The combination of an instrument sensitive to direct current, and a rectifying device whereby alternating currents or voltages can be measured.

rectifier meter—*See* Rectifier Instrument.

Rectifier stack.

rectifier stack—A dry-disc rectifier made up of layers of individual rectifier discs (e.g., a selenium or copper-oxide rectifier).

rectifier transformer—A transformer the primary of which operates at the fundamental frequency of the a-c system and the secondary of which has one or more windings conductively connected to the main electrodes of the rectifier.

rectifying element—A circuit element which conducts current in one direction only.

rectigon—A hot-cathode gas-filled diode that operates at a high pressure. Used most frequently in battery-charging circuits.

rectilineal compliance—A mechanical element that opposes a change in the applied force (e.g., the springiness that opposes a force on the diaphragm of a speaker or microphone).

rectilinear—In a straight line—specifically, moving, forming, or bounded by a straight line.

rectilinear scanning—The scanning of an area in a predetermined sequence of narrow, straight, parallel strips.

rectilinear writing recorder—An oscillograph that records in rectilinear coordinates.

recurrence rate—*See* Repetition Rate.

recursion—The continued repeating of the same operation or group of operations.

recursive—Capable of being repeated.

recyclability—The capability of a battery system to be recharged after it has been discharged.

red gun—In a three-gun color-television pic-

Rectilinear recording.

ture tube, the electron gun whose beam strikes only the phosphor dots that emit the red primary.

redistribution—In a charge-storage tube or television camera tube, the alteration of charges on one area of a storage surface by secondary electrons from any other area of the same surface.

redox cell—A cell designed to convert the energy of the reactants to electrical energy. An intermediate reductant, in the form of a liquid electrolyte, reacts at the anode in a conventional manner; it is then regenerated by reaction with a primary fuel.

red-tape operation — In a computer, operations which do not directly contribute to the results, i.e., those internal operations which are necessary to process data, but do not in themselves contribute to any final answer.

reduced coefficient of performance — The ratio of a given coefficient of performance to the corresponding coefficient of performance of a Carnot cycle.

reduced generator efficiency—The ratio of a given thermoelectric-generator efficiency to the corresponding Carnot efficiency.

redundancy—1. The employment of several devices, each performing the same function, in order to improve the reliability of a particular function. 2. Added or repeated information employed to reduce ambiguity or error in a transmission of information. As the signal-to-noise ratio decreases, redundancy may be employed to prevent an in-

crease in transmission error. 3. As used in reliability, the concept of providing duplicate functional units in electronic equipment which allow continued performance if a failure occurs.

redundancy check—In a computer, the use of extra information for checking purposes only.

red video voltage—The signal voltage that controls the grid of the red gun in a three-gun picture tube. This signal is a reproduction of the output from the red camera at the transmitter.

reed—A thin bar located in a narrow gap and made to vibrate electrically, magnetically, or mechanically by forcing air through the gap.

reed relay—A relay in which two flat magnetic strips mounted inside a coil are attracted to each other when the coil is energized. The relay contacts are mounted on the strips.

re-entrancy—A type of feedback employed in microwave oscillators. In most magnetrons a circuit is used that can be described as a slow-wave structure that feeds back into itself. In beam re-entrancy the beam may be circulated repeatedly through the interaction space.

re-entrant cavity — A resonant cavity in which one or more sections are directed inward with the result that the electric field is confined to a small area or volume.

re-entrant winding—An armature winding that returns to its starting point, thus forming a closed circuit.

reference address—An address used in digital-computer programming as a reference for a group of relative addresses.

reference angle—The angle formed between the center line of a radar beam as it strikes a reflecting surface and the perpendicular drawn to that reflecting surface.

reference black level — The picture-signal level corresponding to a specified maximum limit for black peaks.

reference boresight—A direction defined by an optical, mechanical, or electrical axis of an antenna, established as a reference for the purpose of beam direction or tracking axis alignment.

reference burst—*See* Color-Burst.

reference dipole—A half-wave straight dipole tuned and matched for a given frequency and used as a unit of comparison in antenna measurement work.

reference electrode — In pH measurements, an electrode, usually hydrogen-filled, used to provide a reference potential. (*Also see* Glass Electrode.)

reference frequency—A frequency coinciding with, or having a fixed and specified relation to, the assigned frequency. It does not necessarily correspond to any frequency in an emission.

reference level—The starting point for designating the value of an alternating quantity or a change in it by means of decibel units.

For sound loudness, the reference level is usually the threshold of hearing. For communications receivers, 60 microwatts is normally used. A common reference in electronics is one milliwatt, and power is stated as so many decibels above or below this figure.

reference line—A line from which angular measurements are made.

reference monitor—A receiver (or other similar device of known performance capabilities) used for judging the transmission quality.

reference noise—The magnitude of circuit noise that will produce a noise-meter reading equal to that produced by 10^{-12} watt of electric power at 1,000 hertz.

reference phase—The phase of the color burst transmitted with color-television carriers. It is used in synchronizing the receiver reference oscillator with the transmitted color signals.

reference point—A terminal that is common to both the input and the output circuits.

reference record—In digital-computer programming, a compiler output that lists the operations and their positions in the final specific routine, plus information describing the segmentation and storage allocation of the routine.

reference recording—A recording of a radio program for future reference or checking.

reference time—In a computer, an instant chosen near the beginning of switching as an origin for time measurements. It is taken as the first instant at which either the instantaneous value of the drive pulse, the voltage response of the magnetic cell, or the integrated voltage response reaches a specified fraction of its peak pulse amplitude.

reference tone—A stable tone of known frequency continuously recorder on one track of multitrack signal recordings and intermittently recorded on signal-track recordings by the collection-equipment operators for subsequent use by the data analysts as a frequency reference.

reference voltage—Alternating-current voltage in a synchro servosystem used to determine the in-phase or 180° out-of-phase condition to provide directional sense.

reference volume—The magnitude of complex electric wave, such as that corresponding to speech or music, which gives a reading of zero VU on a standard volume indicator. The sensitivity of the volume indicator is adjusted so that the reference volume or zero VU is read when the instrument is connected across a 600-ohm resistance to which there is delivered a power of 1 milliwatt at 1,000 hertz.

reference white—The light from a nonselective diffuse reflector as a result of the normal illumination of the scene to be televised.

reference white level—In television, the picture-signal level corresponding to a specified maximum limit for white peaks.

reflectance—*See* Reflection Factor.

reflected impedance—1. The apparent impedance across the primary of a transformer when current flows in the secondary. 2. The impedance at the input terminals of a transducer as a result of the impedance characteristics at the output terminals.

reflected power or signal—The power flowing back to the generator from the load.

reflected resistance—The apparent resistance across the primary of a transformer when a resistive load is across the secondary.

Reflected and direct wave.

reflected wave—The wave which has been reflected from a surface, a junction of two different media, or a discontinuity in the medium it is traveling in (e.g., the echo from a target in radar, the sky wave in radio, the wave traveling toward the source from the termination of a transmission line).

reflecting curtain—A vertical array of half-wave reflecting antennas placed one-quarter wavelength behind a radiating curtain of dipoles to form a pine-tree array.

reflecting electrode—A tubular outer electrode or the repeller plate in a microwave oscillator tube corresponding in construction but not function to the plate of an ordinary triode. It is capable of generating extremely high frequencies.

reflecting galvanometer—A galvanometer with a small mirror attached to the moving element. The mirror reflects a beam of light onto a scale.

reflecting grating—An arrangement of wires placed in a waveguide to reflect the desired wave while freely passing one or more other waves.

reflection—The phenomenon in which a wave that strikes a medium of different characteristics is returned to the original medium with the angles of incidence and reflection equal and lying in the same plane.

reflection altimeter—An aircraft altimeter that determines altitude by the reflection of sound, supersonic, or radio waves from the earth.

reflection coefficient—1. At the junction of a uniform transmission line and a mismatched terminating impedance, the vector ratios between the electric fields associated with the reflected and the incident waves. 2. At any specified plane in a uniform transmission medium, the vector ratios between the electric fields associated with the reflected and the incident waves. 3. At any specified plane in a uniform transmission line between a source and an absorber of power, the vector ratio between the electric fields associated with the reflected and the incident waves. It is given by the formula $(Z_2 - Z_1)/(Z_2 + Z_1)$, where Z_1 and Z_2 are the impedances of the source and load, respectively.

reflection color tube—A color picture tube that produces an image by electron reflection in the screen region.

reflection Doppler—A system utilizing the Doppler frequency shift to measure the position and/or velocity of an object not carrying a transponder.

reflection error—In navigation, the error due to the wave energy that reaches the receiver as a result of undesired reflections.

reflection factor—Also called mismatch factor, reflectance, reflectivity, or transition factor. The ratio of the current delivered to a load whose impedance is not matched to the source, to the current that would be delivered to a load of matched impedance. Expressed as a formula:

$$\frac{\sqrt{4Z_1Z_2}}{Z_1 + Z_2}$$

where Z_1 and Z_2 are the unmatched and the matched impedances, respectively.

reflection grating—A wire grating that is placed inside a waveguide so as to reflect a desired wave while at the same time allowing one or more other waves to pass freely.

reflection law—For any reflected object, the angle of incidence is equal to the angle of reflection.

reflection loss—1. That part of transition loss due to the reflection of power at the discontinuity. 2. The ratio (in decibels) of the power incident upon the discontinuity, to the difference between the powers incident upon and reflected from the discontinuity.

reflection sounding—Echo depth sounding in which the depth is measured by reflecting sound or supersonic waves off the bottom of the ocean.

reflective code—See Gray Code.

reflective jamming—See Radar-Confusion Reflectors.

reflective optics—A system of mirrors and lenses used in projection television.

reflectivity—See Reflection Factor.

reflectometer—A microwave system arranged to measure the incidental and reflected voltages and indicate their ratio.

reflector—Also called a reflector element. 1. One or more conductors or conducting surfaces for reflecting radiant energy—specif-

ically, a parasitic antenna element located in other than the general direction of the major lobe of radiation. 2. (*Also see* Repeller.)

reflector satellite—A satellite so designed that radio or other waves bounce off its surface.

reflector element—*See* Reflector.

reflector voltage—The voltage between the reflector electrode and the cathode in a reflex klystron.

reflex baffle—A speaker baffle in which a portion of the radiation from the rear of the diaphragm is propagated forward after a controlled phase shift or other modification. This is done to increase the over-all radiation in some portion of the frequency spectrum.

reflex bunching—In a microwave tube, a type of bunching that is brought about when the velocity-modulated electron stream is made to reverse its direction by means of an opposing d-c field.

reflex circuit—A circuit through which the signal passes for amplification both before and after detection.

Reflex-klystron schematic.

reflex klystron—A klystron with a reflector (repeller) electrode in place of a second resonant cavity, to redirect the velocity-modulated electrons through the resonant cavity which produced the modulation. Such klystrons are well suited for use as oscillators, because the frequency is easily controlled by repositioning the reflector.

refracted wave—Also called the transmitted wave. In an incident wave, the portion that travels from one medium into a second medium.

refraction—The change in direction of propagation of a wavefront due to its passing

Refraction (of radio waves).

obliquely from one medium into another in which its speed is different. Refraction may also occur in a single medium of varying characteristics.

refraction error—In navigation, the error due to the bending of one or more wave paths by undesired refraction.

refraction loss—That part of the transmission loss due to refraction resulting from nonuniformity of the medium.

refractive index — Of a wave-transmission medium, the ratio between the phase velocity in free space and in the medium.

refractive modulus—Also called the excess modified index of refraction. The excess over unity of the modified index of refraction. It is expressed in millionths and is given by the equation:

$$M = (n + h/a - 1)\,10^6$$

where M is the refractive modulus, n is the index of refraction at a height h above sea level, and a is the radius of the earth.

refractivity—Ratio of phase velocity in free space to that in the medium, minus 1.

refractometer—An instrument for measuring the refractive index of a liquid or solid, usually from the critical angle at which total reflection occurs.

refrangible—Capable of being refracted.

regeneration—1. The gain in power obtained by coupling from a high-level point back to a lower-level point in an amplifier or in a system which encloses devices having a power-level gain. (*Also see* Positive Feedback *and* Regenerative Feedback.) 2. In a computer storage device whose information storing state may deteriorate, the process of restoring the device to its latest undeteriorated state. (*Also see* Rewrite.) 3. The replacement of a charge in a charge-storage tube to overcome decay effects, including a loss of charge by reading.

regeneration control—A variable capacitor,

variable inductor, potentiometer, or rheostat used in a regenerative receiver to control the amount of feedback and thereby keep regeneration within useful limits.

regenerative amplification — Amplification where the increased gain and selectivity are given by a feedback arrangement similar to that in a regenerative detector. However, the operation is always kept just below the point of oscillation.

regenerative braking—Dynamic braking in which the momentum, as the equipment is being braked, causes the traction motors to act as generators. A retarding force is then exerted by the return energy to the power-supply system.

regenerative detector—A detector circuit in which regeneration is produced by positive feedback from the output to the input circuit. In this way, the amplification and sensitivity of the circuit are greatly increased.

regenerative divider—Also called a regenerative modulator. A frequency divider in which the output wave is produced by modulation, amplification, and selective feedback.

regenerative feedback—*See* Regeneration.

regenerative modulator — *See* Regenerative Divider.

regenerative receiver—A receiver in which controlled regeneration is used to increase the amplification provided by the detector stage.

regenerative repeater—A repeater that regenerates pulses to restore the original shape. Used in teletypewriter and other code circuits, each code element is replaced by a new code element with specified timing, waveform, and magnitude.

regional channel — A standard broadcast channel within which several stations may operate at five kilowatts or less. However, interference may limit the primary service area of such stations to a given field-intensity contour.

Regenerative detector.

regional interconnections—*See* Interconnection.

region of limited proportionality—The range of applied voltage, below the Geiger-Mueller threshold, where the gas amplification depends on the charge liberated by the initial ionizing event.

register—1. A digital-computer device capable of retaining information, often that contained in a small subset (e.g., one word) of the aggregate information. (*Also see* Storage.) 2. The relative position of all or part of the conductive pattern with respect to a mechanical feature of the board or to another pattern on the obverse side of the printed-circuit board (e.g., pattern-to-hole register or pattern-front-to-pattern-back register). 3. Also called registration. The accurate matching of two or more patterns such as the three images in color television. 4. A range of notes used for playing a particular piece or part of it (e.g., melody or harmony), particularly the range covered by a clavier or manual.

register constant—Symbolized by Kr. The factor by which the register reading must be multiplied in order to provide proper consideration of the register (gear) ratio and the instrument transformer ratios, to obtain the registration in the desired units.

register control—Any device that provides automatic register. In photoelectric register control, a light source and phototube form a scanning head. Whenever a special mark or a part of the design printed on a continuous web of paper arrives at the scanning head, the amount of light reaching the phototube changes. If necessary, the web is then moved slightly to bring it back into register.

register length—The number of digits, characters, or bits which a computer register can store.

register mark—In printed circuits, a mark used to establish the relative position of one or more printed-wiring patterns or portions of patterns with respect to their desired locations on the base.

register of a meter—In a meter, the part which registers the revolutions of the rotor, or the number of impulses received from or transmitted to the meter and gives the answer in units of electric energy or other quantity measured.

registration, conductive pattern-to-board-outline—The location of the printed pattern relative to the overall outline dimensions of the printed-circuit board.

registration, front-to-back—On a printed-circuit board, the location of the printed pattern on one side relative to the printed pattern on the opposite side.

registration of a meter—The apparent amount of electric energy (or other quantity being measured) that has passed through the meter, as shown by the register reading. It is equal to the register reading times the

register constant. During a given period, it is equal to the register constant times the difference between the register readings at the beginning and end of the period.

registry—The superposition of one image onto another (e.g., in the formation of an interlaced scanning raster).

regulated power supply—A unit which maintains a constant output voltage or current for changes in line voltage, output load, ambient temperature, or time.

regulating device—A device that functions to regulate a quantity or quantities such as voltage, current, power, speed, frequency, temperature, and load, at a certain value or between certain limits for machines, tie lines, or other apparatus.

regulating transformer—A transformer for adjusting the voltage or the phase relation (or both) in steps, usually without interrupting the load. It comprises one or more windings excited from the system circuit or a separate source, and one or more windings connected in series with the system circuit.

regulating winding—A supplementary transformer winding connected in series with one of the main windings and used for changing the ratio of transformation or the phase relationship, or both, between circuits.

regulation—1. The difference between the maximum and minimum voltage drops within a specified anode-current range in a gas tube. 2. The holding constant of some condition (e.g., voltage, current, power, or position). 3. In a power supply, the ability to maintain a constant load voltage or current despite changes in line voltage or load impedance.

regulation of a constant-current transformer—The maximum departure of the secondary current from its rated value, expressed in percent of the rated secondary current, with the rated primary voltage and frequency applied and at the rated secondary power factor and with the current variation taken between the limits of a short circuit and rated load.

regulation of a constant-potential transformer—The change in secondary voltage, expressed in percent of rated secondary voltage, which occurs when the rated kva output at a specified power factor is reduced to zero, with the primary impressed terminal voltage maintained constant. In the case of a multiwinding transformer, the loads on all windings at specified power factors are to be reduced from the rated kva to zero simultaneously.

regulator—A device, the function of which is to maintain a designated characteristic at a predetermined value or to vary it according to a predetermined plan.

regulator tube—A two-electrode glow-discharge gas tube that has an essentially constant voltage drop. When series-connected with a resistance across a d-c source, the tube will maintain a constant d-c voltage across its terminal, with wide variations in the d-c source voltage.

reignition— The generation of multiple counts, within a radiation-counter tube, by the atoms or molecules excited or ionized in the discharge accompanying a tube count.

reignition voltage—Also called restriking voltage. That voltage which is just sufficient to re-establish conduction of a gas tube if applied during the deinonization period. It varies inversely with time during the de-ionization period.

Reike diagram—A polar-coordinate load diagram for microwave oscillators, particularly for klystrons and magnetrons.

Reinartz crystal oscillator—A crystal-controlled vacuum-tube oscillator in which the crystal current is kept low by placing, in the cathode lead, a resonant circuit tuned to half the crystal frequency. The resultant re-generation at the crystal frequency improves the efficiency, but without the problem of uncontrollable oscillations at other frequencies.

reinsertion of a carrier— Combining a locally generated carrier signal in a receiver with an incoming suppressed-carrier signal.

rejection band—The frequency range below the cutoff frequency of a uniconductor wave-guide.

rejector circuit—A circuit that suppresses or eliminates signals of the frequency to which it is tuned.

rel—A unit of reluctance, equal to one ampere-turn per magnetic line of force.

relative accuracy—The possible deviation among the standards in a group.

relative address—1. A designation used to identify the position of a memory location in a computer routine or subroutine. 2. A label used to identify a word in a routine or subroutine with respect to its position in that routine or subroutine.

relative bearing—The bearing in which the direction of the reference line is the heading of the vehicle.

relative coding— In a computer, coding in which all addresses refer to an arbitrarily selected position, or in which all addresses are represented symbolically.

relative damping of an instrument—Also called specific damping. Ratio of the actual damping torque at a given angular velocity of a moving element, to the damping torque which would produce critical damping at this same angular velocity.

relative dielectric constant—Ratio of the dielectric constant of a material to that of a vacuum. The latter is arbitrarily given a value of 1.

relative gain of an antenna—The gain of an antenna in a given direction when the reference antenna is a half-wave loss-free dipole isolated in space and the equatorial plane of which contains the given direction.

relative humidity—1. Ratio of the quantity of water vapor in the atmosphere, to the quantity which would saturate at the existing temperature. 2. Ratio of the pressure of water vapor to that of saturated water vapor at the same temperature.

relative luminosity—Ratio of the actual luminosity at a particular wavelength, to the maximum luminosity at the same wavelength.

relative Peltier coefficient—The Peltier co-efficient of a couple made up of the given material as the first-named conductor and a specified standard conductor, commonly platinum, lead, or copper.

relative permeability—Ratio of the magnetic permeability of one material to that of another, or of the same material under different conditions.

relative plateau slope—The average per-centage change in the counting rate of a radiation-counter tube, near the midpoint of the plateau, per increment of applied voltage. It is usually expressed as the per-centage change in counting rate per 100-volt change in applied voltage.

relative power gain (of one transmitting or receiving antenna over another)—The measured ratio of the signal power one antenna produces at the receiver input terminals, to the signal power produced by the other, the transmitting power level re-maining fixed.

relative refractive index—Ratio of the re-fractive indices of two media.

relative response—The ratio, usually ex-pressed in decibels, of the response under some particular conditions to the response under reference conditions (which should be stated explicitly).

relative Seebeck coefficient— The Seebeck coefficient of a couple made up of the given material as the first-named conductor and a specified standard conductor such as platinum, lead, or copper.

relative velocity (of a point with respect to a reference frame)—The rate at which a position vector of that point changes with respect to the reference frame.

relaxation—An action requiring an observa-ble length of time for initiation in response to a sudden change in conditions.

relaxation circuit—A circuit arrangement, usually of vacuum tubes, reactances, and resistances, which has two states or condi-tions, one, both, or neither of which may be stable. The transient voltage produced by passing from one to the other, or the volt-age in the state of rest, can be used in other circuits.

relaxation inverter—An inverter that uses a relaxation-oscillator circuit to convert d-c power to a-c power.

relaxation oscillator— An oscillator which generates a nonsinusoidal wave by gradually charging and quickly discharging a capacitor or an inductor through a resistor. The fre-quency of a relaxation oscillator may be

Relaxation oscillator.

self-determined, or determined by a synchronizing voltage derived from an external source.

relaxation time—1. The time an exponentially decaying quantity takes to decrease in amplitude by a factor of 0.3679. 2. The average time between collisions of an electron with the lattice.

relay—An electromechanical device in which contacts are opened and/or closed by variations in the conditions of one electric circuit and thereby affect the operation of other devices in the same or other electric circuits.

relay bias—Bias produced by a spring on an electromagnet. By acting on the relay armature, the spring tends to hold it in a given position.

relay broadcast station—A station licensed to retransmit, from points where wire facilities are not available, the programs from one or more broadcast stations.

relay contacts—Contacts that are closed or opened by the movement of a relay armature.

relay drop—A relay activated by an incoming ringing current, to call an operator's attention to a telephone subscriber's line.

relay flutter—Erratic rather than positive operation and release of a relay.

relay magnet—A coil and iron core forming an electromagnet which, when energized, attracts the armature of a relay and thereby opens or closes the relay contacts.

relay receiver—A specific assembly of apparatus which accepts a sound or television relay signal at its input terminals, and delivers the amplified signal at its output terminals.

relay selector—A relay circuit associated with a selector, consisting of a magnetic impulse counter, for registering digits and holding a circuit.

relay station—*See* Relay Transmitter.

relay system—Dial switching equipment made up principally of relays instead of mechanical switches.

relay transmitter—Also called a repeater or relay station (but only if the signal is reduced to a composite picture signal at a standard impedance level, and polarity between the receiver and transmitter). The specific assembly of apparatus which accepts a sound or television-relay input signal from the relay receiver, and rebroadcasts it to another station outside the range of the operating station.

release—1. An electromagnetic device that opens a circuit breaker automatically or allows a motor starter to return to its off position when tripped by hand, by an interruption of power-supply operation, or by an excessive current. 2. The condition attained by a relay when it has been de-energized, all contacts have functioned, and the armature (if applicable) has attained a fully opened position.

release current—The maximum current needed to fully release a relay, after it has been fully closed.

release force—The value to which the force on the actuator of a momentary-contact switch must be reduced to allow the contacts to snap from the operated contact position to the normal contact position.

release time—The interval between the time power is removed from a relay coil and the contacts being checked are released.

releasing position—That position of the actuator of a momentary-contact switch at which the contacts snap from the operated contact position to the normal contact position.

reliability—The probability that a device will perform adequately for the length of time intended and under the operating environment encountered.

reliability control—The scientific coordination and direction of technical reliability activities from a system viewpoint.

reliability data—1. Data related to the frequency of failure of an item, equipment, or system. These data may be expressed in terms of "failure rate," "mean time between failure" (mtbf), or "probability of success." 2. Data contained in comprehensive docu-

Relay.

ments that provide a detailed history of the reliability evaluation of component parts, component assemblies, etc., or the entire program during the design, development, production, and major product improvement phases of an equipment, weapon, or weapon system in which engineering studies have been performed to select the most reliable product for the intended application.

reliability engineering—The establishment, during design, of an inherently high reliability in a product.

reliability test — Tests and analyses carried out in addition to other type tests and designed to evaluate the level of reliability in a product, etc. as well as the dependability, or stability, of this level relative to time and use under various environmental conditions.

relieving anode—In a pool-cathode tube, an auxiliary anode which provides an alternative conducting path to reduce the current to another electrode.

reluctance — The resistance of a magnetic path to the flow of magnetic lines of force through it. It is the reciprocal of permeance and is equal to the magnetomotive force divided by the magnetic flux.

reluctance motor—A synchronous motor similar in construction to an induction motor. The member carrying the secondary circuit has salient poles, but no d-c excitation. It starts as an induction motor, but operates normally at synchronous speed.

reluctive transduction—The conversion of the measurand into a change in a-c voltage by changing the reluctance path between two or more coils when a-c excitation is applied.

reluctivity—The ability of a magnetic material to conduct magnetic flux. It is the reciprocal of permeability.

REM—*See* Roentgen Equivalent Man.

remanence—The extent to which a body remains magnetized after removal of a magnetizing field that has brought the body to its saturation (maximum) magnetization. A substance with remanence is known as ferromagnetic.

remanent magnetization — The magnetization retained by a substance after the magnetizing force has been removed.

remodulator—Formerly called SCFM. A device for converting amplitude modulation to audio-frequency–shift modulation for transmission over a voice radio-frequency channel.

remote—*See* Field Pickup.

remote control—Any system of control performed from a distance. The control signal may be conveyed by intervening wires, sound (ultrasonics), light, or radio.

remote-control equipment — *See* Remote Control.

remote-cutoff tube—Also called a variable-mu or extended-cutoff tube. An electron tube used mainly in r-f amplifiers. The

Remote-cutoff tube characteristic.

control-grid wires are farther apart at the center than at the ends. Therefore, the amplification of the tube does not vary in direct proportion to the bias. Also, some plate current will flow, regardless of the negative bias on the grid.

remote error sensing—A means by which the regulator circuit of a related power supply senses the voltage directly at the load. This connection is used to compensate for a voltage drop in the connecting wires.

remote indicator—1. A radar indicator which is connected in parallel with a primary indicator. 2. An indicator located some distance away from the data-gathering element.

remote line—A program transmission line between a remote-pickup point and the studio or transmitter site.

remotely adjustable timer—A time delay having external leads to which a variable or fixed resistor can be attached.

remote metering—*See* Telemetering.

remote pickup—A program which originates away from the studio and is transmitted to the studio or transmitter over telephone lines or a radio link.

remote programming—Power-supply operation which permits control of the regulated output current or voltage by means of a remotely varied resistance or voltage.

remote sensing—The process by which a power supply senses voltage directly at the load. This method eliminated the variations in load lead drop from affecting the load regulation.

renewable fuse—A fuse which may be readily restored to operation by replacing the fused link.

reoperate time—The release time of a thermal relay.

repeatability—1. The ability of a device or an instrument to come back to the same reading after a certain length of time. 2. The ability of an instrument to repeat its readings taken when deflecting the pointer upscale, compared to the readings taken when deflecting the pointer downscale, expressed as a percentage of the full-scale deflection.

repeatability error—The inability to reproduce the same output readings when a given level of measurand is applied repeatedly in the same direction.

repeat-cycle timer—A timer which has any number of load contacts and which continues to repeat its time program as long as power is applied.

repeater—Also called a one-way or two-way repeater. A combination of apparatus for receiving signals from either one or both directions and delivering corresponding signals which have been amplified or reshaped, or both.

repeater jammer—A jamming transmitter used to confuse or deceive the enemy by causing his equipment to present erroneous azimuth, range, or number of targets. This is accomplished by intercepting and reradiating a modified signal on his frequency.

repeater station—*See* Relay Transmitter.

repeating coil—An audio-frequency transformer, usually with a 1:1 ratio, for connecting two sections of telephone line inductively, to permit the formation of simplex and phantom circuits.

repeating flash tube—A flash tube which, by producing rapid, brilliant flashes, permits night aerial photographs to be taken from as high as two miles.

repeating timer—A timer which repeats each operating cycle automatically until excitation is removed.

repeller—Sometimes called a reflector. An electrode, the primary function of which is to reverse the direction of an electron stream.

reperforator—1. A device that converts teletypewriter signals into perforations on tape instead of the usual typed copy on a roll of paper or ticker tape. 2. A machine that reads one punched paper tape or card and punches the same information into another paper tape or card.

repetition frequency—*See* Repetition Rate.

repetition rate—Also called recurrence rate or repetition frequency. The rate at which signals recur or are transmitted.

repetitive peak-inverse voltage—The maximum, allowable instantaneous value of reverse (negative) voltage that may be repeatedly applied to the anode of an scr with the gate open. This value of peak-inverse voltage does not represent a breakdown voltage, but it should never be exceeded (except by the transient rating if the device has such a rating).

reply—In transponder operation, the radio-frequency signal or signals transmitted as a result of an interrogation.

report generation—In a computer, production of complete output reports from only a specification of the desired content and arrangement and from specifications regarding the input file.

report generator—A special computer routine designed to prepare an object routine that, when later run on the computer, produces the desired report.

reproduce—In a computer, to prepare a duplicate of stored information.

reproduce head—An electromagnetic transducer which converts the remnant flux pattern in a magnetic tape into electrical signals during the reproduce (playback) process.

reproducer—A device used to translate electrical signals into sound waves.

reproducibility—The exactness with which measurement of a given value can be duplicated.

reproducing stylus—A mechanical element that follows the modulations of a record groove and transmits the mechanical motion thus derived to the pickup mechanism.

reproduction speed—The area of copy recorded per unit time.

repulsion—A mechanical force tending to separate bodies having a like electric charge or magnetic polarity—or in the case of adjacent conductors, currents flowing in opposite directions.

repulsion-induction motor—A constant or variable-speed repulsion motor with a squirrel-cage winding in the rotor, in addition to the regular winding.

repulsion motor—A single-phase motor in which the stator winding is connected to the source of power and the rotor winding to the commutator. Brushes on the commutator are short-circuited and are placed so that the magnetic axis of the rotor winding is inclined to that of the stator winding. This type of motor has a varying speed characteristic.

repulsion-start, induction-run motor—A single-phase motor which has the same windings as a repulsion motor but operates at a constant speed. The rotor winding is short-circuited (or otherwise connected) to give the equivalent of a squirrel-cage winding. It starts as a repulsion motor, but operates as an induction motor with constant-speed characteristics.

reradiation—1. Scattering of incident radiation. 2. Radiation of the signals amplified in a radio receiver.

rerecording—The process of making a recording by reproducing a recorded sound source and recording this reproduction. (*Also see* Dubbing.)

rerecording system—An association of reproducers, mixers, amplifiers, and recorders capable of being used for combining or modifying various sound recordings to provide a final sound record. Recording of speech, music, and sound effects may be so combined.

rerun—Also called rollback. To run a computer program (or a portion of it) over again.

rerun point—In a computer program, one of a set of preselected points located in a computer program such that if an error is detected between two such points, the problem may be rerun by returning to the last such point instead of returning to the start of the problem.

rerun routine—A computer routine designed to be used, in the event of a malfunction or mistake, to reconstitute a routine from the previous rerun point.

reset—1. To restore a storage device to a prescribed state. 2. To place a binary cell in the initial, or zero, state. (*Also see* Clear.)

reset pulse—A drive pulse which tends to reset a magnetic cell.

reset terminal—*See* Zero-Input Terminal.

reset time—The period required from the time of the reset command until a timer is fully returned to the before-start conditions ready for the next cycle.

reset timer—A timer which can be reset by electrical means. May be either an "on delay" or "off delay" type. 2. A timer with one or more circuits which spring-reset to zero when the clutch is disengaged.

residual—1. The difference between any value and some estimate of the means of such values; e.g., residuals from a curve of regression. (Residual unbalance.) 2. The complement of a set is called a residual set. 3. (adjective) Pertaining to a measure of the output of a transducer under static conditions and with no stimulus applied.

residual charge—The charge remaining on the plates after an initial discharge of the capacitor.

residual current—The vector sum of the currents in the several wires of an electric supply circuit.

residual discharge—A discharge of the residual charge of a capacitor remaining after the initial discharge.

residual deviation — Apparent modulation due to noise and/or distortion in the transmitter.

residual error—The direction-finding errors remaining after errors due to site and antenna effects have been minimized.

residual field—The magnetic field left in an iron-field structure after excitation has been removed.

residual flux—The value of magnetic induction that remains in a magnetic circuit when the magnetomotive force is reduced to zero.

residual f-m—*See* Incidental F-M.

residual frequency modulation — In a klystron, frequency modulation of the fundamental frequency due to shot and ion noises, a-c heater voltage, etc.

residual gases—The small amounts of gases remaining in a vacuum tube despite the best possible exhaustion by vacuum pumps.

residual induction—The magnetic induction which remains in a magnetized material when the effective magnetizing force has been reduced to zero. When the material is a symmetrically cyclic magnetic condition, the residual induction is termed the "normal residual induction." Abbreviated B_r.

residual ionization—Ionization of air or other gas not accounted for in a closed chamber by recognizable neighboring agencies.

residual losses—In a magnetic core, the difference between the total losses and the sum of the eddy-current and hysteresis losses.

residual magnetic induction—Magnetic induction remaining in a ferromagnetic object after the magnetizing force has been removed. The amount depends on the material, shape, and previous magnetic history.

residual magnetism—The magnetism which remains in the core of an electromagnet after the operating circuit has been opened.

residual modulation — *See* Carrier Noise Level.

residual screw—A brass screw in the center of a relay armature. It is used to adjust the residual air gap between the armature and the coil core, to prevent residual magnetism from holding the armature operated after the relay operating circuit has been opened.

residual voltage—The vector sum of the voltages to ground of the several phase wires in an electric supply circuit.

resist—In the preparation of a printed-circuit board, a material, such as ink, paint, metallic plating, etc., used to protect the desired portions of the conductive material from the action of the etchant, solder, or plating.

resistance—1. A property of conductors which—depending on their dimensions, material, and temperature—determines the current produced by a given difference of potential. The practical unit of resistance is the ohm. It is defined as the resistance through which a difference of potential of one volt will produce a current of one ampere. 2. Opposition which a device or material offers to current. 3. A circuit element designed to offer a predetermined resistance to current. 4. That property of a substance which impedes the current and results in the dissipation of the power in the form of heat.

resistance balance—The amount of resistance which is required to null the output of certain transducers or input systems.

resistance box—An assembly of resistors and the necessary switching or other means for changing the resistance connected across its output terminals by known, fixed amounts. (*Also see* Decade Box.)

resistance brazing—Brazing by resistance heating, the joint being part of the electrical circuit.

resistance bridge — A common form of Wheatstone bridge employing resistances in three arms. *Also see* Wheatstone Bridge.

resistance-bridge pressure pickup—A pressure transducer in which the electrical output is derived from the unbalance of a resistance bridge, which is varied according to the applied pressure.

resistance-capacitance–coupled amplifier—An amplifier, the stages of which are connected by a suitable arrangement of resistors and capacitors.

Resistance-bridge pressure pickup.

Resistance-capacitance coupling.

resistance-capacitance coupling—Also called RC coupling. Coupling between two or more circuits, usually amplifier stages, by a combination of resistive and capacitive elements.

resistance-capacitance filter—A filter made up only of resistive and capacitive elements. Abbreviated RC filter.

resistance-capacitance oscillator—An oscillator the output frequency of which is determined by resistance and capacitance elements. Abbreviated RC oscillator.

resistance coupling — Also called resistive coupling. The association of circuits with one another by means of the mutual resistance between circuits.

resistance drop—The voltage drop occurring across two points on a conductor when current flows through the resistance between those points. Multiplying the resistance in ohms by the current in amperes gives the voltage drop in volts.

resistance furnace—An electric furnace in which the heat is developed by the passage of current through a suitable resistor, which may be the charge itself or a resistor imbedded in or surrounding the charge.

resistance grounded—Grounded through a resistance.

resistance lamp—An electric lamp used as a resistance to limit the amount of current in a circuit.

resistance loss—The power lost when current flows through a resistance. Its value in watts is equal to the resistance in ohms multiplied by the square of the current in amperes $(W = R \times I^2)$.

resistance magnetometer—A magnetometer which depends for its operation on the variation in the electrical resistance of a material immersed in the field to be measured.

resistance material—A material having sufficiently high resistance per unit length or volume to permit its use in the construction of resistors.

resistance noise—*See* Thermal Noise.

resistance pad—A network employing only resistances. It is used to provide a fixed amount of attenuation without altering the frequency response.

resistance ratio — In a thermistor, the ratio of the resistances measured at two specified reference temperatures with zero power in the thermistor.

resistance standard—*See* Standard Resistor.

resistance-start motor—A form of split-phase motor having a resistance connected

in series with the auxiliary winding. The auxiliary circuit opens whenever the motor attains a predetermined speed.

resistance strain gage—A strain gage consisting of a small strip of resistance material cemented to the part under test. Its resistance changes when the strip is compressed or stretched.

resistance temperature detector — Also called resistance-thermometer detector or resistance-thermometer resistor. A resistor made of some material for which the electrical resistivity is a known function of the temperature. It is intended for use with a resistance thermometer and is usually in such a form that it can be placed in the region where the temperature is to be determined.

resistance temperature meter—*See* Resistance Thermometer.

Resistance thermometer.

resistance thermometer—Also called resistance temperature meter. An electric thermometer which has a temperature-responsive element called a resistance temperature detector. Since the resistance is a known function of the temperature, the latter can be readily determined by measuring the electrical resistance of the resistor.

resistance-thermometer detector—*See* Resistance Temperature Detector.

resistance-thermometer resistor — *See* Resistance Temperature Detector.

resistance thermometry — A temperature-measuring technique that utilizes the temperature coefficient of a wirewound resistor. Known as a resistance thermometer, this resistor consists of a spiral of nickel or platinum wire. Since the ohmic value of the wire varies with temperature, the resistance of the spiral is thus an indication of temperature.

resistance weld—The junction produced by heat obtained from the resistance of the work to the flow of electric current in a circuit of which the work is a part, and by the application of pressure before and during the flow of current. The term includes all types of bonds produced by the process, which may or may not be classified metallurgically as welds.

resistance wire—A wire made from a metal or alloy having a high resistance per unit length (e.g., nichrome). It is used in wire-wound resistors, heating elements, and other high-resistance circuits.

resist-etchant—Any material deposited onto a copper-clad base material to prevent the conductive area underneath from being etched away.

resistive conductor—A conductor used primarily because of its high electrical resistance.

resistive coupling—*See* Resistance Coupling.

resistive load—A load in which the voltage is in phase with the current.

resistive transduction—The conversion of the measurand into a change in resistance.

resistive unbalance—Unequal resistance in the two wires of a transmission line.

resistivity—1. The resistance of a semiconductor. It is the reciprocal of conductivity. 2. The resistance of a sample of material having specified dimensions. (*Also see* Specific Resistance.)

resistor—1. A device which resists the flow of electric current in a circuit. There are two types—fixed and variable. 2. A device connected into an electrical circuit to introduce a specified resistance.

resistor capacitor transistor logic—Abbreviated RCTL. A logic circuit design that employs a resistor and a speedup capacitor in parallel for each input of the gate. A transistor's base is connected to one end of the RC network. A positive voltage on the RC input will energize the transistor and turn it on, so that the output voltage is nearly zero volts. This circuit is a positive NOR or negative NAND when NPN transistors are used in the circuit.

resistor color code—A code adopted by the Electronic Industries Association to mark the values of resistance on resistors in a readily recognizable manner. The first color represents the first significant figure of the resistor value, the second color the second significant figure, and the third color represents the number of zeros following the first two figures. A fourth color is sometimes added to indicate the tolerance of the resistor.

resistor core—An insulating support around which a resistor element is wound or otherwise placed.

resistor element—1. That portion of a resistor which possesses the property of electric

resistance. 2. That portion of a potentiometer which provides the change in resistance as the shaft is rotated.

resistor housing—The enclosure around the resistance element and the core of a resistor.

resistor transistor logic — Abbreviated RTL. A form of logic that has a resistor as the input component that is coupled to the base of an NPN transistor. As in RCTL the transistor is an inverting element that produces the positive NOR gate or the negative NAND gate junction.

resist plating—Any material which, when deposited on a conductive area, prevents the areas underneath from being plated.

resnatron—Acronym for RESoNAtor-TRON. A high-power, high-efficiency, cavity-resonator tetrode designed to operate in the vhf region.

resolution—1. The deriving of a series of discrete elements from a sound, scene, or other form of intelligence so that the original may subsequently be synthesized. 2. The degree to which nearly equal values of a quantity can be discriminated. 3. The fineness of detail in a reproduced spatial pattern. 4. The degree to which a system or a device distinguishes fineness of detail in a spatial pattern. 5. In facsimile, a measure of the narrowest line width that may be transmitted and reproduced. 6. A measure of the smallest possible increment of change in the variable output of a device. 7. The minimum output voltage (or current) change of a regulated power supply that can be made using the front-panel controls of a power supply. The resolution of "continuously variable" controls shall be defined as 2° of shaft rotation. 8. The minimum output voltage (or current) change that can be made using the front-panel controls of a power supply. The resolution of "continuously variable" controls is defined as 1% of shaft rotation. 9. In a potentiometer, the smallest possible incremental resistance change. 10. The reciprocal number of steps per revolution of a motor shaft, expressed in degrees per step.

resolution chart—A pattern of black and white lines used to determine the resolution capabilities of equipment.

resolution noise—The noise due to the stepped character of the resistance element in wirewound potentiometric transducers.

resolution wedge—A narrow-angled, wedge-shaped pattern calibrated for the measurement of resolution. It is composed of alternate contrasting strips which gradually converge and taper individually to preserve equal widths along a line drawn perpendicular to the axis of the wedge.

resolver—1. A means for resolving a vector into two mutually perpendicular components. 2. A transformer, the coupling between primary and secondary of which can be varied. 3. A small section with a faster access than the remainder of the magnetic-drum memory in a computer. 4. A device which separates or breaks up a quantity into constituent parts or elements. 5. An electro-mechanical transducing device which develops an output voltage proportional to the product of an input voltage and the sine of the shaft angle.

resolving power—The reciprocal of the beam width in a unidirectional antenna, measured in degrees. It may differ from the resolution of a directional-radio system, since the latter is affected by other factors as well.

resolving time—The minimum time interval by which two events must be separated to be distinguishable.

resonance—1. A circuit condition whereby the inductive- and capacitive-reactance (or -impedance) components of a circuit have been balanced. In usual circuits, resonance can be obtained for only a comparatively narrow frequency band or range. 2. In a mechanical system, the frequency at which the maximum displacement occurs.

$$R_1 R_4 = R_2 R_3$$
$$\omega^2 LC = 1$$

Resonance bridge (series).

resonance bridge—A four-arm, alternating-current bridge normally used for measuring inductance, capacitance, or frequency. An inductor and a capacitor are both present in one arm, the other three arms being (usually) nonreactive resistors. The adjustment for balance includes the etablishment of resonance for the applied frequency. Two general types—series or parallel—can be distinguished, depending on how the inductor and capacitor are connected.

resonance characteristic — *See* Resonance Curve.

resonance curve—Also called a resonant curve or resonance characteristic. A graphical representation of how a tuned circuit responds to the various frequencies in and near the resonant frequency.

resonance indicator—A meter, neon lamp, headphone, etc., that indicates when a circuit is at resonance.

resonance radiation—Radiation from a gas or vapor due to excitation and having the same frequency as the exciting source (e.g., sodium vapor irradiated with sodium light).

resonant capacitor—A tubular capacitor that is purposely wound so as to have inductance in series with its capacitance to resonate at a predetermined (i-f) frequency. Used as a bypass capacitor in i-f amplifiers for more effective bypassing.

Resonant cavity.

resonant cavity—A form of resonant circuit in which the current is distributed on the inner surface of an enclosed chamber. By making the chamber of the proper dimensions, it is possible to give the circuit a high Q at microwave frequencies. The resonant frequency can be changed by adjusting screws which protrude into the cavity, or by changing the shape of the cavity.

resonant charging choke—A modulator inductor which sets up an oscillation of a given charging frequency with the effective capacitance of a pulse-forming network in order to charge a line to a high voltage.

resonant circuit—A circuit which contains both inductance and capacitance and is therefore tuned to resonance at a certain frequency. The resonant frequency can be raised or lowered by changing the inductance and/or capacitance values.

resonant-circuit–type frequency indicator—A frequency-indicating device which depends for its operation on the frequency-versus-reactance characteristics of two series-resonant circuits. The circuit is arranged so that the deflecting torque is independent of the amplitude of the signal to be measured.

resonant-current step-up—The ability of a parallel-resonant circuit to circulate a much higher current through its inductor and capacitor than the current fed into the circuit.

resonant curve—*See* Resonance Curve.

resonant diaphragm—In waveguide technique, a diaphragm so proportioned that it does not introduce reactive impedance at the design frequency.

resonant frequency—1. The frequency at which a given system or object will respond with maximum amplitude when driven by an external sinusoidal force of constant amplitude. For an LC circuit, the resonant frequency is determined by the formula:

$$f = \frac{1}{2\pi \sqrt{LC}}$$

where, f is in hertz, L is in henrys, and C is in farads. 2. The frequency of a crystal unit for a particular mode of vibration to which, discounting dissipation, the effective impedance of the crystal unit is zero.

resonant frequency of a crystal unit—For a particular mode of vibration, the frequency to which (discounting dissipation) the effective impedance of the crystal unit is zero.

resonant gap—The small region where the electric field is concentrated in the resonant structure inside a TR tube.

resonant gate transistor—A surface field-effect transistor incorporating a cantilevered beam which resonates at a specific frequency to provide high-Q frequency discrimination.

resonant line—A transmission line in which the distributed inductance and capacitance are such that the line is resonant at the frequency it is handling.

resonant-line oscillator — An oscillator in which one or more sections of transmission line are employed as tanks.

resonant mode—In the response of a linear device, a component characterized by a certain field pattern and, when not coupled to other modes, representable as a single-tuned circuit. When modes are coupled together, the combined behavior is similar to that of single-tuned circuits that have been correspondingly coupled.

resonant-reed relay—A relay with multiple contacts, each actuated by an a-c voltage of the frequency at which the reeds resonate.

resonant resistance—The resistance value to which a resonant circuit is equivalent.

resonant voltage step-up—The ability of an inductor and a capacitor in a series-resonant circuit to deliver a voltage several times greater than the input voltage.

resonant window (switching tubes) — A resonant iris sealed with a suitable dielectric material and constituting a portion of the vacuum envelope of the tube.

resonate — To bring to resonance — i.e., to maximize or minimize the amplitude or other characteristic of a steady-state quantity.

resonating cavity—A waveguide that is adjustable in length and terminates in a metal piston, diaphragm, or other wave-reflecting device at either or both ends. It is used as a filter, a means of coupling between guides of different sizes, or an impedance network.

resonator—An apparatus for setting up and maintaining oscillations of a frequency determined by the physical constants of the system.

resonator cavity—A section of coaxial line or waveguide completely enclosed by conductive walls.

resonator grid—One of the grids attached to a cavity resonator in a velocity-modulation tube.

resonator mode—A condition of operation corresponding to a particular field configuration for which the electron stream introduces negative conductance into the coupled circuit.

resonator wavemeter—A resonant circuit for determining wavelength (e.g., a cavity-resonator wavemeter).

resonistor—An experimental resonating device that is essentially a cantilevered chip of silicon mounted, like a tiny diving board, on a substrate. It measures 0.0350 inch long, 0.090 inch wide, and 0.008 inch thick, and contains two special diffused resistors. When an input signal is applied, it causes the silicon chip to vibrate, and the resonistor then delivers an output voltage with a specific stable frequency.

responder—The part of a transponder that automatically transmits a reply to the interrogator-responsor. By contrast, the responsor is the receiver which accepts and interprets the signals from the transponder.

response—A quantitative expression of the output of a device or system as a function of the input, under conditions which must be explicitly stated. The response characteristic, often presented graphically, gives the response as a function of some independent variable such as frequency or direction.

response curve—1. A plot of output versus frequency for a specific device. 2. A plot of stimulus versus output.

responser—*See* Responsor.

response speed—The time for a control action to start after a temperature change has occurred at the sensor.

response time—1. The time (usually expressed in cycles of the power frequency) required for the output voltage of a magnetic amplifier to reach 63% of its final average value in response to a step-function change of signal voltage. 2. The time required for the pointer of an instrument to come to apparent rest in its new position after the measured quantity abruptly changes to a new, constant value. 3. *See* Recovery Time (6). 4. The time required to reach a specified percentage (e.g., 90, 98, 99%) of the final output value). 5. *See* Transient Recovery Time.

responsor—1. Also spelled responser. The receiver used to receive and interpret the signals from a transponder. 2. An electronic device used to receive an electronic challenge and to display a reply thereto.

resting frequency—*See* Center Frequency.

restore—To return a variable address or other computer word to its initial value.

restorer—*See* D-C Restorer.

restoring spring—Also called return spring. A spring that moves the armature to the normal position and holds it there when the relay is de-energized.

rest potential—The residual potential difference remaining between an electrode and an electrolyte after the electrode has become polarized.

restriking voltage—*See* Reignition Voltage.

resultant—The effect produced by two or more forces or vectors.

retained image—Also called image burn. A change that is produced on the target of a television camera tube by a stationary light image and that results in the production of a spurious electrical signal corresponding to the light image for a large number of frames after the image is removed.

retardation coil—A high inductance coil used in telephone circuits to permit passage of d-c or low-frequency current while blocking audio-frequency currents. *Also see* Inductor.

retarding-field oscillator—Also called a positive-grid oscillator. An oscillator tube in which the electrons move back and forth through a grid which is more positive than the cathode and plate. The frequency depends on the electron-transit time and sometimes on the associated circuit parameters. The field around the grid retards the electrons and draws them back as they pass through it in either direction. Barkhausen-Kurz and Gill-Morell oscillators are examples of a retarding-field oscillator.

retarding magnet—Also called a braking magnet or drag magnet. A magnet used for limiting the speed of the rotor in a motor-type meter.

retard transmitter—A transmitter in which a delay is introduced between the time it is actuated and the time transmission begins.

retentivity—That property of a material measured by the normal residual induction remaining after the removal of an applied magnetizing force corresponding to the saturation induction for the material.

retentivity of vision—The image retained momentarily by the mind after the view has left the field of vision. (*Also see* Persistence of Vision.)

RETMA—Abbreviation for Radio-Electronics-Television Manufacturers Association, now the Electronic Industries Association (EIA).

retrace—*See* Flyback.

retrace blanking—The blanking of a television picture tube during vertical-retrace intervals to prevent the retrace lines from being visible on the screen.

retrace interval—*See* Return Interval.

retrace line—Also called the return line. The line traced by the electron beam in a cathode-ray tube as it travels from the end of one line or field to the start of the next line or field.

retrace time—*See* Return Interval.

retractile spring—The spring which tends to open the armature of an electromagnetic device and which holds the armature open

when its force is not overcome by magnetic attraction.

retrieve—In a computer, to select specific information.

retrodirective reflector—A reflector which redirects incident flux back toward the point of origin of the flux.

return interval—Also called retrace interval, retrace time, or return time. The interval corresponding to the direction of sweep not used for delineation.

return line—*See* Retrace Line.

return lines—Conductors connecting the loads to the lowest-potential power-supply terminal. Lowest potential means most nearly zero with respect to the ground point, regardless of polarity. The term "ground" is reserved for a single point; return lines include all means of connecting the low-potential terminal of the power supply to the load such as ground busses and chassis.

return loss—1. At a discontinuity in a transmission system, the difference between the power incident upon, and the power reflected from, the discontinuity. 2. The ratio in decibels of (1) above.

return spring—*See* Restoring Spring.

return time—*See* Return Interval.

return trace—The path of the scanning spot during the return interval.

return transfer function—In a feedback control device, the transfer function that relates a loop return signal to the corresponding loop input signal.

return wire—The ground, common, or negative wire of a circuit.

reverberation—The persistence of sound due to the repeated reflections from walls, ceiling, floor, furniture, and occupants in a room or auditorium.

reverberation chamber—An enclosure in which all surfaces have been made as sound-reflective as possible. It is used for certain acoustic measurements.

reverberation period—The time required for the sound in an enclosure to die down to one millionth (60 db) of its original intensity.

reverberation strength—The difference between (a.) the level of a plane wave that produces in a nondirectional transducer a response equal to that produced by the reverberation corresponding to a 1-yard range from the effective center of the transducer and (b.) the index level of the pulse transmitted by the same transducer on any bearing.

reverberation time—For a given frequency, the time required for the average sound-energy density, originally in a steady state, to decrease to one-millionth (60 db) of its initial value after the source is stopped.

reverberation-time meter—An instrument for measuring the reverberation time of an enclosure.

reverberation unit—A circuit or device that

adds an artificial echo to a sound being reproduced or transmitted.

reversal—A change in the direction of transmission or polarity.

reverse bias—Also called back bias. An external voltage applied to a semiconductor PN junction to reduce the flow of current across the junction and thereby widen the depletion region. It is the opposite of forward bias.

reverse-blocking PNPN-type switch—A PNPN-type switch which exhibits a reverse-blocking state when its anode-to-cathode voltage is negative and does not switch in the normal manner of a PNPN-type switch.

reverse-breakdown voltage—The voltage that produces a sharp increase in reverse current in a semiconductor, without a significant increase in voltage.

reverse coupler—A directional coupler used for sampling reflected power.

reverse current—*See* Back Current.

reverse-current relay—A relay that operates whenever current flows in the reverse direction.

reversed feedback amplifier—An amplifier in which inverse feedback is employed to reduce harmonic distortion and otherwise improve fidelity.

reverse direction—Also called inverse direction. The direction of greater resistance to current flow through a diode or rectifier—i.e., from the positive to the negative electrode.

reverse emission—*See* Back Emission.

reverse key—A key used in a circuit to reverse the polarity of that circuit.

reverse-phase current relay—Also called phase-balance current relay. A device which functions when the polyphase currents are of reverse-phase sequence, or when the polyphase currents are unbalanced or contain negative phase-sequence components above a given amount.

reverse recovery time—In a semiconductor diode, the time required for the current or voltage to reach a specified state after being switched instantaneously from a specified forward-current condition to a specified reversed bias condition.

reverse resistance—The resistance measured at a specified reverse voltage or current in a diode or rectifier.

reverse saturation current—The reverse current that flows in a semiconductor because of a specified reverse voltage.

reverse voltage—The voltage applied in the reverse direction to a diode or rectifier.

reversible booster—A booster capable of adding to or subtracting from the voltage of a circuit.

reversible capacitance—For a capacitor, the limit, as the amplitude of the applied sinusoidal voltage approaches zero, of the ratio of the amplitude of the in-phase, fundamental-frequency component of transferred charge to the amplitude of the applied voltage,

with a specified constant bias voltage superimposed on the sinusoidal voltage.

reversible capacitance characteristic—The function giving the relation of reversible capacitance to bias voltage.

reversible motor—A motor in which the rotation can be reversed by a switch that changes the motor connections.

reversible permeability—The limit approached by the incremental permeability as the alternating field strength approaches zero.

reversible transducer—*See* Bilateral Transducer.

reversing switch—A switch used for changing the direction of any form of motion—specifically, the direction of motor rotation or the polarity of circuit connections.

reverting call—In telephony, a call made by one party on a line to another party on the same line.

rewind—To return the tape to its starting point in a magnetic recorder.

rewind control—A button or lever for rapidly rewinding magnetic recording tape from the take-up reel to the feed reel.

rewrite—Also called regeneration. In a storage device where the information is destroyed by being read, the restoring of information into the storage.

rf—Abbreviation for radio frequency.

r-f amplifier—1. An amplifier used to increase the voltage or power at the carrier frequency. 2. Any amplifier capable of operation in the radio-frequency portion of the spectrum.

r-f bandwidth—The band of frequencies comprising 99% of the total radiated power extended to include any discrete frequency on which the power is at least 0.25% of the total radiated power.

rfc—Abbreviation for radio-frequency choke.

r-f cavity preselector—An ultrahigh-frequency circuit component which is similar in function to a tuned resonant circuit. A tunable cavity.

r-f choke—A coil used to prevent r-f currents from passing from one circuit to another.

r-f component—The portion of a signal or wave which consists only of the radio-frequency alternations, and not including its audio rate of change in amplitude frequency.

r-f current—Alternating current having a frequency higher than 10,000 hertz.

r-f energy—Alternating-current energy generated at radio frequencies.

r-f generator—A generator that produces sufficient r-f energy at its assigned frequency for induction or dielectric heating.

r-f head—A unit consisting of a radar transmitter and part of a radar receiver, the two contained in a package for ready removal and installation.

RFI (radio-frequency interference)—Radio-frequency energy of sufficient magnitude to possibly influence the operation of other electronic equipment.

r-f indicator—A device that shows the presence of r-f energy. It may consist of a tuned circuit or parallel line connected to an incandescent lamp or other indicator.

r-f interference-shield ground — The grounding technique for all shields that are used to suppress the radiation of interference from leads.

r-f intermodulation distortion—Intermodulation distortion that has its origin in the r-f stages of a receiver.

r-f line—1. A system of metallic tubes (waveguides and/or coaxial lines) which conduct radio-frequency energy from one point to another. 2. A metallic conductor used to transmit radio-frequency energy from one point to another.

r-f oscillator—*See* Radio-Frequency Oscillator.

r-f plumbing—Radio-frequency transmission lines and associated equipment in the form of waveguides.

r-f power supply—A high-voltage power supply consisting of an r-f oscillator the output voltage of which is stepped up and then rectified. Used in television receivers or other equipment to supply the high d-c voltage required by the second anode of cathode-ray tubes.

r-f preselectors—Bandpass filters which improve the selectivity by rejecting unwanted frequencies at the radio-frequency input stage.

r-f probe—1. A resonant conductor which is placed in a waveguide or cavity resonator for the purpose of inserting or withdrawing electromagnetic energy. 2. A detecting device used with a vacuum-tube voltmeter to measure r-f voltages.

r-f pulse—A radio-frequency carrier amplitude-modulated by a pulse. The amplitude of the modulated carrier is zero before and after the pulse. Coherence of the carrier with itself is not applied.

r-f resistance—*See* High-Frequency Resistance.

r-f shift—*See* Frequency Shift.

r-f signal generator—Also called service oscillator. A test instrument that generates several bands of radio frequencies necessary for the alignment and servicing of radios, television, and other electronic equipment.

r-f tolerance—The amount of r-f energy the human body can receive without injury.

r-f transformer — *See* Radio-Frequency Transformer.

R/h—Abbreviation for roentgens per hour.

rheo—Abbreviation for rheostat.

rheostat—A variable resistor which has one fixed terminal and a movable contact (often erroneously referred to as a "two-terminal potentiometer"). Potentiometers may be used as rheostats, but a rheostat cannot be used as a potentiometer because connections can-

not be made to both ends of the resistance element.

RHI—Abbreviation for range-height indicator. A radar display in which the abscissa represents the range to the target, and the ordinate indicates height.

Rhombic antenna.

rhombic antenna—An antenna composed of long-wire radiators comprising the sides of a rhombus. The antenna usually is terminated in an impedance. The sides of the rhombus and the angle between them, the elevation, and the termination are proportioned to give the desired directivity.

rho-theta — A polar-coordinate navigational system providing sufficiently accurate data that a computer can be used which will provide arbitrary course lines anywhere within the coverage area of the system.

rhumbatron—A resonant cavity consisting of lumped inductance and capacitance. It is used, instead of circuits, to act as an oscillator capable of giving an output of several kilowatts at frequencies of several thousand megahertz.

rhythm bar — In some organs, a bar used to permit rhythmic playing of a chord without interrupting the pressure on the keys or chord button.

RIAA curve—1. A standard recording characteristic curve approved for long-playing records by the Record Industry Association of America. 2. The equalization curve for playback of records recorded as in (1).

ribbon—A common intraconnecting material, usually nickel, of rectangular cross section, which is used to connect electronic component parts or modules together into the form of a functioning circuit.

ribbon microphone—A microphone in which the moving conductor is in the form of a ribbon driven directly by the sound waves.

Rice neutralizing circuit—A radio-frequency amplifier circuit that neutralizes the grid-to-plate capacitance of the amplifier tube.

Ribbon microphone.

Richardson effect—*See* Edison Effect.

Richardson equation—An expression for the density of thermionic emission at saturation current, in terms of the absolute temperature of the filament.

ride gain—To continually adjust the volume level of a program while observing a volume indicator so that the resulting audio-frequency signal will have the necessary magnitude for proper operation of the transmission equipment.

ridge waveguide—A circular or rectangular waveguide with one or more longitudinal ridges projecting inwardly from one or both sides. The ridges increase the transmission bandwidth by lowering the cutoff frequency.

Rieke diagram—A special polar-coordinate chart where load conditions can be determined for oscillators such as klystrons, and magetrons. Information from the chart indicates where optimum operation is located, as well as the limitations oscillators have with various loads.

rig—1. A system of components. 2. An amateur station consisting of receiver, transmitter, and all the necessary accessory equipment.

Righi-Leduc effect — The phenomenon whereby, when a metal strip is placed with its plane perpendicular to a magnetic field and heat flows through the strip, a temperature difference is developed across the strip.

right-handed polarized wave—Also called clockwise polarized wave. An elliptically polarized transverse electromagnetic wave in which the electric intensity vector rotates clockwise as an observer looks in the direction of propagation.

right-hand rule—*See* Fleming's Rule.

right-hand taper—The characteristic whereby a potentiometer or rheostat has a higher resistance in the clockwise half of its rotational range than in its counter-clockwise half (looking at the shaft end).

rigid metal conduit—A raceway specially constructed for the purpose of the pulling in or the withdrawing of wires or cables after the conduit is in place. It is made of metal pipes of standard weight and thickness, permitting the cutting of standard threads.

rim drive—The method of driving a phonograph or sound-recorder turntable by means of a small, rubber-covered wheel that is on the shaft of an electric motor and contacts the rim of the turntable.

Rim drive.

rim magnet—*See* Field-Neutralizing Magnet.

ring—1. A ring-shaped contacting part of a plug usually placed in back of but insulated from the tip. 2. An audible alerting signal on a telephone line.

ring-around—In a secondary radar: 1. The undesired triggering of a transponder by its own transmitter. 2. The triggering of a transponder at all bearings, causing a ring presentation on a ppi.

ring circuit—In waveguide practice, a hybrid-T having the physical configuration of a ring with radial branches.

Ring counter.

ring counter—1. A loop of interconnected bistable elements arranged so that only one is in a specified state at any given time. As input signals are counted, the specified state moves in an ordered sequence around the loop. 2. A loop or circuit of interconnected flip-flops so arranged that only one is on at any given time and that as input signals are received, the position of the "on" state moves in sequence from one flip-flop to another around the loop.

ringdown—A method of signaling subscribers and operators using either a 20-hertz a-c signal, a 135-hertz a-c signal, or a 1,000-hertz signal interrupted 20 times per second.

ring head—A magnetic head in which the magnetic material forms an enclosure with one or more air gaps. The magnetic-recording medium bridges one of these gaps and contacts or is close to the pole pieces on one side only.

ringing—1. The production of an audible or visible signal at a station or switchboard by means of an alternating or pulsating current. 2. A damped oscillation in the output signal of a system, as a result of a sudden change in the input signal. 3. High-frequency

431

damped oscillations caused by shock excitation of high-frequency resonances.

ringing current — An alternating current which may or may not be superimposed onto a direct current for telephone ringing.

ringing key—A key which, when operated, sends a ringing current over its circuit.

ring magnet — A ceramic permanent magnet in which the axial length is no greater than the wall thickness and the wall thickness is no less than 15% of the outside diameter.

ring modulator—A modulator used as a balanced modulator, demodulator, or phase detector that has four diodes connected in series to form a ring around which current can easily flow in one direction. Input and output connections are made at the four nodal points of the ring.

ring oscillator — A circuit configuration in which two or more pairs of tubes are operated as push-pull oscillators in a ring-like arrangement. Usually alternate successive pairs of plates and grids are connected to tank circuits, and the load is coupled to the plate circuits.

ring retard—Also called slug retard. A heavy conductor surrounding the iron-flux path in a relay to retard the establishment or the decay of flux in the path.

ring time—In radar, the time during which the output of an echo box remains above a specified level. It is used in measuring the performance of radar equipment.

RIOMETER — Acronym for Relative Ionospheric Opacity METER. An instrument for recording the level of extra-terrestrial cosmic noise at selected frequencies in the hf and vhf regions.

ripple—1. The a-c component arising from sources within a d-c power source. Unless otherwise specified, ripple is the ratio, expressed in per cent, of the root-mean-square value of the ripple voltage to the absolute value of the total voltage. 2. The excursions above and below the average peak ampressed in percent, of the root-mean-square plitude. 3. That portion of the output voltage of a power supply harmonically related in frequency to the input power, and to any internally generated switching frequency. Normally ripple is expressed as an rms percentage, but can also be expressed as peak to peak. Ripple is replaced by a new term known as pard, which includes hum and noise as well as spikes in the output.

ripple current—The alternating component of a substantially steady current.

ripple-current rating—The rms value of the a-c component of the current through a capacitor.

ripple filter—A low-pass filter designed to reduce the ripple current while freely passing the direct current from a rectifier or generator.

ripple frequency—The frequency of the ripple current. In a full-wave rectifier it is twice the supply frequency. In a generator it is a function of the speed and the number of poles.

ripple quantity—The alternating component of a pulsating quantity when this component is small relative to the continuous component.

ripple voltage—The alternating component of the unidirectional voltage from a rectifier or generator.

rise cable — In communication practice: 1. The vertical portion of a house cable extending from one floor to another. 2. Sometimes, any other vertical sections of cable.

rise time—The time required for the leading edge of a pulse to rise from 10% to 90% of its final value. It is proportionate to the time constant and is a measure of the steepness of the wavefront.

rising-sun magnetron—A multicavity vane-type magnetron in which resonators of two different resonant frequencies are arranged alternately for the purpose of mode separation.

rising-sun resonator—A magnetron anode structure in which large and small cavities alternate around the perimeter of the structure.

R/m—Abbreviation for roentgens per minute.

RMA—Abbreviation for Radio Manufacturers Association, now Electronic Industries Association (EIA).

RMA color codes—A term formerly used to designate the EIA Color Codes.

RMI — Abbreviation for radio-magnetic indicator.

rms—Abbreviation for root-mean-square.

rms amplitude—Also called effective value. The amplitude of an alternating-current wave which may be used for an accurate computation of power in watts. In communications particularly, with complex waves involved, the root-mean-square amplitude of a current is said to be that current which is computed from a measurement of power dissipated in a known resistance as a result of that current.

rms (effective) pulse amplitude — The square root of the average of the squares of the instantaneous amplitudes taken over the duration of the pulse.

rms pard—The value of the output waveform of a regulated power supply, omitting the d-c component value.

rms voltage—The effective value of a varying or alternating voltage. That value which would produce the same power loss as if a continuous voltage were applied to a pure resistance. In sine-wave voltages, the rms voltage is equal to 0.707 times the peak voltage.

Roberts rumble—The nickname given to a phenomenon whereby certain radio disturbances appear to be connected with the passage of satellites through the earth's ionosphere. Investigations have been made to determine the feasibility of exploiting this effect for the tracking of satellites.

robot pilot—*See* Autopilot.

Rochelle-salt crystal — A crystal made of sodium potassium tartrate. Because of its pronounced piezoelectric effect, it is used extensively in crystal microphones and phonograph pickups. Perfect Rochelle-salt crystals up to four inches and even more in length can be grown artificially.

rocking—Rotating the tuning control in a superheterodyne receiver back and forth while adjusting the oscillator padder near the low-frequency end of the tuning dial, to obtain more accurate alignment.

rocky-point effect—Transient but violent discharges between electrodes in high-voltage transmitting tubes.

rod gap—A spark gap in which the electrodes are two coaxial rods, with ends between which the discharge takes place, cut perpendicularly to the axis.

roentgen—The unit of radioactive dose of exposure. It is the amount of gamma radiation that will produce one electrostatic unit of charge in one cubic centimeter of air which is surrounded by an infinite mass of air at standard temperature and pressure conditions.

roentgen equivalent man — A radiation-exposure dose which produces the same effects on human tissue as one roentgen of X-ray radiation. Abbreviated REM.

roentgen meter—Also called a roentgenometer. An instrument for measuring the quantity or intensity of roentgen rays (X-rays or gamma rays).

roentgenogram—Also called an X-ray photograph or an X-ray. A photograph taken by showering an object or the human body with X-rays (roentgen rays). Depending on the transparency of the object or body, the interior can thus be seen and recorded.

roentgenology—That branch of science related to the application of roentgen rays (X-rays) for diagnostic or therapeutic purposes.

roentgenometer—*See* Roentgen Meter.

roentgen rays—*See* X-Rays.

roger—A code word used in communications to mean: 1. Your message has been received and is understood. 2. OK—an expression of agreement.

Roget spiral—A helix of wire that contracts in length, when a current is sent through, as a result of the mutual attraction between adjacent turns.

roll—Also called flip-flop, especially when intermittent. The upward or downward movement of a television picture due to lack of vertical synchronization.

rollback—*See* Rerun.

rolling transposition—The method by which two or more conductors of an open-wire circuit are spiral-wound. With two wires, a complete transposition can be executed utilizing two consecutive suspension points.

rolloff—The particular manner in which the amplitude frequency characteristic behaves as it approaches its frequency limits.

roll out—To read out of a computer storage by simultaneously increasing by 1 the value of the digit in each column, repeating this r times (where r is the radix) and, at the instant the representation changes from (r–1) to zero, either generating a particular signal, terminating a sequence of signals, or originating a sequence of signals.

roof filter—A low-pass filter used in repeater and terminal equipment to reduce the unwanted higher frequencies induced into the circuit from external sources.

room noise—*See* Ambient Noise.

root mean square—The square root of the average of the square of the values of a periodic quantity taken throughout one complete period. It is the effective value of a periodic quantity. Abbreviated rms.

root-mean-square value — Of alternating currents and voltages, the effective current or voltage applied. It is that value of alternating current or voltage that produces the same heating effect as would be produced by an equal value of direct current or voltage. It is equal to 0.707 times the maximum alternating-current value.

root-sum square—The square root of the sum of the squares. A common expression of the total harmonic distortion.

rope—Similar to chaff, but longer. Electromagnetic-wave reflectors used to confuse enemy radar. They consist of long strips of metal foil, to which small parachutes may be attached to reduce their rate of fall.

rope-lay conductor or cable — A cable consisting of one or more layers of helically laid groups of wires surrounding a central core.

rosin connection—Also called a rosin joint. A defective connection of a conductor to a piece of equipment or to another conductor. Supposedly the joint is tightly soldered, but actually it is held together only by unburnt rosin flux.

rosin-core solder—Self-fluxing solder consisting of a hollow center filled with rosin.

rosin joint—*See* Rosin Connection.

rotary-beam antenna—A highly directional short-wave antenna system. It is mounted on a mast and can be rotated manually or by an electric-motor drive to any desired position.

rotary converter—*See* Dynamotor.

rotary coupler—*See* Rotating Coupler.

rotary generator (induction-heating usage) — An alternating-current generator adapted to be rotated by a motor or other prime mover.

rotary joint—*See* Rotating Coupler.

rotary phase converter—A machine which converts power from an alternating-current system of one or more phases to an alternating-current system of a different number of phases, but of the same frequency.

rotary plunger relay—A relay in which the linear motion of the plunger is converted mechanically into rotary motion.

rotary relay—1. A relay in which the armature rotates to close the gap between two or more pole faces (usually with a balanced armature). 2. A term sometimes used for stepping relay.

rotary-solenoid relay—A relay in which the linear motion of the plunger is converted into rotary motion by mechanical means.

rotary spark gap—A device used to produce periodic spark discharges. It consists of several electrodes which are mounted on a wheel and rotate past a fixed electrode.

rotary stepping relay—*See* Stepping Relay.

rotary stepping switch—*See* Stepping Relay.

rotary switch—An electromechanical device which is capable of selecting, making, or breaking an electrical circuit. It is actuated by a rotational torque applied to its shaft.

rotary transformer—A term sometimes applied to a rotating machine used to transform direct-current power from one voltage to another.

rotary voltmeter—*See* Generating Voltmeter.

rotatable phase-adjusting transformer—A transformer in which the secondary voltage may be adjusted to have any desired phase relation with the primary voltage by mechanically orienting the secondary winding with respect to the primary. The latter winding consists usually of a distributed symmetrical polyphase winding and is energized from a polyphase circuit. (*Also see* Phase-Shifting Transformer.)

rotating-anode tube—An X-ray tube in which the anode rotates continually to bring a fresh area of its surface into the beam of electrons. This procedure allows a greater output without melting the target.

rotating coupler—Also called rotary coupler and rotary joint. A joint that permits one section of a waveguide to rotate while passing r-f energy.

rotating disc—*See* Drum Memory.

rotating element of a meter—*See* Rotor of a Meter.

rotating field—The magnetic field in the stator of induction motors. Because of excitation from a polyphase source, the field appears to rotate around the stator from pole to pole.

rotating radio beacon—A radio transmitter that rotates a concentrated beam horizontally at a constant speed. Different signals are transmitted in each direction so that ships and aircraft without directional receiving equipment can determine their bearings.

rotational life—The ability of a potentiometer to be operational after a defined number of wiper sweeps across the element.

rotational wave—*See* Shear Wave.

rotation spectrum—An X-ray spectrum of the diffraction pattern obtained when X-rays are sent through a rotating crystal.

rotator—1. A motor-driven assembly which turns an antenna so that it can be aimed in the direction of best reception. 2. In waveguides, a means of rotating the plane of polarization. In rectangular waveguides it is done by simply twisting the guide itself.

Rotator (antenna).

rotoflector—In radar, an elliptically shaped rotating reflector used to divert a vertically directed radar beam at right angles so that it radiates horizontally.

rotor—1. The rotating member of an electric machine. In a motor, it is connected to and turns the drive shaft. In a generator, the rotor is turned to produce electricity by cutting magnetic lines of force. 2. The movable plates of a variable capacitor.

rotor of a meter—Also called the rotating element of a meter. The portion driven directly by electromagnetic action.

rotor plates—The movable plates of a variable capacitor.

round conductor—A solid or stranded conductor with a substantially circular cross section.

rounding—A lack of a sharp corner of a waveform, or a smooth transition from the leading or trailing edge to the limiting final value.

rounding error—The error that results when the less significant digits of a number are dropped and the most significant digits are then adjusted.

round off—1. To delete less significant digits from a number and possibly apply some rule of correction to the part retained. 2. To approximate a number by discarding one or more final digits. If it is 5, 6, 7, 8, or 9 (or 50 . . . , etc.), the new final digit is raised by 1 (e.g., 30.7 would be rounded off to 31, and 519.2 to 519). This is done for ease of calculation, where estimate will suffice.

round-off error—*See* Rounding Error.

round-trip echoes—Multiple-reflection echoes produced when the radar pulse is reflected from a target strongly enough that the echo is reflected back to the target, where it produces a second echo.

routine—A set of computer instructions arranged in a correct sequence and used to direct a computer in performing one or more desired operations.

rpm — Abbreviation for revolutions per minute.

rps — Abbreviation for revolutions per second.

R-S flip-flop — A flip-flop having two inputs, designated R and S. At the application of a clock pulse, a 1 on the S input will set the flip-flop to the 1 or "on" state, and 1 on the R input will reset it to the 0 or "off" state. It is assumed that 1's will never appear simultaneously at both inputs.

R-S-T flip-flop — A flip-flop having three inputs, R, S, and T. The R and S inputs produce states as described for the R-S flip-flop; the T causes the flip-flop to change states.

RTMA — Abbreviation for Radio-Television-Manufacturers Association, now Electronic Industries Association (EIA).

rubber-covered wire — A wire with rubber insulation.

ruby — A type of aluminum-oxide crystal used to produce one form of solid-state laser.

ruby laser — An optically pumped solid-state laser in which a ruby crystal produces an extremely narrow and intense beam of coherent red light. Used for localized heating and for light-beam communication.

Ruby laser.

ruby maser — A maser that has a ruby crystal in the cavity resonator.

ruggedization — The redesign of a piece of equipment or its components, to make them able to withstand prolonged vibration and mechanical shock.

Ruhmkorff coil — An induction coil having a magnetic interrupter. It is used to produce a spark discharge across an air gap.

rumble — Also called turntable rumble. A descriptive term for a low-frequency vibration, which is mechanically transmitted to the recording or reproducing turntable and superimposed onto the reproduction.

runaround cross talk — Cross talk resulting from the coupling of the high-level end of one repeater to the low-level end of another repeater. Often a third repeater or line is the means of coupling; therefore, runaround cross talk may be a form of interaction cross talk.

runaway — Any additive condition to which continued exposure will eventually destroy a device.

run book — All the material needed to document a run of a program on a computer.

run motor — In facsimile equipment, a motor which supplies the power to drive the scanning or recording mechanisms. A synchronous motor is used to limit the speed.

running circuit breaker — A device the principal function of which is to connect a machine to its source of running voltage after having been brought up to the desired speed on the starting connection.

running torque — The turning power of a motor when running at its rated speed.

runway-localizing beacon — A small radio-range beacon that provides accurate directional guidance along the runway of an airport and for some distance beyond it.

rupture — The ability of contacts to break apart or rupture the electrical flow without welding under excessive currents.

rupture (or interrupting) capacity — The maximum current that a protective device will interrupt. Specified as the number of interruptions in amperes (adjusted circuit) without a change in calibration or a failure of dielectric strength.

rush-box — A superregenerative receiver.

rutherford — A quantity of radioactive material that produces one million disintegrations per second. Abbreviated rd.

ryotron — A thin-film inductive superconductive device. An inductive switch capable of inductance variation of better than three orders of magnitude.

R — Y signal — In color television, the red-minus-luminance color-difference signal. When combined with the luminance (Y) signal, it produces the red primary signal.

S

S — Symbol for secondary.

sabin (square-foot unit of absorption) — A measure of the sound absorption of a surface. It is equivalent to 1 square foot of a perfectly absorptive surface. (*Also see* Equivalent Absorption.)

saddle — Insulation placed under a splice in a coil lead.

safety factor — The amount by which the normal operating rating of a device can be exceeded without causing failure of the device.

safety service — A radiocommunication service used permanently or temporarily for the safeguarding of human life and property.

St. Elmo's fire — A visible electric discharge sometimes seen at the tips of aircraft propellers or wings, the mast of a ship, or any other metal point where there is considerable atmospheric difference of potential due to concentration of the electric field at the points of the conductor.

sal-ammoniac cell—A cell in which the electrolyte consists primarily of a solution of ammonium chloride.

salient pole—A pole consisting of a separate radial projection having its own iron pole piece and its own field coil, used in the field system of a generator or motor.

Salisbury darkbox—An isolating chamber used for test work in connection with radar equipment. The walls of the chamber are specially constructed to absorb all imping-ing microwave energy at a certain frequency.

sample—1. A specimen of a product selected to represent all units in a batch for inspec-tion purposes. 2. One or more units of product drawn from a lot, the units being selected at random without regard to their quality.

sample and hold—A circuit used in an ana-log-to-digital converter whenever it is de-sirable to make a measurement of a signal and to know precisely when the input sig-nal corresponds to the results of the mea-surement. It is also used to increase the duration of a signal.

sample pulse—*See* Strobe Pulse.

sampler—*See* Sampling Circuit.

sampling circuit—Also called a sampler. A circuit the output of which is a series of discrete values representative of the values of the input at a series of points in time.

sampling gate—A device which must be activated by a selector pulse before it will extract information from the input wave-form.

sampling oscilloscope—An oscilloscope tech-nique very similar in principle to the use of stroboscopic light to study fast mechani-cal motion. Progressive samples of adja-cent portions of successive waveforms are taken; then they are "stretched" in time, amplified by relatively low-bandwidth am-plifiers, and finally shown, one sample at a time, on the screen of a cathode-ray tube. The graph produced is a replica of the sampled waveforms. The principal difference in appearance between displays made by sampling techniques and conventional dis-plays is that those made by sampling com-prise separate segments or dots. This technique is limited to depicting repetitive signals, since no more than one sample is taken and displayed each time the signal oc-curs and provides a means for examining fast-changing signals of low amplitude that cannot be examined in any other way.

sampling plan—A program for the accept-ance or rejection of a lot based on tests or inspections indicating the quality of pre-determined sample sizes.

sampling rate—The number of times that a particular data channel is sampled by a commutator in one second.

sampling theory—A sampling theorem (de-veloped by Nyquist in 1928) which states

that two samples per cycle will completely characterize a band-limited signal; that is, the sampling rate must be twice the highest-frequency component. (In practice, the sampling rate is ordinarily from five to ten times the highest frequency.)

sand load—An attenuator used as a terminat-ing section on a transmission line to dis-sipate power. The space between inner and outer conductors is filled with a sand and carbon mixture which acts as the dissipative element.

sandwich—A packaging method in which components are placed between boards or layers.

sapphire—A gem used on the tip of quality phonograph needles, and also for bearings in precision instruments.

satellite—A tv station licensed to rebroad-cast the programming of a parent station. It differs from a translator in that satellite power limits are much higher, and satellites may also originate some programming.

saturable-core magnetometer—A magne-tometer in which the change in permeability of a ferromagnetic core provides a measure of the field.

saturable-core oscillator—A relaxation os-cillator in which the occurrence of satura-tion in a magnetic core initiates a change in the conductive state of amplifying or switch-ing elements.

saturable-core reactor—*See* Saturable Re-actor.

saturable reactor—Also called a saturable-core reactor. A magnetic-core reactor, the reactance of which is controlled by chang-ing the saturation of the core by varying a superimposed unidirectional flux.

saturable transformer—A saturable reactor with an additional winding to provide volt-age transformation or isolation from the a-c supply.

saturated color—A pure color—i.e., one not contaminated by white.

saturated recovery time—The recovery time of a thermal relay measured when the relay is de-energized after temperature saturation (equilibrium) has been reached.

saturated reoperate time—Reoperate time of a thermal relay when temperature satu-ration (equilibrium) is reached before the relay is de-energized.

saturating reactor—A magnetic-core reactor capable of operating in the region of satura-tion without independent control means.

saturating signal—In radar, a signal of greater amplitude than the dynamic range of the receiving system.

saturation—1. The attribute of any color per-ception possessing a hue that determines the degree of its difference from the achromatic color perception most resembling it. 2. The operating condition of a transistor when an increase in base current produces no further increase in collector current. 3. The state of magnetism beyond which a metal or alloy is incapable of further magnetization—i.e., the point beyond which the BH curve is a straight line. 4. A circuit condition whereby an increase in the driving or input signal no longer produces a change in the output. 5. The condition when a transistor is driven so hard that it becomes biased in the forward direction. In a switching application, the charge stored in the base region prevents the transistor from turning off quickly under saturation conditions.

saturation absorption—The condition obtainable between pairs of electron energy levels in which, under very high radiation intensity, the absorption coefficient gradually decreases to zero because of the absence of empty levels to which transition can occur.

saturation control—In a color television receiver, a control which regulates the amplitude of the chrominance signal. The latter, in turn, determines the color saturation.

saturation current—1. The current in the plate circuit of a vacuum tube when all electrons emitted by the cathode pass on to the plate. 2. The current that flows between the base and collector of a transistor when an increase in the emitter-to-base voltage causes no further increase in the collector current.

saturation curve—A magnetization curve for a ferromagnetic material.

saturation flux density—*See* Saturation Induction.

saturation induction—Sometimes loosely referred to as saturation flux density. The maximum intrinsic induction possible in a material.

saturation limiting—Limiting the minimum output voltage of a vacuum-tube circuit by operating the tube in the region of plate-current saturation.

saturation magnetization—The magnetic condition of a body when an increase in the magnetizing force produces practically no change in the intensity of magnetization.

saturation noise—The noise arising when a uniformly saturated tape is reproduced. This is often some 15 db higher than the bulk-erased noise and is associated with imperfect particle dispersion.

saturation point—The point beyond which an increase in one of two quantities produces no increase in the other.

saturation resistance—Ratio of voltage to current in a saturated semiconductor.

saturation value—1. The highest value that can be obtained under given conditions. 2. The value of magnetic-flux density beyond which increases in the magnetizing force have no appreciable effect on the flux density in a particular sample of magnetic material.

saturation voltage—1. The voltage drop appearing across a switching transistor that is fully turned on. 2. Generally, the voltage excursion at which a circuit self-limits (i.e.,

is unable to respond to excitation in a proportional manner). In operational amplifiers, the output-voltage saturation limits may be imposed by any stage, from the input to the output, depending in part on the external loading and feedback parameters.

sawtooth current—A current that has a sawtooth waveform.

sawtooth generator—An oscillator providing an alternating voltage with a sawtooth waveform.

sawtooth voltage—A voltage that varies between two values in such a manner that the waveshape resembles the teeth of a saw.

Sawtooth wave.

sawtooth wave—A periodic wave, the amplitude of which varies linearly between two values. A longer interval is required for one direction of progress than for the other.

saxophone— A linear-array antenna with a cosecant-squared radiation pattern.

SBA—Abbreviation for standard beam approach.

S-band—A radio-frequency band of 1,550 to 5,200 MHz, with wavelengths of 19.35 to 5.77 cm.

SBT—Abbreviation for surface-barrier transistor.

scalar—A quantity that has magnitude but no direction (e.g., real numbers).

scalar frequency meter—A frequency meter in which electronic circuits are used for counting and gating electrical signals to indicate their number and/or rate.

scalar function—A function which has magnitude only. Thus, the scalar product of two vectors is a scalar function, as is a real function of a real variable.

scalar quantity— Any quantity which has magnitude only — e.g., time, temperature, quantity of electricity.

scale—1. A series of musical notes, symbols, sensations, or stimuli arranged from low to high by a specified scheme of intervals suitable for musical purposes. 2. The theoretical basis of a numerical system. 3. A series of markings used for measurement or computation. 4. A defined set of values, in terms of which different quantities of the same nature can be measured. 5. In a computer, to change the units of a variable so that the problem is within its capacity.

scale division—The space between two adjacent markings on a scale.

scale factor—1. In analog computing, a proportionality factor which relates the magnitude of a variable to its representation within a computer. 2. In digital computing, the arbitrary factor which may be associated with numbers in a computer to adjust the position of the radix point so that the significant digits occupy specified columns. 3. The factor by which the number of scale divisions indicated or recorded by an instrument must be multiplied to compute the value of the measurand. 4. A value used to convert a quantity from one notation to another.

scale length of an indicating instrument—The length of the path described by the tip of the pointer (or other indicating means) in moving from one end of the scale to the other.

scale-of-ten circuit—*See* Decade Scaler.

scale-of-two counter—A flip-flop circuit in which successive similar pulses are applied at a common point, causing the circuit to alternate between its two conditions of permanent stability.

scaler—Also called a scaling circuit. A circuit which produces an output after a predetermined number of input pulses have been received.

scale span—The algebraic difference between the values of the actuating electrical quantity corresponding to the two ends of the scale of an instrument.

scaling—1. An electronic method of counting electrical pulses occurring too fast to be handled by mechanical recorders. 2. The changing of a quantity from one notation to another. 3. Adjusting the coefficient of a circuit to each of its one or more input-signal terminals. The relative scaling of one input to another is called weighting. 4. In computing, relating problem variables to machine variables.

scaling circuit—*See* Scaler.

scaling factor—Also called the scaling ratio. The number of input pulses per output pulse required by a scaler.

scaling ratio—*See* Scaling Factor.

scalloping distortion—In video tape recording, a series of small, vertical curves in the recorded image. Caused by unequal stretching across the width of the videotape.

scan—1. In facsimile, to analyze the density of successive elemental areas of the subject copy in a predetermined pattern at the transmitter, or to record these areas at the recorder. 2. To examine point by point—e.g., in converting a televised scene or image into a methodical sequence of elemental areas. 3. One sweep of the mosaic in a camera tube or of the screen in a picture tube.

scan-coded tracking system—*See* Monopulse Tracking.

scan converter—A unit for converting electronic-scan data to synchro-bearing data.

scan-converter tube—A device consisting of a cathode-ray tube and a vidicon imaging tube assembled face-to-face in the same envelope.

scanistor—An integrated semiconductor optical-scanning device that converts images into electrical signals. The output analog signal represents both the amount and the position of the light shining on its surface.

scanner—1. An instrument which automatically samples or interrogates the state of various processes, conditions, or physical states and initiates action in accordance with the information obtained. 2. In a facsimile transmitter, the part which systematically translates the densities of the subject copy into the signal waveform.

scanner amplifier—A vacuum-tube amplifier in a facsimile transmitter used to amplify the output-signal voltage of the scanner.

scanning—1. In television, facsimile, or picture transmission, the successive analyzing or synthesizing, according to a predetermined method, of the light values or equivalent characteristics of elements constituting a picture area. 2. In radar, the directing of a beam of radio-frequency energy successively over the elements of a given region, or the corresponding process in reception.

scanning-antenna mount—An antenna support which provides a mechanical means for scanning or tracking with the antenna, and a means for taking off information and using it for indication and control.

scanning beam—A beam of light, a radar beam, or an electron beam that is used in scanning.

scanning circuit—1. A circuit which produces a linear, circular, or other movement of the beam in a cathode-ray tube at regular intervals. 2. Also called sweep circuit. That part of a cathode-ray oscilloscope which provides a time-reference base.

scanning disc—1. A rotating tricolor wheel used between the camera lens and subject, or picture tube and viewer, in field-sequential color television. 2. A Nipkow disc.

scanning frequency—*See* Stroke Speed.

scanning head—A light source and a phototube combined as a single unit for scanning a moving strip of paper, cloth, or metal in photoelectric side-register control systems.

scanning line—1. In television, the single, continuous narrow strip determined by the scanning process. In most systems, the scanning lines are blanked during the return intervals. The number of scanning lines is equal to the ratio of the line to the frame frequency. 2. A single, narrow, continuous strip containing highlights, shadows, and halftones of the picture area, as determined by the scanning process.

scanning linearity—In television, the uniformity of the scanning speed during the trace interval.

scanning-line frequency—The number of scanning lines per second. *Also see* Stroke Speed.

scanning loss—In a radar system employing

a scanning antenna, the reduced sensitivity that occurs in scanning across a target, compared with the sensitivity when a constant beam is directed at the target. This loss is expressed in decibels.

scanning sonar—An echo-ranging system in which the sound pulse is transmitted simultaneously through the entire angle to be searched and a rapidly rotating transducer having a narrow beam angle scans for the returning echoes.

scanning speed—The number of inches per second explored by the spot of light or other source of energy in television, facsimile, radar, etc.

scanning spot—The immediate area being explored at any instant by a spot of light or other energy source in television, facsimile, radar, etc. *Also see* Picture Element.

scanning yoke—A yoke-shaped iron core that supports the electromagnetic deflecting coils around the neck of some cathode-ray tubes.

scannogram—The recording made on paper by a scanner.

scan rate—The rate at which a control computer periodically checks a controlled quantity.

scatter—1. A disordered change in the direction of propagation when radio waves encounter matter. 2. Spurious radar echoes due to reflections from layers of the ionosphere.

scatterband—In pulse systems, the total bandwidth occupied by the frequency spread of numerous interrogations operating on the same nominal radio frequency.

scattered reflections—Reflections from portions of the ionosphere at different virtual heights. These reflections interfere with each other and cause rapid fading of the signal.

scattering—1. The change in direction, frequency, or polarization of radio waves when they encounter matter. 2. In a narrower sense, a disordered change in the incident energy of (1) above. 3. The change of direction of particles or photons colliding with other particles or systems. 4. The diffusion of a sound or light beam due to discontinuities in the transmitting medium.

scattering loss—That part of the transmission lost because of scattering within the medium or the roughness of the reflecting surface.

scatter propagation—Also called beyond-the-horizon propagation, or over-the-horizon transmission. Transmission of high-power radio waves beyond line-of-sight distances by reflecting them from the troposphere or ionosphere.

scatter read—The ability of a computer to distribute data into several memory areas as it is being entered into the system from magnetic tape.

scc wire—Abbreviation for single-cotton-covered wire.

SCEPTRON—Acronym for Spectral ComparativE PaTtern RecOgNizer. A device which

Scatter propagation.

automatically classifies complex signals derived from any type of information that can be changed into an electrical signal.

sce wire—Abbreviation for single-cotton covering over enamel insulation on a wire.

schematic circuit diagram — *See* Schematic Diagram.

schematic diagram—Also called a schematic circuit diagram, diagram, or schematic. A diagram of the electrical scheme of a circuit, with components represented by graphical symbols.

$$C_x R_2 = C_s R_1$$
$$C_x R_x = C_1 R_1$$

Schering bridge.

Schering bridge—A four-arm alternating-current bridge used for measuring capacitance and dissipation factor. The unknown capacitor and a standard loss-free capacitor form two adjacent arms, the arm adjacent to the standard capacitor consists of a resistor and capacitor in parallel, and the fourth arm is a nonreactive resistor.

Schmidt optical system—An optical system for magnifying and projecting a small, brilliant image from a projection-type cathode-ray tube onto a screen.

Schmitt limiter—*See* Schmitt Trigger.

Schmitt trigger—Also called Schmitt limiter. A bistable pulse generator in which an out-

Schmitt trigger.

put pulse of constant amplitude exists only as long as the input voltage exceeds a certain d-c value.

scintillation — 1. In radio propagation, a random and usually relatively small fluctuation of the received field about its mean value. 2. Also called target glint or wander. On a radar display, a rapid apparent displacement of the target from its mean position. 3. The flash of light produced by an ionic action.

scintillation conversion efficiency — In a scintillator, the ratio of the optical photon energy emitted to the energy of the incident particle or photon of ionizing radiation.

scintillation counter — A device that indirectly detects charged particles and gamma rays and neutrons by using a photomultiplier tube to convert the short flashes of light, produced as the particle passes through a transparent scintillating material, into electric signals which can be recorded. One advantage of scintillation counters is that they are very fast; i.e., they have a very small resolving time.

scintillation-counter cesium resolution — The scintillation-counter energy resolution for the gamma ray or conversion electron emitted from cesium-137.

scintillation-counter energy resolution — In a scintillation counter, a measure of the smallest discernible difference in energy between two particles or photons of ionizing radiation.

scintillation-counter energy-resolution constant — The product of the square of the scintillation-counter energy resolution times the specified energy.

scintillation-counter head — The combination of scintillators and photosensitive devices that produces electrical signals in response to ionizing radiation.

scintillation-counter time discrimination — In a scintillation counter, a measure of the smallest time interval between two successive individually discernible events. Quantitatively, the standard deviation of the time-interval curve.

scintillation decay time — The time required for the decrease of the rate of emission of

optical photons in a scintillation from 90% to 10% of the maximum value.

scintillation duration — The interval from the time of emission of the first optical photon of a scintillation to the time when 90% of the optical photons of the scintillation have been emitted.

scintillation rise time — The time interval occupied by the increase of the rate of emission of optical photons of a scintillation from 10% to 90% of the maximum value.

scintillator — The combination of the body of scintillator material and its container.

scintillator material — A material that exhibits the property of emitting optical photons in response to ionizing radiation.

scintillator-material total-conversion efficiency — In a scintillator material, the ratio of the produced optical photon energy to the energy of a particle or photon of ionizing radiation that is entirely absorbed in the scintillator material.

scope — Slang for a cathode-ray oscilloscope.

scophony television system — A mechanical television projection system developed in England. The light-storage phenomenon of a supersonic light valve is utilized, and ingenious optical and mechanical methods provide large, bright images suitable for theater installation as well as home television receivers. The apparent screen brightness is multiplied several hundred times because several hundred picture elements are projected simultaneously.

scoring system — In motion-picture production, a system for recording music in time with the action on the film.

Scott connection — A method of connecting transformers to convert two-phase power to three-phase or vice versa.

scr — Abbreviation for silicon controlled rectifier.

scramble — 1. To transpose and/or invert bands of frequencies, or otherwise modify the form of the intelligence at the transmitting end, according to a prearranged scheme, to obtain secrecy. 2. To make telephony unintelligible to casual interception. 3. To mix, in cryptography, in a random or quasi-random fashion.

scrambled speech — Also called inverted speech. Speech that has been made unintelligible (e.g., for secret transmission) by inverting its frequency. At the receiving end, it can then be converted back into intelligible speech by reinverting the frequency.

scrambler circuit — Also called a speech scrambler. A circuit where essential speech frequencies are divided into several ranges by filters and then inverted to produce scrambled speech. (*Also see* Speech Inverter.)

scratch filter — A low-pass filter which minimizes the needle-scratch output of a phonograph pickup by suppressing the higher audio frequencies.

screen — 1. The surface upon which the

visible pattern is produced in a cathode-ray tube. 2. A metal partition which isolates a device from external electric or magnetic fields. 3. *See* Screen Grid.

screen angle—A vertical angle bounded by a straight line from the radar antenna to the horizon and the horizontal at the antenna, assuming a 4/3 earth's radius.

screen dissipation—The power which the screen grid dissipates as heat after bombardment by the electron stream.

screen grid—Also called a screen. A grid placed between a control grid and an anode and usually maintained at a fixed positive potential. By reducing the electrostatic influence of the anode, it prevents the electrons from bunching in the space between the screen grid and the cathode.

screen-grid modulation — Modulation produced by introducing the signal into the screen-grid circuit of any multigrid tube where the carrier is present.

screen-grid tube—A vacuum tube in which a grid is placed between the control grid and the anode to prevent the latter from reacting with the control grid.

screen-grid voltage — The direct-voltage value applied between the screen grid and the cathode of a vacuum tube.

S-curve—An S-shaped frequency-response curve showing how the output of a frequency-modulation detector or circuit varies with frequency.

sea clutter—*See* Sea Return.

seal—A structure in which a metal part is embedded into glass or ceramic in such a way that the two are tightly bonded together.

sealed contacts—A contact assembly enclosed in a sealed compartment separate from the other parts of the relay.

sealed-gage pressure transducer—A pressure transducer that has the sensing element sealed in its case at room ambient pressure. The sealing method holds the original internal pressure for long periods of time.

sealed meter — A meter constructed so that moisture or vapor cannot enter the meter under specified test conditions.

sealed tube—Used chiefly for pool-cathode tubes. A hermetically sealed electron tube.

sealing compound—A type of wax or pitch compound used in dry batteries, capacitor blocks, transformers, or circuit units to keep out air and moisture.

sealing off—The final closing of the bulb of a vacuum tube or lamp after evacuation.

seam welding—A resistance welding process in which overlapping spot welds are made progressively along a joint by means of circular electrodes. The circular seam-welding wheels roll along the overlapping edges to be welded, and the control circuit is arranged to pass current at sufficiently close intervals to produce the desired degree of overlapping of the spot welds. The primary purpose of a seam-welding joint is to produce liquidtight or airtight containers from comparatively thin sheet metal.

search—1. In radar operation, the directing of the lobe (beam of radiated energy) in order to cover a large area. A broad-beam antenna may be used, or a rotating or scanning antenna. 2. A systematic examination of the available information in a specific field of interest. 3. To scan available stored information.

search coil—*See* Magnetic Test Coil.

search gate—A gate pulse which is made to search back and forth over a certain range.

searchlighting—In radar, the opposite of scanning. Instead, the beam is projected continuously at an object.

searchlight-type sonar — An echo-ranging system employing the same narrow beam pattern for both transmission and reception.

search radar—A radar intended primarily for displaying targets as soon as possible after their entrance into the coverage area.

search receiver—*See* Intercept Receiver.

sea return—Also called sea clutter. In radar, the aggregate received echoes reflected from the sea.

seasonal factors—Factors which are used to adjust sky-wave absorption data for seasonal variations. These variations are due primarily to seasonal fluctuations in the heights of the ionospheric layers.

seasoning—Overcoming a temporary unsteadiness of a component which may appear when the component is first installed.

seating time—The elapsed time after the coil of a relay has been energized to the time required to seat the armature of the relay.

sec—Abbreviation for second or for secondary winding of a transformer.

secondary—1. The transformer output winding where the current flow is due to inductive coupling with another coil called the primary. 2. Low-voltage conductors of a power distributing system.

secondary area—*See* Secondary Service Area.

secondary calibration—Also called sense step. Calibration of accessory equipment in which a transducer is deliberately unbalanced electrically to change the output voltage, current, or impedance. Generally performed by means of a calibration resistor which is placed across one leg of the bridge.

secondary cell—A voltaic cell which, after being discharged, may be restored to a charged condition by an electric current sent through the cell in a direction opposite that of the discharge current. *Also see* Storage Cell.

secondary color—A color produced by combining any two primary colors in equal proportions. In the light-additive process, the three secondary colors are cyan, magenta, and yellow.

secondary electron—The electron knocked loose from a molecule by another electron.

secondary-electron multiplier—An amplifier tube in which the electron stream is focused onto a succession of targets, each of which adds its secondary electrons to the stream. In this way, considerable amplification is provided.

secondary emission—The liberation of electrons from an element, other than the cathode, as a result of being struck by other high-velocity electrons. In a vacuum tube there are usually more secondary than primary electrons—a desirable phenomenon in electron-multiplier or dynatron-oscillator tubes. However, pentodes have a suppressor grid to nullify the undesirable effect of secondary emission.

secondary-emission ratio—The average number of secondary electrons emitted from a surface per incident primary electron.

secondary-emission tube—A tube which makes use of secondary emission to achieve a useful end. The photomultiplier is an example.

secondary failure—1. A failure occurring as a direct result of the abnormal stress on a component brought about by the failure of another part or parts. 2. Any failure that is the direct or indirect result of a primary failure.

secondary grid emission—Emission from the grid of a tube as a result of high-velocity electrons being driven against it and knocking off additional electrons. The effect is the same as for primary grid emission.

secondary line—The conductors connected between the secondaries of distribution transformers and the consumer service entrances.

secondary radar—*See* Radar.

secondary radiation—Random reradiation of electromagnetic waves.

secondary service area—Also called the secondary area. The service area of a radio or television broadcast station within which satisfactory reception can be obtained only under favorable conditions.

secondary standard—A unit (e.g., length, capacitance, weight) used as a standard of comparison in individual countries or localities, but checked against the one primary standard in existence somewhere in the world.

secondary storage—Storage which is not an integral part of a computer, but which is directly linked to and controlled by it.

secondary voltage—The voltage across the secondary winding of a transformer.

secondary winding—The winding on the output side of a transformer.

secondary X-rays—X-rays given off by an object irradiated with X-rays. Their frequency depends on the material in the object.

second breakdown—A condition in which the output impedance of a transistor changes almost instantaneously from a large value to a small limiting value. It may be distinguished from normal transistor operation by the fact that once it occurs, the base no longer controls normal collector characteristics. Second breakdown is associated with imperfections in the device structure, usually being more severe in multiple-diffused, high-speed devices.

second-channel attenuation—*See* Selectance.

second-channel interference—Also called alternate-channel interference. Interference in which the extraneous power originates from an assigned (authorized) signal two channels away from the desired channel.

second detector—Also called a demodulator. In a superheterodyne receiver, the portion that separates the audio component from the modulated intermediate frequency.

section—A four-terminal network which cannot be divided into a cascade of two simpler four-terminal networks.

sectionalized vertical antenna—A vertical antenna in which the continuity is broken at one or more points by the insertion of reactances or driving voltages.

Sectoral horn.

sectoral horn—A horn with two parallel and two diverging sides.

sector cable—A multiconductor cable in which the cross section of each conductor is essentially a sector of a circle, an ellipse, or some figure intermediate between them. Sector cables are used in order to make possible the use of larger conductors in a cable of given diameter.

sector display—A range-amplitude display used with a radar set. The antenna system rotates continuously, and the screen (of the long-persistence type) is excited only while the beam is within a narrow sector centered on the object.

sector scan—A scan in which the antenna oscillates through a selected angle.

sector scanning—Modified circular scanning in which only a portion of the plane or flat cone is generated.

secular variation—A slow variation in the strength of the earth's magnetic field.

Seebeck coefficient of a couple—For homogeneous conductors, the limit, as the difference in temperature approaches zero, of the quotient of the Seebeck emf divided by the temperature difference between the junctions. By convention, the Seebeck coefficient of a couple is considered positive if, at the cold junction, the first-named conductor has a positive potential with respect to the second. It is the algebraic difference between either the relative or absolute Seebeck coefficients of the two conductors.

Seebeck effect—The production of an emf when two properly chosen materials form a closed circuit and one junction is hotter than the other.

Seebeck emf—Also called thermal emf. The emf produced by the Seebeck effect.

seed—A special single crystal from which large single crystals are grown by the Czochralski technique.

segment—1. In a routine, the part short enough to be stored entirely in the internal storage of a computer, yet containing all the coding necessary to call in and jump automatically to other segments. 2. To divide a program into an integral number of parts, each of which performs a part of the total program and is short enough to be completely stored in internal memory.

segmented thermoelectric arm—A thermoelectric arm made up of two or more materials that have different compositions.

segmenting—*See* Partitioning.

seismic mass—The force-summing member for applying acceleration and/or gravitational force in an accelerometer.

seismograph—An instrument for recording the time, direction, and intensity of earthquakes or of earth shocks produced by explosions.

Seitz breakdown theory—Breakdown is due to the attainment of a critical avalanche size which leads to a conducting path.

selectance—1. A measure of the drop in response as a resonant device loses its resonance. It is the ratio of the amplitude of response at the resonant frequency, to the response at some other, specified frequency. 2. Often expressed as adjacent-channel attenuation (aca) or second-channel attenuation (2aca). The reciprocal of the ratio of the sensitivity of a receiver tuned to a specified channel, to its sensitivity at another channel a specified number of channels away.

selected mode—A mode of operation for an encoder selector circuit in which one set of brushes is selected to be read and another inhibited from being read; also a mode of operation for a system controlling several encoder outputs in which the encoder is selected to be read and all others inhibited from being read.

selection check—A verification of a computer instruction, usually automatic, to in-

sure that the correct register or device has been chosen.

selection ratio—The ratio of the least magnetomotive force used to select a cell or core to the maximum magnetomotive force used which is not intended to select a cell or core.

selective—The characteristic of responding to a desired frequency to a greater degree than to other frequencies.

selective absorption—Absorption of rays of a certain group of frequencies only.

selective calling—A means of calling in which code signals are transmitted for the purpose of activating the automatic attention device at the station being called.

selective dump—A dump of a selected area of internal storage.

selective fading—Fading in which the received signal does not have the same variation in strength for all frequencies in the band. Selective fading usually occurs during multipath transmission.

selective interference—Interference the energy of which is concentrated within narrow frequency bands.

selective squelch—*See* Squelch Circuit.

selectivity—1. The characteristic which determines the extent to which the desired signal can be differentiated from disturbances of other frequencies. 2. The ability of a receiver to reject transmissions other than the one to which it is tuned. Usually shown by a curve on which the input-signal voltage required to produce a constant power output is plotted against frequency. 3. The degree to which a radio receiver can accept the signals of one station, while rejecting those of all other stations on adjacent channels.

selectivity control—The control for making a receiver more selective.

select lines—In a core memory array, the wires which pass through magnetic cores and carry the selecting coincident currents.

selector—1. On a punch-card machine, a mechanism which reports a condition and accordingly causes a card or an operation to be selected. 2. In a telephone system, the switch or relay-group switching systems that select the path the call is to take through the system. It operates under the control of the dial at the calling station. 3. A sequential switch, usually multicontact or motor driven.

selector pulse—A pulse used to identify one event of a series.

selector relay—A relay capable of automatically selecting one or more circuits.

selector switch—A multiposition switch that permits one or more conductors to be connected to any of several other conductors.

selectron—A computer-memory tube capable of storing 256 binary digits and permitting very rapid selection and access.

selenium—A chemical element with marked photosensitive properties and a resistance that varies inversely with illumination. It is used as a rectifier layer in metallic rectifiers.

selenium cell—A photoconductive cell consisting of selenium between suitable electrodes.

selenium rectifier—A metallic rectifier in which a thin layer of selenium is deposited on one side of an aluminum plate and a highly conductive metal is coated over it.

Selenium rectifier.

Electrons flow more freely from the coating to the selenium than in the opposite direction, thereby providing rectification.

self-adaptive system—A system which can exhibit the qualities of reorganization and/or learning.

self and systems testing and checkout— Logical and numerical processing for the purpose of exercising and monitoring responses of the system and the functioning of the computer itself.

self-balancing recorder—A recording device operating on the servomechanism principle.

self-bias—1. The voltage developed by the flow of vacuum-tube current through a resistor in a grid or cathode lead. 2. Also called automatic bias. A form of tube bias utilizing the voltage drop developed across a resistor through which either cathode or grid current flows.

self-capacitance — *See* Distributed Capacitance.

self-checking code—In computers, a code in which errors produce forbidden combinations. A single error-detecting code produces a forbidden combination if a digit gains or loses a single bit. A double error-detecting code produces a forbidden combination if a digit gains or loses either one or two bits, and so forth.

self-cleaning contacts—*See* Wiping Contacts.

self-complementing code — A machine language in which the code of the complement of a digit is the complement of the code of the digit.

self-contained instrument — An instrument which has all the necessary equipment built into it or the case.

self-demagnetization—The process by which a magnetized sample of magnetic material tends to demagnetize itself by virtue of the opposing fields created within it by its own magnetization.

self-excitation—The supplying of field current to a generator from its own armature.

self-excited oscillator—An oscillator that operates without external excitation and solely by the direct voltages applied to the electrode. It depends on its resonant circuits for frequency determination (i.e., not crystal controlled).

self-extinguishing — Material which ignites and burns when exposed to flame or elevated temperature, but which stops burning when the flame or high temperature is removed.

self-focused picture tube—A television picture tube with an automatic electrostatic focus designed into the electron gun.

self-generating transducer — A transducer which requires no external electrical excitation to provide an output.

self-healing capacitor—A capacitor that restores itself to operation after a breakdown caused by excessive voltage.

self-heated thermistor—A thermistor the body temperature of which is significantly higher than the temperature of its ambient medium as a result of the power being dissipated in it.

self-impedance—At any pair of terminals of a network, the ratio of an applied potential difference to the resultant current at these terminals (all other terminals open).

self-inductance—The property which determines the amount of electromotive force induced in a circuit whenever the current changes in the circuit.

self-induction — The property whereby a varying current will produce a voltage in a circuit.

self-inductor—An inductor used for changing the self-inductance of a circuit.

self-instructed carry—A system of executing the carry process in a computer by allowing information to propagate to succeeding places as soon as it is generated, without receipt of a specific signal.

self-latching relay—A relay in which the armature remains mechanically locked in the energized position until deliberately reset.

self-locking nut—A nut with an inherent locking action, so it cannot readily be loosened by vibration.

self-organizing machines—Machines that can recognize, or learn to recognize, such stimuli as patterns, characters, and sound, and which can then adapt to a changing environment.

self-powered—Equipment containing its own power supply. It may be either a combination of wet and dry cells, or dry cells in conjunction with a spring-driven motor.

self-pulse modulation — Modulation accomplished by using an internally generated pulse. (*Also see* Blocking Oscillator.)

self-pulsing—A special type of grid-pulsing circuit which automatically stops and starts the oscillations at the pulsing rate.

self-quenched counter tube—A radiation-counter tube in which reignition of the discharge is inhibited.

self-quenched detector—A superregenerative detector in which the grid-leak–grid-capacitor time constant is sufficiently large to cause intermittent oscillation above audio frequencies. As a result, normal regeneration is stopped just before it spills over into a squealing condition.

self-quenching oscillator—An intermittent self-oscillator producing a series of short trains of r-f oscillations separated by intervals of quiescence. The quiescence is caused by rectified oscillatory currents, which build up to the point where they cut off the oscillations.

self-rectifying X-ray tube—An X-ray tube operating with an alternating anode potential.

self regulation — The tendency of a component or system to resist change in its condition or state of operation.

self-repeating timer — A form of time-delay circuit in which relay contacts are used to restart the time delay.

self-reset—Automatically returning to the original position when normal conditions are resumed (applied chiefly to relays and circuit breakers).

self-saturating rectifier—A half-wave rectifying-circuit element connected in series with the output windings of a saturable reactor in a self-saturating magnetic-amplifier circuit.

self-saturation—The saturation obtained in a magnetic amplifier by rectifying the output current of a saturable reactor.

self-screening range—The range at which a target can be detected by a radar in the midst of its jamming mask, with a certain specified probability.

self-selecting V scan—The V-scan method of reading a polystrophic code (primarily the binary code) in which diode logic circuits are used internally in the encoder to perform the necessary bit-to-bit selection to prevent ambiguity in the encoder output data.

self-starting synchronous motor—A synchronous motor provided with the equivalent of a squirrel-cage winding so it can be started like an induction motor.

self-sustained oscillations — Oscillations maintained by the energy fed back from the output to the input circuit.

self-testing—The ability of a piece of equipment to automatically verify the proper operation of its components or subsystems.

self-threading reel—A device for spooling and storing tape; in particular, one which does not require external aid to affix or start the first turn of tape on its winding surface or hub. Flanges on such reels can be continuous and free of windows; winding surfaces are continuous and free of distortion-producing threading slots.

self-wiping contacts—*See* Wiping Contacts.

selsyn—*See* Synchro.

semiactive repeater — A communications satellite which uses a minimum of on-board electronics to take a modulated signal beamed at it from a ground station and transfer its information (modulation) into an unmodulated beam (on a different frequency) sent up by the receiving station. For this transfer it uses Van Atta or other directive arrays and nonlinear elements.

semiautomatic tape relay—A method of communication whereby messages are received and retransmitted in teletypewriter tape form involving manual intervention in the transfer of the tape from the receiving reperforator to the automatic transmitter.

semiconducting material—A solid or liquid having a resistivity midway between that of an insulator and a metal.

semiconductor—A solid or liquid electronic conductor, with resistivity between that of metals and that of insulators, in which the electrical charge carrier concentration increases with increasing temperature over some temperature range. Over most of the practical temperature range, the resistance has a negative temperature coefficient. Certain semiconductors possess two types of carriers, negative electrons and positive holes. The charge carriers are usually electrons, but there may be also some ionic conductivity.

semiconductor chip—A single piece of semiconductor material of any dimension.

semiconductor device—A device in which the characteristic that distinguishes electronic conduction takes place within a semiconducting material.

semiconductor diode—1. An inactive semiconductor device with a nonlinear voltage-characteristic and two terminals. 2. A light-emitting diode that emits coherent light by suitably arranged geometry. Gallium arsenide is used for lasers of this type.

semiconductor-diode parametric amplifier —A parametric amplifier using one or more varactors.

semiconductor integrated circuit—A number of electrical elements inseparably associated on or within a continuous body of semiconductor material to perform a circuit function. *See* Monolithic IC.

semiconductor integrated circuits — Complex circuits fabricated by suitable and selective modification of areas on and in wafers of semiconductor material to produce patterns of interconnected passive and active elements. The circuit may be assembled from several chips and use thin-film elements or discrete components.

semiconductor intrinsic properties—Properties of a semiconductor that are characteristic to the ideal crystal.

semiconductor junction—The region of transition between semiconducting regions of different electrical properties, usually between P-type and N-type materials.

semiconductor laser—A light-emitting diode that uses stimulated emission to produce a coherent-light output. *Also see* Diode Laser.

semiconductor material — A material in which the conductivity ranges between that of a conductor and an insulator. The electrical characteristics of semiconductor materials such as silicon are dependent upon the small amounts of added impurities or dopants.

semidirectional microphone—A microphone, the field response of which is determined by the angle of incidence in part of the frequency range but is substantially independent of the angle of incidence in the remaining part.

semiduplex — In a communications circuit, a method of operation in which one end is duplex and one end simplex. This type of operation is sometimes used in mobile systems with the base station duplex and the mobile station or stations simplex. A semiduplex system requires two operating frequencies.

semimagnetic controller—An electrical controller in which not all its basic functions are performed by electromagnets.

semimetals—Materials such as bismuth, antimony, and arsenic having characteristics that class them between semiconductors and metals.

semiremote control—Radio-transmitter control performed near the transmitter by devices connected to but not an integral part of the transmitter.

semitone—Also called half step. The interval between two sounds. Its basic frequency ratio is equal to approximately the twelfth root of 2.

semitransparent photocathode — A photocathode in which radiant flux incident on one side produces photoelectric emission from the opposite side.

sending-end impedance — Also called the driving-point impedance. The ratio of an applied potential difference of a transmission line, to the resultant current at the point where the potential difference is applied.

sending filter—A filter used at the transmitting terminal to restrict the transmitted frequency band.

sensation level—*See* Level Above Threshold.

sense—1. In navigation, the relationship between the change in indication of a radionavigational facility and the change in the navigational parameter being indicated. 2. In some navigational equipment, the property of permitting the resolution of 180° ambiguities. 3. To examine or determine the status of some system components. 4. To read holes in punched tape or cards.

sense finder—In a direction finder, that portion which permits determination of direction without 180° ambiguity.

sense-reversing reflectivity—The characteristic of a reflector that reverses the sense of an incident ray. (For example, a perfect corner reflector is invisible to a circularly polarized radar because it reverses the sense.)

sense step—*See* Secondary Calibration.

sensing—The process of determining the sense of an indication.

sensing element—*See* Primary Detector.

Sensistor—A silicon resistor the resistance of which varies with temperature, power, and time.

sensitive relay—A relay requiring only a small current. It is used extensively in photoelectric circuits.

sensitive volume—In a radiation-counter tube, the portion responding to a specific radiation.

sensitivity—1. The minimum input signal required in a radio receiver or similar device, to produce a specified output signal having a specified signal-to-noise ratio. This signal input may be expressed as power or voltage at a stipulated input network impedance. 2. Ratio of the response of a measuring device, to the magnitude of the measured quantity. It may be expressed directly in divisions per volt, milliradians per microampere, etc., or indirectly by stating a property from which sensitivity can be computed (e.g., ohms per volt for a stated deflection). 3. The signal current developed in a camera tube per unit incident radiation density (i.e., per watt per unit area).

sensitivity adjustment—Also called span adjustment. The control of the ratio of output signal to excitation voltage per unit measurand. Generally accomplished in a system by changing the gain of one or more amplifiers. The practice of placing excitation control components (such as potentiometers or rheostats) in series with the excitation to a transducer is a sensitivity adjustment for the system. However, in the latter case no significant change is introduced in the output-to-input ratio of the transducer.

sensitivity control—The control that adjusts the amplification of the radio-frequency amplifier stages and thereby makes the receiver more sensitive.

sensitivity-time control—Also called gain-time control or time gain. The portion of a system which varies the amplification of a radio receiver in a predetermined manner.

sensitizing (electrostatography) — The establishing of an electrostatic surface charge of uniform density on an insulating medium.

sensitometer—An instrument used to measure the sensitivity of light-sensitive materials.

sensitometry — Measurement of the light-response characteristics of photographic film.

sensor—1. In a navigational system, the portion which perceives deviations from a reference and converts them into signals. 2. A sensing element.

sentinel—1. A symbol marking the beginning or end of some piece of information in digital-computer programming. 2. *See* Tag.

separate excitation — Excitation in which generator field current is provided by an independent source, or motor field current is provided from a source other than the one connected across the armature.

separately instructed carry—Executing the carry process in a computer by allowing carry information to propagate to succeeding places only when a specific signal is received.

separate parts of a network—The unconnected parts.

separation—The degree to which two stereo signals are kept apart. Stereo realism is dependent on the successful prevention of their mixture before reaching the output terminals of the power amplifier. Tape systems have a separation capability inherently far superior to that of the disc systems.

separation circuit—A circuit that separates signals according to their amplitude, frequency, or some other selected characteristic.

separation filter—A combination of filters used to separate one band of frequencies from another—often, to separate carrier and voice frequencies for transmission over individual paths.

separation loss—The loss that occurs in output when the surface coating of a tape fails to make perfect contact with the surfaces of either the record or reproduce head.

separator—1. An insulating sheet or other device employed in a storage battery to prevent metallic contact between plates of opposite polarity within a cell. 2. An insulator used in the construction of convolutely wound capacitors. 3. *See* Delimiter.

septate coaxial cavity—A coaxial cavity with a vane or septum added between the inner and outer conductors. The result is a cavity that acts as if it had a rectangular cross section bent transversely.

septate waveguide—A waveguide with one or more septa placed across it to control microwave power transmission.

septum—A thin metal vane which has been perforated with an appropriate wave pattern. It is inserted into a waveguide to reflect the wave.

sequence—1. The order in which objects or items are arranged. 2. To place in order. 3. A succession of terms so related that each may be derived from one or more of the preceding terms in accordance with some fixed law.

sequence checking routine—A checking routine which examines every instruction executed and prints certain data concerning this check.

sequence control—Automatic control of a series of operations in a predetermined order.

sequencer—A mechanical or electronic device that may be set to initiate a series of events and to make the events follow in sequence.

sequence relay—A relay which controls two or more sets of contacts in a predetermined sequence.

sequencer register—In a computer, a counter which is pulsed or reset following the execution of an instruction to form the new memory address which locates the next instruction.

sequence timer—A succession of time-delay circuits arranged so that completion of the delay in one circuit initiates the delay in the following circuit.

sequency of operation—A detailed written description of the order in which electrical devices and other parts of the equipment should function.

sequential-access storage—A form of digital computer storage in which the items of stored information become available only in a one-after-another sequence regardless of whether all or only part of the information is desired.

sequential color television—A color television system in which the three primary colors are transmitted in succession and reproduced on the receiver screen in the same manner.

sequential control—Digital-computer operation in which the instructions are set up in sequence and fed to the computer consecutively during the solution of a problem.

sequential element—A device having at least one output channel and one or more input channels, all characterized by discrete states, such that the state of each output channel is determined by the previous states of the input channels.

sequential interlace—A method of interlacing in which the lines of one field are placed directly under the corresponding lines of the preceding field.

sequential lobing—A direction-determining technique utilizing the signals of overlapping lobes existing at the same time.

sequential relay—A relay that controls two or more sets of contacts in a predetermined sequence.

sequential sampling—Sampling inspection in which the decision to accept, reject, or inspect another unit is made following the inspection of each unit.

sequential scanning—In television, rectilinear scanning in which the distance from center to center of successively scanned lines is equal to the nominal line width.

sequential timer—A timer in which each interval is initiated by the completion of the preceding interval. All intervals may be independently adjusted.

serial—Pertaining to time-sequential transmission of storage of, or logical operations on, the parts of a word in a computer—the same facilities being used for successive parts.

serial arithmetic unit—One in which the digits are operated on sequentially. (*Also see* Parallel Arithmetic Unit.)

serial digital computer—One in which the digits are handled serially. Mixed serial and parallel machines are frequently called serial or parallel, according to the way the arithmetic processes are performed. An example of a serial digital computer is one which handles decimal digits serially, although the bits which comprise a digit might be handled either serially or in parallel. (*Also see* Parallel Digital Computer).

serial operation — Computer operation in which numbers are processed one character at a time—as opposed to parallel operation, where several numbers are processed simultaneously.

serial-parallel—Having the property of being partially serial and partially parallel.

serial printed—A device capable of printing characters one at a time across a page.

serial programming — Programming of a digital computer in such a manner that only one arithmetical or logical operation can be executed at one time.

serial storage — In a computer, storage in which time is one of the coordinates used in the location of any given bit, character, or word.

serial transfer—Data transfer in which the characters of an element of information are transferred in sequence over a single path.

serial transmission—Information transmission in which the characters of a word are transmitted in sequence over a single line.

series—1. The connecting of components end to end in a circuit, to provide a single path for the current. 2. An indicated sum of a set of terms in a mathematical expression (e.g., in an alternating or arithmetic series).

Series circuit.

series circuit—A circuit in which resistances or other components are connected end to end so that the same current flows throughout the circuit.

series connection—A way of making connections so as to form a series circuit.

series excitation—The field excitation obtained in a motor or generator by allowing the armature current to flow through the field winding.

series-fed vertical antenna—A vertical antenna which is insulated from ground and energized at the base.

series feed—The method by which the d-c voltage to the plate or grid of a vacuum tube is applied through the same impedance in which the alternating current flows.

series field—In a machine, the part of the total magnetic flux due to the series winding.

series loading—Loading in which reactances are inserted in series with the conductors of a transmission circuit.

series modulation—Modulation in which the plate circuits of a modulating tube and a modulated amplifier tube are in series with the same plate-voltage supply.

series motor—A motor in which the field and armature circuits are connected in series. In small motors with laminated field frames, the performance will be similar when operated on direct current or alternating current. For this reason, the series motor is frequently called a "universal" motor.

series operation—The connection of two or more power supplies together to obtain an output voltage of the combination equal to the sum of the individual supplies. A common current passes through all the supplies.

series-parallel network—Any network which contains only resistors, inductors, and capacitors and in which successive branches are connected in series and/or in parallel.

series-parallel switch — A switch which changes the connections of lamps or other devices from series to parallel or vice versa.

series peaking—*See* Peaking Network.

series regulator—A device that is placed in series with a source of power and is able to automatically vary its series resistance, thereby controlling the voltage or current output.

series resistor—A resistor generally used for adapting an instrument so that it will operate on some designated voltage or voltages. It forms an essential part of the voltage circuit and may be either internal or external to the instrument.

series resonance—1. The steady-state condition which exists when the current in a circuit comprising inductance and capacitance in series is in phase with the voltage across the circuit. 2. Resonance exhibited by a capacitor and inductor connected in series, characterized by low series attenuation at the resonant or tuned frequency, and high series attenuation at all others. 3. The condition existing in a circuit when the source of electromotive force is in series with an inductance and capacitance, the reactances of which cancel each other at the applied frequency, thereby reducing the impedance to minimum.

series-resonant circuit—A circuit in which an inductor and capacitor are connected in series and have values such that the inductive reactance of the inductor will be equal to the capacitive reactance of the capacitor at the desired resonant frequency. At resonance, the current through a series-resonant circuit is at maximum.

series-shunt network—*See* Ladder Network.

series T-junction—*See* E-plane T-junction.

series winding—In a motor or generator, a field winding that carries the same current as the armature; i.e., this winding is in series with the armature rather than in parallel with it. Series-wound motors are used in fractional horsepower, a-c–d-c applications, such as fans and electric mixers. Their other chief use is in heavy-duty d-c traction equipment such as electric locomotives, because of their extremely high starting torque.

series-wound motor—A commutator motor

in which the field and armature circuits are in series.

serrated pulse—A vertical synchronizing pulse divided into a number of small pulses, each acting for the duration of half a line in a television system.

serrated rotor plate—Also called a slotted or split-rotor plate. A rotor plate with radial slots which permit different sections of the plate to be bent inward or outward so that the total capacitance of a variable-capacitor section can be adjusted during alignment.

serration—1. The sawtooth appearance of vertical and near-vertical lines in a television picture. This is caused by their starting at different points during the horizontal scan. 2. A designed irregular surface used as a reservoir to retain excess infiltrating material and/or multiple points to obtain high-current-density resistance welding or resistance brazing.

serrodyne—A frequency translator or frequency converter, based on linear sawtooth modulation of phase shift or time delay. One convenient modulable device for serrodyne use is a traveling-wave tube, which provides gain as well as frequency translation.

serve—With reference to cable construction, a type of separator applied directly over the conductor or conductors. The serve may consist of one or more materials such as paper, cotton, silk, nylon, or rayon. These materials may be applied spirally or laterally.

serviceability—Those properties of an equipment design that facilitate service and repair in operation.

service area—1. The area within which a navigational aid is of use. 2. The area, surrounding a broadcasting station, where the signal is strong enough for satisfactory reception at all times (i.e., not subject to objectionable interference or fading).

service band—The band of frequencies allocated to a class of radio service.

service channel—A band of frequencies, usually including a voice channel, utilized for maintenance and fault indication on a communication system.

service life—The length of time a primary cell or battery needs to reach a specified final electrical condition on a service test that duplicates normal usage.

service oscillator—*See* R-F Signal Generator.

service routine—In digital computer programming, a routine designed to assist in the actual operation of the computer.

service switch—A switch, usually in a box, for disconnecting the line voltage from the circuits it services.

service unit—In a microwave system, the equipment or facilities used for maintenance communications and transmission of fault indications.

serving (of a cable)—A wrapping applied around the core before a cable is leaded, or over the lead if the cable is armored. Some common materials are jute, cotton, or duck tape.

servo—Short for servomotor. A device that contains and delivers power to move a control or controls.

servoamplifier—A servo unit in which information from a synchro is amplified to control the speed and direction of the servomotor output.

servo loop—In a servoamplifier, the entire closed loop formed by feedback from output to input. In a position servo, the output position is compared to a command signal at the input.

servomechanism—1. An automatic feedback-control system in which one or more of its signals represent mechanical motion. 2. A system in which the output is mechanically driven by the difference between the input and the output for the purpose of making the output agree with the input.

servomotor—A motor used in a servo system. Its rotation or speed (or both) are controlled by a corrective electric signal that has been amplified and fed into the motor circuit.

servo noise—The hunting of the tracking servomechanism of a radar as a result of backlash and compliance in the gears, shafts, and structures of the mount.

servo oscillation—An unstable condition in which the load tends to hunt back and forth about the ordered position.

servo system—An automatic control system for maintaining a condition at or near a predetermined value by activation of an element such as a control rod. It compares the required condition (desired value) with the actual condition and adjusts the control element in accordance with the difference (and sometimes the rate of change of the difference).

servo techniques—Methods of studying the performance of servomechanisms or other control systems.

servovalve—(Electrohydraulic flow control.) An electrical-input, fluid-control valve capable of continuous control.

set—1. To place a storage device in a prescribed state. 2. To place a binary cell in the *1* state. 3. A permanent change, attributable to any cause, in a given parameter. 4. *See* Equipment.

set analyzer—A test instrument designed to permit convenient measurement of voltages and currents.

set composite—A signaling circuit in which two signaling or telegraph legs may be superimposed on a two-wire interoffice trunk by means of one of the balanced pairs of high-impedance coils connected to each side of the line with an associated capacitor network.

set noise—Inherent random noise caused in a receiver by thermal currents in resistors and by variations in the emission currents of vacuum tubes.

set point — In a feedback control loop, the point which determines the desired value of the quantity being controlled.

set pulse — A drive pulse which tends to set a magnetic cell.

set-reset flip-flop — A standard flip-flop except that if both the set and reset inputs are a 1 at the same time, the flip-flop will assume a prescribed state.

set terminal — *See* One-Input Terminal.

settling time — 1. The time interval, following the initiation of a specified stimulus to a system, required for a specified variable to enter and remain within a specified narrow band centered on the final value of the variable. 2. The time required for the output of an amplifier to become stable after the application of a step-function input.

setup — In television, the ratio between the reference black and reference white levels, both measured from the blanking level. It is usually expressed in per cent.

setup time — The time, measured from the point of 10% input change, required for a capacitor-diode gate to open or close after the occurrence of a change of input level.

seven-unit teleprinter code — Frequently called Teletype code. A code that represents the letters of the alphabet, the numerals, the punctuation marks, and the various control functions necessary on a teleprinter (such as line feed, carriage return, upshift, and downshift) by five-unit combinations of *mark* and *space* conditions. (In addition to the five units which indicate the letter or other data, the code contains a "start" unit, which is always a "space," and a "stop" unit, which is always a "mark," to indicate the beginning and ending of each character.

sexadecimal notation — Also called dekahexadecimal notation. A scale of notation for numbers in which the base is 16.

sferics — Contraction of the term "atmospherics," meaning interference.

sferics receiver — Also called lightning recorder. A type of radio direction finder which measures electronically the direction of arrival, intensity, and rate of occurrence of atmospherics. In its simplest form the instrument consists of two orthogonally crossed antennas. Their output signals are connected to an oscillograph so that one loop measures the east-west components. These are combined vertically to give the azimuth.

sg - -Abbreviation for screen-grid electrode (of a vacuum tube).

shaded-pole motor — A single-phase induction motor provided with one or more auxiliary short-circuited stator windings that are displaced magnetically from the main winding.

shading — 1. A brightness gradient in the reproduced picture not present in the original scene, but caused by the camera tube. 2. Compensating for the spurious signal generated in a camera tube during the trace intervals. 3. Controlling the directivity pattern of a transducer through the distribution of phase and amplitude of the transducer action over the active face.

shading coil — *See* Shading Ring.

shading ring — A shorted turn placed around part of the pole of an alternating-current magnet to delay the change of magnetic flux in that part.

shading signal — A signal that increases the gain of the amplifier in a television camera while the electron beam is scanning a dark portion.

shadow attenuation — Attenuation of radio waves over a sphere in excess of that over a plane when the distance over the surface and other factors are the same.

shadow factor — The ratio of the electric field strength which would result from propagation over a sphere, to that which would result from propagation over a plane (other factors being the same).

shadow mask — *See* Aperture Mask.

shadow region — A region in which, under normal propagation conditions, an obstruction reduces the field strength from a transmitter to the point where radio reception or radar detection is ineffective or virtually so.

shadow tuning indicator — A vacuum tube in which a moving shadow shows how accurately a radio receiver is tuned.

shaft — The axial member to which torque is applied to cause rotation of an adjustable component.

shaft position encoder — Also called converter or coder. An analog-to-digital converter which transduces a mechanical analog shaft rotation to an electrical digital representation.

shaker — An electromagnetic device capable of imparting known and/or controlled vibratory acceleration to a given object.

shake-table test — A laboratory test in which a device or component is placed in a vibrator to determine the reliability of the device or component when subjected to vibration.

shank — 1. The part of a phonograph needle which is clamped into position in the pickup or cutting head. 2. The cylindrical or rodlike portion of a connector or contact. 3. That part of a fastener lying between the head and the extreme opposite end.

Shannon limit — The maximum signal-to-noise ratio improvement which can be achieved by the best modulation technique, as implied by Shannon's theorem relating channel capacity to signal-to-noise ratio.

shaped-beam antenna — An antenna whose directional pattern over a certain angular range is designed to a special shape for some particular use.

shaped-beam display tube — A cathode-ray tube in which the beam is first deflected through a matrix, then repositioned along the axis of the tube, and finally deflected into the desired position on the faceplate. A typical tube is the Charactron.

shape factor — 1. For a filter, the ratio (usually maximum) comparing a high-attenuation–level bandwidth and a low-attenuation–level bandwidth. 2. The ratio of the 60-db bandwidth to the 6-db bandwidth. Defines the selectivity of an amplifier stage.

shaping—Adjustment of a plan-position-indicator pattern set up by a rotating magnetic field.

shaping network—An electrical network designed to be inserted into a circuit to improve its transmission or impedance properties, or both. *Also see* Corrective Network.

sharp-cutoff tube—The opposite of a remote-cutoff tube. A tube in which the control-grid spirals are uniformly and closely spaced. As the grid voltage is made more and more negative, the plate current decreases steadily to cutoff.

sharp tuning—Responsive to a limited range of frequencies.

shaving—In mechanical recording, the removal of material from the surface of a recording medium for the purpose of obtaining a new surface.

shear wave—1. Also called a rotational wave. A wave, usually in an elastic solid, which causes an element of the solid to change its shape but not its volume. 2. A wave in which particle displacement is at right angles to the direction of propagation.

sheath—1. The external conducting surface of a shielded transmission line. 2. A metal wall of a waveguide. 3. Part of a discharge in a rarefied gas, in which there is a space charge due to an accumulation of electrons or ions.

sheath-reshaping converter—A converter in which the pattern of the wave is changed by gradual reshaping of the waveguide sheath and the metal sheets mounted longitudinally in the guide.

sheet grating—A three-dimensional grating consisting of thin metal sheets extending along the inside of a waveguide for about one wavelength. It is used to stop all but the predetermined wave, which passes unimpeded.

sheet resistivity—Also called ohms per square. The electrical resistance measured across the opposite side of a square pattern of deposited film material.

Sheffer-stroke function—The Boolean operator that gives a truth-table value of true only when both of the variables that the operator connects are not true.

shelf corrosion—Consumption of the negative electrode of a dry cell as a result of local action.

shelf life—The length of time under specified conditions that a material or component retains its usability.

shell—1. A group of electrons having a common energy level that forms part of the outer structure of an atom. 2. The outer section of a plug or receptacle that mechanically supports the assembly and in some cases provides coupling and locking.

shell-type transformer—A transformer in which the magnetic circuit completely surrounds the windings.

shf—Abbreviation for super-high frequency.

shield—1. Also called shielding. A screen or other housing (usually conducting) placed around devices or circuits to reduce the effect of electric or magnetic fields on them. 2. *See* Braid.

shield coverage—*See* Shield Percentage.

shielded building—In modern practice, a building in which shielding was incorporated in the basic architectural design. Shielded buildings often employ structural steel members as an integral part of RFI shielding.

shielded cable—A single- or multiple-conductor cable surrounded by a separate conductor (the shield) intended to minimize the effects of adjacent electrical circuits.

shielded-conductor cable—A cable in which the insulated conductor or conductors are enclosed in a conducting envelope or envelopes, almost every point on the surface of which is at ground potential or at some predetermined potential with respect to ground.

shielded enclosure—A room, hangar, or box, shielded or screened so as to provide a controlled electromagnetic environment.

shielded joint—A cable joint having its insulation so enveloped by a conducting shield that substantially every point on the surface of the insulation is at ground potential, or at some predetermined potential with respect to ground.

shielded line—A transmission line the elements of which confine propagated radio waves to an essentially finite space inside a tubular conducting surface called the sheath, thus preventing the line from radiating radio waves.

shielded pair—A two-wire transmission line surrounded by a metallic sheath.

shielded transmission line—A transmission line, the elements of which confine the propagated electrical energy inside a conducting sheath.

shielded wire—An insulated wire covered with a metal shield—usually of tinned, braided copper wire.

shielded X-ray tube—An X-ray tube enclosed in a grounded metal container, except for a small opening through which the X-rays emerge.

shield effectiveness—The relative ability of a shield to screen out undesirable radiation.

shield factor—Ratio between the noise (or induced current or voltage) in a telephone circuit when a source of shielding is present and when it is not.

shield grid (of a gas tube)—A structure which shields the control electrode from the anode or cathode, or both. It prevents the radiation of heat from and the depositing of thermionic activating material on them. It also reduces the electrostatic influence of the anode, and may be used as a control electrode in some applications.

shielding—The practice of confining the dielectric field of an electric cable to the inside of the cable insulation or insulated conductor assembly by surrounding the insulation or assembly with a grounded conducting medium called a shield.

shielding effectiveness—The relative reduction of radiated electromagnetic energy levels occasioned by the use of an enclosure either to contain or exclude the energy.

shield percentage—Also called shield coverage. The physical area of a circuit or cable actually covered by shielding material, expressed in percent.

shield wire—A wire employed for reducing the effects of extraneous electromagnetic fields on electric supply or communication circuits.

shift—Displacement of an ordered set of computer characters one or more places to the left or right. If the characters are the digits of a numerical expression, a shift is equivalent to multiplying by a power of the base.

shift counter—A shift register in which the first stage, through logic feedback, produces a pattern of ones or zeros as a function of the state of other states in the register. The pattern of ones and zeros so produced is termed a ring code.

shift-frequency modulation—A form of frequency modulation in which the modulating wave shifts the output frequency between predetermined values, and the output wave is coherent, with no phase discontinuity.

shift out—In a computer, to move information within a register toward one end so that, as the information leaves this one end, 0's are entered into the other end.

shift pulse—A drive pulse which initiates the shifting of characters in a register.

shift register—An element in the digital family which utilizes flip-flops to perform a displacement or movement of a set of digits one or more places to the right or left. If the digits are those of a numerical expression, a shift may be the equivalent of multiplying the number by a power of the base.

ship error—A radio direction-finder error that occurs when radio waves are reradiated by the metal structure of a ship.

ship-heading marker—On a ppi scope, an electronic radial sweep line indicating the heading of the ship on which the equipment is installed.

ship's emergency transmitter—A ship's transmitter to be used exclusively on a distress frequency for distress, urgency, or safety purposes.

ship station—A radio station operated in the maritime-mobile service and located on board a vessel which is not permanently moored.

ship-to-shore communication—Communication by radio between a ship at sea and a shore station.

shock—1. An abrupt impact applied to a stationary object. It is usually expressed in gravities (g). 2. An acceleration transient of short duration and nonrepetitive occurrence.

shock absorber—A device for dissipating vibratory energy, to modify the response of a mechanical system to an applied shock.

shock excitation—*See* Impulse Excitation.

shock-excited oscillations—*See* Free Oscillations.

shock isolator—Also called a shock mount. A resilient support which tends to isolate a system from applied shock.

Shockley diode — A four-layer controlled semiconductor rectifier diode without a base connection, used as a trigger or switching diode.

shock motion—In a mechanical system, transient motion characterized by suddenness and by significant relative displacements.

shock mount—*See* Shock Isolator.

Shockover capacitor.

shockover capacitor—A capacitor connected between the grid and cathode of a thyratron to prevent premature firing.

shock pulse—Usually a single disturbance that is characterized by an increase and a decrease of acceleration in a relatively short period of time.

shodop—Acronym for Short-range Doppler.

shoran—Acronym for Short Range Air Navigation. A precision distance-measuring system employing the pulse timing principle to measure the distance from an aircraft to one or more fixed responder ground stations. Fundamentally, the system consists of a mobile transmitter-receiver-indicator unit and a fixed receiver-transmitter unit (transponder). Pulses are sent from the mobile transmitter and returned to the originating point by the transmitter. The indicator measures the time interval required for the travel of a pulse between stations and converts this information into distance to the nearest thousandth of a mile.

shore effect—The bending of radio waves toward the shore line when traveling over water, due presumably to the slightly greater velocity of radio waves over water than over land. This effect causes errors in radio direction-finder indications.

shore-to-ship communication—Communication by radio between a shore station and a ship at sea.

short—*See* Short Circuit.

short base-line system—A system which uses continuous waves and which has a base-line length that is short in comparison to the target signal.

short circuit—Also called a short. An abnormal connection of relatively low resistance between two points of a circuit. The result is a flow of excess (often damaging) current between these points.

short-circuit driving-point admittance — The driving-point admittance between the j terminal of an n-terminal network and the reference terminal when all other terminals have zero alternating components of voltage with respect to the reference point.

short-circuit feedback admittance (of an electron-device transducer) — The short-circuit transfer admittance from the output terminals to the input terminals of a specified socket, the associated filters, and the electron device.

short-circuit forward admittance (of an electron-device transducer) — The short-circuit transfer admittance from the input terminals to the output terminals of a specified socket, the associated filters and the electron device.

short-circuit impedance—The driving-point impedance of a line or four-terminal network when its far end is short-circuited.

short-circuiting or grounding device—A power or stored-energy operated device which functions to short-circuit or ground a circuit in response to automatic or manual means.

short-circuit input admittance (of an electron-device transducer)—The short-circuit driving-point admittance at the input terminals of a specified socket, the associated filters, and the electron device.

short-circuit output admittance (of an electron-device transducer) — The short-circuit driving-point admittance at the output terminals of a specified socket, the associated filters, and the electron device.

short-circuit output capacitance (of an n-terminal electron device) — The effective capacitance determined from the short-circuit output admittance.

short-circuit parameters—In an equivalent circuit of a transistor, the resultant parameter when independent variables are selected for the input and output voltages.

short-circuit protection (automatic)—A current-limiting system which enables a power supply to continue operating without damage into any output overload, including short circuits. The output voltage must be restored to normal when the overload is removed, as distinguished from a fuse or circuit-breaker system, which opens at overload and must be reclosed to restore power.

short-circuit transfer admittance — The transfer admittance from terminal j to terminal l of an n-terminal network when all terminals except j have zero complex alternating components of voltage with respect to the reference point.

short-circuit transfer capacitance (of an electron device)—The effective capacitance determined from the short-circuit transfer admittance.

short code—A system of instructions that causes an automaton to behave as if it were another, specified automaton.

short-contact switch—A selector switch in which the movable contact is wider than the distance between its clips, so that the new circuit is made before the old one is broken.

short-distance navigational aid—An equipment or system which provides navigational assistance to a range not exceeding 200 miles.

shorted out—Made inactive by connecting a heavy wire or other low-resistance path around a device or portion of a circuit.

short-gate gain—Video gain on a short-range gate.

shorting noise—A noise which occurs in wirewound potentiometric transducers, even when no current is drawn from the device. It is due to the shorting out of adjacent turns of the wire as the slider traverses the winding. The portion of the interturn current which flows through the slider appears as noise.

shorting switch—A switch type in which contact is made for a new position before breaking contact with the previous position. Classified as a "make-before-break" switch.

short plug—A plug designed to connect the springs of a jack together or to short them.

short-range navigation—A precision position-fixing system using a pulse transmitter and receiver in connection with two transponder beacons at fixed points.

short-slot coupler—*See* Three-db Coupler.

short-time duty—A service requirement that demands operation at a substantially constant load for a short, specified time.

short time limits—Values of minimum and maximum trip time measured at various percentages of overload.

short-time rating—The rating that defines the load which a machine, apparatus, or device can carry at approximately the room temperature for a short, specified time.

short wave—Radio frequencies which fall above the commercial broadcasting band from 1.5 to 30 MHz) and are used for skywave communication over long distances.

short-wave converter—An electronic unit designed to be connected between a receiver and its antenna system to permit reception of frequencies higher than those the receiver ordinarily handles.

short-wave transmitter—A radio transmitter that radiates short waves, which ordinarily are shorter than 200 meters.

453

shot effect—Noise voltages developed by the random travel of electrons within a tube. The effect is characterized by a steady hiss from a radio, and by snow or grass in a television picture.

shot noise—1. Noise generated due to the random passage of discrete current carriers across a barrier or discontinuity, e.g., a semiconductor junction. Shot noise is characteristic of all transistors and diodes and is directly proportional to the square root of the applied current. 2. Noise caused by thermal agitation in vacuum tubes.

short code—A system of instructions that causes an automaton to behave as if it were another, specified automaton.

shunt—1. A precision low-value resistor placed across the terminals of an ammeter to increase its range. 2. Any part connected, or the act of connecting any part, in parallel with some other part. 3. In an electric circuit, a branch the winding of which is in parallel with the external or line circuit.

Shunt.

shunt calibration—A procedure in which a parallel resistance is placed across a (similar) element to obtain a known and deliberate electrical change.

shunt-fed vertical antenna—A vertical antenna connected to the ground at the base, and energized at a suitable point above the grounding point.

shunt feed—*See* Parallel Feed.

shunt field—Part of the magnetic flux produced in a machine by the shunt winding connected across the voltage source.

shunt-field relay—A special polarized relay with two coils on opposite sides of a closed magnetic circuit. The relay operates only when the currents in its two windings flow in the same direction.

shunting effect—A reduction in signal amplitude caused by the load which an amplifier or measuring instrument imposes on the signal source. For d-c signals the shunting effect is directly proportional to the output impedance of the signal source and inversely proportional to the input impedance of the amplifier.

shunting or discharge switch—A switch which serves to open or to close a shunting circuit around any piece of apparatus (except a resistor) such as a machine field, a machine armature, a capacitor, or a reactor.

shunt leads—Those leads which connect the circuit of an instrument to an external shunt. The resistance of these leads must be taken into account when the instrument is adjusted.

shunt loading—Loading in which reactances are applied in parallel across the conductors of a transmission circuit.

shunt neutralization—*See* Inductive Neutralization.

shunt peaking—*See* Peaking Network.

shunt regulator—A device placed across the output of a regulated power supply to control the current through a series-dropping resistance in order to maintain a constant output voltage or current.

shunt T-junction—*See* H-plane T-junction.

shunt-wound generator—A direct-current generator in which the field coils and armature are wound in parallel.

shunt-wound motor—A direct-current motor in which the field circuit and armature circuit are connected in parallel.

Shunt-wound d-c generator.

shutter—A movable cover that prevents light from reaching the film or other light-sensitive surface in a still, movie, or television camera except during the exposure time.

side armature—An armature which rotates about an axis parallel to that of the core, with the pole face on a side surface of the core of a relay.

sideband attenuation—Attenuation in which the relative transmitted amplitude of one or more components of a modulated signal (excluding the carrier) is smaller than the amplitude produced by the modulation process.

sideband power—The power contained in the sidebands. This is the power to which a receiver responds when receiving a modulated wave, not the carrier power.

sidebands—1. The frequency bands on both sides of the carrier frequency. The frequencies of the wave produced by modulation fall within these bands. 2. The wave components lying within such bands. During amplitude modulation with a sine-wave carrier, the upper sideband includes the sum (carrier plus modulating) frequencies, and the lower sideband includes the difference (carrier minus modulating) frequencies.

side circuit—A circuit arrangement for deriving a phantom circuit. In four-wire circuits, the two wires associated with the "go" channel form one "side circuit" and those associated with the return channel form another. (*Also see* Phantom Circuit.)

side echo—An echo due to a side lobe of an antenna.

side frequency—One of the frequencies of a sideband.

side lobe—A portion of the beam from an antenna, other than the main lobe. It is usually much smaller than the main lobe.

side-lobe blanking—A technique which compares relative signal strengths between an omnidirectional antenna and the radar antenna.

sideswiper—A telegraph key which operates from side to side rather than up and down.

side thrust—In disc recording, the radial component of force on a pickup arm caused by the stylus drag.

sidetone—The reproduction, in a telephone receiver, of sounds received by the transmitter of the same telephone set (e.g., hearing one's own voice in the receiver of a telephone set when speaking into the mouthpiece).

sidetone telephone set—A telephone set with no balancing network for reducing sidetone.

siemens—The new and preferred term for mho.

sight check—To verify the sorting or punching of punched cards by looking through the pattern of punched holes.

sign—1. A symbol which distinguishes negative from positive quantities. 2. A symbol which indicates whether a quantity is greater or less than zero. 3. A binary indicator of the position of the magnitude of a number relative to zero.

signal—1. A visible, audible, or other conveyor of information. 2. The intelligence, message, or effect to be conveyed over a communication system. 3. A signal wave. 4. The physical embodiment of a message.

signal attenuation—The reduction in the strength of electrical signals.

signal bias—A form of teletypewriter signal distortion brought about by the lengthening or shortening of pulses during transmission. When marking pulses are all lengthened, a marking-signal bias results; when marking pulses are all shortened, a spacing-signal bias results.

signal-carrier f-m recording—A method of recording in which the input signal is frequency modulated onto a carrier, and the carrier is recorded on a single track at saturation and without bias.

signal conditioning—To process the form or mode of a signal so as to make it intelligible to, or compatible with, a given device, including such manipulation as pulse shaping, pulse clipping, digitizing, and linearizing.

signal converter—A circuit that reduces, filters, and (if necessary) rectifies incoming signals to logic system levels.

signal delay—The transmission time of a signal through a network. The time is always finite, and it may be undesired or purposely introduced.

signal-distortion generator—An instrument furnished and designed to apply distortion on a signal for the purpose of ranging and adjusting teletypewriter equipment or for furnishing a clear signal.

signal electrode—The electrode from which the signal output of a camera tube is taken.

signal element—Also called a unit interval. That part of a signal which occupies the shortest interval of the signaling code. It is considered to be of unit duration in building up signal combinations.

signal-frequency shift—In a frequency-shift facsimile system, the numerical difference between the frequencies corresponding to the white and black signals at any point in the system.

signal generator—Also called a standard voltage generator. A device which supplies a standard voltage of known amplitude, frequency, and waveform for measuring purposes.

signal ground—The ground return for low-level signals such as inputs to audio amplifiers or other circuits that are susceptible to coupling through ground-loop currents.

signaling channel—A tone channel used for signaling purposes.

signaling key—A key used in wire or radio-telegraphy to control the sequence of current impulses that form the code signals.

signal injector—A test instrument, usually small, which contains an audio-frequency pulse oscillator. A signal injected at points in the circuitry aids in troubleshooting.

signal intelligence—A generic term which includes both communications intelligence and electronics intelligence.

signal interpolation—*See* Interpolation.

signal lamp—A lamp that indicates, when lit or out, the existence of certain conditions in a circuit (e.g., signal lamps on switchboards, or pilot lamps in radio sets).

signal leakage—Interference in a given playback channel which has its origin in the recording system. Such interference occurs during simultaneous record/reproduce, and has a leading time displacement with reference to the signal on the tape.

signal level—The difference between the measure of the signal at any point in a transmission system, and the measure of an arbitrary reference signal. (Audio signals are often stated in decibels—thus their difference can be conveniently expressed as a ratio.)

signal-muting switch—A switch used on a record changer to ground (mute) the signal from the pickup during a change cycle.

signal-noise ratio—*See* Signal-to-Noise Ratio.

signal plate—A metal plate that backs up the mica sheet containing the mosaic in one type of cathode-ray television camera tube. The electron beam acts on the capacitance between this plate and each globule of the mosaic to produce the television signal.

signal plus noise and distortion—A radio-receiver sensitivity measurement based on the signal input required to produce 50% of the rated output at a 12-decibel ratio (4:1 voltage ratio) of signal plus noise and distortion to noise and distortion alone.

signal-separation filter—A bandpass filter which selects the desired signal or channel from a composite signal.

signal-shaping network—An electric network inserted into a telegraph circuit, usually at the receiving end, to improve the waveshape of the signals.

signal-shield ground—A ground technique for all shields used for the protection from stray pickup of leads carrying low-level, low-frequency signals.

signal shifter—A variable-frequency oscillator for shifting amateur transmitters to a less crowded frequency within a given band.

signal strength—The strength of the signal produced by a transmitter at a particular location. Usually it is expressed as so many millivolts per meter of the effective receiving-antenna length.

signal-strength meter—Also called an S meter. A meter connected in the avc circuit of a receiver and calibrated in db or arbitrary "S" units to read the strength of a received signal.

signal-to-noise ratio—Also called signal-noise ratio. 1. Ratio of the magnitude of the signal to that of the noise (often expressed in decibels). 2. In television transmission, the

ratio in decibels of the maximum peak-to-peak voltage of the video television signal (including the synchronizing pulse), to the rms voltage of the noise at any point. 3. The ratio of the amplitude of a signal after detection to the amplitude of the noise accompanying the signal. It may also be considered as the ratio, at any specific point of a circuit, of signal power to total circuit-noise power. Abbreviated s/n ratio or snr.

signal tracer—A test instrument used for tracing a signal through the circuit in order to find faulty wiring or components.

signal tracing—The tracing of a signal through each stage in order to locate a fault.

signal voltage—The effective (root-mean-square) voltage value of a signal.

signal wave—A wave with characteristics that permit it to carry intelligence.

signal-wave envelope—The contour of a signal wave which is composed of a series of wave cycles.

signal winding—Also called an input winding. In a saturable reactor, the control winding to which the independent variable (signal wave) is applied.

signature (target)—The characteristic pattern of the target displayed by detection and classification equipment.

sign-control flip-flop—In computers, a flip-flop in the arithmetic unit used for storing the sign of the result of an operation.

sign digit—A character (+ or −) used to designate the algebraic sign of a number.

significant digits (of a number)—A set of digits from consecutive columns, beginning with the most significant digit other than zero, and ending with the least significant digit the value of which is known or assumed to be relevant. The digits of a number can be ordered according to their significance, which is greater when occupying a column corresponding to a higher power of the radix.

silent discharge—The gradual and nondisruptive discharge of electricity from a conductor into the atmosphere. It is sometimes accompanied by the production of ozone.

silent period—An hourly period during which ship and shore radio stations must remain silent and listen for distress calls.

silica gel—A moisture-absorbent chemical used for dehydrating waveguides, coaxial lines, pressurized components, shipping containers, etc.

silicon—A metallic element often mixed with iron or steel during smelting to provide desirable magnetic properties for transformer-core materials. In its pure state, it is used as a semiconductor.

silicon capacitor—*See* Varactor.

silicon controlled rectifier—A three-junction semiconductor device that is normally an open circuit until an appropriate gate signal is applied to the gate terminal, at which time it rapidly switches to the con-

ANODE

P	J1
N	J2
P	J3
N	

GATE

CATHODE

Silicon controlled rectifier.

ducting state. Its operation is equivalent to that of a thyratron.

silicon controlled switch—A PNPN semiconductor device with leads to all four semiconductor regions.

silicon detector—*See* Silicon Diode.

silicon diffused epitaxial mesa transistor—A silicon transistor that has high voltage and power ratings and low storage time and saturation voltage.

silicon diode—Also called a silicon detector. A crystal detector used for rectifying or detecting uhf and shf signals. It consists of a metal contact held against a piece of silicon in a particular crystalline state.

silicon double-base diode—*See* Unijunction Transistor.

silicone—A member of the family of polymeric materials characterized by a recurring chemical group that contains silicon and oxygen atoms as links in the main chain. These compounds are presently derived from silica (sand) and methyl chloride. One of their important properties is resistance to heat.

silicon monoxide—A dielectric material often used in the fabrication of a microelectronic device to form an insulator, substrate, or a thin-film capacitor dielectric.

silicon oxide—A dielectric material commonly used in the surface passivation of microelectronic circuits. Silicon oxide contains various combinations of silicon monoxide and silicon dioxide.

silicon planar transistor—A silicon transistor produced by the planar process and consisting of a series of etchings and diffusions to produce a transistor with a thin oxide layer within the planes of a silicon substrate.

silicon rectifier—One or more silicon rectifying cells or cell assemblies.

silicon rectifying cell—An elementary two-terminal silicon device which consists of a positive and a negative electrode and conducts current effectively in only one direction.

silicon solar cell—A photovoltaic cell designed to convert light energy into power for electronic and communication equipment. It consists essentially of a thin wafer of specially processed silicon.

silicon steel—Steel containing 3% to 5% silicon. Its magnetic qualities make it de-

sirable for use in the iron cores of transformers and in other a-c devices.

silicon transistor—A transistor in which silicon is used as the semiconducting material.

silicon unijunction transistor—*See* Unijunction Transistor.

silk-covered wire—A wire covered with one or more layers of fine floss silk. It is a better insulator than cotton. Also, it is more moisture-resistant and permits more turns of wire within a given space.

silver—A precious metal which is more conductive than copper. Because it does not readily corrode, it is used for contact points of relays and switches. Its chemical symbol is Ag.

silvered-mica capacitor—A mica capacitor that has a coating of silver deposited directly on the mica sheets instead of using conducting metal foil.

silvering—*See* Silver Spraying.

silver migration—The ionic displacement of metallic silver through an insulating medium. Usually·it is caused by a combination of extended time, high humidity, temperature variations, and d-c potential.

silver solder—A solder that is composed of copper, silver, and zinc. It has a melting point lower than that of silver, but higher than that of lead-tin solder.

silver spraying—Also calling silvering. Metallizing the surface of an original master disc recording by using a dual spray nozzle in which ammoniated silver nitrate and a reducer are combined in an atomized spray to precipitate the metallic silver.

silverstat—An arrangement of closely spaced contactors. Sometimes used as a step-by-step device to unbalance the arms of a resistance bridge.

silverstat regulator—A multitapped resistor, the taps of which are connected to single-leaf silver contacts. Variation of voltage causes a solenoid to open or close these contacts, shorting out more or less of the resistance in the exciter circuit as a means of regulating the output voltage to the desired value.

simple harmonic current—Also called sinusoidal current. A symmetrical alternating

DIFFUSED BORON LAYER

P-TYPE SILICON

ARSENIC-DOPE N-TYPE SILICON

LOAD

Silicon solar cell.

current, the instantaneous value of which is equal to the product of a constant, and the sine or cosine of an angle having a value varying linearly with time.

simple harmonic electromotive force—Instantaneous values of a symmetrical alternating electromotive force which are equal to the product of a constant and the cosine or sine of an angle, the values of which vary linearly with time.

simple quad—*See* S-quad.

simple scanning—Scanning of only one scanning spot at a time.

simple sound source—A source which radiates sound uniformly in all directions under free-field conditions.

simple steady-state vibration—A periodic motion made up of a single sinusoid.

simple target—In radar, a target the reflecting surface of which does not cause the amplitude of the reflected signal to vary with the aspect of the target (e.g., a metal sphere).

simple tone—1. A sound wave, the instantaneous sound pressure of which is a simple sinusoidal function of time. 2. Also called a pure tone. A sound sensation characterized by its singleness of pitch.

simplex—A form of communication satellite operation which involves communication in only one direction at a time (mainly for facsimile, television, and some data).

simplex channel — A path for electrical transmission of information in one direction between two or more terminals.

simplex coil—A repeating coil used on a pair of wires to derive a commercial simplex circuit.

simplexed circuit—A two-wire metallic circuit from which a simplex circuit is derived, the metallic and simplex circuits being capable of simultaneous use.

simplex operation — Communication that takes place in only one direction at a time between two stations. Included in this classification are ordinary transmit-receive or press-to-talk operation, voice-operated carrier, and other forms of manual or automatic switching from transmit to receive.

simulation—A type of problem in which a physical model and the conditions to which the model may be subjected are all represented by mathematical formulas.

simulator—A device which represents a system or phenomenon and which reflects the effects of changes in the original so that it may be studied, analyzed, and understood from the behavior of that device.

simulcast—1. To broadcast a program simultaneously over more than one type of broadcast station, e.g., to broadcast a stereophonic program over an a-m and f-m station. 2. A program so broadcast.

simulcasting—Broadcasting a stereo program over an a-m and f-m station. An a-m and f-m tuner are required for stereo reception.

simultaneous lobing—In radar, a direction-

determining technique utilizing the received energy of two concurrent and partially overlapped signal lobes. The relative phase or power of the two signals received from a target is a measure of the angular displacement of the target from the equiphase or equisignal direction.

sine—The sine of an angle of a right triangle is equal to the side opposite that angle, divided by the hypotenuse (the long side opposite the right angle).

sine galvanometer—An instrument resembling a tangent galvanometer except that its coil is in the plane of the deflecting needle. The sine of the angle of deflection will then be proportionate to the current.

sine law—The law which states that the intensity of radiation in any direction from a linear source varies in proportion to the sine of the angle between a given direction and the axis of the source.

sine potentiometer — A d-c voltage divider (potentiometer), the output of which is proportionate to the sine of the shaft-angle position.

Sine wave.

sine wave—A wave which can be expressed as the sine of a linear function of time, space, or both.

singing—An undesired self-sustained oscillation at a frequency in or above the pass-band of a system or component.

singing margin—Also called gain margin. The excess of loss over gain around a possible singing path at any frequency, or the minimum value of such excess over a range of frequencies.

singing point—1. The condition of a circuit or transmission path where the sum of the gains exceeds the sum of the losses. When expressed in decibels, it is the gain that can be added to the circuit equivalent before singing will begin. 2. The amount of total gain in a transmission system (most commonly used in connection with two-wire repeaters) which causes the system to begin to lose efficiency of performance because the self-oscillating point is too closely approached. 3. The singing point of a circuit which is coupled back to itself is the point at which the gain is just sufficient to make the circuit break into oscillation.

single-address code—An instruction which contains the location of the data and the operation or sequence of operations to be performed on these data.

single amplitude—With reference to vibratory conditions, the peak displacement of an oscillating structure from its average or mean position.

single-anode tank—*See* Single-Anode Tube.

single-anode tube—Also called a single-anode tank. An electron tube with one anode (used chiefly for pool-cathode tubes).

single-axis gyro—A type of gyro in which the spinning rotor is mounted in a gimbal arranged so as to tilt about only one axis relative to the stable element.

single-button carbon microphone—A microphone having a carbon-filled buttonlike container on one side of its flexible diaphragm. As the sound waves move the diaphragm, the resistance of the carbon changes and the microphone current constitutes the desired audio-frequency signal.

single-carrier f-m recording—The method of recording in which the input signal is frequency-modulated onto a carrier and the carrier is recorded on a single track at saturation and without bias.

single-channel—A carrier-only or single-tone modulated radio control transmitter and matching receiver installation.

single-channel monopulse tracking system—*See* Monopulse Tracking.

single-channel simplex — Nonsimultaneous communication between stations over the same frequency channel.

single circuit—A telegraph circuit capable of nonsimultaneous two-way communication.

single-degree-of-freedom system—A system for which only one co-ordinate is required to define the configuration of the system.

single-dial control—Control of a number of different devices or circuits by means of a single adjustment (e.g., in tuning all variable-capacitor sections of a radio receiver).

single-ended—Unbalanced, such as grounding one side of a circuit or transmission line.

single-ended amplifier — An amplifier in which only one tube is normally employed in each stage—or if more than one tube is used, they are connected in parallel so that operation is asymmetric with respect to ground.

single-ended push-pull amplifier circuit—An amplifier circuit having two transmission paths designed to operate in a complementary manner and connected to provide a single unbalanced output. (No transformer is used.)

single-ended tube—A metal tube in which all electrodes—including the control grid—are connected to base pins and there is no top connection. The letter *S* after the first numerals in a receiving-tube designation (e.g., 6SN7) indicates a single-ended tube.

single-groove stereo — *See* Monogroove Stereo.

single-gun color tube—A color picture tube with a single electron gun that produces only one beam, which is sequentially deflected across the phosphor dots.

single harmonic distortion—The ratio of the power at the fundamental frequency measured at the output of the transmission system considered, to the power of any single harmonic observed at the output of the system because of its nonlinearity, when a single-frequency signal of specified power is applied to the input of the system. It is expressed in db.

single-hop propagation — Transmission in which the radio waves are reflected only once in the ionosphere.

single-junction photosensitive semiconductor—Two layers of semiconductor materials with an electrode connection to each material. Light energy controls the amount of current flow.

single-line diagram — A form of schematic diagram in which single lines are used to show component interconnections even though two or more conductors are required in the actual circuit.

single-loop feedback — A loop in which feedback may' occur only through one electrical path.

single-phase circuit—Either an alternating-current circuit with only two points of entry, or one with more than two points of entry but energized in such a way that the potential differences between all pairs of points of entry are either in phase or 180° out of phase. A single-phase circuit with only two points of entry is called a single-phase, two-wire circuit.

single-phase synchronous generator — A generator which produces a single alternating electromotive force at its terminals.

single phasing—The tendency of the rotor (of a motor tach generator) to continue to rotate when one winding is opened and the other winding remains excited.

single-point grounding—A grounding system that attempts to confine all return currents to a network which serves as the circuit reference. It does not imply that the grounding system is limited to one earth connection. To be effective, no appreciable current is allowed to flow in the circuit reference; i.e., the sum of the above return currents is zero.

single-polarity pulse—A pulse which departs from normal in one direction only.

single pole—A contact arrangement in which all contacts in the arrangement connect, in one position or another, to a common contact.

single-pole, double-throw—Abbreviated spdt. A three-terminal switch or relay contact for connecting one terminal to either of two other terminals.

single-pole-piece magnetic head — A magnetic head with only one pole piece on one side of the recording medium.

single-pole, single-throw—Abbreviated spst. A two-terminal switch or relay contact which either opens or closes one circuit.

single sampling plan—The plan which consists of a single sample size with associated acceptance and rejection criteria.

single-shield solid enclosure—An all-metal enclosure providing higher attenuation than cell-type units. It is usually a rigid, free-standing enclosure.

single-shot blocking oscillator—A blocking oscillator modified to operate as a single-shot trigger circuit.

single-shot multivibrator — Also called a single-trip multivibrator. A multivibrator modified to operate as a single-shot trigger circuit. *Also see* Monostable Multivibrator.

single-shot trigger circuit—Also called a single-trip trigger circuit. A trigger circuit in which the pulse initiates one complete cycle of conditions ending with a stable condition.

single-sideband filter—A bandpass filter in which the slope on one side of the response curve is greater than on the other side. So-called because it is used in systems to suppress a carrier frequency and transmit one or both sidebands.

single-sideband modulation—Abbreviated ss or ssb. Modulation whereby the spectrum of the modulating wave is translated in frequency by a specified amount, either with or without inversion.

single-sideband suppressed carrier—Modulation resulting from the partial or complete elimination of the carrier and all components of one sideband from an amplitude-modulated wave.

single-sideband system — A type of radio-telephone service in which one set of sidebands (either the upper or lower) is completely suppressed and the transmitted carrier is partially suppressed.

single-sideband transmission—Transmission of only one sideband, the other sideband being suppressed. The carrier wave may be transmitted or suppressed.

single-sideband transmitter—A transmitter in which only one sideband is transmitted.

single-signal receiver—A superheterodyne receiver equipped for single-signal reception. A crystal filter, usually in the intermediate-frequency amplifier, can be shorted out by a switch when high selectivity is not needed.

single-signal reception—Use of a piezoelectric quartz crystal and associated coupling circuits as a crystal filter, to provide the high degree of selectivity required for reception in a crowded band.

single sweep—The operating mode for a triggering-sweep oscilloscope in which the

sweep must be reset for each operation, thus preventing unwanted multiple display; it is particularly useful for trace photography. In the interval after the sweep is reset and before it is triggered, the oscilloscope is said to be armed.

single throw — A contact arrangement in which each contact form included is a single contact pair.

single-throw circuit breaker — A circuit breaker in which only one set of contacts need be moved to open or close the circuit.

single-throw switch—A switch in which only one set of contacts need be moved to open or close the circuit.

single-tone keying—Keying in which the carrier is modulated with a single tone for one condition, which may be either marking or spacing, but not for the other.

single-track magnetic system—A magnetic-recording system, the medium of which has only one track.

single-track recorder — A tape recorder which records or plays only one track at a time on or from the tape. *Also see* Monaural Recorder.

single-trip multivibrator — *See* Single-Shot Multivibrator.

single-trip trigger circuit—*See* Single-Shot Trigger Circuit.

single-tuned amplifier—An amplifier characterized by resonance at a single frequency.

single-tuned circuit—A circuit which may be represented by a single inductance and capacitance, together with associated resistances.

single-turn potentiometer—A potentiometer in which the slider travels the complete length of the resistive element with only one revolution of the shaft.

single-unit semiconductor device—A semiconductor device having one set of electrodes associated with a single carrier stream.

single-wire line—A transmission line that uses the ground as one side of the circuit.

single-wound resistor—A resistor in which only one layer of resistance wire or ribbon is wound around the base or core.

sink—In communication practice: 1. A device which drains off energy from a system. 2. A place where energy from several sources is collected or drained away.

sins—Acronym for a Ship's Inertial marine Navigational System especially applicable to submarine use.

sintered plate—A powder which holds the active plate material used for both the

Single-sideband transmitter.

anode and cathode in secondary cells. This provides a large surface area for the active material, allowing better cycle life, higher discharge rates, and better efficiency than the pocket-type plate design.

sinusoid — A curve having ordinates proportional to the sine of the abscissa.

sinusoidal—Varying in proportion to the sine of an angle or time function (e.g., ordinary alternating current).

sinusoidal current—*See* Simple Harmonic Current.

sinusoidal electromagnetic wave — In a homogeneous medium, a wave with an electric field strength proportionate to the sine (or cosine) of an angle that is a linear function of time, distance, or both.

sinusoidal field—A field in which the magnitude of the quantity at any point varies as the sine or cosine or an independent variable such as time, displacement, or temperature.

sinusoidal quantity—A quantity that varies in the manner of a sinusoid.

sinusoidal vibration—A cyclical motion in which the object moves linearly. The instantaneous position is a sinusoidal function of time.

sinusoidal wave—A wave the displacement of which varies as the sine (or cosine) of an angle that is proportional to time, distance, or both.

site error—In navigation, the error that occurs when the radiated field is distorted by objects near navigational equipment.

six-phase circuit—A combination of circuits energized by alternating electromotive forces which differ in phase by one-sixth of a cycle (60°).

size control—On a television receiver, a control which varies the size of the picture either horizontally or vertically.

skew—1. In facsimile, the nonrectangular received frame due to asynchronism between the scanner and recorder. Numerically it is the tangent of the angle of this deviation. 2. The motion characterized on a magnetic tape by an angular velocity between the gap center line and a line perpendicular to the tape center line. 3. In magnetic thin film, the deviation of the easy axis during fabrication.

skewed distribution—A frequency distribution of any natural phenomenon in which zero or infinity is one of its limits.

skewness—A statistical measure of the asymmetry existing in a distribution.

skiatron—1. A dark-trace oscilloscope tube. (*Also see* Darktrace Tube.) 2. A display employing an optical system with a dark-trace tube.

skin depth—In a current-carrying conductor, the depth below the surface at which the current density has decreased one neper below the current density at the surface.

skin effect—Also called radio-frequency resistance. The tendency of r-f currents to

flow near the surface of a conductor. Thus they are restricted to a small part of the total sectional area, which has the effect of increasing the resistance.

skinner—A wire brought out at the end of a cable prepared for soldering to a terminal.

skinning—Peeling the insulation from a wire.

skip—1. A digital-computer instruction to proceed to the next instruction. 2. In a computer, a "blank" instruction.

skip distance — The distance separating two points on the earth between which radio waves are transmitted by reflection from the ionized layers of the ionosphere.

skip fading—Fading due to fluctuations of ionization density at the place in the ionosphere where the wave is reflected, which causes the skip distance to increase or decrease.

skip keying—The reduction of the radar pulse-repetition frequency to a submultiple of that normally used, to reduce the mutual interference between radars or to increase the length of the radar time base.

skip zone—Also called zone of silence. A ring-shaped space or region within the transmission range wherein signals from a transmitter are not received. It is the distance between the farthest point reached by the ground wave and nearest point at which the refracted sky waves come back to earth.

sky error—*See* Ionospheric Error.

sky hook—Amateur term for antenna.

sky noise—Noise produced by radio energy from stars.

sky wave—*See* Ionospheric Wave *and* Indirect Wave.

sky-wave correction—In navigation, a correction for sky-wave propagation errors applied to measured positional data. The amount of the correction is established on the basis of an assumed position and on the height of the ionosphere.

sky-wave station error—In sky-wave–synchronized loran, the station-synchronization error due to the effect of the ionosphere on the synchronizing signal transmitted from one station to the other.

sky-wave–synchronization loran — A loran system in which the range is extended by using ionosphere-reflected signals for synchronizing the two ground stations.

sky-wave transmission delay—The longer time taken by a transmitted pulse when carried by sky waves reflected once from the E-layer, compared with the same pulse carried by ground waves.

slab—A relatively thick crystal from which blanks are cut.

slant range—In radar, the line-of-sight distance from the measuring point to the target, particularly an aerial target.

slave antenna—A directional antenna that is positioned in azimuth and elevation by a servo system. The information controlling the servo system is supplied by a tracking or positioning system.

slave drive—*See* Follower Drive.

slaved tracking—A method of interconnecting two or more regulated power supplies so that the master supply operates to control other power supplies called slaves.

slave relay—*See* Auxiliary Relay.

slave station—A radionavigational station, the emissions of which are controlled by a master station.

slave sweep—A time base which is synchronized or triggered by a waveform from an external source. It is used in navigational systems for displaying or utilizing the same information at different locations, or in displaying or utilizing different information with a common or related time base.

slaving—The use of a torque to maintain the orientation of the spin axis of a gyro relative to an external reference such as a pendulum or magnetic compass.

sleeping sickness — In transistors, the gradual appearance of leakage.

sleeve—1. A cylindrical contacting part usually placed in back of the tip or ring of a plug and insulated from it. 2. An iron core (usually a thin-walled cylinder) used as an electromagnetic shield around an inductor.

sleeve antenna—A vertical half-wave antenna the lower half of which is a metallic sleeve through which the concentric feed line runs. The upper radiating portion, which is one-quarter wavelength, is connected to the center of the line.

sleeve-dipole antenna—A dipole antenna with a coaxial sleeve around the center.

sleeve-stub antenna—An antenna consisting of half of a sleeve-dipole antenna projecting from an extended conducting surface.

sleeve wire—1. A third conductor when associated with a pair. 2. Wire which connects to the sleeve of a plug or jack. By extension, it is common practice to designate by this term the conductors having similar functions or arrangements in circuits where plugs or jacks may not be involved.

slewing—Rapid change of a mechanism associated with either end of a data-transmission system when it stops following one target and takes up another.

slewing rate—Also called rate limit or voltage velocity limit. The rate at which an output can be driven from limit to limit over the dynamic range. The time-rate-of-voltage change.

slew range—The high-speed range in which a motor can run continuously but cannot stop, start, or reverse without losing step count.

slice—An alternate term for "wafer."

slicer—Also called an amplitude gate or a clipper-limiter. A transducer which transmits only portions of an input wave lying between two amplitude boundaries.

slicked switch — An alacritized mercury

switch in which the rolling surface has been treated with an oily material.

slideback—The technique of applying a d-c voltage to one input of a differential amplifier in order to change the vertical position on the crt screen of the signal applied to the other input.

slideback voltmeter—A vacuum-tube voltmeter that measures effective voltage values indirectly by measuring the change in grid-bias voltage required to restore the plate current of the vacuum tube to the value it had before the unknown voltage was applied to the grid circuit.

slider—A sliding contact.

slide-rule dial—A tuning dial in which a pointer moves in a straight line over a straight scale. So called because it resembles a slide rule.

Slide switch.

slide switch—A switch which is positioned by sliding it back and forth.

slide wire—A bare resistance wire and a slider that can be set anywhere along the wire to provide a continuously variable resistance.

slide-wire bridge—A simplified Wheatstone bridge in which the resistance ratio is determined by the position of a slider on a resistance wire.

slide-wire rheostat—A long single-layer coil of resistance wire with a sliding contact. The resistance is varied by moving the slider.

sliding contact—*See* Wiping Contact.

slip—1. In facsimile, a distorted image similar to skew but caused by slippage in the mechanical drive system. 2. The difference between the synchronous and operating speed of a motor.

slip clutch—A protective device used in gear trains to disengage the load when it exceeds a specified value.

slip ring—A device for making electrical connections between stationary and rotating contacts.

slip rings—*See* Collector Rings.

slope — The essentially linear portion of the grid-voltage, plate-current characteristic curve of a vacuum tube. This is where the operating point is chosen when linear amplification is desired.

slope-based linearity—A manner of expressing nonlinearity as the deviation from a straight line for which only the slope is specified.

slope detection—A discriminator operation on one of the slopes of the response curve for a tuned circuit. It is rarely used in f-m receivers because the linear portion of the response curve is too narrow for large-signal operation.

slope detector—A detector in which slope detection is employed.

slot—One of the grooves formed in the iron core of a motor or generator armature for the conductors forming the armature winding.

slot antenna—A radiating element formed by a slot in a conducting surface.

slot armor — An insulator in the slot of a magnetic core of a machine; it may be on the coil or separate from it.

slot cell—A formed sheet of insulation that is separate from the coil and placed in the slot of a magnetic core.

slot coupling—A method of transferring energy between a coaxial cable and a waveguide by means of two coincident narrow slots, one in the sheath of the guide and the other in the sheath of the coaxial cable. E- or H-waves are launched into the guide, depending on whether the cable and guide are parallel or perpendicular to each other.

slot-discharge resistance — See Corona Resistance.

slot effect—The minimum voltage of rated frequency applied to the control-voltage winding of a motor tach generator necessary to start the rotor turning at no-load conditions with rated voltage and frequency on the fixed-voltage winding.

slot insulation—Flexible sheet-type insulation inserted into the slots of armatures and stators to insulate the windings from the core.

slot radiator—A primary radiating element in the form of a slot cut in the walls of a metal waveguide or cavity resonator or in a metal plate.

slotted line—See Slotted Section.

slotted rotor plate — See Serrated Rotor Plate.

slotted section—Also called a slotted line or slotted waveguide. A section of a waveguide or shielded transmission line, the shield of which is slotted to permit examination of the standing waves with a traveling probe.

slotted swr measuring equipment—A device in which standing and/or reflected waves are measured with a slotted line and a detecting probe.

sloted waveguide—See Slotted Section.

slow-acting relay—See Slow-Operating Relay.

slow-action relay—See Time-Delay Relay.

slow death—The gradual change of transistor characteristics with time. This change is attributed to ions which collect on the surface of the transistor.

slowed-down video—A technique of transmitting radar data over narrow-bandwidth circuits. The radar video is stored over the time required for the antenna to move through one beamwidth, and is subsequently sampled at such a rate that all range intervals of interest are sampled at least once each beam width or once per azimuth quantum.

slow memory—A computer memory, or storage, with a relatively long access time.

slow-operate, fast-release relay—A relay designed specifically for a long make and short release time.

slow-operate, slow-release relay—A slow-speed relay designed specifically for both a long make and a long release time.

slow-operating relay—Also called a slow-acting relay. One which is slow to attract its armature after its winding is energized.

Slotted section.

A copper slug, or collar, at the armature end of the core delays the operation momentarily after the operating circuit is completed. Such a relay is often marked SO on circuit diagrams.

slow-release relay—*See* Slow-Releasing Relay.

slow-releasing relay—Also called a slow-release relay. A slow-acting relay in which a copper slug, or collar, at the heelpiece end of the core delays the restoration momentarily after the operating circuit is opened. Such a relay is often marked SR on circuit diagrams.

slow-speed relay—A relay designed specifically for long operate or release time, or both.

slow-wave circuit—A microwave circuit in which the phase velocity of the waves is considerably below the speed of light. Such waves are used in traveling-wave tubes.

slow-wave structure—A circuit composed of selected inductance and capacitance that causes a wave to be propagated at a speed slower than the speed of light.

slug—1. A heavy metal ring or short-circuited winding used on a relay core to delay operation of the relay. 2. A metallic core which can be moved along the axis of a coil for tuning purposes.

slug tuner—A waveguide tuner containing one or more longitudinally adjustable pieces of metal or dielectric.

slug tuning—Varying the frequency of a resonant circuit by introducing a slug of material into the electric or magnetic fields, or both.

small signal—That value of an a-c voltage or current which, when halved or doubled, will not affect the characteristic being measured beyond the normal accuracy of the measurement of that characteristic.

small-signal analysis—Consideration of only small excursions from the no-signal bias, so that a vacuum tube or transistor can be represented by a linear equivalent circuit.

small-signal characteristics—The characteristics of an amplifier operating in the linear amplification region.

small-signal current gain (current-transfer ratio)—The output current of a transistor with the output circuit shorted, divided by the input current. The current components are understood to be small enough that linear relationships hold between them.

small-signal, open-circuit forward-transfer impedance—In a transistor, the ratio of the a-c output voltage to the a-c input current when the a-c output current is zero.

small-signal, open-circuit input impedance—In a transistor, the ratio of the a-c input voltage to the a-c input current when the a-c output current is zero.

small-signal, open-circuit output admittance—In a transistor, the ratio of the a-c output current to the a-c voltage applied to the output terminals when the a-c input current is zero.

small-signal, open-circuit output impedance—In a transistor, the ratio of the a-c voltage applied to the output terminals to the a-c output current when the a-c input current is zero.

small-signal, open-circuit reverse-transfer impedance—In a transistor, the ratio of the a-c input voltage to the a-c output current when the a-c input current is zero.

small-signal, open-circuit, reverse-voltage transfer ratio—In a transistor, the ratio of the a-c input voltage to the a-c output voltage when the a-c input current is zero.

small-signal power gain—In a transistor, the ratio of the a-c output power to the a-c input power under specified small-signal conditions. Usually expressed in db.

small-signal, short-circuit, forward-current transfer ratio—In a transistor, the ratio of the a-c output current to the a-c input current when the a-c output voltage is zero.

small-signal, short-circuit forward-transfer admittance—In a transistor, the ratio of the a-c output current to the a-c input voltage when the a-c output voltage is zero.

small-signal, short-circuit input admittance—In a transistor, the ratio of the a-c input current to the a-c input voltage when the a-c output voltage is zero.

small-signal, short-circuit input impedance—In a transistor, the ratio of the a-c input voltage to the a-c input current when the a-c output voltage is zero.

small-signal, short-circuit output admittance—In a transistor, the ratio of the a-c output current to the a-c output voltage when the a-c input voltage is zero.

small-signal, short-circuit reverse-transfer admittance—In a transistor, the ratio of the a-c input current to the a-c output voltage when the a-c input voltage is zero.

small-signal transconductance—In a transistor, the ratio of the a-c output current to the a-c input voltage when the a-c output voltage is zero.

smear—Television-picture distortion in which objects appear stretched out horizontally and are blurred.

S-meter—A built-in meter used in some communications receivers to indicate the strength of the received signal. *See* Signal-Strength Meter.

Smith chart—1. A special polar coordinate diagram designed to solve problems concerning transmission lines. It was developed by P. H. Smith. 2. A special graph laid out in such a way that transmission-line impedances can conveniently be found on it.

smoothing choke—An iron-core choke coil that filters out fluctuations in the output current of a vacuum-tube rectifier or direct-current generator.

smoothing circuit—A combination of inductance and capacitance employed as a filter circuit to remove fluctuations in the output current of a vacuum-tube or semiconductor rectifier or direct-current generator.

Smith chart.

smoothing factor—The factor expressing the effectiveness of a filter in smoothing out ripple voltages.

smoothing filter—1. A filter used to remove fluctuations in the output current of a vacuum-tube or semiconductor rectifier or direct-current generator. 2. A low-pass filter in the vertical-deflection amplifier of a spectrum analyzer. It is used to smooth amplitude fluctuation, in order to display spectral density and the average level of random signals as single lines. (The time constant of a smoothing filter is generally variable.)

SMPTE—Abbreviation for the Society of Motion Picture and Television Engineers.

snake—A tempered steel wire, usually of rectangular cross-section. The snake is pushed through a run of conduit or through an inaccessible space such as a partition and used for drawing in wires.

snap-action—1. In a mercury switch, the rapid motion of the mercury pool from one position to another. 2. A rapid motion of the contacts from one position to another position, or their return. This action is relatively independent of the rate of travel of the actuator.

snap-action contacts—A contact assembly such that the contacts remain in one of two positions of equilibrium with substantially constant contact pressure during the initial motion of the actuating member until a point is reached at which stored energy causes the contacts to move abruptly to a new position of equilibrium.

snap magnet—A permanent magnet used in thermostatic, pressure, and other control instruments to provide quick make-and-break action at the contact and thereby minimize sparking. The magnet pulls the armature in suddenly against the spring to close the contacts and hold them closed until the spring is compressed enough to make them fly apart.

snap-off diode—A modified very high-speed, planar, epitaxial, passivated diode in which the charge stored during conduction of the diode is held close to the junction.

snapshot—In a computer, a dynamic printout of selected data in storage that occurs at breakpoints and checkpoints during the computing operations as opposed to a static printout.

snap switch—A switch (e.g., a light switch) in which the contacts are separated or brought together suddenly as the operating knob or lever compresses or releases a spring.

sneak circuit—That part of a complete electrical circuit which carries an unintentional (sneak) current. Sneak currents may prevent proper operation of interconnected equipment.

Snell's law—The sine of the angle of incidence, divided by the sine of the angle of refraction, equals a constant called the index of refraction when one of the mediums is air.

snivet—A straight, jagged, or broken vertical black line that appears near the right edge of the screen of a television receiver.

snooperscope—A night viewing device to permit a user to see objects in total darkness. It consists of an infrared source, an infrared image converter, and a battery-operated high-voltage d-c-to-d-c converter. Infrared radiation sent out is reflected back to the snooperscope, where it is then converted into a visible image on the fluorescent screen of the image converter tube.

snow—1. A speckled background caused by random noise on an intensity-modulated display. 2. White specks in a television picture (usually indicative of a weak signal).

snowflake transistor — A high-speed medium-power switching transistor for use as a thin-film or core driver. It employs a six-pointed emitter geometry that permits the optimum ratio of emitter periphery to emitter area.

snr—Abbreviation for signal-to-noise ratio.

s/n ratio—Abbreviation for signal-to-noise ratio.

soak—In an electromagnetic relay, the condition that exists when the core is approximately saturated.

soakage—The disability of a capacitor to come up to voltage instantaneously without voltage lag or creep during or after charging. The lower the soakage, the lower the lag and creep.

soak time—The period of time required following activation for the electrolyte in a cell or battery to be sufficiently absorbed into the active materials.

soak timer—A reset timer, usually dial-adjustable, as applied in a temperature-control system for controlling the length of time the temperature is held at a predetermined level.

soak value—The voltage, current, or power applied to the coil of the relay coil to insure that a condition approximating magnetic saturation exists.

socket—An opening that supports and electrically connects to vacuum tubes, bulbs or other devices or components when they are inserted into it.

socket adapter—A device placed between a tube and its socket so that the tube can be used in a socket designed for some other base, or so that current or voltage can be measured at the electrodes while the tube is in use.

socket contact—A hollow female contact designed to mate with a male contact. It is

normally connected to the "live" side of a circuit.

sodar — Acronym for SOund Detecting And Ranging. A device which detects large changes in temperature overhead by the amount of sound returned as echoes (the colder the atmosphere, the louder the echoes). The sound, which is within the range of human hearing, is launched upward and the echoes are changed into oscilloscope patterns.

sodium amalgam-oxygen cell—A fuel-cell system in which materials functioning in the dual capacity of fuel and anode are consumed continuously. Low operating temperatures and high power-to-weight ratios are significant characteristics of the system.

sodium-vapor lamp—A gas-discharge lamp containing sodium vapor. It is used chiefly for highway illumination.

sofar—Acronym for SOund Fixing And Ranging. An underwater sound system with which air and ship survivors can be located within a square mile and as far as 2,000 miles away. Survivors drop a TNT charge into the water. The charge, which is timed to explode at 3,000 to 4,000 feet, sets up underwater sound waves that can be picked up by hydrophones at shore stations.

soft magnetic material—Also called a low-energy material. Ferromagnetic material which, once having been magnetized, is very easily demagnetized (i.e., requires only a slight coercive force to remove the resultant magnetism).

soft phototube—A gas phototube.

soft tube—1. A high-vacuum tube which has become defective because of the entry of a small amount of gas. 2. An electronic tube into which a small amount of gas has purposely been put to obtain the desired characteristics. 3. Also called gassy tube.

software — A program package available for work on general-purpose, digital-computer hardware.

soft X-rays—X-rays with comparatively long wavelengths and hence poor penetrating power.

solar absorber—A surface that has the property of converting solar radiation into thermal energy.

solar cell—A silicon photovoltaic cell that converts solar energy directly into electrical energy.

solar concentrator—A device that increases the intensity of solar energy by optical means.

solar-energy conversion — The process of changing solar radiation into electrical or mechanical power, either directly or by using a heat engine.

solar noise—Electromagnetic radiation from the sun at radio frequencies.

solder—A readily meltable metal or alloy that produces a bond at a junction of two metal surfaces. True solder must have a lower melting point than the metals being joined and must also be capable of uniting with the metals to be joined.

solderability—1. In a printed-circuit board, a measure of the ability of the conductive pattern to be wet by solder. 2. The property of a metal surface which allows it to be wetted by solder.

solder eye—A solder-type terminal provided with a hole at its end through which a wire can be inserted prior to being soldered. A ring-shaped contact termination of a printed-circuit connector for the same purpose.

solder ground—A conducting path to ground due to dripping or overhanging solder.

soldering—The joining of metallic surfaces (e.g., electrical contacts) by melting a metal or an alloy (usually tin and lead) over them.

soldering iron—A soldering tool consisting of a heating element to heat the tip and melt the solder, plus a heat-insulated handle.

solderless connector—A device for clamping two wires firmly together to provide a good connection without solder. A common form is a cap with tapered internal threads, which are twisted over the exposed ends of the wires.

solderless wrap—Also called wire wrap. A method of connection in which a solid wire is tightly wrapped around a rectangular, square, or V-shaped terminal by means of a special tool.

solder short—A defect which occurs when solder forms a short-circuit path between two or more conductors.

Solenoid.

solenoid—1. A coil of wire which, when a current flows through it, will act as a magnet and tend to pull a movable iron core to a central position. 2. An electric conductor wound as a spiral with a small pitch, or as two or more coaxial spirals. 3. An electromagnet having an energized coil approximately cylindrical in form and an armature the motion of which is reciprocating within and along the axis of the coil.

solenoid valve—A combination of an electromagnet plunger or an orifice to which a disc or plug can be positioned to either restrict or completely shut off a flow. (Orifice closure or restriction occurs when the electromagnet actuates a magnet plunger.)

solid—A state of matter in which the motion of the molecules is restricted. They tend to remain in one position, giving rise to a crystal structure. Unlike a liquid or gas, a solid has a definite shape and volume.

solid circuit—A semiconductor network fabricated in one piece of material by alloying, diffusing, doping, etching, cutting, and the use of necessary jumper wires.

solid conductor—A wire—i.e., a conductor composed of a single strand.

solid-electrolyte fuel cell—A self-contained fuel cell in which oxygen is the oxidant and hydrogen is the fuel. The oxidant and fuel are kept separated by a solid electrolyte which has a crystalline structure and a low conductivity.

solid-electrolyte tantalum capacitor—Also called solid tantalum capacitor. A tantalum capacitor with a solid semiconductor electrolyte instead of a liquid. A wire anode is used for low capacitance values and a sintered pellet for higher values.

solidly grounded — Also called directly grounded. Grounded through an adequate grounded connection in which no impedance has been inserted intentionally.

solid-state—1. Pertaining to circuits and components using semiconductors. 2. The physics of materials in their solid form. Examples of solid-state materials are: transistors, diodes, solid-state lasers, metals and alloys, etc.

solid-state atomic battery—A device in which a radioactive material and a solar cell are combined. The radioactive material emits particles that enter the solar cell, which in turn produces electrical energy.

solid-state circuit — A complete circuit formed from a single block of semiconductor material. *Also see* Monolithic Integrated Circuit.

Solid-electrolyte tantalum capacitor.

solid-state component — A component the operation of which depends on the control of electric or magnetic phenomena in solids (e.g., a transistor, crystal diode, or ferrite).

solid-state computer — A computer built primarily from solid-state electronic circuit elements.

solid-state device—Any element that can control current without moving parts, heated filaments, or vacuum gaps. All semiconductors are solid-state devices, although not all solid-state devices (e.g., transformers) are semiconductors.

solid-state integrated circuit—The class of integrated componets in which only solid-state materials are used.

solid-state physics—The branch of physics that deals with the structure and properties of solids, including semiconductors (i.e., a material the electrical resistivity of which is between that of insulators and conductors). Generally used semiconductors are silicon and germanium.

solid-state relay — A relay that employs solid-state semiconductor devices as components.

solid tantalum capacitor—*See* Solid-Electrolyte Tantalum Capacitor.

solion—Contraction of SOLution ION. An electrochemical sensing and control device in which ions in solution carry electric charges to give amplification corresponding to that of vacuum tubes and transistors.

solion integrator—A precision electrochemical cell housed in glass and containing four small platinum electrodes in a solution of potassium iodide and iodine. The integrator anode and cathode make up the covers of a small cylindrical volume (less than 0.00025 cubic inch) for storing electrical information in the form of ions. The integrator cathode contains a fixed amount of hydraulic porosity for completing the internal-solution path to the other two electrodes.

solo manual—*See* Swell Manual.

Sommerfeld formula—An approximate wave-propagation relationship that may be used when distances are short enough that the curvature of the earth may be neglected in the computations.

Sonalert—A solid-state tone-emitting device.

Sonar.

sonar—Acronym for SOund Navigation And Ranging. Also called active sonar if it radiates underwater acoustic energy, or passive (listening) sonar if it merely receives the energy generated from a distant source. Apparatus or technique of obtaining information regarding objects or events underwater through the transmission and reception of acoustic energy. Two well-known uses are to detect submarines and fish.

Solion integrator.

sonar background noise—In sonar, the total noise, presented to the final receiving element, that interferes with the reception of the desired signal.

sone—A unit of loudness. A simple tone of frequency 1,000 hertz, 40 db above a listener's threshold, produces a loudness of 1 sone. The loudness of any sound that is judged by the listener to be n times that of the 1-sone tone is n sones.

sonic—1. Pertaining to the speed of sound. 2. Utilizing sound waves.

sonic altimeter—An altimeter that determines the height of an aircraft above the earth by measuring the time the sound waves take to travel from the aircraft to the ground and back, based on the fact that the velocity of sound at sea level is 1,080 feet per second through dry air at 0°C. (32°F.).

sonic applicator—A self-contained electromechanical transducer for local application of sound for therapeutic purposes.

sonic boom—An explosionlike sound heard and felt when the shock wave that is generated by aircraft flying at supersonic speed reaches the ground.

sonic cleaning—The cleaning of contaminated materials by the action of intense sound waves produced in the liquid into which the material is immersed.

sonic delay line—A device in which electroacoustic transducers and the propagation of an elastic wave through a medium are used to produce the delay of an electrical signal.

sonic depth sounder—*See* Fathometer.

sonic drilling—The cutting or shaping of materials with an abrasive slurry driven by a reciprocating tool attached to an electromechanical transducer.

sonic frequencies—Vibrations which can be heard by the human ear (from about 15 hertz to approximately 20,000 hertz).

sonic soldering—The method of joining metals by the use of mechanical vibration to break up the surface oxides.

sonic speed—*See* Speed of Sound.

sonic thermocouple—A thermocouple so designed that gas moves past the junction with a velocity of mach 1 or greater, resulting in maximum heat transfer to the junction.

sonne—Also called consol. A radionavigational aid that provides a number of rotating characteristic signal zones. A bearing may be determined by observation (and interpolation) of the instant when transition occurs from one zone to the following zone.

sonobuoy—Also called a radiosonobuoy. A device used to locate a submerged target (e.g., a submarine). By means of a hydrophone system in the water, a sonobuoy detects the noises and converts them into radio signals, which are transmitted to a receiver in an airplane. Each sonobuoy transmits on one of several possible frequencies, and the receiver in the airplane has a channel selec-

tor so the operator can switch from one to another.

sonoluminescence—The creation of light in liquids by sonically-induced cavitation.

sonometer—A frequency meter that depends for its operation on mechanical resonance with the vibrations of a variable length of stretched wire.

sonoptography—The use of sound waves to obtain a 3-D image of an object. No lenses are required. In essence, a two stage process in which the diffraction pattern of an object irradiated by sound waves is biased by a coherent sound wave and recorded. The resultant pattern, like the hologram, then is interrogated with a suitable coherent light source to obtain a three-dimensional image.

sophisticated—A piece of equipment, system, etc., which is complex and intricate, or requires special skills to operate.

sophisticated vocabulary—An advanced and elaborate set of computer instructions, enabling the computer to perform such intricate operations as linearizing, extracting square roots, selecting the highest number, etc.

sort—To arrange items of information according to rules which depend on a key or field contained by the items.

sorter—A machine which sorts cards according to the position of coded holes.

S O S—A distress signal used in radiotelegraphy.

sound—1. Also called a sound wave. An alteration in pressure, stress, particle displacement or velocity, etc., propagated in an elastic material, or the superposition of such propagated alterations. 2. Also called a sound sensation. The auditory sensation usually evoked by the alterations described in (1) above.

sound absorption—The conversion of sound energy into some other form (usually heat) in passing through a medium or on striking a surface.

sound-absorption coefficient—The incident sound energy absorbed by a surface or medium, expressed in the form of a fraction.

sound analyzer—A device for measuring the amplitude and frequency of the components of a complex sound. It usually consists of a microphone, an amplifier, and a wave analyzer.

sound articulation—The per cent of articulation obtained when the speech units are fundamental sounds (usually combined into meaningless syllables).

sound bars—Alternate dark and light horizontal bars caused in a television picture by a-f voltage reaching the video-input circuit of the picture tube.

sound carrier—The frequency-modulated carrier which transmits the sound portion of television programs.

sound concentrator—A parabolic reflector

used with a microphone at its focus to obtain a highly directive pickup response.

sound-effect filter—A filter, usually adjustable, designed to reduce the passband of a system at low and/or high frequencies in order to produce special effects.

sound energy—The total energy in a given part of a medium, minus the energy which would exist there if no sound waves were present.

sound-energy density—At a point in a sound field, the sound energy contained in a given infinitesimal part of the medium, divided by the volume there. The commonly used unit is the erg per cubic centimeter.

sound-energy flux—The average rate at which sound energy flows through any specified area for a given period. The commonly used unit is the erg per second.

sound-energy flux density—*See* Sound Intensity.

sounder—*See* Telegraph Sounder.

sound field—A region in any medium containing sound waves.

sound film—Motion-picture film having a sound track along one side of the picture frames, for simultaneous reproduction of the sounds that accompany the film. A beam of light is projected through the sound track and is modulated at an audio rate by the variations in the width or density of the track. A phototube and amplifier then convert these modulations into sound.

sound gate—A mechanical device through which film is passed in a projector, to convert the sound track into audio signals that can be amplified and reproduced. In a television camera used for pickups, a sound gate provides the sound accompaniment for the motion picture being televised. Associated with the sound gate are an exciter lamp, a lens assembly, and a phototube.

sound head—The part of a sound motion-picture projector which converts the photographic or magnetic sound track on the film into audible sound signals.

sounding—Determination of the depth of water or the altitude above the earth.

sound intensity—Also called specific sound-energy flux or sound-energy flux density. The average rate of sound energy transmitted in a specified direction through a unit area normal to this direction at the point considered. The common unit is the erg per second per square centimeter, although sound intensity expressed in watts per square centimeter may occasionally be used.

sound-level meter—An instrument—including a microphone, amplifier, output meter, and frequency-weighting networks—for the measurement of noise and sound levels. The measurements approximate the loudness level obtained for pure tones by the more elaborate ear-balance method.

sound-on-sound recording — A method by which material previously recorded on one

track of a tape may be recorded on another track while simultaneously adding new material to it.

sound-powered telephone set—A telephone set in which the transmitter and receiver are passive transducers; operating power is obtained from the speech input only.

sound-power level—The ratio, expressed in db, of the sound power emitted by a source to a standard reference power of 10^{-13} watts.

sound power of a source—The total sound energy radiated by the source per unit of time. The common unit is the erg per second, but the power may also be expressed in watts.

sound pressure—The instantaneous pressure minus the static pressure at some point in a medium when a sound wave is present.

sound-pressure level — Abbreviated spl. In decibels, 20 times the logarithm of the ratio of the pressure of a sound to the reference pressure, which must be explicitly stated (usually, either 2×10^{-4} or 1 dyne per square centimeter).

sound probe—A small microphone (or tube added to a conventional microphone) for exploring a sound field without significantly disturbing it.

sound recordings—Records, tapes, or other sonic components upon which audio intelligence is inscribed or recorded or can be reproduced.

sound-recording system—A combination of transducing devices and associated equipment for storing sound in a reproducible form.

sound-reflection coefficient — Also called acoustical reflectivity. Ratio at which the sound energy reflected from a surface flows on the side of incidence, to the incident rate of flow.

sound-reproducing system—A combination of transducers and associated equipment for reproducing prerecorded sound.

sound sensation—*See* Sound.

sound spectrum—The frequency components included within the range of audible sound.

sound takeoff—The connection or coupling at which the 4.5-MHz frequency-modulated sound signal in a television receiver is obtained.

sound track—The narrow band which carries the sound in a movie film. It is usually along the margin of the film, and more than one band may be used (e.g., for stereophonic sound).

sound-transmission coefficient (of an interface or septum)—Also called acoustical transmittivity. The ratio of the transmitted to the incident sound energy. Its value is a function of the angle of incidence of the sound.

sound wave—*See* Sound.

source—1. The device which supplies signal power to a transducer. 2. In a field-effect transistor, the electrode that corresponds to the cathode of a vacuum tube.

source data automation—The methods of recording information in coded forms on paper tapes, punched cards, or tags that can be used repeatedly to produce many other records without rewriting.

source impedance—The impedance which a source of energy presents to the input terminals of a device.

source language—The language used to prepare a problem as the input for a computer operation.

source program — A computer program written in a language designed for ease of expression of a class of problems or procedures by humans. A generator, assembler, translator, or compiler routine translates the source program into an object program in machine language.

sourcing—Redesign or modification of existing equipment to eliminate a source of emi. When sourcing is not feasible, engineers are forced to resort to suppression, filtering, or shielding.

south pole—In a magnet, the pole into which magnetic lines of force are assumed to enter after emerging from the north pole.

space—1. An impulse which, in a neutral circuit, causes the loop to open or causes the absence of a signal, while in a polar circuit it causes the loop current to flow in a direction opposite to that for a mark impulse. A space impulse is equivalent to a binary 0. 2. In some codes, a character which causes a printer to leave a character width with no printed symbol.

space attenuation—The loss of energy, expressed in decibels, of a signal in free air caused by such factors as absorption, reflection, scattering, and dispersion.

space charge—1. The electrical charge caused in space by the presence of electrons or ions. 2. The electron cloud around the hot cathode of a vacuum tube.

space-charge debunching—In a microwave tube, a process in which the bunched electrons are dispersed due to the mutual interactions between electrons in the stream.

space-charge effect—Repulsion of electrons emitted from the cathode of a thermionic vacuum tube by electrons accumulated in the space charge near the cathode.

space-charge field — The electric field that occurs inside a plasma due to the net space charge in the volume of the plasma.

space-charge grid—A grid, usually positive, that controls the position, area, and magnitude of a potential minimum, or of a virtual cathode adjacent to the grid.

space-charge region — 1. The region where the net charge density of a semiconductor differs significantly from zero. (*Also see* Depletion Layer.) 2. The region in a semiconductor in which the mobile carrier charge density is insufficient to neutralize the net charge density of the fixed donor and acceptor ions.

space-charge tube—A tube in which the space charge is used to greatly increase the transconductance. A positively charged grid is placed next to the cathode, in front of the control grid. This enlarges the space charge, moving it out to where the control grid can have a greater effect on it and hence on the plate current.

space coordinates—A three dimensional system of rectangular co-ordinates. The x and y co-ordinates lie in a reference plane tangent to the earth, and the z co-ordinate is perpendicular.

space current—The total current flowing between the cathode and all other electrodes in a tube.

spaced antenna—An antenna system used for minimizing local effects of fading at short-wave receiving stations. So called because it consists of several antennas spaced a considerable distance apart.

spaced-antenna direction finder—A direction finder comprising two or more similar but separate antennas coupled to a common receiver.

space diversity—*See* Space-Diversity Reception.

space-diversity reception—Also called space diversity. Diversity reception from receiving antennas placed in different locations.

spaced-loop direction finder—A spaced-antenna direction finder in which the individual antennas are loops.

space factor — Ratio of the effective area utilized, to the total area in a winding section.

space harmonics—Harmonics in the distribution of flux in the air gap of a resolver. They may be determined as a percent of fundamental by a Fourier analysis of the flux distribution pattern. Space harmonics cause angular inaccuracy.

space pattern—On a test chart, a pattern designed for the measurement of geometric distortion. The EIA ball chart is an example.

space permeability — The factor that expresses the ratio of magnetic induction to magnetizing force in a vacuum. In the cgs electromagnetic system of units, the permeability of a vacuum is arbitrarily taken as unity.

space phase—Reaching corresponding peak values at the same point in space.

space quadrature—The difference in the position of corresponding points of a wave in space, the points being separated by one quarter of the wavelength in question.

space-to-mark transition—The transition, or switching, from a spacing impulse to a marking impulse. (Teletypewriter term.)

space wave—The radiated energy consisting of the direct and ground waves.

spacing—The distance between microphones or speakers in stereo recording or reproduction.

spacing end distortion — End distortion which lengthens the spacing impulse by advancing the mark-to-space transition. (Teletypewriter term.)

spacing interval—The interval between successive telegraph signal pulses. During this interval, either no current flows or the current has the opposite polarity from that of the signal pulses.

spacing pulse—In teletypewriter operation, the signal interval during which the selector unit does not operate.

spacing wave—Also called back wave. In telegraphic communication, the emission which takes place between the active portions of the code characters or while no code characters are being transmitted.

spacistor—A semiconductor device consisting of one PN junction and four electrode connections. It is characterized by a low transient time for carriers to flow from the input to the output.

spade bolt—A bolt with a threaded section and one spade-shaped flat end through which there is a hole for a screw or rivet. It is used for fastening shielded coils, capacitors, and other components to the chassis.

spade contact—A contact with fork-shaped female members designed to dovetail with spade-shaped male members. Alignment in this type of connection is very critical if good conductivity is to be achieved.

spade tips—Notched, flat metal strips connected to the end of a cord or wire so that it can be fastened under a binding screw.

spaghetti — Heavily varnished cloth tubing sometimes used to provide insulation for circuit wiring.

span—1. The part or space between two consecutive points of support in a conductor, cable, suspension strand, or pole line. 2. The reach or spread between two established limits such as the difference between high and low values in a given range of physical measurements.

spark—1. The abrupt, brilliant phenomenon which characterizes a disruptive discharge. 2. A single, short electrical discharge between two electrodes.

spark capacitor — A capacitor connected across a pair of contact points, or across the inductance which causes the spark, for the purpose of diminishing sparking at these points.

spark coil—An induction coil used to produce spark discharges.

spark frequency—The total number of sparks occurring per second in a spark transmitter (not the frequency of the individual waves).

spark gap—The arrangement of two electrodes between which a disruptive discharge of electricity may occur, and such that the insulation is self-restoring after the passage of a discharge.

spark-gap modulation—Modulation in which a controlled spark-gap breakdown produces one or more pulses of energy for application to the element in which the modulation is to take place.

spark-gap modulator — A modulator employed in certain radar transmitters. A pulse-forming line is discharged across either a stationary or a rotary spark gap.

spark-gap oscillator — A type of oscillator consisting essentially of an interrupted high-voltage discharge and a resonant circuit.

sparking — Intentional or accidental spark discharge, as between the brushes and commutator of a rotating machine, between the contacts of a relay or switch, in a solid tantalum capacitor, or at any other point at which a circuit is broken.

sparking voltage—The minimum voltage at which a spark discharge occurs between electrodes of a given shape, at a given distance apart, under given conditions.

spark killer—An electric network, usually a capacitor and resistor in series, connected across a pair of contact points (or across the inductance which causes the spark) to diminish sparking at these points.

spark lag—The interval between attainment of the sparking voltage and passage of the spark.

sparkover—Breakdown of the air between two electrical conductors, permitting the passage of a spark.

spark plate—In an automobile radio, a metal plate insulated from the chassis by a thin sheet of mica. It bypasses the noise signals picked up by the wiring under the hood.

spark-quenching device — See Spark Suppressor.

spark recorder—A recorder in which the recording paper passes through a spark gap formed by a metal plate underneath and a moving metal pointer above the paper. Sparks from an induction coil pass through the paper, periodically burning small holes that form the record trace.

spark spectrum—The spectrum produced in a substance when the light from a spark passes between terminals made of that substance or through an atmosphere of that substance.

spark suppressor — Also called a spark-quenching device or an arc suppressor. An electric network, such as a capacitance and resistance in series, or a diode connected across a pair of contacts to diminish sparking (arcing) at these contacts.

spark test—A test performed on wire and cable to determine the amount of detrimental porosity or defects in the insulation.

spark transmitter—A radio transmitter in which the source of radio-frequency power is the oscillatory discharge of a capacitor through an inductor and a spark gap.

spatial distribution—The directional properties of a speaker, transmitting antenna, or other radiator.

spdt — Abbreviation for single-pole, double-throw.

speaker—Abbreviated spkr. Also called a loudspeaker. An electroacoustic transducer that radiates acoustic power into the air with essentially the same waveform as that of the electrical input.

Speaker.

speaker efficiency—Ratio of the total useful sound radiated from a speaker at any frequency, to the electrical power applied to the voice coil.

speaker impedance—The rated impedance of the voice coil of a speaker.

speaker-reversal switch—A switch for connecting the left channel to the right speaker and vice versa on a stereo amplifier. It is a means of correcting for improper left-right orientation in the program source.

speaker system—A combination of one or more speakers and all associated baffles, horns, and dividing networks used to couple the driving electric circuit and the acoustic medium together.

speaker voice coil—In a moving-coil speaker, the part which is moved back and forth by electric impulses and is fastened to the cone in order to produce sound waves.

speaking arc—A d-c arc on which audio-frequency currents have been superimposed. As a result, the arc reproduces sounds in a manner similar to a speaker, and its light output will vary at the audio rate required for sound-film recording.

special-purpose computer—A computer designed to solve a restricted class of problems, as contrasted with a general-purpose computer.

special-purpose motor—A motor possessing special operating characteristics and/or special mechanical construction, designed for a particular application, and not included in the definition of a general-purpose motor.

special-purpose relay—A relay the application of which requires special features not characteristic of general-purpose or definite-purpose relays.

specific acoustic impedance — Also called unit-area acoustic impedance. The complex ratio of sound pressure to particle velocity at a point in a medium.

specific acoustic reactance—The imaginary component of the specific acoustic impedance.

specific acoustic resistance—The real component of the specific acoustic impedance.

specific coding—Digital-computer coding in which all addresses refer to specific registers and locations.

specific conductance—*See* Electrolytic Conductivity.

specific conductivity—The conducting ability of a material in mhos per cubic centimeter. It is the reciprocal of resistivity.

specific damping of an instrument — *See* Relative Damping of an Instrument.

specific dielectric strength—The dielectric strength per millimeter of thickness of an insulating material.

specific gravity—The weight of a substance compared with the weight of the same volume of water at the same temperature.

specific heat—The capacity of a material to be heated at a given temperature (expressed as calories per degree C. per gram), compared to water, which has a specific heat of 1.

specific inductive capacity — *See* Dielectric Constant.

specific program—Digital-computer programming for solving a specific problem.

specific repetition rate—In loran, one of a set of closely-spaced repetition rates derived from the basic rate and associated with a specific set of synchronized stations.

specific resistance—The resistance of a conductor. It is expressed in ohms per unit length per unit area, usually circular mil feet. (*Also see* Resistivity.)

specific routine—A digital-computer routine expressed in specific computer coding and used to solve a specific mathematical, logical, or data-handling problem.

specific sound-energy flux—*See* Sound Intensity.

spectral characteristic — The relationship between the radiant sensitivity of a phototube and the wavelength of the incident radiant flux. It is usually shown by a graph.

spectral contour plotter—A spectrum analyzer that presents a three-dimensional contour plot of analog signals, heart sounds, brain waves, etc.

spectral response—Also called spectral sensitivity characteristic. The relative amount of visual sensation produced by one unit of radiant flux of any one wavelength. The human eye or a photocell exhibits greatest spectral response to the wavelengths producing yellow-green light.

spectral sensitivity—The color response of a photosensitive device.

spectral sensitivity characteristic — *See* Spectral Response.

spectral voltage density — The rms voltage corresponding to the energy contained in a frequency band having a width of one hertz. For the spectral voltage density at a given frequency, the band is centered on the given frequency.

spectrograph—An instrument with an entrance slit and dispersing device that uses photography to obtain a record of the spectral range. The radiant power passing through the optical system is integrated over time, and the quantity recorded is a function of the radiant energy.

spectrometer—A test instrument that determines the frequency distribution of the energy generated by any source and displays all components simultaneously.

spectrophotoelectric—Pertaining to the dependence of photoelectric phenomena on the wavelength of the incident radiation.

spectroscope — An instrument used to disperse radiation into its component wavelengths and to observe or measure the resultant spectrum.

spectroscopy — The branch of optics that deals with radiations in the infrared, visible, and ultraviolet regions of the spectrum.

spectrum—A continuous range of electromagnetic radiations, from the longest known radio waves to the shortest known cosmic rays. Light, which is the visible portion of the spectrum, lies about midway between these two extremes.

spectrum analysis — The study of energy distribution across the frequency spectrum for a given electrical signal.

spectrum analyzer—A scanning receiver that automatically tunes through a selected frequency spectrum and displays on a crt or a chart a plot of amplitude versus frequency of the signals present at its input. A spectrum analyzer is, in effect, an automatic Fourier analysis plotter.

spectrum intervals—Frequency bands represented as intervals on a frequency scale.

spectrum level—For a specified signal at a particular frequency, the level of that part contained within a band one hertz wide, centered at the particular frequency.

spectrum-selectivity characteristic — A measure of the increase in the minimum input-signal power over the minimum detectable signal required to produce an indication on a radar indicator, if the received signal has a spectrum different from that of the normally received signal.

spectrum signature analysis—The evaluation of emi from transmitting and receiving equipment in order to determine operational and environmental compatibility.

spectrum utilization characteristics—The compiled data of either transmitters or receivers which describe operational parameters such as bandwidth, sensitivity, stability, antenna pattern, power output, etc. Also describes the capabilities of the equipment to either reject or suppress unwanted electromagnetic energy.

specular reflection — Reflection of light, sound, or radio waves from a surface so smooth that its inequalities are small in comparison with the wavelength of the incident rays. As a result, each incident ray produces a reflected ray in the same plane.

SPEDAC—Acronym for Solid-state, Parallel, Expandable, Differential-Analyzer Computer. A high-speed digital differential analyzer using parallel logic and arithmetic, solid-state circuitry, and modular construction and capable of being expanded in computing capacity, precision, and operating speed.

speech amplifier—A voltage amplifier made specifically for a microphone.

speech audiometer—An audiometer for measuring either live or recorded speech signals.

speech clipper—A speech-amplitude–limiting circuit which permits the average modulation percentage of an amplitude-modulated transmitter to be increased.

speech frequency—*See* Voice Frequency.

speech interpolation—The method of obtaining more than one voice channel per voice circuit by giving each subscriber a speech path in the proper direction only at the times when his speech requires it.

speech inverter—An apparatus that interchanges high and low speech frequencies by removing the carrier wave and transmission of only one sideband in a radiotelephone. This renders the speech unintelligible unless picked up by apparatus capable of replacing the carrier wave in the correct manner. (*Also see* Scrambler Circuit.)

speech level — The energy of speech (or music), measured in volume units on a volume indicator.

speech scrambler—*See* Scrambler Circuit.

speech synthesizer—A system used in research to generate speech from electrical signals in order to study human vocal patterns.

speed limit—A control function that prevents the controlled speed from exceeding prescribed limits.

speed of light—The speed at which light travels, or 186,284 miles per second.

speed of sound—Also called sonic speed. The speed at which sound waves travel through a medium (in air and at standard sea-level conditions, about 750 miles per hour or 1,080 feet per second).

speed of transmission — Also called rate of transmission. The instantaneous rate of processing information by a transmission facility. Usually measured in characters or bits per unit time.

speed-ratio control — A control function which maintains a preset ratio of the speeds of two drives.

speed regulation—The speed change of a motor between full-load and no-load, expressed in per cent of full-load speed.

speed regulator—A regulator which maintains or varies the speed of a motor at a predetermined rate.

speed-up capacitor—A capacitor used in RCTL to permit faster turn-on of the transistor in response to a change in input; it also helps overcome the storage delay of the transistor itself.

sphere gap—A spark gap with spherical electrodes. It is used as an excess-voltage protective device.

sphere-gap voltmeter—An instrument for measuring high voltages. It consists of a sphere gap, and the electrodes are moved together until the spark will just barely pass. The voltage can be calculated from the gap spacing and the electrode diameter, or read directly from a calibrated scale.

spherical aberration—Image defects (e.g., blurring) due to the spherical form of a lens or mirror. These defects cause a blurred image because the lens or mirror brings the central and marginal rays to different focuses. Common types of spherical aberration are astigmatism and curvature of the field.

spherical candlepower—In a lamp, the average candlepower in all directions in space. It is equal to the total luminous flux of the lamp, measured in lumens, divided by 4π.

spherical coordinates—A system of polar coordinates which originate in the center of a sphere. All points lie on the surface of the sphere, and the polar axis cuts the sphere at its two poles.

spherical-earth factor—Ratio between the electric field strengths that would result from propagation over an imperfectly conducting spherical earth and a perfectly conducting plane.

spherical wave—A wave in which the wavefronts are concentric spheres.

spider—A highly flexible ring, washer, or punched flat member used in a dynamic speaker to center the voice coil on the pole piece without appreciably hindering the in-and-out motion of the voice coil and its attached diaphragm.

spider-web antenna—An all-wave receiving antenna having several lengths of doublets connected somewhat like the web of a spider, to give favorable pickup characteristics over a wide range of frequencies.

spider-web coil—A flat coil having an open weave somewhat like the bottom of a woven basket. It was used in older radio receivers.

spike—An abrupt transient which comprises part of a pulse but exceeds its average amplitude considerably.

spike discriminator—A circuit used in a transponder to discriminate against pulses of extremely short duration, such as might be caused by ignition noise.

spike-leakage energy—The radio-frequency energy per pulse transmitted through TR and pre-TR tubes before and during the establishment of the steady-state radio-frequency discharge.

spike noise—In a chopper, the static field noise caused by insulating material; can be observed if the chopper is followed by a wideband amplifier.

spiking—Short, multiple, irregular bursts of laser-output radiation. Spiking is characteristic of pulse lasers, especially flash-pumped solid-dielectric types (e.g. ruby, neodymium in glass). The spike duration is typically 0.2 to 2 μsec.

spill—The redistribution and hence loss of information from a storage element of a charge-storage tube.

spindle—The upward-projecting shaft used on a phonograph turntable for positioning and centering the record.

spinner—An automatically rotatable radar antenna, together with its associated equipment.

spinning electron—An electron that spins with an angular momentum.

spinthariscope—An instrument for viewing the scintillations of alpha particles on a luminescent screen.

spin wave—A moving magnetic disturbance in a ferrite. The presence of an alternating magnetic field with its frequency near that of the natural precessional frequency of a spin tends to increase the precession angle. This increase in precession angle is passed from atom to atom by dipole and exchange interactions.

spin-wave amplitude—The difference between the precession angles of two spins.

spiral distortion—In camera tubes or image tubes using magnetic focusing, a form of distortion in which image rotation varies with distance from the axis of symmetry of the electron optical system.

spiral four—A quad in which the four conductors are twisted about a common axis, the two sets of opposite conductors being used as pairs.

spiral scanning—Scanning in which the maximum radiation describes a portion of a spiral, with the rotation always in one direction.

spkr—Abbreviation for speaker.

spl—Abbreviation for sound-pressure level.

splashproof—A device or machine so constructed and protected that external splashing will not interfere with its operation.

splashproof motor—An open motor in which the ventilating openings are so constructed that drops of liquid or solid particles falling on it, or coming toward it in a straight line at any angle not greater than 100° from the vertical, cannot enter either directly or by striking and running along a surface of the motor.

splatter—Adjacent-channel interference due to overmodulation of a transmitter by abrupt peak audio signals. It is particularly noticeable for sounds containing high-frequency harmonics.

splice insulation—Insulation used over a splice.

splicing block—A grooved metal or plastic device for holding magnetic recording tape while being spliced. The ends of the tape are inserted into the groove.

splicing tape—A pressure-sensitive, nonmagnetic tape used for splicing magnetic tape together.

split—1. Of radar tracks, the separation of radar data from a single track to such a degree that one or more additional tracks can be initiated manually or automatically; a similar condition exists when a raid is separated to such an extent that it can be represented on a situation display as two or more raids. 2. Initiation of split tracks, raids, or groups by a direction center-track monitor or by programming means.

split-anode magnetron—A magnetron with an anode divided into two segments, usually by parallel slots.

split-conductor cable—A cable in which each conductor is composed of two or more insulated conductors normally connected in parallel.

split fitting—A conduit fitting, bend, elbow, or tee split longitudinally so that it can be positioned after the wires have been drawn into the conduit. The two parts are held together usually by screws.

split gear—A type of gear designed to minimize backlash. The method consists of splitting one gear of a meshing pair and so connecting a spring between the two halves that pressure is exerted on both sides of the teeth of the other gear.

split hydrophone—A directional hydrophone in which the electroacoustic transducers are divided and arranged so that each division can induce a separate electromotive force between its own terminals.

split image—Two or more scenes appearing on a television screen as a result of trick "photography" at the studio.

split-phase motor—A single-phase induction motor having an auxiliary winding connected in parallel with the main winding, but displaced in a magnetic position from the main winding so as to produce the required rotating magnetic field for starting. The auxiliary circuit is generally opened when the motor has reached a predetermined speed.

split projector—A directional projector in which electroacoustic transducing elements are divided and arranged so that each division can be energized separately through its own terminals.

split-rotor plate—*See* Serrated Rotor Plate.

split-sound system—An early television receiver i-f system in which the audio and video i-f signals are separated right after the mixer stage and are amplified in separate i-f stages. Replaced by the more current intercarrier sound system.

split-stator variable capacitor—A variable capacitor with a rotor section common to two separate stator sections. Used for balancing in the grid and plate tank circuits of transmitters.

split transducer—A directional transducer in which electroacoustic transducing elements are divided and arranged so that each division is electrically separate.

split winding—An equal division of a winding which will allow series or parallel external connection of the divided winding (four external leads) of a servomotor.

spontaneous emission—Emission occurring without stimulation or quenching after excitation.

spool—A flanged form serving as the foundation on which a coil is wound.

sporadic E-layer—A portion that sometimes breaks away from the normal E-layer in the ionosphere and exhibits unusual erratic characteristics.

sporadic reflections—Also called abnormal reflections. Sharply defined, intense reflections from the sporadic E-layer. Their frequencies are higher than the critical frequency of the layer, and they occur anytime, anywhere, and at any frequency.

spot—1. The area instantaneously affected by the impact of an electron beam of a cathode-ray tube. 2. *See* Land.

spot noise factor—*See* Spot Noise Figure.

spot noise figure—Also called spot noise factor. Ratio of the output noise of a transducer, to the portion attributable to the thermal noise in the input termination when the termination has a standard noise temperature ($290°K$). The spot noise figure is a point function of input frequency.

spot projection—In facsimile: 1. An optical method in which the scanning or recording spot is delineated by an aperture between the light source and the subject copy or record sheet. 2. The optical system in which the scanning or recording spot is the size of the area being scanned and reproduced.

spot speed—1. In facsimile, the length of the scanning line times the number of lines per second. 2. In television, the product of the length (in units of elemental area, i.e., in spots) of the scanning line and the number of scanning lines per second.

spottiness—Bright spots scattered irregularly over the reproduced image in a television receiver, due to man-made or static interference entering the television system at some point.

spot welding—A resistance welding process whereby welds are made between two or more overlapping sheets of metal by pressing them together between two electrodes arranged to conduct current to the outer surfaces of the overlapped sheets. The tips of one or both of the electrodes are restricted in area to approximately the diameter of the spot weld desired.

spot wobble—An externally produced oscillating movement of an electron beam and its resultant spot. Spot wobble is used to eliminate the horizontal lines across the screen and thus make the picture more pleasing.

spreader—1. An insulating crossarm used to hold the wires of a transmission line apart. 2. The crossarm separating the parallel wire elements of an antenna.

spread groove—A groove cut between recordings. The groove, which has an abnormally high pitch, separates the recorded material but still enables the stylus to travel from one to the next.

spreading anomaly—That part of the propagation anomaly that is identifiable with the geometry of the ray pattern.

spreading loss—The transmission loss suffered by radiant energy. The effect of spreading, or divergence, is measured by this loss.

spread spectrum transmission—A communications technique in which many different signal waveforms are transmitted in a wide band. Power is spread thinly over the band so narrow-band radios can operate within the wide band without interference.

spring—A resilient, flat piece of metal forming or supporting a contact member in a jack or a key.

spring-actuated stepping relay—A stepping relay in which cocking is done electrically and operation is produced by spring action.

spring contact—A relay or switch contact, usually of phosphor bronze and mounted on a flat spring.

spring curve—A plot of the spring force on the armature of a relay versus armature travel.

spring-finger action—The design of a contact, as used in a printed-circuit connector or a socket contact, permitting easy stress-free spring action to provide contact pressure and/or retention.

spring pile-up—An assembly of all contact springs operated by one armature lever.

spring-return switch—A switch which returns to its normal position when the operating pressure is released.

spring stop—In a relay, the member used to control the position of a pretensioned spring.

spring stud—In a relay, an insulating member that transmits the armature motion from one movable contact to another in the same pileup.

spst—Abbreviation for single-pole, single-throw.

spurious emanations — Unintentional and undesired emissions from a transmitting circuit.

spurious count—*See* Spurious Tube Counts.

spurious emission—*See* Spurious Radiation.

spurious pulse—In a scintillation counter, a pulse not purposely generated or directly due to ionizing radiation.

spurious pulse mode—An unwanted pulse mode which is formed by the chance combination of two or more pulse modes and is indistinguishable from a pulse interrogation or reply.

spurious radiation — Also called spurious emission. Emissions from a radio transmitter at frequencies outside its assigned or intended emission frequency. Spurious emissions include harmonic emissions, parasitic emissions, and intermodulation products, but exclude emissions in the immediate vicinity of the necessary band, which are a result of the modulation process for the transmission of information.

spurious response — 1. Any undesired response from an electric transducer or similar device. 2. The sensitivity of a circuit to signals of frequencies other than the frequency to which the circuit is tuned.

spurious-response attenuation—The ability of a receiver to discriminate between a desired signal to which it is resonant and an undesired signal at any other frequency to which it is simultaneously responsive.

spurious-response ratio—Ratio of the field strength at the frequency which produces a spurious response, to the field strength at the desired frequency, each field being applied in turn to produce equal outputs. Image ratio and intermediate-frequency response ratio are special forms of spurious-response ratio.

spurious signal—An unwanted signal generated either in the equipment itself or externally and heard (or seen) as noise.

spurious transmitter output—Any component of the radio-frequency output that is not implied by the type of modulation and the specified bandwidth.

spurious transmitter output, conducted—A spurious output of a radio transmitter that is conducted over a tangible transmission path such as a power line, control circuit, radio-frequency transmission line, waveguide, etc.

spurious transmitter output, extraband—A spurious transmitter output that lies outside the specified band of transmission.

spurious transmitter output, inband—A spurious transmitter output that lies within the specified band of transmission.

spurious transmitter output, radiated—A spurious output radiated from a radio transmitter. (The associated antenna and transmission lines are not considered part of the transmitter.)

spurious tube counts—Also called spurious counts. The counts in radiation-counter tubes, other than background counts and those caused directly by the radiation to be measured. They are caused by electrical leakage, failure of the quenching process, etc.

sputtering—1. Also called cathode sputtering. A process sometimes used in the production of the metal master disc. In this process the original is coated with an electric conducting layer by means of an electric discharge in a vacuum. 2. Ejection of atoms from a surface when bombarded by atomic particles.

spygmogram—A graphic recording of the movements, forms, and forces of an arterial pulse.

s-quad—Also called simple quad. An arrangement of two parallel paths, each of which contains two elements in series.

square-law demodulator — *See* Square-law Detector.

square-law detection—Detection in which the output voltage is substantially proportional to the square of the input voltage over the useful range of the detector.

square-law detector—Also called square-law demodulator. A detector in which the output voltage is essentially proportional to the square of the r-f input voltage.

square-law scale meter—A meter in which the deflection is proportional to the square of the applied energies.

square-loop ferrite—A ferrite with a rectangular hysteresis loop.

squareness ratio—1. For a magnetic material in a symmetrically cyclically magnetized condition, the ratio of the flux density at zero magnetizing force, to the maximum flux density. 2. The ratio of the flux density to the maximum flux density when the magnetizing force has changed halfway from zero toward its negative limiting value.

Square wave (ideal).

square wave—A square- or rectangular-shaped periodic wave which alternately assumes two fixed values for equal lengths of time, the transition time being negligible in comparison with the duration of each fixed value.

square-wave amplifier—A resistance-coupled amplifier (in effect, a wideband video amplifier) which amplifies a square wave with a minimum of distortion.

square-wave generator—A signal generator for producing square or rectangular waves.

square-wave response—In camera tubes, the ratio of the peak-to-peak signal amplitude given by a test pattern consisting of alternate black and white bars of equal widths, to the difference in signal between large-area blacks and whites having the same illuminations as the bars. Horizontal square-wave response is measured if the bars are perpendicular to the horizontal scan, and vertical square-wave response is measured if they are parallel.

squaring circuit—1. A circuit which changes a sine wave or other wave into a square wave. 2. A circuit which contains nonlinear elements and which produces an output voltage proportional to the square of the input voltage.

squawker — The midrange speaker of a three-way system.

squeal—Audible tape vibrations, primarily in the longitudinal node, caused by a frictional excitation at the heads and guides.

squealing — The high-pitched noise heard along with the desired intelligence in a radio receiver. It is due to interference between stations or to oscillation in one of the receiver circuits.

squeezable waveguide—In radar, a variable-width waveguide for shifting the phase of the radio-frequency wave traveling through it.

squeeze section—A length of waveguide, the critical dimension of which can be altered to correspond to changes in the electrical length.

squeeze track — A variable-density sound track in which variable width with greater signal-to-noise ratio is obtained by means of adjustable masking of the recording light beam and simultaneous increase of the electric signal applied to the light modulator.

squegger — A self-quenching oscillator in which the suppression occurs in the grid circuit.

squegging—A self-blocking condition in an oscillator circuit.

squegging oscillator — *See* Blocking Oscillator.

squelch—To automatically quiet a receiver by reducing its gain in response to a specified characteristic of the input.

squelch circuit—A circuit for preventing a radio receiver from producing an audio-frequency output in the absence of a signal having predetermined characteristics. A squelch circuit may be operated by signal energy in the receiver passband, by noise quieting, or by a combination of the two (ratio squelch). It may also be operated by a signal having special modulation characteristics (selective squelch).

squint—In radar, an ambiguous term, meaning either the angle between the two major-lobe axes in a lobe-switching antenna, or the angular difference between the axis of antenna radiation and a selected geometric axis such as the axis of the reflector.

squint angle—The angle between the physical axis of the antenna center and the axis of the radiated beam.

squirrel-cage induction motor—An induction motor in which the secondary circuit, usually the rotor, consists of a squirrel-cage winding (two discs connected along their circumference with copper bars) arranged in slots in the iron core.

squirrel-cage winding—A permanently short-circuited winding which is usually uninsulated, has its conductors uniformly distributed around the periphery of the machine, and is joined by continuous end rings.

squitter—In radar, random firing (intentional or otherwise) of the transponder transmitter in the absence of interrogation.

ss—*See* Single-Sideband Modulation.

ssb—*See* Single-Sideband Modulation.

ssfm—A system of multiplex in which the single-sideband subcarriers are used to frequency-modulate a second carrier.

sspm—A system of multiplex in which the single-sideband subcarriers are used to phase-modulate a second carrier.

stability—1. The ability of a component or device to maintain its nominal operating characteristics after being subjected to changes in temperature, environment, current, and time. It is usually expressed in either percent or parts per million for a given period of time. 2. The ability of a power supply to maintain a constant output voltage (or current) over a period of time under fixed conditions of input, load and temperature. Usually expressed in terms of a voltage (or current) change over a fixed length of time. 3. The ability to maintain effectiveness within reasonable bounds in spite of large changes in environment. *Also see* Drift. 4. For a feedback-control system or element, the property such that its output is asymptomatic (i.e., will ultimately attain a steady-state d-c level within the linear range and without continuing external stimuli).

stability factor—The measure of the bias stability of a transistor amplifier. It is defined as the change in collector current, I_c, per change in cutoff current, I_{co}.

stabilivolt—A gas-filled tube containing a number of concentric, coated iron electrodes. It is used as a source of practically constant voltage for apparatus drawing only small currents.

stabilization—1. The introducing of stability into a circuit. 2. A treatment of a magnetic material designed to increase its magnetic permanency.

stabilized feedback—*See* Negative Feedback.

stabilized flight—A type of flight in which control information is obtained from inertia-stabilized references such as gyroscopes.

stabilized local oscillator — An extremely stable radio-frequency oscillator used as a local oscillator in the superheterodyne radar receiver in a moving-target indicator system.

stabilized shunt-wound motor — A shunt-wound motor to which a light series winding has been added to prevent a rise in speed, or to reduce the speed when the load increases.

stabilized winding — Also called tertiary winding. An auxiliary winding used particularly in star-connected transformers: a. To stabilize the neutral point of the fundamental frequency voltage. b. To protect the transformer and the system from excessive third-harmonic voltages. c. To prevent telephone interference caused by third-harmonic currents and voltages in the lines and earth.

stabistor—A voltage-limiting semiconductor. A diode designed to break over and conduct at a certain voltage. This is the normal forward conduction of a diode and is also characteristic of zener diodes, which avalanche into conduction when breakdown (backward) voltage is exceeded.

stable element—In navigation, an instrument or device which maintains a desired orientation independently of the vehicle motion.

stable oscillation—A response which does not increase indefinitely with time; the opposite of an unstable oscillation.

stable platform—Also called a gyrostabilized platform. A gyro instrument which provides accurate azimuth, pitch, and roll attitude information. In addition to serving as reference elements, they are used for stabilizing accelerometers, star trackers, and similar devices in space.

stack—1. That portion of a computer memory and/or registers used to temporarily hold information. 2. *See* Pileup.

stacked array—An antenna consisting of elements placed one above the other. This is done to increase the sensitivity.

stacked dipole antenna—Antennas in which the antenna directivity is increased by providing a number of identical dipole elements, excited either directly or parasitically. The resultant radiation pattern will depend on the number of dipole elements used, the spacing and phase difference between the elements, and the relative magnitudes of the currents.

stacked heads—Also called in-line heads. An arrangement of magnetic recording heads used for stereophonic sound. The two heads are directly in line, one above the other.

stage—1. A term usually applied to an amplifier to mean one step, especially if part of a multistep process; or the apparatus employed in such a step. 2. A hydraulic amplifier used in a servovalve. Servovalves may be single-stage, two-stage, three-stage, etc.

stage-by-stage elimination — A method of locating trouble in electronic equipment by using a signal generator to introduce a test signal into each stage, one at a time, until the defective stage is found.

stage efficiency — Ratio of useful power (alternating current) delivered to the load, to the power at the input (direct current).

staggered heads—An infrequently-used arrangement of magnetic recording heads for stereophonic sound. The heads are $1\frac{7}{32}$ inch apart. Stereo tapes recorded with staggered heads cannot be played on recorders using stacked heads, and vice versa.

staggered tuning—A means of producing a wide bandwidth in a multistage i-f amplifier by tuning to different frequencies by a specified amount.

staggering—The offsetting of two channels of different carrier systems from exact sideband-frequency coincidence, in order to avoid mutual interference.

staggering advantage—A reduction in intelligible cross talk between identical channels of adjacent carrier systems as a result of using slightly different frequency allocations for the different systems.

stagger time — The interval between the times of actuation of any two contact sets.

stagger-tuned amplifier—An amplifier consisting of two or more stages, each tuned to a different frequency.

stagnation thermocouple—A type of thermocouple in which a high recovery factor is achieved by stagnating the flow in a space

Staggered tuning.

surrounding the junction. This results in a high response time as compared with an exposed junction.

staircase generator — A special-purpose signal generator that produces an output which increases in steps; thus its output waveform has the appearance of a staircase.

staircase signal—A waveform consisting of a series of discrete steps resembling a staircase.

stalled-torque control — A control function used to control the drive torque at zero speed.

stall torque—1. The torque which the rotor of an energized motor produces when restrained from motion. 2. The torque developed by a servomotor at speed in excess of 1 rpm but less than $\frac{1}{2}\%$ of the synchronous speed with a rated voltage and frequency of the proper phase relationship applied to both windings.

stalo—1. Acronym for STAbilized Local Oscillator used as part of a moving-target indication device in conjunction with a radar. 2. A highly stable oscillator, usually stabilized by feedback from a very high-Q LC circuit such as a high-Q cavity.

stamper—A negative (generally made of metal by electroforming), from which finished records are molded.

standard—An exact value, or a concept established by authority, custom, or agreement, to serve as a model or rule in the measurement of a quantity or in the establishment of a procedure.

standard antenna—An open single-wire antenna, including the lead-in wire, having an effective height of four meters.

standard beam approach—Abbreviated sba. A vhf 40-MHz, continuous-wave, low-approach system using a localizer and markers. The two main-signal lobes are tone-modulated with the Morse-code letters *E* and *T* (• and —). These modulations form a continuous tone when the aircraft is on its course. The airborne equipment is usually instrumented for visual reference, but may be used aurally in some applications.

standard broadcast band—The band of frequencies extending from 535 to 1605 kilohertz.

standard broadcast channel—The band of frequencies occupied by the carrier and two sidebands of a broadcast signal. The carrier frequency is at the center, with the sidebands extending 5 kHz on either side.

standard broadcast station—A radio station operated on a frequency between 535 and 1,605 kHz for the purpose of transmitting programs intended for reception by the general public.

standard candle — A unit of candlepower equal to a specified fraction of the visible light radiated by a group of 45 carbon-filament lamps preserved at the National Bureau of Standards, the lamps being operated at a specified voltage. The standard candle was originally the amount of light radiated by a tallow candle of specified composition and shape.

standard capacitor—A capacitor in which its capacitance is not likely to vary. It is used chiefly in capacitance bridges.

Standard cell.

standard cell—A primary cell which serves as a standard of voltage.

standard component—A component which is regularly produced by some manufacturer and is carried in stock by one or more distributors.

standard deflection — 1. In a galvanometer having an attached scale, one scale division. 2. In a galvanometer without an attached scale, 1 millimeter when the scale distance is 1 meter.

standard deviation—A measure of the variation of data from the average. It is equal to the root mean square of the individual deviations from the average.

standard eye—An observer that has red and infrared luminosity functions.

standard facility—In programming actions, a basic communications electronics functional entity which is engineered to satisfy a specific communications electronics operational requirement. An associated standard facility equipment list describes the facility functionally and indicates the material required for the standard facility.

standard-frequency service — A radiocommunication service that transmits for general reception specified standard frequencies of known high accuracy.

standard-frequency signal — One of the highly accurate signals broadcast by the National Bureau of Standards radio station WWV on 2.5, 5, 10, 15, 20, 25, 30, and 35 MHz at specific times. Used for testing and calibrating radio equipment all over the world.

standard-gain horn — A waveguide device that has essentially flared out its waveguide dimensions to specific lengths that match (with certain gain) the incoming energy to the atmosphere. The applications include using these horns for reflectors and lenses, pickup horns for sampling power, and receiving and transmitting antennas.

standardization—The process of establishing by common agreement engineering criteria, terms, principles, practices, materials, items, processes, equipment, parts, subassemblies, and assemblies to achieve the greatest practicable uniformity of items of supply and engineering practices, to insure the minimum feasible variety of such items and practices, and to effect optimum interchangeability of equipment parts and components.

standard microphone—A microphone, the response of which is known for the condition under which it is to be used.

standard noise temperature — A standard reference temperature (T) for noise measurements, taken as 290° K.

standard observer—A hypothetical observer who requires standard amounts of primaries in a color mixture to match every color.

standard pitch—The tone *A* at 440 hertz.

standard propagation—Propagation of radio waves over a smooth, spherical earth of uniform dielectric constant and conductivity, under standard atmospheric refraction.

standard reference temperature—In a thermistor, the body temperature for which the nominal zero-power resistance is specified.

standard refraction—The refraction which would occur in an idealized atmosphere; the index of refraction decreases uniformly with height at the rate of 39×10^{-6} per kilometer.

standard register of a motor meter—Also called a dial register. A four- or five-dial register, each dial being divided into ten equal parts numbered from zero to nine. The dial pointers are geared so that adjacent ones move in opposite directions at a 10-to-1 ratio.

standard resistor—Also called a resistance standard. A resistor which is adjusted to a specified value, is only slightly affected by variations in temperature, and is substantially constant over long periods of time.

Standard resistor.

standard rod gap—A gap between the ends of two half-inch square rods. Each rod is cut off squarely and mounted on supports so that it overhangs the inner edge of each support by a length equal to or greater than half the gap spacing. It is used for approximate measurements of crest voltages.

standard sea-water conditions—Sea water with a static pressure of 1 atmosphere, a temperature of 15° C., and a salinity such that the velocity of sound propagation is exactly 1,500 meters per second.

standard sphere gap—A gap between two metal spheres of standard dimensions. It is used for measuring the crest value of a voltage, by observing the maximum gap spacing at which sparkover occurs when a voltage is applied under known atmospheric conditions.

standard subroutine—In a computer, a subroutine which is applicable to a class of problems.

standard television signal—A signal which conforms to accepted specifications.

standard test conditions—The environmental conditions under which measurements should be made when disagreement of data obtained by various observers at different times and places may result from making measurements under other conditions.

standard test-tone power—One milliwatt (0 dbm) at 1,000 hertz.

standard voltage generator — *See* Signal Generator.

standard volume indicator—A volume indicator with the characteristics prescribed by the American Standards Association.

standby — 1. The condition of equipment which will permit complete resumption of stable operation within a short period of time. 2. A duplicate set of equipment to be used if the primary unit becomes unusable because of malfunction.

standby battery—A storage battery held in reserve to serve as an emergency power source in event the regular power facilities at a radio station, hospital, etc., fail.

standby register — A register in which accepted or verified information can be stored to be available for a rerun in the event of a mistake in the program or a malfunction in the computer.

standby transmitter—A transmitter installed and maintained ready for use whenever the main transmitter is out of service.

standing-on-nines carry—A system of executing the carry process in a computer. If a carry into a given place produces a carry from there, the incoming carry information is routed around that place.

standing wave—1. The distribution of current and voltage on a transmission line formed by two sets of waves traveling in opposite directions, and characterized by the presence of a number of points of successive maxima and minima in the distribution curves. Also called stationary wave. 2. The sinusoidal distribution of current and voltage amplitudes along a transmission line as a result of the reflection of energy from a point where a mismatch of impedance occurs.

standing-wave detector—See Standing-Wave Meter.

standing-wave indicator—See Standing-Wave Meter.

standing-wave loss factor — Ratio of the transmission loss in a waveguide when it is unmatched, compared with the loss when it is matched.

standing-wave meter—Also called a standing-wave indicator or detector. An instrument for measuring the standing-wave ratio in a transmission line. It may also include means for finding the location of maximum and minimum amplitudes.

standing-wave ratio — Abbreviated swr. 1. The ratio of current (or voltage) at a loop (maximum) in the transmission line to the value at a (minimum) node. It is equal to the ratio of the characteristic impedance of the line to the impedance of the load connected to the output end of the line. 2. The ratio of the amplitude of a standing wave at an antinode to the amplitude at a node.

standing-wave-ratio bridge — Abbreviated swr bridge. A bridge for measuring the standing-wave ratio on a transmission line to check the impedance match.

standoff insulator—An insulator used to hold a wire or other radio component away from the structure on which it is mounted.

star chain—A group of navigational radio transmitting stations comprising a master station about which three or more slave stations are symmetrically located.

star-connected circuit—A polyphase circuit

in which all current paths within the region that limits the circuit extend from each of the points of entry of the phase conductors to a common conductor (which may be the neutral conductor).

star connection—See Wye Connection.

stark effect—The splitting of spectral lines due to an applied electric field.

star network — A set of three or more branches with one terminal of each connected at a common node.

star-quad cable—Four wires laid together and twisted as a group.

starter—1. An auxiliary electrode used to initiate conduction in a glow-discharge, cold-cathode tube. 2. Sometimes referred to as a trigger electrode. A control electrode, the principal function of which is to establish sufficient ionization to reduce the anode breakdown voltage in a gas tube. 3. An electric controller for accelerating a motor from rest to normal speed.

starter breakdown voltage—The voltage required to initiate conduction across the starter gap of a glow-discharge, cold-cathode tube, all other tube elements being held at cathode potential before breakdown.

starter gap—The conduction path between a starter and the other electrode to which the starting voltage is applied in a glow-discharge, cold-cathode tube.

starter voltage drop — The voltage drop across the starter gap after conduction is established there in a glow-discharge, cold-cathode tube.

starting anode—The anode that establishes the initial arc in a mercury-arc rectifier tube.

starting circuit breaker — A device the principal function of which is to connect a machine to its source of starting voltage.

starting current of an oscillator — The value of oscillator current at which self-sustaining oscillations will start under specified loading.

starting electrode—The electrode that establishes the cathode spot in a pool-cathode tube.

starting reactor—A reactor for decreasing the starting current of a machine or device.

starting torque—Also called pull-in torque. The maximum load torque with which motors can start and come to synchronous speed.

starting-to-running transition contactor—A device which operates to initiate or cause the automatic transfer of a machine from the starting to the running power connection.

starting voltage—The voltage necessary for a gaseous voltage regulator to become ionized or to start conducting. As soon as this happens, the voltage drops to the operating value.

start lead—Also called inside lead. The inner termination of a winding.

startover—A program function that causes an inactive computer to become active.

start-record signal—In facsimile transmission, the signal that starts the converting of the electrical signal to an image on the record sheet.

start signal—The signal that converts fac-simile-transmission equipment from standby to active.

start-stop multivibrator — *See* Monostable Multivibrator *and* Flip-Flop Multivibrator.

start-stop-printing telegraphy — Printing telegraphy in which the signal-receiving mechanisms are started and stopped at the beginning and end of each transmitted character.

starved amplifier — An amplifier employing pentode tubes in which the screen voltage is set 10% below the plate voltage and the plate-load resistance is increased to 10 times the normal value. Thus, the amplification factor is greatly increased— often a stage gain of 2,000 is achieved.

stat—A prefix used to identify electrostatic units in the cgs system. (*Also see* Statampere, Statcoulomb, Statfarad, Stathenry, Statmho, Statohm, *and* Statvolt.)

statampere—The cgs electrostatic unit of current, equal to 3.3356×10^{-10} ampere (absolute).

statcoulomb—The cgs electrostatic unit of charge equal to 3.3356×10^{-10} coulomb (absolute).

state—The condition of a circuit, system, etc.

state of charge—The condition of a storage cell or battery in terms of the remaining capacity.

statfarad — The cgs electrostatic unit of charge equal to 1.11263×10^{-12} farad (absolute).

stathenry—The cgs electrostatic unit of inductance equal to 8.98766×10^{11} henrys (absolute).

static—*See* Atmospherics.

static behavior—The behavior of a control system or an individual unit under fixed conditions (as contrasted to dynamic behavior, under changing conditions).

static characteristic—The relationship between a pair of variables such as electrode voltage and electrode current, all other voltages being maintained constant. This relationship is usually represented by a graph.

static charge — The accumulated electric charge on an object.

static check—Of a computer, consists of one or more tests of computing elements, their interconnections, or both, performed under static conditions.

static convergence — Convergence of the three electron beams at the center of the aperture mask in a color picture tube. The term "static" applies to the theoretical paths the beams would follow if no scanning forces were present.

static decay—In a storage tube, decay that is a function only of storage surface properties such as lateral or transverse leakage.

static device—As associated with electronic

and other control or information-handling circuits, the term "static" refers to devices with switching functions that have no moving parts.

static electricity—Stationary electricity—i.e., in the form of a charge in equilibrium, or considered independently of the effects of its motion.

static eliminator—A device for reducing atmospheric static interference in a radio receiver.

static field—A field that is present between the poles of either a permanent magnet or an electromagnet that has a direct current passing through its coils.

static focus—The focus attained when the electron beam is theoretically at rest or is at the position it would occupy if scanning energy were not applied.

static forward-current transfer ratio—In a transistor, the ratio, under specified test conditions, of the d-c output current to the d-c input current.

static input resistance—In a transistor, the ratio of the d-c input voltage to the d-c input current.

staticizer—A storage device which is able to take information sequentially in time and put it out in parallel.

static machine—A machine for generating an electric charge, usually by induction.

static measurement—A measurement taken under conditions where neither the stimulus nor the environmental conditions fluctuate.

static pressure—Also called hydrostatic pressure. The pressure that would exist at a certain point in a medium with no sound waves present. In acoustics, the commonly used unit is the microbar.

static printout—In a computer, a printout of data that is not one of the sequential operations and occurs after conclusion of the machine run.

static register—A computer register which retains its information in static form.

static regulator—A transmission regulator in which the adjusting mechanism is in self-equilibrium at any setting and control power must be applied to change the setting.

static sensitivity—In phototubes, the direct anode current divided by the incident radiant flux of constant value.

static skew—A measure of the distance that the output from one track is ahead or behind (i.e., leading or lagging) the output of another track as a tape is transported over the read head.

static storage — In computers, storage in which the information does not change position (e.g., electrostatic storage, flip-flop storage, binary magnetic-core storage, etc.). The opposite of dynamic storage.

static subroutine—A digital-computer subroutine involving no parameters, other than the addresses of the operands.

static torque—*See* Locked-Rotor Torque.

static transconductance—In a transistor, the

ratio of the d-c output current to the d-c input voltage.

station—One or more transmitters, receivers, and accessory equipment required to carry on a definite radio communication service. The station assumes the classification of the service in which it operates.

stationary battery—A storage battery designed for service in a permanent location.

stationary contacts—Those members of contact pairs that are not moved directly by the actuating system.

stationary field—A constant field—i.e., one where the scalar (or vector) at any point does not change during the time interval under consideration.

stationary wave—*See* Standing Wave.

station break—1. A cue given by the station originating a program, to notify network stations that they may identify themselves to their audiences, broadcast local items, etc. 2. The actual time taken in (1) above.

statmho—The cgs electrostatic unit of conductance equal to 1.1126×10^{-12} mho (absolute).

statohm—The cgs electrostatic unit of resistance equal to 8.98766×10^{11} ohms (absolute).

stator—1. The nonrotating part of the magnetic structure in an induction motor. It usually contains the primary winding. 2. The stationary plates of a variable capacitor. 3. The conducting surfaces of a switch. Similar to the commutator in electrical rotating mechanisms.

stator of an induction watthour meter—A voltage circuit, one or more current circuits, and a magnetic circuit combined so that the reaction with currents induced in an individual, or a common, conducting disc exerts a driving torque on the rotor.

stator plates—The fixed plates of a variable capacitor.

statvolt—The cgs electrostatic unit of voltage equal to 299.796 volts (absolute).

stave—One of the number of individual longitudinal elements which comprise a sonar transducer.

stay cord—A component of a cable, usually a high-tensile textile used to anchor the cable ends at their points of termination, to keep any pull on the cable from being transferred to the electrical connection.

steady state—A condition in which circuit values remain essentially constant, occurring after all initial transients or fluctuating conditions have settled down.

steady-state deviation—The difference between the final value assumed by a specified variable after the expiration of transients and its ideal value.

steady-state oscillation—Also called steady-state vibration. Oscillation in which the motion at each point is a periodic quantity.

steady-state regulation—Slow changes in the output voltage of a power supply following an input-voltage and/or load-im-

pedance variation; it is usually expressed in volts ($\triangle V$) or as a percentage of the nominal output.

steady-state vibration—*See* Steady-State Oscillation.

steatite—A ceramic consisting chiefly of a silicate of magnesium. Because of its excellent insulating properties—even at high frequencies—it is used extensively in insulators.

steerable antenna—An antenna the major lobe of which can be readily shifted in direction.

Stefan-Boltzmann law—The total emitted radiant energy per unit of a black body is proportionate to the fourth power of its absolute temperature.

Steinmetz coefficient—A factor by which the 1.6th power of the magnetic flux density must be multiplied to give the approximate hysteresis loss of an iron or steel sample in ergs per cubic centimeter per cycle when that sample is undergoing successive magnetization cycles having the same maximum flux density.

stenode circuit—A superheterodyne receiving circuit in which a piezoelectric unit is used in the intermediate-frequency amplifier to balance out all frequencies except signals at the crystal frequency, thereby giving very high selectivity.

step-by-step switch—A bank-and-wiper switch in which the wipers are moved by individual electromagnet ratchet mechanisms.

step calibration—Also called interval calibration. Often confused with sense step, that is, the application of a calibration resistor to produce a deliberate electrical unbalance.

step counter—In a computer, a counter used in the arithmetical unit to count the steps in multiplication, division, and shift operation.

step-down transformer—A transformer in which the voltage is reduced as the energy is transferred from its primary to its secondary winding.

step function—A signal having one or more sudden discontinuities.

step-function response—*See* Transient Response.

step generator—A device for testing the linearity of an amplifier. A step wave is applied to the amplifier input and the step waveform observed, on an oscilloscope, at the output.

step input—A sudden but sustained change in an input signal.

step load change—An instantaneous change in the magnitude of the load current.

stepper motor—A motor the normal operation of which consists of discrete angular motions of essentially uniform magnitude, rather than continuous rotation.

stepping—*See* Zoning.

stepping relay—Also called rotary stepping switch (or relay) or stepping switch. A multiposition relay in which moving wiper contacts mate with successive sets of fixed contacts in a series of steps, moving from one step to the next in successive operations of the relay.

Stepping relay.

stepping switch—*See* Stepping Relay.

step-recovery diode—A varactor in which forward voltage injects carriers across the junction, but before the carriers can combine, the voltage reverses and carriers return to their origin in a group. The result is the abrupt cessation of reverse current and a harmonic-rich waveform.

step-servo motor — A device that, when properly energized by d-c voltage, indexes in definite angular increments.

step-strobe marker — A form of strobe marker in which the discontinuity is in the form of a step in the time base.

step-up transformer — A transformer in which the voltage is increased as the energy is transferred from the primary to the secondary winding.

step-voltage regulator—A device consisting of a regulating transformer and a means for adjusting the voltage or the phase relation of the system circuit in steps, usually without interrupting the load.

steradian—A solid spherical angle which encloses a surface equal, on a sphere, to the square of the radius of the sphere.

stereo—A prefix meaning three-dimensional—specifically (especially without the hyphen), stereophonic.

stereo adapter—Also called a stereo control unit. A device used with two sets of monophonic equipment to make them act as a single stereo system.

stereo amplifier—An audio-frequency amplifier, with two or more channels, for a stereo sound system.

stereo broadcasting—*See* Stereocasting.

stereo cartridge—A phonograph pickup for reproduction of stereophonic recordings. Its high-compliance needle is coupled to two independent voltage-producing elements.

stereocasting—Also called stereo broadcasting. Broadcasting over two sound channels to provide stereo reproduction. This may be done by simulcasting, multicasting, or multiplexing.

stereocephaloid microphone—Two or more

microphones arranged to simulate the acoustical patterns of human hearing.

stereo control unit—*See* Stereo Adapter.

stereo microphones—Two or more microphones spaced as required for stereo recording.

stereophonic—Multichannel sound, creating a sense of depth due to the separation of or variation between the signals received by each ear.

stereophonic reception—Reception involving the use of two receivers having a phase difference in their reproduced sounds. The sense of depth given to the received program is analogous to the listener's being in the same room as the orchestra or other medium.

stereophonic separation—The ratio of the electrical signal caused in the right (or left) stereophonic channel to the electrical signal caused in the left (or right) stereophonic channel by the transmission of only a right (or left) signal.

stereophonic sound system—A sound system with two or more microphones, transmission channels, and speakers arranged to give depth to the reproduced sound.

stereophonic subcarrier—A subcarrier having a frequency which is the second harmonic of the pilot subcarrier frequency and which is employed in f-m stereophonic broadcasting.

stereophonic system—A sound-reproducing system in which a plurality of microphones, transmission channels, and speakers (or earphones) are arranged to afford a listener a sense of the spatial distribution of the sound sources.

stereophonic subchannel—The band of frequencies from 23 to 53 kilohertz containing the stereophonic subcarrier and its associated sidebands.

stereo pickup—A phonograph pickup used with single-groove, two-channel stereo records.

stereo recording—The impressing of signals from two channels onto a tape or disc in such a way that the channels are heard separately on playback. The result is a directional, three-dimensional effect.

stereoscopic television—A system of television broadcasting in which the images appear to be three-dimensional.

stereosonic system—A recording technique using two closely-spaced directional microphones with their maximum directions of reception 45° from each other. In this way, one picks up sound largely from the right and the other from the left, similar to mid-side recording.

stick circuit — A circuit used to maintain energization of a relay or similar unit through its own contacts.

sticking—In computers, the tendency of a flip-flop to remain in, or to spontaneously switch to, one of its two stable states.

stiffness factor—The angular lag between the input and output of a servosystem.

still—Photographic or other stationary illustrative material used in a television broadcast.

stimularity—An arbitrary measure of sensitivity to stimulation. It is proportional to the quantum efficiency relative to incident radiation.

stimulated emission—The emission of radiation by a system going from an excited electron energy level to a lower energy level under the influence of a radiation field. The emitted radiation is in phase with the stimulating radiation and produces a negative-absorption condition.

stimulus—*See* Excitation *and* Measurand.

stirring effect—The circulation in a molten conductive charge due to the combined motor and pinch effects.

stochastic—The characteristic of events changing the probabilities of various responses.

stochastic process—A group of random variables.

stock reel—Also called supply reel or storage reel. On a tape recorder, the reel from which unrecorded or unplayed tape is taken as the machine records on or plays it.

stoichiometric impurity—A crystalline imperfection caused in a semiconductor by a deviation from the stoichiometric composition.

stop-cycle timer — A timer which runs through a single cycle and then stops until the starting signal is reinitiated.

stop opening — In a camera, the size of the aperature that controls the amount of light passing through the lens.

stopping potential—The voltage required to stop the outward movement of electrons emitted by photoelectric or thermionic action.

stop-record signal—A facsimile signal used for stopping the conversion of the electric signal into an image on the record sheet.

stop signal—The signal that transfers facsimile equipment from active to standby.

storage—1. The act of storing information (*Also see* Store.) 2. Sometimes called a memory. Any device in which information can be stored. 3. A computer section used primarily for storing information in electrostatic, ferroelectric, magnetic, acoustic, optical, chemical, electronic, electrical, mechanical, etc., form. Such a section is sometimes called a memory, or a store, in British terminology. 4. A device into which data can be entered, held, and retrieved at a later time.

storage access time—In a computer, the time required to transfer information from a storage location to the local storage register or other location, where the information then becomes available for processing.

storage battery—Two or more storage cells connected in series and used as a unit.

Storage battery.

storage capacity—Also called memory capacity. The amount of information that can be retained in a storage (memory) device. It is often expressed as the number of words (given the number of digits and the base of the standard word).

storage cell—1. Also called a secondary cell. A cell which, after being discharged, can be recharged by sending an electric current through it in the opposite direction from the discharging current. 2. An elementary unit of storage (e.g., binary cell, decimal cell).

storage device—A device into which data can be inserted, in which it can be retained, and from which it can be retrieved.

storage element—An area which retains information distinguishable from that of adjacent areas on the storage area of charge-storage tubes.

storage integrator—In an analog computer, an integrator used to store a voltage in the hold condition for future use while the rest of the computer assumes another computer control state.

storage laser—Any laser which stores unusually high energy prior to discharge. For example, a storage diode laser is a laser in which some carriers are electrically excited for a time longer than the lasing period.

storage life—The minimum length of time over which a device, system, or transducer can be exposed to specified environmental storage conditions without changing the performance beyond a specified tolerance.

storage location—A computer storage position that holds one machine word and usually has a specific address.

storage medium—Any recording device or medium into which data can be copied and held until some later date, and from which the entire original data can be obtained.

storage oscilloscope — An instrument that has the ability to store a crt display in order that it may be observed for any required time. This stored display may be instantly erased to make way for storage of a later event.

storage temperature—The temperature of the medium, immediately adjacent to the device, at which the device, without power applied, may be stored indefinitely without deterioration.

storage time—1. The time during which the

output current or voltage of a pulse is falling from maximum to zero after the input current or voltage has been removed. 2. In a transistor, the time required to sweep current carriers from the collector region when the switch is turned off.

storage tube — *See* Electrostatic Memory Tube.

store—1. To retain information in a device from which the information can later be withdrawn. 2. To introduce information into the device in (1) above. 3. A British synonym for storage.

stored-energy welding—A method of welding in which electric energy is accumulated (stored) electrostatically, electromagnetically, or electrochemically at a relatively slow rate and is then released at the required rate for welding.

stored program—A set of instructions in the computer memory specifying the operations to be performed and the location of the data on which these operations are to be performed.

stored-program computer — 1. Also called general-purpose computer. A computer in which the instructions specifying the program to be performed are stored in the memory section along with the data to be operated on. 2. A digital computer which, under control of its own instructions, can synthesize, alter, and store instructions as though they were data and can subsequently execute these new instructions.

store transmission bridge—A transmission bridge which consists of four identical impedance coils (the two windings of the back-bridge relay and the live relay of a connector, respectively) separated by two capacitors. It couples the calling and called telephones together electrostatically for the transmission of voice-frequency (alternating) currents, but separates the two lines for the transmission of direct current for talking purposes (talking current).

storm loading—The mechanical loading imposed on the components of a pole line by wind, ice, etc., and by the weight of the components themselves.

straight dipole—A half-wave antenna consisting of one conductor, usually center-fed.

straight-line capacitance — The variable-capacitor characteristic obtained when the rotor plates are shaped so that the capacitance varies directly with the angle of rotation.

straight-line code—The repetition of a sequence of instructions, with or without address modification, by explicitly writing the instructions for each repetition. Generally straight-line coding will require less execution time and more space than equivalent loop coding. If the number of repetitions is large, this type of coding is tedious unless a generator is used. The feasibility of straight-line coding is limited by the space required as well as the difficulty of coding a variable number of repetitions.

straight-line frequency—The variable-capacitor characteristic obtained when the rotor plates are shaped so that the resonant frequency of the tuned circuit containing the capacitor varies directly with the angle of rotation.

straight-line wavelength — The variable-capacitor characteristic obtained when the rotor plates are shaped so that the wavelength of resonance in the tuned circuit containing the capacitor varies directly with the angle of rotation.

strain—The physical deformation, deflection, or change in length resulting from stress (force per unit area). The magnitude of strain is normally expressed in microinches per inch.

strain anisotropy—A force that directs the magnetization of a particle along a preferred direction relative to the strain.

strain gage—A measuring element for converting force, pressure, tension, etc., into an electrical signal.

strain-gage based—An instrument or transducer with a sensing element composed of bonded or unbonded strain gages.

strain-gage transduction—The conversion of the measurand into a change in resistance caused by strain in four or, more rarely, two arms of a Wheatstone bridge.

strain insulator—A single insulator, an insulator string, or two or more strings in parallel designed to transmit the entire pull of the conductor to, and insulate the conductor from, the tower or other support.

strain pickup—A phonograph pickup cartridge using the principle of the strain gage.

strain wire—Wire having a composition such that it exhibits favorable strain-gage performance. Also the strain-sensitive filaments which constitute the transfer electrical elements in certain transducers.

strand—One of the wires or groups of wires of any stranded conductor.

stranded conductor—*See* Stranded Wire.

stranded wire—Also called stranded conductor. A conductor composed of a group of wires or any combination of groups of wires. The wires in a stranded conductor are usually twisted or braided together.

End view.   **Perspective view.**

Straps on cavity-magnetron anode.

strap—A wire or strip connected between the ends of the segments in the anode of a cavity magnetron to promote operation in the desired mode.

strapping — The suppressing of undesired modes of oscillation in a magnetron.

stratosphere—A calm region of the upper atmosphere characterized by little or no temperature change throughout. It is separated from the lower atmosphere (troposphere) by a region called the tropopause.

stray capacitance—The capacitance introduced into a circuit by the leads and wires connecting the circuit components.

stray current—A portion of the total current that flows over paths other than the intended circuit.

stray-current corrosion—Corrosion that results when a direct current from a battery or other external source causes a metal in contact with an electrolyte to become anodic with respect to another metal in contact with the same electrolyte. Accelerated corrosion will occur at the electrode where the current direction is from the metal to the electrolyte and will generally be in proportion to the total current.

stray field—The leakage magnetic flux that spreads outward from an inductor and does no useful work.

strays—*See* Atmospherics.

streaking—Distortion in which televised objects appear stretched horizontally beyond their normal boundaries. It is most apparent at the vertical edges, where there is a large transition from black to white or white to black, and is usually expressed as short, medium, or long streaking. Long streaking may extend as far as the right edge of the picture, and in extreme low-frequency distortion, even over a whole line interval.

streamer breakdown—Breakdown caused by an increase in the field due to the accumulation of positive ions produced during electron avalanches.

streaming—The production of a unidirectional flow of currents in a medium where sound waves are present.

strength of a simple sound source—The rms magnitude of the total air flow at the surface of a simple source in cubic meters per second (or cubic centimeters per second), where a simple source is taken to be a spherical source the radius of which is small compared with one-sixth wavelength.

strength of a sound source—The maximum instantaneous rate of volume displacement produced by the source when emitting a sinusoidal wave.

stress—The force producing strain in a solid.

stretched dislay—A ppi display having the polar plot expanded in one rectangular dimension. The equal-range circles of the normal ppi display becomes ellipses.

striation technique—Rendering sound waves visible by using their individual ability to refract light waves.

striking an arc—Starting an electric arc by

touching two electrodes together momentarily.

striking distance — The effective separation of two conductors having an insulating fluid between them.

striking potential—1. The voltage required to start an electric arc. 2. The lowest grid-to-cathode potential at which plate current begins flowing in a gas-filled triode.

string — In a list of items, a group of items that are already in sequence according to a rule.

string electrometer—An electrostatic voltage-measuring instrument consisting of a conducting fiber stretched midway between and parallel to two conducting plates. The electrostatic field between the plates displaces the fiber laterally in proportion to the voltage between the plates.

string-shadow instrument—An instrument in which the indicating means is the shadow (projected or viewed through an optical system) of a filamentary conductor, the position of which in a magnetic or an electric field depends on the measured quantity.

strip—To remove insulation from a wire or cable.

stripper—A hand-operated or motor-driven tool for removing insulation from wires.

strip transmission line — A transmission component that is similar to a microstrip except that it has a second ground plane placed above the conductor strip.

strobe—1. An intensified spot in the sweep of a deflection-type indicator, used as a reference mark for ranging or expanding the presentation. 2. An intensified sweep on a plan-position indicator or B-scope. Such a strobe may result from certain types of interference or it may be purposely applied as a bearing or heading marker. 3. On a console oscillator, a line representing the azimuth data generated by a jammed radar site. 4. *See* Electronic Flash.

strobe marker—A small birght spot, a short gap, or other discontinuity produced on the line trace of a radar display to indicate the part of the time base which is receiving attention.

strobe pulse—1. Also called sample pulse. A pulse used to gate the output of a core-memory sense amplifier into a trigger in a register. 2. A pulse of a duration less than the time period of a recurrent phenomenon used for making a close investigation of that phenomenon. The frequency of the strobe pulse bears a simple relation to that of the phenomenon, and the relative timing is usually adjustable.

strobolume—A trade name used to describe a high-intensity electronic stroboscope manufactured by General Radio Company.

stroboscope — A device that indicates frequency of operation by creating the optical illusion of slowing down or stopping a moving pattern, which is illuminated by a light that flashes at a known frequency.

Stroboscope disc.

stroboscopic disc—A printed disc having several rings, each with a different number of dark segments. The pattern is placed on a rotating phonograph turntable and illuminated at a known frequency by a flashing discharge tube. The speed can then readily be determined by noting which pattern appears to stand still or rotate the slowest.

stroboscopic tachometer — A stroboscope with a scale calibrated in flashes or in revolutions per minute. The stroboscopic lamp is directed onto the rotating device being measured, and the flashing rate is adjusted until the device appears to be standing still. The speed can then be read directly from the scale.

strobotron—A type of glow lamp that produces intense flashes of light when fed with accurately timed voltage pulses. It is used in electronic stroboscopes for visual inspection of high-speed moving parts.

stroke speed—Also called scanning line frequency or scanning frequency. The number of times per minute that a fixed line, perpendicular to the direction of scanning, is crossed in one direction by a scanning or recording spot in a facsimile system.

structureborne noise — Undesired vibration in, or of, a solid body.

stub—1. A short length of transmission line or cable joined as a branch to another transmission line or cable. 2. A short section of transmission line, open or shorted at the far end, connected in parallel with a transmission line to match the impedance of the line to that of an antenna or transmitter.

stub angle—A right-angle elbow for a coaxial r-f transmission line, the inner conductor being supported by a quarter-wave stub.

stub cable—A short branch from a principal cable. The end is often sealed until used. Pairs in the stub are referred to as stubbed-out pairs.

stub matching—Using a stub to match a transmission line to an antenna or load.

stub-supported coaxial—A coaxial cable the inner conductor of which is supported by short-circuited coaxial stubs.

stub tuner—A stub terminated by movable short-circuiting means and used for matching impedance in the line to which it is joined as a branch.

stunt box—A device for controlling the non-printing functions of a teletype terminal.

stutter—In facsimile, a series of undesired black and white lines sometimes produced when the signal amplitude changes sharply.

stylus—1. Also called a needle. The needle-like object used in a sound recorder to cut or emboss the record grooves. Generally it is made of sapphire, stellite, or steel. The plural is styli. 2. The pointed element that contacts the record sheet in a facsimile recorder.

stylus alignment—The position of the stylus with respect to the record. The correct position is perpendicular.

stylus drag—Also called needle drag. The friction between the reproducing stylus and the surface of the recording medium.

stylus force—Also called vertical stylus force, tracking force, and formerly called needle pressure or stylus pressure. The downward force, in grams or ounces, exerted on the disc by the reproducing stylus.

stylus oscillograph—An instrument in which a pen or stylus records, on paper or another suitable medium, the value of an electrical quantity as a function of time.

stylus pressure—*See* Stylus Force.

subassembly—Parts and components combined into a unit for convenience in assembling or servicing. A subassembly is only part of an operating unit; it is not complete in itself.

subatomic—Smaller than atoms—i.e., electrons or protons.

subatomic particles — The particles that make up the atom—i.e., protons, electrons, and neutrons.

subcarrier—A carrier used to generate a modulated wave which is applied, in turn, as a modulating wave to modulate another carrier.

subcarrier band—A band associated with a given subcarrier and specified in terms of maximum subcarrier deviation.

subcarrier channel—The channel required to convey the telemetric information of a subcarrier band.

subcarrier discriminator tuning unit—A device which tunes the discriminator to a particular subcarrier.

subcarrier frequency shift—The use of an audio-frequency shift signal to modulate a radio transmitter.

subcarrier oscillator—1. In a telemetry system, the oscillator which is directly modulated by the measurand or its equivalent in terms of changes in the transfer elements of a transducer. 2. In a color television receiver, the crystal oscillator operating at the chrominance subcarrier frequency of 3.58 MHz.

subchassis—The chassis on which closely associated components such as those of an amplifier or power supply are mounted. A subchassis is a building block, easily changed and usable in a variety of systems.

subcommutation—In a computer, the act of connecting one data source to a sampled data system less frequently than other data sources.

subcommutation frame—In pcm systems, a recurring integral number of subcommutator words which include a single subcommutation frame synchronization word. The number of subcommutator words in a subcommutation frame is equal to an integral number of primary commutator frames. The length of a subcommutation frame is equal to the total number of words or bits generated as a direct output of the subcommutator.

subcycle generator—A frequency-reducing device used in telephone equipment to furnish ringing power at a submultiple of the power-supply frequency.

subdivided capacitor—A capacitor in which several capacitors known as sections are mounted so that they may be used individually or in combination.

subelement—A distinguishable portion of a circuit element (e.g., the emitter, collector, and base are subelements of an integrated bipolar transistor).

subframe—A complete sequence of frames during which all subchannels of a specific channel are sampled once.

subharmonic—A sinusoidal quantity, the frequency of which is an integral submultiple of the fundamental frequency of its related periodic quantity. A wave with half the frequency of the fundamental of another wave is called the second subharmonic of that wave; one with a third of the fundamental frequency is called a third subharmonic, etc.

subject copy—Also called copy. In facsimile, the material in graphic form to be transmitted for reproduction by the recorder.

submarine cable—A cable designed for service underwater; usually a lead-covered cable with a steel armor applied between layers of jute.

submerged-resistor induction furnace—A furnace for melting metal. It comprises a melting hearth, a depending melting channel closed through the hearth, a primary induction winding, and a magnetic core which links the melting channel and primary winding.

submersible transformer—A transformer so constructed that it will operate when submerged in water under predetermined conditions of pressure and time—e.g., a subway transformer.

subminiature tube—A small electron tube used generally in miniaturized equipment.

subminiaturization—The technique of packaging discrete miniaturized parts, using assembly techniques which result in increased volumetric efficiency (e.g., a hybrid circuit).

submultiple resonance—Resonance at a frequency that is a submultiple of the frequency of the exciting impulses.

subnanosecond—Less than a nanosecond.

subpanel—An assembly of electrical devices connected together which forms a simple functional unit in itself.

subprogram—A part of a computer program.

subroutine—1. In computer technology, the portion of a routine that causes a computer to carry out a well-defined mathematical or logical operation. 2. Usually called a closed subroutine. One to which control may be transferred from a master routine, and returned to the master routine at the conclusion of the subroutine.

subscriber's drop—The line from a telephone cable to a subscriber's building.

subscriber set—Also called a customer set. An assembly of apparatus for originating or receiving calls on the premises of a subscriber to a communication or signaling service.

subscription television—See Pay Television.

subscription television broadcast program—A television broadcast program intended to be received in intelligible form by members of the public only for a fee or charge.

subset—1. In a telephone system, the handset or deskset at the station location. 2. Also known as a modem, data set, or subscriber set. A modulation/demodulation device designed to make business-machine signals compatible with communications facilities.

subsidiary conduit—The terminating branch of an underground conduit run extending from a manhole or handhole to a nearby building, handhole, or pole.

subsonic frequency—See Infrasonic Frequency.

subsonic speed—A speed less than the speed of sound.

substation—Any building or outdoor location at which electric energy in a power system is transformed, converted, or controlled.

substep—A part of a computer step.

substitute—In a computer, to replace one element of information by another.

substitution interference measurements—

Subminiature tube.

A measurement in which the noise level of the source being measured is compared to a known level from a calibrated source: impulse generator for broad-band noise or sine-wave generator for cw.

substitution method—A three-step method of measuring an unknown quantity in a circuit. First, some circuit effect dependent on the unknown quantity is measured or observed. Then a similar but measurable quantity is substituted in the circuit. Finally, the latter quantity is adjusted to produce a like effect. The unknown value is then assumed to be equal to the adjusted known value.

substrate (of an integrated circuit)—1. The supporting material upon or within which an integrated circuit is fabricated or to which an integrated circuit is attached. 2. A material on the surface of which an adhesive substance is spread for bonding or coating; any material which provides a supporting surface for other materials, especially materials used to support printed-circuit patterns.

subsurface wave—An electromagnetic wave propagated through water or land. Operating frequencies for communications may be limited to approximately 35 kHz due to attenuation of high frequencies.

subsynchronous—Having a frequency that is a submultiple of the driving frequency.

subsynchronous reluctance motor—A form of reluctance motor with more salient poles than the number of electrical poles in the primary winding. As a result, the motor operates at a constant average speed which is a submultiple of its apparent synchronous speed.

subsystem—1. A major, essential, functional part of a system. The subsystem usually consists of several components. 2. An interconnected combination of a set of related circuits or integrated circuits to form a logical subdivision of an equipment or operational system.

subtractive filter—An optical filter which is of a certain color and eliminates that color when placed in the path of white light.

subtractor—An operational amplifier circuit in which the output is proportional to the difference between its two input voltages or between the net sums of its positive and negative inputs.

subway transformer—A transformer of submersible construction.

success ratio—The ratio of the number of successful attempts to the total number of trials. It is frequently used as a reliability index.

suckout—A hole in the response pattern of a tuned circuit due to the self-resonance of components at certain frequencies.

sudden commencement—Magnetic storms which start suddenly (within a few seconds) and simultaneously all over the earth.

sudden ionospheric disturbances—The sudden increase in ionization density in lower parts of the ionosphere, caused by a bright solar chromospheric eruption. It gives rise to a sudden increase of absorption in radio waves propagated through the low parts of the ionosphere, and sometimes to simultaneous disturbances of terrestrial magnetism and earth current. The change takes place within one or a few minutes, and conditions usually return to normal within one or a few hours.

Suhl effect—When a strong transverse magnetic field is applied to an N-type semiconducting filament, the holes injected into the filament are deflected to the surface. Here they may recombine rapidly with electrons and thus have a much shorter life, or they may be withdrawn by a probe as though the conductance had increased.

suicide control — A control function which uses negative feedback to reduce and automatically maintain the generator voltage at approximately zero.

sulfating—The accumulation of lead sulfate on the plates of a lead-acid storage battery. This reduces the energy-storing ability of the battery and causes it to fail prematurely.

sum channel—A combination of left and right stereo channels identical to the program, which may be recorded or transmitted monophonically.

summary punch — A punch-card machine which may be attached to another machine in such a way that it will punch information produced, calculated, or summarized by the other machine.

summary recorder—In computers, output equipment which records a summary of the information handled.

summation check—A redundant computer check in which groups of digits are summed, usually without regard to overflow. The sum is then checked against a previously computed sum to verify the accuracy of the computation.

summation frequency—A frequency which is the sum of two other frequencies that are being produced simultaneously.

summation tone—A combination tone, heard under certain circumstances, the pitch of which corresponds to a frequency equal to the sum of the frequencies of the two components.

summing point—1. A mixing point, the output of which is obtained by adding its inputs (with the prescribed signs). 2. The input terminal to which the feedback loop from the output of an amplifier is returned.

supercommutation — Commutation at a higher rate by connection of a single data input source to equally spaced contacts of the commutator (cross patching). Corresponding cross patching is required at the decommutator.

superconducting — Exhibiting superconductivity.

superconductivity—The decrease in resist-

Superheterodyne receiver.

ance of certain materials (lead, tin, thallium, etc.) as their temperature is reduced to nearly absolute zero. When the critical (transition) temperature is reached, the resistance will be almost zero.

superconductor — A material that exhibits superconductivity.

super-emitron—*See* Image Iconoscope.

supergroup—A group of 60 channels occupying the range of frequencies between 312 kHz and 552 kHz.

superhet—Slang for a superheterodyne receiver.

superheterodyne receiver — A receiver in which the incoming modulated r-f signals are usually amplified in a preamplifier and then fed into the mixer for conversion into a fixed, lower carrier frequency (called the intermediate frequency). The modulated i-f signals undergo very high amplification in the i-f-amplifier stages and are then fed into the detector for demodulation. The resultant audio or video signals are usually further amplified before being sent to the output.

superheterodyne reception—A method of receiving radio waves in which heterodyne reception converts the voltage of the received wave into a voltage having an intermediate, but usually superaudible, frequency which is then detected.

superhigh frequency—Abbreviated shf. The frequency band extending from 3,000 to 30,000 megahertz.

Supermalloy—Trade name of Arnold Engineering Company for a magnetic alloy with a maximum permeability greater than 1,000,000.

supermode laser—A frequency-modulated laser, the output of which is passed through a second phase modulator driven 180° out of phase and with the same modulation index as the first modulator. All of the energy of the previously existing laser modes is compressed into a single frequency, with nearly the full power of the laser concentrated in that signal.

superposed circuit—An additional channel obtained in such a manner from one or more circuits normally provided for other channels that all channels can be used simultaneously, without mutual interference.

superposition theorem—When a number of voltages (distributed in any manner throughout a linear network) are applied to the network simultaneously, the current that flows is the sum of the component currents that would flow if the same voltages had

acted individually. Likewise, the potential difference that exists between any two points is the component potential difference that would exist there under the same conditions.

superpower—The comparatively large power (sometimes over 1,000,000 watts) used by a broadcasting station in its antenna.

superradiance—A rapid increase in intensity of fluorescent-line emission with increasing excitation (pump) power. This intensity increase and associated line narrowing are attributed to coherent reinforcement of spontaneously emitted photons during a single pass through the active region. (Laser term.)

superrefraction—Abnormally large refraction of radio waves in the lower layers of the atmosphere, leading to abnormal ranges of operation.

superregeneration—A form of regenerative amplification frequently used in radio-receiver detecting circuits. Oscillations are alternately allowed to build up and are quenched at a superaudible rate.

superregenerative detector—A detector that functions on superregeneration to achieve extremely high sensitivity with a minimum number of amplifier stages.

superregenerative receiver—A receiver in which the regeneration is varied in such a manner that the circuit is periodically rendered oscillatory and nonoscillatory.

supersensitive relay—A relay that operates on extremely small currents (usually less than 250 microamperes).

supersonic—Faster than the speed of sound (approximately 750 mph). These speeds are usually referred to by the term "mach" or "mach number." Mach 1 equals the speed of sound; mach 2, twice the speed of sound, etc.

supersonic communication—Communication through water by manually keying the sound output of echo-ranging equipment used on ships.

supersonic frequency—*See* Ultrasonic Frequency.

supersonics—1. The general term covering phenomena associated with speeds higher than that of sound (e.g., aircraft and projectiles which travel faster than sound). 2. The general term covering the use of frequencies above the range of normal hearing.

supersonic sounding—A system of determining ocean depths by measuring the time interval between the production of a supersonic wave just below the surface of the water, and the arrival of the echo reflected from the bottom. The sounds are transmitted and received by either magnetostriction or piezoelectric units, and electronic equipment is employed to provide a continuous indication of depth (sometimes with a permanent recording).

supersync signal—A combination horizontal- and vertical-sync signal transmitted at the end of each scanning line in commercial television.

superturnstile antenna—A stacked antenna array in which each element is a batwing antenna.

supervisory control—A system by which selective control and automatic indication of remote units is provided by electrical means over a relatively small number of common transmission lines. (Carrier-current channels on power lines can be used for this purpose.)

supervisory signal—A signal for attracting the attention of an attendant in connection with switching apparatus, etc.

supervoltage—A voltage applied to X-ray tubes operating between 500 and 2,000 kilovolts.

supply voltage—The voltage obtained from a power supply to operate a circuit.

suppressed carrier—That type of system which results in the suppression of the carrier frequency from the transmission medium. (The intelligence of a carrier wave after modulation is contained in either sideband, and normally only one sideband is transmitted; the other sideband and carrier frequency are suppressed. The intelligence is recovered at the receiving end by inserting a carrier frequency from a local source which, when combined with the incoming signal, produces the original frequencies with which the transmitting carrier was modulated.)

suppressed-carrier operation—*See* Suppressed-Carrier Transmission.

suppressed-carrier transmission—Transmission in which the carrier frequency is either partially or totally suppressed. One or both sidebands may be transmitted.

suppressed time delay—Deliberate displacement of the zero of the time scale with respect to the time of emission of a pulse, in order to simulate electrically a geographical displacement of the true position of a transponder.

suppressed-zero instrument—An indicating or recording instrument in which the zero position is below the end of the scale markings.

suppression—1. Elimination of any component of an emission—e.g., a particular frequency or group of frequencies in an audio- or radio-frequency signal. 2. Reduction or elimination of noise pulses generated by a motor or motor generator. 3. Elimination of unwanted signals or interference by means of shielding, filtering, grounding, component relocation, or sometimes redesign.

suppression pulse—The pulse generated in an airborne transponder by coincidence of the first interrogation pulse and the control pulse. This pulse, also known as a killer pulse, is used to suppress unwanted interrogations from the side lobes.

suppressor—1. A resistor used in an electron-tube circuit to reduce or prevent oscillation or the generation of unwanted r-f signals. 2. A resistor in the high-tension lead of the ignition system in a gasoline engine.

suppressor grid—A grid interposed between two positive electrodes (usually the screen grid and the plate) primarily to reduce the flow of secondary electrons from one to the other.

suppressor pulse—The pulse used to disable an ionized flow field or beacon transponder during intervals when interference would be encountered.

surface analyzer—An instrument that measures or records irregularities in a surface. As a crystal-pickup stylus or similar device moves over the surface, the resulting voltage is amplified and fed to an indicator or recorder that magnifies the surface irregularities as high as 50,000 times.

surface asperities—Small projecting imperfections on the surface coating of a tape that limit and cause variations in head-to-tape contact. A term useful in discussions of friction and modulation noise.

surface barrier—A barrier formed automatically at a surface by the electrons trapped there.

surface-barrier transistor — Abbreviated SBT. A wafer of semiconductor material into which depressions have been etched electrochemically on opposite sides. The emitter- and collector-base junction or metal-to-semiconductor contacts are then formed by electroplating a suitable metal onto the semiconductor in the etched depressions. The original wafer constitutes the base region.

surface-controlled avalanche transistor—A transistor in which the avalanche breakdown voltage is controlled by an external field applied through surface insulating layers, and which permits operation at frequencies up to the 10-GHz range.

surface duct—An atmospheric duct for which the lower boundary is the surface of the earth.

surface insulation—Also called oxalizing or insulazing. A coating applied to magnetic-core laminations to retard the passage of current from one lamination to another.

surface leakage—The passage of current over the boundary surfaces of an insulator, as distinguished from passage through its volume.

surface noise—Also called needle scratch. In mechanical recording, the noise caused in the electric output of a pickup by irregular contact surfaces in the groove.

surface of position—Any surface defined by a constant value of some navigational coordinate.

surface recombination rate—The rate at which free electrons and holes recombine at the surface of a semiconductor.

surface recording—Storage of information on a coating of magnetic material such as that which is used on magnetic tape, magnetic drums, etc.

surface reflection—Also called Fresnel loss. The part of the incident radiation that is reflected from the surface of a refractive material. It is directly proportional to the refractive index of the material and is reduced for a given wavelength by application of an appropriate surface coating.

surface resistance—Ratio of the d-c voltage applied to two electrodes on the surface of a specimen, to that portion of the current between the electrodes and in a thin layer of moisture or other semiconducting material that may be native to or deposited on the surface.

surface resistivity—The resistance between opposite edges of a surface film 1 cm square. It is measured by determining the resistance between two straight conductors 1 cm apart, pressed upon the surface of a slab of the material. Water-absorbent materials usually show a lower resistivity than nonabsorbent ones.

surface states—Discontinuities and contaminants at the surface of a semiconductor device which tend to change the surface characteristics and promote device parameter instability.

surface-temperature resistor—A platinum-resistance thermometer designed for installation directly on the surface whose temperature is being measured.

surface wave—A subclassification of the ground wave. So called because it travels along the surface of the earth.

surface-wave transmission line—A single-conductor line having a relatively thick dielectric sheath, often 3 or more times the diameter of the conductor, and a conical horn at each end exciting a mode of propagation on the line that is practically non-radiating.

surge—Sudden current or voltage changes in a circuit.

surge admittance—Reciprocal of surge impedance.

surge-crest ammeter—A special magnetometer used with magnetizable links to measure the crest value of transient electric currents.

surge generator—*See* Impulse Generator.

surge impedance—*See* Characteristic Impedance.

surge voltage (or current)—A large, sudden change of voltage (or current), usually caused by the collapse of a magnetic field or by a shorted or open circuit element.

surge-voltage recorder—*See* Lichtenberg Figure Camera.

surround—The part of a speaker cone by which its outside edge is anchored, usually corrugated.

surveillance—Systematic observation of air, surface, or subsurface areas by visual, electronic, photographic, or other means.

surveillance radar—In air-traffic control systems, a radar set or system used in a ground-controlled approach system to detect aircraft within a certain radius of an airport and to present continuously to the radar operator information as to the position, in distance and azimuth, of these aircraft.

surveillance radar station—In the aeronautical radionavigation service, a land station employing radar to detect the presence of aircraft.

susceptance—The reciprocal of reactance, and the imaginary part of admittance. It is measured in mhos.

susceptibility—1. Ratio of the induced magnetization to the inducing magnetic force. 2. The undesired response of an equipment to emissions, interference, or transients, or to signals other than those to which the equipment is intended to be responsive.

susceptibility meter—A device for measuring low values of magnetic susceptibility.

susceptiveness—The tendency of a telephone system to pick up noise and low-frequency induction from a power system. It is determined by telephone-circuit balance, transpositions, wire spacing, and isolation from ground.

suspension—A wire that supports the moving coil of a galvanometer or similar instrument.

Suspension galvanometer.

suspension galvanometer—An early type of moving-coil instrument in which a coil of wire was suspended in a magnetic field and would rotate when it carried an electric current. A mirror attached to the coil deflected a beam of light, causing a spot of light to travel on a scale some distance from the instrument. The effect was a pointer of greater length but no mass.

suspension lines—The main lines leading from the canopy to the suspended load. Often mistakenly called "shroud" lines.

sustain—In an organ, the effect produced by circuitry which causes a note to diminish gradually after the key controlling the note has been released.

sustained oscillation—1. Oscillation in which forces outside the system but controlled by it maintain a periodic oscillation at a period or frequency that is nearly the natural period of the system. 2. Continued oscillation due to insufficient attenuation in the feedback path.

sustained start—An electrical signal for starting a timer which is of any duration longer than the timer setting.

sw—Abbreviation for short wave.

swamping resistor—In transistor circuits, a resistor placed in the emitter lead to mask (minimize the effects of) variations caused in the emitter-base junction resistance by temperature variations.

sweep—The crossing of a range of values of a quantity for the purpose of delineating, sampling, or controlling another quantity. Examples of swept quantities are the displacement of a scanning spot on the screen of a cathode-ray tube, and the frequency of a wave.

sweep accuracy—The accuracy of the trace horizontal displacement in an oscilloscope compared with the reference independent variable, usually expressed in terms of average rate error as a percent of full scale.

sweep amplifier—An amplifier stage designed to increase the amplitude of the sweep voltage.

sweep circuit—1. A circuit which produces, at regular intervals, an approximately linear, circular, or other movement of the beam in a cathode-ray tube. 2. The part of a cathode-ray oscilloscope that provides a time-reference base.

sweep delay—The time between the application of a pulse to the sweep-trigger input of an oscilloscope and the start of the sweep.

sweep-delay accuracy—The accuracy of an indicated sweep delay in an oscilloscope, usually specified in error terms.

sweep expander—*See* Sweep Magnifier.

sweep-frequency generator—A signal source capable of changing frequency automatically and in synchronism with a display device. The frequency sweep can be obtained by either mechanical or electronic means.

sweep-frequency record—A test record on which a series of constant-amplitude frequencies have been recorded. Each frequency is typically repeated 20 times per second, starting at 50 Hz and continuing up to 10 kHz or higher.

sweep generator—Also called timing-axis oscillator. A circuit which applies voltages or currents to the deflection elements in a cathode-ray tube in such a way that the deflection of the electron beam is a known function of time, against which other periodic electrical phenomena may be examined, compared, and measured.

sweeping receivers—Automatically and continuously tuned receivers designed to stop and lock on ·when a signal is found or to continually plot band occupancy.

sweep jammer—An electronic jammer which sweeps a narrow band of electronic energy over a broad bandwidth.

sweep linearity—The maximum displacement error of the independent variable between specified points on the display area in an oscilloscope.

sweep lockout—A means for preventing multiple sweeps when operating an oscilloscope in a single-sweep mode.

sweep magnifier—Also called sweep expander. A circuit or control for expanding part of the sweep display of an oscilloscope.

sweep oscillator—An oscillator used to develop a sawtooth voltage which can be amplified to deflect the electron beam of a cathode-ray tube. *Also see* Sweep Generator.

sweep switching—The alternate display of two or more time bases or other sweeps using a single-beam crt. Comparable to dual- or multiple-trace operation of a deflection amplifier.

sweep test—Pertaining to cable, checking the frequency response by generating an r-f voltage, the frequency of which is varied back and forth through a given frequency range at a rapid constant rate while observing the results on an oscilloscope.

sweep-through—A jamming transmitter that sweeps through a radio-frequency band and jams each frequency briefly, producing a sound like that of an aircraft engine.

sweep time—The reciprocal of sweep rate.

sweep voltage—The voltage used for deflecting an electron beam. It may be applied to either the magnetic deflecting coils or the electrostatic plates.

swell manual—Also called solo manual. In an organ, the upper manual normally used to play the melody. (*Also see* Manual.)

swept resistance—The portion of the total resistance of a potentiometric transducer over which the slider travels when the device is operated through its total range.

swing—The variation in frequency or amplitude of an electrical quantity.

swinging—Momentary variations in frequency of a received wave.

swinging arm—A type of mounting and feed used to move the cutting head at a uniform rate across the recording disc in some recorders. All phonograph pickups are of the swinging-arm type.

swinging choke—An iron-core choke coil designed so that its effective inductance varies with the current passing through it. It is used as the input choke in some power-supply filter circuits.

"swiss-cheese" packaging—Also called imitation 2-D. A high-density packaging technique in which passive and active components are inserted into holes punched in printed-circuit-board substrates and attached by soldering or thermocompression bonding or by means of conductive epoxy adhesive.

switch—A mechanical or electrical device that completes or breaks the path of the current or sends it over a different path.

switchboard—1. A manually operated apparatus at a telephone exchange. The various circuits from subscribers and other exchanges terminate here, so that operators can establish communications between two subscribers on the same exchange, or on different exchanges. 2. A single large panel or an assembly of panels on which are mounted the switches, circuit breakers, meters, fuses, and terminals essential to the operation of electrical equipment.

switch detector—A detector which extracts information from the input waveform only at instants determined by a selector pulse.

switch gear—A general term covering switching interrupting, control, metering, protective, and regulating devices; also assemblies of these devices and associated interconnections, accessories, and supporting structures, used primarily in connection with the generation, transmission, and distribution of electric power.

switching—Making, breaking, or changing the connections in an electrical circuit.

switching center—1. A location at which data from an incoming circuit are routed to the proper outgoing circuit. 2. A group of equipment within a relay station for automatically or semiautomatically relaying communications traffic.

switching characteristics—An indication of how a device responds to an input pulse under specified driving conditions.

switching circuit—A circuit which performs a switching function. In computers, this is performed automatically by the presence of a certain signal (usually a pulse signal). When combined, switching circuits can perform a logical operation.

switching coefficient—The derivative of applied magnetizing force with respect to the reciprocal of the resultant switching time. It is usually determined as the reciprocal of the slope of a curve of reciprocals of switching times versus the values of applied magnetizing forces, which are applied as step functions.

switching device—Any device or mechanism,

either electrical or mechanical, which can place another device or circuit in an operating or nonoperating state.

switching time—1. The interval between the reference time and the last instant at which the instantaneous-voltage response of a magnetic cell reaches a stated fraction of its peak value. 2. The interval between the reference time and the first instant at which the instantaneous integrated-voltage response reaches a stated fraction of its peak value.

switchplate—A small plate attached to a wall to cover a push-button or other type of switch.

swr—Abbreviation for standing-wave ratio.

swr bridge—*See* Standing-Wave-Ratio Bridge.

syllabic companding—Companding in which the effective gain variations are made at speeds allowing response to the syllables of speech but not to individual cycles of the signal wave.

syllable articulation—Also called percent-of-syllable articulation. The percent of articulation obtained when the speech units considered are syllables (usually meaningless and usually of the consonant-vowel-consonant type).

symbol—1. A simplified design representing a part in a schematic circuit diagram. 2. A letter representing a particular quantity in formulas. 3. A sign, mark, or drawing agreed upon to represent an electrical device or component part thereof.

symbolic—Having to do with the representation of something by a conventional sign.

symbolic address—Also called a floating address. In digital-computer programming, a label chosen in a routine to identify a particular word, function, or other information independent of the location of the information within the routine.

symbolic coding—In digital computer programming, any coding system using symbolic rather than actual computer addresses.

symbolic logic—A form of logic in which nonnumerical relationships for a computer are expressed by symbols suitable for calculation.

symbolic programming—A program using symbols instead of numbers for the operations and locations in a computer. Although the writing of a program is easier and

Simple switch.   Vacuum tube.   Thyratron.

Switching circuits.

faster, an assembly program must be used to decode the symbol into machine language and assign instruction locations.

symmetrical — Balanced—i.e., having equal characteristics on each side of a central line, position, or value.

symmetrical alternating quantity—An alternating quantity for which all values separated by a half period have the same magnitude but opposite sign.

symmetrical avalanche rectifier—An avalanche rectifier which can be triggered in either direction. After triggering, it presents a low impedance in the triggered direction.

symmetrically, cyclically magnetized condition—The condition of a cyclically magnetized material when the limits of the applied magnetizing forces are equal and of opposite sign.

symmetrical transducer (with respect to specified terminations)—A transducer in which all possible pairs of specified terminations can be interchanged without affecting the transmission.

symmetrical transistor — A transistor in which the collector and emitter are made identical, so either can be used interchangeably.

sync—Short for synchronous, synchronization, synchronizing, etc.

sync compression—The reduction in gain applied to the sync signal over any part of its amplitude range with respect to the gain at a specified reference level.

Synchro.

synchro—1. A small motorlike device containing a stator and a rotor. When several synchros are correctly connected together, all rotors will line up at the same angle of rotation. 2. An inductive device capable of transforming an angular-position input into an electrical output or an electrical input into an angular output.

synchro-control differential generator—A rotary component for modifying the synchro-control generator output signal to correspond to the addition or subtraction from the generator shaft angle. Usually used with a synchro-control generator and synchro-control transducer.

synchro-control generator—A rotary component for transforming the shaft angle to a corresponding set of electrical signals for

ultimate retransformation to the shaft position in a remote location.

synchro-control transformer — A rotary component which accepts signals from a generator or differential generator for reconversion to the shaft angle with the aid of a servomechanism. Often used by itself as an angle-to-signal transducer, but usually with a synchro-control generator and synchro-control differential generator.

synchro differential generator—A synchro unit which receives an order from a synchro generator at its primary terminals, modifies this order mechanically by any desired amount according to the angular position of the rotor, and transmits the modified order from its secondary terminals to other synchro units.

synchro differential motor—A motor which is electrically similar to the synchro differential generator except that a damping device is added to prevent oscillation. Its rotor and stator are both connected to synchro generators, and its function is to indicate the sum or difference between the two signals transmitted by the generators.

synchro generator—A synchro which has an electrical output proportional to the angular position of its rotor.

Synchroguide—A type of control circuit for horizontal scanning in which the sync signal, oscillator voltage pulse, and scanning voltage are compared and kept in synchronism.

synchro motor—A synchro in which the rotor-shaft position is dependent on the electrical input.

synchronism—1. The phase relationship between two or more quantities of the same period when their phase difference is zero. 2. Applied to the synchronous motor, the condition under which the motor runs at a speed which is directly related to the frequency of the power applied to the motor and is not dependent upon other variables.

synchronization—1. The precise matching of two waves or functions. 2. The process of keeping the electron beam on the television screen in the same position as the scanning beam at the transmitter. 3. In a carrier, that degree of matching, in frequency, between the carrier used for modulation and the carrier used for demodulation which is sufficiently accurate to permit efficient functioning of the system.

synchronization error — In navigation, the error due to imperfect timing of two operations (may or may not include the signal transmission time).

synchronize—1. To adjust the periodicity of an electrical system so that it bears an integral relationship to the frequency of the periodic phenomenon under investigation. 2. To lock one element of a system into step with another. The term usually refers to locking a receiver to a transmitter, but it can refer to locking the data-terminal equipment bit rate to the data set frequency.

synchronized sweep—A sweep which would free-run in the absence of an applied signal, but in the presence of the signal is synchronized by it.

synchronizer—1. The component of a radar set which generates the timing voltage for the complete set. *Also see* Timer. 2. A computer storage device used to compensate for a difference in a rate of flow of information or time of occurrence of events when information is being transmitted from one device to another.

synchronizing (in television)—Maintaining two or more scanning processes in phase.

synchronizing-pulse selector — A circuit used to separate synchronizing pulses from commutated pulse trains.

synchronizing reactor—A current-limiting reactor that is connected momentarily across the open contacts of a circuit-interrupting device for synchronizing purposes.

synchronizing relay—A relay which functions when two alternating-current sources are in agreement within predetermined limits of phase angle and frequency.

synchronizing separator—*See* Amplitude Separator.

synchronizing signal—*See* Sync Signal.

synchronous—1. In step or in phase, as applied to two devices or machines. 2. A term applied to a computer, in which the performance of a sequence of operations is controlled by equally spaced clock signals or pulses.

synchronous booster converter — A synchronous converter connected in series with an a-c generator and mounted on the same shaft. It is used for adjusting the voltage at the commutator of the converter.

synchronous capacitor—A rotating machine running without mechanical load and designed so that its field excitation can be varied in order to draw a leading current (like a capacitor) and thereby modify the power factor of the a-c system, or influence the load voltage through such change in power factor.

synchronous clock—An electric clock driven by a synchronous motor, for operation on an a-c power system in which the frequency is accurately controlled.

synchronous computer—A digital computer in which all ordinary operations are controlled by equally spaced signals from a master clock.

synchronous converter—A synchronous machine which converts alternating current to direct current or vice versa. The armature winding is connected to the collector rings and commutator.

synchronous demodulator — Also called a synchronous detector. A demodulator in which the reference signal has the same frequency as the carrier or subcarrier to be demodulated. It is used in color television receivers to recover either the I or the Q signals from the chrominance sidebands.

synchronous detector—*See* Synchronous Demodulator.

synchronous gate—A time gate in which the output intervals are synchronized with the incoming signal.

synchronous generator—A circuit designed to synchronize an externally generated signal with a train of clock pulses. The generator produces precisely one output pulse for each cycle of the input signal. The output pulse thus has a width equal to that of the period of the clock-pulse train.

synchronous inverter—*See* Dynamotor.

synchronous machine—A machine which has an average speed exactly proportionate to the frequency of the system to which it is connected.

synchronous motor — An induction motor which runs at synchronous speed. Its stator windings have the same arrangement as in nonsynchronous induction motors, but the rotor does not slip behind the rotating magnetic stator field.

synchronous rectifier—A rectifier in which contacts are opened and closed at the correct instant by either a synchronous vibrator or a commutator driven by a synchronous motor.

synchronous speed—A speed value related to the frequency of an a-c power line and the number of poles in the rotating equipment. Synchronous speed in revolutions per minute is equal to the frequency in hertz divided by the number of poles, with the result multiplied by 120.

synchronous torque—The maximum load torque with which a motor can be loaded after it comes to synchronous speed. These torques are usually higher than starting torques.

Synchronous-vibrator power supply.

synchronous vibrator—An electromagnetic vibrator that simultaneously converts a low d-c voltage to a low alternating voltage and applies it to a power transformer, from which a high alternating voltage is obtained and rectified. In power packs, it eliminates the need for a rectifier tube.

synchroscope—1. An instrument used to determine the phase difference or degree of synchronism of two alternating-current generators or quantities. 2. An oscilloscope on which recurrent pulses or waveforms may be observed, and which incorporates a sweep generator that produces one sweep for each pulse.

synchro system—A system for obtaining remote indication or control by means of self-synchronizing motors such as selsyns and equivalent types.

synchro-torque receiver—A relatively low-impedance positioning device that generates its own torque when driven by a suitable synchro-torque transmitter.

synchro-torque transmitter—A positioning device that generates electrical information of sufficient power to drive a suitable torque receiver.

synchrotron—A device for accelerating charged particles (e.g., electrons) in a vacuum. The particles are guided by a changing magnetic field while being accelerated many times in a closed path by a radio-frequency electric field.

synchrotron radiation—Also called magnetic *bremsstrahlung*. The radiation produced by relativistic electrons as they travel in a region of space containing magnetic fields.

sync level—The level of the peaks of the sync signal.

sync limiter—A circuit used in television circuits to prevent sync pulses from exceeding a predetermined amplitude.

sync pulse—Part of the sync signal in a television system.

sync section—A color tv circuit comprising a keyer, burst amplifier, phase detector, reactance tube, subcarrier oscillator, and quadrature amplifier.

sync separator—The circuit which separates the picture signals from the control pulses in a television system.

sync signal—Also called a synchronizing signal. The signal employed for synchronizing the scanning. In television it is composed of pulses at rates related to the line and field frequencies.

sync-signal generator—A synchronizing signal generator for a television receiver or transmitter.

synthesizer frequency meter—A device for measuring frequency by utilizing a synthesized crystal-based signal for the internally generated signal.

synthetic display generation—Logical and numerical processing to display collected or calculated data in symbolic form.

syntony—The condition in which two oscillating circuits have the same resonant frequency.

system—1. An assembly of component parts linked together by some form of regulated interaction into an organized whole. 2. A collection of consecutive operations and procedures required to accomplish a specific objective.

systematic errors—Those errors which have an orderly character and can be corrected by calibration.

systematic inaccuracies—Those inaccuracies due to inherent limitations in the equipment.

system deviation—The instantaneous difference between the value of a specified system variable and the ideal value of the variable.

system element—One or more basic elements, together with other components necessary to form all or a significant part of one of the general functional groups into which a measurement system can be classified.

system engineering—A method of engineering approach whereby all the elements in the control system are considered, even the smallest value and the process itself.

system failure rate—The number of occasions during a given time period on which a given number of identical systems do not function properly.

system layout—In a microwave system, a chart or diagram showing the number, type, and terminations of circuits used in the system.

system noise—The output of a system when it is operating with zero input signal.

system of beams—The three electron beams emitted by the triple electron-gun assembly in a color tube. They occupy positions equidistant from a common axis and are spaced 120° apart around the axis.

system of units—An assemblage of units for expressing the magnitudes of physical quantities.

system overshoot—The largest value of system deviation following the dynamic crossing of the ideal value as a result of a specified stimulus.

system reliability—The probability that a system will perform its specified task properly under stated conditions of environment.

T

T—1. Symbol for transformer or absolute temperature. 2. Abbreviation for the prefix "tera" (10^{12}).

tab—*See* Land.

table lookup—In a computer, a method of controlling the location to which a jump or transfer is made. It is used especially when there is a large number of alternatives, as in function evaluation in scientific computations.

tabulator—A machine (e.g., a punch-card machine) which reads information from one medium and produces lists, totals, or tabulations on separate forms or continuous paper strips.

tachometer—An instrument used to measure

MOTOR
WHOSE SPEED IS
TO BE MEASURED

D-C OR A-C TACHOMETER

SHAFT COUPLER

D-C VOLTMETER (WITH D-C TACHOMETER)
OR FREQUENCY METER (WITH A-C TACHOMETER)
CALIBRATED IN RPM.

Tachometer.

the frequency of mechanical systems by the determination of angular velocity.

tachometer generator—A small generator attached to a rotating shaft for the purpose of generating a voltage proportional to the shaft speed. In speed-control circuits, a tachometer may be coupled to the shaft of the motor whose speed is to be controlled. A change of motor speed will produce a change of tachometer output voltage. This change of voltage can be used as an error signal to restore the speed to the desired value.

tag—Also called a sentinel. In digital-computer programming, a unit of information the composition of which differs from that of other members of the set so that it can be used as a marker or label.

tail—A small pulse following the main pulse and in the same direction, or the slow decay following the main body of the pulse.

tail clipping—A method of sharpening the trailing edge of a pulse.

tailing—*See* Hangover.

tail-warning radar sets—A radar set placed in the tail of an aircraft to warn of aircraft approaching from the rear.

take-up reel—The reel which accumulates the tape as it is recorded or played on a tape recorder.

talbot—A unit of luminous energy in the mksa system equal to 1 lumen-second.

talker echo—An echo which reaches the ear of the person who originated the sound.

talk-listen switch—A switch on an intercommunication unit to switch the speaker as required to function either as a reproducer or as a microphone.

tandem—Also called cascade. Two terminal-pair networks are in tandem when the output terminals of one network are connected directly to the input terminals of the other network.

tandem transistor—Two transistors in one package and internally connected together.

tangent—A straight line which touches the circumference of a circle at one point.

tangent galvanometer—A galvanometer consisting of a small compass mounted horizontally in the center of a large vertical coil of wire. The current through the coil is proportional to the tangent of the angle at which the compass needle is deflected.

tangential component—A component acting at right angles to a radius.

tangential sensitivity—A term generally applied as an indication of quality in a receiving system. This term can be used to define the minimum signal level that can be detected above the background noise. However, it is usually expressed as that signal power level which causes a 3-db rise above the noise-level reading.

tangential sensitivity on look-through—The strength of the target signal, measured at the receiver terminals, required to produce a signal pulse having twice the apparent height of the noise.

tangential wave path—In radio-wave propagation of a direct wave over the earth, a path which is tangential to the surface of the earth. The tangential wave path is curved by atmospheric refraction.

tangent sensitivity—The slope of the line tangent to the response curve at the point being measured.

tank—1. A unit of acoustically operating delay-line storage containing a set of channels. Each channel forms a separate recirculation path. 2. (*Also see* Tank Circuit.)

tank circuit—1. A circuit capable of storing electrical energy over a band of frequencies continuously distributed about a single frequency at which the circuit is said to be resonant or tuned. The selectivity of the circuit is proportionate to the ratio between the energy stored in the circuit and the energy dissipated. This ratio is often called the Q of the circuit. 2. Also called a tank. A parallel-resonant circuit connected in the plate circuit of an electron-tube generator.

tantalum (electrolytic) capacitor—An electrolytic capacitor with a tantalum foil or sintered-slug anode.

Tantalum capacitor.

Tape deck.

tantalum-foil electrolytic capacitor—A capacitor which consists of two tantalum foil electrodes with an oxide on the anode, and separated by layers of absorbent paper saturated with an operating electrolyte.

T-antenna—Any antenna consisting of one or more horizontal wires, with the lead-in connected approximately in the center.

tap—1. A fixed electrical connection to a specified position on the element of a potentiometer, transformer, etc. 2. A branch. Applies to conductors such as a battery tap, and to miscellaneous general use.

tape—1. Magnetic recording tape with one or more recording strips (tracks). 2. (*Also see* Punched Tape.) 3. A ribbon of flexible material—e.g., friction, magnetic, punched, etc. 4. A linear medium for storing information which can be used as the input or output to a computer (e.g., magnetic tape).

tape cable—Also called flat flexible cable. A form of flexible multiple conductor in which parallel strips of metal are imbedded in an insulating material.

tape cartridge—A magazine or holder for a length of magnetic tape which by its design avoids the necessity for manual threading or handling. Usually compatible only with one specific type of machine. *Also see* Tape Magazine.

tape character—Information consisting of bits stored across the several longitudinal channels of a tape.

tape-controlled carriage—A paper-feeding device automatically controlled by a punched paper tape.

tape copy—A message received in tape form as the result of a transmission.

tape deck—A tape recorder designed for use in a high-fidelity music system. Usually it consists only of the motorboard mechanism and does not include a preamplifier, power amplifier, speaker, or case.

tape feed—A mechanism which feeds the tape to be read or sensed by a computer or other data-handling system.

tape guides—Grooved pins of nonmagnetic material mounted at either side of the recording-head assembly. Their function is to position the magnetic tape on the head as it is being recorded or played.

tape lifters—A system of movable guides which automatically divert tape from contact with the recorder heads during the fast forward or rewinding mode of operation.

tape loop—A length of magnetic tape with the ends joined together to form an endless loop. Used either on a standard recorder, a special message-repeater unit, or in conjunction with a cartridge device, it enables a recorded message to be played back repetitively; there is no need to rewind the tape.

tape magazine—Also called a tape cartridge. A container holding a reel of magnetic recording tape, which can be played without being threaded manually.

tape mark—A special record indicating end of file.

tape monitor—A circuit which permits the checking of recordings by taking the signal directly from the tape a moment after the recording is made. This is only possible on three-head recorders.

tape-on surface-temperature resistor—A surface-temperature resistor installed by adhering the sensing element to the surface with a piece of pressure-sensitive tape.

tape-path center line—The locus or path traced by an imaginary point, located on the recording tape midway between its edges, as it travels from reel to reel through guides, past heads, and between capstan and pressure rollers. For correct tracking and minimum tape distortion, the entire path should lie in a single plane located above the

501

motor board at a height compatible with head-gap locations.

tape phonograph—*See* Tape Player.

tape player—Sometimes called a tape phonograph or a tape reproducer. A unit for playing recorded tapes. It has no facilities for recording.

taper—In communication practice, a continuous or gradual change in electrical properties with length—e.g., as obtained by a continuous change of cross section of a waveguide or by the distribution and change of resistance of a potentiometer or rheostat.

tape recorder—A mechanical-electronic device for recording voice, music, and other audio-frequency material. Sound is converted to electrical energy, which in turn sets up a corresponding magnetic pattern on iron-oxide particles suspended on paper or plastic tape. During playback, this magnetic pattern is reconverted into electrical energy and then changed back to sound through the medium of headphones or a speaker. The recorded material may be converted to a visual display by the use of an oscilloscope, other visual indicator, or a graphic recorder. Also used for magnetically recording the video material for television programs.

tapered potentiometer—A continuously adjustable potentiometer, the resistance of which varies nonuniformly along the element—being greater or less for equal slider movement at various points along the resistance element.

tapered transmission line—*See* Tapered Waveguide.

tapered waveguide—Also called a tapered transmission line. A waveguide in which a physical or electrical characteristic changes continuously with distance along the axis of the guide.

tape reproducer—*See* Tape Player.

tape reservoir—That part of a magnetic tape system used to isolate the tape storage inertia (i.e., tape reels, etc.) from the drive system.

tape skew—The deviation of a tape from following a linear path when transported across the heads, causing a time displacement between signals recorded on different tracks

and amplitude differences between the outputs from individual tracks owing to variations in azimuth alignment. The adjectives "static" and "dynamic" are used to distinguish between the steady and fluctuating components of the tape skew.

tape speed—The speed at which tape moves past the head in the recording or playback mode. The standard tape speed for home use is 7½ ips or half this speed (3¾ ips). One-fourth or even one-eighth this speed is also used, but usually only for music when special high-quality tape is utilized. The professional recording speed for music mastering is usually 15 ips.

tape-speed errors—Any variation in tape speed from the normal speed over the record or reproduce head, regardless of cause.

tape-speed variations—*See* Flutter.

tape splicer—A device for splicing magnetic tape automatically or semiautomatically.

tape threader—A device that makes easier the threading of magnetic recording tape onto the reel.

tape-to-head speed—The relative speed of the tape and head during normal recording or replay. (The tape-to-head speed coincides with the tape speed in conventional longitudinal recording, but it is considerably greater than the tape speed in systems where the heads are scanned across or along the tape.)

tape-to-tape converter—A device for changing from one form of input/output medium or code to another, i.e., magnetic tape to paper tape (or vice versa) or eight-channel code to five-channel code.

tape transmitter—A machine for high-speed keying of telegraph code signals previously recorded on tape.

tape-transport mechanism—*See* Motor Board.

tape-wound core—A magnetic core consisting of a plastic or ceramic toroid around which is wound a strip of thin magnetic tape possessing a square-hysteresis-loop characteristic. Also known as bimag, a tape-wound core is used principally as a shift-register element.

tap lead—The lead connected to a tap on a coil winding.

Tape recording.

tapped control—A rheostat or potentiometer having a fixed tap at some point along the resistance element, usually to provide fixed grid bias or automatic tone compensation.

tapped line—A delay line in which more than two terminal pairs are associated with a single sonic-delay channel.

tapped resistor—A wirewound fixed resistor having one or more additional terminals along its length, generally for voltage-divider applications.

tapped winding—A coil winding with connections brought out from turns at various points.

tap switch—A multicontact switch used chiefly for connecting a load to any one of a number of taps on a resistor or coil.

target—1. In a camera tube, a structure employing a storage surface which is scanned by an electron beam to generate an output-signal current corresponding to the charge-density pattern stored thereon. 2. Also called an anticathode. In an X-ray tube, an electrode or part of an electrode on which a beam of electrons is focused and from which X-rays are emitted. 3. In radar, a specific object of radar search or surveillance. 4. Any object which reflects energy back to the radar receiver.

target capacitance—In camera tubes, the capacitance between the scanned area of the target and backplate.

target cutoff voltage—In camera tubes, the lowest target voltage at which any detectable electrical signal, corresponding to a light image on the sensitive surface of the tube, can be obtained.

target discrimination—The characteristic of a guidance system that permits it to distinguish between two or more targets in close proximity.

target fade—The loss or decrease of signal from the target due to interference or other phenomena.

target glint—*See* Scintillation.

target identification—A visual procedure by which a radar target is positively identified as either hostile or friendly.

target language—The language into which some other language is to be properly translated.

target noise—Reflections of a transmitted radar signal from a target that has a number of reflecting elements randomly oriented in space.

target reflectivity—The degree to which a target reflects electromagnetic energy.

target scintillation—The apparent random movement of the center of reflectivity of a target observed during the course of an operation.

target seeker—In a missile homing system, the element that senses some feature of the target so that the resulting information can be used to direct appropriate maneuvers to maintain a collision course.

target voltage—In a camera tube with low-velocity scanning, the potential difference between the thermionic cathode and the backplate.

taut-band meter—An instrument the moving element of which is supported by two thin metal ribbons kept under tension by elastic members at each end of the assembly. This construction eliminates physical contact between the moving parts, and thus does away with friction.

tearing—Distortion observed on the television screen when the horizontal synchronization is unstable.

teaser transformer—A transformer of two T-connected, single-phase units for three-phase to two-phase or two-phase to three-phase operation; it is connected between the midpoint of the main transformer and the third wire of the three-phase system.

teasing—In the life-testing of switches, the slow movement of rotor contacts making and breaking with stator contacts.

technician license—A class of amateur radio license issued in the United States by the FCC for the primary purpose of operation and experimentation on frequencies above 50 MHz.

tecnetron—A high-power multichannel field-effect transistor similar to a triode tube in that it has anode and cathode connections (and a grid connection between) on opposite ends of a small germanium rod.

tee junction—Also spelled T-junction. A junction of waveguides in which the longitudinal guide axes form a T. The guide which continues through the junction is called the main guide; the one which terminates at a junction, the branch guide.

telautograph—Also called a telewriter. A writing telegraph instrument in which the movement of a pen in the transmitting apparatus varies the current and thereby causes the corresponding movement of a pen at the remote receiving instrument.

telecamera—Acronym for a TELEvision CAMERA.

telecardiophone—An amplifying stethoscope which permits heart sounds to be heard at a distance.

telecast—Acronym for TELEvision broadCASTing—specifically, a television program, or the act of broadcasting a television program.

telecasting—The broadcasting of a television program.

telecommunication—1. Any communication at a distance. Broadly, all forms of electrical transmission of intelligence. This includes the telegraph, telephone, radio, telephotograph, and television, listed in their chronological order of development. (*Also see* Communication.) 2. Data transmission between a computing system and remotely located devices via a unit that performs the necessary format conversion and controls the rate of transmission.

teleconference—A conference between persons who are remote from one another but linked together by a telecommunications system.

telegenic—The suitability of a subject or model for televising.

telegraph central office—A telephone switching unit installed in a telephone system providing service to the general public, having the necessary equipment and operating arrangements for terminating and interconnecting lines and trunks.

telegraph channel—The transmission media and intervening apparatus involved in the transmission of telegraph signals in a given direction between two intermediate telegraph installations. A means of one-way transmission of telegraph signals.

telegraph circuit—A complete circuit over which signal currents flow between transmitting and receiving apparatus in a telegraph system. It sometimes consists of an overhead wire or cable and a return path through the ground.

telegraph concentrator — A switching arrangement by means of which a number of branch or subscriber lines or station sets may be connected to a lesser number of trunk lines, operating positions, or instruments through the medium of manual or automatic switching devices to obtain more efficient use of facilities.

telegraph distributor—A device which effectively associates one direct current or carrier telegraph channel in rapid succession with the elements of one or more signal-sending or -receiving devices.

telegraph grade circuit—A circuit suitable for transmission by teletypewriter equipment. Normally the circuit is considered to employ d-c signalling at a maximum speed of 75 bauds.

telegraph key—A hand-operated device for opening and closing contacts to modulate the current with telegraph signals.

Telegraph key.

telegraph-modulated waves — Continuous waves, the amplitude or frequency of which is varied by means of telegraphic keying.

telegraph selector — A device which performs a switching operation in response to a definite signal or group of successive signals received over a controlling circuit.

telegraph signal distortion—The time displacement of transitions between conditions such as marking and spacing, with respect to their proper relative positions in perfectly timed signals. The total distortion is the algebraic sum of the bias and the characteristic and fortuitous distortions.

telegraph sounder—A telegraph receiving instrument in which an electromagnet attracts an armature each time a pulse arrives. This armature makes an audible sound as it hits against its stops at the beginning and end of each current impulse, and the intervals between these sounds are translated from code into the received message by the operator.

telegraph transmission speed—The rate at which signals are transmitted. This may be measured by the equivalent number of dot-cycles per second or by the average number of letters or words transmitted and received per minute.

telegraph transmitter—A device for controlling a source of electric power in order to form telegraph signals.

telegraphy—1. A system of telecommunication for the transmission of graphic symbols, usually letters or numerals, by the use of a signal code. It is used primarily for record communication. 2. Any system of telecommunication for the transmission of graphic symbols or images for reception in record form, usually without gradation of shade values.

telelectrocardiograph—A device for transmission and remote reception of electrocardiograph signals.

telemeter—1. To transmit analog or digital reports of measurements and observations over a distance (e.g., by radio transmission from a guided missile to a control or recording station on the ground). 2. A complete measuring, transmitting, and receiving apparatus for indicating, recording, or integrating the value of a quantity at a distance by electric translating means.

telemetering—Also called telemetry or remote metering. Measurement which, through intermediate means, can be interpreted at a distance from the primary detector. A receiving instrument converts the transmitted electrical signals into units of data, which can then be translated by data reduction into appropriate units.

telemeter service—Metered telegraph transmission between paired telegraph instruments over an intervening circuit adapted to serve a number of such pairs on a shared-time basis.

telemetry—The science of sensing and measuring information at some remote location and transmitting the data to a convenient location to be read and recorded.

telemetry beacon—A system whereby two or more reply pulses are transmitted by the beacon for the transmission of data from the test vehicle to the ground station.

telemetry frame—In pcm systems, one complete sampling of words or channels of information at a given rate; in time-division multiplexing, one complete commutator revolution.

telemetry-frame rate—The frequency derived from the period of one frame.

telephone—Combination of apparatus for converting speech energy to electrical waves, transmitting the electrical energy to a distant point, and there reconverting the electrical energy to audible sounds.

telephone capacitor—A fixed capacitor connected in parallel with a telephone receiver to bypass r-f and higher audio frequencies and thereby reduce noise.

telephone carrier current—A carrier current used for telephone communication so that more than one channel can be obtained on a single pair of wires.

telephone channel—A channel suitable for the transmission of telephone signals.

telephone circuit—A complete circuit over which audio and signaling currents travel between two telephone subscribers communicating with each other in a telephone system.

telephone current—An electric current produced or controlled by the operation of a telephone transmitter.

telephone jack—*See* Phone Jack.

telephone pickup—Any of several devices used to monitor telephone conversations, usually without direct connection to the telephone line and operating on the principle of mutual magnetic coupling.

telephone plug—*See* Phone Plug.

telephone receiver—The earphone used in a telephone system.

telephone repeater—An assemblage of amplifiers and other equipment employed at points along the line to rebuild the signal strength in a telephone circuit.

telephone ringer—An electric bell that operates on low-frequency alternating or pulsating current and is used for indicating a telephone call to the station being alerted.

telephone system—A group of telephones plus the lines, trunks, switching mechanisms, and all other accessories required to interconnect the telephones.

telephone transmitter—A microphone used in a telephone system. (*Also see* Microphone.)

telephony—The transmission of speech current over wires, enabling two persons to converse over almost any distance.

telephoto—Also called telephotography. A photoelectrical transmission system for point-to-point or air-to-ground transmission of high-definition pictorial information.

telephotography—*See* Telephoto.

telephoto lens—A lens system that is physically shorter than its rated focal length. It is used in still, movie, and television cameras to enlarge images of objects photographed at comparatively great distances.

teleprinter—1. *See* Printer. 2. Trade name used by Western Union for its telegraph terminal equipment.

teleran—A navigational system in which radar and television transmitting equipment are employed on the ground, with television receiving equipment in the aircraft, to televise the image of the ground radar ppi scope to the aircraft along with map and weather data.

telering—A frequency-selector device for the production of ringing power.

telesynd—Telemeter or remote-control equipment which is synchronous in both speed and position.

teletype—A system used for transmitting messages over some distance, employing keyboard or paper-tape sending and printed receiving.

teletypewriter—1. *See* Printer. 2. A generic term referring to the basic equipment made by Teletype Corporation and to teleprinter equipment. The teletypewriter uses electromechanical functions to generate codes (Baudot) in response to a human input to a manual keyboard.

teletypewriter code—A special code in which each code group is made up of five units, or elements, of equal length which are known as marking or spacing impulses. The five-unit start-stop code consists of five signal impulses preceded by a start impulse and followed by a stop impulse. Each impulse except the stop impulse is 22 milliseconds in length; the stop impulse is 32 milliseconds (based on 60-word-per-minute operation).

televise—The act of converting a scene or image field into a television signal.

television—Abbreviated tv. A telecommunication system for transmission of transient images of fixed or moving objects.

television and radar navigation—A navigational system which; a. employs ground-based search radar equipment along an airway to locate aircraft flying near that airway, b. transmits, by television means, information pertaining to these aircraft and other information to the pilots of properly equipped aircraft, and c. provides information to the pilots appropriate for use in the landing approach.

television broadcast band—The frequencies assignable to television broadcast stations in the band extending from 54 to 890 MHz. These frequencies are grouped into channels, as follows: Channels 2 through 4, 54 to 72 MHz; Channels 5 and 6, 76 to 88 MHz; Channels 7 through 13, 174 to 216 MHz; and Channels 14 through 83, 470 to 890 MHz.

television broadcast station—A radio station for transmitting visual signals, and usually simultaneous aural signals, for general reception.

television camera—A pickup unit used in a television system to convert into electric signals the optical image which is formed by a lens.

television channel—A channel suitable for the transmission of television signals. The channel for associated sound signals may or may not be considered part of the television channel.

television engineering—*See* Radio Engineering.

television interference—Interference in the reception of the sound and/or video portion of a television program by a transmitter or another device.

television pickup station—A land mobile station used for the transmission of television program material and related communications from the scenes of events occurring at points removed from television broadcast station studios, to the television broadcast stations.

television receiver—A radio receiver for converting incoming electric signals into television pictures and the associated sound.

television reconnaissance — Air reconnaissance by optical or electronic means to supplement photographic and visual reconnaissance.

television relay system—A system of two or more stations for transmitting television relay signals from point to point, using radio waves in free space as a medium. Such transmission is not intended for direct reception by the public.

television repeater—A repeater used in a television circuit.

television screen—In a television receiver, the fluorescent screen of the picture tube.

television signal—The audio signal and video signal that are broadcast simultaneously to produce the sound and picture portions of a televised scene.

television transmitter—The aggregate radio-frequency and modulating equipment necessary to supply, to an antenna system, the modulated radio-frequency power by which all component parts of a complete television signal (including audio, video, and synchronizing signals) are concurrently transmitted.

televoltmeter — A telemeter that measures voltage.

telewattmeter — A telemeter that measures power.

telewriter—*See* Telautograph.

telex—An audio-frequency teleprinter system used in Great Britain to provide teletypewriter service over telephone lines.

telluric current—*See* Earth Current.

Telstar—A low-altitude active communications satellite used for microwave communication and satellite tracking.

temperature coefficient—1. A factor used to calculate the change in the characteristics of a substance, device, or circuit element with changes in its temperature. 2. The percentage change in the output voltage (or current) of a regulated power supply due to a variation of ambient temperature. The values are usually expressed as a percentage per degree Celsius and restricted to the specified ambient range of the unit.

temperature coefficient of frequency—The rate at which the frequency changes with temperature, expressed in hertz per megahertz per degree Celsius at a given temperature.

temperature coefficient of permeability—A coefficient expressing the change in permeability as the temperature rises or falls. It is expressed as the rate of change in permeability per degree.

temperature coefficient of resistance—The ratio of the change in resistance (or resistivity) to the original value for a unit change in temperature. The temperature coefficient over the temperature range from t to t_1, referred to the resistance R_t at temperature t, is determined by the following equation:

$$\frac{R_{t1} - R_t}{R_t (t_1 - t)}$$

where t is the temperature, preferably in degrees C. The value will be positive unless otherwise indicated by a negative sign.

temperature coefficient of voltage drop — The change in the voltage drop of a glow-discharge tube, divided by the change in ambient temperature or in the temperature of the envelope.

temperature coefficient value—The expected percentage change per degree of temperature difference from a specified temperature.

temperature-compensated zener diode—A positive temperature-coefficient reversed-bias zener diode (PN junction) connected in series with one or more negative-temperature forward-biased diodes within a single package.

temperature-compensating capacitor—A capacitor the capacitance of which varies with temperature in a known and predictable manner. It is used extensively in oscillator circuits, to compensate for changes due to temperature variations in the values of other components.

temperature compensation—The process whereby the effects of an increase or decrease in ambient temperature are canceled (e.g., as in the case of an oscillator that is required to maintain a stable output frequency regardless of ambient temperature changes).

temperature control — 1. A switch actuated by a thermostat responsive to changes in temperature, and used to maintain temperature within certain limits. 2. A control device responsive to temperature.

temperature derating—Lowering the voltage, current, or power rating of a device or component when it is used at elevated temperatures.

temperature detector—An instrument used to measure the temperature of a body. Any physical property that is dependent on temperature may be employed, such as the differential expansion of two bodies, thermoelectromotive force at the junction of two metals, change of resistance of a metal, or the radiation from a hot body.

temperature-limited—The condition of a cathode when all the electrons emitted from it are drawn away by a strong positive field. The only way to increase the flow of electrons is to raise the cathode temperature.

temperature relay—A relay which functions at a predetermined temperature.

temperature rise—The difference between the initial and final temperature of a component or device. Temperature rise is expressed in degrees C or F, usually referred to an ambient temperature, and equals the hot-spot temperature minus the ambient temperature.

temperature saturation—*See* Filament Saturation.

temperature shock—A rapid change from one temperature extreme to another.

temperature-wattage characteristic—In a thermistor, the relationship, for a specific ambient temperature, between the temperature of the thermistor and the applied steady-state power.

temporary magnet—A magnetized material having a high permeability and low retentivity.

temporary storage—Internal storage locations in a computer reserved for intermediate and partial results.

TEM wave—Abbreviation for transverse electromagnetic wave.

tensiometer—A device for determining the tautness of a supporting wire or cable.

tension—1. Mechanical—the condition of strain which tends to stretch. 2. Electrical—the potential or electrostatic voltage.

tenth-power width—In a plane containing the direction of the maximum of a lobe, the full angle between the two directions in that plane, about the maximum in which the radiation intensity is one-tenth the maximum value of the lobe.

tera—Prefix for the numerical quantity of 10^{12}. Abbreviated T.

terahertz—One million megahertz, or 10^{12} hertz. Abbreviated THz.

teraohm—One million megohms, or 10^{12} ohms.

teraohmmeter—An instrument used to measure extremely high resistance.

terminal—1. A point of connection for two or more conductors in an electrical circuit. 2. A device attached to a conductor to facilitate connection with another conductor.

terminal area—1. A portion of a microelectronic circuit used for making electrical connections to the conductor pattern—e.g., an enlarged pad (area) on a semiconductor die. *Also see* Pad. 2. A portion of a printed circuit used for making electrical connections to the conductive pattern, such as the enlarged portion of conductor material surrounding a component mounting hole.

terminal block—An insulating base or slab

equipped with one or more terminal connectors for the purpose of making electrical connections thereto.

Terminal boards.

terminal board—Also called a terminal strip. An insulating base or slab equipped with terminals for connecting wiring.

terminal box—A housing where cable pairs are brought out to terminations for connections.

terminal brush—A brush with long bristles for cleaning fuses and terminals in a terminal box.

terminal cutout pairs—Numbered, designated pairs brought out of a cable at a terminal.

terminal equipment—1. At the end of a communications channel, the equipment essential for controlling the transmission and/or reception of messages. 2. Telephone and teletypewriter switchboards and other centrally located equipment to which wire circuits are terminated.

terminal guidance—1. Guidance applied to a guided missile between midcourse guidance and arrival at the target. 2. Electronic, mechanical, visual, or other assistance given an aircraft pilot to facilitate arrival at, landing upon, or departure from an air landing or air-drop facility.

terminal impedance—The complex impedance seen at the unloaded output or input terminals of transmission equipment or a line in otherwise normal operating condition.

terminal leg—*See* Terminal Stub.

terminal lug—1. A threaded lug to which a wire may be fastened in a terminal box. 2. A cylindrical piece of metal, either solid or hollow and of two or more diameters, which can be stacked, flared, swaged, or pressed into a hole for the purpose of connecting leads or external wires to the conductive pattern.

terminal pad—An alternate term for "terminal area" or "pad."

terminal pair—An associated pair of accessible terminals (e.g., the input or output terminals of a device or network).

terminal repeater—1. An assemblage of equipment designed specifically for use at the end of a communication circuit—as contrasted with the repeater, which is designed for an intermediate point. 2. Two microwave terminals arranged to provide for the interconnection of separate systems, or separate sections of a system.

terminal station — The microwave equipment and associated multiplex equipment employed at the ends of a microwave system.

terminal strip—*See* Terminal Board.

terminal stub—Also called terminal leg. A piece of cable which comes with a cable terminal for splicing into the main cable.

terminal unit—Equipment usable on a communication channel for either input or output.

terminal vhf omnirange — Very-high-frequency omnirange, normally low powered, complete with a local monitoring device which will automatically shut down the facility if it is not operating properly.

terminated line—A transmission line terminated in a resistance equal to the characteristic impedance of the line, so that there is no reflection or standing waves.

terminating—The closing of the circuit at either end of a line or transducer by connection of some device. Terminating does not imply any special condition, such as the elimination of reflection.

termination—1. A load connected to a transmission line or other device. To avoid wave reflections, it must match the characteristic of the line or device. 2. A waveguide technique; the point at which energy flowing along a waveguide continues in a nonwave guide mode of propagation.

ternary — 1. A numerical system of notation using the base 3 and employing the characters 0, 1, and 2. 2. Able to assume three distinct states.

ternary code—A code in which each element may be any one of three distinct kinds or values.

ternary pulse-code modulation—A form of pulse-code modulation in which each element of information is represented by one of three distinct values, e.g., positive pulses, negative pulses, and spaces.

terrain-avoidance radar — Airborne radar which provides a display of terrain ahead of a low-flying airplane to permit horizontal avoidance of obstacles.

terrain-clearance indicator—A device for measuring the distance from an aircraft to the surface of the sea or earth.

terrain error—In navigation, the error resulting from distortion of the radiated field by the nonhomogeneous characteristics of the terrain over which the radiation in question has been propagated.

terrain-following radar — Airborne radar which provides a display of terrain ahead of a low-flying aircraft to permit manual control, or signals for automatic control, to maintain constant altitude above the ground.

terrestrial-reference flight—Stabilized flight in which control information is obtained

from terrestrial phenomena (e.g., flight in which basic information derived from the magnetic field of the earth, atmospheric pressure, and the like is fed into a conventional automatic pilot).

Tertiary coil.

tertiary coil—A third coil used in the output transformer of an audio amplifier to supply a feedback voltage.

tertiary winding—1. A winding added to a transformer, in addition to the conventional primary and secondary windings, to suppress third harmonics or to make connections to a power-factor–correcting device. 2. *See* Stabilized Winding.

tesla—A unit of magnetic induction equal to 1 weber per square meter in the mksa system.

Tesla coil—An air-core transformer used for developing high-voltage discharge at a very high frequency. It has a few turns of heavy wire as the primary and many turns of fine wire as the secondary.

test—A procedure or sequence of operations for determining the manner in which equipment is functioning or the existence, type, and location of any trouble.

test bench—Equipment designed specifically for making over-all bench tests on equipment in a particular test set-up under controlled conditions.

test board—A switchboard equipped with testing apparatus, arranged so that connections can be made from it to telephone lines or central office equipment for testing purposes.

test clip—A spring clip fastened to the end of an insulated wire to enable quick temporary connections when circuits or devices are being tested.

testing level—The value of power used for reference represented by 0.001 watt working into 600 ohms.

test lead — A flexible insulated lead used chiefly for connecting meters and test instruments to a circuit under test.

test oscillator—A test instrument that can be set to generate an unmodulated or tone-modulated radio-frequency signal at any frequency needed for aligning or servicing receivers and/or amplifiers.

Test pattern.

test pattern—A geometric pattern containing a group of lines and circles, and used for testing the performance of a television receiver or transmitter by revealing the following video-signal characteristics: horizontal linearity, vertical linearity, contrast, aspect ratio, interlace, streaking, ringing, vertical resolution, and horizontal resolution.

test prod—A sharp metal point used for making a touch connection to a circuit terminal. It has an insulated handle and a means for electrically connecting the point to a test lead.

test record—A phonograph disc designed to test the quality and characteristics of turntables, pickups, amplifiers, etc.

test routine (in a computer)—1. A synonym for check routine. 2. Generally both the check and the diagnostic routines.

test set—One or more instruments required for servicing of a particular type of equipment.

tetrad—A group of four, especially a group of four pulses used to express a digit in the scale of 10 or 16.

Tetrode.

tetrode—A four-electrode electron tube containing an anode, a cathode, a control electrode (grid), and one additional electrode that is ordinarily a screen grid.

tetrode junction transistor—*See* Double-Base Junction Transistor.

tetrode transistor—A junction transistor with two electrode connections to the base to reduce interelement capacitance (in addition to the normal emitter and collector elements, each having one connection).

Te value—The temperature at which the resistance of a centimeter cube is of 1 megohm.

TE wave—Abbreviation for transverse electric wave.

T flip-flop—Also called binary. A type of flip-flop the outputs of which change state each time the input-signal voltage falls from 1 to 0 and remain unchanged when the input-signal voltage rises from 0 to 1. Thus, there is one change in output state for every two changes in input signal. Thus the frequency of the output is half the frequency of the input.

thallofide cell — A photoconducting cell which has thallium oxysulfide as the light-sensitive agent.

theoretical acceleration at stall—A figure of merit derived from the stall-torque to rotor-inertia ratio, which indicates how rapidly a motor will accelerate from stall.

theoretical cutoff — *See* Theoretical Cutoff Frequency.

theoretical cutoff frequency—Also called theoretical cutoff. The frequency at which, disregarding the effects of dissipation, the attenuation constant of an electric structure changes from zero to a positive value or vice versa.

theoretical electrical travel—The shaft travel over which the theoretical function characteristic of a precision potentiometer extends, as determined from the index point.

theremin—An electronic musical instrument consisting of two radio-frequency oscillators which beat against each other to produce an audio-frequency tone, in a manner similar to a beat-frequency audio oscillator. The pitch and volume are varied by hand capacitance.

thermal—A general term for all forms of thermoelectric thermometers, including a series of couples, thermopiles, and single thermocouples.

thermal agitation—1. Movement of the free electrons in a material. In a conductor they produce minute pulses of current. When these pulses occur at the input of a high-gain amplifier in the conductors of a resonant circuit, the fluctuations are amplified together with the signal currents and heard as noise. 2. Also called thermal effect. Minute voltages arising from random electron motion, which is a function of absolute temperature expressed in degrees Kelvin.

thermal-agitation voltage — The potential difference produced in circuits by thermal agitation of the electrons in the conductor.

thermal ammeter—*See* Hot-Wire Ammeter.

thermal breakdown — 1. A form of breakdown in which decomposition or melting occurs due to the temperature rise resulting from the applied electric stress. 2. A runaway condition in a dielectric, the loss factor of which increases with temperature. Dielectric loss heats the material, producing an increase in temperature. Therefore, the dielectric loss increases still more, producing a further increase in temperature, and so on.

thermal circuit breaker—A circuit breaker the operation of which depends on temperature expansion due to electrical heating.

thermal coefficient of resistance — The change in the resistivity of a substance due to the effects of temperature only. Usually expressed in ohms per ohm per degree change in temperature.

thermal compensation—A method employed to reduce or eliminate the thermal effects on one or more of the performance parameters of a transducer.

thermal conduction—The transfer of thermal energy by processes having no net movement of mass and having rates proportional to the temperature gradient.

thermal conductivity—A measure of the ability of a substance to conduct heat. Expressed in terms of calories of heat conducted per second per sq. cm. per cm. of thickness per degree C difference in temperature from one surface to the other.

thermal conductor—A material which readily transmits heat by conduction.

thermal contraction—The shrinkage exhibited by most metals when cooled.

thermal converter—Also called thermocouple converter, thermoelectric converter, thermoelectric generator, or thermoelement. One or more thermojunctions in thermal contact with an electric heater or integral, so that the electromotive force developed by thermoelectric action at its output terminals gives a measure of the input current in its heater.

thermal cutout—An overcurrent protective device which contains a heater element that affects a fusible member and thereby opens the circuit.

thermal detector—*See* Bolometer.

thermal drift—A change in the output of a regulated power supply over a period of time, due to changes in internal ambient temperatures not normally related to environmental changes. Thermal drift is usually associated with changes in line voltage and/or load changes.

thermal effect—*See* Thermal Agitation.

thermal emf—The electromotive force generated when the junction of two dissimilar metals is heated. *Also see* Seebeck EMF.

thermal endurance—1. An indication of the relative life expectancy of a product when exposed to operating temperatures much higher than normal room temperature. 2. *See* Heat Endurance.

thermal expansion—The increase in length caused by heating, generally expressed in

inches of increase per inch of original length per degrees of temperature.

thermal flasher—An electric device that automatically opens and closes a circuit at regular intervals, owing to alternate heating and cooling of a bimetallic strip heated by a resistance element in series with the circuit being controlled.

thermal generation—The creation of a hole and a free electron by freeing a bound electron through the addition of heat energy.

thermal instrument—An instrument that depends on the heating effect of an electric current for its operation (e.g., thermocouple and hot-wire instruments).

thermal ionization—Ionization due to high temperature (e.g., in the electrically conducting gases of a flame).

thermal junction—*See* Thermocouple.

thermal lag—The time expended in raising the entire mass of a cathode structure to the temperature of the heater.

thermal life—The operating life of a device under varying ambient temperatures.

thermal microphone—A microphone depending for its action on the variation in the resistance of an electrically heated conductor that is being alternately increased and decreased in temperature by sound waves.

thermal noise—1. Also called resistance noise. Random circuit noise associated with the thermodynamic interchange of energy necessary to maintain thermal equilibrium between the circuit and its surroundings. (*Also see* Johnson Noise.) 2. Noise generated by the random thermal motion of charged particles.

thermal protector—A current- and temperature-responsive device used to protect another device against overheating due to overload.

thermal radiation — Commonly known as heat. Radiation produced by the action of heat on molecules or atoms. Its frequency extends between the extremes of infrared and ultraviolet.

thermal rating—A statement of the permissible temperature rating beyond which unsatisfactory performance occurs.

thermal relay—A relay that responds to the heating effect of an energizing current, rather than to the electromagnetic effect.

thermal resistance—1. Ratio of the temperature rise to the rate at which heat is generated within a device under steady-state conditions. 2. The resistance of a substance to the conductivity of heat.

thermal resistor—An electronic device which makes use of the change in resistivity of a semiconductor with changes in temperature.

thermal response time—The time from the occurrence of a step change in power dissipation until the junction temperature reaches 90% of the final value of junction-temperature change, when the device-case or ambient temperature is held constant.

thermal runaway—A condition in which the

Thermal relay.

dissipation in a transistor or other device increases so rapidly with higher temperature that the temperature keeps on rising.

thermal sensitivity set — A permanent change in sensitivity due to temperature effects only. Usually expressed as the difference in sensitivity at room temperature before and after a temperature cycle over the operating temperature range of the transducer.

thermal shock—1. A sudden, marked change in the temperature of the medium in which a component or device operates. 2. The effect of heat or cold applied at such a rate that nonuniform thermal expansion or contraction occurs within a given material or combination of materials.

thermal telephone receiver — Also called thermophone. An electroacoustic transducer, such as a telephone receiver in which the temperature of a conductor is caused to vary in response to the current input, thereby producing sound waves as a result of the expansion and contraction of the adjacent air.

thermal time constant — 1. The time from the occurrence of a step change in power dissipation until the junction temperature reaches 63.2% of the final value of junction-temperature change, when the device-case or ambient temperature remains constant. 2. In a thermistor, the time required for 63.2% of the change from initial to final body temperature after the application of a step change in temperature under zero-power conditions.

thermal time-delay relay—A type of relay in which the time interval between energization and actuation is determined by the thermal storage capacity of the actuator critical operating temperature, power input, and thermal insulation.

thermal time-delay switch—An overcurrent-protective device containing a heater element and thermal delay.

thermal tuning—Adjusting the frequency of a cavity resonator by using thermal expansion to vary its shape.

thermal tuning time (cooling)—In microwave tubes, the time required to tune through a specified frequency range when the tuner power is instantaneously changed from the specified maximum to zero. The initial condition must be one of equilibrium.

thermal tuning time (heating) — In microwave tubes the time required to tune through a specified frequency range when the tuner power is instantaneously changed from zero to the specified maximum. The initial condition must be one of equilibrium.

thermion—An ion, either positive or negative, which has been emitted from a heated body. Negative thermions are electrons (thermoelectrons).

thermic—Pertaining to heat.

thermionic—Pertaining to the emission of electrons by heat.

thermionic cathode—*See* Hot Cathode.

thermionic converter—Also called thermionic generator or thermoelectron engine. A device which produces electrical power directly from heat. One type contains a heated cathode to emit electrons and a cold anode to collect them, thereby causing a flow of current. Both electrodes are enclosed in a vacuum or gas-filled envelope.

thermionic current—Current due to directed movements of thermions (e.g., the flow of electrons from the cathode to the plate in a thermionic vacuum tube).

thermionic detector—A detector circuit in which a thermionic vacuum tube delivers an audio-frequency signal when fed with a modulated radio-frequency signal.

thermionic diode — A diode electron tube which has a heated cathode.

thermionic emission—Liberation of electrons due to the temperature rise of the cathode alone, independent of any other element within the tube.

thermionic energy conversion—The direct production of electricity by means of the electron emission from a heated substance.

thermionic generator—*See* Thermionic Converter.

thermionic grid emission—Also called primary grid emission. The current produced by the electrons thermionically emitted from a grid. Generally it is due to excessive grid temperatures or to contamination of the grid wires by cathode-coating material.

thermionic rectifier—A rectifier utilizing a thermionic vacuum tube to convert alternating current into unidirectional current.

thermionic tube—*See* Hot-Cathode Tube.

thermionic work function—The energy required to transfer electrons from a given metal to a vacuum or some other adjacent medium during thermionic emission.

thermistor—A solid-state semiconducting device, the electrical resistance of which varies with the temperature. Its temperature coefficient of resistance is high, nonlinear, and negative.

thermoammeter—Also called a thermocouple

511

EXCESS HEAT RADIATED AWAY

ENVELOPE THERMAL CONDUCTION LOSSES

ANODE

$T_a \sim 600\,C$

ELECTRON FLOW

CERAMIC SEAL

EXTERNAL LOAD

CATHODE

$T_c \sim 1100\,C$

SPACER

THERMAL CONDUCTION LOSSES THROUGH SPACES

RADIATION LOSSES FROM CATHODE TO ANODE

HEAT ENERGY INPUT

ELECTRON COOLING AT THE CATHODE CAUSED BY ELECTRONS BOILING OFF

Thermionic converter.

TYPICAL E-I CURVE OF THERMISTOR

Thermistor characteristics.

ammeter. An ammeter that is actuated by the voltage generated in a thermocouple through which the current to be measured is sent. It is used chiefly for measuring radio-frequency currents.

thermocompensator—In pH meters, a temperature-sensitive device sometimes used to make electronic adjustments in the circuit that are required due to changes in the temperature of the solution.

thermocouple—Also called thermal junction. A device for measuring temperature where two electrical conductors of dissimilar metals are joined at the point of heat application and a resulting voltage difference, directly proportional to the temperature, is developed across the free ends and is measured

LEAD WIRE

Bead.

Disc.

Washer.

Rod.

Thermistors.

THERMO JUNCTION

HEATER FILAMENT

FILAMENT SUPPORT

THERMOCOUPLE WIRE

GLASS ENVELOPE

Thermocouple.

potentiometrically. Reference to standard tables is made to determine the temperature.

thermocouple ammeter — *See* Thermoammeter.

thermocouple contact—A contact of special material used in connectors employed in thermocouple applications. Materials often used are iron, constantan, copper, chromel, alumel, and others.

thermocouple converter—*See* Thermal Converter.

thermocouple instrument—An electrothermic instrument in which one or more thermojunctions are heated by an electric current, causing a direct current to flow through the coil of a suitable direct-current mechanism such as one of the permanent-magnet, moving-coil type.

thermocouple thermometer—*See* Thermoelectric Thermometer.

thermocouple vacuum gage — A vacuum gage which depends for its operation on the thermal conduction of the gas present. The pressure being measured is a function of the electromotive force of a thermocouple, the measuring junction of which is in thermal contact with a heater carrying a constant current. Thermocouple vacuum gages ordinarily are used over a pressure range of 10^{-1} to 10^{-3} mm Hg.

thermocouple wire—A wire drawn from special metals or alloys and calibrated to established specifications for use as a thermocouple pair (e.g., iron, constantan, alumel, etc.).

thermodynamics—The study of the relationship between heat and other forms of energy.

thermoelectric arm — Also called thermoelectric leg. The portion of a thermoelectric device having the electric current density and the temperature gradient approximately parallel or antiparrallel and having electrical connections made at its extremities to a part in which the opposite relation between the direction of the temperature gradient and the electric current density exists.

thermoelectric converter—A device capable of converting heat energy directly into electrical energy (bismuth telluride). *Also see* Thermal Converter.

thermoelectric cooler—A device utilizing the Peltier phenomenon to provide a silent, nonmoving cooler having a controllable cooling rate.

Thermoelectric couple.

thermoelectric couple—A thermoelectric device in which there are two arms of unlike composition.

thermoelectric device — A general term for thermoelectric heat pumps and generators.

thermoelectric effect — The electromotive force produced by the difference in temperature between two junctions of dissimilar metals in the same circuit.

thermoelectric generator — *See* Thermal Converter.

thermoelectric heating device—A thermoelectric heat pump used for adding thermal energy to a body.

thermoelectric heat pump — A device in which the direct interaction of an electrical current and heat flow is used to transfer thermal energy between bodies.

thermoelectricity—1. The direct conversion of heat into electricity. 2. The reciprocal use of electricity to create heat or cold. (*Also see* Seebeck Effect, Peltier Effect, *and* Thomson Effect.)

thermoelectric junction—A thermojunction, as in a thermocouple.

thermoelectric leg—*See* Thermoelectric Arm.

thermoelectric manometer — A manometer (pressure-measuring instrument) that depends on the variation of thermoelectromotive force (voltage due to heat) with pressure.

thermoelectric series—A series of metals arranged in the order of their thermoelectric powers.

thermoelectric thermometer—Also called a thermocouple thermometer. A thermometer employing one or more thermocouples, of which one set of measuring junctions is in thermal contact with the body whose temperature is to be measured, while the temperature of the reference junctions is either known or otherwise taken into account.

thermoelectromotive force—The voltage developed due to the differences in temperature between parts of a circuit containing two or more different metals.

thermoelectron—The electron emitted from a heated body.

thermoelectron engine — *See* Thermionic Converter.

thermoelement—A device consisting of a thermocouple and a heating element arranged for measuring small currents. *Also see* Thermal Converter.

thermogalvanometer — An instrument for measuring small high-frequency currents from their heating effect. Generally it consists of a d-c galvanometer connected to a thermocouple that is heated by a filament carrying the current to be measured.

thermojunction—One of the contact surfaces between the two conductors of a thermocouple. The thermojunction in thermal contact with the body under measurement is called the measuring junction, and the other thermojunction is called the reference junction.

thermojunction battery—A nuclear-type battery which converts heat into electrical energy directly by the thermoelectric or the Seebeck effect.

thermoluminescence—The production of light in a material by moderate heat.

thermomagnetic—1. Pertaining to the effect of temperature on the magnetic properties of a substance. 2. Pertaining to the effect of a magnetic field on the temperature distribution in a conductor.

thermometer—An instrument for measuring temperature. Electrical versions depend on the change in resistance of a material with temperature, the voltage produced in a thermocouple, or various other effects of temperature.

thermophone—An electroacoustic transducer

thermopile   **thin film**

Thermopiles.

in which sound waves of calculable magnitude are produced by the expansion and contraction of the air adjacent to a conductor, the temperature of which varies in response to a current input.

thermopile—A group of thermocouples connected in series-aiding. Specifically: 1. A device used to measure radiant power or energy. 2. A source of electric energy.

thermoplastic flow test — For an insulating material, a measure of the resistance to deformation when subjected to heat and pressure.

thermoplastic material—A plastic material that can be softened by heat and rehardened into a solid state by cooling. This remelting and remolding can be done many times.

thermoplastic recording—A recording process in which information is placed onto plastic tape electronically. A special electron gun, fed by a digital or scanner input, writes a charge in narrow bands on a moving film coated with a plastic that has a low melting point. The film is heated by an r-f heater that melts the plastic coating, permitting it to be deformed by electrostatic and surface-tension forces in proportion to the charge laid down by the beam of the electron gun. The ridges cool quickly and form a diffraction grating that can then be viewed, projected by suitable optics, or read out by a flying-spot scanner. The system operates in a high vacuum.

thermosetting material—Plastic which hardens when heat and pressure are applied. Unlike a thermoplastic, it cannot be remelted or remolded.

thermostat—A mechanism that can be set

ADJUSTING SLUG
CONTACT PRELOADING SPRING
SIDE SPRING
FRICTION SPRING
FRAME
RIGID STRIP
ADJUSTING SCREW
MICA INSULATION
BIMETAL
CONTACTS
FLEXIBLE SILVER CONNECTOR
FRAME SUPPORT LEAD
LEAD WIRE

Thermostat.

to operate at definite temperatures and can convert the expansion of heated metal or fluid into sufficient movement and power to operate small devices, control electric circuits or small valves, etc.

thermostatic switch—A temperature-operated switch that receives its operating energy by thermal conduction or convection from the device being controlled or operated.

theta polarization—The state of the wave whereby the E vector is tangential to the meridian lines of some given spherical frame of reference.

Thevenin's theorem—The current that will flow through an impedance Z_1 when connected to any two terminals of a linear network between which a voltage E and an impedance Z previously existed, is equal to the voltage E divided by the sum of Z and Z_1.

thick-film circuit—A microcircuit in which passive components of a ceramic-metal composition are formed on a suitable substrate by screening and firing. Discrete active elements are attached separately.

thick-film process—A method in which electronic circuit elements—resistors, conductors, capacitors, etc.—are produced by applying specially formulated pastes to a ceramic substrate in a defined pattern and sequence. The substrate containing the "green pattern" is fired at a relatively high temperature to mature the circuit elements and bond them integrally to the substrate. The term "thick film" distinguishes this technology from thin-film practice, in which circuit elements are made by evaporation or sputtering in a high-vacuum environment. Circuits produced by this technology are identified by several descriptive phrases: thick-film passive circuits or thick-film hybrid circuits when active devices are included.

thick films—Layers of resistive, dielectric, and conductive inks that are deposited on a substrate. The deposition process, similar to graphic silk screening, employs a fine-mesh screen to hold the pattern for the components that are to be deposited. The pattern is produced by photographic means, and wherever the inks are not to be deposited, the holes in the mesh are blocked by an emulsion.

thickness vibration—Vibration of a piezoelectric crystal in the direction of its thickness.

thin film—1. Having to do with the branch of

microelectronics in which thin layers of material are deposited on an insulating base in a vacuum. 2. A coating up to a thickness of about 10^4 angstrom.

thin-film capacitor—A capacitor utilizing a metal oxide as the dielectric or insulating material. Both the electrodes and the dielectric are deposited in layers on a substrate. This device is usually associated with microelectronics and integrated and thin-film circuits.

thin-film circuit—A circuit that is formed on a substrate by sputtering or vacuum deposition to make up the passive circuit elements such as resistors and interconnections. Active components are added and their connections made after the thin films have been laid down.

thin-film formation—A process that is either additive by pattern formation through masks, or subtractive by selective etching of predeposited films from a substrate.

thin-film integrated circuit—An integrated circuit consisting of a passive substrate on which the various passive elements (resistors and capacitors) are deposited in the form of thin-patterned films of conductive or nonconductive material. Active components (transistors and diodes) are attached separately as individually packaged devices or in unpacked (chip) form, or may be formed integrally by thin-film techniques. *Also see* Hybrid Thin-Film Circuit.

thin-film memory—In a computer, a storage device made of thin discs of magnetic material deposited on a nonmagnetic base. Its operation is similar to the core memory. (*Also see* Storage *and* Core Memory.)

thin-film microelectronics — Circuits made up of two-dimensional passive and essentially two-dimensional active elements mounted or deposited on thin wafers of an insulating substrate material.

thin-film semiconductor—A semiconductor produced by the deposition of an appropriate single-crystal layer on a suitable insulator.

thin-wall ring magnet — A type of ceramic permanent magnet in which the axial length is greater than the wall thickness or the wall thickness is less than 15% of the outside diameter.

third harmonic — A sine-wave component having three times the fundamental frequency of a complex wave.

Thomson bridge—*See* Kelvin Bridge.

Thomson effect—The net absorption or generation of heat that results, in addition to the joule heat, when an electric current is passed between two points of a homogeneous conductor having a temperature gradient.

Thomson electromotive force—The voltage that exists between two points that are at different temperatures in a conductor.

Thomson heat—The thermal energy absorbed or produced due to the Thomson effect.

thoriated filament—A tungsten vacuum-tube filament to which a small amount of thorium has been added to improve emission. The thorium comes to the surface and is primarily responsible for the electron emission.

thread—*See* Chip.

threaded core—A core with a threaded body.

threading slot—A slot, in the cover plate of a recording-head assembly, into which the tape is slipped in threading the reels of a recorder.

three-address code—Also called instruction code. In computers, a multiple-address code which includes three addresses, usually two addresses from which data are taken and one address where the result is entered. Location of the next instruction is not specified, and instructions are taken from storage in preassigned order.

three-address instruction—In computers, an instruction which includes an operation and specifies the location of three registers. *Also see* Three-Address Code.

three-channel stereo—A stereo recording or reproduction system which uses three spaced microphones for recording and three sound reproducers for playback.

three-db coupler—The junction of two waveguides having a common H wall. The two guides are coupled together by an H-type aperture coupling. Also called the Riblet coupler or short-slot coupler.

three-gun color picture tube—Also called a tri-gun color picture tube. A color-television picture tube with three individually controlled electron guns, one for each of the three primary colors (blue, green, and red).

three-level laser—A laser involving three electronic energy levels. The ground state (level 1) is pumped to level 3. This is followed by a transition to the upper laser level 2, which in turn is followed by stimulated emission back to the ground state.

three-phase circuit—A combination of circuits energized by alternating electromotive forces which differ in phase by one-third of a cycle, or 120 electrical degrees. In practice, the phases may vary several degrees from the specified angle.

three-phase current — A current delivered through three wires—each wire serving as the return for the other two, and the three current components differing in phase successively by one-third of a cycle, or 120 electrical degrees.

three-phase, four-wire system—An a-c supply system comprising four conductors—three connected as in a three-phase, three-wire system and the fourth to the neutral point of the supply, which may be grounded.

three-phase motor—An a-c motor operated from a three-phase circuit.

three-phase, seven-wire system—A system of a-c supply from groups of three single-phase transformers connected in a Y. Thus, a three-phase, four-wire, grounded-neutral system of a higher voltage for power is obtained, the neutral wire being common to both systems.

three-phase, three-wire system — An a-c supply system comprising three conductors, between successive pairs of which are maintained alternating differences of potential successively displaced in phase by one-third of a cycle.

three-plus-one instruction—In digital computer programming, a four-address instruction in which one of the addresses always specifies the location of the next instruction to be performed.

three-pole switch—An arrangement of three single-pole switches coupled together to operate three contacts simultaneously.

three-position relay—Sometimes called a center-stable polar relay.

three-pulse cascade canceler—A moving-target indicator technique in which two "two-pulse cancelers" are cascaded together. This improves the velocity response.

Three-quarter bridge.

three-quarter bridge—A bridge connection in which one of the diode rectifiers has been replaced by a resistor.

three-way speaker system—A sound-reproducing system using three separate speakers, each designed for a specific portion of the audio spectrum (high, low, and middle frequencies). The high- and low-frequency speakers are known as the tweeter and woofer, respectively.

three-way switch—A switch which can connect one conductor to any one of two other conductors.

three-wire system—A system of electric supply comprising three conductors, one of which (known as the neutral wire) is maintained at a potential midway between the potential of the other two (referred to as the outer conductor). Part of the load may be connected directly between the outer conductors, the remainder being divided as evenly as possible into two parts, each of which is connected between the neutral and one outer conductor. There are thus two distinct supply voltages, one being twice the voltage of the other.

threshold—1. The point at which an effect is first produced, observed, or otherwise indicated. 2. In a modulation system, the smallest value of carrier-to-noise ratio at the input of the demodulator for all values above which a small percentage change in the input carrier-to-noise ratio produces a

substantially equal or smaller percentage change in the output signal-to-noise ratio. 3. That point at which an indication exceeds the background or ambient.

threshold current—The minimum current at which a gas discharge becomes self-sustaining.

threshold decoding—A decoding procedure so arranged that the decision on the symbol that was transmitted is based on a majority count of the parity-check equations involving that symbol.

threshold field—The least magnetizing force in a direction which tends to decrease the remanence, which, when applied either as a steady field of long duration or as a pulsed field appearing many times, will cause a stated fractional change of remanence.

threshold frequency—The frequency at which the quantum energy is just sufficient to release photoelectrons from a given surface.

threshold of audibility—Also called threshold of detectability or threshold of hearing. For a specified signal, the minimum effective sound pressure of a signal capable of evoking an auditory sensation in a specified fraction of the trials. The characteristics of the signal, the manner in which it is presented to the listener, and the point at which the sound pressure is measured must all be specified. This threshold is usually expressed in decibels relative to 0.0002 μb.

threshold of detectability—*See* Threshold of Audibility.

threshold of discomfort—Also called threshold of feeling. For a specified signal, the minimum effective sound-pressure level which, in a specified fraction of the trials by a battery of listeners, will stimulate the ear to the point where the sensation of feeling becomes uncomfortable. This threshold is customarily expressed in decibels relative to 0.0002 μb.

threshold of feeling—*See* Threshold of Discomfort.

threshold of hearing — *See* Threshold of Audibility.

threshold of luminescence — *See* Luminescence Threshold.

threshold of sensitivity—The smallest stimulus or signal that will result in a detectable output. This phrase is frequently used to describe the voltage point at which an operations monitor or event marker will trigger.

threshold signal—In navigation, the smallest signal capable of producing a recognizable change in the positional information.

threshold value—1. The minimum input that produces a corrective action in an automatic control system. 2. The minimum level for which there is a measurable output.

throat—1. Part of the flare or tapered parallel-plate guide immediately adjacent to and connected to the main run of a waveguide. 2. The smaller cross-sectional area of a horn.

throat microphone — A microphone worn

around the throat and actuated by vibrations of the larynx as the user talks. It is used in jet airplanes, tanks, and other places where background noise would drown out the conversation.

through path—The transmission path from the loop input signal to the loop output signal in a feedback control loop.

through repeater—A microwave repeater that is not equipped to provide for connections to any local facilities other than the service channel.

through transfer function—The transfer function of the through path in a feedback control loop.

throw—1. In an electric motor or generator, the number of core slots spanned between the bottom leg of a coil and the top leg of the same coil. 2. The span between the bottom leg of a coil and the top leg of the same coil, expressed in the number of core slots spanned.

throwing power—Referring to the ability of an anode used in an impressed-current cathodic-protection system to distribute its current over a large surface. It is principally dependent upon the anode voltage, current, surface area, position of the anode with respect to the cathode, and the salinity and flow velocity of the water.

throw-out spiral—*See* Lead-Out Groove.

thru-hole connection—Also called feed-thru connection and plated thru hole. A conductive material used to make electrical and mechanical connection between the conductive patterns on opposite sides of a printed-circuit board.

thru repeater—In a microwave system, a repeater station that is not equipped to be connected to any local facilities other than the service channel.

thump—1. A low-frequency transient disturbance in a system or component. 2. The noise caused in a receiver by telegraph currents when the receiver is connected to a telephone circuit on which a direct-current telegraph channel is superimposed.

Thyratron.

thyratron—A hot-cathode gas tube in which one or more control electrodes initiate the anode current, but do not limit it except under certain operating conditions.

thyratron gate—In computers, an AND gate consisting of a multielement gas-filled tube

in which conduction is initiated by the coincident application of two or more signals. Conduction may continue after one or more of the initiating signals have been removed.

thyratron inverter—An inverter circuit in which thyratron tubes convert the d-c power to a-c power.

thyristor—A bistable device comprising three or more junctions. At least one of the junctions can switch between reverse- and forward-voltage polarity within a single quadrant of the anode-to-cathode voltage–current characteristics. Used in a generic sense to include silicon controlled rectifiers and gate-control switches, as well as multilayer two-terminal devices. (Many countries use the term "thyristor" in place of the term "PNPN-type switch.")

thyrite—A silicon-carbide ceramic material with nonlinear resistance characteristics. Above a critical voltage, the resistance falls considerably.

THz—Abbreviation for terahertz (10^{12} hertz).

tickler—A small coil connected in series with the anode circuit of an electron tube and inductively coupled to a grid-circuit coil. The tickler coil is used chiefly in regenerative detector circuits, to establish feedback or regeneration.

tie cable—1. A cable between two distributing frames or distributing points. 2. A cable between two private branch exchanges. 3. A cable between a private branch exchange switchboard and the main office. 4. A cable connecting two other cables.

tie line—1. *See* Interconnection. 2. A leased communications circuit or channel.

tie point—An insulated distributing point (other than an active terminal connection) where junctions of component leads are made in circuit wiring.

tier array—An array of antenna elements, one above the other.

tie trunk—A telephone line or channel directly connecting two private branch exchanges.

tie wires—Short pieces of wire used to tie open-line wires to insulators.

tight coupling—*See* Close Coupling.

tilt—In radar, the angle between the axis of radiation in the vertical plane, and a reference axis which is normally the horizontal. *Also see* Wave Tilt.

tilt angle—In radar, the angle between the vertical axis of radiation and a reference axis (normally the horizontal).

tilt controls—In a color television receiver employing the magnetic-convergence principle, the three controls used to tilt the vertical center rows in the three colored patterns produced by a dot-generator signal.

tilt error—1. In navigation, the ionospheric error component due to nonuniform height. 2. The difference between the true tilt and the mechanical tilt. The sign is such that when it is algebraically added to the mechanical tilt, the result is the true tilt. *Also see* Antenna Tilt Error.

tilting—1. Forward inclination of the wave front of radio waves traveling along the ground. The amount of tilt depends on the electrical constants of the ground. 2. Changing the angle of a television camera to follow a moving object being televised. 3. Changing the vertical angle of a directional antenna.

timbre—Also called tone color or musical quality. The character of a musical tone that distinguishes one musical instrument from another playing the same note. The difference between two steady tones having the same pitch and degree of volume is called the difference in timbre. Timbre depends mostly on the relative intensity of the different harmonics and the frequencies of the most prominent harmonics.

time—The measure of the duration of an event. The fundamental unit of time is the second.

time assignment speech interpolation—Telephone switching equipment whereby a person is connected to idle circuits when he starts talking, and is disconnected when he stops talking.

time base—A voltage generated by the sweep circuit of a cathode-ray–tube indicator. Its waveshape is such that the trace is either linear with respect to time or, if nonlinear, is still at a known timing.

time clock—A loosely used term sometimes referring to time switches, sometimes to interval timers, or to any type of timer.

time-code generator—A timer with an absolute time reference having digital outputs suitable for machine interpretation. Dial or numeric display may be included.

time constant—The time required for an exponential quantity to change by an amount equal to 0.632 times the total change that will occur. Specifically: 1. In a capacitor-resistor circuit, the number of seconds required for the capacitor to reach 63.2% of its full charge after a voltage is applied. 2. In an inductor-resistor circuit, the number of seconds required for the current to reach 63.2% of its final value. 3. The time constant, in seconds, of an inductor having an inductance L in henrys and resistance R in ohms is equal to L/R. 4. The time constant of a capacitor having a capacitance C in farads in series with a resistance R in ohms is equal to R × C. 5. The time required for the motor to accelerate from 0 to 63.2% of its final no-load speed when the rated voltage, with the proper phase relationship, is applied.

time constant of fall—The time required for a pulse to fall from 70.7% to 26.0% of its maximum amplitude, excluding spikes.

time constant of rise—The time required for a pulse to rise from 26.0% to 70.7% of its maximum amplitude, excluding spikes.

time-current characteristics of a fuse—

The relation between the root-mean-square alternating current or direct current and the time for the fuse to perform the whole or some specified part of its interrupting function. Usually shown as a curve.

timed acceleration—A control function that automatically controls the speed increase of a drive as a function of time.

timed deceleration—A control function that automatically controls the speed decrease of a drive as a function of time.

time delay—1. The time required for a signal to travel between two points in a circuit. 2. The time required for a wave to travel between two points in space. 3. The total elapsed time or lag required for a given command to be effected after the command is given.

time-delay circuit—A circuit that delays the transmission of an impulse signal, or the performance of a transducer, for a definite desired length of time.

time-delay closing relay — *See* Time-Delay Starting Relay.

time-delay generator—A device which accepts an input signal and provides a delay in time before the initiation of an output signal.

time-delay relay—Also called slow-action relay. A relay in which there is an appreciable interval of time between the energizing or de-energizing of the coil and the movement of the armature. (e.g., slow-operating relays and slow-release relays).

time-delay starting (or closing) relay—Also called time-delay closing relay. A device which functions to give a desired amount of time delay before or after any point or operation in a switching sequence or protective relay system.

time-delay stopping or opening relay—A time-delay device which serves in conjunction with the device that initiates the shutdown, stopping, or opening operation in an automatic sequence.

time-derived channel—Any of the channels obtained by time-division multiplexing of a channel.

time discriminator—A circuit in which the sense and magnitude of the output is a function of the time difference of, and relative time sequence between, two pulses.

time-distribution analyzer—Also called time sorter. An instrument that indicates the number or rate of occurrence of time intervals falling within one or more specified ranges. The time interval is defined by the separation between members of a pulse pair.

time-division data link—Radiocommunications which use time-division techniques for channel separation.

time-division multiplex—A system for transmitting information about two or more quantities (measurands) over a common channel, by dividing available time intervals among the measurands to form a composite train. Information may be transmitted by a variation of pulse duration, pulse amplitude, or pulse position, or by a pulse code.

time flutter—A variation in the synchronization of components of a radar system, leading to variations in the position of the observed pulse along the time base, and reducing the accuracy with which the time of arrival of a pulse may be determined.

time frame—In telemetry, the time period containing all elements between corresponding points of two successive reference markers.

time gain—*See* Sensitivity-Time Control.

time gate—A transducer which has an output during chosen time intervals only.

time harmonics — High-frequency components generated by nonlinearity in a resolver magnetic circuit. In a-c resolvers with no d-c components present, time harmonics are odd multiples of the fundamental frequency. Time harmonics appear as a component of null voltage.

time-interval selector—A circuit that functions to produce a specified output pulse when and only when the time interval between two input pulses is between set limits.

time lag—1. The interval between application of any force and full attainment of the resultant effect. 2. The interval between two phenomena.

time-mark generator — A circuit that produces accurately spaced pulses for display on the screen of an oscilloscope.

time pattern—A picture-tube presentation of horizontal and vertical lines or rows of dots generated by two stable frequency sources operating at multiples of the line and field frequencies.

time phase—Reaching corresponding peak values at the same instants of time, though not necessarily at the same points in space.

time pulse distributor—A device or circuit for allocating timing pulses or clock pulses to one or more conducting paths or control lines in a specified sequence.

time quadrature—Differing by a time interval corresponding to one-fourth the time of one cycle of the frequency in question.

timer—1. A part of an electronic circuit which starts pulse transmission and synchronizes it with the beginning of an indicator sweep or the timing of gates, range markers, etc. 2. A special clock mechanism or motor-operated device used to perform switching operations at predetermined time intervals. 3. An assembly of electric circuits and associated equipment which provides the following: trigger pulses, sweep circuits, intensifier pulses, gate voltages, blanking voltages, and power supplies. 4. The part of the radar set that initiates pulse transmission and synchronizes this with the beginning of indicator sweeps, timing of gates, range markers, etc. *Also see* Synchronizer.

time response — An output, expressed as a function of time, that results from a speci-

fied input applied under specified operating conditions.

timer motor—A synchronous clock motor having a definite output speed determined by the number of poles in the stator and the reduction of the associated gear train.

time-sequencing—In a computer, switching signals generated by a program purely as a function of accurately measured elapsed time.

time sharing—1. A computer-use technique whereby several operators may use a computer at the same time. *Also see* Interlace Operation *and* Interrupt. 2. The use of a device for two or more purposes during the same overall time interval, accomplished by interspersing component actions in time.

time signals—Time-controlled radio signals broadcast by government-operated radio station WWV at regular intervals each day on several frequencies.

time sorter — *See* Time Distribution Analyzer.

time switch—A clock-controlled switch used to open or close a circuit at one or more predetermined times. Usually refers to repeat cycle timers with a dial graduated with time of day (in 24-hour type) or with time and day in 7-day type. Has means of adjusting the time when circuits are turned on or off, usually with pins or clips. Used for turning lights on at night, ringing bells in offices, schools, etc.

time-to-digital conversion—The process of converting an interval of time into a digital number.

timing axis oscillator—*See* Sweep Generator.

timing-pulse distributor—Also called waveform generator. A computer circuit driven by pulses from the master clock. It operates in conjunction with the operation decoder to generate timed pulses needed by other machine circuits to perform the various operations.

timing relay—A form of auxiliary relay used to introduce a definite time delay in the performance of a function.

timing signal—Any signal recorded simultaneously with data to provide a time index.

tinkertoy—An attempt at modularization where wafers, with one or more component parts printed or mounted on them, are stacked vertically, with interconnecting wiring stiff enough to provide support running through holes around the periphery of the wafer.

tinned—Covered with metallic tin to permit easy soldering.

tinned wire—A copper wire that has been coated with a layer of tin or solder to prevent corrosion and to simplify soldering.

tinsel conductor—A type of electrical conductor comprising a number of tiny threads, each thread having a fine, flat ribbon of copper or cadmium bronze closely spiraled about it. Used for small cables requiring limpness and extra-long flex life (e.g., used with headsets or handsets).

tip—1. The contacting part at the end of a plug or probe. 2. Also called tip side. The end of the plug used to make circuit connections in a manual switchboard. The tip is the connector attached to the positive side of the common battery which powers the station equipment. By extension, it is the positive battery side of a communications line.

tip·jack—Also called a pup jack. A small single-hole jack for a single-pin contact plug.

tipoff—The last portion of a vacuum-tube bulb to be melted and sealed after evacuation of the bulb.

tip side—Also called a tip wire. The conductor of a circuit associated with the tip of a plug or the tip spring of a jack. *Also see* Tip.

tip wire—*See* Tip Side.

T-junction—*See* Tee Junction.

TM$_{m, n}$ wave—In a rectangular waveguide, the transverse magnetic wave for which m and n are the number of half-period variations of the magnetic field along the longer and shorter transverse dimensions, respectively.

TM wave—Abbreviation for transverse magnetic wave.

T-network.

T-network—A network composed of three branches. One end of each branch is connected to a common junction point. The three remaining ends are connected to an input terminal, an output terminal, and a common input and output terminal, respectively.

to-from indicator—An instrument that forms part of the omnirange facilities and is used for resolving the 180° ambiguity.

Toggle switch.

toggle switch—A two-position snap switch operated by a projecting lever to open or close circuits.

tolerance—A permissible deviation from a specified value. A frequency tolerance is expressed in hertz or as a percentage of the nominal frequency; an orientation tolerance,

in minutes of arc; a temperature tolerance, in degrees Celsius, and a dimensional tolerance, in decimals or fractions.

toll center—Also called toll office and toll point. The basic toll switching entity; a central office where channels and toll-message circuits terminate. While this is usually one particular central office in a city, larger cities may have several central offices where toll-message circuits terminate.

toll-terminal loss—On a toll connection, that part of the over-all transmission loss attributable to the facilities from the toll center, through the tributary office to and including the subscriber's equipment.

tone—1. A sound wave capable of exciting an auditory sensation having pitch. 2. A sound sensation having pitch.

tone arm—*See* Pickup Arm.

tone burst—A single sine-wave frequency, 50 to 500 microseconds long having a rectangular envelope, used for testing the transient response of speakers.

tone channel—An intelligence or signalling circuit in which on-off or frequency-shift modulation of a frequency (usually an audio frequency) is used as a means of transmission.

Tone control.

tone control—A control, usually part of a resistance-capacitance network, used to alter the frequency response of an amplifier so that the listener can obtain the most pleasing sound. In effect, a tone control accentuates or attenuates the bass or treble portion of the audio-frequency spectrum.

tone generator—A device for providing an audio-frequency current suitable for testing audio-frequency equipment or for signaling.

tone keyer—An instrument device which converts direct-current impulses to audio tones, for line transmission or for keying a transmitter.

tone localizer—*See* Equisignal Localizer.

tone-modulated waves—Waves obtained from continuous waves by amplitude-modulating them at an audio frequency in a substantially periodic manner.

tone modulation—A type of code-signal transmission obtained by causing the radio-frequency carrier amplitude to vary at a fixed audio frequency.

tone reversal—Distortion of the recorder copy in facsimile. It causes the various shades of black and white not to be in the proper order.

Tonotron—A multimode, selective-erasure storage tube.

top cap—A terminal in the form of a metal cap at the top of some vacuum tubes and connected to one of the electrodes.

top-loaded vertical antenna—A vertical antenna that is larger at the top, resulting in a modified current distribution, which gives a more desirable radiation pattern vertically. A series reactor may be connected between the enlarged portion of the antenna and the remaining structure.

topology—The surface layout of the elements comprising an IC.

tornadotron — A millimeter wave device which generates radio-frequency power from an enclosed, orbiting electron cloud excited by a radio-frequency field when subjected to a strong, pulsed magnetic field.

torn-tape relay—A method of receiving messages in tape form, breaking the tape, and retransmitting the message in tape form.

toroid—1. A surface, or its closed solid, generated by any closed plane rotating about a straight line in its own plane—the resulting configuration being doughnut shaped. 2. A highly efficient type of coil wound upon a ring or "doughnut" type of core. The toroid provides for a highly concentrated magnetic field within itself, and has a minimum magnetic flux leakage (external field).

toroidal coil—A coil wound in the form of a toroidal helix.

toroidal core—A ring-shaped core.

toroidal permeability—Under stated conditions, the relative permeability of a toroidal body of the given material. The permeability is determined from measurements of a coil wound on the toroid such that stray fields are minimized or can be neglected.

torque—1. A force that tends to produce rotation or twisting. 2. Force applied rotationally as around the axis of a nut, bolt, or screw so that these elements can assume their share of stress. This tightening operation is measured in inch-pounds, foot-pounds, or inch-ounces.

torque amplifier—A device with input and output shafts and supplying work to rotate the output shaft so that its position corresponds to that of the input shaft but does not impose any significant torque on the latter.

torque-coil magnetometer—A magnetometer which depends for its operation on the torque developed by a known current in a coil capable of turning in the field to be measured.

torque gradient—The torque required in inch-ounces to pull a specific energized synchro 1° away from its normal position.

torque of an instrument—Also called deflecting torque. The turning moment produced on the moving element by the quantity to be measured or by some quantity dependent thereon acting through the mechanism.

torquer—A device which produces torque

about an axis of freedom in response to a signal input.

torque-to-inertia ratio—*See* Acceleration At Stall.

torsiometer—An instrument for measuring the amount of power which a rotating shaft is transmitting.

torsion galvanometer—A galvanometer in which the force between the fixed and moving systems is measured by the angle through which the supporting head of the moving system must be rotated to return the moving system to zero.

torsion-string galvanometer — A sensitive galvanometer in which the moving system is suspended by two parallel fibers that tend to twist around each other.

total capacitance—The capacitance between a given conductor and all other conductors in a system when all other conductors are connected together. The total capacitance of a conductor equals the ratio of the sum of its direct capacitances to the other conductors.

total combined regulation—The change in output of a regulated power supply arising from simultaneous changes in all of the specified operating conditions, when the direction of such changes is such as to make their effects additive. It may be stated as a percentage of the specified output and/or an absolute value.

total distortion—The sum total of all forms of signal distortions.

total emission—The magnitude of the current produced when electrons are emitted from a cathode under the influence of a voltage such that all the electrons emitted are drawn away from the cathode.

total emissivity—The ratio of radiation emitted by a surface to the radiation emitted by the surface of a black body under identical conditions. Important conditions which affect emissivity of a material are surface finish, color, temperature, and wavelength of radiation. Emissivity may be expressed for radiation of a single wavelength (monochromatic emissivity), for total radiation of a specified range of wavelengths (total spectral emissivity), or for total radiation of all wavelengths (total emissivity).

total excursion—The application of a stimulus, in a controlled manner, over the span of an instrument.

total harmonic distortion—The ratio of the power at the fundamental frequency measured at the output of the transmission system considered, to the power of all harmonics observed at the output of the system because of its nonlinearity when a single frequency signal of specified power is applied to the input of the system. It is expressed in decibels.

total internal reflection—When light passes from one medium to another which is optically less dense (e.g., from glass to air), the ray is bent away from the normal. If the incident ray meets the surface at such an angle that the refracted ray must be bent away at an angle of more than 90°, the light cannot emerge at all, and is totally internally reflected.

totalizing—To register a precise total count from mechanical, photoelectric, electromagnetic, or electronic inputs or detectors.

total losses of a ferromagnetic part—Under stated conditions, the power absorbed and then dissipated as heat when a body of ferromagnetic material is placed in a time-varying magnetic field.

total losses of a transformer—The losses represented by the sum of the no-load and load losses.

total luminous flux—The total light emitted in all directions by a light source.

totally enclosed motor—A motor so enclosed as to prevent the free exchange of air between the inside and the outside of the case, but not sufficiently enclosed to be termed airtight.

totally unbalanced currents—See Push-Push Currents.

total range of an instrument—Also called the range of an instrument. The region between the limits within which the quantity measured is to be indicated or recorded.

total regulation—The · arithmetic sum of changes in output of a regulated power supply arising from changes in each of the specified operating conditions (current, voltage, or power) when such changes are applied individually, and in a manner to make their effects additive. It may be stated as a percentage of the specified output and/or absolute value.

total resistance—The d-c resistance of a (precision) potentiometer between the input terminals with the shaft positioned so as to give a maximum resistance value.

total spectral emissivity—See Total Emissivity.

total telegraph distortion—Telegraph transmission impairment expressed in terms of time displacement of mark-space and space-mark transitions from their proper positions and given in per cent of the shortest perfect pulses called the unit pulse.

total transition time—In a circuit, the time interval between the point of 10% input change and the point of 90% output change. It is equal to the sum of the delay time and rise (or fall) time.

touch control—A control circuit that actuates a circuit when two metal areas or a preselected area are bridged by one's finger or hand.

touch-tone dialing—Push-button telephone dialing in which the direct-current pulsing technique of the rotating dial is replaced by a combination of tones to provide the proper automatic switching.

tourmaline—A strongly piezoelectric natural or synthetic crystal.

tower—A structure usually used when an antenna must be mounted higher than 50 feet.

Tower radiator.

tower radiator—A metal tower structure used as a transmitting antenna.

Townsend criterion—The relationship expressing the minimum requirement for breakdown in terms of the ionization coefficients.

Townsend discharge—An electrical discharge in a gas at moderate pressure (above about 0.1 millimeter of mercury). It corresponds to corona, and is free from space charges.

Townsend Ionization Coefficient—The average number of ionizing collisions made by an electron as it drifts a unit distance in the direction of an applied electric force.

T-pad—A pad made up of resistance elements arranged in a T-network (two resistors inserted in one line, with a third between their junction and the other line).

trace—1. The pattern on the screen of a cathode-ray tube. 2. The visible line or lines produced on the screen of a cathode-ray tube by the deflection of the electron stream.

trace interval—The interval corresponding to the direction of sweep used for delineation.

tracer—1. A radioisotope which is mixed with a stable material to trace the material as it undergoes chemical and physical changes. 2. A thread of contrasting color woven into the insulation of a wire for identification purposes. 3. See Signal Tracer.

trace width—The distance between two points on opposite sides of a trace on an oscilloscope at which luminance is 50% of maximum. If the trace departs from a well-behaved (approximately Gaussian) form, it should be smoothed for the purpose of measurement.

tracing distortion—The nonlinear distortion introduced in the reproduction of mechanical recording when the curve traced by the reproducing stylus is not an exact replica of the modulated groove. For example, in the case of sine-wave modulation in vertical recording, the curve traced will be a poid.

track—1. A path which contains reproducible information left on a medium by recording means energized from a single channel. 2. In electronic computers, that portion of a moving-type storage medium accessible to a given reading station (e.g., film, drum, tapes, discs). (*Also see* Band *and* Channel.) 3. An area of tape surface that coincides with the location of the recorded magnetization produced by one record gap.

track-command guidance — A missile-guidance method in which both target and missile are tracked by separate radars and commands are sent to the missile to correct its course.

track hold memory—A circuit that, in its "track" mode, develops an output that follows (ideally) the input exactly, or is proportional to it; and then, in its "hold" mode, maintains the output constant (ideally) at the value it had at the instant the circuit was commanded to change from "track" to "hold."

track homing—The process of following a line of position known to pass through an object.

tracking—1. The process of keeping a radio beam, or the cross hairs of an optical system, set on a target—usually while determining the range of the target. 2. The maintenance of proper frequency relationships in circuits designed to be simultaneously varied by ganged operation. 3. The accuracy with which the stylus of a phonograph pickup follows a prescribed path over the surface of the record. 4. The ability of a multigun tube to superimpose simultaneously information from each gun. Tracking error is the maximum allowable distance between the displays of any two guns. 5. The ability of an instrument to indicate at the division line being checked when energized by corresponding proportional values of actual end-scale excitation. 6. The interconnecting of power supplies in such a manner that one unit serves to control all units in series operation. In this manner, the output voltage of the slave units follows the variations of the master. 7. The difference at any shaft position between the output ratios of any two commonly actuated similar electrical elements expressed as a percentage of the single total voltage applied to them. 8. Motion given to the major lobe of an antenna so that a preassigned moving target in space is always contained within the major lobe. 9. The process of following the movement of a satellite or rocket by telescope, radar, radio, or photographic observations.

tracking accuracy—The ability to indicate at a division line being checked when a meter is energized by corresponding proportional values of actual end-scale excitation, expressed as a percentage of actual end-scale value. Tracking accuracy is usually within one and one-half times the rated full-scale accuracy of the meter.

tracking antenna—A directional antenna system which automatically changes in position or characteristics to follow the motion of a moving signal source.

tracking error — In lateral mechanical recording, the angle between the vibration axis of the mechanical system of the pickup and a plane which contains the tangent to the unmodulated record groove and is perpendicular to the recording surface at the point of needle contact.

tracking force—*See* Stylus Force.

tracking jitter—*See* Jitter.

tracking resistance—*See* Arc Resistance.

tracking spacing—The distance between the center line of adjacent tracks on a recording tape. In the typical case of longitudinal tracks 50 mils wide, the tracking spacing is 70 mils.

tracking spot—A moving spot used for target indication on a radar.

track-while-scan—A radar system utilizing electronic-computer techniques whereby raw data are used to track an assigned target, compute target velocity, and predict its future position without interfering with the scanning rate.

track width—The width of the track on a recording tape, corresponding to a given record gap. The most common track widths encountered in longitudinal recording are 48 and 50 mils, several such tracks being accommodated on a half-inch-wide tape.

tractive force—The force which a permanent magnet exerts on a ferromagnetic object.

traffic—Messages handled by communication or amateur stations.

trailers—Bright streaks at the right of large dark areas, or dark areas or streaks at the right of bright areas, in the televised picture. The usual cause is insufficient gain at low video frequencies.

trailing blacks—*See* Following Blacks.

trailing edge—The major portion of the decay of a pulse.

trailing-edge pulse time—The time at which the instantaneous amplitude last reaches a stated fraction of the peak pulse amplitude.

trailing reversal—*See* Following Whites *and* Following Blacks.

trailing whites—*See* Following Whites.

trainer—1. The representation of an operating system by computers and its associated equipment and personnel. 2. Electronic equipment, used for training operators of radar or sonar apparatus by simulating signals received under operating conditions in the field.

tramlines—A pattern on an *A* scope appearing as a number of horizontal lines above the baseline. The effect is produced by cw modulated with a low-frequency signal.

trans—Abbreviation for transmitter. Also abbreviated xmtr or xmitter.

transaction file — In a computer, a file containing information relating to current activities or transactions.

transadmittance—From one electrode to another, the alternating components of the current of the second electrode divided by the alternating component of the voltage of the first electrode, all other electrode voltages being maintained constant. As most precisely used, the term refers to infinitesimal amplitudes.

transadmittance compression ratio—Ratio of the magnitude of the small-signal forward transadmittance of the tube to the magnitude of the forward transadmittance at a given input-signal level.

transceiver — 1. The combination of radio transmitting and receiving equipment in a common housing, usually for portable or mobile use and employing some common circuit components for both transmitting and receiving. 2. A device which transmits and receives data from punched card to punched card. It is essentially a conversion device which, at the sending end, reads the card and transmits the data over the wire. At the receiving end, it punches the data into a card.

transceiver data link—Integrated data processing by means of punched cards, using transceivers as terminal equipment. The transmission path can be wire or radio.

transconductance — Symbolized g_m. Also called mutual conductance. An electron-tube rating equal to the change in anode current divided by the change in grid voltage causing the anode-current change. The unit of transconductance is the mho; a more commonly used unit is the micromho (10^{-6}mho).

transconductance amplifier—An amplifier that supplies an output current proportional to its input voltage. From its output terminals the amplifier appears to be a current source with a high output impedance R_o. Its input impedance $R_{1n} >> R_g$ and the output impedance $R_o >> R_L$, where R_g and R_L are the source and load impedances.

transconductance meter—Also called a mutual-conductance meter. An instrument for indicating the transconductance of a grid-controlled electron tube.

transconductance tube tester—Also called a mutual-conductance or dynamic-mutual-conductance tube tester. A tube tester with circuits set up in such a manner that the test is made by applying an a-c signal of known voltage to the control grid and the tube amplification factor or mutual conductance is measured under dynamic operating conditions.

transconductor—An active or passive network, the short-circuit output current of which is a specific, accurately known, often nonlinear function of the input voltage.

transcribe—1. To copy, with or without translating, from one external storage medium of a computer to another. 2. To copy from a computer into a storage medium or vice versa.

transcriber—Equipment associated with a computing machine for the purpose of transferring input or output data from a record of information in a given language to the medium and language used by a digital computing machine, or from a computing machine to a record of information.

transcription—An electrical recording (e.g., a high-fidelity, 33⅓-rpm record) containing part or all of a (radio) program. It may be either an instantaneous recording disc or a pressing.

transdiode—A transistor so connected that the base and collector are actively maintained at equal potentials, although not connected together. The logarithmic transfer relationship between collector current and base-emitter voltage very closely approximates that of an ideal diode.

transducer—A device by means of which energy can be made to flow from one or more transmission systems to one or more other transmission systems. The energy may be in any form, such as electrical, mechanical, acoustical, etc. The term "transducer" is often restricted to a device in which the magnitude of an applied stimulus is converted into an electrical signal proportionate to the quantity of the stimulus. Usually, the variations of the phenomenon being measured are referenced to time.

transducer-coupling system efficiency—The power output at the point of application, divided by the electrical power input into the transducer.

transducer efficiency—Ratio of the power output to the electrical power input at the rated power.

transducer equivalent noise pressure (of an electroacoustic transducer or system used for sound reception) — Also called equivalent noise pressure. For a sinusoidal plane-progressive wave, the rms sound pressure which, if propagated parallel to the principal axis of the transducer, would produce an open-circuit signal voltage equal to the rms of the inherent open-circuit noise voltage of the transducer in a transmission band having a bandwidth of 1 hertz and centered on the frequency of the plane sound wave.

transducer gain—Ratio of the power that the transducer delivers to the load under specified operating conditions, to the available power of the source.

transducer insertion loss — *See* Insertion Loss.

transducer loss — Ratio of the available power of the source, to the power that the transducer delivers to the load under specified operating conditions.

transducer pulse delay — The interval of time between a specified point on the input pulse and on its related output pulse.

transfer—1. To transmit, or copy, information from one device to another. 2. To jump. 3. The act of transferring. 4. In electrostatography, the act of moving a developed image, or a portion thereof, from one surface to another without altering its geometrical configuration (e.g., by electrostatic forces or by contact with an adhesive-coated surface).

transfer admittance—The complex ratio of the current at the second pair of terminals of an electrical transducer, to the electromotive force applied between the first pair, all pairs of terminals being terminated in any specified manner.

transfer characteristic—1. The relationship, usually shown by a graph, between the voltage of one electrode and the current to another electrode, all other electrode voltages being maintained constant. 2. The characteristics pertaining to the degree of output activity for an input stimulus, or vice versa.

transfer check—In a computer, verification of transmitted data by temporarily storing, retransmitting, and comparing. Also a check to see if the transfer or jump instruction was properly performed.

transfer circuit—A circuit which connects communication centers of two or more separate networks in order to transfer the traffic between the networks.

transfer constant—Also called the image-transfer constant. One-half the natural logarithm of the complex ratio of the voltage times current entering a transducer, to that leaving the transducer when it is terminated in its image impedances.

transfer contact—*See* Break-Make Contact.

transfer control—*See* Jump.

transfer current—The starter-gap current required to cause conduction across the main gap of a glow-discharge, cold-cathode tube.

transfer function—1. The relationship between two system variables that enables the second variable to be determined from the first. 2. A mathematical expression frequently used by control engineers which expresses the relationship between the outgoing and the incoming signals of a process or control element. The transfer function is useful in studies of control problems. 3. A mathematical expression which describes the relationship between physical conditions at two different points in time or space in a given time, and perhaps, also describes the role played by the intervening time or space.

transfer impedance—Ratio of the potential difference between any two pairs of terminals of a network applied at one pair of terminals, to the resultant current at the other pair of terminals (all terminals being terminated in any specified manner).

transfer instruction—An instruction, signal, or operation which conditionally or unconditionally specifies the location of the next instruction and directs a computer to that instruction.

transfer operation—An operation which moves data from one storage location or one storage medium to another. Transfer is sometimes taken to refer specifically to movement between different media; storage to movement within the same medium.

transfer ratio—From one point to another in a transducer at a specified frequency, the complex ratio of the generalized force or velocity at the second point to that applied at the first point.

transferred charge—The net electric charge moved from one terminal of a capacitor to another through an external circuit.

transferred charge characteristic — The mathematical function that relates transferred charge to capacitor voltage.

transfer switch—A form of air switch arranged so that a conductor connection can be transferred from one circuit to another without interrupting the current.

transfer time—1. The time required for a transfer to be made in a digital computer. 2. In a relay, the total time—after contact bounce has ceased—between the breaking of one set of contacts and the making of another.

Transfluxor — A trade name (RCA) for a binary magnetic core having two or more openings. Control of the transfer of magnetic flux between the three or more legs of the magnetic circuits provides ways to store information, gate electrical signals, etc.

transform—1. To convert a current or voltage from one magnitude to another, or from one type to another. 2. In digital-computer programming, to change information in structure or composition without significantly altering the meaning or value at the same time.

transformation point—The temperature at which an alloy or metal changes from one crystal state to another as it heats or cools.

transformation ratio — The ratio between electrical output and input under certain specified conditions.

transformer—An electrical device which, by electromagnetic induction, transforms electric energy from one or more circuits to one or more other circuits at the same frequency, but usually at a different voltage and current value.

transformer build—The amount of window area used in constructing a transformer.

transformer-coupled amplifier—An amplifier, the stages of which are coupled together by transformers.

transformer coupling—Use of a transformer,

between stages of an amplifier, i.e., to connect the anode circuit of one stage to the grid circuit of the following stage.

transformerless receiver—A receiver in which the power-line voltage is applied directly to series-connected tube heaters or filaments and to a rectifier circuit instead of first being stepped up or down in voltage by a power transformer.

transformer load loss—Losses in a transformer which are incident to the carrying of the load. Load losses include I^2R loss in the windings due to load current, stray loss due to stray fluxes in the winding core, clamps, etc., and to circulating current, if any, in parallel windings.

transformer loss—Expressed in decibels, the ratio of the signal power that an ideal transformer of the same impedance ratio would deliver to the load impedance, to the signal power delivered by the actual transformer.

transformer oil—A high-quality insulating oil in which windings of large power transformers are sometimes immersed to provide high dielectric strength, insulation resistance, and flash point, plus freedom from moisture and oxidation.

transformer vault—An isolated enclosure, either above or below ground, with fire-resistant walls, ceiling, and floor for unattended transformers and their auxiliaries.

transformer voltage ratio—The ratio of the root-mean-square primary terminal voltage to the root-mean-square secondary terminal voltage under specified conditions of load.

transforming section—A length of waveguide or transmission line of modified cross section, or with a metallic or dielectric insert, used for impedance transformation.

transhybrid loss—The transmission loss at a given frequency measured across a hybrid circuit when connected to a given two-wire termination and balancing network.

transient—1. The instantaneous surge of voltage or current produced by a change from one steady-state condition to another. 2. A phenomenon caused in a system by a sudden change in conditions, and which persists for a relatively short time after the change. 3. A distinct line or series of lines perpendicular to the direction of scanning produced in the recorded copy immediately following a sudden change in density. 4. A damped oscillatory quantity occurring in the output of a system as a result of a sudden change in input. 5. In a power supply, a variable observed during transition from one steady-state operating condition to another (or between two successive states in which the response is constant or identically repetitive). 6. A momentary surge on a signal or power line. It may produce false signals or triggering impulses and cause insulation or component breakdowns and failures.

transient analyzer—An electronic device for repeatedly producing a succession of equal electric surges of small amplitude and of

adjustable waveform in a test circuit and presenting this waveform on the screen of an oscilloscope.

transient behavior—In a power supply, the general attitude of response in terms of amplitude and time.

transient distortion—Distortion due to the inability of a system to reproduce or amplify transients linearly.

transient magnistor—A high-speed saturable reactor in which an alternating electric current in the form of a sine-wave carrier or pulses is passed through a signal winding and modulated by variations of current passing through a control coil.

transient motion—Any motion which has not reached, or has ceased to be, a steady state.

transient oscillation—A momentary oscillation which occurs in a circuit during switching.

transient overshoot—The largest transient deviation of the measured quantity following the dynamic crossing of the final value as a result of the application of a specified stimulus.

transient peak-inverse voltage—Under specified conditions, the maximum allowable instantaneous value of nonrecurrent reverse (negative) voltage that may be applied to the anode of an scr with gate open.

transient phenomena—Rapidly changing actions occurring in a circuit during the interval between closing of a switch and settling to steady-state conditions, or between any other temporary actions occurring after some change in a circuit or its constants.

transient recovery time—Also called recovery time, transient response time, or response time. 1. The intervals between the time a transient deviated from a specified amplitude range and the time it returns and remains within the specified amplitude range. The amplitude range centered about the average of the steady-state values that exist immediately before and after the transient. 2. The time required for the output voltage of a power supply to come back to within a level approximating the normal d-c output following a sudden change in load current.

transient response—1. The transient of a dependent variable resulting from an abrupt change of an independent variable with all other variables constant. 2. Also called step-function response. Commonly, the characteristic response of a system to a unit sweep or unit impulse. The elements of transient response most commonly specified are: rise time, fall time, overshoot, undershoot, preshoot, and ringing. 3. (input line changes) The transient of an output variable (voltage, current, or power) of a electronic power supply resulting from an abrupt specified change of input line voltage, with all other conditions held constant. 4. (load changes)

The transient of an output variable (voltage current, or power) of an electronic power supply resulting from an abrupt specified change of load, with all other conditions held constant.

transient response time—*See* Transient Recovery Time.

transient state—A temporarily abnormal condition of a variable.

transinformation (of an output symbol about an input symbol)—Also called mutual information. The difference between the information content of the input symbol and the conditional information content of the input symbol which is given the output symbol.

transistance — The characteristic of an electrical element which makes possible the control of voltages, currents, or flux so as to produce gain or switching action in a circuit. Examples of the physical realization of transistance occur in transistors, diodes, saturable reactors, etc.

transistor—An active semiconductor device, usually made of silicon or germanium, having three or more electrodes. The three main electrodes used are the emitter, base, and collector. Conduction is by means of electrons (elementary particles having the smallest negative electrical charge that can exist) and holes (mobile electron vacancies equivalent to a positive charge).

transistor action—The physical mechanism of amplification in a junction transistor.

transistor amplifier—An amplifier in which the required amplification is produced by one or more transistors.

transistor base — The region between an emitter and a collector of a transistor, into which minority carriers are injected.

transistor chip—An unencapsulated transistor element of very small size used in microcircuits.

transistor digital computer—A computer designed to operate satisfactorily in aircraft flying at supersonic speeds. Vacuum-tube failure and heat are eliminated by use of approximately 800 transistors. The power required for operation is less than 100 watts.

transistor dissipation — The power dissipated in the form of heat by the collector. The difference between the power supplied to the collector and the power delivered by the transistor to the load.

transistorized—Pertaining to equipment or a design in which transistors instead of vacuum tubes are used.

transistor oscillator—An oscillator which uses a transistor in place of an electron tube.

transistor pentode—A transistor designed for mixing, modulating, or switching, and containing the equivalent of three emitters, a base, and a collector.

transistor radio—A radio receiver which uses transistors in place of electron tubes.

transistor resistor logic—Abbreviated TRL

An early form of logic-circuit design that was employed prior to the advent of monolithic circuits. The input elements are resistors; however, unlike RTL there is only one active output transistor. In discrete circuit designs, this logic form was the least expensive since it required a minimum number (one) of active devices.

transistor seconds — Also called fallouts. Those transistors that remain after the firsts (units meeting rigid specifications for a specific application) have been removed from the production line.

transistor transistor logic — Abbreviated TTL or T²L. Also called multiemitter transistor logic. A logic circuit design similar to DTL, with the diode inputs replaced by a multiple emitter transistor. In a four-input DTL gate, there are four diodes at the input. A four-input TTL gate will have four emitters of a single transistor as the input element. TTL gates using NPN transistors are positive-level NAND gates or negative-level NOR gates.

transit angle—The product of angular frequency and the time taken for an electron to cross a given path.

transition—A change in the state of a teletypewriter line—the act of a line going from a marking state to a spacing state, or vice versa.

transition card — A card which signals the computer that the reading-in of a program has ended and that the carrying out of the program has started.

transition error—In an encoder, the difference between the shaft angle at which a code-position change should occur and the angle at which it actually does occur.

transition factor—*See* Reflection Factor.

transition frequency — 1. Also called crossover frequency. In a disc-recording system, the frequency corresponding to the point of intersection of the asymptotes, to the constant-amplitude and the constant-velocity portions of its frequency-response curve. This curve is plotted with output-voltage ratio in decibels as the ordinate, and the logarithm of the frequency as the abscissa. 2. In a transistor, the product of the magnitude of the small-signal, common-emitter, forward-current transfer ratio times the frequency of measurement when this frequency is high enough that the magnitude is decreasing with a slope of approximately 6 db per octave.

transition layer—*See* Transition Region.

transition-layer capacitance—*See* Depletion-Layer Capacitance.

transition loss—At any point in a transmission system, the ratio of the available power from that part of the system ahead of the point under consideration, to the power delivered to that part of the system beyond the point under consideration.

transition point—A point at which the circuit constants change in such a way that a wave being propagated along the circuit is reflected.

transition region — Also called transition layer. The region, between two homogeneous semiconductor regions, in which the impurity concentration changes.

transition temperature — The temperature below which the electrical resistance of a material becomes too small to be measured.

transitron — A thermionic tube circuit the action of which depends on the negative transconductance of the suppressor grid of a pentode with respect to the screen grid.

Transitron oscillator.

transitron oscillator — A negative-transconductance oscillator employing a pentode tube with a capacitor connected between the screen and suppressor grids. The suppressor grid periodically divides the current between the screen grid and anode, thereby producing oscillations.

transit time — 1. The time taken for a charge carrier to cross a given path. 2. The average time a minority carrier takes to diffuse from emitter to collector in a junction transistor. 3. The time an electron takes to cross the distance between the cathode and anode.

transit-time mode — A condition of oscillator operation, corresponding to a limited range of drift-space transit angle, for which the electron stream introduces a negative conductance into the coupled circuit.

translate — To change computer information from one language to another without significantly affecting the meaning.

translational morphology — The structural characterization of an electronic component in which it is possible to identify the areas of patterns of resistive, conductive, dielectric, and active materials in or on the surface of the structure with specific corresponding devices assembled to perform an equivalent function.

translation loss — Also called playback loss. The loss in the reproduction of a mechanical recording, whereby the amplitude of motion of the reproducing stylus differs from the recorded amplitude in the medium.

translator — 1. A device which transforms signals from the form in which they were generated, into a useful form for the purpose at hand. (*Also see* Program Assembly.) 2. A television receiver and low-power trans-

mitter which receives television signals on one channel and retransmits them on another channel (usually any uhf channel from 70 to 83) to valleys and like areas which cannot receive the direct signals. 3. In telephone equipment, the device that converts dialed digits into call-routing information.

transmissibility — Ratio of the response amplitude of the system in steady-state forced vibration, to the excitation amplitude. The ratio may be between forces, displacements, velocities, or accelerations.

transmission — Conveying electrical energy from point to point along a path.

transmission anomaly — The difference, in decibels, between the total loss in intensity and the reduction in intensity that would be due to an inverse-square divergence.

transmission band — The frequency range above the cutoff frequency of a waveguide.

transmission band filter — A frequency band of free transmission; i.e., a frequency band in which, if dissipation is disregarded, the attenuation constant is zero.

transmission coefficient — For a transition or discontinuity between two transmission media at a given frequency, the ratio of some quantity associated with the transmitted wave at a specified point in the second medium, to the same quantity associated with the incident wave at a specified point in the first medium.

transmission facility — The transmission medium and all the associated equipment required to transmit a message.

transmission gain — *See* Gain.

transmission level — The level of signal power at any point in a transmission system. It is equal to the ratio of the power at that point to the power at some point in the system chosen as a reference point. This ratio is usually expressed in decibels.

Transmission lines.

transmission line — A material structure forming a continuous path from one place to another, and used for directing the transmission of electromagnetic energy along this path.

transmission-line coupler — A coupler that allows the passage of electric energy in either direction between balanced and unbalanced transmission lines.

transmission-line-tuned, absorption-type frequency meter — A frequency meter using a tuned length of wire or a coaxial cavity as the frequency-determining element.

transmission-line-tuned, transmission-type frequency meter — A frequency meter using a tuned length of wire or a coaxial cavity as the frequency-determining element.

transmission loss — In communication, a general term denoting a decrease in power in transmission from one point to another. Usually expressed in decibels.

transmission measuring set—A measuring instrument comprising a signal source and a signal receiver having known impedances, for measuring the insertion loss or gain of a network or transmission path connected between those impedances.

transmission mode—A form of propagation characterized by the presence of any one of the elemental types of TE, TM, or TEM waves along a transmission line.

transmission primaries—The set of three primaries, either physical or nonphysical, each chosen to correspond in amount to one of the three independent signals contained in the color-picture signal. The I, Q, and Y signals.

transmission regulator — A device which maintains the transmission substantially constant over a system.

transmission response—The conversion of electrical energy traveling at the speed of light to sonic energy traveling at the speed of sound.

transmission speed—The number of information elements sent per unit time, usually expressed as bits, characters, word groups, or records per second or per minute.

transmission system—An assembly of elements capable of functioning together to transmit signal waves.

transmission time—The absolute time interval between transmission and reception of a signal.

transmission-type frequency meter—A frequency meter in which a tuned electrical circuit or a cavity is used to transmit the energy from the signal source under test to a detecting load.

transmit—To send a program, message, or other information from one location to another.

Transmit-receive switch.

transmit-receive switch—Also called a TR switch, TR box, TR tube, or duplex assembly. An automatic device employed in a radar to prevent the transmitted energy

from reaching the receiver, but allowing the received energy to do so without appreciable loss.

transmit-receive tube—*See* TR Tube.

transmittance—1. Of a material, the ratio of the radiant power transmitted through the material, to the incident radiant power. 2. As a transfer function, a response function for which the variables are measured at different ports (terminal pairs).

transmitted-carrier operation—Amplitude-modulated carrier transmission in which the carrier wave is transmitted.

transmitted wave—*See* Refracted Wave.

transmitter—1. Equipment used to generate and amplify an r-f carrier signal, modulate this carrier with intelligence, and radiate the modulated r-f carrier into space. 2. In telephony, the microphone that converts sound waves into electrical signals at an audio-frequency rate.

transmitter distributor — In teletypewriter operations, a motor-driven device which translates teletypewriter code combinations from perforated tape into electrical impulses, and transmits these impulses to one or more receiving stations.

transmitter frequency tolerance—The extent to which the carrier frequency of a transmitter may legally depart from the assigned frequency.

transmitter start code—Usually a two-letter call that is sent to an outlying machine to automatically turn on its tape transmitter.

transmitting antenna—A device for converting electrical energy into electromagnetic radiation capable of being propagated through space.

transmitting current response—Of an electroacoustic transducer used for sound emission, the ratio of the sound pressure apparent at a distance of 1 meter in a specified direction from the effective acoustic center of the transducer, to the current flowing at the electric input terminals. Usually expressed in decibels above a reference-current response of 1 microbar per ampere.

transmitting efficiency (projector efficiency)—Ratio of the total acoustic power output of an electroacoustic transducer, to the electric power input.

transmitting loop loss—That part of the repetition equivalent assignable to the station set, subscriber line, and battery supply circuit which are on the transmitting end.

transmitting power response (projector power response) — Of an electroacoustic transducer used for sound emission, the ratio of the effective sound pressure apparent at a distance of 1 meter in a specified direction from the effective acoustic center of the transducer, to the electric power input. Usually expressed in decibels above a reference response of 1 microbar square per watt of electric power input.

transmitting station—A location at which the transmitter of a radio system and its antenna and associated equipment are grouped.

transmitting voltage response—Of an electroacoustic transducer used for sound emission, the ratio of the sound pressure apparent at a distance of 1 meter in a specified direction from the effective acoustic center of the transducer, to the signal voltage applied at the electric input terminals. Usually expressed in decibels above a reference-voltage response of 1 microbar per volt.

transonic speed—A speed of 600 to 900 miles per hour, corresponding to about Mach 0.8 to Mach 1.2.

transponder — A radio transmitter-receiver which transmits identifiable signals automatically when the proper interrogation is received. (*Also see* Pulse Repeater.)

transponder dead time—The time interval between the start of a pulse and the earliest instant at which a new pulse can be received or produced by a transponder.

transponder efficiency—A ratio expressed as a percentage of the number of replies to the number of interrogations from a transponder.

transponder suppressed time delay — The over-all fixed delay between reception of an interrogation and the transmission of a reply.

transportable transmitter—Sometimes called a portable transmitter. A transmitter designed to be readily carried from place to place, but normally not operated while in motion.

transport time—In an automatic system, the time required to move an object, element, or information between two predetermined positions.

transposition—An interchange of the positions of the conductors of a circuit. The term is most frequently applied to open-wire circuits.

transposition blocks — Spreaders used to space and reverse the relative positions of two conductors at fixed intervals.

transposition section—A length of open-wire line to which a fundamental transposition design or pattern is applied as a unit.

transrectification — The rectification that occurs in one circuit when an alternating voltage is applied to another circuit.

transrectification characteristic — The graph obtained by plotting the direct voltage values for one electrode of a vacuum tube as abscissas against the average current values in the circuit of that electrode as ordinates, for various values of alternating voltage applied to another electrode as a parameter. The alternating voltage is held constant for each curve, and the voltages on other electrodes are maintained constant.

transrectification factor — The change in average current of an electrode, divided by the change in the amplitude of the alternating sinusoidal voltage applied to another electrode (the direct voltages of this and other electrodes being maintained constant).

transrectifier—A device, ordinarily a vacuum tube, in which rectification occurs in one electrode circuit when an alternating voltage is applied to another electrode.

transresistance amplifier—An amplifier that supplies an output voltage proportional to an input current. The transfer function of the amplifier is $e_o/l_m = R_m$, where R_m is the transresistance.

transverse-beam traveling-wave tube — A traveling-wave tube in which the electron beam intersects the signal wave rather than moving in the same direction.

transverse cross-talk coupling—Between a disturbing and a disturbed circuit in any given section, the vector summation of the direct couplings between adjacent short lengths of the two circuits, without dependence on intermediate flow in nearby circuits.

transverse electric wave — Abbreviated TE wave. In a homogeneous isotropic medium, an electromagnetic wave in which the electric field vector is everywhere perpendicular to the direction of propagation.

transverse electromagnetic wave — Abbreviated TEM wave. In a homogeneous isotropic medium, an electromagnetic wave in which the electric and magnetic field vectors both are everywhere perpendicular to the direction of propagation.

transverse-field traveling-wave tube — A traveling-wave tube in which the traveling electric fields which interact with the electrons are essentially transverse to the average motion of the electrons.

transverse interference — Interference occurring across terminals or between signal leads.

transverse magnetic E-mode — A type of mode in which the longitudinal component of the magnetic field is zero and the longitudinal component of the electric field is not zero.

transverse magnetic wave—Abbreviated TM wave. In a homogeneous isotropic medium, an electromagnetic wave in which the magnetic field vector is everywhere perpendicular to the direction of propagation.

transverse magnetization—Magnetization of a recording medium in a direction perpendicular to the line of travel and parallel to the greatest cross-sectional dimension.

transverse recording—The technique of recording with rotating heads which are oriented perpendicular to the edge and surface of the tape.

transverse wave — A wave in which the direction of displacement is perpendicular to the direction of propagation at each point of the medium.

trap—1. A selective circuit that attenuates undesired signals but does not affect the desired ones. (*Also see* Wave Trap.) 2. A crystal imperfection which can trap carriers.

trapezoidal distortion—Distortion in which a televised picture has the shape of a trapezoid (wide at top or bottom) instead of a rectangle. It is due to the interaction between the vertical- and horizontal-deflection coils (or plates) of the cathode-ray tube.

trapezoidal generator—An electronic circuit that produces a trapezoidal voltage wave.

Trapezoidal pattern.

trapezoidal pattern—An oscilloscope pattern which indicates the percentage of modulation in an amplitude-modulated system.

trapezoidal wave—1. A trapezoidal-shaped waveform. 2. A square wave onto which a sawtooth has been superimposed. It is the voltage wave necessary to give a linear deflection current through the coils of a magnetic cathode-ray tube.

trapped flux — In a material in the superconducting state, magnetic flux linked with a closed superconducting loop.

trapping—The holding of electrons or holes by any of several mechanisms in a crystal, thereby preventing them from moving.

traveling detector—A probe mounted on a slider and free to move along a longitudinal slot cut into a waveguide or coaxial transmission line. The traveling detector is connected to auxiliary measuring apparatus and used for examining the relative magnitude of any standing-wave system.

traveling plane wave—A plane wave in which each frequency component has an exponential variation of amplitude and a linear variation of phase in the direction of propagation.

traveling wave—The resulting wave when the electric variation in a circuit takes the form of translation of energy along a conductor, such energy being always equally divided between current and potential forms.

traveling-wave magnetron — A traveling-wave tube in which the electrons move in crossed static electric and magnetic fields that are substantially normal to the direction of wave propagation.

traveling-wave magnetron oscillations — Oscillations sustained by the interaction between the space-charge cloud of a magnetron and a traveling electromagnetic field with approximately the same phase velocity as the mean velocity of the cloud.

traveling-wave parametric amplifier — A parametric amplifier which has a continuous iterated structure incorporating nonlinear reactors and in which the signal, pump, and difference-frequency waves are propagated along the structure.

traveling-wave phototube — A traveling-wave tube that has a photocathode and a window that admits a modulated laser beam, which causes the emission of a current-modulated photoelectron beam. This beam is then accelerated by an electron gun and directed into the helical slow-wave structure of the tube.

traveling-wave tube — Abbreviated twt. A tube in which a stream of electrons interacts continuously or repeatedly with a guided electromagnetic wave moving substantially in synchronism with it, and in such a way that there is a net transfer of energy from the stream to the wave.

traveling-wave tube amplifier — A power-amplifying piece of equipment yielding about 30 db of gain over broad bandwidths. The units are built around certain twt's in the most commonly used frequency bands, and they have external modulation circuitry incorporated.

traveling-wave-tube interaction circuit — An extended electrode arrangement used in a traveling-wave tube to propagate an electromagnetic wave in such a manner that the traveling electromagnetic fields are retarded to the point where they extend into the space occupied by the electron stream.

TR box—*See* Transmit-Receive Switch.

TR cavity—The resonant portion of a **TR** switch.

treating—Any of the processes of applying

SCHEMATIC DIAGRAM SHOWING BASIC COMPONENTS OF A TRAVELING-WAVE-TUBE AMPLIFIER

Traveling-wave tube.

varnishes or other insulating compounds to insulation, coils, or windings. This includes the processes of impregnation, soaking, and surface coating by any of the various methods.

treble—The higher part in harmonic music or voice; of high or acute pitch. In music, the frequencies from middle *C* (256 hertz) and upward.

treble boost—Deliberate adjustment of the amplitude-frequency response of a system or component to accentuate the higher audio frequencies.

tree—A set of connected branches without meshes.

treeing — A progressive type of insulation failure in which branching hollow channels slowly penetrate the insulation at rather low applied voltages.

tremolo—1. The amplitude modulation of an audio tone. 2. A warbling or fluctuating effect approximately seven times per second, to the tone of an instrument characterized by a variation in intensity rather than pitch. (*Also see* Vibrato).

trf—Abbreviation for tuned radio frequency.

tri—Abbreviation for triode.

Triac—A General Electric trade name for a gate-controlled full-wave a-c silicon switch designed to switch from a blocking state to a conducting state for either polarity of applied voltage with positive or negative gate triggering.

Triac.

triad—1. Three radio stations operated as a group for determining the position of aircraft or ships. 2. A group of three dots, one of each color-emitting phosphor, on the screen of a color picture tube. 3. A group of three bits or three pulses, usually in sequence on one wire or simultaneously on three wires.

triangulation—A method of finding the location of a third point by taking bearings from two fixed points a known distance apart. The third point will be at the intersection of the two bearing lines.

triax—A type of shielded conductor that em-

ploys a shield and jacket over the primary insulation, plus a second shield and jacket over all. Aside from applications requiring maximum attenuation of radiated signals or minimum pickup of external interference, this cable can also be used to carry two separate signals.

triaxial cable—A special form of coaxial cable containing three conductors.

triaxial speaker—A dynamic speaker unit consisting of three independently driven units combined into a single speaker.

tribo—A prefix meaning due to or pertaining to friction.

triboelectric—Pertaining to electricity generated by friction.

triboelectricity — Electrostatic charges generated due to friction between different materials.

triboelectric series—A list of substances arranged so that any of them can become positively electrified when rubbed with one farther down the list, or negatively charged when rubbed with one farther up the list.

tributary circuit—A circuit which connects an individual drop, or drops, to a switching center.

tributary station—A communications terminal consisting of equipment compatible for the introduction of messages into, or reception from, its associated relay station.

trickle charge—1. A continuous charge of a storage battery at a slow rate approximately equal to the internal losses and suitable to maintain the battery in a fully charged condition. 2. Very slow rates of charge suitable not only in compensating for internal losses, but in restoring small, intermittent discharges to the load circuit delivered from time to time.

trickle charger—A device for charging a storage battery at a low rate continuously, or for several hours at one time.

tricolor camera—A television camera designed to separate reflected light into three frequency groups, each corresponding to the light energies of the three primary colors. The camera transforms the intensity variations of each primary into amplitude variations of an electrical signal.

Tricolor camera.

tricolor picture tube—A picture tube which reproduces a scene in terms of the three light primaries.

MID FREQUENCY
UNIT

LOW-FREQUENCY
UNIT

LOW-
FREQUENCY
DIAPHRAGM

HIGH-
FREQUENCY
UNIT

HIGH-
FREQUENCY
HORN

MID FREQUENCY
HORN

Triaxial speaker.

tricon—A radionavigational system in which the airborne receiver accepts pulses from a triplet (chain of three stations) in a variable time sequence so that the pulses arrive at the same time even though traveling over paths of various lengths.

trigatron—An electronic switch in which breakdown of an auxiliary gap initiates conduction.

trigger—1. To start action in another circuit, which then functions for a certain length of time under its own control. 2. A pulse that starts an action.

trigger action—The instantaneous initiation of main current flow by a weak controlling impulse in a device.

trigger circuit—1. A circuit with two conditions of stability, with means for passing spontaneously or through application of an external stimulus from one to the other when certain conditions are satisfied. 2. A circuit in which an electron tube performs the function of a relay. Impulses applied to the input of the tube produce corresponding impulses in the output circuit, starting a chain of events. 3. *See* Flip-Flop Circuit.

trigger countdown—A process that reduces the repetition rate of a triggering signal.

trigger diode — A symmetrical three-layer avalanche diode used to control scr's and Triacs. It has a symmetrical switching mode, and therefore fires whenever the breakover voltage is exceeded in either polarity of applied voltage.

triggered blocking oscillator—A blocking oscillator that can be reset to its starting condition by the application of a trigger voltage.

triggered spark gap—A fixed spark gap in which the discharge passes between two electrodes and is struck (started) by an auxiliary electrode called the trigger, to which low-power pulses are applied.

triggered sweep — In a cathode-ray oscilloscope, a sweep initiated by a signal pulse.

trigger electrode—*See* Starter.

triggering—The starting of circuit action, which then continues for a predetermined time under its own control.

triggering signal—The signal from which a trigger is derived.

trigger level—1. In a transponder, the minimum receiver input capable of causing the transmitter to emit a reply. 2. The instantaneous level of a triggering signal at which a trigger is to be generated. Also the name of the control which selects the level.

trigger point—The amplitude point on the input pulse at which triggering of the sweep of a cathode-ray oscilloscope occurs.

trigger pulse—A pulse used for triggering.

trigger-pulse steering—In transistors, the routing or directing of trigger signals (usually pulses) through diodes or transistors (called steering diodes or transistors) so that the signals affect only one of several associated circuits.

trigistor—A bistable PNPN semiconductor component with characteristics comparable to those of a flip-flop or bistable multivibrator.

tri-gun color picture tube—*See* Three-Gun Color Picture Tube.

trim control—On some regulated power supplies, a control used to make minor adjustments of output voltage.

Trigistor Flip-Flop

Conventional Transistor Flip-Flop

THIS EQUALS THIS

Trigistor.

trimmer—*See* Trimmer Capacitor.

trimmer capacitor—Also called a trimmer. A small variable capacitor associated with another capacitor and used for fine adjustment of the total capacitance of the combination.

trimmer potentiometer—A lead-screw–actuated potentiometer.

trimmer resistor—A small rheostat used in place of a fixed resistor to permit adjustment of resistance values in a circuit during initial calibration of an equipment or when recalibration is required.

trimming—The fine adjustment of capacitance, resistance, or inductance in a circuit.

trinistor—A three-terminal silicon semiconductor device with characteristics similar to those of a thyratron and used for controlling large amounts of power.

trinoscope—Any assembly of three kinescopes producing the red, green, and blue images required for tricolor television optical projection (e.g., for theater tv).

triode—A three-electrode electron tube containing an anode, a cathode, and a control electrode (grid).

Trinoscope.

triode amplifier—An amplifier in which only triode tubes are used.

triode-heptode converter—A superheterodyne converter circuit which uses a triode local oscillator and a heptode converter, both contained in one envelope.

triode-hexode converter—A superheterodyne converter circuit which uses a triode local oscillator and a hexode converter, both contained in one envelope.

triode-pentode—A dual-purpose vacuum tube containing a triode and a pentode in the same envelope.

triode PNPN-type switch—A PNPN-type switch having an anode, cathode, and gate terminal.

CATHODE

CONTROL GRID

PLATE

Triode.

trip coil—An electromagnet in which a moving armature trips a circuit breaker or other protective device and thereby opens a circuit under abnormal conditions.

triple detection—*See* Double Superheterodyne Reception.

triplet—1. Three radionavigational stations operated as a group for the determination of position. 2. The waveform of the output voltage of a delay line when the input pulse has a width approximately equal to the resolution of the delay line.

ARCO 461

Trimmer capacitors.

triplex cable—A cable made up of three insulated single-conductor cables twisted together with or without a common insulating covering.

triplexer—A dual duplexer which permits the use of two receivers simultaneously and independently in a radar system by disconnecting the receivers during the transmitted pulse.

tripod—A three-legged camera support.

tripping device—A mechanical or electromagnetic device used for opening (turning off) a circuit breaker or starter, either when certain abnormal electrical conditions occur or when a catch is actuated manually.

tripping relay—Also called trip-free relay. A device which functions to trip a circuit breaker, contactor, or equipment or to permit immediate tripping by other devices; or to prevent immediate reclosure of a circuit interrupter, in case it should open automatically even though its closing circuit is maintained closed.

trisistor — A fast-switching semiconductor consisting of an alloyed junction PNP device in which the collector is capable of electron injection into the base. Its characteristics resemble those of a thyratron electron tube, and the switching time is in the nanosecond range.

tristimulus values—The amounts of each of the three primary colors that must be combined to match a sample.

tri-tet oscillator—A crystal-controlled, electron-coupled vacuum-tube oscillator which is isolated from the output circuit through use of the screen-grid electrode as the oscillator anode. Used for multiband operation because it generates strong harmonics of the crystal frequency.

tritium — A radioactive isotope of hydrogen with an atomic number of 3.

TRL — Abbreviation for transistor resistor logic.

trombone—An adjustable U-shaped coaxial-line matching assembly.

tropicalization—A chemical treatment developed to combat the fungi that ruin electronic equipment in hot, humid jungle regions.

tropo—*See* Tropospheric Scatter Communication.

troposphere—The lower layer of the earth's atmosphere, extending to about 60,000 feet at the equator and 30,000 feet at the poles. In this area, the temperature generally decreases with altitude, clouds form, and convection is active.

tropospheric scatter — The propagation of radio waves by scattering as a result of irregularities or discontinuities in the physical properties of the troposphere.

tropospheric scatter communication—Also called tropo. A method or system of transmitting, within the troposphere, microwaves in the uhf or shf bands to effect radiocommunication between two points on the earth's surface separated by moderate distances of from 70 to 600 miles. Such a span or hop may be augmented by other spans in tandem to permit end-to-end or through circuits up to many thousands of miles. More specifically, this method of communication is now generally understood to embrace a radio system that permits communication over the distances indicated, with excellent reliability and good information capacity, using relatively high transmitted power, frequency modulation, and highly sensitive receiving apparatus.

tropospheric superrefraction — The phenomenon occurring in the troposphere whereby radio waves are bent sufficiently to be returned to the earth.

tropospheric wave—A radio wave that is propagated by reflection from a place of abrupt change in the dielectric constant or its gradient in the troposphere. In some cases, the ground wave may be so altered that new components appear to arise from reflections in regions of rapidly changing dielectric constants; when these components are distinguishable from the other components, they are called tropospheric waves.

trouble—Failure of a circuit or element to perform in a standard manner.

trouble-location problem—A computer test problem, the incorrect solution of which supplies information on the location of faulty equipment. It is used after a check problem has shown that a fault exists.

troubleshoot—To look for, locate, and repair malfunctions in equipment.

TR switch—*See* Transmit-Receive Switch.

TR tube—A gas-filled radio-frequency switching tube used to protect the receiver in pulsed radio-frequency systems. (*Also see* Transmit-Receive Switch.)

true bearing—A bearing given in relation to geographic north, as opposed to a magnetic bearing.

true course—A course in which the direction of the reference line is true rather than magnetic north.

true homing—The following of a course in such a way that the true bearing of an aircraft or other vehicle is held constant.

true north—Geographic north.

true ohm—The actual value of the practical unit of resistance. It is equal to 10^9 absolute electromagnetic units of resistance.

true power—The average power consumed by a circuit during one complete cycle of alternating current.

true radio bearing—*See* Radio Bearing.

true random noise—A noise characterized by a normal or Gaussian distribution of amplitudes.

truncate—To drop digits of a number of terms in a series, thereby lessening precision. For example, the value 3.14159265 (π) when truncated to five figures is 3.1415, whereas it could be rounded off to 3.1416.

truncated paraboloid—A paraboloid reflector in which a portion of the top and bottom have been cut away to broaden the main radiated lobe in the vertical plane.

truncation error—The error resulting from the use of only a finite number of terms of an infinite series, or from the approximation of operations in the infinitesimal calculus by operations in the calculus of finite differences.

trunk—1. A single message circuit between two points, both of which are switching centers and/or individual message distribution points. 2. A communications channel between two different offices, or between groups of equipment within the same office. 3. A telephone line or channel between two central offices or switching devices, which is used in providing telephone connections between subscribers.

trunk circuit—A circuit which connects two switching centers.

trunk loss—That part of the repetition equivalent assignable to the trunk used in the telephone connection.

truth table—A logic function listing all possible combinations of input values and indicating, for each combination, the true output values.

T$_s$—Abbreviation for color temperature.

Tschebyscheff filters—Filter networks that are designed to exhibit a predetermined ripple in the passband (ripple amplitudes from 0.01 db to 3 db are common) in exchange for which they provide a more rapid attenuation above cutoff—which, unlike their passband response, is monotonic.

TSC—Abbreviation for transmitter start code.

T²L or TTL—Abbreviation for transistor transistor logic.

tuba—A powerful land-based radar jamming transmitter operated between 480 to 500 MHz. It was developed during World War II for use against night fighter planes.

tube—A hermetically sealed glass or metal envelope in which conduction of electrons takes place through a vacuum or gas.

tube bridge—An instrument used in the precise measurement of vacuum-tube characteristics. It contains one or more bridge-type measuring circuits, plus power supplies and signal sources for all possible electrode combinations.

tube coefficients—Constants that describe the characteristics of a thermionic vacuum tube (e.g., amplification factor, mutual conductance, a-c plate resistance, etc.).

tube complement—The number and types of electron tubes required in an electronic equipment.

tube count—A terminated discharge produced by an ionizing event in a radiation-counter tube.

tube drop—The voltage measured across a tube, from plate to cathode, when the tube is conducting at its normal current rating.

tube electrometer—A thermionic vacuum tube adapted for use as an electrometer, to measure potential difference.

tube heating time—The time required for the coolest portion of a mercury-vapor tube to attain its operating temperature.

tube noise—Noise originating in a vacuum tube (e.g., from shot effect, thermal agitation, etc.).

Tube shield.

tube shield—A metallic enclosure placed over a vacuum tube to prevent external fields from interfering with the function of the tube.

tube socket—A receptacle which provides mechanical support and electrical connection for a vacuum tube.

tube tester—A test instrument for indicating the condition of vacuum tubes used in electronic equipment.

tube voltage drop—1. The anode voltage in an electron tube during conduction. 2. In a gas tube, the anode voltage during the conducting period.

tubing—Extruded nonsupported plastic materials designed as protection and electrical insulation for exposed components of electrical and electronic assemblies, as opposed to coated, braided, woven tube termed sleeving.

tubular capacitor—A paper, ceramic, or electrolytic capacitor shaped like a cylinder; leads or lugs project from one or both ends.

tunable echo box—An echo box consisting of an adjustable cavity operating in a single mode. When the echo box is calibrated, the setting of the plunger at resonance will indicate the wavelength.

tunable magnetron—A magnetron that can be tuned mechanically or electronically over a limited band of frequencies.

tuned—Adjusted to resonate or operate at a specified frequency.

tuned amplifier—An amplifier in which the load is a tuned circuit. Thus, the load impedance and amplifier gain vary with the frequency.

tuned-anode oscillator — *See* Tuned-Plate Oscillator.

tuned antenna—An antenna designed, by means of its own inductance and capacitance, to provide resonance at the desired operating frequency.

tuned-base oscillator—A transistor oscillator comparable to a tuned-grid electron-tube oscillator. The frequency-determining device (resonant circuit) is located in the base circuit.

tuned circuit—A circuit consisting of inductance and capacitance which can be adjusted for resonance at the desired frequency.

tuned-collector oscillator—A transistor oscillator comparable to the tuned-plate electron-tube oscillator. The frequency-determining device is located in the collector circuit.

tuned dipole—A dipole antenna that resonates at its operating frequency.

tuned filter—A resonant arrangement of electronic components which either attenuates signals at a particular frequency and passes signals at other frequencies, or vice versa.

tuned filter oscillator—An oscillator in which a tuned filter is used.

tuned-grid oscillator—An oscillator, the frequency of which is determined by a parallel-tuned tank in the grid circuit. The tank is coupled to the plate to provide the required feedback.

tuned-grid–tuned-anode oscillator — *See* Tuned-Grid Tuned-Plate Oscillator.

Tuned-grid, tuned-plate oscillator.

tuned-grid, tuned-plate oscillator — Also called tuned-grid–tuned-anode oscillator. An oscillator having parallel-resonant circuits in both the plate and the grid circuits. The necessary feedback is provided by the plate-to-grid interelectrode capacitance.

tuned-plate oscillator — Also called tuned-anode oscillator. An oscillator, the frequency of which is determined by a parallel-tuned tank in the plate circuit. The tank is coupled to the grid to provide the required feedback.

tuned radio-frequency amplifier—A tuned amplifier using resonant-circuit coupling and designed to operate at radio frequencies.

tuned radio-frequency receiver—A radio receiver consisting of several amplifier stages, which are tuned to resonance at the carrier frequency of the desired signal by a ganged variable-tuning capacitor. The amplified signals at the original carrier frequency are fed directly into the detector for demodulation. The resultant audio-frequency signals are again amplified, and are then reproduced by a speaker.

tuned radio-frequency transformer — A transformer used for selective coupling in radio-frequency stages.

tuned-reed frequency meter—A vibrating-reed instrument for measuring the frequency of an alternating current.

tuned relay—A relay having mechanical or other resonating arrangements that limit the response to currents at one particular frequency.

tuned resonating cavity—A resonating cavity half a wavelength long or some multiple of a half wavelength, used in connection with a waveguide to produce a resultant wave with the amplitude in the cavity greatly exceeding that of the wave in the guide. For reception of waves, a detecting grating can be placed at the point of maximum amplitude in the cavity, to convert the energy to a form suitable for amplification in a telephone or television circuit. A tuned cavity is a nonreflecting termination for a guide.

tuned rope—Long lengths of chaff cut to the various lengths necessary for tuning to different wavelengths.

tuned transformer—A transformer, the associated circuit elements of which are adjusted as a whole to be resonant at the frequency of the alternating current supplied to the primary, thereby causing the secondary voltage to build up to higher values than would otherwise be obtained.

tuner—In the broad sense, a device for tuning. Specifically, in radio-receiver practice: 1. A packaged unit capable of producing only the first portion of the functions of a receiver and delivering either r-f, i-f, or demodulated information to some other equipment. 2. That portion of a receiver which contains the circuits that are tuned to resonance at the received-signal frequency and those which are tuned to the local-oscillator frequency.

tungar rectifier—A gaseous rectifier containing argon gas. It is employed in battery chargers and low-voltage power supplies.

tungar tube—A phanatron (hot-cathode, gas-filled rectifier tube) having a heated filament serving as the cathode and a graphite disc as the anode in a bulb filled with low-pressure argon. Used chiefly in battery chargers.

tungsten—A metal used in the manufacture of filaments for vacuum tubes and in making contact points for switches and other parts where sparking may occur. After the tungsten is made ductile by rolling, swaging, and hammering, it is very tough.

tungsten filament—A filament used in incandescent lamps, and in thermionic vacuum tubes and other tubes requiring an incandescent cathode. Smaller tungsten filaments are operated in a vacuum, while those for larger lamps are used in an inert gas at about ordinary atmospheric pressure.

tuning—The adjustment relating to frequency of a circuit or system to secure optimum performance. Commonly, the adjustment of a circuit or circuits to resonance.

tuning capacitor—A variable capacitor for

adjusting the natural frequency of an oscillatory or resonant circuit.

tuning circuit—A circuit containing inductance and capacitance, either or both of which may be adjusted to make the circuit responsive to a particular frequency.

tuning coil—A variable inductance for adjusting the natural frequency of an oscillatory or resonant circuit.

tuning control—A control knob that adjusts all tuned circuits simultaneously.

tuning core—Normally a molded iron core for permeability tuning, into which an adjusting screw has been cemented or molded.

tuning eye—Slang for a cathode-ray tuning indicator.

tuning fork—A two-pronged hard-steel device that vibrates at a definite natural frequency when struck or when set in motion by electromagnetic means. Used in some electronic equipment as an accurately controllable source of signals, because its vibrations can be formed readily into audiofrequency signals by means of pickup coils.

tuning-fork drive—Control of an oscillator by continuous vibrations of a tuning fork. A high harmonic of the oscillating signal obtained from the fork is selected by filter circuits and is strongly amplified to determine the main-oscillator frequency in a transmitter or other equipment.

tuning in—Adjusting the tuning controls of a receiver to obtain maximum response to the signals of the station it is desired to receive.

tuning indicator—A device that indicates whether or not a receiver is tuned accurately. It is connected to some circuit in which current or voltage is maximum or minimum when the receiver is accurately tuned to give the strongest output signal.

tuning meter—A direct-current meter connected to a receiver circuit and used for determining whether the receiver is accurately tuned to a station.

tuning probe—An essentially lossless probe of adjustable penetration extending through the wall of a waveguide or cavity resonator.

tuning range—The frequency range over which a tuned circuit can be adjusted.

tuning screw—In waveguide technique, an impedance-adjusting element in the form of a rod whose depth of penetration through the wall into a waveguide or cavity is adjustable by rotating a screw.

tuning stubs—Inductor elements, usually adjustable, which are connected to transmission lines at intervals to improve the voltage distribution.

tuning susceptance—The normalized susceptance of an ATR tube in its mount due to its deviation from the desired resonance frequency.

tuning wand—*See* Neutralizing Tool.

tunnel cathode — A metal insulator-metal sandwich. Electrons tunnel from the metal substrate and appear in the metal film as hot electrons. Some of the hot electrons have sufficient energy to pass over the cathode surface barrier into the vacuum.

Tunnel diode characteristics.

tunnel diode—Also called Esaki diode. A semiconductor consisting of a PN junction which has been especially constructed to optimize the characteristics desired. It is designated P_tN and has an extremely narrow junction and large impurity concentrations in both regions. It is extremely stable and has excellent environmental characteristics, withstanding large temperature changes and radiation bombardment. The P_tN junction may be combined with other junctions. In operation, the tunnel diode differs from other types of PN junctions, in that it exhibits negative resistance and the current is carried by electrons that travel across the PN barrier by quantum mechanical tunneling. It is so stable that it could be operated in an unencapsulated state under severe moisture and contamination conditions.

tunnel effect—1. The probability that a particle of given potential energy can penetrate a finite barrier of higher potential. 2. Piercing of a rectangular potential barrier in a semiconductor by a particle that does not have sufficient energy to go over the barrier.

tunneling—*See* Tunnel Diode.

tunnel triode — A transistorlike device in which the emitter-base junction is a tunnel diode and the collector-base junction is a conventional diode.

tunneluminescence—The emission of light from a phosphor film deposited on the surface of a thin-film metal-oxide-metal sandwich.

turbidimeter—*See* Opacimeter.

turn—One complete loop of wire.

turn factor — Under stated conditions, the number of turns that a coil of given shape and dimensions placed on a core in a given position must have for a coefficient of self-inductance of 1 henry to be obtained for the core.

turnoff delay time — The time interval between occurrence of the trailing edge of a fast input pulse and the occurrence of the 90% point of the negative-going output waveform.

turn-off reversal—A polarity reversal of the output of the electronic power supply occurring from the turning off of the power of a regulated power supply.

turnoff time—The time that a switching circuit (gate) takes to stop the flow of current in the circuit it is controlling.

turnon delay time—The time interval from the occurrence of the leading edge of a fast input pulse to the occurrence of the 10% point of the positive-going output waveform, assuming that the rise time of the incoming pulses is 1/10 of the rise time of the element to be measured under loaded conditions.

turn-on overshoot — Overshoots occurring from the turning on of power of a regulated power supply.

turn-on reversal—A polarity reversal of the output of the power supply occurring from the turning on of the power supply of a regulated power supply.

Turnover cartridge.

turnover cartridge—A phonograph cartridge adapted, by the use of two styli, to play both large- and fine-groove records.

turnover frequency—In disc recording, the frequency below which constant-amplitude recording is used and above which constant-velocity recording is employed.

turnover pickup—Also called dual pickup. A pickup designed for playing both standard and microgroove records, using a single magnetic structure. (*Also see* Turnover Cartridge.)

turns ratio—The ratio of the number of turns in the primary winding to the number in the secondary winding of a transformer.

turnstile antenna—An antenna composed of two dipole antennas normal to each other and with their axes intersecting at their midpoints. Usually the currents are equal and in phase quadrature.

turntable—A revolving platform used in recording or playing phonograph records.

turntable rumble—*See* Rumble.

turret—A revolving plate mounted at the

front of some television cameras and carrying two or more lenses of different types, to permit rapid interchange of lenses.

turret tuner—A television-receiver tuner containing a separate set of resonating circuit elements for each channel. Each set is mounted on an insulating strip or strips placed on a drum rotated from the channel-selector control, which selects the drum position for the desired channel.

tv—Abbreviation for television.

tvi—Abbreviation for television interference.

tv recording—A permanent record of video signals recorded photographically, electronically, or by other means, and which may be displayed through a television system or projected as a motion-picture film.

tweeter—Also called a high-frequency unit. A speaker intended to reproduce the very high frequencies, usually those above 3,000 Hz, in a high-fidelity audio system.

twenty-one type repeater—A two-wire telephone repeater in which one amplifier serves to amplify the telephone currents in both directions. The circuit is arranged so that the input and output terminals of the amplifier are in one pair of conjugate branches, while the lines in the two directions are in another pair.

twenty-two type repeater—A two-wire telephone repeater with two amplifiers. One amplifies the telephone currents being transmitted in one direction, and the other the telephone currents being transmitted in the other direction.

twin cable—A cable composed of two parallel insulated, stranded conductors having a common covering.

twin check—A continuous check of computer operations accomplished by duplication of equipment and automatic comparison of results.

Twin lead.

twin lead—Also called twin line. A type of transmission line covered by a solid insulation and comprising two parallel conductors, the impedance of which is determined by their diameter and spacing. The three most common impedance values are 75, 150, and 300 ohms.

twin line—*See* Twin Lead.

twinning—The intergrowth of two crystal regions having opposite oriented axes. Two types of twinning may occur; electrical and optical. In electrical twinning the electrical sense of the crystal axes are reversed and the twinned regions will interfere with one another piezoelectrically. It is this effect which limits the high-temperature utility of quartz as a piezoelectric material.

twin-T network—*See* Parallel-T Network.

twin triode—Two triode vacuum tubes in a single envelope.

twin wire—A cable composed of two small, parallel insulated conductors having a common covering.

twist—1. The progressive rotation of the cross section of a waveguide about the longitudinal axis. 2. The deviation from a plane surface measured from one corner to the corner diagonally opposite.

twisted joint—A union of two conductors wound tightly around each other. A sleeve may be used, and it and the conductors twisted.

twisted pair—A cable composed of two small insulated conductors twisted together without a common covering. The two conductors of a twisted pair are usually substantially insulated, so that the combination is a special case of a cord.

twister—A piezoelectric crystal that generates a voltage when twisted.

twistor—A computer memory element containing inclined helical windings of magnet wire on a nonmagnetic wire, with another winding over the helix. Information is stored in the form of polarized helical magnetization.

two-address—In a computer, having the property that each complete instruction includes an operation and specifies the location of two registers, usually one containing an operand and the other the result of the operation.

two-dimensional circuitry—See Thin-Film Integrated Circuitry.

two-fluid cell—A cell having unlike electrolytes at the positive and negative electrodes.

two-level system—A laser which uses only two electron energy levels. Electrons in the ground state (level 1) are pumped to the excited state (level 2). The electrons then surrender their energy by stimulated emission and return to the ground state.

two-phase—Also called quarter phase. Having a phase difference of 90 electrical degrees, or one quarter-cycle.

two-phase current—Two currents delivered through two pairs of wires at a phase difference of one quarter-cycle (90°) between them.

two-phase, five-wire system—An alternating-current supply in which four of its conductors are connected as in a four-wire, two-phase system and the fifth is connected to the neutral points of each phase and usually grounded. Despite its name, it is strictly a four-phase, five-wire system.

two-phase, four-wire system—A system of alternating-current supply comprising two pairs of conductors, between one pair of which is maintained an alternating difference of potential displaced in phase by one quarter of a period from an alternating difference of potential of the same frequency maintained between the other pair.

two-phase, three-wire system—An alternating-current supply consisting of three conductors. Between one conductor (known as

the common return) and each of the other two, alternating differences of potential which are 90° out of phase with each other are maintained.

two-pilot regulation—The use of two pilot frequencies within a transmitted band so that the change in attenuation due to twist can be detected and compensated for by a regulator.

two-port network—A network with two ports.

two-pulse canceler—A moving-target indicator canceler which compares the phase variation of two successive pulses received from a target. It discriminates against signals with radial velocities which produce a Doppler frequency equal to a multiple of the pulse-repetition frequency.

two-quadrant multiplier—Of an analog computer, a multiplier in which operation is restricted to a single sign of one input variable only.

two-source frequency keying—Keying in which the modulating wave shifts the output frequency between predetermined values derived from independent sources.

two-terminal network—A network that is connected by only two terminals to an external system.

two-terminal-pair network—Also called a four-pole, quadripole, or quadrupole network. A network with four accessible terminals grouped in pairs. One terminal of each pair may coincide with a network node.

two-tone keying—Keying in which the modulating wave causes the carrier to be modulated with one frequency for the marking condition, and a different frequency for the spacing condition.

two-tone modulation—1. A method of modulation in which two different carrier frequencies are used for the two signaling conditions. 2. In teletypewriter operation, a method of modulation in which two different carrier frequencies are employed for the two signaling conditions. The transition from one frequency to the other is abrupt, with resultant phase discontinuities.

two-track recording—On quarter-inch-wide tape, the arrangement by which only two channels of sound may be recorded, either as a stereo pair in one direction or as separate monophonic tracks (usually in opposite directions).

two-value capacitor motor—A capacitor motor that uses different values of effective capacitance for starting and running.

two-wattmeter method—A method of measuring total power in a balanced or unbalanced three-phase system by adding the readings of two wattmeters, each with its current coil in one phase and its voltage coil connected between it and the third phase.

two-way amplifier—An amplifier in which the right and left channels of a stereo system are both amplified simultaneously by the same tubes, using push-pull circuitry but feeding one signal to the input grids in parallel instead of push-pull. The parallel and push-pull signals are then separated by two output transformers in a matrixing circuit.

two-way communication — Communication between radio stations, each having both transmitting and receiving equipment.

two-way repeater—*See* Repeater.

two-way switch—A switch used for controlling electrical or electronic equipment, components, or circuits from either of two positions.

two-way system—A speaker in which the low and the high frequencies are reproduced separately by two electrically independent speaker elements, each of which is provided with a suitable sound-radiating system.

two-wire channel — A two-way circuit for transmission in either direction.

two-wire circuit—A metallic circuit formed by two conductors insulated from each other. It is possible to use the two conductors as either a one-way transmission path, a half-duplex path, or a duplex path. Also used in contrast with a four-wire circuit to indicate a circuit using one line or channel for transmission of electric waves in both directions.

two-wire repeater — A telephone repeater which provides for transmission in both directions over a two-wire telephone circuit.

two-wire system—A system of electric supply comprising two conductors, with the load connected between them.

twt—Abbreviation for traveling-wave tube.

Twystron — A very high power, hybrid microwave tube combining the input section of a high-power klystron with the output section of a traveling-wave tube. It is characterized by high operating efficiency and wide bandwidths.

type-A facsimile—Facsimile communication in which the images are built up of lines of constant-intensity dots.

type-A waves—Continuous waves.

type A_1 waves—Unmodulated, keyed, continuous waves.

type A_2 waves—Modulated, keyed, continuous waves.

type A_3 waves—Continuous waves modulated by music, speech, or other sounds.

type A_4 waves—Superaudio frequency-modulated continuous waves, as used in a facsimile system.

type A_5 waves—Superaudio frequency-modulated continuous waves as used in television.

type A_9 waves—Composite transmissions and cases not covered by type-A thru type-A_5 waves.

type-B facsimile—Facsimile communication in which the images are built up of lines of dots having a varying intensity (e.g., in telephotography and photoradio).

type-B waves—Keyed, damped waves.

type-printed telegraphy — Telegraphy in which the message is automatically printed at the receiving station.

U

ubitron—An amplifier or oscillator in which an undulating electron beam interacts with an r-f wave. The kinetic energy of the beam is converted into r-f energy (0-type interaction). The undulation of the beam is produced by a periodic magnetic field. This field gives the beam a transverse-velocity component which interacts with the r-f wave.

U bolt.

U-bolt—A U-shaped bolt threaded on both ends, for fastening antennas to masts.

uhf—Abbreviation for ultrahigh frequency.

UL—Abbreviation for Underwriters Labora-

tories, a corporation supported by some underwriters for the purpose of establishing safety standards on types of equipment or components.

ultimately controlled variable—The quantity whose control is the end purpose of an automatic control system.

ultimate sensitivity or threshold — One-half the deadband in a graphic recorder. When the instrument is balanced at the center of the deadband, it denotes the minimum change in measured quantity required to initiate pen response.

ultimate trip current—The smallest value of current that will cause tripping of a circuit breaker under a given set of ambient conditions.

ultimate trip limits—The values of overload of a circuit breaker at which the minimum and maximum limits of the time-current curve become asymptotic; i.e., the limits of current that will trip or not trip the breaker "ultimately." Minimum and maximum limits of ultimate trip are often called calibration.

ultor—An adjective used to identify the picture-tube anode or element farthest from the cathode, the anode to which the highest voltage is applied, or the voltage itself (e.g., the ultor anode is the second anode of the picture tube, and the ultor voltage is the voltage applied to it).

ultor element—The element which receives the highest d-c voltage in a cathode-ray tube.

ultra-audible frequency — *See* Ultrasonic Frequency.

ultra-audion—Any of several special vacuum-tube circuits employing regeneration.

ultra-audion circuit—A regenerative detector circuit in which a parallel-resonant circuit is connected between the grid and the plate of a vacuum tube, and a variable capacitor is connected between the plate and cathode to control the amount of regeneration.

ultra-audion oscillator—*See* Colpitts Oscillator.

Ultrafax—A trade name of RCA for a system in which printed information is transmitted by radio, facsimile, and television at high speeds.

ultrahigh frequency—Frequency band; 300 to 3,000 MHz. Wavelength: 10 to 100 centimeters. Abbreviated uhf.

ultrahigh-frequency converter — A circuit used to convert uhf television signals to vhf, to permit uhf television reception on a vhf receiver.

ultrahigh-frequency generator—Any device for generating ultrahigh-frequency alternating currents (e.g., a conventional negative-grid generator; a positive-grid, or Barkhausen, generator; a magnetron; and a velocity-modulation, or electron-beam generator such as the klystron).

ultrahigh-frequency loop—Generally a single-loop antenna used in ultrahigh-frequency work to secure a nondirectional radiation pattern in the plane of the loop. The doughnut-shaped pattern is perpendicular to the loop.

ultrahigh-frequency translator — A television-broadcast translator station that transmits on a uhf television-broadcast channel.

ultralinear amplifier—A high-power output, low-distortion amplifier used in high-fidelity systems. It requires a specially wound output transformer.

ultramicrometer—An instrument for measuring very small displacements by electrical means (e.g., by the variation in capacitance produced by the movement being measured).

ultramicroscope — A dark-field microscope with which very small particles are illuminated by refracted light so that diffraction rings may be observed.

ultramicrowave — Having wavelengths of about 10^{-1} to 10^{-4} cm.

ultrashort waves—Radio waves shorter than 10 meters in wavelength (about 30 MHz in frequency). Waves shorter than 1 meter are called microwaves.

ultrasonic—Having a frequency above that of audible sound—i.e., between sonic and hypersonic.

ultrasonic brazing—*See* Ultrasonic Soldering.

Ultrasonic cleaning tank.

ultrasonic cleaning tank — A heavy-gage, polished stainless-steel tank with transducers mounted on the bottom or sides.

ultrasonic coagulation — The bonding together of small particles by the action of ultrasonic waves.

ultrasonic cross grating—Also called grating. The two- or three-dimensional space grating produced when ultrasonic beams having different directions of propagation intersect.

ultrasonic delay line—Also called an ultrasonic storage cell. A contained medium (usually a liquid such as mercury) in which the signal is delayed because of the longer propagation time of the sound waves in the medium.

ultrasonic densitometer—An instrument device for determining the thickness or density of an object or material, based on the time required for an ultrasonic signal to penetrate to a receiver and/or "echo" back to a receiver adjacent to another transmitter.

ultrasonic detector—A device—either mechanical, electrical, thermal, or optical—for detecting and measuring ultrasonic waves.

ultrasonic diagnosis—A method of obtaining information from within the body in a visual presentation without employing ionizing radiation. It differs from X-ray techniques in that the form of energy used is high-frequency sound. Also, in contrast to X-ray techniques, in which the film is placed behind the tissue being examined, ultrasonic information is picked up at the original point of transmission in the form of echoes from internal structures.

ultrasonic disintegrator—An apparatus for

using the pressure wave produced by an ultrasonic generator to tear cells apart.

ultrasonic drill—A special type of drill that has a magnetostrictive transducer attached to a tapered cone that serves as a velocity transformer. With an appropriate tool, practically any shape of hole can be drilled in brittle and hard material.

ultrasonic flaw detector—Equipment comprising an ultrasonic generator, transducer, detector, and display and used to detect flaws or cracks in solids from the reflection pattern of ultrasonic signals observed on a cathode-ray tube.

ultrasonic frequency—Also called an ultra-audible frequency. Any frequency above the audio range, but commonly applied to elastic waves propagated in gases, liquids, or solids.

ultrasonic generator—An electrical device that converts electrical power to an appropriate frequency for use with an electromechanical transducer.

ultrasonic grating constant—The distance between diffracting centers of the sound wave producing particular light-diffraction spectra.

ultrasonic inspection — A nondestructive testing method of locating internal defects in a part by sending ultrasonic impulses (inaudible high-frequency sound waves of 0.5 to 11 megahertz) into the part and measuring the time required for these impulses to penetrate the material, be reflected from the opposite side or from the defect, and return to the sending point.

ultrasonic level detector—A level detector consisting of an ultrasonic receiver and transmitter located in one wall of a container or vessel. With nothing to obstruct the beam, it is reflected from the opposite wall. When the level of the liquid or other material in the container reaches the beam, the liquid or material acts as a reflector, thus reducing the reflection time and indicating that a given level has been reached.

ultrasonic light diffraction—The formation of optical diffraction spectra when a beam of light is passed through a longitudinal sound-wave field. The diffraction results from the periodic variation of the light refraction in the sound field.

ultrasonic light modulator—A device containing a fluid which, by action of ultrasonic waves passing through the fluid, modulates a beam of light passed transversely through the fluid.

ultrasonic material dispersion—The production of suspensions or emulsions of one material in another by the action of high-intensity ultrasonic waves.

ultrasonic plating—The chemical or electrochemical deposition and bonding of one or more solid materials to the surface of another material by the use of vibrational wave energy.

ultrasonic probe—A rod for directing ultra-sonic force, used in a disintegration or foreign-body location application.

ultrasonics—The general subject of sound in the frequency range above 15 kilohertz.

ultrasonic soldering—A method of forming a nonporous, continuously metallic connection between metal or alloy parts without necessarily employing chemicals or mechanical abrasives. Instead, vibrational wave energy, heat, and a separate alloy or metal having a melting point below 800° F. and also below that of the metals or alloys being joined is used.

ultrasonic space grating—Also called grating. A periodic spatial variation in the index of refraction caused by the presence of acoustic waves within the medium.

ultrasonic storage cell—*See* Ultrasonic Delay Line.

ultrasonic stroboscope—A light interrupter in which the light beam is modulated by an ultrasonic field.

ultrasonic therapy—The use of ultrasonic vibrations for therapeutic purposes.

ultrasonic thickness gage—A thickness gage in which the propagation time of an ultrasonic beam through a sheet of material is translated into a measure of the thickness of the material.

Ultrasonic transducer.

ultrasonic transducer—A device which takes the electrical oscillations produced by the ultrasonic generator and transforms them into mechanical oscillations. Typical transducer materials are piezoelectric (e.g., quartz or barium titanate) or magnetostrictive (e.g., nickel).

ultrasonic waves—Waves having a frequency in the ultrasonic range.

ultrasonic welding — A solid-state bonding process in which metals being joined never reach melting temperatures. They are joined by clamping them together and applying the ultrasonic energy in the plane of the weld without the application of heat.

ultraviolet—Electromagnetic radiation at frequencies higher than those of visible light and with wavelengths of about 200 to 4,000 angstrom units.

ultraviolet lamp—A lamp providing a high proportion of ultraviolet radiation (e.g., arc lamps, mercury-vapor lamps, or incandescent lamps in bulbs of a special glass that is transparent to ultraviolet rays).

ultraviolet rays—Radiation in the ultraviolet region.

umbilical cord—A quickly detachable cable through which missiles or rockets are powered and controlled until the moment of launching.

umbrella antenna—An antenna in which the wires are guyed downward in all directions from a central pole or tower to the ground, somewhat like the ribs of an open umbrella.

unamplified back bias—A degenerative voltage developed across a fast time-constant circuit within an amplifier stage itself.

unbalanced—1. Lacking the conditions for balance. 2. Frequently, a circuit having one side grounded. 3. Differential mutual impedance or mutual admittance between two circuits which ideally would have no coupling.

unbalanced circuit—A circuit, the two sides of which are electrically unlike.

unbalanced line—A transmission line in which the voltages on the two conductors are not equal with respect to ground (e.g., a coaxial line).

unbalanced output—An output where one of the two output terminals is substantially at ground potential.

unbalanced wire circuit—A circuit, the two sides of which are electrically unlike.

unblanking—The turning on of the crt beam.

unblanking generator—A circuit for producing pulses that turn on the beam of a cathode-ray tube.

unblanking pulse—A pulse that turns on the beam of a cathode-ray tube.

unbonded strain gage — A pressure-sensing element made up of resistance strain-gage wire elements arranged in a Wheatstone bridge. It can have two or four active arms, which respond to a pressure applied to the transducer. The unbonded strain-gage wires are suspended in air and are activated by a mechanism attached to a diaphragm or other pressure-responding element.

uncharged — Having a normal number of electrons and hence no electrical charge.

unconditional—In a computer, not subject to conditions external to the specific instruction.

unconditional jump—A computer instruction which interrupts the normal process of obtaining the instructions in an ordered sequence and specifies the address from which the next instruction must be taken.

unconditional transfer of control—In a digital computer which obtains its instructions serially from an ordered sequence of addresses, an instruction which causes the following instruction to be taken from an address that becomes the first of a new sequence.

undamped natural frequency — The frequency at which a system with a single degree of freedom will oscillate, in the absence of damping, upon momentary displacement from the rest position by a transient force.

undamped oscillations — Oscillations that have a constant amplitude for their duration.

undamped wave—A constant-amplitude wave.

underbunching—The condition whereby the buncher voltage of a velocity-modulation tube is lower than the value required for optimum bunching of the electrons.

undercompounded—A generator in which the output voltage drops as the load is increased.

undercurrent relay—A relay that functions when its coil current falls below a predetermined value.

undercut—In a printed-circuit board, the reduction of the cross section of a metal-foil conductor due to the removal of metal from beneath the edge of the resist by the etchant.

undercutting—A cutting with too shallow a groove or with insufficient lateral movement of the stylus during sound disc recordings.

underdamped—A degree of damping that is not sufficient to prevent oscillation in the output of a system following application of an abrupt stimulus.

underdamping—1. In a system, the condition whereby the amount of damping is so small that the system executes one or more oscillations when subjected to a single disturbance (either constant or instantaneous). 2. Oscillation of the transducer output about a final steady value in response to a step change in the measurand. After an initial overshoot, the oscillation amplitude decreases.

underflow—In a computer, the generation of a quantity smaller than the accepted minimum (e.g., floating-point underflow).

underground cable—A cable installed below the surface of the earth.

under insulation—The insulation under wire that is brought from the center of a coil over the top or bottom wall.

underlap—Recorded elemental areas that are smaller than normal—specifically, the space between the recorded elemental area in one recording line of a facsimile system and the adjacent elemental area in the next recording line, or the elemental areas in the direction of the recording line.

underload relay—A relay that operates when the load in a circuit drops below a certain value.

undermodulation—Insufficient modulation of a transmitter, due to maladjustment or to insufficient modulation signal.

underpower relay—A relay which functions when the power decreases below a predetermined value.

undershoot—The initial transient response to a unidirectional change in input which precedes the main transition and is opposite in sense. (*Also see* Precursor.)

underthrow distortion—Distortion resulting when the maximum amplitude of the signal wavefront is less than the steady-state amplitude which would be attained by a prolonged signal wave.

undervoltage protection—Also called low-voltage protection. The effect of a device to cause and maintain the interruption of power to the main circuit upon the reduction or failure of voltage.

undervoltage relay—A relay which operates when its coil voltage falls below a predetermined value.

underwater sound projector—An electroacoustic transducer designed to convert electric waves into sound waves, which are radiated in water for reception at a distance.

undistorted wave—A periodic wave in which both the attenuation and the velocity of propagation are the same for all sinusoidal components, and in which the same sinusoidal component is present at all points.

undisturbed-one output—A 1 output of a magnetic cell to which no partial-read pulses have been applied since that cell was last selected for writing.

undisturbed-zero output—A 0 output of a magnetic cell to which no partial-write pulses have been applied since that cell was last selected for reading.

unfired tube—The condition of TR, ATR, and pre-TR tubes when there is no radio-frequency glow discharge at either the resonant gap or the resonant window.

unfurlable antenna—A device which can be unfolded to form a larger antenna.

ungrounded—Not intentionally connected to ground except through high-impedance devices.

ungrounded system—A system in which no point is directly connected to earth except through potential or ground-detecting transformers or other very-high-impedance devices.

uniaxial magnetic anistropy—A property of magnetic thin film in which the direction of magnetization is always parallel to the easy axis unless an external force acts upon it.

uniconductor waveguide—A waveguide consisting of a rectangular or cylindrical metallic surface surrounding a uniform dielectric medium.

unidirectional—Flowing in only one direction (e.g., direct current).

unidirectional antenna—An antenna with a single, well-defined direction of maximum gain.

unidirectional coupler—A directional coupler which samples only one direction of transmission.

unidirectional current—A direct current—i.e., one that is always positive or always negative—never alternating.

unidirectional microphone—A microphone that responds predominantly to sound from a single solid angle of one hemisphere or less.

unidirectional pulses—Single-polarity pulses which all rise in the same direction.

unidirectional pulse train—A pulse train in which all pulses rise in the same direction.

unidirectional transducer—Also called a unilateral transducer. A transducer, the out-

put of which cannot be actuated by waves to supply related waves at its input.

uniform field—A field in which the scalar (or vector) has the same value at every point in the region under consideration at that instant.

uniformity—In terms of magnetic tape properties, a figure of merit relating to the ability of the tape to deliver a steady and consistent output level upon being recorded with a constant input. Usually expressed in db variation from average at a midrange frequency.

uniform line—A line with substantially identical electrical properties throughout its length.

uniform plane wave—A plane wave with constant-amplitude electric and magnetic field vectors over the equiphase surfaces. Such a wave can only be found in free space, at an infinite distance from the source.

uniform precession—The condition in which the magnetic moments of all atoms in a sample are parallel and precess in phase about the magnetic field. Uniform precession occurs in regions where the magnetic field is uniform. A spin wave is a phase distortion of this condition.

uniform waveguide—A waveguide in which the physical and electrical characteristics do not change with distance along its axis.

Unijunction transistor.

unijunction transistor—Also called a silicon double-base diode or silicon unijunction transistor. A three-terminal semiconductor device exhibiting stable open-circuit, negative-resistance characteristics. The internal construction consists of a uniformly doped N-type, single-crystal semiconductor with ohmic contacts at each end and the emitter wire attached between them.

unilateral area track—A sound track in which only one edge of the opaque area is modulated in accordance with the recorded signal. However, there may be a second edge modulated by a noise-reduction device.

unilateral bearing—A bearing obtained with a radio direction finder having a unilateral response, eliminating the chance of a 180° error.

unilateral conductivity—Conductivity in only one direction (e.g., in a perfect rectifier).

unilateral element—A two-terminal element

with a zero voltage-to-current characteristic (or the equivalent) on one side of the origin.

unilateralization—A special case of neutralization in which the feedback parameters are completely balanced out. In transistors, these feedback parameters include a resistive in addition to a capacitive component. Unilateralization changes a network from bilateral to unilateral.

unilateral network—A network in which any driving force applied at one pair of terminals produces a response at a second pair, but yields no response when the driving force is applied in the other direction.

unilateral transducer — *See* Unidirectional Transducer.

unipolar field-effect transistor — A field-controlled majority-carrier device wherein the conductance of a semiconductor channel is modulated by a transverse electric field. The field is controlled by the combination of gate bias voltage V_{gs} and the net voltage V_{ds} between channel drain and source.

unipolar transistor—A transistor in which charge carriers are of only one polarity. *Also see* Field-Effect Transistor.

unipole—1. An all-pass filter section with one pole and one zero. 2. A hypothetical antenna which radiates and receives equally in all directions. *Also see* Isotropic Antenna.

unipotential cathode—*See* Indirectly-Heated Cathode.

unit—1. A computer portion or subassembly which constitutes the means of accomplishing some inclusive operation or function (e.g., an arithmetic unit). 2. The specific magnitude of a quantity set apart by appropriate definition and serving as a basis for the comparison or measurement of like quantities.

unit-area acoustic impedance—*See* Specific Acoustic Impedance.

unitary code—A code having only one digit, the number of times it is repeated determining the quantity it represents.

unit charge—The electrical charge which will repel a force of one dyne on an equal and like charge one centimeter away in a vacuum, assuming each charge is concentrated at a point.

unit interval—*See* Signal Element.

unit length—The basic element of time for determining code speeds in message transmission.

unit magnetic pole—A pole with a strength such that when it is placed 1 cm away from a like pole, the force between the two is 1 dyne.

unitor — In computers, a device or circuit which performs a function corresponding to the Boolean operation of union. *Also see* OR Circuit.

unit pulse—*See* Baud.

unit record equipment — Equipment using punched cards as input data, such as collators, tabulating machines, etc.

unit sequence starting relay — A device which functions to start the next available unit in a multiple-unit equipment on the failure or on the nonavailability of the normally preceding unit.

unit sequence switch — A switch used to change the sequence in which units may be placed in and out of service in multiple-unit equipment.

unit step current (or voltage)—A current (or voltage) which undergoes an instantaneous change in magnitude from one constant level to another.

unit substation transformer—A transformer which is mechanically and electrically connected to and coordinated in design with one or more switch-gear or motor-controlled assemblies or combinations thereof.

unit troque gradient—The torque gradient of a synchro, measured when the synchro is electrically connected to another synchro of the same size.

unitunnel diode—A diode similar to a tunnel diode, but specially treated to give peak reverse currents in the microampere region while providing high forward conductance at low voltage levels.

unity coupling—Perfect magnetic coupling between two coils, so that all the magnetic flux produced by the primary winding passes through the entire secondary winding.

unity-gain crossover frequency—The frequency at which the open-loop voltage gain of an amplifier curve crosses through unity gain, or zero db.

unity power factor—A power factor of 1.0. It is obtained only when current and voltage are in phase (e.g., in a circuit containing only resistance, or in a reactive circuit at resonance).

Universal motor.

universal motor—A series-wound motor designed to operate at approximately the same speed and output on direct current or on a single-phase alternating current of not more than 60 hertz and approximately the same rms voltage.

universal output transformer—An output transformer having a number of taps on its winding. By proper choice of connections, it can be used between the audio-frequency output stage and the speaker of practically any radio receiver or audio amplifier.

universal receiver—Also called an a-c/d-c receiver. A receiver with no power transformer and thus capable of operating from either a-c or d-c power lines, without changes in its internal connections.

universal shunt—*See* Ayrton Shunt.

universe — *See* Population.

unload—In a computer. 1. To remove the tape from the columns of a recorder by raising or lowering the recording head. 2. To remove a portion of the address part of an instruction. 3. *Also see* Dump.

unloaded antenna — An antenna with no added inductance or capacitance.

unloaded applicator impedance (dielectric heaters)—The complex impedance measured at the point of application and at a specified frequency without the load material in position.

unloaded Q (switching tubes)—Also called the intrinsic Q. The Q of a tube unloaded by either the generator or termination.

unloading amplifier—An amplifier capable of reproducing or amplifying a given voltage signal while drawing negligible current from the voltage source.

unloading circuit—In an analog computer, a computing element or combination of computing elements capable of reproducing or amplifying a given voltage signal while drawing negligible current from the voltage source, thus decreasing the load errors.

unmodulated—Having no modulation—e.g. a carrier that is transmitted during moments of silence in radio programs, or a silent groove in a disc recording.

unmodulated groove—Also called a blank groove. In mechanical recording, the groove made in the medium with no signal applied to the cutter.

unoriented—A structure in which the crystallographic axes of the grains of a metal are not aligned to give directional magnetic properties.

unpack—In a computer, to separate combined items of information, each into a separate machine word.

untuned—Not resonant at any of the frequencies being handled.

unwind—In a computer, to code all the operations of a cycle, at length and in full, for the express purpose of eliminating all red-tape operations.

up-converter—A type of parametric amplifier which is characterized by the frequency of the output signal being greater than the frequency of the input signal.

update—To search the file (such as a particular record in a computer tape) and select one entry, then perform some operation to bring the entry up-to-date.

updating—The act of bringing information up to the current value.

upper operating temperature — The maximum temperature to which a material can be subjected and still maintain specified operating characteristics within limits.

upper sideband—The higher frequency or group of frequencies produced by an amplitude-modulation process.

upset-duplex system—A direct-current telegraph system in which a station between any two pieces of duplex equipment may transmit signals by opening and closing the line circuit and thereby upsetting the duplex balance.

upset welding—A resistance-welding process wherein the weld is made simultaneously over the entire area of abuting surfaces or progressively along the joint with the aid of rolls or clamps which force the abutting surfaces together. The pressure is applied before heating starts and is maintained throughout the heating period.

up time — The time during which an equipment is either operating or available for operation as opposed to down time when no productive work can be accomplished.

urea plastic material—A thermosetting plastic material, with good dielectric, used for radio-receiver cabinets, instrument housings, etc.

USASI—Abbreviation for United States of America Standards Institute, the successor to ASA (American Standards Association).

"U" scan—A parallel reading method to prevent ambiguity in the readout of polystrophic codes at the code-position transitions by reading one of two sets of brushes, depending on the state of a control or selector bit.

useful life—The total time a device operates between debugging and wearout.

utilization factor—In electrical power distribution, the ratio of the maximum demand of a system (or part of a system) to the rated capacity of the system (or part) under consideration.

utilogic—A line of digital IC's built around a basic AND and a basic NOR circuit. The AND has multiple-emitter inputs; the NOR has emitter-follower inputs. The output for the AND is an emitter follower, and for the NOR, a totem-pole arrangement. J-K binary element is also included in the line.

V

V—1. Symbol for volt or voltmeter. 2. Schematic symbol for vacuum tube.

VA—Abbreviation for volt-ampere.

vac—Abbreviation for vacuum.

vacuum—Abbreviated vac. Theoretically, an enclosed space from which all air and gases have been removed. However, since such a perfect vacuum is never attained, the term is taken to mean a condition whereby sufficient air has been removed so that any remaining gas will not affect the characteristics beyond an allowable amount.

vacuum capacitor—A capacitor consisting usually of two concentric cylinders enclosed in a vacuum to raise the breakdown voltage.

vacuum deposition—A process in which a substance is deposited on a surface by heating the substance in a vacuum until vaporization occurs.

vacuum envelope—The airtight envelope which contains the electrodes of an electron tube.

vacuum gage—A device that indicates the absolute gas pressure in a vacuum system (e.g., in the evacuated parts of a mercury-arc rectifier).

vacuum impregnation—Filling the spaces between electric parts or turns of a coil with an insulating compound while the coil or parts are in a vacuum.

vacuum phototube—A phototube which is evacuated to such a degree that its electrical characteristics are essentially unaffected by gaseous ionization.

vacuum range—For a communications system, the maximum range computed for an atmospheric attenuation of zero.

vacuum seal—An airtight junction between component parts of an evacuated system.

vacuum switch—A switch in which the contacts are enclosed in an evacuated bulb, usually to minimize sparking.

vacuum tank—An airtight metal chamber which contains the electrodes and in which the rectifying action takes place in a mercury-arc rectifier.

vacuum tube—An electron tube evacuated to such a degree that its electrical characteristics are essentially unaffected by the presence of residual gas or vapor.

vacuum-tube amplifier—An amplifier in which electron tubes are used to control the power from the local source.

vacuum-tube characteristics—Data that show how a vacuum tube will operate under various electrical conditions.

vacuum-tube keying—A code-transmitter keying system in which a vacuum tube is connected in series with the plate-supply lead going to the winding in the plate circuit of the final stage. The grid of the tube is connected to its filament through the transmitting key so that when the key is open, the tube is blocked, interrupting the plate supply to the output stage. Closing the key allows plate current once more to flow through the keying tube and the output tubes.

vacuum-tube modulator—A modulator in which a vacuum tube is the modulating element.

vacuum-tube oscillator—A circuit in which a vacuum tube is used to convert d-c power into a-c power at the desired frequency.

vacuum-tube rectifier—A tube which changes an alternating current to a unidirectional pulsating direct current.

vacuum-tube transmitter—A radio transmitter in which electron tubes are utilized to convert the applied electric power into radio-frequency power.

vacuum-tube voltmeter—Abbreviated vtvm. *See* Electronic Voltmeter.

valence—A number representing the proportion in which the atom is able to combine with other atoms. It generally depends on the number and arrangement of electrons in the outermost shell of each type of atom.

valence band—In the spectrum of a solid crystal, the range of energy states containing the energies of the valence electrons which bind the crystal together. In a semiconductive material, it is just below the conduction band.

valence bond—Also called a bond. The bond formed between the electrons of two or more atoms.

valence electrons—The electrons of an atom in the outer shell that determine the chemical valency of the atom.

valence shell—The electrons which form the outermost shell of an atom.

validity—Correctness—specifically, how closely repeated approximations approach the desired (i.e., correct) result.

valley—A dip between two peaks in a curve.

valley current—In a tunnel diode, the current measured at the positive voltage for which the current has a minimum value from which it will increase if the voltage is further increased.

valley voltage—In a tunnel diode, the voltage corresponding to the valley current.

value—The magnitude of a physical quantity.

valve—1. A British term for a vacuum tube. 2. A device permitting current flow in one direction only (e.g., a rectifier). 3. A device or system which is capable of flow diversion, cutoff, or modulation.

valve tube—*See* Kenotron.

Van Allen radiation belts—Two doughnut-shaped belts of high-energy particles which surround the earth and are trapped in its magnetic field. They were first discovered by Dr. James A. Van Allen of Iowa State University.

Van de Graaff accelerator—An electrostatic-generator type of particle accelerator from

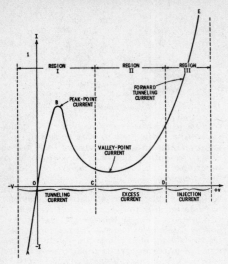

Valley current.

which the voltage is obtained by picking up static electricity at one end of the machine (on a rubber belt) and carrying it to the other end, where it is stored.

vane-anode magnetron—A cavity magnetron in which the walls between adjacent cavities have parallel plane surfaces.

vane attenuator—A waveguide device designed to present attenuation in a circuit by sliding a resistive element from the side wall of the waveguide to the center for maximum attenuation. This method of attenuation is used in precision calibrated attenuation readings, and resetting must be made. Some of its countless applications are calibrations of other attenuators, directional couplers, filters, and other lossy components, in antenna-pattern measurements, noise-level measurements, and for setting power levels to desired values.

Vane-type instrument.

vane-type instrument—A measuring instrument in which the pointer is moved by the force of repulsion between fixed and mov-able magnetized iron vanes, or by the force between a coil and a pivoted vane-shaped piece of soft iron.

vane-type magnetron—A cavity magnetron in which the walls between adjacent cavities have plane surfaces.

V-antenna.

V antenna—A V-shaped arrangement of conductors, the two branches being fed equally in opposite phase at the apex.

vapor pressure—The pressure of the vapor accumulated above a confined liquid (e.g., in a mercury-vapor rectifier tube).

var—1. Abbreviation for volt ampere reactive. The unit of reactive power, as opposed to real power in watts. One var is equal to one reactive volt-ampere. 2. Abbreviation for visual aural range.

varactor—1. A PN junction semiconductor diode designed for low losses at high frequencies. Its capacitance varies with the applied voltage. 2. Also called varactor diode, silicon capacitor, voltage-controlled capacitor, and voltage-variable capacitor. A two-terminal solid-state device that utilizes the voltage-variable capacitance of a PN junction. In the normal semiconductor diode, efforts are made to minimize inherent capacitance, while in the varactor, this capacitance is emphasized. Since the capacitance varies with the applied voltage, it is possible to amplify, multiply, and switch with this device.

varhour meter—Also called a reactive volt-ampere-hour meter. An electricity meter which measures and registers the integral (usually in kilovarhours) of the reactive power of the circuit into which the meter is connected.

variable—Any factor or condition which can be measured, altered, or controlled (e.g., temperature, pressure, flow, liquid level, humidity, weight, chemical composition, color, etc.).

variable-area track—A sound track divided laterally into opaque and transparent areas. A sharp line of demarcation between these areas forms an oscillographic trace of the waveshape of the recorded signal.

variable-capacitance diode—Abbreviated vcd. A semiconductor diode in which the junction capacitance present in all semiconductor diodes has been accentuated. An appreciable change in the thickness of the junction-depletion layer and a corresponding change in the capacitance occur when the d-c voltage applied to the diode is changed.

variable-capacitance transducer—A transducer which measures a parameter or a change in a parameter by means of a change in capacitance.

Variable capacitor.

variable capacitor—A capacitor which can be changed in capacitance by varying the useful area of its plates, as in a rotary capacitor, or by altering the distance between them, as in some trimmer capacitors.

variable-carrier modulation — *See* Controlled-Carrier Modulation.

variable connector — 1. A flowchart symbol representing a sequence connection which is not fixed, but which can be varied by the flowcharted procedure itself. 2. The device which inserts instructions in a program corresponding to the selection of paths appearing in a flowchart. 3. The computer instructions which cause a logical chain to take one of several alternative paths.

variable coupling—Inductive coupling that can be varied by moving the windings.

variable-cycle operation—Computer operation in which any cycle is started at the completion of the previous cycle, instead of at specified clock times.

variable-density track—A sound track of constant width and usually, but not necessarily, of uniform light transmission on any instantaneous transverse axis. The average light transmission varies along the longitudinal axis in proportion to some characteristic of the applied signal.

variable-depth sonar—A sensor that can be lowered by cable from a ship or helicopter, through thermal layers, to detect submarines operating at deeper levels.

variable-erase recording—The method of recording on magnetic tape by selective erasure of a prerecorded signal.

variable field—A field in which the scalar (or vector) at any point changes during the time under consideration.

variable-frequency oscillator — Abbreviated vfo. A stable oscillator, the frequency of which can be adjusted over a given range.

variable inductance—A coil the inductance of which can be varied.

variable-inductance pickup—A phonograph

Variable inductance.

pickup in which the movement of a stylus causes the inductance to vary accordingly.

variable-inductance transducer — A transducer in which the output voltage is a function of the change in a variable-inductance element.

variable monoergic—A type of emission in which the magnitude of the homogeneous particle or radiation energy is continuously variable over broad limits; e.g., the proton energy from some types of accelerators can be controlled by varying the high voltage.

variable-mu pressure transducer—A device which converts mechanical input pressure to a proportional electrical output based on the change of the mu of its magnetic circuit due to the applied pressure (Villari effect).

variable-mu tube—*See* Remote-Cutoff Tube.

variable radio-frequency radiosonde — A radiosonde the carrier frequency of which is modulated by the magnitude of the meteorological variables being sensed.

variable-reluctance microphone—Also called a magnetic microphone. A microphone which depends for its operation on the variations in reluctance of a magnetic circuit.

Variable-reluctance pickup.

variable-reluctance pickup — Also called a magnetic pickup or cartridge. A phonograph pickup which depends for its operation on the variations in reluctance of a magnetic circuit.

variable-reluctance transducer—Also called a magnetic transducer. A transducer that depends for its operation on the variations in reluctance of a magnetic circuit.

variable-resistance pickup—A phonograph pickup which depends for its operation on the variation of a resistance.

variable-resistance transducer — A transducer in which the signal output depends on the change in a resistance element.

variable resistor—A wirewound or composi-

Variable resistors.

tion resistor, the resistance of which may be changed. (*Also see* Rheostat *and* Potentiometer.)

variable-speed motor—A motor the speed of which can be adjusted within certain limitations, regardless of load.

variable-speed scanning—A scanning method whereby the optical density of the film being scanned determines the speed at which the scanning beam in the cathode-ray tube of a television camera is deflected.

variable transformer—An iron-core transformer with provision for varying its output voltage over a limited range, or continuously from zero to maximum—generally by the movement of a contact arm along exposed turns of the secondary winding.

Variac—Trade name of General Radio Co. for a variable transformer.

variate — *See* Random Variable.

variations—The angular difference between a true and a magnetic bearing or heading.

varicap—*See* Varactor.

varindor—An inductor, the inductance of which varies markedly with the current in the winding.

variocoupler — A radio transformer with windings that have an essentially constant self-impedance, but the mutual impedance between them is adjustable.

variolosser—A device whose loss can be controlled by a voltage or current.

variometer—A variable inductor in which the inductance is changed by the relative position of two or more coils.

varistor—A two-electrode semiconductor device with a voltage-dependent nonlinear resistance that drops markedly as the applied voltage is increased.

Varley loop—A type of Wheatstone-bridge circuit which gives, in one measurement, the difference in resistance between two wires of a loop.

varmeter—Also called a reactive volt-ampere meter. An instrument for measuring reactive power in either vars, kilovars, or megavars. If the scale is graduated in kilovars or megavars, the instrument is sometimes designated a kilovarmeter or megavarmeter.

varnished cambric—A linen or cotton fabric that has been impregnated with varnish or insulating oil and baked. It is used as insulation in coils and other radio parts.

varying duty—A requirement of service that demands operation at loads and for intervals of time, both of which may be subject to wide variation.

varying-speed motor—A motor which slows

down as the load increases (e.g., a series motor, or an induction motor with a large amount of slip).

varying-voltage control—A form of armature-voltage control obtained by impressing, on the armature, a voltage which varies considerably with a change in load and consequently changes the speed of the motor (e.g., by using a differentially compound-wound generator or a resistance in the armature circuit).

V-beam system—A radar system for measuring elevation. The antenna emits two fan-shaped beams, one vertical and the other inclined, which intersect at ground level. Each beam rotates continuously about a vertical axis, and the time elapsing between the two echoes from the target provides a measure of its elevation.

vcd — Abbreviation for variable-capacitance diode.

V-cut—A type of crystal-oscillator cut in which the major plane surfaces are not parallel to the X, Y, or Z planes.

vector—The term for a symbol which denotes a directed quantity—i.e., one which cannot be completely described except in terms of both magnitude and direction (e.g., wind velocities, voltages and currents of electricity, and forces of all kinds).

vector admittance—The ratio for a single sinusoidal current and potential difference in a portion of a circuit of the corresponding complex harmonic current to the corresponding complex potential difference.

vector-ampere—The unit of measurement of vector power.

vector cardiograph — An instrument that measures both the magnitude and the direction of heart signals by displaying cardiograph signals on any desired set of axes, usually X, Y, and Z.

vector diagram—An arrangement of vectors showing the relationships between alternating quantities having the same frequency.

vector field—In a given region of space, the total value of some vector quantity which has a definite value at each point of the region (e.g., the distribution of magnetic intensity in a region surrounding a current-carrying conductor.

vector function—A function which has both magnitude and direction (e.g., the magnetic intensity at a point near an electric circuit is a vector function of the current in that circuit).

vector impedance—The ratio for a simple sinusoidal current and potential difference in a portion of a circuit of the corresponding complex harmonic potential difference to the corresponding complex current.

vector power—A vector quantity equal to the square root of the sum of the squares of the active and reactive powers. The unit is the vector-ampere.

vector power factor—Ratio of the active power to the vector power. In sinusoidal quantities, it is the same as power factor.

vector quantity—A quantity with both magnitude and direction.

velocimeter—A c-w reflection Doppler system used to measure the radial velocity of an object.

velocity—1. A vector quantity that includes both magnitude (speed) and direction in relation to a given frame of reference. 2. Rate of motion in a given direction, employed in its higher magnitudes as a means of overcoming the force of gravity.

velocity error—The amount of angular displacement existing between the input and output shafts of a servomechanism when both are turning at the same speed.

velocity filter—A storage-tube device which blanks all targets that do not move more than one resolution cell in less than a predetermined number of antenna scans.

velocity hydrophone—A type of hydrophone in which the electric output is substantially proportional to the instantaneous particle velocity in the incident sound wave.

velocity-lag error—A lag, between the input and output of a device, that is proportional to the rate of variation of the input.

velocity level—In decibels of a sound, 20 times the logarithm to the base 10 of the ratio of the particle velocity of the sound to the reference particle velocity. The latter must be stated explicitly.

velocity microphone—A microphone in which the electric output corresponds substantially to the instantaneous particle velocity in the impressed sound wave. It is a gradient microphone of order one, and is inherently bidirectional.

velocity-modulated amplifier—Also called a velocity-variation amplifier. An amplifier in which velocity modulation is employed for amplifying radio frequencies.

velocity-modulated oscillator—Also called a velocity-variation oscillator. An electron-tube structure in which the velocity of an electron stream is varied (velocity-modulated) in passing through a resonant cavity called a buncher. Energy is extracted from the bunched electron stream at a higher level in passing through a second cavity resonator called the catcher. Oscillations are sustained by coupling energy from the catcher cavity back to the buncher cavity.

velocity modulation—Also called velocity variation. Modification of the velocity of an electron stream by the alternate acceleration and deceleration of the electrons with a period comparable to that of the transit time in the space concerned.

velocity of light—A physical constant equal to 2.99796×10^{10} centimeters per second. (More conveniently expressed as 186,280 statute miles per second, 161,750 nautical miles per second, or 328 yards per microsecond.)

velocity of propagation—1. The speed at which a disturbance (sound, radio, light, etc., waves) is radiated through a medium.

2. The ratio of the speed of the flow of an electric current in an insulated cable to the speed of light, expressed in percentage. In the case of coaxial cables, this ratio is 65-66%, where the insulation is polyethylene.

velocity resonance—*See* Phase Resonance.

velocity sorting—The selecting of electrons according to their velocity.

velocity spectrograph—An apparatus for separating an emission of electrically charged particles into distinct streams, in accordance with their speed, by means of magnetic or electric deflection.

velocity transducer—A transducer which generates an output proportionate to the imparted velocities.

velocity variation—*See* Velocity Modulation.

velocity-variation amplifier—*See* Velocity-Modulated Amplifier.

velocity-variation oscillator—*See* Velocity-Modulated Oscillator.

Venn diagrams—Diagrams in which circles or ellipses are used to give a graphic representation of basic logic relations. Logic relations between classes, operations on classes, and the terms of the propositions are illustrated and defined by the inclusion, exclusion, or intersection of these figures. Shading indicates empty areas, crosses indicate areas that are not empty, and blank spaces indicate areas that may be either. Named for English logician John Venn, who devised them.

vent—A controlled weakness somewhere in the enclosure of an aluminum electrolytic capacitor to permit pressure relief in case of failure due to shorting or improper installation of the capacitor.

vented baffle—An enclosure designed to properly couple a speaker to the air.

venturi tube—A short tube with flaring ends and a constricted throat. It is used for measuring flow velocity by measurement of the throat pressure, which decreases as the velocity increases.

verification—The process of checking the results of one data transcription against those of another, both transcriptions usually involving manual operations. (*Also see* Check.)

verifier—Of computers, a device on which a record can be compared or tested for identity character by character with a retranscription or copy as it is being prepared.

verify—1. To check, usually with an automatic machine, one recording of data against another in order to minimize the number of human errors in the data transcription. 2. To make certain that the information being prepared for a computer is correct.

vernier—1. An auxiliary scale comprising subdivisions of the main measuring scale and thus permitting more accurate measurements than are possible from the main scale alone. 2. An auxiliary device used for obtaining fine adjustments.

vernier capacitor—A variable capacitor

placed in parallel with a larger tuning capacitor and used to provide a finer adjustment after the larger one has been set to the approximate desired position.

vernier dial—A type of tuning dial used chiefly for radio equipment. Each complete rotation of its control knob moves the main shaft only a fraction of a revolution and thereby permits fine adjustment.

vernitel — A precision device which makes possible the transmission of data with high accuracy over standard frequency-modulated–frequency-modulated telemetering systems.

Versatile Automatic Test Equipment — A computer-controlled tester for missile electronic systems. It troubleshoots faults by deductive logic and isolates them to the plug-in module or component level.

vertex—*See* Node.

vertex plate—A matching plate placed at the vertex of a reflector.

vertical—In 45/45 recording, the signal produced by a sound arriving at the two microphones simultaneously and 180° out of phase, causing the cutting stylus to move vertically.

vertical amplification — Signal gain in the circuits of an oscilloscope that produce vertical deflection on the screen.

vertical-amplitude controls — *See* Parabola Controls.

vertical antenna—A vertical metal tower, rod, or suspended wire that is used as a receiving and/or transmitting antenna.

vertical blanking—The blanking applied to a cathode-ray tube to eliminate the trace during flyback.

vertical-blanking pulse — In television, a pulse transmitted at the end of each field to cut off the cathode-ray beam while it returns to start the next field.

vertical-centering control—A control provided in a television receiver or cathode-ray oscilloscope to shift the entire image up or down on the screen.

vertical compliance—The ability of a reproducing stylus to move vertically while in the reproducing position on a record.

vertical-deflection electrodes—The pair of electrodes that move the electron beam up and down on the screen of a cathode-ray tube employing electrostatic deflection.

vertical dynamic convergence—Convergence of the three electron beams at the aperture mask of a color picture tube during the scanning of each point along a vertical line at the center of the tube.

vertical field-strength diagram—A representation of the field strength at a constant distance from, and in a vertical plane passing through, an antenna.

vertical-frequency response—In an oscilloscope, the band of frequencies passed, with amplification between specified limits, by the amplifiers that produce vertical deflection on the screen.

vertical-hold control—*See* Hold Control.

vertical-incidence transmission—The transmission of a radio wave vertically to the ionosphere and back. The transmission remains practically the same for a slight departure from the vertical (e.g., when the transmitter and receiver are a few kilometers apart).

vertical-lateral recording—A technique of making stereo phonograph discs by recording one signal laterally, as in monophonic records, and the other vertically, as in hill-and-dale transcriptions.

vertical-linearity control—A control that permits adjustment of the spacing of the horizontal lines on the upper portion of the picture to effect linear vertical reproduction of a televised scene.

vertically polarized wave—1. An electromagnetic wave with a vertical electric vector. 2. A linearly polarized wave with a horizontal magnetic field vector.

vertical polarization—Transmission in which the transmitting and receiving antennas are placed in a vertical plane, so that the electrostatic field also varies in a vertical plane.

vertical quarter-wave stub — An antenna with a vertical portion that is electrically one quarter-wavelength long. It is used generally with a ground plane at the base of the stub.

vertical radiator—A transmitting antenna perpendicular to the earth's surface.

vertical recording—Also called hill-and-dale recording. Mechanical recording in which the groove modulation is perpendicular to the surface of the recording medium.

vertical redundance—In a computer, an error condition which exists when a character fails a parity check, i.e., has an even number of bits in an odd-parity system, or vice versa.

vertical resolution—On a television test pattern, the number of horizontal wedge lines that can be clearly discerned by the eye before they merge together.

vertical retrace—The return of the electron beam from the bottom of the image to the top after each vertical sweep.

vertical speed transducer—An instrument which furnishes an electrical output that is proportionate to the vertical speed of the aircraft or missile in which it is installed.

vertical stylus force—*See* Stylus Force.

vertical sweep—The downward movement of the scanning beam from top to bottom of the televised picture.

vertical-synchronizing pulse — Also called picture-synchronizing pulse. One of the six pulses transmitted at the end of each field in a television system. It maintains the receiver in field-by-field synchronism with the transmitter.

very high frequency—Frequency band: 30 to 3000 MHz. Wavelength: 1 to 10 meters. Metric waves. Abbreviated vhf.

very long range—A classification of ground radar sets by slant range, applied to those with a maximum range exceeding 250 miles.

Vestigial-sideband television channel.

very low frequency—Frequency band: below 30 kHz. Wavelength: above 10,000 meters. Abbreviated vlf.

very short range—Classification of ground radar sets by slant range, applied to those with a maximum range of less than 25 miles.

vestigial—Pertaining to a remnant or remaining part.

vestigial sideband — Amplitude-modulated transmission in which a portion of one sideband has been largely suppressed by a transducer having a gradual cutoff in the neighborhood of the carrier frequency.

vestigial-sideband filter—A filter that is inserted between an a-m transmitter and its transmitting antenna to suppress part of one of the sidebands.

vestigial-sideband transmission — Also called asymmetrical sideband transmission. Signal transmission in which one normal sideband and the corresponding vestigial sideband are utilized.

vestigial-sideband transmitter — A transmitter in which one sideband and only a portion of the other are transmitted.

vfo—Abbreviation for variable-frequency oscillator.

vhf—Abbreviation for very high frequency.

vhf omnirange—Abbreviated vor. A specific type of range operating at vhf and providing radial lines of position in a direction determined by the bearing selection within the receiving equipment. A nondirectional reference modulation is emitted, along with a rotation pattern which develops a variable modulation of the same frequency as the reference modulation. Lines of position are determined by comparing the phase of the variable with that of the reference.

vibrating bell—A bell having a mechanism designed to strike repeatedly and as long as it is actuated.

vibrating-reed meter — A frequency meter consisting of a row of steel reeds, each having a different natural frequency. All are excited by an electromagnet fed with the alternating current whose frequency is to be measured. The reed whose frequency corresponds most nearly with that of the current vibrates, and the frequency is read on a scale beside the row of reeds.

vibrating-reed relay — A type of relay in which an alternating or a self-interrupted voltage is applied to the driving coil so as to produce an alternating or pulsating magnetic field that causes a reed to vibrate.

vibrating-wire transducer — A transducer which utilizes a thin wire suspended in a magnetic field; the change in tension of the wire reflects a frequency-modulating output.

vibration — 1. A continuously reversing change in the magnitude of a given force. 2. A mechanical oscillation or motion about a reference point of equilibrium.

vibration analyzer—A device used to analyze mechanical vibrations.

vibration galvanometer—An a-c galvanometer in which a reading is obtained by making the natural oscillation frequency of the moving element equal to the frequency of the current being measured.

vibration isolator—A resilient support that tends to isolate a system from steady-state excitation or vibration.

vibration meter—Also called a vibrometer. An apparatus comprising a vibration pickup, calibrated amplifier, and output meter, for the measurement of displacement, velocity, and acceleration of a vibrating body.

vibration pickup—A microphone that responds to mechanical vibrations rather than to sound waves. In one type a piezoelectric unit is employed; the twisting or bending of a Rochelle-salt crystal generates a voltage that varies with the vibration being analyzed.

vibration sensitivity — The peak instantaneous change in output at a given sinusoidal vibration level for any one stimulus value within the range of an instrument or equipment. It is usually expressed in percentage of full-scale output per vibratory "g" over a given frequency range. It may also be specified as a total error in percentage of full-scale output for a given vibratory acceleration level.

vibration survey—A method of determining the natural frequency of a transducer by observation of the output waveform upon the application of a shock or tapping of sufficient magnitude to initiate oscillation of the instrument.

vibrato—A musical embellishment which depends primarily on periodic variations of frequency, often accompanied by variations in amplitude and waveform. The quantitative description of vibrato is usually in terms of the corresponding modulation of frequency (5-7 Hz), amplitude, or waveform, or all three.

A—ACTUATING COIL
B—VIBRATOR REED
C—CONTACTS
D—CONTACTS
E—FRAME
F—CONNECTING LEADS
G—CASE
H—CONNECTING PINS
I—SPONGE RUBBER

Vibrator.

vibrator—A vibrating reed which is driven like a buzzer and has contacts arranged to interrupt direct current to the winding(s) of a transformer resulting in an alternating current being supplied from another winding to the load.

vibrator power supply—A power supply incorporating a vibrator, step-up transformer, rectifier, and filters for changing a low d-c voltage to a high d-c voltage.

vibratron—A triode with an anode that can be moved or vibrated by an external force. Thus, the anode current will vary in proportion to the amplitude and frequency of the applied force.

vibrograph—An apparatus for recording mechanical vibrations.

vibrometer—*See* Vibration Meter.

video—1. Pertaining to the bandwidth and spectrum position of the signal resulting from radar or television scanning. In current usage, video means a bandwidth on the order of several megahertz. 2. A prefix to the name of television parts or circuits which carry picture signals. 3. Radar or television signals which actuate the cathode-ray tube; frequencies extend from approximately 60 hertz to several megahertz.

video amplifier—An amplifier which provides wideband operation in the frequency range of approximately 15 hertz to 5 megahertz.

video carrier—The television signal whose modulation sidebands contain the picture, sync, and blanking signals.

videocast—1. To broadcast a program by means of television. 2. A program so broadcast.

video detector—The demodulator circuit which extracts the picture information from the amplitude-modulated intermediate frequency in a television receiver.

video discrimination—A radar circuit that reduces the frequency band of the video-amplifier stage in which it is used.

video frequency—1. The frequency of the signal voltage containing the picture information which arises from the television scanning process. In the present United States television system, these frequencies are limited from approximately 30 Hz to 4 MHz. 2. A band of frequencies extending from approximately 100 hertz to several megahertz.

video-frequency amplifier—A device capable of amplifying those signals that comprise the periodic visual presentation.

video-gain control—A control for adjusting the amplitude of a video signal. Two such controls are provided in the matrix section of some color television receivers so that the proper ratios between the amplitudes of the three color signals can be obtained.

video integration—A method of improving the output signal-to-noise ratio by utilizing the redundancy of repetitive signals to sum the successive video signals.

video integrator—1. An electric counter-countermeasure device used to reduce the response to nonsynchronous signals such as noise; it is useful against random pulse signals and noise. 2. A device which uses the redundancy of repetitive signals to improve the output signal-to-noise ratio by summing the successive video signals.

video mapping—The procedure whereby a chart of an area is electronically superimposed on a radar display.

video mixer—A circuit or device used to combine the signals from two or more television cameras.

video recording (magnetic tape)—The methods of recording data having a bandwidth in excess of 100 kHz on a single track.

video signal—The picture signal in a television system—generally applied to the signal itself and the required synchronizing and equalizing pulses.

video stretching—In navigation, a procedure whereby the duration of a video pulse is increased.

video tape—A wide magnetic tape designed for recording and playing back a composite black and white or color television signal.

video tape recording—Abbreviated vtr. A method of recording television picture and sound signals on tape for reproduction at some later time.

vidicon—A camera tube in which a charge-density pattern is formed by photoconduction and stored on that surface of the photoconductor which is scanned by an electron beam, usually of low-velocity electrons.

viewfinder—An auxiliary optical or electronic device attached to a television camera so the operator can see the scene as the camera sees it.

viewing mirror—A mirror used in some tele-

FOCUSING COIL

HORIZONTAL AND VERTICAL
DEFLECTING COILS

ALIGNMENT COIL

GLASS
FACEPLATE

GRID #2
GRID #1

CATHODE

GRID #3

TARGET
TARGET CONNECTION
GRID #4

Vidicon.

vision receivers to reflect the image formed on the screen of the picture tube at an angle convenient to the viewer.

viewing screen—The face of a cathode-ray tube on which the image is produced.

Villari effect—A phenomenon in which a change in magnetic induction occurs when a mechanical stress is applied along a specified direction to a magnetic material having magnetostrictive properties.

vinyl resin—A soft plastic used for making phonograph records.

virgin tape—*See* Raw Tape.

virtual address—In a computer, an immediate, or real-time, address.

virtual cathode—An electron cloud that forms around the outer grid in a thermionic vacuum tube when the inner grid is maintained slightly more positive than the cathode.

virtual height—The height of the equivalent reflection point that will cause a wave to travel to the ionosphere and back in the same time required for an actual reflection. In determining the virtual height, the wave is assumed to travel at uniform speed and the height is determined by the time required to go to the ionosphere and back at the assumed velocity of light.

virtual image—The optical counterpart of an object, formed at imaginary focuses by prolongations of light rays (e.g., the image that appears to be behind an ordinary mirror).

virtual ppi reflectoscope—A device for superimposing a virtual image of a chart onto the ppi pattern. The chart is usually prepared with white lines on a black background to the scale of the ppi range scale.

viscometer—Also called a viscosimeter. A device for measuring the degree to which a liquid resists a change in shape.

viscosimeter—*See* Viscometer.

viscosity—The frictional resistance offered by one part or layer of a liquid as it moves

past an adjacent part or layer of the same liquid.

viscous and magnetic damping—Damping by virtue of the viscosity of a fluid around the sensing element or of a magnetic field.

viscous-damped arm—A phonograph pickup arm mounted on a liquid cushion of oil, which provides high damping to eliminate arm resonances. It also protects the record groove and stylus; the arm does not fall on the record when dropped, but floats down gently.

visibility factor—Also called display loss. Ratio of the minimum input-signal power detectable by ideal instruments connected to the output of a receiver, to the minimum signal power detectable by a human operator through a display connected to the same receiver. The visibility factor may include the scanning loss.

visible radiation—Radiation with wavelengths ranging from about 4,000 to 8,000 angstrom units, corresponding to the visible spectrum of light.

visual aural range—Abbreviated var. A special type of vhf range providing a pair of radial lines of position which are reciprocal in bearing and are displayed to the pilot on a zero-center, left-right indicator. This facility also provides a pair of reciprocal radial lines of position located 90° from the above visually indicated lines. These are presented to the pilot as aural A-N radiorange signals, which provide a means for differentiating between the two visually indicated lines (and vice versa).

visual carrier frequency—The frequency of the television carrier which is modulated by the picture information.

visual communication—Communication by optical signs such as flags and lights.

visual radio range—Abbreviated vrr. A radio range, the course of which is followed by means of visual instruments.

visual transmitter—Also called a picture

transmitter. In television, the radio equipment for transmission of the picture signals only.

visual transmitter power—The peak power output during transmission of a standard television signal.

vitreous—Having the nature of glass.

vlf — Abbreviation for very low frequency.

vocabulary—A list of operating codes or instructions available for writing the program for a given problem and for a specific computer.

vodas—Acronym for Voice-Operated Device, Anti-Sing. A system for preventing the overall voice-frequency singing of a two-way telephone circuit by disabling one direction of transmission at all times.

voder—Acronym for Voice Operation DEmonstratoR. An electronic device capable of artificially producing voice sounds. It uses vacuum tubes in connection with electrical filters controlled through a keyboard.

vogad—Acronym for Voice-Operated Gain-Adjusting Device. A voice-operated device used to give a substantially constant volume output for a wide range of inputs.

voice coil—Also called a speaker voice coil. A coil attached to the diaphragm of a dynamic speaker and moved through the air gap between the pole pieces.

voice filter—A parallel-resonant circuit connected in series with a line feeding several speakers. Its purpose is to remove the tubbiness of the male voice. The frequency of resonance is adjusted somewhere between 125 and 300 Hz.

voice frequency—Also called the speech frequency. The audible range of frequencies (32-16,000 Hz). In telephony, the voice range for speech is about 100-3,500 Hz.

voice-frequency carrier telegraphy—Carrier telegraphy in which the carrier currents have frequencies such that the modulated currents may be transmitted over a voice-frequency telephone channel.

voice-frequency dialing—A method of dialing by which the direct-current pulses from the dial are transformed into voice-frequency alternating-current pulses..

voice-frequency telephony — Telephony in which the frequencies of the components of the transmitted electric waves are substantially the same as the frequencies of corresponding components of the actuating acoustical waves.

voice-grade channel—A channel suitable for the transmission of speech, digital or analog data, or facsimile, generally with a frequency range of about 300 to 3,000 hertz.

voice-grade circuit—A circuit suitable for the transmission of speech, digital or analog data, or facsimile, generally with a frequency range of about 300 to 3,000 hertz.

voice-operated device—A device which permits the presence of voice or sound signals to effect a desired control.

voice-operated device antising—A system for preventing the overall voice-frequency singing of a two-way telephone circuit by disabling one direction of transmission at all times.

voice-operated gain-adjusting device — A voice-operated device used to give a substantially constant-volume output for a wide range of inputs.

voice-operated loss control and suppressor—A voice-operated device which switches the loss out of the transmitting branch and inserts the loss into the receiving branch under control of the subscriber's speech.

volatile—1. A computer storage medium in which information cannot be retained without continuous power dissipation. 2. Capable of evaporating.

volatile memory—In computers, any memory which can return information only as long as energizing power is applied. The opposite of nonvolatile memory.

volatile storage—A computer storage device in which the stored information is lost when the power is removed (e.g., acoustic delay lines, electrostatics, capacitors, etc.).

volatile store—A storage device in which stored data are lost when the applied power is removed (e.g., an acoustic delay line).

Voldicon—The trade name of Adage, Inc., for a family of high-speed, all-semiconductor, current-balancing devices that use digital logic and readout for high-speed precision measurement of analog signals.

volt—Abbreviated V. The unit of measurement of electromotive force. It is equivalent to the force required to produce a current of 1 ampere through a resistance of 1 ohm.

Volta effect—*See* Contact Potential.

voltage—1. Electrical pressure—i.e., the force which causes current to flow through an electrical conductor. 2. Symbolized by **E**. The greatest effective difference of potential between any two conductors of a circuit.

voltage amplification—Also called voltage gain. Ratio of the voltage across a specified load impedance connected to a transducer, to the voltage across the input of the transducer.

voltage amplifier—An amplifier used specifically to increase a voltage. It is usually capable of delivering only a small current.

voltage-amplifier tube—A tube that is designed primarily as a voltage amplifier. It has high gain, but delivers very little output power.

voltage and power directional relay — A device which permits or causes the connection of two circuits when the voltage difference between them exceeds a given value in a predetermined direction, and causes these two circuits to be disconnected from each other when the power flowing between them exceeds a given value in the opposite direction.

voltage attenuation—Ratio of the voltage across the input of a transducer, to the voltage delivered to a specified load impedance connected to the transducer.

voltage balance relay — A device which operates on a given difference in voltage between two circuits.

voltage breakdown—1. The voltage necessary to cause insulation failure. 2. A rapid increase of current flow, from a relatively low value to a relatively high value, upon the application of a voltage to a PN junction or dielectric.

voltage-breakdown test—A test whereby a specified voltage is applied between given points in a device, to ascertain that no breakdown will occur at that specified voltage.

voltage calibrator—Test equipment which supplies accurate a-c voltages for comparison on a scope screen with other waveforms to determine their voltage level.

voltage circuit of a meter—The combination of conductors and windings of the meter itself, excluding multipliers, shunts, or other external circuitry, to which is applied the voltage to be measured, a definite fraction of that voltage, or a voltage dependent on it.

voltage coefficient of capacitance — Also called voltage sensitivity. The quotient of the derivative with respect to voltage of a capacitance characteristic at a point divided by the capacitance at that point.

voltage comparator—An amplifying device with a differential input that will provide an output polarity reversal when one input signal exceeds the other. When operating with open loop and without phase compensation, operational amplifiers make fast and accurate voltage comparators.

voltage-controlled capacitor—*See* Varactor.

voltage-controlled crystal oscillator — A crystal oscillator the operating frequency of which can be changed by applying a controlling voltage to introduce a phase shift in the oscillator circuit.

voltage-controlled oscillator—An oscillator the frequency of oscillation of which can be varied by a changing voltage.

voltage corrector—An active source of regulated power placed in series with the output of an unregulated supply. The voltage corrector senses changes in the output voltage (or current) and corrects for these changes automatically by varying its own output in the opposite direction so as to maintain the total output voltage constant.

voltage/current crossover—The characteristic of a power supply that automatically converts the mode of operation of a power supply from voltage regulation to current regulation (or vice versa) as required by preset limits. The constant-current and constant-voltage settings are independently adjustable over specified limits. The region near the intersection of the constant-voltage and constant-current curves is described by the term "crossover characteristics."

voltage-directional relay—1. A relay which functions in conformance with the direction of an applied voltage. 2. A device which operates when the voltage across an open circuit breaker or contacter exceeds a given value in a given direction.

voltage divider—Also called a potential divider. A resistor or reactor connected across a voltage and tapped to make a fixed or variable fraction of the applied voltage available. (*Also see* Potentiometer and Rheostat.)

Voltage doubler.

voltage doubler—A voltage multiplier which rectifies each half cycle of the applied alternating voltage separately, and then adds the two rectified voltages to produce a direct voltage having approximately twice the peak amplitude of the applied alternating voltage.

voltage drop—The difference in voltage between two points, due to the loss of electrical pressure as a current flows through an impedance.

voltage feed—Excitation of a transmitting antenna by applying voltage at a point of maximum potential (at a voltage loop or antinode).

voltage feedback—A form of amplifier feedback in which the voltage drop across part of the load impedance is put in series with the input-signal voltage.

voltage gain—*See* Voltage Amplification.

voltage generator—A two-terminal circuit element with a terminal voltage independent of the current through the element.

voltage gradient — The voltage per unit length along a resistor or other conductive path.

voltage inverter—A circuit having a response (output) proportional to a constant (the gain) times the input signal, but opposite in sign to it. In a unit-gain inverter, the output is (−1) times the input.

voltage jump—An abrupt change or discontinuity in the tube voltage drop during operation of glow-discharge tubes.

voltage level—Ratio of the voltage at any point in a transmission system, to an arbitrary value of voltage used as a reference. In television and other systems where waveshapes are not sinusoidal or symmetrical about a zero axis and where the sum of the maximum positive and negative excursions of the wave is important in system performance, the two voltages are given as peak-to-peak values. This ratio is usually expressed in dbv, signifying decibels referred to 1 volt peak-to-peak.

voltage limit—A control function that maintains a voltage between predetermined values.

voltage loop—A point of maximum voltage in a stationary wave system. A voltage loop exists at the ends of a half-wave antenna.

voltage-measuring equipment — Equipment for measuring the magnitude of an alternating or direct voltage.

voltage multiplier — 1. A rectifying circuit which produces a direct voltage approximately equal to an integral multiple of the peak amplitude of the applied alternating voltage. 2. A series arrangement of capacitors charged by rapidly rotating brushes in sequence, giving a high direct voltage equal to the source voltage multiplied by the number of capacitors in series. 3. A precision resistor used in series with a voltmeter to extend its measuring range.

voltage node—A point having zero voltage in a stationary-wave system (e.g., at the center of a half-wave antenna).

Voltage quadrupler.

voltage quadrupler—A rectifier circuit in which four diodes are employed to produce a d-c voltage of four times the peak value of the a-c input voltage.

voltage-range multiplier—Also called an instrument multiplier. A series resistor installed external to the measurement device to extend its voltage range.

voltage rating—Also called the working voltage. The maximum voltage which an electrical device or component can sustain without breaking down.

voltage ratio (of a transformer)—Ratio of the rms primary terminal voltage to the rms secondary terminal voltage under specified load conditions.

voltage-ratio box—*See* Measurement Voltage Divider.

voltage reference—A highly regulated voltage source used as a standard to which the output voltage of a power supply is continuously compared for purposes of regulation.

voltage-reference tube—A gas tube in which the voltage drop is essentially constant over the operating range of current, and is relatively stable at fixed values of current and temperature.

voltage reflection coefficient—The ratio of the complex electric field strength or voltage of a reflected wave to that of the incident wave.

voltage-regulating transformer — A saturated-core type of transformer which holds the output voltage to within a few percent, with input variations up to ±20%. Considerable harmonic distortion results unless extensive filters are employed.

voltage regulation—A measure of the degree to which a power source maintains its output-voltage stability under varying load conditions.

voltage regulator—1. A device that maintains or varies the terminal voltage of a generator or other machine at a predetermined value. 2. A gas-filled electronic tube which has the property of maintaining a nearly constant voltage across its terminals over a considerable range of current through the tube. It is used in an electronic voltage regulator.

Voltage-regulator tube.

voltage-regulator tube—Also called a VR tube. A glow-discharge, cold-cathode tube in which the voltage drop is essentially constant over the operating range of current, and which is designed to provide a regulated direct-voltage output.

voltage relay—A relay that functions at a predetermined value of voltage.

voltage saturation—*See* Plate Saturation.

voltage-sensitive resistor—A resistor (e.g., a varistor), the resistance of which varies with the applied voltage.

voltage sensitivity—1. The voltage that produces standard deflection of a galvanometer when impressed on a circuit made up of the galvanometer coil and the external critical-damping resistance. The voltage sensitivity is equal to the product of the current sensitivity and the total circuit resistance. 2. *See* Voltage Coefficient of Capacitance.

voltage-stabilizing tube—A gas-filled glow-discharge tube normally working in that part of characteristic where the voltage is practically independent of current drop within a given range.

voltage standard — An accurately known voltage source (e.g., a standard cell) used for comparison with or calibration of other voltages.

voltage standing-wave ratio — Abbreviated vswr. Ratio between the sum and difference of the incident and reflected voltage waves.

voltage to ground—The voltage between any live conductor of a circuit and earth (or common reference plane).

voltage transformer—*See* Potential Transformer.

voltage tripler—A rectifier circuit in which three diodes are employed to produce a d-c voltage equal to approximately three times the peak a-c input voltage.

voltage-tunable magnetron — A high-frequency, continuous-wave oscillator operating in the microwave region. Power outputs begin in the milliwatts range and extend through hundreds of watts.

voltage-tunable tube — An oscillator tube the operating frequency of which can be changed by varying one or more of its electrode voltage (e.g., a backward-wave magnetron).

voltage-type telemeter — A telemeter in which the translating means is the magnitude of a single voltage.

voltage-variable capacitor—*See* Varactor.

voltage velocity limit—*See* Slewing Rate.

voltaic cell—Early name for a primary cell.

voltaic couple—Two dissimilar metals in contact, resulting in a contact potential difference.

voltaic pile—A voltage source consisting of alternate pairs of dissimilar metal discs separated by moistened pads, forming a number of elementary primary cells in series.

volt-ammeter—An instrument, calibrated to read both voltage and current.

volt-ampere—Abbreviated VA. A unit of apparent power in an a-c circuit containing reactance. It is equal to the potential in volts multiplied by the current in amperes, without taking phase into consideration.

volt-ampere-hour meter — An electricity meter which measures the integral, usually in kilovolt-ampere-hours, of the apparent power in the circuit where the meter is connected.

volt-ampere meter—An instrument for measuring the apparent power in an alternating-current circuit. Its scale is graduated in volt-amperes or kilovolt-amperes.

volt-ampere reactive—Abbreviated var. Also called reactive volt-ampere. The unit of reactive power.

Volta's law—When two dissimilar conductors are placed in contact, the same contact potential is developed between them, whether the contact is direct or through one or more intermediate conductors.

volt box—*See* Measurement Voltage Divider.

volt-electron — An obsolete expression for electron-volt.

voltmeter — An instrument for measuring potential difference. Its scale is usually graduated in volts. If graduated in millivolts or kilovolts, the instrument is usually designated as a millivoltmeter or a kilovoltmeter.

voltmeter-ammeter—A voltmeter and an ammeter combined into a single case, but with separate circuits.

voltmeter sensitivity—Expressed in ohms-per-volt, the ratio of the total resistance of a voltmeter, to its full-scale reading in volts.

volt-ohm-milliammeter—A test instrument with several ranges, for measuring voltage, current, and resistance.

volume—1. Also called power level. 2. The magnitude (measured on a standard volume indicator) of a complex audio-frequency wave, expressed in volume units. In addition, the term "volume" is used loosely to signify either the intensity of a sound or the magnitude of an audio-frequency wave. 3. The amount or a measure of energy in an electrical or acoustical train of waves.

volume compression—Also called automatic volume compression. The limiting of the volume range to about 30 to 40 decibels at the transmitter, to permit a higher average percentage modulation without overmodulation. Also used in recording to raise the signal-to-noise ratio.

volume compressor—A circuit which provides volume compression.

volume conductivity—*See* Conductivity.

volume control—A variable resistor for adjusting the loudness of a radio receiver or amplifying device.

volume equivalent—A measure of the loudness of speech reproduced over a complete telephone connection. It is expressed numerically in terms of the trunk loss of a working reference system which has been adjusted to give equal loudness.

volume expander—A circuit which provides volume expansion.

volume expansion—*See* Automatic Volume Expansion.

volume indicator—An instrument for indicating the volume of a complex electric wave such as that corresponding to speech.

volume lifetime—The average time interval between the generation and recombination of minority carriers in a homogeneous semiconductor.

volume limiter—An amplifier the gain of which is automatically reduced when the average input volume to the amplifier exceeds a predetermined value, so that the output for all inputs in excess of this value is substantially constant. A volume limiter differs from a peak limiter in that it is controlled by the average volume instead of by the instantaneous peaks.

volume-limiting amplifier — An amplifier which reduces the gain whenever the input volume exceeds a predetermined level, so

that the output volume is maintained sub-
_____ ____ant. The normal gain is re-
_____ the input volume drops be-
_____mined limit.

_____striction—The relative vol-
_____ body of ferromagnetic ma-
_____ magnetization of the body
_____ zero to a specified value
_____on) under specified condi-

_____. Of a transmission system,
_____pressed in db, between the
_____inimum volumes which the
_____factorily handle. 2. Of a
_____equency signal, the differ-
_____ db, between the maximum
_____volumes occurring over a

_____ation rate—The rate at
_____rons and holes recombine
_____e of a semiconductor.
_____e—Ratio of the d-c voltage
_____electrodes in contact with
_____ a specimen, to that portion
_____between them distributed
_____imen.
_____y—1. Ratio of the potential
_____ to the current in a mate-
_____nt density. (*Also see* Re-

s_____ ____ __so called specific insulation resistance. The electrical resistance between
opposite faces of a 1-cm cube of insulating
material, commonly expressed in ohm-centi-
meters.

volumetric displacement — The change in
volume required to displace the diaphragm
of a pressure transducer from its rest position to a position corresponding to the
application of a stimulus equal to the rated
range of the transducer.

volumetric efficiency—Also called packing
factor. The ratio of parts volume to total
equipment volume, expressed in percent.
In modules, it is usually taken as the volume
of component bodies only (not including
leads, other interconnecting media, insulators, heat sinks, and so on) and based on
nominal sizes of components and nominal
outside module dimensions.

volumetric radar—A radar capable of producing three-dimensional position data on
several targets.

volume unit—1. The unit of transmission
measurement for measuring the level of
nonsteady-state currents. Zero level is the

steady-state reference power of 1 milliwatt
in a circuit of 600 ohms characteristic impedance. 2. A measure of the power level
of the voice wave. Zero volume unit is
equivalent to +4 dbm for simple electrical
waves (single frequencies). 3. A standardized
unit for specifying the power of voice or
music.

volume-unit indicator—Also called a VU indicator or volume-unit meter. An instrument
calibrated to read audio-frequency power
levels directly in volume units.

volume-unit meter—Abbreviated VU meter.
See Volume-Unit Indicator.

volume velocity—The rate at which a medium flows through a specified area due to
a sound wave.

Von Hippel breakdown theory—Also called
low-energy criterion. Breakdown occurs at
fields for which the rate of recombination
of electrons and positive holes is less than
the rate of collisional ionization. Assumes
no distribution in electron energies.

vor—Abbreviation for vhf omnirange.

vowel articulation—The percent of articulation obtained when the speech units considered are vowels, usually combined with
consonants into meaningless syllables.

V ring — In commutator construction, a specially shaped insulating structure having one
or more V-shaped sections.

vrr—Abbreviation for visual radio range.

vr tube — Abbreviation for voltage-regulator
tube.

vswr — Abbreviation for voltage standing-
wave ratio.

VTL — Abbreviation for variable threshold
logic.

vtm—*See* voltage-tunable magnetron.

vtr — Abbreviation for video-tape recording.

vtvm — Abbreviation for vacuum-tube voltmeter.

VU—Abbreviation for volume unit.

VU indicator—Abbreviation for volume-unit
indicator.

VU meter — Abbreviation for volume-unit
meter. A volume indicator with a decibel
scale and specified dynamic and other characteristics. It is used to obtain correlated
readings of speech power necessitated by
the rapid fluctuations in level of voice
currents.

vulcanized fiber—A laminated plastic insulation made of paper and cellulose dried
under heavy pressure.

PROGRAM LINE   600 OHM LOAD   VU METER

A   B   C   7500Ω   ←3900Ω→

VU meter.

W

W—Symbol for energy, watt, or work.

wafer—1. A thin semiconductor slice of silicon or germanium with parallel faces on which matrices of microcircuits or individual semiconductors can be formed. After processing, the wafer is separated into dice or chips containing individual circuits. 2. A single section of a wafer switch.

wafer socket—A vacuum-tube socket that consists of two punched sheets or wafers of an insulating material, separated by spring-metal clips that grip the terminal pins of the inserted tube.

wafer switch—A rotary multiposition switch with fixed terminals on ceramic or Bakelite wafers. The rotor arm, in the center, is positioned by a shaft. Several decks may be stacked onto one switch and rotated by a common shaft.

Wagner ground—A bridge with an additional pair of ratio arms, onto which the ground connection to the bridge is moved in order to effect a perfect balance, free from error.

waiting time—In certain tubes (e.g., thyratrons), the time that must elapse between the turning on of their heaters and the application of plate voltage. (*Also see* Access Time.)

Walkie-lookie.

walkie-lookie—A compact, portable television camera used for remote broadcasts. The resultant electrical pulses are transmitted by microwave radio to a local control point for retransmission over a standard television station.

walkie-talkie—A two-way radio communication set designed to be carried by one per-

Walkie-talkie.

son, usually strapped to his back, and capable of being operated while in motion.

wall box—A metal box placed in the wall and containing switches, fuses, etc.

wall outlet—A spring-contact device to which a portable lamp or appliance is connected by means of a plug attached to a flexible cord. The wall outlet is installed in a box, and connected permanently to the power-line wiring of a home or building.

walls—The sides of the groove in a disc record.

wamoscope—Acronym for a WAve-MOdulated oscilloSCOPE. A cathode-ray tube which includes detection, amplification, and display of a microwave signal in a single envelope, thus eliminating the local oscillator, mixer, i-f amplifier, detector, video amplifier, and associated circuitry in a conventional radar receiver. Tubes are available for a range of 2,000 to 4,000 MHz.

wander—*See* Scintillation.

warble-tone generator—An oscillator, the frequency of which is varied cyclically at a subaudio rate over a fixed range. It is usually used with an integrating detector to obtain an averaged transmission or cross-talk measurement.

warm-up time—1. In an indirectly-heated tube, the time which elapses, after the heater is turned on, before the cathode reaches its optimum operating temperature. 2. The time, following power application to a device, required for the output to stabilize within specifications. 3. In a regulated power

SECTION A-A

Wafer switch.

supply, the time, following power application to the supply, required for the output voltage (or current) to stabilize within specifications.

watch—*See* Radio Watch.

water-activated battery—A primary which contains the electrolyte but requires the addition of (or immersion in) water before it becomes usable.

water-cooled tube—A vacuum tube having an anode structure projecting through the glass envelope and constructed to permit circulation of water around the anode for cooling purposes during operation.

water load—A matched waveguide termination in which the electromagnetic energy is absorbed in water. The output power is calculated from the difference in temperature between the water at the input and output.

waterproof motor—A totally enclosed motor so constructed that it will exclude water applied in the form of a stream from a hose. Leakage may occur around the shaft, provided it is prevented from entering the oil reservoir and provision is made for automatically draining the motor. The means for automaitc draining may be a check valve, or a tapped hole at the lowest part of the frame which will serve for application of a drain pipe.

watt—1. Abbreviated W. A unit of the electric power required to do work at the rate of 1 joule per second. It is the power expended when 1 ampere of direct current flows through a resistance of 1 ohm. 2. Practical unit of electric power. In an alternating-current circuit, the true power in watts is effective volts multiplied by the circuit power factor (there are 746 watts in 1 horsepower).

wattage rating—The maximum power that a device can safely handle.

watt-hour—A unit of electrical work indicating the expenditure of 1 watt of electrical power for 1 hour. Equal to 3,600 joules.

watt-hour capacity—The number of watt-hours delivered by a storage battery at a specified temperature, rate of discharge, and final voltage.

watt-hour constant of a meter—The registration, expressed in watt-hours, corresponding to one revolution of the rotor.

watt-hour–demand meter—A combined watt-hour meter and demand meter.

watt-hour meter—An electricity meter which measures and registers the integral, usually in kilowatt-hours, of the active power of the circuit into which the meter is connected. This power integral is the energy delivered to the circuit during the integration interval.

wattless component—A reactive component.

wattless power—*See* Reactive Power.

wattmeter—An instrument for measuring the magnitude of the active power in an electric circuit. Its scale is usually graduated in watts. If graduated in kilowatts or mega-

watts, the instrument is usually designated as a kilowattmeter or megawattmeter.

watt-second—The amount of energy corresponding to 1 watt acting for 1 second. It is equal to 1 joule.

watt-second constant of a meter—The registration, in watt-seconds, corresponding to one revolution of the rotor.

wave—A physical activity that rises and falls, or advances and retreats, periodically as it travels through a medium.

wave amplitude—The maximum change from zero of the characteristic of a wave.

wave analyzer—An electric instrument for measuring the amplitude and frequency of the various components of a complex current or voltage wave.

wave angle—The angle at which a wave is propagated from one point to another.

wave antenna—Also called a Beverage antenna. A directional antenna composed of parallel horizontal conductors one-half to several wavelengths long, and terminated to ground in its characteristic impedance at the far end.

wave band—A band of frequencies, such as that assigned to a particular type of communication service.

wave-band switch—A multiposition switch for changing the frequency band tuned by a receiver or transmitter.

wave clutter—Clutter caused on a radar screen by echoes from sea waves.

wave converter—A device for changing a wave from one pattern to another (e.g., baffle-plate, grating, and sheath-reshaping converters for wave guides).

wave duct—1. A tubular waveguide capable of concentrating the propagation of waves within it. 2. A natural duct formed in air by atmospheric conditions. Waves of certain frequencies travel through it with more than average efficiency.

wave equation—An equation that gives a mathematical specification of a wave process, or describes the performance of a medium through which a wave is passing.

wave filter—A transducer for separating waves on the basis of their frequency. It introduces a relatively small insertion loss to waves in one or more frequency bands, and a relatively large insertion loss to waves of other frequencies. (*Also see* Filter.)

waveform—1. The shape of an electromagnetic wave. 2. The graphic representation of the wave in (1) above, showing the variations in amplitude with time.

waveform-amplitude distortion—Sometimes called amplitude distortion. Nonlinear waveform distortion caused by unequal attenuation or amplification between the input and output of a device.

waveform analyzer—An instrument that measures the amplitude and frequency of the components in a complex waveform.

waveform generator—*See* Timing-pulse Distributor.

waveform influence—The change in meter indication, caused solely by a change in waveform from a specified waveform, of the applied current and/or voltage.

waveform monitor — An oscilloscope designed especially for viewing the waveform of a video signal.

waveform synthesizer—Equipment for generating a signal of a desired waveform.

wavefront—1. In a progressive wave in space, a continuous surface which is a locus of points having the same phase at a given instant. 2. That part of a signal-wave envelope between the initial point of the envelope and the point at which the envelope reaches its crest.

wave function—In a wave equation, a point function that specifies the amplitude of a wave.

waveguide—1. A system of material boundaries capable of guiding electromagnetic waves. 2. A transmission line comprising a hollow conducting tube within which electromagnetic waves are propagated on a solid dielectric or dielectric-filled conductor.

waveguide attenuator — A waveguide device for producing attenuation by some means (e.g., by absorption and reflection).

waveguide connector—Also called a waveguide coupling. A mechanical device for electrically joining parts of a waveguide system together.

waveguide coupling—See Waveguide Connector.

waveguide critical dimension—The dimension of waveguide cross section which determines the cutoff frequency.

waveguide cutoff frequency — Also called the critical frequency. The frequency limit of propagation, along a waveguide, for waves of a given field configuration.

waveguide dummy load—Sections of waveguide for dissipating all the power entering the input flange.

Waveguide elbows.

waveguide elbow—A bend in a waveguide.

waveguide flange—See Flange.

waveguide lens — A microwave device in which the required phase changes are produced by refraction through suitable waveguide elements acting as lenses.

waveguide mode suppressor—A filter used to suppress undesired modes of propagation in a waveguide.

waveguide phase shifter—A device for adjusting the phase of the output current or voltage relative to the phase at the input of a device.

waveguide plunger — In a waveguide, a plunger used for reflecting the incident energy.

waveguide post — In a waveguide, a rod placed across the waveguide and behaving substantially like a shunt susceptance.

waveguide propagation—Long-range communications in the 10-kHz to 35-kHz frequency range by the waveguide characteristics of the atmospheric duct formed by the ionospheric D-layer and the surface of the earth. *Also see* Atmospheric Duct.

waveguide resonator—A waveguide device intended primarily for storing oscillating electromagnetic energy.

waveguide shim—A thin metal sheet inserted between waveguide components to insure electrical contact.

waveguide shutter—A vane within a waveguide, used to protect the receiver system from adjacent radar power by establishing an electrical short across the waveguide when a companion transmitter is operating.

waveguide stub — An auxiliary section of wave guide that has an essentially nondissipative termination and is joined to the main section of the waveguide.

waveguide switch — A transmission-line switch for connecting a transmitter or receiver from one antenna to another or to a dummy load.

waveguide taper—A section of tapered wave guide.

waveguide tee — A junction for connecting a branch section of waveguide in series or parallel with the main transmission line.

waveguide transformer — A device, usually fixed, added to a waveguide for the purpose of impedance transformation.

waveguide tuner — An adjustable device added to a waveguide for the purpose of impedance transformation.

waveguide twist—A waveguide section in which the cross section rotates about the longitudinal axis.

waveguide wavelength—Also called a guide wavelength. For a traveling plane wave at a given frequency, the distance along the waveguide, between the points at which a field component (or the voltage or current) differs in phase by 2π radians.

wave heating—The heating of a material by energy absorption from a traveling electromagnetic wave.

wave impedance (of a transmission line)—At every point in a specified plane, the complex ratio between the transverse components of the electric and magnetic fields. (Incident and reflected waves may both be present.)

wave interference—The phenomenon which results when waves of the same or nearly same type and frequency are superimposed.

It is characterized by variations in the wave amplitude which differ from that of the individual superimposed waves.

wavelength—1. In a periodic wave, the distance between points of corresponding phase of two consecutive cycles. The wavelength (λ) is related to the phase velocity (v) and frequency (f) by the formula $\lambda = v/f$. 2. The quotient of the velocity of propagation divided by the frequency.

wavelength constant—The imaginary part of the propagation constant—i.e., the part that refers to the retardation in phase of an alternating current passing through a length of transmission line.

wavelength shifter—A photofluorescent compound employed with a scintillator material. Its purpose is to absorb photons and emit related photons of a longer wavelength, thus permitting more efficient use of the photons by the phototube or photocell.

wave mechanics—A general physical theory whereby wave characteristics are assigned to the components of atomic structure and all physical phenomena are interpreted in terms of hypothetical waveforms.

wavemeter—An instrument for measuring the wavelength of a radio-frequency wave. Resonant-cavity, resonant-circuit, and standing-wave meters are representative types.

wave normal—A unit vector normal to an equiphase surface, with its positive direction taken on the same side of the surface as the direction of propagation. In isotropic media, the wave normal is in the direction of propagation.

wave number—The number of waves per unit length. The usual unit of wave number is the reciprocal centimeter, cm-1. In terms of this unit, the wave number is the reciprocal of the wavelength when the latter is in centimeters in a vacuum.

wave packet—A short pulse of waves (e.g., spin waves).

wave propagation—*See* Propagation.

waveshape—A graph of a wave as a function of time or distance.

wave tail—That part of a signal-wave envelope between the steady-state value (or crest) of an envelope and the end.

wave tilt—The forward inclination of a radio wave due to its proximity to ground.

wave train—A limited series of wave cycles caused by periodic short-duration disturbances.

wave trap — 1. Also called a trap. A device used to exclude unwanted signals or interference from a receiver. Wave traps are usually tunable to enable the interfering signal to be rejected or the true frequency of a received signal to be determined. 2. A resonant circuit connected into the antenna system of a radio receiver to suppress undesired signals at a particular frequency.

wave velocity—A quantity which specifies the speed and direction at which a wave travels through a medium.

way-operated circuit—A circuit shared by three or more stations on a "party-line" basis. One of the stations may be a switching center. May be a single or duplex circuit.

way point—A selected point having some particular significance on a radionavigational course line.

way station—In telegraphy, one of the stations on a multipoint network.

wax—In mechanical recording, a blend of waxes with metallic soaps.

wax master—*See* Wax Original.

wax original—Also called a wax master. An original recording on a wax surface, from which the master is made.

weak coupling—Loose coupling in a radio-frequency transformer. *Also see* Loose Coupling.

wearout—The point at which the continued operation and repair of an item becomes uneconomical because of the increased frequency of failure. The end of the useful life of the item.

wearout failure—A failure that is predictable on the basis of known wearout characteristics. This type of failure is due to deterioration processes or mechanical wear, the probability of occurrence of which increases with time.

weather-protected motor—An open motor the ventilating passages of which are so designed as to minimize the entrance of rain, snow, and airborne particles to the electric parts.

weber—The practical unit of magnetic flux equal to the amount which, when linked at a uniform rate with a single-turn electric circuit during an interval of 1 second, will induce an electromotive force of 1 volt in the circuit. One weber equals 10^8 maxwells.

wedge—1. The fan-shaped pattern of equidistant black and white converging lines in a television test pattern. 2. A waveguide termination consisting of a tapered length of dissipative material, such as carbon, introduced into the guide.

wedge bonding—A type of thermocompression bonding used in intergrated-circuit manufacturing where a wedge-shaped tool is used to press a small section of the lead wire onto the bonding pad.

Wehnelt cathode—A hot cathode that consists of a metallic core coated with alkaline-earth oxides. It is widely used in vacuum tubes.

weight—The force with which a body is attracted toward the earth.

weight coefficient of a thermoelectric generator—The quotient of the electrical power output of the thermoelectric generator divided by the weight of the generator.

weight coefficient of a thermoelectric generator couple—The quotient of the electrical power output of the thermoelectric couple divided by the weight of the couple.

weighted distortion factor—The weighting

of harmonics in proportion to their harmonic relationship.

weighted noise level — The noise level weighted in accordance with the 70-decibel equal-loudness contour of the human ear and expressed in dbm.

weighting—The artificial adjustment of measurements in order to account for factors which, during normal use of a device, would otherwise differ from the conditions during measurement. For example, background-noise measurements may be weighted by applying factors or introducing networks to reduce the measured values in inverse ratio to their interference.

weightlessness—1. A condition in which no acceleration, whether of gravity or other force, can be detected by an observer within the system in question. 2. A condition in which gravitational and other external forces acting on a body produce no stress, either internal or external, in the body. Weightlessness occurs when gravity forces are exactly balanced by other forms of acceleration (zero g).

weld—The consolidation of two metals, usually by application of heat to the proposed joint.

weldgate pulse — A waveform used in controlling the flow of welding current.

welding transformer—A power transformer with a secondary winding consisting of only a few turns of very heavy wire. It is used to produce high-value alternating currents at low voltages for welding purposes.

weld junction—A junction formed by heat or metallurgical fusion of conductors. It provides a strong electrical connection with good conductivity. It is widely used in microelectronic packaging. Wires, ribbons, or films as small as 0.0005-inch thick can be joined by resistance and electron-beam welding methods.

weld-on surface-temperature resistor — A surface-temperature resistor installed by welding the sensing element to the surface being measured.

weld polarity—Certain material combinations have a different resistance to a weld current, depending on the direction of the current. In d-c welding, a suitable weld may be possible in only one direction of current. A weld schedule must define the proper polarity for such cases.

weld time—The interval during which current is allowed to flow through the work during the performance of one weld. In pulsation welding, the weld period includes the "cool" time intervals.

Wertheim effect—When a wire placed in a longitudinal magnetic field is twisted, there will be a transient voltage difference between the ends of the wire.

Western Union joint—A strong, highly conductive splice made by crossing the cleaned ends of two wires, twisting them together, and soldering.

Western Union joint.

Weston normal cell—A standard cell of the saturated cadmium type in which the positive electrode is cadmium and the electrolyte is a cadmium-sulphate solution.

Westrex system—*See* Forty-five/Forty-five.

wet—Term describing the condition in which the liquid electrolyte in a cell is free-flowing.

wet cell—A cell the electrolyte of which is in liquid form and free to flow and move.

wet-charged stand—The period of time that a charged, wet secondary cell can stand before losing a specified, small percentage of its capacity.

wet contact—A contact through which direct current flows.

wet electrolytic capacitor—An electrolytic capacitor that has a liquid electrolyte.

wet flashover voltage—The voltage at which the air surrounding a clean, wet insulator shell breaks down completely between electrodes. This voltage will depend on the conditions under which the test is made.

wet-reed relay—A reed-type relay containing mercury at the relay contacts to reduce arcing and contact bounce.

wet shelf life—The period of time that a wet secondary cell can remain discharged without deteriorating to a point where it cannot be recharged.

wet tantalum capacitor—A polar capacitor the cathode of which is a liquid electrolyte (a highly ionized acid or salt solution). Characteristics: highest capacity per unit volume, low impedance, lowest d-c leakage, excellent shelf life.

wetting—The formation of a uniform, smooth, unbroken, and adherent film of solder to a base metal.

Wheatstone bridge—Also called resistance bridge. A null-type resistance-measuring circuit in which resistance is measured by direct comparison with a standard resistance.

wheel static—Auto-radio interference due to a static charge building up between the brake drum and the wheel spindle.

whiffletree switch—In computers, a multiposition electronic switch composed of gate tubes and flip-flops. It is so named because its circuit diagram resembles a whiffletree.

$$R_x = R_3 R_2 / R_1$$

Wheatstone bridge.

whip antenna — A simple vertical antenna consisting of a slender whiplike conductor supported on a base insulator.

whisker — 1. *See* Catwhisker. 2. Ultrapure elongated metal and ceramic filaments of extremely high tensile strengths.

whistler mode propagation — The transmission of radio waves between conjugate points with respect to the geomagnetic equator; i.e., points of opposite geomagnetic latitude and equal geomagnetic longitude by the apparent ducting of waves long the flux lines of the geomagnetic field.

whistlers — 1. High-frequency atmospherics that decrease in pitch and then tend to rise again. 2. Audio-frequency waves from lightning-stroke radiation that have penetrated the ionosphere.

white — 1. For color tv, white is a mixture of red, green, and blue. In the picture this is produced by exciting all three dots in each phosphor trio. Since the eye cannot distinguish the individual dots, the mixture appears white. 2. The facsimile signal produced when an area of subject copy having minimum density is scanned.

white circuit — A cathode follower with another tube replacing the cathode resistor. By driving this additional tube with a signal that is out of phase with the original signal, low-impedance, broad-band characteristics are obtained.

white compression — Also called white saturation. The reduction in gain applied to a picture signal at those levels corresponding to light areas in a picture.

white-dot pattern — *See* Dot Pattern.

white level — The carrier-signal level which corresponds to maximum picture brightness in television and facsimile.

white light — Radiation producing the same color sensation as average sunlight at noon.

white noise — 1. Random noise (e.g., shot and thermal noise) whose constant energy per unit bandwidth is independent of the central frequency at the band. The name is taken from the analogous definition of white light. 2. The electrical disturbance caused by the random movement of free electrons in a conductor or semiconductor. Since its electrical energy is evenly distributed throughout the entire frequency spectrum, it is useful for testing the frequency response of amplifiers, speakers, etc. 3. Continuous, random noise distributed uniformly across the frequency spectrum.

white object — An object which reflects all wavelengths of light with substantially equal high efficiencies and considerable diffusion.

white peak — A peak excursion of the picture signal in the white direction.

white raster — *See* Chroma-Clear Raster.

white recording — 1. In an amplitude-modulation system, that form of recording in which the maximum received power corresponds to the minimum density of the record medium. 2. In a frequency-modulation system, that form of recording in which the lowest received frequency corresponds to the minimum density of the record medium.

white room — An area in which the atmosphere is controlled to eliminate dust, moisture, and bacteria. It is used in the production and assembly of components and systems, the reliability or functions of which might be adversely affected by the presence of foreign matter.

white saturation — *See* White Compression.

white signal — The facsimile signal produced when a minimum-density area of the subject copy is scanned.

white-to-black amplitude range — 1. In a facsimile system employing positive amplitude modulation, the ratio of signal voltage (or current) for picture white to that for picture black at any point in the system. 2. In a facsimile system employing negative amplitude modulation, the ratio of the signal voltage (or current) for picture black to that for picture white. Both ratios are often expressed in decibels.

white-to-black frequency swing — In a facsimile system employing frequency modulation, the numerical difference between the signal frequencies corresponding to picture white and picture black at any point in the system.

white transmission — 1. In an amplitude-modulation system, that form of transmission in which the maximum transmitted power corresponds to the minimum density of the subject copy. 2. In a frequency-modulation system, that form of transmission in which the lowest transmitted frequency corresponds to the minimum density of the subject copy.

whole step — *See* Whole Tone.

whole tone — Also called a whole step. The interval between two sounds with a basic frequency ratio approximately equal to the sixth root of 2.

wicking—1. The flow of solder up under the insulation on covered wire. 2. The act of drawing moisture through a fabric or thread, like the action of a wick in an oil lamp when it draws oil up to the flame.

wide-angle lens—A lens that picks up a wide area of a television stage setting at a short distance.

wideband—Capable of passing a broad range of frequencies (said of a tuner or amplifier). Especially vital to good multiplex reception, and for faithful audio reproduction.

wideband amplifier — An amplifier capable of passing a wide range of frequencies with equal gain.

wideband axis—In phasor representation of the chrominance signal, the direction of the phasor representing the fine-chrominance primary.

wideband communications system—A communications system which provides numerous channels of communications on a highly reliable and secure basis; the channels are relatively invulnerable to interruption by natural phenomenon or counter-measures. Included are multichannel telephone cable, tropospheric scatter, and multichannel line-of-sight radio systems such as microwave.

wideband improvement — Ratio of the signal-to-noise ratio of the system in question, to the signal-to-noise ratio of a reference system.

wideband ratio — Ratio of the occupied-frequency bandwidth to the intelligence bandwidth.

wide open—Refers to the untuned characteristic or lack of frequency selectivity.

wide-open receiver—A receiver that has essentially no tuned circuits and is designed to receive all frequencies simultaneously in the band of coverage.

width—1. The distance between two specified points of a pulse. 2. The horizontal dimension of a television or facsimile display.

width coding—Modifying the duration of the pulses emitted from the transponder according to a prearranged code for recognition in the display.

width control—A television-receiver or an oscilloscope control which varies the amplitude of the horizontal sweep and hence the width of the picture.

Wiedemann effect—The direct Wiedemann effect is the twist produced in a wire placed in a longitudinal magnetic field when a current flows through the wire; the twist is due to the helical resultant of the impressed longitudinal field and the circular field of the wire. The magnetic material expands (or contracts) parallel to the helical lines of force and hence the twist. The inverse Wiedemann effect is the axial magnetization of a current-carrying wire when twisted.

Wiedemann-Franz law—A theoretical result which states that the ratio of thermal conductivity to electrical conductivity is the same for all metals at the same temperature.

Wien bridge—An alternating-current bridge used to measure inductance or capacitance in terms of resistance and frequency. *Also see* Wien Capacitance Bridge *and* Wien Inductance Bridge.

Wien-bridge oscillator—An oscillator, the frequency of which is controlled by a Wien bridge.

$$\frac{C_3}{C_4} = \frac{R_2}{R_1} - \frac{R_4}{R_3} \qquad C_2 C_4 = \frac{1}{\omega^2 R_3 R_4}$$

Wien capacitance bridge.

Wien capacitance bridge—A four-arm, alternating-current capacitance bridge used for measuring capacitance in terms of resistance and frequency. Two adjacent arms contain capacitors—one in series and the other in parallel with a resistor—while the other two are normally nonreactive resistors. The balance depends on the frequency, but the capacitance of either or both capacitors can be computed from the resistances of all four arms and from the frequency.

Wien inductance bridge—A four-arm alternating-current inductance bridge used for measuring inductance in terms of resistance and frequency. Two adjacent arms contain inductors—one in series and the other in parallel with a resistor—while the other two are normally nonreactive resistors. The balance depends on the frequency, but the inductances of either or both inductors can be computed from the resistances of the four arms and from the frequency.

Wien's law—Better known as Wien's displacement law. The wavelength of maximum radiation intensity is inversely proportional to the absolute temperature of a black body, and the intensity of radiation at this maximum wavelength varies as the fifth power of the absolute temperature.

Williamson amplifier—A high-fidelity, push-pull, audio-frequency amplifier using triode-connected tetrodes. The circuit was developed by D. T. N. Williamson.

Williams-tube storage—A type of electrostatic storage using a cathode-ray tube.

$$\frac{L_3}{L_4} = \frac{R_1(R_L + R_3)}{R_2R_3 - R_1R_4}$$

$$\omega^2 L_3 L_4 = R_4(R_L + R_3) - R_L R_3 \frac{R_2}{R_1}$$

Wien inductance bridge.

Wimshurst machine—A common static machine or electrostatic generator consisting of two coaxial insulating discs rotating in opposite directions. Sectors of tinfoil are arranged, with respect to a connecting rod and collecting combs, so that static electricity is produced for charging Leyden jars or discharging across a gap.

wind—The way in which recording tape is wound onto a reel. An A wind is one in which the tape is wound so that the coated surface faces toward the hub; a B wind is one in which the coated surface faces away from the hub. A uniform, as opposed to an uneven, wind is one giving a flat side tape pack, free from laterally displaced, protruding layers.

wind charger—A wind-driven d-c generator for changing batteries (e.g., 32-volt batteries formerly used on many farms).

winding—A conductive path, usually wire, inductively coupled to a magnetic core or cell. Windings may be designated according to function—e.g., sense, bias, drive, etc.

winding arc—In an electrical machine, the length of a winding stated in terms of degrees.

winding factor—The ratio of the total area of wire in the center hole of a toroid to the window area of a toroid or transformer core.

window—1. Strips of metal foil, wire, or bars dropped from aircraft or fired from shells or rockets as a radar countermeasure. 2. The small area through which beta rays enter a Geiger-Mueller tube.

Window area.

window area—The opening in the laminations of a transformer.

window corridor—Also called the infected area or lane. An area where window has been sown.

window jamming — Reradiation of electromagnetic energy by reflecting it from a window to jam enemy electronic devices.

windshield—In radar, a streamlined cover placed in front of airborne paraboloid antennas to minimize wind resistance. The cover material is such as to present no appreciable attenuation to the radiation of the radar energy.

wing spot generator—An electronic circuit that grows wings on the video target signal of a type-G indicator. These wings are inversely proportional in size to the range.

wiper—1. The moving contact which makes contact with a terminal in a stepping relay or switch. 2. In a potentiometer, the contact that moves along the element, dividing the

Wimshurst inductance static machine.

resistance according to its mechanical position.

wiper arm—In a pressure potentiometer, the movable electrical contact that is driven by the sensing element and moves along the coil.

wiping action—The action which occurs when contacts are mated with a sliding action. Wiping has the effect of removing small amounts of contamination from the contact surfaces, thus establishing better conductivity.

wiping contact—Also called self-cleaning contact, sliding contact, and self-wiping contact. A switch or relay contact designed to move laterally with a wiping motion when engaging with or disengaging from a mating contact.

wire—A solid or stranded group of solid cylindrical conductors having a low resistance to current flow, together with any associated insulation.

wire communication—Transmission of signs, signals, pictures, and sounds of all kinds over wire, cable, or other similar connections.

wired-program computer — A computer in which nearly all instructions are determined by the placement of interconnecting wires held in a removable plugboard. This arrangement allows for changes of operations by simply changing plugboards. If the wires are held in permanently soldered connections, the computer is called a fixed-program type.

wired radio—Communication whereby the radio waves travel over conductors.

wire drawing—The pulling of wire through dies made of tungsten carbide or diamond with a resultant reduction in the diameter of the wire.

wire dress—Arranging of wires or conductors in preparation for a mechanical hookup.

wire gage—Also called American Wire Gage (AWG), and formerly Brown and Sharpe (B&S) Gage. A system of numerical designations of wire sizes, starting with 0000 as the largest size and going to 000, 00, 1, 2, and beyond for the smaller sizes.

wire grating—An arrangement of wires set into a waveguide to pass one or more waves while obstructing all others.

wire-guided—In missile terminology, guided by electrical impulses sent over a closed wire circuit between the guidance point and the missile.

wireless—1. A British term for radio. 2. Used in the United States, in the sense of (1) above, when the word "radio" might be misinterpreted (e.g., wireless record player).

wireless device—Any apparatus (e.g., a wireless record player) that generates a radio-frequency electromagnetic field for operating associated apparatus not physically connected and at a distance in feet not greater than 157,000 divided by the frequency in kilohertz. Legally, the total electromagnetic field produced at the maximum operating distance cannot exceed 15 microvolts per meter.

wireless record player—*See* Wireless Device.

wire-link telemetry—Also called hard-wire telemetry. Telemetry in which a hard-wire link is used as the transmission path, no radio link being used.

wirephoto—Transmission of a photograph or other single image over a telegraph system. The image is scanned into elemental areas in orderly sequence, and each area is converted into proportional electric signals which are transmitted in sequence and reassembled in correct order at the receiver.

wire printer—A high-speed printer that prints characterlike configurations of dots through the proper selection of wire ends from a matrix of wire ends, rather than conventional characters through the selection of type faces.

wire recorder—A magnetic recorder in which the recording medium is a round stainless-steel wire about 0.004 inch in diameter rather than magnetic tape.

wire recording — A recording method in which the medium is a thin stainless-steel wire (instead of a tape or disc).

wiresonde—An atmospheric sounding instrument which is supported by a captive balloon and used to obtain temperature and humidity data from ground level to a height of a few thousand feet. Height is determined by means of a sensitive altimeter, or from the amount of cable released and the angle which the cable makes with the ground. The information is telemetered to the ground station through a wire cable.

wire splice—An electrically sound and mechanically strong junction of two or more conductors.

wireways—Sheet-metal troughs with hinged covers for housing and protecting electrical conductors and cable, and in which conductors are laid in place after the wireway has been installed as a complete system.

Wirewound resistor (adjustable).

wirewound resistor—A resistor in which the resistance element is a length of high-resistance wire or ribbon wound onto an insulating form.

wire wrap—*See* Solderless Wrap.

wire wrapping—A technique for terminating conductors.

wiring connector—A device for joining one or more wires together.

wiring diagram—A drawing that shows electrical equipment and/or components, together with all interconnecting wiring.

wobble—*See* Flicker.

wobble stick—A rod extending from a pendant station to operate the "stop" contacts; it will function when pushed in any direction.

wobbulator—More commonly called a sweep generator. A signal generator, the frequency of which is varied automatically and periodically over a definite range. It is used, together with a cathode-ray tube, for testing frequency response. One form consists of a motor-driven variable capacitor, which is used to vary the output frequency of a signal generator periodically between two limits.

woofer—A speaker designed to reproduce the bass frequencies. It is usually used with a crossover network and a tweeter.

word—A group of characters occupying one storage location in a computer. It is treated by the computer circuits as an entity, by the control unit as an instruction, and by the arithmetic unit as a quantity.

word length—1. The number of bits or characters handled as a physical unit by a computer or other device. 2. The size of a field.

word pattern—The smallest meaningful language unit recognized by a machine. It is usually composed of a group of syllables and/or words.

word rate—The frequency derived from the elapsed period between the beginning of the transmission of one word and the beginning of transmission of the next word.

word size—In computer terminology, the number of decimal or binary bits comprising a word.

word time—*See* Minor Cycle.

work—The magnitude of a force times the distance through which that force is applied. (*Also see* Load.)

work coil—*See* Load Coil.

work function—1. The minimum energy (commonly expressed in electron volts) required to remove an electron from the Fermi level of a material and send it into field-free space. 2. A general term applied to the energy required to transfer electrons or other particles from the interior of one medium, across a boundary, into an adjacent medium.

work hardening—The strengthening of a crystalline material resulting from plastic deformation.

working memory—*See* Working Storage.

working Q—*See* Loaded Q.

working storage—Also called the working memory. In a computer storage (internal), a portion reserved by the program for the data upon which the operations are being performed.

working voltage—1. *See* Voltage Rating. 2. The recommended maximum voltage of operation for an insulated conductor. It is usually set at approximately one-third of the breakdown voltage. 3. The voltage rating of a fixed capacitor. It is the recommended

maximum voltage at which the unit should be operated.

worm—A gear with teeth in the form of screw threads.

worst-case circuit analysis—A type of circuit analysis used to determine the worst possible effect on the output parameters due to changes in the values of circuit elements. The circuit elements are set to the values within their anticipated ranges that produce the maximum detrimental changes in the output.

worst-case design—An extremely conservative design approach in which the circuit is designed to function normally, even though all component values have simultaneously assumed the worst possible condition that can be caused by initial tolerance, aging, etc. Worst-case techniques are also applied to obtain conservative derating of transient and speed specifications.

worst-case noise pattern—Maximum noise appearing when half of the half-selected cores are in a 1 state and the other half are in a 0 state. Sometimes called checkerboard or double-checkerboard pattern.

wound-rotor induction motor—An induction motor in which the secondary circuit consists of a polyphase winding or coils with either short-circuited terminals or ones closed through suitable circuits.

wow—Distortion caused in sound reproduction by variations in speed of the turntable or tape. (*Also see* Flutter.)

wow meter—An instrument that indicates the instantaneous speed variation of a turntable or similar equipment.

wrap—1. One winding of ferromagnetic tape. 2. The length of the path of a magnetic recording tape along which the tape and head are in intimate physical contact. It is sometimes measured as the angle of arrival and departure of the tape with respect to the head.

wrap-around—The amount of curvature exhibited by the magnetic tape or film in passing over the pole pieces of the magnetic heads.

wrapper—An insulating barrier applied to a coil by wrapping a sheet of insulating material around the coil periphery so as to form an integral part of the coil.

wrapping—A method of applying insulation to wire by serving insulating tapes around the conductor.

wratten filter—An optical filter used for filtering a given band of light. It is used in film-recorder optical systems when recording directly on color film (direct positive). It is also extensively used in photography.

wrinkle finish—An exterior paint that dries to a wrinkled surface when applied to cabinets or panels.

write—In a computer: 1. To copy, usually from internal to external storage. 2. To transfer elements of information to an output medium. 3. To record information in a register, location, or other storage device or medium. 4. To establish a charge pattern corresponding to the input (charge-storage tubes). (*Also see* Read.)

write pulse—In a computer, a pulse that is used to enter information into one or more magnetic cells for storage purposes.

writing rate—The maximum speed at which the spot on a cathode-ray tube can move and still produce a satisfactory image.

writing speed—The rate of writing on successive storage elements in a charge-storage tube.

wvdc—Abbreviation for working voltage, direct current. This is the maximum safe d-c operating voltage that can be applied across the terminals of a capacitor at its maximum operating temperature.

WWV—Call letters of the radio station of the National Bureau of Standards in Washington, D. C. WWV provides radio-broadcast technical services, including time signals, standard radio and audio frequencies, and radio-propagation disturbance warnings at 2.5, 5, 10, 15, 20, 25, 30, and 35 megahertz.

WWVH—Call letters of the National Bureau of Standards' radio station at Maui, Hawaii. It broadcasts on 5, 10, and 15 MHz for many locations not served by WWV.

wye connection—Also called a star connection. A Y-shaped winding connection.

wye junction—A Y-shaped junction of waveguides.

X

X—Symbol for reactance.

X and Z demodulation—A system of color-tv demodulation in which the two reinserted 3.58-MHz subcarrier signals differ by approximately 60° rather than the usual 90°. The R-Y, B-Y, and G-Y voltages are derived from the demodulated signals, and these voltages control the three guns of the picture tube. An important advantage of this system is that receiver circuitry is simpler than that required with I and Q demodulation.

X-axis—1. The reference axis in a quartz crystal. 2. The horizontal axis in a system of rectangular coordinates.

X-band—A radio-frequency band of 5,200 to 11,000 MHz, with wavelengths of 5.77 to 2.75 cm.

X-bar—A rectangular crystal bar, usually cut from a Z-section, elongated parallel to X and with its edges parallel to X, Y, and Z.

X_C—Symbol for capacitive reactance.

X-cut crystal—A crystal cut so that its major surfaces are perpendicular to an electrical (X) axis of the original quartz crystal.

xenon—A rare gas used in some thyratron and other gas tubes.

xerographic printer—A device for printing an optical image on paper; light and dark areas are represented by electrostatically charged and uncharged areas on the paper. Powdered ink, dusted on the paper, adheres to the charged areas and is subsequently melted into the paper by the application of heat.

xerographic recording — A recording produced by xerography.

xerography—That branch of electrostatic electrophotography in which images are formed onto a photoconductive insulating medium by infrared, visible, or ultraviolet radiation. The medium is then dusted with a powder, which adheres only to the electrostatically charged image. Heat is then applied in order to fuse the powder into a permanent image.

xeroprinting—Printing by xerography.

xeroradiography—Xerography in which X- or gamma rays are used.

xistor—Abbreviation for transistor.

X_L—Symbol for inductive reactance.

xmitter — Abbreviation for transmitter. Also abbreviated trans or xmtr.

xmsn—Abbreviation for transmission.

xmtr—Abbreviation for transmitter. Also abbreviated trans or xmitter.

X-particle—A particle having the same negative charge as an electron, but a mass between that of an electron and a proton. It is produced by cosmic radiation impinging on gas molecules or actually forming a part of cosmic rays.

X-ray apparatus—An X-ray tube and its accessories, including the X-ray machine.

X-ray crystallography—Use of X-rays in studying the arrangement of the atoms in a crystal.

X-ray detecting device—A device which detects surface and volume discontinuities in solids by means of X-rays.

X-ray diffraction camera—A camera that directs a beam of X-rays into a sample of unknown material and allows the resultant diffracted rays to act on a strip of film.

X-ray diffraction pattern—The pattern produced on film exposed in an X-ray diffraction camera. It is made up of portions of circles having various spacings, depending on the material being examined.

X-ray goniometer—An instrument that determines the position of the electrical axes of a quartz crystal by reflecting X-rays from the atomic planes of the crystal.

X-rays—Also called roentgen rays. Penetrating radiation similar to light, but having much shorter wavelengths (10^{-7} to 10^{-10} cm). They are usually generated by bombarding a metal target with a stream of high-speed electrons.

X-ray spectrometer—An instrument for producing an X-ray spectrum and measuring the wavelengths of its components.

X-ray spectrum—An arrangement of a beam of X-rays in the order of wavelength.

X-ray thickness gage—A contactless thickness gage used to measure and indicate the thickness of moving cold-rolled sheet steel during the rolling process. An X-ray beam directed through the sheet is absorbed in proportion to the thickness of the material and its atomic number, and a measure of the amount of absorption gives a continuous indication of sheet thickness.

X-ray tube—A vacuum tube in which X-rays are produced by bombarding a target with high-velocity electrons accelerated by an electrostatic field.

xtal—Abbreviation for crystal.

X-wave—One of the two components into which the magnetic field of the earth divides a radio wave in the ionosphere. The other component is the ordinary, or O-, wave.

XY-cut crystal—A crystal cut so that its characteristics fall between those of an X- and a Y-cut crystal.

XY plotter—A device used in conjuction with

X-ray tube.

a computer to plot coordinate prints in the form of a graph.

XY recorder—A recorder that traces, on a chart, the relationship between two variables, neither of which is time. Sometimes the chart moves and one of the variables is controlled so that the relationship does increase in proportion to time.

XY switch—A remote-controlled bank-and-wiper switch arranged so that the wipers move back and forth horizontally.

Y

Y—Symbol for admittance.

Yagi antenna.

Yagi antenna—A type of directional antenna array consisting usually of one driven half-wavelength dipole section, one parasitically excited reflector, and several parasitically excited directors.

Y antenna—*See* Delta Matched Antenna.

Y-axis — 1. A line perpendicular to two parallel faces of a quartz crystal. 2. The vertical axis in a system of rectangular coordinates.

Y-bar—A crystal bar cut in Z-sections, with its long direction parallel to Y.

Y-connected circuit — A star-connected, three-phase circuit.

Y-connection—*See* Y-network.

Y-cut crystal—A crystal cut in such a way that its major flat surfaces are perpendicular to the Y axis of the original quartz crystal.

yield map—A microcircuit or semiconductor wafer on which dots indicate those devices that failed the test criteria.

yield strength—*See* Yield Value.

yield value—Also called yield strength. The lowest stress at which a material undergoes plastic deformation. Below this stress, the material is elastic; above it, viscous.

Y-junction—A junction of waveguides in which their longitudinal axes form a Y.

Y-match.

Y-match — Also called a delta match. A method of connecting to an unbroken dipole. The transmission line is fanned out and connected to the dipole at the points where the impedance is the same as that of the line.

Y-network—Also called a Y-connection. A star network of three branches.

yoke—A set of coils placed over the neck of a magnetically deflected cathode-ray tube to deflect the electron beam horizontally and vertically when suitable currents are passed through them.

Young's modulus—A constant that expresses the ratio of unit stress to unit deformation for all values within the proportional limit of the material.

Y-signal—A luminance transmission primary which is 1.5 to 4.2 MHz wide and equivalent to a monochrome signal. For color pictures, it contributes the finest details and brightness information. *Also see* Luminance Signal.

Yoke.

Z

Z—Symbol for impedance.

Zamboni pile—A primary electrochemical system capable of supplying very high electrical potentials in comparatively little space. The anode material in the pile is aluminum, and the cathode is manganese dioxide and carbon black. The electrolyte in the chemical system is aluminum chloride.

Z-angle meter—An electronic instrument for measuring impedance in ohms and phase angle in electrical degrees.

Z-axis modulation—Also called beam modulation or intensity modulation. Varying the intensity of the electron stream of a cathode-ray tube by applying a pulse or square wave to the control grid or cathode.

Z-bar—A rectangular crystal bar usually cut from X sections and elongated parallel to Z.

Zebra time—An alphabetic expression denoting Greenwich mean time.

Zeeman effect—If an electric discharge tube or other light source emitting a bright-line spectrum is placed between the poles of a powerful electromagnet, a very powerful spectroscope will show that the action of the magnetic field has split each spectrum line into three or more closely spaced but separate lines, the amount of splitting or the separation of the lines being directly proportional to the strength of the magnetic field.

zener breakdown—A breakdown caused in a semiconductor device by the field emission of charge carriers in the depletion layer.

Zener breakdown theory—A critical current density is attained by internal field emission, or tunneling, due to the high applied field.

zener diode—A two-layer device that, above a certain reverse voltage (the zener value), has a sudden rise in current. If forward-biased, the diode is an ordinary rectifier. But, when reversed-biased, the diode exhibits a typical knee, or sharp break, in its current-voltage graph. The voltage across the device remains essentially constant for any further increase of reverse current, up to the allowable dissipation rating. The zener diode is a good voltage regulator, overvoltage protector, and voltage reference.

Zener effect—A reverse-current breakdown due to the presence of a high electric field at the junction of a semiconductor or insulator.

zener impedance—*See* Breakdown Impedance.

zener voltage—*See* Breakdown Voltage.

zeppelin antenna—A horizontal antenna that is a multiple of a half-wavelength long. One end is fed by one lead of a two-wire transmission line that is also a multiple of a half-wavelength long.

zero (in a computer)—Positive binary zero is indicated by the absence of a digit or pulse in a word. In a coded-decimal computer, decimal zero and binary zero may not have the same configuration. In most computers, there are distinct representations for plus and minus zero conditions.

Zener diode characteristic.

zero-access storage—Computer storage for which the waiting time is negligible (e.g., flip-flop, trigger, or indicator storage).

zero-address instruction — A digital-computer instruction specifying an operation in which the locations of the operands are defined by the computer code; no explicit address is required.

zero adjuster—A device for adjusting a meter so that the pointer will rest exactly on zero when the electrical quantity is zero.

zero adjustment—1. The act of nulling out the output from a system or device. 2. The circuit or other means by which a no-output condition is obtained from an instrument when properly energized.

zero-axis symmetry—A type of symmetry in which a waveform is symmetrical about an axis and does not exhibit a net d-c component.

zero beat—The condition whereby two frequencies being mixed are exactly the same and therefore produce no beat note.

zero-beat reception—*See* Homodyne Reception.

zero bias—1. The absence of a potential difference between the control grid and the cathode. 2. When the received teletypewriter signal is equal to the transmitted signal (neither longer nor shorter), the circuit is said to have zero bias.

zero-bias tube—A vacuum tube designed to be operated as a class-B amplifier with no negative bias applied to its control grid.

zero compensation—A method by which, in certain transducers, the effects of temperature on the output at zero measurand may be minimized and maintained within known limits.

zero compression—In computers, any of several techniques used to eliminate the storage of non-significant leading zeros.

zero-cut crystal—A quartz crystal cut in such a direction that its temperature coefficient with respect to the frequency is essentially zero.

zero drift—*See* Zero Shift.

zero elimination—In a computer, the editing or deleting of nonsignificant zeros appearing to the left of the integral part of a quantity.

zero error—The delay time occurring within the transmitter and receiver circuits of a radar system. For accurate range data, this delay time must be compensated for when the range unit is calibrated.

zero-field emission — Thermionic emission from a hot conductor which is surrounded by a region of uniform electric potential.

zero-gravity switch—Also called weightlessness switch. A switch that closes when weightlessness or zero gravity is approached.

zero-input terminal—Also called a reset terminal. The terminal which, when triggered, will put a flip-flop in the zero (starting) condition—unless the flip-flop is already in a zero condition, in which event it will not change.

zero level—A reference level for comparing sound or signal intensities. In audio-frequency work, it is usually a power of .006 watt; and in sound, the threshold of hearing.

zero method—*See* Null Method.

zero-modulation noise—The noise arising when reproducing an erased tape with the erase and record heads energized as they would be in normal operation, but with zero input signal (usually 3 to 4 db higher than the bulk-erased noise).

zero-output terminal—The terminal which produces an output (of the correct polarity to trigger a following circuit) when a flip-flop is in the zero condition.

zero pole—1. A reference point for an open-wire poleline. 2. The dead-end pole at the origin of the line. 3. The lowest-numbered pole.

zero phase-sequence relay—A relay which functions in conformance with the zero phase-sequence component of the current, voltage, or power of the circuit.

zero potential—The potential of the earth, taken as a convenient reference for comparison.

zero-power resistance—In a thermistor, the resistance at a specified temperature when the electrical power dissipation is zero.

zero-power resistance-temperature characteristic—In a thermistor, the function relating the zero-power resistance and body temperature.

zero-power temperature coefficient of resistance—In a thermistor, the ratio, at a specified temperature, of the rate of change with temperature of zero-power resistance to the zero-power resistance.

zero set—1. A permanent change in the output of a device at zero measurand due to any cause. 2. A control on a vtvm to set the pointer to zero. 3. A control for adjusting a range counter to give the correct range.

zero shift—Also called zero drift. The amount by which the zero or minimum reading of an instrument deviates from the calibrated point as a result of aging or the application of an external condition to the instrument.

zeros of a network function—Those values of p (real or complex) for which the network function is zero.

zero stability—The ability of an instrument to withstand effects which might cause zero shift. Usually expressed as a percentage of full scale.

zero state—In a magnetic cell, the state wherein the magnetic flux through a specified cross-sectional area has a negative value, from an arbitrarily specified direction. (*Also see* One State.)

zero-subcarrier chromaticity—The chromaticity normally displayed when the subcarrier amplitude is zero in a color television system.

zero suppression—1. In a recording system, the injection of a controllable voltage to balance out the steady-state component of the input signal. 2. In a computer, the elimination of zeros to the left of the significant integral part of a quantity.

zero time reference—In a radar, the time reference of the schedule of events during one cycle of operation.

Z factor—In thermoelectricity, an accepted figure of merit which denotes the quality of the material.

zigzag reflections—From a layer of the ionosphere, high-order multiple reflections which may be of abnormal intensity. They occur in waves which travel by multihop ionosphere reflections and finally turn back toward their starting point by repeated reflections from a slightly curved or sloping portion of an ionized layer.

zinc—A bluish-white metal which, in its pure form, is used in dry cells.

Z marker—Also called a zone marker. A marker beacon that radiates vertically and is used for defining a zone above a radio range station.

Z₀—Symbol for characteristic impedance—i.e., the ratio of the voltage to the current at every point along a transmission line on which there are no standing waves.

zone—1. Any of the three top positions (12, 11 or 0) on a punch card. 2. A part of internal computer storage allocated for a particular purpose.

zone bits—1. The two leftmost binary digits in a digital computer in which six binary digits are used for characters and the four rightmost are used for decimal digits. 2. Any bit in a group of bit positions that are used to indicate a specific class of items (e.g., numbers, letters, special signs, and commands).

zone blanking—A method of turning off the cathode-ray tube during part of the sweep of the antenna.

zone leveling—In semiconductor processing, the passage of one or more molten zones along a semiconductor body, for the purpose of uniformly distributing impurities throughout the material.

zone marker—*See* Z-marker.

zone of silence—An area—between the points at which the ground wave becomes too weak to be detected and the sky wave first returns to earth—where normal radio signals cannot be heard. *Also see* Skip Zone.

zone plate antenna—A rapid-scanning antenna in which the reflector consists of arcs of confocal parabolas with focal lengths which differ by T/λ and which lie close to a circle centered at the focus, where λ is the wavelength.

zone-position indicator—An auxiliary radar set for indicating the general position of an object to another radar set with a narrower field.

zone punch—*See* Overpunch.

zone purification—In semiconductor processing, the passage of one or more molten zones along a semiconductor to reduce the impurity concentration of part of the ingot.

zoning—1. Also called stepping. Displacement of the various portions of the lens or surface of a microwave reflector, so that the resulting phase front in the near field remains unchanged. 2. Purifying a metal by passing it through an induction coil; the impurities are swept ahead of the heating effect. Specifically used in purifying semiconductor crystals.

zoom—To enlarge or reduce on a continuously variable basis the size of a televised image. It may be done electronically or optically.

zoom lens—An optical lens with some elements made movable so that the focal length or angle of view can be adjusted continuously without losing the focus.

PRONUNCIATION GUIDE

Here is an alphabetical listing of more than 1,100 often-mispronounced electronic terms taken from the dictionary proper. Turn to this section whenever you are in doubt about the pronunciation of a word.

You will note the use of accents, and also of diacritical marks over the vowels. For simplicity, no secondary accents are shown—only primary accents. The normal inflection of your voice will automatically stress the secondary accents, once you know where to place the primary accents. For example, the word "ther-mo-e-lec-TRIC-i-ty" would normally have a secondary accent on "ther," but you'll notice that your inflection tends to put it there.

The following pronunciation key, with diacritical markings, shows how the vowels are pronounced.

ā as in ace	ê as in here	o͞o as in moon
å as in chaotic	ē as in her	o͝o as in foot
ä as in arm	ī as in ice	ou as in how
ă as in map	ĭ as in it	ū as in huge
â as in dare	ō as in note	ů as in unite
ē as in me	ȯ as in obey	ŭ as in cup
ė as in event	ŏ as in not	û as in urn
ĕ as in met	ô as in or	ü as in blue
	oi as in oil	

At first glance it may seem difficult to distinguish between ā and å, ē and ė, ō and ȯ, or ū and ů. The first are called long vowels, and the second, half-long vowels. Just remember that their use is relative—for example, in the word "photograph," the first *o* is a bit longer than the second. The slight differentiation is difficult to hear, but it is there.

Also remember that unaccented syllables are not given the full brunt of the pronunciation. For example, in speech we do not say "PLAT-IN-NUM"—we say "PLAT-i-num" and tend to "swallow" the *i* (although it can be heard). By the same token, the word "photography" is pronounced "fo-TOG-ruf-e," not "FO-TOG-RAFF-FEE."

By keeping these few pointers in mind, you will find the "Pronunciation Guide" an easy—as well as a handy—tool.

A

a′bac (ă′băc)
ab′am·pere (ăb′ăm·pēr)
ab·cou′lomb (ăb·ko͞o′lŏm)
ab·er·ra′tion (ăb·ēr·ā′shŭn)
ab′far·ad (ăb′făr·ăd)
ab′hen·ry (ăb′hĕn·rē)
ab′mho (ăb′mō)
ab′ohm (ăb′ōm)
a·bort′ (ä·bôrt′)
ab·scis′sa (ăb·sĭs′ä)
ab′volt (ăb′vōlt)
ac·cel·er·om′e·ter (ăk·sĕl·ēr·ŏm′ĕ·tēr)
ac·cen·tu·a′tion (ăk·sĕn·tū·ā′shŭn)
ach·ro·mat′ic (ăk·rō·măt′ĭk)
a·clin′ic (ă·klĭn′ĭk)
a·cous′tic (ä·ko͞os′tĭk)
a·cous·to·e·lec′tric (ä·ko͞os·tō·ė·lĕk′trĭk)
ac·tin′ic (ăk·tĭn′ĭk)
ac·tin′i·um (ăk·tĭn′ĭ·ŭm)
ac′tu·a·tor (ăk′tū·ä·tēr)

ad′dend (ăd′ĕnd)
ad′di·tron (ă′dĭ·trŏn)
ae′o·light (å′ō·līt)
aer′i·al ((âr′ĭ·ŭl)
aer·o·dy·nam′ics (âr·ō·dī·năm′ĭks)
aer′o·phare (âr′ō·fâr)
a·gon′ic (ă·gŏn′ĭk)
a·lac′ri·tized (ă·lăk′rĭ·tīzd)
al·ge·bra′ic (ăl·jĕ·brā′ĭk)
al′gol (ăl′gŏl)
al′go·rithm (ăl′gȯ·rĭth′m)
al′ka·line (ăl′kä·līn)
al·lo·ca′tion (ăl·ō·kā′shŭn)
al′ni·co (ăl′nĭ·kō)
al′pha (ăl′fä)
al·tim′e·ter (ăl·tĭm′ĕ·tēr)
al·to·trop′o·sphere (ăl·tō·trŏp′ȯ·sfĕr)
a·lu′mi·nized (ä·lū′mĭ·nīzd)
am′bi·ent (ăm′bĭ·ĕnt)
am′me·ter (ăm′mē·tēr)
am′pere (ăm′pēr)
am′pli·dyne (ăm′plĭ·dīn)
am′pli·stat (ăm′plĭ·stăt)

an·a·cous'tic (ăn·ä·kōōs'tĭc)
an·as'tig·mat (ăn·ăs'tĭg·măt)
an'chor (ăng'kẽr)
an·cil'lar·y (ăn·sĭ'lẽr·ē)
an·e·cho'ic (ăn·ĕ·kǒ'ĭk)
an·e·mom'e·ter (ăn·ĕ·mǒm'ĕ·tẽr)
an'i·on (ăn'ĭ·ŏn)
an·i·so·trop'ic (ăn·ĭ·sō·trŏp'ĭk)
an·i·sot'ro·py (ăn·ī·sŏt'rŏ·pē)
an·nealed' (ă·nēld')
an'nu·lar (ăn'ū·lẽr)
an·nun·ci·a'tion (ă·nŭn·sĭ·ā'shŭn)
an·nun'ci·a·tor (ă·nŭn'sĭ·ā·tẽr)
an'o·diz·ing (ăn'ō·dīz·ĭng)
a·nom'a·lous (ä·nŏm'ä·lŭs)
an·ti·air'craft (ăn·tĭ·âr'krăft)
an·ti·ca·pac'i·tance (ăn·tĭ·kä·pă'sĭ·tŭns)
an·ti·co·in'ci·dence (ăn·tĭ·kō·ĭn'sĭ·dĕns)
an·ti·fer·ro·e·lec·tric'i·ty (ăn·tĭ·fĕrō·ĕ·lĕk·trĭ'sĭ·tē)
an·ti·fer·ro·mag·net'ic (ăn·tĭ·fĕr·ō·măg·nĕt'ĭk)
an·ti·log'a·rithm (ăn·tĭ·lŏg'ä·rĭth'm)
an·ti·mi·cro·phon'ic (ăn·tĭ·mĭ·krō·fŏn'ĭk)
an'ti·nodes (ăn'tĭ·nōds)
an·ti·pro'ton (ăn·tĭ·prō'tŏn)
an·ti·side'tone (ăn·tĭ·sīd'tōn)
a·pe·ri·od'ic (ā·pĕ·rĭ·ŏd'ĭk)
a'per·ture (ă'pẽr·chẽr)
ap·pli·que' (ăp·lĭ·kā')
a·qua·dag (ăk'wä·dăg)
a·rith·met'ic [adj.] (ä·rĭth·mĕt'ĭk)
a·rith'me·tic [noun] (ä·rĭth'mĕ·tĭk)
as·bes'tos (ăs·bĕs'tŭs)
as'pect ra'tio (ăs'pĕkt rā'shō)
as·per'i·ties (ăs·pĕr'ĭ·tēs)
a·spher'ic (ä·sfêr'ĭc)
a·sym·met'ric (ä·sĭ·mĕt'rĭk)
a'sta·ble (à'stā'b'l)
a·stig'ma·tism (ä·stĭg'mä·tĭzm)
a'symp·tote (ă'sĭm·tōt)
a·symp·tot'ic (ă·sĭm·tŏt'ĭk)
a·syn'chro·nous (ä·sĭng'krō·nŭs)
at'mos·phere (ăt'môs·fẽr)
at·mos·pher'ic (ăt·môs·fẽr'ĭk)
at·ten·u·a'tion (ă·tĕn·ū·ā'shŭn)
at'to (ăt'tō)
au·di·om'e·ter (ô·dĭ·ŏm'ĕ·tẽr)
au'di·on (ô'dĭ·ŏn)
au'di·o·phile (ô'dĕ·ō·fīl)
au'gend (ô'jĕnd)
au'ral (ô'rŭl)
au·ro'ra (ô·rô'rä)
au·ro'ral (ô·rô'răl)
au'to·dyne (ô'tō·dīn)
au·to·ma'tion (ô·tō·mā'shŭn)
au·to·ra·di·og'ra·phy (ô·tō·rä·dĭ·ŏg'rä·fē)

au·to·reg·u·la'tion (ô·tō·rĕg·ū·lā'shŭn)
Au'to·syn (ô'tō·sĭn)
au·to·trans'form·er (ô·tō·trăns'fôr·mẽr)
aux·il'ia·ry (ôg·zĭl'yû·rē)
a'va·lanche (ăv'ä·lănch)
a·vi·a'tion (ā·vĭ·ā'shŭn)
a·vi·on'ics (ā·vē·ŏn'ĭks)
A·vo·ga'dro's (ä·vŏ·gä'drōz)
ax'i·al (ăk'sĭ·ŭl)
ax'is (ăk'sĭs)
Ayr'ton-Per'ry (âr'tŭn) (pĕr'ē)

B

bab'ble (băb'·'l)
baf'fle (băf'·'l)
Ba'ke·lite (bā'kä·līt)
bal·lis'tic (bä·lĭs'tĭk)
bal'un (băl'ŭn)
ban'tam (băn'tŭm)
bar'i·um (bâr'ĭ·ŭm)
Bark'haus·en-Kurz (bärk'houz'n) (kẽrz)
ba·rom'e·ter (bä·rŏm'ĕ·tẽr)
bar'ret·ter (bâr'ĕt·ẽr)
bar'ri·er (bâr'ĭ·ẽr)
bass [music] (bās)
bath·y·con·duc'tor·graph (băth·ĭ·kŏn- dŭk'tẽr·grăf)
bath·y·ther'mo·graph (băth·ĭ·thẽr'mŏ- gráf)
baud (bôd)
bay·o·net' (bā·ŏ·nĕt')
ba·zoo'ka (bä·zōō'kä)
bel (bĕl)
Bel·li'ni-To'si (bĕl·lē'nĕ) (tō'sĕ)
Be·ni'to (bĕ·nē'tŏ)
be'ta (bā'tä)
be'ta·tron (bā'tä·trŏn)
bev'a·tron (bĕv'ä·trŏn)
Bev'er·age (bĕv'ẽr·ĕj)
bez'el (bĕz'·'l)
bi'as (bī'ŭs)
bi·con'i·cal (bī·kŏn'ĭ·k'l)
bi·di·rec'tion·al (bī·dĭ·rĕk'shŭn·'l)
bi·fi'lar (bī·fī'lẽr)
bi·lat'er·al (bī·lăt'ẽr·ôl)
bi·me·tal'lic (bī·mĕ·tăl'ĭk)
bi'na·ry (bī'nâ·rē)
bin·au'ral (bīn·ô'rôl)
bi·nis'tor (bī·nĭs'tẽr)
bi·no'mi·al (bī·nō'mĭ·ôl)
bi·o·met'rics (bī·ŏ·mĕt'rĭks)
bi·on'ics (bī·ŏn'ĭks)
bi·qui'na·ry (bī·kwī'nâ·rē)
bis'cuit (bĭs'kĭt)
bi·stab'le (bī·stā'b'l)
blip (blĭp)

bli'vet (blĭ'vĕt)
Bloch wall (blŏk) (wôl)
bof'fle (bŏf''l)
bo'gey (bō'gē)
bo·lom'e·ter (bô·lŏm'ĕ·tēr)
Bool'e·an (bōōl'ê·ŭn)
byte (bīt)

C

cad'mi·um (kăd'mē·ŭm)
cal'i·brate (kăl'ĭ·brāt)
cal'o·mel (kăl'ô·mĕl)
cal·o·rim'e·ter (kăl·ô·rĭm'ĕ·tēr)
ca·nal' ray (kä·năl') (rā)
can·do·lu·mi·nes'cence (kăn·dô·lōo-
    mĭ·nĕs'ĕns)
ca·pac'i·tance (kä·pă'sĭ·tŭns)
cap'stan (kăp'stăn)
Car·bo·run'dum (kär·bô·rŭn'dŭm)
car·ci'no·tron (kär·sĭ'nô·trŏn)
Car'dew (kär'dōo)
car'di·oid (kär'dĭ·oid)
Car·not' (kär·nō')
cas·cade' (kăs·kād')
cas'code (kăs'kōd)
cat·a·stroph'ic (kăt·ä·strŏf'ĭk)
ca·te'na (kă·tē'nä)
cath·am'pli·fi·er (kăth·ămp'lĭ·fī·ēr)
cath·o·do·lu·mi·nes'cence (kăth·ô·dɷ
    lōo·mĭ·nĕs'ĕns)
cat'i·on (kăt'ī·ŏn)
cav·i·ta'tion (kăv·ĭ·tā'shŭn)
cel'lu·lose (sĕl'ŭ·lōs)
Cel'si·us (sĕl'sĭ·ŭs)
cen'ti- (sĕn'tĭ)
cen·trif'u·gal (sĕn·trĭf'ŭ·gôl)
cen·trip'e·tal (sĕn·trĭp'ĕ·tôl)
ce·ram'ic (sē·răm'ĭk)
Cer'en·kov (sĕr'ĕn·kôf)
ce'si·um (sē'zĕ·ŭm)
chad (chăd)
chem·i·sorp'tion (kĕm·ĭ·sôrp'shŭn)
chro'ma (krō'mä)
chro·mat'ic (krō·măt'ĭk)
chro·ma·tic'i·ty (krō·mä·tĭ'sĭ·tē)
chro'mi·nance (krō'mĭ·năns)
chron'o·graph (krŏn'ô·grăf)
chron·om'e·ter (krŏn·ŏm'ĕ·tēr)
chron'o·scope (krŏn'ô·skōp)
cir'clo·tron (sûr'klô·trŏn)
cla'vi·er (klä'vĭ·ēr)
co·ax'i·al (kō·ăk'sĭ·ôl)
co'-chan·nel (kō'-chăn 'l)
co'dan (kō'dăn)
co·ef·fi'cient (kō·ĕ·fīsh'ĕnt)
co·er'cive (kô·ēr'sĭv)
co·er·civ'i·ty (kō·ēr·sĭv'ĭ·tē)
cog'ging (kŏg'ĭng)
co·her'ent (kô·hĭr'ĕnt)
co·her'er (kô·hĭr'ēr)
co'li·dar (kō'lĭ·där)

col·late' (kô·lāt')
col·li·ma'tion (kŏl·ĭ·mā'shŭn)
col'li·ma·tor (kŏl'ĭ·mā·tēr)
col·lin'e·ar (kô·lĭn'ê·ēr)
col·or·i·met'ric (kŭl·ēr·ĭ·mĕt'rĭk)
col·or·i'me·try (kŭl·ēr·ĭ'mĕ·trē)
Col'pitts (kōl'pĭts)
col'umn (kŏl'ŭm)
com·mu·ta·tor (kŏm'ŭ·tā·tēr)
com·pan'der (kŏm·păn'dēr)
com·par'a·tor (kŏm·păr'ĕ·tēr)
com·pat·i·bil'i·ty (kŏm·păt·ĕ·bĭl'ĭ·tē)
com·po'nent (kŏm·pō'nĕnt)
com·pos'ite (kŏm·pŏz'ĭt)
con·cat'e·nate (kŏn·kăt''n·āt)
con·cen'tric (kŏn·sĕn'trĭk)
Con'dor (kŏn'dôr)
con'duit (kŏn'dōo·ĭt)
con'el·rad (kŏn'ăl·răd)
con'i·cal (kŏn'ĭ·kăl)
con'ju·gate [adj.] (kŏn'jŏō·gȧt)
con'o·scope (kŏn'ŏ·skōp)
con'sol (kŏn'sŭl)
con'sole (kŏn'sōl)
con'so·nance (kŏn'sô·nŭns)
Cor·bi'no effect (kôr·bē'nô)
co·se'cant (kô·sē'kănt)
cou'lomb (kōō'lōm)
cou·lom'e·ter (kōō·lŏm'ĕ·tēr)
Coul'ter (kōl'tēr)
co·va'lent (kō·vä'lĕnt)
Crookes (krŏŏks)
cry·o·gen'ics (krī·ô·jĕn'iks)
cry'o·stat (krī'ô·stăt)
cry'o·tron (krī'ô·trŏn)
cu'rie (kû'rē)
Cur·pis'tor (kûr·pĭs'tēr)
cy·ber·net'ics (sī·bēr·nĕt'ĭks)
cy'clic (sī'klĭk)
cy'cli·cal·ly (sī'klĭ·kô·lē)
cy'clo·gram (sī'klô·grăm)
cy'clo·tron (sī'klô·trŏn)
cy·lin'dri·cal (sĭ·lĭn'drĭ·kôl)
Czo·chral'ski (zō·krôl'skē)

D

Da'mon (dā'mŭn)
Dan'iell (dăn'yĕl)
dar'af (dăr'ŭf)
D'Ar·son·val' (där'sŏn·vŭl)
da'ta (dā'tä)
De·bye' (dĕ·bī')
dec'ade (dĕk'ād)
de·ca·les'cent (dē·kä·lĕs'ĕnt)
dec'ca (dĕk'ä)
de·cel'er·at·ing (dē·sĕl'ēr·āt·ĭng)
dec'i- (dĕs'ĭ-)
dec'i·bel (dĕs'ĭ·bĕl)
dec'i·log (dĕs'ĭ·lôg)
dec·i·met'ric (dĕs·ĭ·mĕt'rĭk)
dec'i·ne·per (dĕs'ĭ·nä·pēr)

dec·li·na′tion (děk·lǐ·nā′shǔn)
dec·li·nom′e·ter (děk·lǐ·nǒm′ě·tēr)
dee (dē)
de′fect (dě′fěkt)
de·gaus′sing (dē·gous′ǐng)
de·gen′er·a·cy (dě·jěn′ēr·ě·sē)
de·i·on·i·za′tion (dě·ī·ǒn·ǐ·zā′shǔn)
dek′a (děk′ä)
dek·a·hex·a·dec′i·mal (děk·ä·hěks·ä-děs′ǐ·môl)
de·lim′it·er (dě·lǐm′ǐ·tēr)
Del′lin·ger (děl′ǐn·jēr)
de·mag·net·i·za′tion (dē·măg·nět-ǐ·zā′shǔn)
Dem′ber (děm′bēr)
de·mod·u·la′tion (dē·mǒd·ů·lā′shǔn)
den′a·ry (děn′â·rē)
den′drite (děn′drīt)
den·drit′ic (děn·drǐt′ǐc)
den·si·tom′e·ter (děn·sǐ·tǒm′ě·tēr)
de·ple′tion (dě·plē′shǔn)
de·po·lar·i·za′tion (dē·pō·lär·ǐ·zā′shǔn)
de·riv′a·tive (dě·rǐv′ä·tǐv)
Des′triau (děs′trîô)
de·tec′to·phone (dē·těk′tô·fōn)
de′tent (dě′těnt)
deu·te′ri·um (dů·târ′ě·ǔm)
deu′ter·on (dū′tēr·ǒn)
de·vi·a′tion (dē·vē·ā′shǔn)
Dew′ar (dū′ēr)
di·ag·nos′tic (dī·ăg·nǒs′tǐk)
di·ag′no·tor (dī·ăg′nô·tēr)
di·a·mag·net′ic (dī·ä·măg·nět′ǐk)
di·a·pa′son (dī·ä·pā′z′n)
di′a·phragm (dī′ä·frăm)
di′a·ther·my (dī′ä·thēr·mē)
di·chro′ic (dī·krō′ǐk)
di′chro·ism (dī′krô·ǐzm)
di·e·lec′tric (dī·ě·lěk′trǐk)
dig′i·ralt (dǐj′ǐ·rălt)
dig′i·tal (dǐj′ǐ·tôl)
di·hep′tal (dī·hěp′tôl)
di·op′ter (dī·ǒp′tēr)
di′plex·er (dī′plěks·ēr)
di·rec·tiv′i·ty (dě·rěk·tǐv′ǐ·tē)
dis′cone (dǐs′kōn)
dis·crete′ (dǐs·krēt′)
dis·crim′i·na·tor (dǐs·krǐm′ǐ·nā·tēr)
dis·per′sion (dǐs·pēr′zhǔn)
dis·sec′tor (dǐ·sěk′tēr)
dis·si·pa′tion (dǐs·ǐ·pā′shǔn)
dis·so·ci·a′tion (dǐ·sō·sǐ·ā′shǔn)
dis′so·nance (dǐs′ô·nǔns)
dis·sym·met′ri·cal (dǐ·sǐ·mět′rǐ·kôl)
di·verg′ing (dī·vērj′ǐng)
di·ver′si·ty (dī·vēr′sǐ·tē)
Doh′er·ty (dō′ēr·tē)
do′nor (dō′nēr)
do′pant (dō′pǎnt)
Dop′pler (dǒp′lēr)
dos′age (dōs′âj)

do·sim′e·ter (dǒ·sǐm′ě·tēr)
dou′blet (dǔb′lět)
drunk·om′e·ter (drǔnk·ǒm′ě·tēr)
du·o·dec′al (dōō·ō·děk′ôl)
du·o·di′ode (dōō·ō·dī′ōd)
du·o·lat′er·al (dōō·ō·lăt′ēr·ôl)
du′o·pole (dōō′ô·pōl)
dy′na·quad (dī′nä·kwäd)
dy′na·mo (dī′nä·mō)
dy·na·mo·e·lec′tric (dī·nä·mō·ě-lěk′trǐk)
dy·na·mom′e·ter (dī·nä·mǒm′ě·tēr)
dy′na·mo·tor (dī′nä·mō·tēr)
dy′na·tron (dī′nä·trǒn)
dyne (dīn)
dy·nis′tor (dī·nǐs′tēr)
dy′node (dī′nōd)

E

eb·i·con·duc·tiv′i·ty (ěb·ǐ·cǒn·dǔk-tǐv′·ǐ·tē)
ec·cen′tric (ěk·sěn′trǐk)
ec·cen·tric′i·ty (ěk·sěn·trǐs′ǐ·tē)
Ec′cles-Jor′dan (ěk′ls) (jôr′d′n)
ech′e·lon (ěsh′ě·lǒn)
Eint′ho·ven (īnt′hō·věn)
e·las′tance (ě·lǎs′tǔns)
e·las·tiv′i·ty (ē·lǎs·tǐv′ǐ·tē)
e·lec′tra (ě·lěk′trä)
e·lec′tral·loy (ě·lěk′trä·loi)
e·lec′tret (ě·lěk′trět)
e·lec·tro·a·cous′tic (ě·lěk·trō·ă-kōōs′tǐk)
e·lec·tro·a·nal′y·sis (ě·lěk·trō·ä-năl′ǐ·sǐs)
e·lec·tro·bi·os′co·py (ě·lěk·trô·bī-ǒs′kǒ·pē)
e·lec·tro·car′di·o·gram (ě·lěk·trō-kär′dǐ·ô·grǎm)
e·lec·tro·co·ag′u·la′tion (ě·lěk·trō-kō·ăg·ů·lā′shǔn)
e·lec·tro·cu′tion (ě·lěk·trō·kū′shǔn)
e·lec·tro·dep·o·si′tion (ě·lěk·trō-děp·ô·zǐsh′ǔn)
e·lec·tro·di·a·lyt′ic (ě·lěc·trō·dī·ä-lǐt′ǐk)
e·lec·tro·dy·nam′ic (ě·lěk·trō·dī-năm′ǐk)
e·lec·tro·dy·na·mom′e·ter (ě·lěk-trō·dī·nä·mǒm′ě·tēr)
e·lec·tro·en·ceph′a·lo·graph (ě·lěk-trō·ěn·sěf′ä·lô·grǎf)
e·lec·tro·graph′ic (ě·lěk·trō·grǎf′ǐk)
e·lec·tro·ki·net′ics (ě·lěk·trō·kǐ-nět′ǐks)
e·lec·tro·lu·mi·nes′cence (ě·lěk·trō-lū·mǐ·něs′ ′ns)
e·lec·trol′y·sis (ě·lěk·trǒl′ǐ·sǐs)
e·lec·tro·lyte (ě·lěk·trō·līt)
e·lec·tro·lyt′ic (ě·lěk·trō·lǐt′ǐk)

e·lec·tro·met'al·lur·gy (ê·lĕk·trō-mĕt'l·ûr·jē)
e·lec·trom'e·ter (ê·lĕk·trŏm'ê·tēr)
e·lec·tro·my·og'ra·phy (ê·lĕk·trō·mī-ŏg'rä·fē)
e·lec·troph'o·rus (ê·lĕk·trŏf'ô·rŭs)
e·lec·tro·pho·tog'ra·phy (ê·lĕk·trō-fô·tŏg'rä·fē)
e·lec·tro·sta·tog'ra·phy (ê·lĕk·trō·stă-tŏg'rä·fē)
e·lec·tro·stric'tion (ê·lĕk·trō-strĭk'shŭn)
e·lec·tro·ther'a·py (ê·lĕk·trō-thâr'ä·pē)
e·lec·tro·ther'mal (ê·lĕk·trō·thēr'mŭl)
e·lec·tro·win'ning (ê·lĕk·trō·wĭn'ĭng)
em·bed'ment (ĕm·bĕd'mĕnt)
em'i·tron (ĕm'ĭ·trŏn)
em·pir'i·cal (ĕm·pêr'ĭ·käl)
en·cap·su·la'tion (ĕn·kăp·sŭ·lā'shŭn)
en'do·dyne (ĕn'dō·dīn)
en'tro·py (ĕn'trô·pē)
en·vi·ron·men'tal (ĕn·vīr·ŭn·mĕn'tôl)
e·pi·tax'i·al (ê·pĭ·tăks'ĭ·ôl)
e·pox'y (ê·pŏks'ē)
ep'si·lon (ĕp'sĭ·lŏn)
e·qui·lib'ri·um (ê·kwĭ·lĭb'rĭ·ŭm)
e'qui·phase (ê'kwĭ·fāz)
e·qui·po·ten'tial (ê·kwĭ·pô·tĕn'shŭl)
e·qui·sig'nal (ê·kwĭ·sĭg'nôl)
e·quiv'a·lent (ê·kwĭv'ä·lĕnt)
e·quiv·o·ca'tion (ê·kwĭv·ô·kā'shŭn)
E·sa'ki (ê·sä'kē)
es·cutch'eon (ĕs·kŭch'ŭn)
Es'ti·a·tron (ĕs'tê·ä·trŏn)
etch'ant (ĕch'ănt)
Et'ting·shaus·en (ĕt'ĭng·shouz 'n)
eu·re'ka (yōō·rē'kä)
ex'ci·ton (ĕks'ĭ·tŏn)
ex'ci·tron (ĕks'ĭ·trŏn)
ex'o·sphere (ĕks'ô·sfêr)
ex·o·ther'mic (ĕks·ô·ther'mĭk)
ex·po·nen'tial (ĕks·pô·nĕn'shôl)
ex·trin'sic (ĕks·trĭn'sĭk)

F

fa'com (fā'kŏm)
fac·sim'i·le (făk·sĭm'ĭ·lē)
Fahne'stock (fŏn'stŏk)
fa·rad'ic (fâ·răd'ĭk)
far'ad·me·ter (fâr'ăd·mē·tēr)
fa·thom'e·ter (fă·thŏm'ê·tēr)
fa·tigue' (fä·tēg')
Faure (fôr)
fem'to- (fĕm'tō)
fem·to·am'pere (fĕm·tō·ăm'pēr)
Fer'mi (fâr'mê)
fer'reed (fēr'ēd)
fer·ri·mag·net'ic (fâr·ĭ·măg·nĕt'ĭk)
fer'ris·tor (fâr'ĭs·tēr)

fer'rod (fâr'ŏd)
fer·ro·dy·nam'ic (fâr·ô·dī·năm'ĭk)
fer·ro·man'ga·nese (fâr·ô·măng'gä-nēz)
fer·rom'e·ter (fâr·ŏm'ê·tēr)
fer·ro·spi·nel' (fâr·ô·spī·nĕl')
fer'rous (fâr'ŭs)
fer'rule (fâr'ŭl)
fil·a·men'ta·ry (fĭl·ä·mĕn'tä·rē)
fi'nite fī'nīt)
fis'sion (fĭsh'ŭn)
Fle·wel'ling (flü·wĕl'ĭng)
Flin'ders (flĭn'dērz)
flu·o·rem'e·ter (flōō·ŏr·rĕm'ê·tēr)
flu·o·res'cence (flōō·ŏr·ĕs'äns)
flu·or·os'co·py (flōō·ŏr·ŏs'kŏ·pē)
fo·com'e·ter (fô·kŏm'ê·tēr)
For·mi'ca (fôr·mī'kä)
FOR'TRAN (fôr'trăn)
for·tu'i·tous (fôr·tū'ĭ·tŭs)
Fou·cault' (fōō·kō')
Fou'rier (fōō·ryä')
Frahm (främ)
Fraun'ho·fer (froun'hō·fēr)
Fres·nel' (frâ·nĕl')
Fus'e·stat (fūz'ŭ·stăt)
Fus'e·tron ((fūz'ŭ·trŏn)

G

ga·le'na (gä·lē'nä)
gal·van'ic (găl·văn'ĭk)
gal·va·nom'e·ter (găl·vä·nŏm'ê·tēr)
gam'ma (găm'ä)
gas'ton (găs'tŭn)
gauss (gous)
Gei'ger-Muel'ler (gī'gēr) (mül'ēr)
Geiss'ler (gīs'lēr)
gen'e·mo·tor (jĕn'ê·mō·tēr)
ge·o·des'ic (jē·ô·dĕs'ĭk)
ger·ma'ni·um (jēr·mā'nĭ·ŭm)
gi'ga- (jī'gä)
gi'ga·cy·cle (jī'gä·sī·k'l)
gig'ohm (jĭg'ōm)
Gill-Mor·rell' (gĭl) (môr·ĕl')
gim'bal (gĭm'bôl)
gimp (gĭmp)
Gi·or'gi (jē·ôr'jê)
go'bo (gō'bō)
Gold'schmidt (gōld'smĭt)
go·ni·om'e·ter (gŏ·nĭ·ŏm'ê·tēr)
goo'gol (gōō'gŏl)
gramme (grăm)
graph'e·chon (grăf'ê·kŏn)
grat'i·cule (grăt'ĭ·kūl)
Gratz (grătz)
Green'wich (grĕn'ĭch)
grom'met (grŏm'ĕt)
Gud'den-Pohl (gŏod'n) (pōl)
Guil'le·min ((gĭl'ê·mĭn)
gut'ta-per'cha (gūt'ä-pēr'chä)

gy·ro·fre′quen·cy (jĭ·rȯ·frē′kwĕn·sē)
gy·ro·scop′ic (jĭ·rȯ·skŏp′ĭk)

H

ha′lo (hā′lō)
hal′o·gen (hăl′ȯ·jĕn)
Heav′i·side (hĕv′ĭ·sīd)
hec′to- (hĕk′tȯ-)
Hef′ner (hĕf′nēr)
Hei′sing (hī′sĭng)
hel′i·cal (hēl′ĭ·k'l)
he·li·on′ics (hē·lĭ·ŏn′ĭks)
he′lix (hē′lĭks)
Helm′holtz (hĕlm′hōlts)
hem·i·mor′phic (hĕm·ĭ·môr′fĭk)
her·maph·ro·dit′ic (hēr·măf·rȯ·dĭt′ĭc)
her·met′ic (hēr·mĕt′ĭk)
hertz (hērts)
Hertz′i·an (hērt′sĭ·ŭn)
het·er·o·ge·ne′i·ty (hĕt·ēr·ȯ·gĕ·nē′ĭ·tē)
heu·ris′tic (hŭ·rĭs′tĭk)
hex·a·dec′i·mal (hĕks·ä·dĕs′ĭ·mäl)
HI·PER′NAS (hĭ·pēr′năs)
his′to·gram (hĭs′tȯ·grăm)
ho′mo·dyne (hō′mȯ·dīn)
ho·mo·ge·ne′i·ty (hō·mō·gĕ·nē′ĭ·tē)
ho·mo·ge′ne·ous (hō·mȯ·jē′nė·ŭs)
ho·mol′o·gous (hō·mŏl′ȯ·gŭs)
ho·mo·po′lar (hō·mȯ·pō′lēr)
ho·ri′zon (hô·rī′z'n)
hy′brid (hī′brĭd)
hy·dro·a·cous′tics (hī·drȯ·ä·kōōs′tĭks)
hy·drom′e·ter (hī·drŏm′ė·tēr)
hy′dro·phone (hī′drȯ·fōn)
hy·grom′e·ter (hī·grŏm′ė·tēr)
hy·gro·scop′ic (hī·grō·skŏp′ĭk)
hy′gro·stat (hī′grȯ·stăt)
hy·per′bo·la (hī·pēr′bȯ·lä)
hy·per·bol′ic (hī·pēr·bŏl′ĭk)
hy·per·son′ic (hī·pēr·sŏn′ĭk)
hys·ter·e′si·graph (hĭs·tēr·ė′sĭ·grăf)
hys·ter·e′sis (hĭs·tēr·ė′sĭs)

I

i·con′o·scope (ī·kŏn′ȯ·skōp)
id·i·o·chro·mat′ic (īd·ĭ·ȯ·krō·măt′ĭk)
ig·ni′tion (ĭg·nĭ′shŭn)
ig·ni′tor (ĭg·nī′tēr)
ig′ni·tron (ĭg′nĭ·trŏn)
il·lu′mi·nant (ĭ·lū′mĭ·nŭnt)
il·lu·mi·nom′e·ter (ĭ·lū·mĭ·nŏm′ė·tēr)
im·preg·na′tion (ĭm·prĕg·nā′shŭn)
in·can·des′cence (ĭn·kän·dĕs′ĕns)
in′ci·dence (ĭn′sĭ·dĕns)
in·cip′i·ent (ĭn·sĭp′ĭ·ĕnt)
in·cli·na′tion (ĭn·klĭ·nā′shŭn)
in·cli·nom′e·ter (ĭn·klĭ·nŏm′ė·tēr)
in·co·her′ent (ĭn·kȯ·hêr′ĕnt)

in·cre·duc′tor (ĭn·krĕ·dŭk′tēr)
in′cre·ment (ĭn′krä·mĕnt)
in·fin·i·tes′i·mal (ĭn·fĭn·ĭ·tĕs′ĭ·môl)
in·hib′it·ing (ĭn·hĭb′ĭ·tĭng)
in·spec′to·scope (ĭn·spĕk′tȯ·skōp)
in′su·laz·ing (ĭn′sȯ·lāz·ĭng)
in′te·ger (ĭn′tĕ·jēr)
in′teg·ral (ĭn′tĕg·rȯl)
in·ten·si·tom′e·ter (ĭn·tĕn·sĭ·tŏm′ė·tēr)
in·ter·dig′i·tal (ĭn·tēr·dĭj′ĭ·tôl)
in·ter·fer·om′e·ter (ĭn·tēr·fēr-
    ŏm′ė·tēr)
in·ter·po·la′tion (ĭn·tēr·pȯ·lā′shŭn)
in·ter′pre·tive (ĭn·tēr′prē·tĭv)
in·ter·ro·ga′tion (ĭn·tēr·ȯ·gā′shŭn)
in·ter′ro·ga·tor (ĭn·târ′ȯ·gā·tēr)
in′ter·ties (ĭn′tēr·tīz)
in·to·na′tion (ĭn·tō·nā′shŭn)
in·trin′sic (ĭn·trĭn′sĭk)
In′var (ĭn′vär)
i′on (ī′ŏn)
i·on′ic (ī·ŏn′ĭk)
i·on′o·sphere (ī·ŏn′ȯ·sfêr)
i′so·bar (ī′sȯ·bär)
i′so·chrone (ī′sȯ·krōn)
i·soch′ro·nous (ī·sŏk′rȯ·nŭs)
i·so·clin′ic (ī·sȯ·klĭn′ĭk)
i′so·mer (ī′sȯ·mēr)
i·so·stat′ic (ī·sō·stăt′ĭc)
i·so·trop′ic (ī·sȯ·trŏp′ĭk)
it′er·a·tive (ĭt′ēr·ä·tĭv)

J

jaff (jăf)
jez′a·bel (jĕz′ä·bĕl)
joule (jōōl)

K

ke·no·pli′o·tron (kē·nȯ·plī′ȯ·trŏn)
ke′no·tron (kē′nȯ·trŏn)
ke·rau′no·phone (kē·rä′nȯ·fōn)
Kerr (kēr)
Ki·kuch′i (kĭ·kōō′chė)
kil′o- (kĭl′ō)
kil′ohm·me·ter (kĭl′ōm·mē·tēr)
kil′o·me·ter (kĭl′ȯ·mē·tēr)
kil·o·met′ric (kĭl·ȯ·mĕ′trĭk)
kil′o·var (kĭl′ȯ·vär)
kin′e·scope (kĭn′ĕ·skōp)
ki·net′ic (kĭ·nĕt′ĭk)
Kirch′hoff (kērk′ôff)
kly·don′o·graph (klī·dŏn′ȯ·grăf)
kly′stron (klī′strŏn)
kur·to′sis (kēr·tō′sĭs)
ky′mo·graph (kī′mȯ·grăf)

L

la′bile (lā′bĭl)

lab'y·rinth (lăb'ĭ·rĭnth)
lac'quer (lăk'ēr)
lamb'da (lăm'dä)
La·mont's' (lä·mŏnts')
Lan'ge·vin (lăn'gĕ·vĭn)
Lang'muir (lăng'mūr)
La·place' (lä·pläs')
la·ryn·ga·phone (lă·rĭng'gä·fōn)
la'ser (lā'sēr)
la'ten·cy (lā'tĕn·sē)
la'tent (lā'tĕnt)
lat'er·al (lăt'ēr·ôl)
la·va·lier' (lă·vä·lêr')
LA'WEB (lä'wĕb)
leak'ance (lēk'ŭns)
Lech'er (lĕch'ēr)
Le·clan·che' (lĕ·klän·shä')
Le'nard (lā'närt)
Le·pel' (lĕ·pĕl')
Lich'ten·berg (lĭk'tĕn·bērg)
Lis'sa·jous ((lĭ'sä·zhoō)
lith'i·um (lĭth'ĭ·ŭm)
litz (lĭtz)
lo'dar (lō'där)
log·a·rith'mic (lŏg·ä·rĭth'mĭk)
lok'tal (lŏk'tôl)
lo·rac' (lô·răc')
lo·rad' (lô·răd')
lo·ran' (lô·răn')
lor'humb (lôr'ŭmb)
Los'sev (lō'sĕf)
lou'ver (loō'vēr)
lu'men (lū'mĕn)
lu·min·aire' (lū·mĭn·âr')
lu·mi·nes'cence (lū·mĭ·nĕs'ĕns)
lu·mi·nos'i·ty (lū·mĭ·nŏs'ĭ·tē)

M

mac·ro·son'ics (măk·rô·sŏn'ĭks)
mag'amp (măg'ămp)
mag'nal (măg'nôl)
mag·ne'si·um (măg·nē'sĭ·ŭm)
Mag'ne·syn (măg'nĕ·sĭn)
mag'net·ite (măg'nĕ·tīt)
mag·ne'to (măg·nē'tō)
mag·ne·to·hy·dro·dy·nam'ic (măg·nē-
  tô·hī·drô·dī·năm'ĭk)
mag·ne·to·i·on'ic (măg·nē·tô·ī·ŏn'ĭk)
mag·ne·tom'e·ter (măg·nĕ·tŏm'ĕ·tēr)
mag·net'tor (măg·nĕt'ēr)
Mag·nis'tor (măg·nĭs'tēr)
man'ga·nin (măn'gä·nĭn)
ma·nom'e·ter (mă·nŏm'ĕ·tēr)
Mar·co'ni (mär·kō'nĭ)
ma'trix (mā'trĭks)
ma'trix·er (mā'trĭk·sēr)
Mat·te·u'cci (mät·tå·oōt'chĕ)
Mc·Nal'ly (mŭk·năl'ē)
Mea'cham (mē'chŭm)

mea'con·ing (mē'kŭn·ĭng)
me'di·an (mē'dĭ·ŭn)
meg'a- (mĕg'ä)
Meiss'ner (mīz'nēr)
mel (mĕl)
me'sa (mā'sä)
mes'on (mĕs'ŏn)
met'a·dyne (mĕt'ä·dīn)
me·te·or·o·log'i·cal (mē·tĭ·ēr·ŏ-
  lŏj'ĭ·k'l)
met're·chon (mĕt'rĕ·kŏn)
mho (mō)
mi'cro- (mī'krō)
mi·cro·cir'cui·try (mī·krō·sēr'kĭ·trē)
mi·cro·log'ic (mī·krō·lŏj'ĭk)
mi·cro·mas·sage' (mī·krō·mäs·säzh')
mi·cro·min·i·a·tur·i·za'tion (mī·krō-
  mĭn·ĭ·ä·chēr·ĭ·zā'shŭn)
mi·cro·mod'ule (mī·krō·mŏd'ŭl)
mi·cro·ra·di·om'e·ter (mī·krô·rā·dĕ·
  ŏm'ĕ·tēr)
mil'li- (mĭl'ĭ)
mil·li·roent'gen (mĭl·ĭ·rĕnt'gĕn)
min·i·a·tur·i·za'tion (mĭn·ĭ·ä·chēr·ĭ-
  zā'shŭn)
Min'ter (mĭn'tēr)
mitte-seite (mĭt-sīt)
mne·mon'ic (nĕ·mŏn'ĭk)
mod'ule (mŏd'ūl)
moi're (mō'rā)
mol (mōl)
mol·ec·tron'ics (mŏl·ĕk·trŏn'ĭks)
mo·lec'u·lar (mŏ·lĕk'ŭ·lēr)
mol'e·cule (mŏl'ĕ·kūl)
mo·lyb'de·num (mŏ·lĭb'dĕ·nŭm)
mon·au'ral (mŏn·ô'rŭl)
mon·o·chro'ma·tor (mŏn·ô·krō'må·tēr)
mon'o·chrome (mŏn'ô·krōm)
mor·pho·log'i·cal (môr·fô·lŏj'ĭ·kŭl)
mor·phol'o·gy (môr·fŏl'ô·gē)
mo·sa'ic (mŏ·zā'ĭk)
mu (mū)
Mul'ler (mŭl'ēr)
mul·ti·cel'lu·lar (mŭl·tĭ·sĕl'ŭ·lēr)
mul·ti·proc'es·sor (mŭl·tĭ·prŏs'ĕs·ēr)
Mu'met·al (mū'mĕt·ŭl)
Mun'sell (mŭn'sŭl)
My'ca·lex (mī'kä·lĕks)
My'lar (mī'lär)

N

nan'o (năn'ō)
Na·per'i·an (nå·pêr'ĭ·ŭn)
na'pi·er (nā'pē·ēr)
Nav'a·globe (năv'ä·glōb)
na'var (nā'vär)
nav'ar·ho (năv'är·hô)
neg'a·tron (nĕg'ä·trŏn)
ne'mo (nē'mō)

ne′per (nē′pẽr)
Nernst (nẽrnst)
neu·ris′tor (nṳ·rĭs′tẽr)
neu·ro·e·lec·tric′i·ty (nṳ·rȯ·ė·lĕk-
trĭs′ĭ·tē)
neu·tri′no (nōō·trē′nō)
neu′tron (nṳ′trŏn)
Ni′chrome (nī′krōm)
Nip′kow (nĭp′kou)
noc′to·vi·sion (nŏk′tȯ·vĭ·zhŭn)
nod′al (nōd′′l)
node (nōd)
nod′ules (nŏd′ūls)
no′mo·graph (nō′mȯ·grăf)
non·e·quiv′a·lence (nŏn·ė·kwĭv′ä·lĕns)
non·e·ras′a·ble (nŏn·ė·răs′ä·b′l)
nov′al (nōv′′l)
nov′ice (nŏv′ĭs)
nu·cle·ar (nū′klė·ẽr)
nu·cle·a′tion (nōō·klĭ·ā′shŭn)
nu·cle·on′ics (nū·klė·ŏn′ĭks)
nu·cle·us (nū′klė·ŭs)
nu′tat·ing (nū′tāt·ĭng)
nu·vis′tor (nōō·vĭs′tẽr)
Ny′quist (nī′kwĭst)

O

o·blique′ (ō·blēk′)
o′boe (ō′bō)
ob·so·les′cence (ŏb·sȯ·lĕs′ĕns)
oc·clude′ (ŏ·klōōd′)
oc′tal (ŏc′tŭl)
o′do·graph (ō′dȯ·grăf)
oer′sted (ẽr′stĕd)
o·me·ga (ō·mĕ′gä)
om·ni·bear·ing (ŏm′nĭ·bâr·ĭng)
om·ni·di·rec′tion·al (ŏm·nĭ·dĭ-
rĕk′shŭn·äl)
on′do·graph (ŏn′dȯ·grăf)
o·pac′i·me·ter (ō·păs′ĭ·mĕ′tẽr)
op′er·and (ŏp′ẽr·ănd)
op·to·e·lec·tron′ic (ŏp·tȯ·ė·lĕk-
trŏn′ĭk)
op′to·phone (ŏp′tȯ·fōn)
or′i·fice (ŏr′ĭ·fĭs)
or′thi·con (ŏr′thĭ·kŏn)
or′tho·code (ŏr′thō·cōd)
or·thog′o·nal (ŏr·thŏg′ȯ·nôl)
os′cil·la·to·ry (ŏs′ĭ·lä·tôr·ė)
os·cil′lo·gram (ŏ·sĭl′ȯ·grăm)
o′zone (ō′zōn)

P

pan·o·ram′ic (păn·ô·răm′ĭk)
pa·rab′o·la (pä·răb′ȯ·lä)
par·a·bol′ic (pâr·ä·bŏl′ĭk)
pa·rab′o·loid (pä·răb′ȯ·loid)
pa·rab·o·loi′dal (pä·răb·ȯ·loi′d′l)
par′af·fin (pâr′ä·fĭn)

pár′al·lax (pâr′ä·lăks)
pa·ram′e·ter (pä·răm′ĕ·tẽr)
par·a·me′tric (pâr·ă·mĕ′trĭk)
pa·ram′e·tron (pä·răm′ĕ·trŏn)
par·a·mis′tor (pâr·ä·mĭs′tẽr)
par·a·sit′ic (pâr·ä·sĭt′ĭk)
Pas′chen′s (păs′kĕnz)
Pel·tier′ (pĕl·tyä′)
per·cep′tron (pẽr·sĕp′trŏn)
per·cus′sive (pẽr·cŭs′ĭv)
per·i·od′ic (pẽr·ĭ·ŏd′ĭk)
pe·riph′er·al (pẽr·ĭf′ẽr·ŭl)
per·me·a·bil′i·ty (pẽr·mė·ä·bĭl′ĭ·tē)
per·me·am′e·ter (pẽr·mĕ·ăm′ĕ·tẽr)
per·mit·tiv′i·ty (pẽr·mĭt·tĭv′ĭ·tē)
per·sis′tor (pẽr·sĭs′tẽr)
phan′o·tron (făn′ȯ·trŏn)
phan′tas·tron (făn′täs·trŏn)
phas′i·tron (fāz′ĭ·trŏn)
phas′ma·jec·tor (fāz′mä·jĕk·tẽr)
pha′sor (fā′zẽr)
phe·nol′ic·(fė·nŏl′ĭk)
phi (fē)
phon (fŏn)
pho′nemes (fō′nēmz)
pho·net′ic (fȯ·nĕt′ĭk)
pho′non (fō′nŏn)
phos·pho·res′cence (fŏs·fȯ·rĕs′ĕns)
pho·to·e·las·tic·i·ty (fō·tō·ė·lăs-
tĭ′sĭ·tē)
pho·to·mag·ne′to·e·lec′tric (fō·tō-
măg·nē′tō·ė·lĕk′trĭk)
pho·tom′e·ter (fȯ·tŏm′ĕ·tẽr)
pho·tom′e·try (fȯ·tŏm′ĕ·trē)
pho′to·sphere (fō′tō·sfêr)
pho·to·vol·ta′ic (fō·tō·vŏl·tā′ĭk)
pi (pī)
pi′co (pī′kō)
pi·e·zo·di·e·lec′tric (pī·ė·zō·dī·ė-
lĕk′trĭk)
pi·e·zo·e·lec′tric (pī·ė·zō·ė·lĕk′trĭk)
pi′e·zo·id (pī′ė·zoid)
Pi·ra′ni (pī·rä′nė)
planch′et (plăn′chĭt)
Planck′i·an (plănk′ĭ·ŭn)
Planck′s (plănks)
plas′ma·tron (plăz′mä·trŏn)
plas′ti·ciz·er (plăs′tĭ·sīz·ẽr)
pla·teau′ (plă·tō′)
pla·tin′o·tron (plă·tĭn′ȯ·trŏn)
plat′i·num (plăt′ĭ·nŭm)
pli·o·dy′na·tron (plī·ȯ·dī′nä·trŏn)
pli′o·tron (plī′ŏ·trŏn)
plu·to′ni·um (plōō·tō′nĭ·ŭm)
poid (poid)
Pois·son′s′ (poi·sŏnz′)
pol·y·es′ter (pŏl·ĭ·ĕs′tẽr)
pol·y·eth′yl·ene (pŏl·ĭ·ĕth′ĭ·lĕn)
pol·y·sty′rene (pŏl·ĭ·stī′rēn)
por·ta·men′to (pôr·tä·mĕn′tō)

pos′i·tron (pŏz′ĭ·trŏn)
po·tas′si·um (pŏ·tăs′ĭ·ŭm)
po·ten′tial (pŏ·těn′shŭl)
po·ten·ti·om′e·ter (pŏ·těn·shĭ·ŏm′ĕ-
   tẽr)
Po·tier′ (pō·tyā′)
Poyn′ting′s (poin′tĭngz)
pre·ces′sion (prĕ·sĕsh′ŭn)
pre·cip′i·ta·tor (prĕ·sĭp′ĭ·tā·tẽr)
pre·cip′i·tron (prĕ·sĭp′ĭ·trŏn)
pre·cur′sor (prĕ·kẽr′sẽr)
pro·fi·lom′e·ter (prŏ·fĭ·lŏm′ĕ·tẽr)
pro·me′thi·um (prŏ·mē′thĭ·ŭm)
pseu′do·code (sōō′dō·cōd)
Pu′pin (pŭ′pĕn)
py′lon (pī′lŏn)
py·ram′i·dal (pĭ·răm′ĭ·dŭl)
pyr·he·li·om′e·ter (pīr·hē·lĭ·ŏm′ĕ·tẽr)
py·ro·e·lec′tric (pī·rō·ė·lĕk′trĭk)
py·rom′e·ter (pī·rŏm′ĕ·tẽr)
Py·thag·o·re′an (pĭ·thăg·ȯ·rē′ŭn)

Q

quad (kwôd)
quad′rant (kwŏd′rănt)
quad·ran′tal (kwŏd·răn′tŭl)
quad′ri·pole (kwŏd′rĭ·pōl)
quad′ru·pole (kwŏd′rōō·pōl)
quan·ti·za′tion (kwŏn·tĭ·zā′shŭn)
quan′tize (kwŏn′tīz)
quan′tum (kwŏn′tŭm)
qua′si- (kwā′sī-)
qui·es′cent (kwī·ĕs′ĕnt)

R

ra′con (rā′kŏn)
rad (răd)
ra′dar (rā′där)
ra′di·ac (rā′dĭ·ăk)
ra′di·al (rā′dĭ·ŭl)
ra′di·a·tive (rā′dĭ·ā·tĭv)
ra·di·ol′o·gy (rā·dĭ·ŏl′ŏ·jĭ)
ra·di·o·paque′ (rā·dĭ·ȯ·pāk′)
ra·di·o·son′o·buoy (rā·dĭ·ȯ·sŏn′ŏ·boi)
ra·di·o·te·leg′ra·phy (rā·dĭ·ȯ·tĕ-
   lĕg′rä·fē)
ra·di·o·te·leph′o·ny (rā·dĭ·ȯ·tĕ-
   lĕf′ȯ·nē)
ra·di·o·ther′a·py (rā·dĭ·ȯ·thâr′ä·pē)
ra·di·o·ther′mics (rā·dĭ·ȯ·thēr′mĭks)
ra′dix (rā′dĭks)
ra′dome (rā′dōm)
ra′dux (rā′dŭks)
ra′mark (rā′märk)
Ram′sauer (răm′sour)
ras′ter (răs′tẽr)
ray′dist (rȧ′dĭst)
Ray′leigh (rā′lĭ)
re·ac·qui·si′tion (rĕ·ăk·wĭ·zĭ′shŭn)

re·bec′ca-eu·re′ka (rĕ·bĕk′ä-ů·rē′kä)
re·ca·les′cent (rē·kä·lĕs′ĕnt)
re·cip′ro·cal (rĕ·sĭp′rŏ·kŭl)
rec·i·pros′i·ty (rĕs·i·prŏs′i·tē)
re·con′nais·sance (rĕ·kŏn′ĭ·sŭns)
rec′ti·gon (rĕk′tĭ·gŏn)
rec·ti·lin′e·al (rĕk·tĭ·lĭn′ė·ŭl)
rec·ti·lin′e·ar (rĕk·tĭ·lĭn′ė·ēr)
re·cur′sion (rĕ·kûr′zhŭn)
re·dun′dan·cy (rĕ·dŭn′dŭn·sē)
re·flec·tom′e·ter (rĕ·flĕk·tŏm′ĕ·tẽr)
re·frac·tom′e·ter (rĕ·frăk·tŏm′ĕ·tẽr)
re·fran′gi·ble (rĕ·frăn′jĭ·b′l)
re·ig·ni′tion (rĕ·ĭg·nĭ′shŭn)
Rei′ke (rī′kė)
Rei′nartz (rī′närts)
rel (rĕl)
re·lax′or (rĕ·lăk′sẽr)
rem′a·nence (rĕm′ä·nĕns)
re·per′fo·ra·tor (rĕ·pẽr′fȯ·rā·tẽr)
re·sid′u·al (rĕ·zĭd′ů·ŭl)
re·sis·tiv′i·ty (rĕ·zĭs·tĭv′ĭ·tē)
res′na·tron (rĕz′nä·trŏn)
ret·ro·di·rec′tive (rĕt·rō·dĭ·rĕk′tĭv)
re·ver·ber·a′tion (rĕ·vẽr·bẽr·ā′shŭn)
rhe′o·stat (rē′ȯ·stăt)
rhom′bic (rŏm′bĭk)
rho·the′ta (rō·thā′tä)
rhum′ba·tron (rōōm′bä·trŏn)
Rig′hi-Le·duc′ (rē′gė·lŭ·dūk′)
RI·OM′E·TER (rĭ·ŏm′ĕ·tẽr)
Ro·chelle′ (rō·shĕl′)
roent′gen (rĕnt′gĕn)
roent·gen′o·gram (rĕnt·gĕn′ȯ·grăm)
roent·gen·ol′o·gy (rĕnt·gĕn·ŏl′ŏ·jē)
roent·gen·om′e·ter (rĕnt·gĕn·ŏm′ĕ·tẽr)
Ruhm′korff (rŭm′kôrf)

S

scin·til·la′tion (sĭn·tĭ·lä′shŭn)
sel′en·ide (sĕl′ĕn·īd)
sep′tate (sĕp′tāt)
se·quen′tial (sė·kwĕn′shŭl)
ser′rat·ed (sĕr′āt·ĕd)
sex·i·dec′i·mal (sĕk·sĭ·dĕs′ĭ·mŭl)
sfer′ics (sfêr′ĭks)
sho·ran′ (shō·răn′)
sil′i·ca (sĭl′ĭ·kä)
sil′i·con (sĭl′ĭ·kŏn)
sil′i·cone (sĭl′ĭ·kŏn)
si′mul·cast·ing (sī′mŭl·kăst·ĭng)
sine (sīn)
sins (sĭnz)
si·nus·oi′dal (sī·nů·soi′dŭl)
skew (skū)
ski′a·tron (skē′ä·trŏn)
sniv′et (snĭv′ĕt)
so′dar (sō′där)
so′di·um (sō′dĭ·ŭm)
so′far (sō′fär)

so'lar (sō'lẽr)
sol'der (sŏd'ẽr)
so'len·oid (sō'lĕn·oid)
so'li·on (sō'lĭ·ŏn)
so'nar (sō'när)
sone (sōn)
son'ic (sŏn'ĭk)
son'ne (sŏn'ẽ)
son'o·buoy (sŏn'ȯ·boi)
son·om'e·ter (sŏn·ŏm'ĕ·tẽr)
so·phis'ti·cat·ed (sȯ·fĭs'tĭ·kāt·ĕd)
spa·cis'tor (spā·sĭs'tẽr)
spa·ghet'ti (spä·gĕt'ē)
spa'tial (spā'shŭl)
spec'tral (spĕk'trôl)
spec·trom'e·ter (spĕk·trŏm'ĕ·tẽr)
spec'u·lar (spĕk'ů·lẽr)
sphere (sfêr)
spher'i·cal (sfêr'ĭ·kŭl)
spin·thar'i·scope (spĭn·thâr'ĭ·skōp)
spo·rad'ic (spȯ·răd'ĭk)
spur'i·ous (spēr'ĭ·ŭs)
squeg'ger (skwĕg'ẽr)
squelch (skwĕlch)
squint (skwĭnt)
squit'ter (skwĭt'ẽr)
sta·bil'i·volt (stä·bĭl'ĭ·vȯlt)
sta'lo (stā'lō)
stat (stăt)
ste'a·tite (stĕ'ä·tīt)
Stef'an-Boltz'mann (stĕf'ŭn-bōltz'mŭn)
Stein'metz (stīn'mĕts)
sten'ode (stĕn'ōd)
ste·ra'di·an (stĕ·rā'dĭ·ŭn)
ster·e·o·ceph'a·loid (stâr·ĕ·ȯ·sĕf'ä-
loid)
stim'u·lus (stĭm'ů·lŭs)
sto·chas'tic (stō·kăs'tĭk)
sto·chi·o·met'ric (stō·kĭ·ȯ·mĕt'rĭk)
strat'o·sphere (străt'ȯ·sfêr)
stri·a'tion (strī·ā'shŭn)
strob'o·scope (strōb'ȯ·skōp)
strob·o·scop'ic (strōb·ȯ·skōp'ĭk)
strob'o·tron (strōb'ȯ·trŏn)
Suhl (sool)
sur·veil'lance (sẽr·vā'lăns)
sus·cep·ti·bil'i·ty (sŭ·sĕp·tĭ·bĭl'ĭ·tē)
sym·bol'ic (sĭm·bŏl'ĭk)
syn'chro·tron (sĭn'krȯ·trŏn)
syn'the·siz·er (sĭn'thĕ·sīz·ẽr)

T

tach·om'e·ter (tăk·ŏm'ĕ·tẽr)
tan·gen'tial (tăn·jĕn'shŭl)
tan'ta·lum (tăn'tä·lŭm)
tec'ne·tron (tĕk'nĕ·trŏn)
tel·e·gen'ic (tĕl·ĕ·jĕn'ĭk)
te·leg'ra·phy (tĕ·lĕg'rä·fē)
te·lem'e·ter (tĕ·lĕm'ĕ·tẽr)
te·lem'e·try (tĕ·lĕm'ĕ·trē)

te·leph'o·ny (tĕ·lĕf'ȯ·nē)
tel'e·ran (tĕl'ĕ·răn)
tel'e·synd (tĕl'ĕ·sĭnd)
tel'ex (tĕl'ĕks)
ten·si·om'e·ter (tĕn·sĭ·ŏm'ĕ·tẽr)
ten'sion (tĕn'shŭn)
ter'a (târ'ä)
ter'na·ry (tẽr'nä·rē)
ter·rain' (tẽr·ān')
ter·res'tri·al (tẽr·ĕs'trĭ·ŭl)
ter'ti·ar·y (tẽr'shĭ·âr·ē)
tes'la (tĕs'lä)
thal'lo·fide (thăl'ȯ·fīd)
ther'e·min (thâr·ĕ·mĭn)
ther'mi·on (thẽr'mĭ·ŏn)
ther·mi·on'ic (thẽr·mĭ·ŏn'ĭk)
ther·mis'tor (thẽr·mĭs'tẽr)
the'ta (thã'tä)
Thev'e·nin's (thĕv'ĕ·nĭns)
tho'ri·at·ed (thō'rĭ·āt·ĕd)
thy'ra·tron (thī'rä·trŏn)
thy'ris·tor (thī'rĭs·tẽr)
thy'rite (thī'rīt)
tim'bre (tĭm'bẽr)
Ton'o·tron (tŏn'ȯ·trŏn)
to·roi'dal (tȯ·roi'dôl)
torque (tôrk)
tor·si·om'e·ter (tôr·sĭ·ŏm'ĕ·tẽr)
tor'sion (tôr'shŭn)
tour'ma·line (toor'mä·lĭn)
trans·hy'brid (trăns·hī'brĭd)
tran'sient (trăn'shĕnt)
tran·sis'tance (trăn·sĭs'tŭns)
tran·si'tion (trăn·zĭsh'ŭn)
tran'si·tron (trăn'sĭ·trŏn)
trans·mis·si·bil'i·ty (trăns·mĭs·ĭ-
bĭl'ĭ·tē)
tran·son'ic (trăn·sŏn'ĭk)
trans·pon'der (trăns·pŏn'dẽr)
trap·e·zoi'dal (trăp·ĕ·zoi'd'l)
tri·ax'i·al (trī·ăx'ĭ·ôl)
tri·bo·e·lec'tric (trī·bȯ·ĕ·lĕk'trĭk)
tri'con (trī'kŏn)
trig'a·tron (trĭg'ä·trŏn)
tri·gis'tor (trī·jĭs'tẽr)
tri·nis'tor (trī·nĭs'tẽr)
trin'o·scope (trĭn'ȯ·skōp)
tri·stim'u·lus (trī·stĭm'ů·lŭs)
trit'i·um (trĭt'ĭ·ŭm)
trop'o·sphere (trŏp'ȯ·sfêr)
trop·o·spher'ic (trŏp·ȯ·sfĕr'ĭk)
trun'cate (trŭn'kāt)
tun'gar (tŭn'gär)
tung'sten (tŭng'stĕn)
tur·bid'i·me·ter (tẽr·bĭd'ĭ·mȧ·tẽr)

U

ul'tor (ŭl'tôr)
ul·tra·mi·crom'e·ter (ŭl·trä·mī-
krŏm'ĕ·tẽr)
um·bil'i·cal (ŭm·bĭl'ĭ·kŭl)

V

va'lence (vā'lĕns)
va·lid'i·ty (vä·lĭd'ĭ·tē)
Van' de Graaff (văn'dĕ·grăf)
var'ac·tor (vâr'ăk·tēr)
var'hour (vär'our)
Var'i·ac (vâr'ĭ·ăk)
var·in·dor (vâr'ĭn·dēr)
var·i·om'e·ter (vâr·ĭ·ŏm'ĕ·tēr)
var·is'tor (vâr·ĭs'tēr)
ver'ni·er (vēr'nĭ·ēr)
ves·tig'i·al (vĕs·tĭj'ĭ·ŭl)
vi·bra'to (vĭ·brä'tŏ)
vi'bra·tron (vī'brä·trŏn)
vi·brom'e·ter (vī·brŏm'ĕ·tēr)
vi'di·con (vĭ'dĭ·kŏn)
Vil·la'ri (vĭ·lâr'ĕ)
vi'nyl (vī'nŭl)
vis·com'e·ter (vĭs·kŏm'ĕ·tēr)
vis·co·sim'e·ter (vĭs·kŏ·sĭm'ĕ·tēr)
vis·cos'i·ty (vĭs·kŏs'ĭ·tē)
vis'cous (vĭs'kŭs)
vo'das (vō'dŭs)
vo'der (vō'dēr)
vo'gad (vō'gäd)
vol'a·tile (vŏl'ŭ·tĭl)
vol·ta'ic (vŏl·tā'ĭk)
vol·u·met'ric (vŏl·ŭ·mĕt'rĭk)

W

Wag'ner (wăg'nēr)
wa'mo·scope (wā'mŏ·skōp)
web'er (wĕb'ēr)
Weh'nelt (vā'nĕlt)
Wert'heim (wērt'hīm)
Wie'de·mann (wē'dŭ·mŭn)
Wie'de·mann-Franz (wē'dŭ·mŭn-fränz)
Wien (wēn)
Wims'hurst (wĭmz'hērst)
wob'bu·la·tor (wŏb'ŭ·lā·tēr)

X

xe'non (zē'nŏn)
xe·ro·graph'ic (zē·rŏ·grăf'ĭk)
xe·rog'ra·phy (zē·rŏg'rä·fē)

Y

Ya'gi (yä'gē)

Z

ze'ner (zē'nēr)
zep'pe·lin (zĕp'ĕ·lĭn)
zinc (zĭngk)

589

SCHEMATIC SYMBOLS

SCHEMATIC SYMBOLS

ABBREVIATIONS

A—Ammeter; ampere; area
a—Ampere
AC, a.c., a-c, ac—Alternating current
AF, a.f., a-f, af—Audio frequency
AFC, afc—Automatic frequency control
AGC, agc—Automatic gain control
AM, am—Amplitude modulation
Amp, amp., Amps, amps.—Ampere; amperes
Ant, ant.—Antenna
AVC, a.v.c., avc—Automatic volume control
B—Susceptance
b—Magnetic flux density
BC, bc—Broadcast
BFO, bfo—Beat-frequency oscillator
C—Capacitance; capacitor
°C—Degrees Celsius or centigrade
cm—Centimeter
cps—Cycles per second
CW, cw—Continuous wave
db—Decibels
DC, d.c., d-c, dc—Direct current
d.c.c, dcc—Double cotton-covered
DPDT, d.p.d.t., dpdt—Double-pole, double-throw
DPST, d.p.s.t., dpst—Double-pole single-throw
d.s.c, dsc—Double silk-covered
E, e—Voltage
e.c., ec—Enamel-covered
EMF, emf—Electromotive force
ERP—Effective radiated power
F, f—Farad
f—Frequency
°F—Degrees Fahrenheit
FM, f.m., fm—Frequency modulation
G—Conductance
G_m, gm, g_m—Mutual conductance
GCT—Greenwich Civil Time
gnd—Ground
H, h—Henry
HF, h.f., h-f, hf—High frequency
hp—Horsepower
hy—Henry
Hz—Hertz
I—Current
IF, i.f., i-f, if—Intermediate frequency
ips—Inches per second
j—Joule; an imaginary number; an operator to rotate a vector quantity 90° counterclockwise
K—× 1000; dielectric constant; a numerical value that does not change during a given period
k—Dielectric constant
KC, kc—Kilocycle
KHz—Kilohertz
kv—Kilovolt
kva—Kilovolt ampere
KW, kw—Kilowatt
KWH, kwh—Kilowatt hour
L—Inductance; inductor

l—Length
LF, l.f., l-f, lf—Low frequency
M—Mutual inductance; × 1000
m—Meter
ma—Milliampere
MC, Mc, mc—Megacycle
mcw—Modulated continuous wave
meg—Megohm
MF, m.f., m-f, mf—Medium frequency
mf, mfd—Microfarad
mh—Millihenry
MHz—Megahertz
mm—Millimeter
mmf, mmfd—Micromicrofarad
mv—Millivolt (sometimes microvolt)
mw—Milliwatt (sometimes microwatt)
NC—No connection
OD—Outside diameter
P—Power
pf—Power factor; picofarad
p-p—Peak-to-peak
Q—Merit of a coil or capacitor; quantity of electricity
R—Resistance; resistor
RC, R-C—Product of resistance time capacitance; resistor-capacitor
RF, r.f., r-f, rf—Radio frequency
RFC—Radio-frequency choke coil
rms—Root mean square
rpm—Revolutions per minute
s.c.c., scc—Single cotton-covered
s.c.e., sce—Single cotton enamel
sec—Second; secondary
SHF, s.h.f., shf—Super-high frequencies
s.s.c., ssc—Single silk-covered
SW, sw—Short wave
t—Time
T—Temperature
trf—Tuned radio frequency
UHF, uhf—Ultrahigh frequency
V, v—Volt; voltmeter
VHF, vhf—Very high frequencies
VOM, vom—Volt-ohm-milliammeter
VTVM, vtvm—Vacuum-tube voltmeter
VU—Volume unit
W—Watt; work
w—Watt
wh, whr—Watt-hour
X—Reactance
X_c—Capacitive reactance
X_L—Inductive reactance
Y—Admittance
Z—Impedance
μa—Microampere
μf—Microfarad
μh—Microhenry
$\mu\mu f$—Micromicrofarad
∿—Cycles per second

The Greek alphabet is given below. The items for which each letter is a symbol are also listed. The small Greek letter is the symbol for all the items listed unless a capital letter is indicated (cap).

Letter Small	Letter Capital	Name	Designates
α	A	Alpha	Angles, coefficients, attenuation constant, absorption factor, area.
β	B	Beta	Angles, coefficients, phase constant.
γ	Γ	Gamma	Specific quantity, angles, electrical conductivity, propagation constant, complex propagation constant (cap).
δ	Δ	Delta	Density, angles, increment or decrement (cap or small), determinant (cap), permittivity (cap).
ϵ	E	Epsilon	Dielectric constant, permittivity, base of natural (Napierian) logarithms, electric intensity.
ζ	Z	Zeta	Co-ordinate, coefficients.
η	H	Eta	Intrinsic impedance, efficiency, surface charge density, hysteresis, co-ordinates.
θ	Θ	Theta	Angular phase displacement, time constant, reluctance, angles.
ι	I	Iota	Unit vector.
κ	K	Kappa	Susceptibility, coupling coefficient.
λ	Λ	Lambda	Wavelength, attenuation constant, permeance (cap).
μ	M	Mu	Prefix *micro-*, permeability, amplification factor.
ν	N	Nu	Reluctivity, frequency.
ξ	Ξ	Xi	Co-ordinates.
o	O	Omicron	——
π	Π	Pi	3.1416 (circumference divided by diameter).
ρ	P	Rho	Resistivity, volume charge density, co-ordinates.
σ	Σ	Sigma	Surface charge density, complex propagation constant, electrical conductivity, leakage coefficient, sign of summation (cap).
τ	T	Tau	Time constant, volume resistivity, time-phase displacement, transmission factor, density.
υ	Υ	Upsilon	——
ϕ	Φ	Phi	Magnetic flux, angles, scalar potential (cap).
χ	X	Chi	Electric susceptibility, angles.
ψ	Ψ	Psi	Dielectric flux, phase difference, co-ordinates, angles.
ω	Ω	Omega	Angular velocity ($2\pi f$), resistance in ohms (cap), solid angles (cap).

The following symbols and abbreviations have been adopted as standard by the Electronic Industries Association (EIA) and the National Electrical Manufacturers Association (NEMA).

B, b—Base electrode for units employing a single base

b_1, b_2, etc.—Base electrodes for more than one base

BV_{CBO}—Breakdown voltage, collector to base, emitter open

BV_{CEO}—Breakdown voltage, collector to emitter, base open

BV_{CER}—Breakdown voltage, collector to emitter, with specified resistance between base and emitter

BV_{CES}—Breakdown voltage, collector to emitter, with base short-circuited to emitter

BV_{EBO}—Breakdown voltage, emitter to base, collector open

BV_R—Breakdown voltage, reverse

C, c—Collector electrode

C_{1b}—Input capacitance (common base)

C_{1c}—Input capacitance (common collector)

C_{1e}—Input capacitance (common emitter)

C_{ob}—Output capacitance (common base)

C_{oc}—Output capacitance (common collector)

C_{oe}—Output capacitance (common emitter)

E, e—Emitter electrode

h_{1b}—Static value of the input resistance (common base)

h_{1b}—Small-signal value of short-circuit input impedance (common base)

h_{1C}—Static value of the input resistance (common collector)

h_{1c}—Small-signal value of short-circuit input impedance (common emitter)

h_{1E}—Static value of the input resistance (common emitter)

h_{1e}—Small-signal value of short-circuit input impedance (common emitter)

h_{1e} (real)—Real part of small-signal value of short-circuit input impedance (common emitter)

h_{OB}—Static value of open-circuit output conductance (common base)

h_{ob}—Small-signal value of open-circuit output admittance (common base)

h_{OC}—Static value of open-circuit output conductance (common collector)

h_{oc}—Small-signal value of open-circuit output admittance (common collector)

h_{OE}—Static value of open-circuit output conductance (common emitter)

h_{oe}—Small-signal value of open-circuit output admittance (common emitter)

i_F—Forward current (instantaneous)

I_O—Average output (rectified) current

I_R—Reverse current (DC)

i_R—Reverse current (instantaneous)

K_p—Thermal derating factor

L_C—Conversion loss

N, n—Region of a device where electrons are the majority carriers

NF—Noise figure

P, p—Region of a device where holes are the majority carriers

P_{BE}—Total power input (DC or average) to the base electrode with respect to the emitter electrode

p_{BE}—Total power input (instantaneous) to the base electrode with respect to the emitter electrode

P_{CB}—Total power input (DC or average) to the collector electrode with respect to the base electrode

p_{CB}—Total power input (instantaneous) to the collector electrode with respect to the base electrode

P_{CE}—Total power input (DC or average) to the collector electrode with respect to the emitter electrode

p_{CE}—Total power input (instantaneous) to the collector electrode with respect to the emitter electrode

R_C—External collector resistance

r_{CE} (sat)—Collector-to-emitter saturation resistance

R_E—External emitter resistance

R_L—Load resistance

T—Temperature

T_A—Ambient temperature

T_C—Case temperature

t_d—Delay time

t_f—Fall time

t_{fr}—Forward recovery time

T_J—Junction temperature

T_{opr}—Operating temperature

t_p—Pulse average time

t_r—Rise time

t_{rr}—Reverse recovery time

t_s—Storage time

T_{stg}—Storage temperature

t_w—Pulse average time

θ—Thermal resistance

θ_{J-A}—Thermal resistance, junction-to-ambient

θ_{J-C}—Thermal resistance, junction-to-case

V_{BB}—Base supply voltage (DC)

V_{BC}—Base-to-collector voltage (DC)

v_{bc}—Base-to-collector voltage (rms)

v_{bc}—Base-to-collector voltage (instantaneous)

V_{BE}—Base-to-emitter voltage (DC)

f_{hfb}—Small-signal, short-circuit, forward-current, transfer-ratio cutoff frequency (common base)

f_{hfc}—Small-signal, short-circuit, forward-current, transfer-ratio cutoff frequency (common collector)

f_{hfe}—Small-signal, short-circuit, forward-current, transfer-ratio cutoff frequency (common emitter)

f_{max}—Maximum frequency of oscillation

G_{PB}—Large-signal average power gain (common base)

G_{pb}—Small-signal average power gain (common base)

G_{PC}—Large-signal average power gain (common collector)

G_{pc}—Small-signal average power gain (common collector)

G_{PE}—Large-signal average power gain (common emitter)

G_{pe}—Small-signal average power gain (common emitter)

h_{FB}—Static value of the forward-current transfer ratio (common base)

h_{fb}—Small-signal, short-circuit, forward-current transfer ratio (common base)

h_{FC}—Static value of the forward-current transfer ratio (common collector)

h_{fc}—Small-signal, short-circuit, forward-current transfer ratio (common collector)

h_{FE}—Static value of the forward-current transfer ratio (common emitter)

h_{fe}—Small-signal, short-circuit, forward-current transfer ratio (common emitter)

h_{rb}—Small-signal value of open-circuit, reverse-voltage transfer ratio (common base)

h_{rc}—Small-signal value of open-circuit, reverse-voltage transfer ratio (common collector)

h_{re}—Small-signal value of open-circuit, reverse-voltage transfer ratio (common emitter)

I, i—Intrinsic region of a device (where neither holes nor electrons predominate)

I_B—Base current (DC)

I_b—Base current (rms)

i_b—Base current (instantaneous)

I_C—Collector current (DC)

I_c—Collector current (rms)

i_c—Collector current (instantaneous)

I_{CBO}—Collector cutoff current (DC), emitter open

I_{CEO}—Collector cutoff current (DC), base open

I_{CER}—Collector cutoff current (DC), with specified resistance between base and emitter

I_{CES}—Collector cutoff current (DC), with base short-circuited to emitter

I_{CEX}—Collector cutoff current (DC), with specified circuit between base and emitter

I_E—Emitter current (DC)

I_e—Emitter current (rms)

i_e—Emitter current (instantaneous)

I_{EBO}—Emitter cutoff current (DC), collector open

I_F—Forward current (DC)

P_{EB}—Total power input (DC or average) to the emitter electrode with respect to the base electrode

p_{EB}—Total power input (instantaneous) to the emitter electrode with respect to the base electrode

P_{IB}—Large-signal input power (common base)

P_{ib}—Small-signal input power (common base)

P_{IC}—Large-signal input power (common collector)

P_{ic}—Small-signal input power (common collector)

P_{IE}—Large-signal input power (common emitter)

P_{ie}—Small-signal input power (common emitter)

P_{OB}—Large-signal output power (common base)

P_{ob}—Small-signal output power (common base)

P_{OC}—Large-signal output power (common collector)

P_{oc}—Small-signal output power (common collector)

P_{OE}—Large-signal output power (common emitter)

P_{oe}—Small-signal output power (common emitter)

P_T—Total power input (DC or average) to all electrodes

p_T—Total power input (instantaneous) to all electrodes

R_B—External base resistance

V_{be}—Base-to-emitter voltage (rms)

v_{be}—Base-to-emitter voltage (instantaneous)

V_{CB}—Collector-to-base voltage (DC)

V_{cb}—Collector-to-base voltage (rms)

v_{cb}—Collector-to-base voltage (instantaneous)

V_{CBF}—DC open-circuit voltage (floating potential) between collector and base, with emitter biased in reverse direction with respect to base

V_{CO}—Collector supply voltage (DC)

V_{CE}—Collector-to-emitter voltage (DC)

V_{ce}—Collector-to-emitter voltage (rms)

v_{ce}—Collector-to-emitter voltage (instantaneous)

V_{CE} (sat)—Collector-to-emitter saturation voltage

V_{EB}—Emitter-to-base voltage (DC)

V_{eb}—Emitter-to-base voltage (rms)

v_{eb}—Emitter-to-base voltage (instantaneous)

V_{EC}—Emitter-to-collector voltage (DC)

V_{ec}—Emitter-to-collector voltage (rms)

v_{ec}—Emitter-to-collector voltage (instantaneous)

V_{ECF}—DC open-circuit voltage (floating potential) between emitter and collector, with base biased in reverse direction with respect to collector

V_{EE}—Emitter supply voltage (DC)

V_F—Forward voltage (DC)

v_F—Forward voltage (instantaneous)

V_R—Reverse voltage (DC)

v_R—Reverse voltage (instantaneous)

V_{RT}—Reach-through voltage

Ohm's Law for A-C Circuits

The fundamental Ohm's law formulas for a-c circuits are given by

$$I = \frac{E}{Z}, \qquad Z = \frac{E}{I},$$

$$E = IZ, \qquad P = EI \cos \theta$$

where I = current in amperes,

Z = impedance in Ohms,

E = volts across Z,

P = power in watts,

θ = phase angle in degrees.

Phase Angle

The phase angle is defined as the difference in degrees by which current leads voltage in a capacitive circuit, or lags voltage in an inductive circuit, and in series circuits is equal to the angle whose tangent is given by the

ratio $\frac{X}{R}$ and is expressed by

$$\text{arc tan } \frac{X}{R}$$

where X = the inductive or capacitive reactance in ohms,

R = the non-reactive resistance in ohms,

of the combined resistive and reactive components of the circuit under consideration.

Therefore

in a purely resistive circuit, $\theta = 0°$

in a purely reactive circuit, $\theta = 90°$

and in a resonant circuit, $\theta = 0°$

also when

$\theta = 0°$, $\cos \theta = 1$ and $P = EI$,

$\theta = 90°$, $\cos \theta = 0$ and $P = 0$.

Degrees $\times$ 0.0175 = radians.

1 radian = 57.3°.

Power Factor

The power-factor of any a-c circuit is equal to the true power in watts divided by the apparent power in volt-amperes which is equal to the cosine of the phase angle, and is expressed by

$$p.f. = \frac{EI \cos \theta}{EI} = \cos \theta$$

where

$p.f.$ = the circuit load power factor,

$EI \cos \theta$ = the true power in watts,

EI = the apparent power in volt-amperes,

E = the applied potential in volts,

I = load current in amperes.

Therefore

in a purely resistive circuit.

$$\theta = 0° \text{ and } p.f. = 1$$

and in a reactive circuit,

$$\theta = 90° \text{ and } p.f. = 0$$

and in a resonant circuit,

$$\theta = 0° \text{ and } p.f. = 1$$

Ohm's Law for D-C Circuits

The fundamental Ohm's law formulas for d-c circuits are given by,

$$I = \frac{E}{R}, \qquad R = \frac{E}{I},$$

$$E = IR, \qquad P = EI.$$

where I = current in amperes,

R = resistance in ohms,

E = potential across R in volts,

P = power in watts.

Ohm's Law Formulas for D-C Circuits

Known Values	Formulas for Determining Unknown Values of . . .			
	I	R	E	P
I & R			IR	I^2R
I & E		$\dfrac{E}{I}$		EI
I & P		$\dfrac{P}{I^2}$	$\dfrac{P}{I}$	
R & E	$\dfrac{E}{R}$			$\dfrac{E^2}{R}$
R & P	$\sqrt{\dfrac{P}{R}}$		$\sqrt{PR}$	
E & P	$\dfrac{P}{E}$	$\dfrac{E^2}{P}$		

Ohm's Law Formulas for A-C Circuits

Known Values	Formulas for Determining Unknown Values of . . .			
	I	Z	E	P
I & Z			IZ	$I^2Z\cos\theta$
I & E		$\dfrac{E}{I}$		$IE\cos\theta$
I & P		$\dfrac{P}{I^2\cos\theta}$	$\dfrac{P}{I\cos\theta}$	
Z & E	$\dfrac{E}{Z}$			$\dfrac{E^2\cos\theta}{Z}$
Z & P	$\sqrt{\dfrac{P}{Z\cos\theta}}$		$\sqrt{\dfrac{PZ}{\cos\theta}}$	
E & P	$\dfrac{P}{E\cos\theta}$	$\dfrac{E^2\cos\theta}{P}$		

Trigonometric Relationships

In any right triangle, if we let

θ = the acute angle formed by the hypotenuse and the base leg,

ϕ = the acute angle formed by the hypotenuse and the altitude leg,

H = the hypotenuse,

A = the side adjacent θ and opposite ϕ,

O = the side opposite θ and adjacent ϕ,

then

$$\text{sine of } \theta = \sin \theta = \frac{O}{H}$$

$$\text{cosine of } \theta = \cos \theta = \frac{A}{H}$$

$$\text{tangent of } \theta = \tan \theta = \frac{O}{A}$$

$$\text{cosecant of } \theta = \csc \theta = \frac{H}{O}$$

$$\text{secant of } \theta = \sec \theta = \frac{H}{A}$$

$$\text{cotangent of } \theta = \cot \theta = \frac{A}{O}$$

also

$$\sin \theta = \cos \phi \qquad \csc \theta = \sec \phi$$
$$\cos \theta = \sin \phi \qquad \sec \theta = \csc \phi$$
$$\tan \theta = \cot \phi \qquad \cot \theta = \tan \phi$$

and

$$\frac{1}{\sin \theta} = \csc \theta \qquad \frac{1}{\csc \theta} = \sin \theta$$

$$\frac{1}{\cos \theta} = \sec \theta \qquad \frac{1}{\sec \theta} = \cos \theta$$

$$\frac{1}{\tan \theta} = \cot \theta \qquad \frac{1}{\cot \theta} = \tan \theta$$

The expression "arc sin" indicates, "the angle whose sine is" . . .; likewise arc tan indicates, "the angle whose tangent is" . . . etc. See formulas in table below.

Known Values	Formulas for Determining Unknown Values of . . .				
	A	O	H	θ	ϕ
A & O			$\sqrt{A^2 + O^2}$	arc tan $\dfrac{O}{A}$	arc tan $\dfrac{A}{O}$
A & H		$\sqrt{H^2 - A^2}$		arc cos $\dfrac{A}{H}$	arc sin $\dfrac{A}{H}$
A & θ		$A \tan \theta$	$\dfrac{A}{\cos \theta}$		$90° - \theta$
A & ϕ		$\dfrac{A}{\tan \phi}$	$\dfrac{A}{\sin \phi}$	$90° - \phi$	
O & H	$\sqrt{H^2 - O^2}$			arc sin $\dfrac{O}{H}$	arc cos $\dfrac{O}{H}$
O & θ	$\dfrac{O}{\tan \theta}$		$\dfrac{O}{\sin \theta}$		$90° - \theta$
O & ϕ	$O \tan \phi$		$\dfrac{O}{\cos \phi}$	$90° - \phi$	
H & θ	$H \cos \theta$	$H \sin \theta$			$90° - \theta$
H & ϕ	$H \sin \phi$	$H \cos \phi$		$90° - \phi$	

Mathematical Symbols

$\times$ or $\cdot$	Multiplied by
$\div$ or $:$	Divided by
$+$	Positive. Plus. Add
$-$	Negative. Minus. Subtract
$\pm$	Positive or negative. Plus or minus
$\mp$	Negative or positive. Minus or plus
$=$ or $::$	Equals
$\equiv$	Identity
$\cong$	Is approximately equal to
$\neq$	Does not equal
$>$	Is greater than
$\gg$	Is much greater than
$<$	Is less than
$\ll$	Is much less than
$\geqq$	Greater than or equal to
$\leqq$	Less than or equal to
$\therefore$	Therefore
$\angle$	Angle
Δ	Increment or Decrement
$\perp$	Perpendicular to
$\parallel$	Parallel to
$\lvert n \rvert$	Absolute value of n

Mathematical Constants

$\pi = 3.14$	$\sqrt{\pi} = 1.77$
$2\pi = 6.28$	$\sqrt{\dfrac{\pi}{2}} = 1.25$
$(2\pi)^2 = 39.5$	
$4\pi = 12.6$	$\sqrt{2} = 1.41$
$\pi^2 = 9.87$	$\sqrt{3} = 1.73$
$\dfrac{\pi}{2} = 1.57$	$\dfrac{1}{\sqrt{2}} = 0.707$
$\dfrac{1}{\pi} = 0.318$	$\dfrac{1}{\sqrt{3}} = 0.577$
$\dfrac{1}{2\pi} = 0.159$	$\log \pi = 0.497$
$\dfrac{1}{\pi^2} = 0.101$	$\log \dfrac{\pi}{2} = 0.196$
	$\log \pi^2 = 0.994$
$\dfrac{1}{\sqrt{\pi}} = 0.564$	$\log \sqrt{\pi} = 0.248$

Decimal Inches

$$\text{Inches} \times \quad 2.540 \quad = \text{Centimeters}$$
$$\text{Inches} \times 1.578 \times 10^{-5} = \text{Miles}$$
$$\text{Inches} \times \quad 10^3 \quad = \text{Mils}$$

Inches			Decimal Equivalent	Millimeter Equivalent
1/64			.0156	0.397
	1/32		.0313	0.794
3/64			.0469	1.191
		1/16	.0625	1.588
5/64			.0781	1.985
	3/32		.0938	2.381
7/64			.1094	2.778
		1/8	.1250	3.175
9/64			.1406	3.572
	5/32		.1563	3.969
11/64			.1719	4.366
		3/16	.1875	4.762
13/64			.2031	5.159
	7/32		.2188	5.556
15/64			.2344	5.953
		1/4	.2500	6.350
17/64			.2656	6.747
	9/32		.2813	7.144
19/64			.2969	7.541
		5/16	.3125	7.937
21/64			.3281	8.334
	11/32		.3438	8.731
23/64			.3594	9.128
		3/8	.3750	9.525
25/64			.3906	9.922
	13/32		.4063	10.319
27/64			.4219	10.716
		7/16	.4375	11.112
29/64			.4531	11.509
	15/32		.4688	11.906
31/64			.4844	12.303
		1/2	.5000	12.700
33/64			.5156	13.097
	17/32		.5313	13.494
35/64			.5469	13.891
		9/16	.5625	14.287
37/64			.5781	14.684
	19/32		.5938	15.081
39/64			.6094	15.478
		5/8	.6250	15.875
41/64			.6406	16.272
	21/32		.6563	16.669
43/64			.6719	17.067
		11/16	.6875	17.463
45/64			.7031	17.860
	23/32		.7188	18.238
47/64			.7344	18.635
		3/4	.7500	19.049
49/64			.7656	19.446
	25/32		.7813	19.842
51/64			.7969	20.239
		13/16	.8125	20.636
53/64			.8281	21.033
	27/32		.8438	21.430
55/64			.8594	21.827
		7/8	.8750	22.224
57/64			.8906	22.621
	29/32		.9063	23.018
59/64			.9219	23.415
		15/16	.9375	23.812
61/64			.9531	24.209
	31/32		.9688	24.606
63/64			.9844	25.004
		1.0	1.0000	25.400

MEMORANDA

Science Fair®
America's Favorite
Electronic Kits

Using the unique "P-Box"® concept, each kit is a useful device that demonstrates important electronic principles. Teacher-written instructions let you learn as you build! Top-quality components assure long-life and fine performance.

Each Kit with All Parts!

"P-Box" Material withstands soldering—remount parts or make wiring changes at will!

Quality Components!

Detailed schematics and pictorial diagrams for easiest possible assembly!

Waste-Free Package Design! Special pre-punched chassis "top" lets you mount parts easily; clear plastic bottom protects wiring!

22 P-BOX KITS AVAILABLE—PRICES LOW AS 1.49

Shortwave Radio

Electronic Thermometer

Electronic Organ

28-100. Single-Tube DC Radio.
28-101. Seven-Note Electronic Organ.
28-102. 2-Transistor Radio
28-103. Wireless AM Transmitter.
28-104. AC/DC Power Supply.
28-105. 3-Way Code Oscillator.
28-106. OTL Monophonic Amplifier.
28-107. "Rise-Fall" Siren Alarm.
28-110. 3-Transistor Shortwave Radio.
28-112. Bell/Buzzer Code Key.
28-116. Telephone Amp with Speaker.

28-118. Adujstable Metronome.
28-122. All-Purpose Electronic VOM.
28-123. 8-Ohm Extension Speaker.
28-126. Photoelectric Nite-Light.
28-128. Light-Operated Burglar Alarm.
28-129. Solar-Powered AM Radio.
28-130. "GoofyLite" Lamp Flasher.
28-131. Voice-Controlled Relay.
28-132. Moisture-Detector Relay.
28-133. WWV AM Radio Converter.
28-135. Indoor/Outdoor Thermometer.

At Over 1000 Allied Radio Shack Stores Nationwide

The Professional Electronic Kits with the "Built-In Instructors"

"A staff of experts" guides your way to kit-building confidence. Detailed assembly manuals tell you what to do, when to do it, and a finished Knight-Kit compares to factory assembled units that cost twice as much!

Knight-Kit

STEP-BY-STEP ASSEMBLY WITH CHECK-OFF SYSTEM
Oversize illustrations and diagrams cover each series of steps. Check box provided when step is completed so you always know where you are and what comes next.

OPERATING INSTRUCTIONS
Once you've assembled your Knight-Kit, the operating section of the manual shows you how to get the full benefit of every feature with detailed explanations and illustrations.

THEORY SECTION
An education in itself — this section provides the background in theory and electrical operation of your equipment. Really adds to the satisfaction of owning and operating your kit.

EXPERT SERVICE NATIONWIDE
In case you need it, service is as close as your neighborhood ARS store. We have factory-trained technicians and complete service facilities. Replacement parts are stocked at all 6 Regional Warehouses and available through all stores.

Knight-Kits for Every Need — You Build Them Better Because They're Designed Better!

29-3387. Three-Channel Color Organ Kit. Reds, blues, greens dance to your music.

29-3383. Two-Station Wireless Intercom Kit Keeps You in Touch from Any Room in Your House.

29-3950. 240-Watt AM/FM Stereo Receiver Kit. The most powerful you can buy! Every hi-fi feature.

29-3986. Compact VOM Kit with 50,000 Ohms/Volt Sensitivity. Reads volts, current, Ohms, dB.

Plus — 40 More!

29-3323. Solid - State Auto Analyzer Kit for Tuneups, Troubleshooting.

At Over 1000 Allied Radio Shack Stores Nationwide

Allied Radio Shack Will Give You Free Educational Material...You Buy Nothing!

TEACHERS & EDUCATORS

Special "No Strings" Offer!

"The Science Fair® Story of Electronics . . . Man's Greatest Discovery" is a unique, 24-page, full color "comic book" we're offering free—in any quantity—for your class or school! It touches on electricity in nature, the first electric light and telegraph, radio waves, the laser beam—and much more! It also covers the Science Fair Hall of Fame: Edison, Faraday, Franklin, Marconi, Morse—to mention a few! Here's the potential to spark a real interest in science for all students.

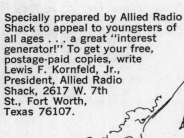

Specially prepared by Allied Radio Shack to appeal to youngsters of all ages . . . a great "interest generator!" To get your free, postage-paid copies, write Lewis F. Kornfeld, Jr., President, Allied Radio Shack, 2617 W. 7th St., Fort Worth, Texas 76107.

Get Acquainted With Sixteen "Great Men In Electronics"

Biographies! Photos! Illustrations!

Now available at a very special price! An attractive 64-page reference book containing biographies of men who pioneered supreme achievements in electronics . . . Morse, Bell, Sarnoff, DeForest, Hammond, and others! Concisely written, factual — an ideal guide for teachers, students, hobbyists. Mail your order to: Electronics Digest — Great Men, P. O. Box 9108, Fort Worth, Texas 76107. Only $1 postpaid — and well worth it!

Reg. 1 95

Now 1 00

Published by Electronic Digest Periodicals, Inc.

ALLIED RADIO SHACK Technical Publications
A "Must" for Hobbyist and Pro

Learn more about the electronics field that interests you!
Authoritative publications written by industry leaders. All are written in easy-to-understand laymen's language. Expand your knowledge of the particular electronics field that interests you. Get yours today.

TUBE SUBSTITUTION HANDBOOK. 96 pages. 62-1326. ....1.75

TRANSISTOR SUBSTITUTION HANDBOOK. 160 pages. 62-1327. ....2.25

SHORTWAVE LISTENER'S GUIDE. 96 pages. 62-1328. ....1.95

RADIO LICENSE HANDBOOK. 136 pages. 62-1329. ....2.50

TV TUBE SYMPTOMS AND TROUBLESHOOTING. 96 pages. 62-1330. ....1.95

CB/HAM/SWL LOG BOOK. 80 pages. 62-1364. ....1.00

HOW TO BUILD ELECTRONIC KITS. 96 pages. 62-7066. ....95¢

BEST WAYS TO USE YOUR VOM AND VTVM. 96 pages. 62-7067. ....95¢

ELECTRONICS DATA HANDBOOK. 112 pages. 62-7398. ....1.25

UNDERSTANDING TRANSISTORS AND TRANSISTOR PROJECTS. 112 pages. 62-7602. ..95¢

INTEGRATED CIRCUIT FUNDAMENTALS AND PROJECTS. 96 pages. 62-7625. ....95¢

ALL ABOUT HIGH-FIDELITY AND STEREO. 96 pages. 62-7699. ....95¢

UNDERSTANDING AND USING CB RADIO. 112 pages. 62-7701. ....95¢

GETTING STARTED IN ELECTRONICS. 112 pages. 62-7705. ....95¢

USING YOUR TAPE RECORDER. 112 pages. 62-7730. ....95¢

DICTIONARY OF ELECTRONIC TERMS. 112 pages. 62-7756. ....1.25

ENCYCLOPEDIA OF ELECTRONIC COMPONENTS. 128 pages. 62-7930. ....1.25

UNDERSTANDING SCHEMATIC DIAGRAMS. 112 pages. 62-7931. ....95¢

UNDERSTANDING AND USING YOUR OSCILLOSCOPE. 112 pages. 62-7932. ....95¢

Prices Slightly Higher in Canada and Alaska

At Over 1000 Allied Radio Shack Stores Nationwide

Over 1000 ALLIED RADIO SHACK Stores in 49 States and Canada

Stop in at the Store Near You .. or Order by Mail!

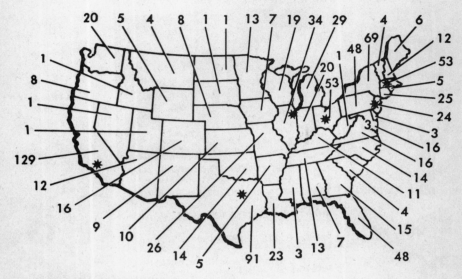

*the most convenient shopping ever
from the world's largest electronic store chain*

1000 STORES

With managers who understand electronic needs!

with quantity-buying power for the best values!

with exclusive products sold nowhere else!

with quality standards and quality controls!

* 7 Giant Regional Warehouses strategically located to keep all our stores stocked with everything we sell. No wasted trips—You get what you want, when you want it, at any Allied Radio Shack Store!

(Prices slightly higher in Canada and Alaska)

Four manufacturing plants in the U. S. and abroad—we make most of our own products—and pass the savings on to you!

 A TANDY CORPORATION COMPANY

At Over 1000 Allied Radio Shack Stores Nationwide